THE CAMBRIDGE SHORTER HISTORY
OF INDIA

THE
CAMBRIDGE SHORTER HISTORY
OF INDIA

by

J. ALLAN, M.A.

Keeper of the Department of Coins and Medals, British Museum

SIR T. WOLSELEY HAIG, K.C.I.E., C.S.I., C.M.G., M.A.

Lecturer in Persian in the School of Oriental Studies, University of London

H. H. DODWELL, M.A.

Professor of the History and Culture of the British Dominions in Asia,
the University of London

Edited by H. H. DODWELL

1969

S.   CHAND   &   CO.

DELHI—NEW DELHI—JULLUNDUR—LUCKNOW
BOMBAY—CALCUTTA—MADRAS—HYDERABAD

S. CHAND & CO.

Ram Nagar	—	New Delhi
Fountain	—	Delhi
Mai Hiran Gate	—	Jullundur
Aminabad Park	—	Lucknow
167, Lamington Road	—	Bombay
32, Ganesh Chandra Ave.	—	Calcutta
35, Mount Road	—	Madras
Sultan Bazar	—	Hyderabad

Third Indian Reprint : 1969

Reprinted in India by S. Chand & Co., with the kind permission
of the Cambridge University Press, London.

*Published by S. Chand & Co., Ram Nagar, New Delhi-55 and
Printed at Rajendra Printers, Ram Nagar, New Delhi-55.*

PREFACE

The *Cambridge Shorter History of India* seeks to provide the general reader with a complete account of Indian political history from its beginning down to the year in which the reforms of 1919 were initiated. For many reasons no single person could hope to succeed in such an attempt. No living person possesses, or indeed is likely to possess, an adequate knowledge of the Sanskrit and Pali texts and inscriptions, of the Persian and Marathi chronicles and documents, and of the administrative records of the English Government. A co-operative method is therefore unavoidable. But it was thought that, if the collaboration were limited to three persons, a volume might be produced founded in each of its sections on original materials, and yet possessing, so far as each section went, a unity of conception and treatment unattainable when individual topics are handled by individual specialists.

The general aim of the authors has been to take full advantage of the knowledge and experience embodied in the various volumes of the *Cambridge History of India,* but to reserve to themselves complete liberty of judgment. The present volume is far from being a mere *résumé* of the larger work, and it is hoped that it will provide in a compact form that survey of Indian history as a whole which has long been sorely needed and which no existing volume satisfactorily supplies.

In two respects the present volume departs from the practice of the later volumes of the Cambridge History. In order to bring them into line with the *Cambridge History of the British Empire* of which they also form a part, diacritical marks were omitted, and no maps were included. But the considerations which justified those decisions do not apply to the present volume. The general reader cannot be expected to be familiar with the pronunciation of the less common Indian names. The long vowels have therefore been marked in order to provide him with a rough guide. For a similar reason a series of maps has been included. With one exception these maps have been specially drawn. But the editor has gratefully to acknowledge the courtesy of Dr C. C. Davies, in allowing him to illustrate the North-West Frontier with a section of a map which appeared in Dr Davies's work on that subject.

June, 1934   H. H. D.

BIBLIOGRAPHICAL NOTE

In general the reader is referred to the full bibliographies printed in the volumes of the *Cambridge History of India*, of which volumes II and IV have still to appear. These will cover the period from the beginning of the Christian era to the Muslim conquest, and the period of the Mughal empire. On their appearance up-to-date bibliographies for these periods will become available. As regards the other periods of Indian history, the following are the most important works which have appeared since the compilation of the bibliographies of the published volumes:

PART I: EARLY INDIA

Hemchandra Raychaudhuri. Political History of Ancient India. Calcutta, 1923.

Marshall, Sir John. Mohenjo-Daro and the Indus Civilization. 3 vols. 1931.

La Vallée-Poussin, L. de. L'Inde jusque vers 300 av. J.-C. Paris, 1924.

—— L'Inde au temps des Mauryas. Paris, 1930.

Pargiter, F. E. Ancient Indian Historical Tradition. Oxford, 1922.

Chamanlal, J. Shah. Jainism in Northern India. 1931.

Law, B. C. Ancient Indian Tribes. Lahore, 1928.

—— Ksatriya Clans in Buddhist India. Calcutta, 1922.

—— Ksatriya Tribes of Ancient India. Calcutta, 1923.

Stein, O. Megasthenes und Kautilya. Vienna, 1921.

Meyer, Eduard. Blüte und Niedergang des Hellenismus in Asien. Berlin, 1925.

Konow, Sten. Corpus inscriptionum Indicarum. Vol. II, Part I. Kharoshthi Inscriptions. Calcutta, 1929.

PART III: BRITISH INDIA

PORTUGUESE

Andrada, Ruy Freyre de. Commentaries. Ed. C. R. Boxer. 1929.

Queroz, Fernão de. Conquest of Ceylon. Trans. Fr. S. G. Perera. 3 vols. 1930.

Prestage, E. The Portuguese Pioneers. 1932.

DUTCH

Reisebeschreibungen von Deutschen Beampten und Kriegsleuter im Dienst der Niederländischen West- und Ost-Indischen Kompagnien, 1602–1797. 12 vols. The Hague, 1931–2.

FRENCH

Martin, F. Mémoires. Ed. Martineau. 2 vols. Paris, 1931–2.
Dalgleish, W. H. Company of the Indies in the Days of Dupleix. 1933.
Bussy, Journal de. Ed. Martineau. 1933.
Besson, —. Les aventuriers français aux Indes, 1775–1820. 1932.
Martineau, A. Le général Perron. 1931.

ENGLISH

Collet, Joseph. Private Letter-books. Ed. Dodwell and Collet. 1933.
Burnell, John. Bombay in the Days of Queen Anne. Hak. Soc., x. 1933.
Weitzman, S. Warren Hastings and Philip Francis. Manchester, 1929.
Das Gupta, A. P. The Central Authority in British India. Calcutta, 1931.
Richmond, Sir H. W. The Navy in India, 1763–83. 1931.
Furber, H. Life of Henry Dundas. Oxford, 1931.
—— The Private Record of an Indian Governor-generalship. Harvard, 1933.
Roberts, P. E. India under Wellesley. 1929.
Morison, J. L. Lawrence of Lucknow. 1934.
Early British Relations with Assam. Ed. Suryyakumar Bhuyan. Calcutta, 1928.
Turner, Ralphe. James Silk Buckingham. 1934.
Pentland, Lady. Lord Pentland: a Memoir. 1928.

CONTENTS

Contents

PART II: MUSLIM INDIA

xii Contents

PART III: BRITISH INDIA

Contents

Contents

Contents   xxi

MAPS

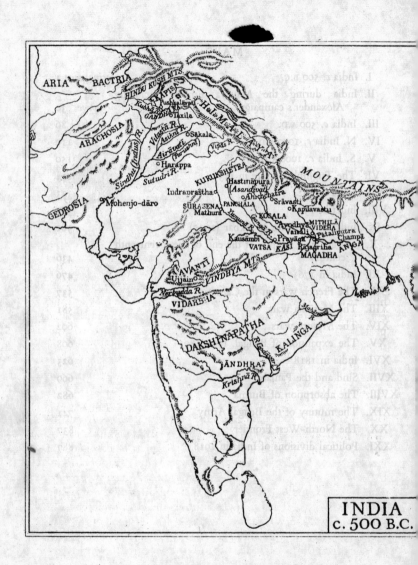

INDIA
c. 500 B.C.

CHAPTER I

Sources and Early History

The most striking feature of the literature of ancient India when compared with European literature is the absence of historical works. It has no Herodotus or Thucydides, no Livy or Tacitus. The early literature is entirely religious and exegetic in origin, and, while important data regarding the social life of the people can be deduced from it, it contains little reference to historical events and still less matter of chronological value. The two great epics, while throwing light on life in the heroic age, contain little of importance for political history. The *Purāṇas*, whose authors might in some ways be compared to our medieval chroniclers, are mainly legendary and mythological collections; they contain a certain amount of genealogical matter, the historical significance of which it is very difficult to estimate. The only professedly historical work, the late twelfth-century chronicle of Kashmīr, contains a certain amount of historical information about a limited period, but the bulk of it is of little value. Bāna's *Harshacharita*, a pseudo-biographical work, contains disappointingly little of historical value and belongs to literature rather than history. A certain number of fragments of historical information are preserved in the most unlikely sources, such as the chance illustrations of the use of words by a grammarian.

It is therefore to other sources that we have to look to reconstruct the history of ancient India. The historical data that can be gathered from Sanskrit and Pāli literature cannot be despised, but interpretation is often difficult and there is an entire lack of chronological data. It is with the help of synchronisms given by foreign, mainly Greek and Chinese, writers that the chronology of Indian history has been built up. In addition to the casual references to India in classical literature, we have what has survived of the contemporary and later accounts of Alexander's Indian expedition, of the descriptions of India by Megasthenes, the Seleucid ambassador at the court of the Mauryas, and other Greek visitors to India. Chinese literature has contributed its share not only in the narratives of pilgrims like Fa Hien in the fifth and Hiuen Tsang in the seventh century, who came to India to visit the sacred sites of Buddhism and study the law at the great schools there, but also in numerous references in historical works, notably to the migrations of various invaders of India from central Asia. Such foreign references are only occasional glimpses, and it is for their chronological value that they are important. The whole chronology of India has been built up from the identification of the Sandracottus of the Greek writers with Chandragupta Maurya.

Our most valuable source is still a native one; the epigraphic and numismatic evidence: countless inscriptions on rock, stone and copper plates have been discovered and read in the last century and a half. Some of these are official and are commemorative and historical documents of the first importance, like the edicts of Asoka or the Allahabad pillar of Samudragupta; others are of a private nature, recording donations by individuals of land or other gifts to temples or for other religious purposes; in these it is facts casually stated like the name of the reigning king that give them their present value. One important feature of such inscriptions is that they are commonly dated in eras which it has been possible to ascertain. They also contain geographical data frequently of interest.

Coins also have survived in large numbers from the third century B.C. onwards. It was on the study of the bilingual inscription of the Greek kings of India that the foundations of Indian epigraphy were laid. Coins have restored to history whole dynasties which had been forgotten. They are sometimes dated, but it is a comparison of types and styles or a study of finds that frequently supplies important chronological information. It is, however, a curious fact that many important rulers do not seem to have issued coins at all and that many others were content to be anonymous on their coinages. Other branches of archaeology have also contributed their share in illuminating dark places in the history of India and the work of the Archaeological Survey in the last thirty years at sites like Taxila, Pātaliputra, and Mohenjo-dāro have been of the utmost value for the history of Indian culture.

Until quite recently our earliest knowledge of the people of India was derived from the hymns of the *Rig-Veda*, from which a picture of the life and culture of the Āryan invaders of India can be drawn. Archaeological research has now taken us back some fifteen hundred years further. An examination of sites in the upper and lower Indus valleys and in Balūchistān has revealed that India possesses relics of a culture as old and as advanced as the ancient civilisations of Sumeria and Elam, with which it has links and similarities. The two most important of these sites are Harappa in the Montgomery district of the Panjab and Mohenjo-dāro—the "city of the dead"—on the lower Indus in the Lārkāna district of Sind. The latter, a place so little known twenty-five years ago, that it was not even mentioned in the Imperial Gazetteer, has been carefully excavated as far as the water permeating its lower levels from the Indus will permit, and the site has revealed the fact that 5000 years ago a well-built, flourishing city stood there. Enough is known of other sites of this culture to show that their organisation was similar. The city was built of brick, the walls above ground being of baked brick set in mud or gypsum mortar, while crude brick was used only for the foundations where they were not exposed to weathering; stone for building purposes, of course, was not procurable in the region of Mohenjo-dāro. The streets were laid out with great regularity. Most of the houses had their own wells from which they drew water that had filtered through from the river. Many of them had bathrooms; all had a good drainage system which, however, only led out into the street and was not carried outside the town. A remarkable feature of the houses is a rubbish chute with a bin outside into which the refuse fell. The civilisation of these cities is remarkable for the large number and excellence of the ordinary dwelling-houses, which is in contrast with what we find in Mesopotamia where the ordinary citizen seems to have lived in very wretched conditions, and where the buildings are either palaces or hovels. In addition to private houses, Mohenjo-dāro contained several larger buildings of uncertain use. They may have been places of worship, but there seems to be an absence of anything in the nature of images in them. A great pillared hall is one of the most striking buildings in the town and is thought to have been a place of assembly. The most prominent building is, however, a great public bath with ancillary buildings.

It has been possible to gather a certain amount of information about the life and habits of the citizens. They cultivated wheat and barley, and bred cattle, sheep, pigs and poultry for food; they also freely used the fish in the river—a food the early Āryans do not seem to have cared for. Other animals of which remains have been discovered were the buffalo, camel, elephant and various kinds of deer. The tiger, the monkey and the hare were known to them, for they are depicted on their seals. Traces of the dog and horse have been found, but the date of these remains is uncertain. They may be much later.

They were acquainted with various metals—gold, silver, copper and lead. Silver was well known, while it was almost unknown to the Indians of the *Rig-Veda*, who called it white gold when they did come across it. Copper was used for weapons and utensils and humbler personal ornaments. Stone is naturally scarce in this region, but we find steatite used for mill-stones and a few other purposes. Numerous semi-precious stones like agate were used for beads and other ornaments; bone and ivory and shells were similarly used; wool and cotton were woven, and numerous spindle-whorls have been found. That the community was wealthy is evident from the ornaments discovered.

The weapons used were spears, axes, daggers, bows and slings— numerous sling-balls have been found. The sword does not appear to have been known, nor is there any trace of defensive armour. The earthenware was turned on the wheel. Many children's toys of clay have survived—rattles, dolls, whistles and carts, the latter being probably the earliest known representations of wheeled vehicles. Like Indians in all ages, they were extremely fond of gaming and numbers of dice have been found.

The most remarkable discovery was that of numerous seals bearing inscriptions in a pictographic character recalling other early systems of writing—Sumerian and Proto-Elamite, and probably having a common origin with them. These seals show a high degree of skill in engraving, and many animals, especially bulls, buffaloes and unicorns, appear upon them. Inscriptions in the same characters are found on pottery, but so far there is no trace of clay tablets or regular documents. The inscriptions have not been read; the characters are not an alphabet but signs, each representing a word. The Chinese system of writing is the modern parallel, and is probably the sole survivor of a group of systems having a common origin to which this Indus script belonged. This system of writing—specimens of which have also come from Harappa—disappeared completely in India; indeed it is difficult to assert that writing, as we know it, was practised in India much before the third century B.C. Conjectures as to the language of these people are almost hopeless; one may confidently assert that it was not Sanskrit, and it is doubtful if it was a Dravidian language.

Not only seal-engraving but also the art of sculpture reached a high pitch among these people: a very fine torso of a man executed in red stone, which was discovered at Mohenjo-dāro, was at first thought to be of Greek workmanship, but it is now certain that it is 2500 years earlier.

Something has been gleaned about the religion of this period. The principal deity seems to have been the Mother Goddess who is so prominent in all early cults; a three-headed deity seems to be a prototype of Siva; if this is so, and there is no reason to doubt it, then he must have forced his way into the Āryan pantheon. There is ample evidence of the cult of baetylic stones and of phallic worship. Trees and animals also seem to have played their part in the religion of this people. The dead were either buried or cremated.

The culture of the Indus valley bears a general resemblance to that of Elam and Mesopotamia. It was essentially a city culture. The name chalcolithic has been given to it, because it was a period in which the use of stone for implements had not quite died out, although it was being supplanted by metals. Features common to these early cultures are the pictographic script and the high development of the minor arts. Seals of the Indus-valley type have been found in Elam and there are other evidences of intercourse; from our knowledge of Mesopotamian chronology it has been possible to establish that the Mohenjo-dāro culture flourished about 3000 B.C. Whether this civilisation extended into the Ganges valley is not yet known; it may be that the Indus, as in later times under the Achaemenids, marked a boundary between east and west and that this culture should be linked with Mesopotamia and Irān rather than with India proper.

The picture thus offered of life in ancient India in this period is very different from that presented by the *Rig-Veda*. The Āryans were a pastoral people, and represent the aborigines with whom they wage a continual struggle as similar in pursuits to themselves. There are no references to strong cities like Mohenjo-dāro, and one thinks only of the existence of primitive villages with rudimentary defences. There are many points of difference. The bull was the great animal with the people of the Indus-valley culture and the cow with the Āryans. The horse was perhaps unknown to the Mohenjo-dāro people, but it was well known to the Vedic Āryans. The metals as known to the two peoples were different. It is evident that the civilisation of this early period is quite different and cut off from that of the Vedas. It seems, however, to contain the germs of much that was to play a great part in the life of the people of India; if this culture owes a great deal to lands to the west with which it has obvious links, it is already, when we meet with it, firmly rooted in India with an Indian character of its own.

Our earliest literary source for the history of India is the hymns of the *Rig-Veda*, the date of which is from about 1500 to 1000 B.C. This is the literature of the early Āryan invaders of India, and, while purely religious in character, gives us a certain amount of information about the life of the community and a number of historical allusions. The hymns are addressed to various gods, and their matter is mainly mythological. The number of secular poems is very small, so that any historical information contained in the Vedic hymns can only be incidental. The poems bear no trace of a memory of the Āryan invasion of India and seem to have been composed in India. The geographical allusions cover a wide area, but are entirely Indian. The Āryans can be shown to be occupying the north-west corner of India, the Panjab. A number of rivers are mentioned, most of which can be identified and nearly all of them belong to the Indus system. Of the north-western tributaries of the Indus are mentioned the Kubhā (Kābul), Suvāstu (Swāt), the Gomatī (Gomal) and Krumu (Kurram). Most frequently mentioned is the river *par excellence*, the Sindhu, through an Iranian form of which the western world got the name of India, and the Sarasvatī (Sarsutī). The five rivers of the Panjab are all known: the Vitastā (Jhelum), Asiknī (Chināb), Parushnī (or Irāvatī from which its modern name Rāvi came), the Sutudrī (Sutlej) and the Vipās (Beās). Of these the Parushnī is the most prominent. The sea was unknown, the word *samudra* still having only its etymological sense of a collection of waters and being applied to large rivers. Mountains are frequently mentioned and are still in the vicinity of the poets. The Ganges and Jumna are just mentioned but the Vindhya mountains and the

Nerbudda are not. The fauna mentioned is in keeping with the geographical allusions. The lion is known but the tiger is not; the gradually increasing reference to the latter animal in late Vedic literature throws an interesting light on the eastward advance of the Āryans. The elephant is known, but is called *mriga hastin*—the "animal with the hand"—a name which could have been given only by strangers who had originally been unfamiliar with it; in time, however, *hastin* becomes the regular name.

The historical allusions in the *Rig-Veda* are confused and obscure. It is clear that the Āryas consisted of a number of tribes who were continually waging war on the aborigines and frequently on one another. They call themselves Āryas, meaning "noble of birth and race" in contrast to the native Dasyus or Dāsas, who are "black", "of *dāsa* colour", in opposition to the *ārya* colour. It is probably to this distinction of colour (*varna*— later, "caste") that we have to go back for the origins of the caste system. Besides their colour, one interesting record of the physical features of the Dasyus has been preserved. They are called *anāsah*, "those who have no noses", which suggests they had noses of the flat Dravidian type, which struck the invaders as contrasting very much with their own clear-cut features. A war of extermination seems to have been waged on them by the invaders and those not slain were made slaves; *dāsa* and *dasī* came to mean "slave" in Sanskrit just as "slave" in the Teutonic language was originally Slav. There is some evidence that Āryan tribes on occasion did not disdain Dāsa help against their kinsmen.

Five tribes are occasionally mentioned together as if they were allied, the Pūrus, Turvasas Yadus, Anus and Druhyus. Of these the Pūrus, who lived on both banks of the Sarasvatī, were important; the Turvasas and Yadus were also of note. These appear with five other tribes in the battle of the ten kings, the great event in Vedic history, in which Sudās, king of the Tritsus, successfully routed a confederation of his enemies. His victory is commemorated by his chief priest Vasishtha. The river itself seems to have played an important part in the tactics of the battle. Sudās was equally successful in a campaign in the east of his kingdom, where he defeated three tribes led by Bheda on the banks of the Jumna. Our information is not sufficient to tell us whether, as is not improbable, there was any co-operation between his eastern enemies and those on the north-west. If there were, he seems to have been an able strategist. Sudās came of a military family, for his grandfather Divodāsa was also a mighty warrior and a great enemy of the Dāsas, on whom he waged relentless war. The greatest leader of the Dāsas was named Sambara.

The Pūrus were also a powerful tribe, and we know the names of a number of their princes. One of these, Trasadasyu, seems to have earned this name in wars with the natives. There is some evidence that the Pūrus later amalgamated with another Vedic tribe, the Bhāratas, against whom they had fought, and that this combination formed the Kurus, who are not mentioned in the Vedas but play an important part in the Brahmanic age.

Scanty as is the information preserved regarding the warfare among the Āryas themselves, still less is known about what must have been much more important, their struggle with the aborigines, whom they gradually exterminated or absorbed. Very little is recorded of the divisions or leaders of the latter. The fact that they did not worship the gods of the Āryas brings them the constant reproach of godlessness and impiety. Their wealth seems to have consisted mainly in cattle, which they drove into the shelter of primitive defences when attacked. The capture of their poor defences is frequently extolled in the Vedic hymns. Of contact between the Vedic Indians and the external world, such as is suggested by the discoveries of Mohenjo-dāro for India and Elam, there is practically no trace, a possible loan-word or two only.

As to the mode of life of the Vedic Indians, we gather something from their literature. Their towns, if one may use the term, were nothing more than villages with some rude earthworks around as a defence. There is nothing in the literature to suggest well-planned cities such as have been revealed in the Indus-valley sites. They were a pastoral people. Cattle provided their main wealth, and the poetry is full of metaphors from pastoral life. They had horses for their chariots and for riding, and the dog for hunting and guarding their flocks. Agriculture was another important source of livelihood, and many aspects of it are touched upon. Their cereal was *yava*, which may be barley; they were also keen huntsmen, using the bow and arrow, snares and traps. They were wood-workers and smiths; the poets borrow metaphors from the trade of the wheelwright. They were exceedingly fond of chariot-racing, and seem to have been devoted to gambling.

Fishing is not mentioned, and navigation only of a very rudimentary nature. Milk and ghee and fruit were important articles of diet, but they seem also to have been mingled with considerable quantities of meat. They had musical instruments and dances. Their weapons were the bow, spear, sword, axe and sling. They cremated and buried their dead, who went to join Yāma, the first of men to die.

As to their political organisation, the tribe was the unit, ruled by its king or petty chief, who was by no means an autocrat, his power being limited by the tribal assembly. The kingship was usually hereditary. The king was the leader in battle, but we know little about his activities in time of peace. A very important post was held by his *purohita*, or domestic priest, and we know from the influence wielded by Visvāmitra and Vasishtha that he held great power. The priests had already developed a very elaborate ritual, which is in contrast to the picture of a primitive state of society that one gathers from allusions to other aspects of social life.

Most of the gods are personifications of natural phenomena like the Sun, Dawn and Fire. The two most important gods are Indra, the thunder-god, and Varuna, the god of the sky and the upholder of moral order; it is only in the hymns addressed to the latter that we find sublimity of thought and high ethical tone. Indra seems gradually to have ousted him from his supremacy. Vishnu is not yet the great deity he became in later times. Sacrifices were made to obtain boons from the gods. The offerings consisted of ghee and *soma*, and the personification of the *soma* plant is one of the deities worshipped. The *soma* owed its place to its intoxicating quality, which led it to be regarded as promising divine powers. In the later hymns a few abstract deities begin to appear. The only goddess of importance is Ushās, the "shining dawn", to whom some of the most poetical hymns are addressed. Sarasvatī, the river goddess, later became the goddess of wisdom. The few secular hymns throw light on wedding and funeral customs; one is of a philosophical nature and the earliest specimen of Indian speculation which later took form as the Sānkhya system.

In the later Vedic period, for which our sources are the literature of the later Vedas and the *Brāhmanas*, the centre of Āryan

culture has moved from the Panjab eastwards, and the land of
the five rivers plays an insignificant part compared with Madhyadesa, the Middle Country, the land between the Jumna and the
Ganges. Kurukshetra is now the headquarters of Brahmanical
culture; its inhabitants, the Kurus, with their immediate neighbours and close allies, the Panchālas, are the people whose example
is to be followed in every way. Their Brāhmans are the most
celebrated, and their kings are models of what a king should be.
The language spoken there is the standard which others seek to
copy; nowhere else are sacrifices performed so perfectly as in the
land of the Kurus. The Kurus and Panchālas now occupy the
place held by the Bhāratas in the earlier books of the *Rig-Veda*.
The memory of the Bhāratas was still esteemed, but they were
no longer a political unit. This was also true of other Rig-Vedic
tribes like the Tritsus and Pūrus. The Kurus are not mentioned
as a people in the *Rig-Veda*, but the occurrence in it of a name
like Kurusravana, the "glory of the Kurus", shows that the
family already existed. The first component of the name Panchāla
suggests that they were formed by an alliance of five tribes. They
are said to have been formerly called the Krivis. Neighbours of
the Kuru-Panchālas were the Vasas and Usīnaras, of whom little
is known. The Srinjayas are closely connected with the Kurus,
whose fortunes they shared. Farther east lay the kingdoms of
Kosala (Oudh) and Videha (northern Bihar), both destined to
great futures. Magadha, which was later on to surpass them all,
is barely mentioned and then with but little respect; this is also
true of the Angas, the neighbours of Magadha on the east. In the
south the Āndhras and other great peoples are mentioned only
as still quite beyond the pale of Āryan culture.

A number of famous cities were now in existence, and everything points to a more settled form of civilisation. The capital
of the Kurus was Asandīvat, better known as the Hastināpura of
the epics. Kāsi, the capital of the kingdom of the same name, is
the later Benares. Kausāmbī is another great city to which we
have early references.

It is quite impossible to give a consecutive account of Indian
history for the first half of the first millennium B.C., roughly the
period covered by the literature of the *Brāhmanas*. Our sources
are entirely religious in character, and preserve only incidentally
anecdotes of a secular nature. The dynastic lists of the *Purānas*

are corrupt, and in any case contain little more than strings of
names. These sources are supplemented by references in the epics.
It has not yet been found possible to make a coherent story out
of the mass of obscure and contradictory references of a historical
nature that have been industriously gathered from these texts.
The flashes of light that are occasionally obtained suggest that a
great deal of early history was perfectly well known to the com-
pilers of the vast sacerdotal literature of the period, but that they
never thought of it as worthy of systematic record. One can
therefore only outline the rise and fall in importance of certain
kingdoms, and give a vague picture of the political history of
India down to the rise of Magadha in the sixth century B.C.

There is a well known passage in the *Brihad Āranyaka Upanishad*
in which Yājnavalkya is asked where the Pārikshitas have gone
and answers that they have gone where those who have performed
the horse-sacrifice go. The Pārikshitas were the first of the many
dynasties recorded in Indian history that attained great power and
then suddenly collapsed. Pārikshit, the founder of the line, was
a king of the Kurus. According to a hymn of the *Atharva-Veda*,
his reign was a kind of golden age in which the people flourished
exceedingly, granaries were filled to overflowing, and the hus-
bandman had a choice of beverages. Little definite is known
about him, however, except that he had a number of sons, of
whom the eldest and best known was his successor Janamejaya.
The latter was a great conqueror, and among his conquests was
the famous city of Taxila in the north. He performed the snake-
sacrifice and at least one horse-sacrifice. Echoes of some dispute
he had with the Brāhmans have survived in various sources. His
capital was Asandīvat and it was at his court that Vaisampāyana
related the story of the great epic. His three brothers, Bhīmasena,
Ugrasena, and Srutasena, all performed the horse-sacrifice. There
is a hint in the *Satapatha-Brāhmana* that they did this to atone for
the guilt of slaying Brāhmans. If all four brothers did perform
a sacrifice indicative of paramount sovereignty, it suggests a
division of the Pārikshit kingdom among them, whether peaceful
or otherwise we do not know. The names of later members of
the line have survived, but beyond vague references to their misfortunes we know nothing of them. In the reign of one of them,
Nichakshu, the capital was removed to Kausāmbī because the
old capital had suffered greatly from the inundations of the

Ganges. The cause of the collapse of the dynasty is not known, but it is clear that great misfortunes came upon the Kurus; a plague of locusts forced large numbers to migrate, and the prophecy that the Kurus would be driven from Kurukshetra looked like being fulfilled. Although it was henceforth never of the same political importance, the land of the Kurus still retained a reputation as a centre of learning.

With the disappearance of the Parikshitas from the scene, interest is transferred to the kingdom of Videha, the most notable of whose kings was the great Janaka. Videha corresponded to part of the modern Bihar, and its capital was Mithila, which is a great city in the epics and in the *Jataka*. Janaka was not much later in date than the last of the Parikshitas, for we find their fall discussed at his court as an event of recent occurrence. He was a great monarch—a *samraj* or emperor. Of his wars and conquests little is recorded, but there is evidence of a long rivalry and ultimate war with Kasi, whose king, Ajatasatru, was exceedingly jealous of Janaka's fame. His court was a celebrated centre of learning to which Brahmans came from all parts of India to take part in the philosophical discussions in which Janaka delighted, like Menander and Akbar in later times. It is from the names of such Brahmans and the references to their origins that we learn a few details of contemporary history and geography. The greatest ornament of his court was the sage, Yajnavalkya Vajasaneya. The names of the successors of Janaka are preserved in several sources in very contradictory fashion. The *Arthasastra* records the story of the downfall of the last of them, Karala, who lost his throne as a punishment for an assault on a young Brahman woman; not only did he lose his life and throne, but the kingship was abolished and replaced by a republic.

Adjoining Videha was the kingdom of Kosala, the royal family of which traced its descent from the Vedic hero, Ikshvaku; it corresponded roughly to the modern Oudh, and attained greater prominence at a later date. Its most important town was Ayodhya, while others were Sravasti and Saketa. The genealogy of its kings is given down to Prasenajit, the Pasenadi of the Buddhist literature. He was a contemporary of Buddha, with whom he was on intimate terms. He was extremely interested in the teacher's views, but did not himself become a Buddhist. By this time Kosala seems to have absorbed the neighbouring kingdom of

Kāsi. In Prasenajit's old age he had a war with Ajātasatru of
Magadha; during his absence from the country his son, Vidudabha,
was proclaimed in his stead. The aged king went to seek assistance
against the usurper but died on the way. Kosala thenceforth sank
into insignificance with the rise of Magadha, into which it was
ultimately incorporated.

Closely associated in the early period with Kosala was the little
kingdom of Kāsi: Ajātasatru was the name of the king of Kāsi
when Janaka ruled in Videha; he was likewise a philosopher and
patron of learning, who liked to take part in disputations. He is
reputed to have been jealous of the lustre shed on Janaka's court
by the learned men who frequented it. The earliest recorded
dynasty of Kāsi traced its descent from the Bhāratas, but Ajātasatru
seems to have belonged to a later dynasty known as the Brāhma-
dattas who came originally from Videha. Kāsi was for a time
a great power and the wealth of its capital was celebrated. There
are numerous references in the *Jātaka* to it. On one occasion it
was besieged by seven kings. At one time Kāsi completely subdued Kosala in a war, in which the king of the latter was slain
and his queen carried off prisoner. The tables seem soon to have
been turned, however, for Kāsi finally passed to Kosala, one of
whose kings earned the epithet "conqueror of Benares". Kosala
absorbed Kāsi completely, probably in the seventh century B.C.
By Buddha's time Kāsi was a province of Kosala, but the fact
that it had once been independent was not yet completely forgotten. It shared the fate of Kosala and became a part of the
growing empire of Magadha.

Gandhāra which passed to the Achaemenids in the sixth century
is occasionally mentioned in this period. Its towns, Taxila and
Pushkalavatī, are already celebrated. The former in particular very
early achieved the great reputation as a centre of learning which
it enjoys in Buddhist literature. Pāṇini, the great Sanskrit grammarian, was a native of this region. South of Gandhāra lay the
land of the Kaikeyas, one of whose kings, Asvapati, had a great
reputation as a teacher. Several celebrated philosophers are recorded to have studied under him. In the period of the later
Brāhmanas there were Āryan kingdoms in the Deccan of which
we have no hint in the *Rig-Veda*. One of the most important
of these was Vidarbha, which corresponded to the modern Berar;
Kalinga, prominent in the last centuries before the Christian era,

is early mentioned. The Bhojas, who are a people of the Deccan in Asoka's inscriptions, are mentioned in the early Brāhmanical literature. Of non-Āryan people of the south the *Aitareya Brāhmana* mentions tribes known as the Āndhras who later were a great people, the Pulindas who crop up again as contemporaries of Asoka, and the Sabaras, who, like some other peoples beyond the sphere of Āryan influence, had a reputation for their knowledge of occult science.

Buddhist and Jain sources represent northern India as divided among sixteen large states—*mahājanapadas*—in the period before the rise of Buddhism and Jainism, that is the late seventh and early sixth centuries B.C. Many of these were republics ruled by popular assemblies. The more important like Kosala and Magadha, with longer histories, are dealt with separately elsewhere. Beyond Magadha lay Anga with its famous capital Champā, one of the six great cities of India, worthy of being chosen by Buddha as the scene of his death. It had commercial relations with the Further East. Anga at one time was a much more important state than Magadha, but it was conquered by Bimbisāra, who slew its last king, and thenceforth Anga became a province of Magadha.

We have already seen that the Videhans drove out their kings and set up a republic. They appear to have joined a confederation of similarly organised tribes, one of whose number, the Vajjis, gave its name to the confederation. The Vajjis were very powerful in the last years of Buddha's life and a formidable obstacle to the ambitions of Ajātasatru of Magadha, who saw that they must be uprooted if his career of conquest was to be successful. He therefore sent a messenger to the aged Buddha to seek a prediction from him regarding the fate of the Vajjis. Buddha's remarks on the Vajjis show that they were very powerful and he stated that so long as certain conditions were fulfilled, notably the regular holding of assemblies, they would never be subdued. Ajātasatru's envoy saw that the Vajjis could be overcome by the king of Magadha not in open battle, but only by diplomacy and breaking up the alliance. Another passage in Buddhist literature records how Sunidha and Vassakāra, ministers of Magadha, built a new fortified town at Pātaligama to repel the Vajjis, and Buddha prophesied a great future for it. It became the Pātaliputra of history. The most celebrated family in the Vajji confederacy was the Lichchhavis, who wielded considerable influence in the seventh and sixth centuries B.C. Ajātasatru's mother was a Lichchavi, and 800 years later we find Samudragupta proudly recording that his mother came of this ancient line. Another clan was the Jnātrikas, in which Mahāvīra was born (whence his name Nātaputta).

Neighbours of the Lichchhavis were the Mallas, who had come to be of little importance by the time they appear in history and were easily conquered by Magadha. The Vatsas were an important community with the ancient city of Kausāmbī as their capital; hither came the people of Hastināpura when the old capital of the Kurus was destroyed. The kings of Vatsa traced their descent from the Bhārata family. One of the most famous kings of the Vatsas was Udayana (Udena), son of Satānīka Parantapa, and one of the great heroes of Sanskrit literature. Little definite is known about him, but the memory of his important matrimonial alliances through his queen Vāsavadattā with Avantī and through Padmavatī with Magadha is preserved by the dramatists; and his renown as a conqueror survived till the time of Somadeva in the eleventh century A.D. The Kurus and Panchālas are still included among the great states, but they had sunk from their former greatness and seem to have accepted a republican constitution like their neighbours.

Mathura was already an important city, the capital of the Sūrasenas. Originally ruled by members of the ancient Yādava family, from which dynasties of the Deccan in later centuries liked to trace their descent, the Sūrasenas became a republic. They still retained their individuality in the time of Megasthenes, but they must by then have long passed under the sway of Magadha. One of the *mahājanapadas*, Avantī, corresponding to the modern Mālwā, seems to have always been ruled by a king; little is known of its earlier history. Its capital was Ujjain and the earliest dynasty seems to have been the Haihayas. A change of dynasty must have taken place in the sixth century, for Pradyota, the first king of whom anything definite is known, was a usurper, an able and powerful man but with a reputation for cruelty. His dynasty raised Avantī to a position of considerable eminence and it was the most powerful rival of Magadha for the hegemony of northern India. In the final struggle Magadha, led by Sisunāga, was triumphant.

In the sixth century B.C. two great teachers arose in India, Mahāvīra and Buddha; Jain and Buddhist literature, therefore, is able to supplement the *Purānas* as a source for the history of India, more particularly of Magadha, at this period. Both these teachers were of aristocratic birth and connected with important families, with the result that much valuable information has been preserved which might otherwise have been lost. Vardhamāna, who on attaining supreme knowledge became known as Mahāvīra or Jina, was the son of an important chief and his wife, the sister of Chetaka, king of Vaisālī, and the aunt of Bimbisāra of Magadha; while Gautama, the Buddha, was the son of a chief of the ancient Sākya family. It is, however, not entirely by accident that Magadha begins to play the most prominent part in the recorded history of northern India. The lists of kings of Magadha in the *Purānas* show that it must have had a long history. The earliest references in the later Vedic literature show that the region was not yet wholly under the influence of Brahmanic culture. Of the earliest recorded dynasty, that founded by Brihadratha, nothing is known except that it came to an end in the sixth century; its last monarch seems to have been overthrown by the Pradyotas of Avantī. Their hold over Magadha, if it was ever complete, must have been short, for when we enter the historical period as documented by the Buddhist and Jain sources, we find Magadha ruled by a powerful monarch called Bimbisāra, whom the Jains knew as Srenika. He had probably taken advantage of the troubles that had accompanied the fall of the last dynasty to seize power and consolidate his position, much as Chandragupta Maurya did at a later date. Tradition makes him the son of Bhattiya, a petty dynast who had suffered much at the hands of his powerful neighbour, Brāhmadatta, king of Anga. Bimbisāra's first task was to avenge these insults to his father, which he did most thoroughly. He slew the last of the Brāhmadatta dynasty, occupied Champā, his capital, and annexed the territory of Anga, thus bringing the territory of Magadha down to the coast and putting an end to the long rivalry between the two kingdoms. There is, perhaps, an echo of this campaign in the *Jātaka* which tells how a king, Ugrasena, helped a defeated king of Magadha to conquer Anga and combine the two kingdoms under his rule. This seems to have been done by Bimbisāra in his father's lifetime, for it is recorded that he acted as his father's viceroy in the conquered territory. The importance of Magadha under Bimbisāra may be gathered from his matrimonial alliances; among his wives were the daughter of the king of Kosala and sister of Pasenadi, and Chellanā, the daughter of Chetaka, king of Vaisāli, two of his more important neighbours. He maintained diplomatic relations with remoter kingdoms, for it is recorded that Pukkusāti, king of Gandhāra, sent him an embassy. As Gandhāra had passed to the Achaemenids by 516 B.C., this statement is of some value for Indian chronology. Bimbisāra probably reigned c. 540–490 B.C. His capital was at first the ancient one of Girivrāja, but he seems to have been the founder of the new city of Rājagriha, which arose around the new "king's house". His kingdom is said to have included 80,000 townships, the overseers of which all became Buddhists. Various meetings between Bimbisāra and Buddha are recorded; one is a very early one in which the king offers the young ascetic wealth and preferment and all that the world can give. Numerous benefactions made by him to Buddhist communities are recorded. His kind-heartedness and considerateness are illustrated by the stories of his abolishing fares at ferries for ascetics and of the bhikkhus feasting on his mangoes. That he realised the importance of a strong army and would tolerate no weakening of its moral is evident from the Mahāvagga, where we are told of the prompt steps he took to get Buddha to prevent the ordination of his soldiers when some of them began to desert the profession of arms for a religious life. He was succeeded by his son Ajātasatru, the Kūnika of the Jains, whose mother was the daughter of the king of Kosala; he had been his father's viceroy in his Anga dominions, which seem to have become the regular appanage of the yuvarāja. Buddhist tradition makes the prince in his early days a friend of Buddha's great opponent, his cousin Devadatta and the arch-enemy of Buddhism. It says that he once wanted to take his father's life, but the plot was discovered and he was forgiven; finally he put Bimbisāra in prison, where, if he did not actually slay him, he at least caused his death by starvation. He afterwards became a Buddhist and expressed contrition for his crime to the then aged Buddha. How much of this story is true it is impossible to say. Bimbisāra may, like many Indian kings, have abdicated in his old age in favour of his son. The matrimonial alliances, which had been one cause of Bimbisāra's strength, provoked the wars of his son's reign.

Ajātasatru's mother had died of grief at her husband's death, and her brother, Pasenadi, king of Kosala, claimed back a village, the revenues of which had supplied her pin-money. Ajātasatru claimed it as his inheritance; a war resulted in which fortune favoured first one and then the other side. At one time the king of Kosala looked like being routed; finally, however, he was so successful as to take his nephew prisoner. The quarrel was settled by his giving a daughter in marriage to Ajātasatru and settling the revenues of the disputed village upon her. The next war was with another of Bimbisāra's brothers-in-law, the king of Vaisālī. Bimbisāra had given a celebrated elephant and some valuable jewels to his son by the Lichchhavi princess. These Ajātasatru claimed on his accession to the throne, but his half-brother fled with his treasures to his uncle in Vaisāli. The latter took his part and refused to surrender the fugitive. When the king of Magadha declared war on him, the Kosala ruler summoned his allies to his assistance, and the war lasted many years. The support given to the king of Vaisāli shows that his neighbour already feared the rising power of Magadha. After a long struggle Magadha was triumphant, and Vaisāli passed under its rule. Ajātasatru is said to have owed his success to his artillery, a kind of ballista which threw huge stones, and to an ancestor of the armoured car, a chariot fitted with death-dealing weapons which wrought great havoc. Buddhist tradition makes Ajātasatru's success the result of his tact and diplomacy as well as of his prowess in the field. He is said to have reigned eighteen years and must therefore have lived till about 460 B.C.

Ajātasatru was succeeded by his sons, Darsaka and Udayibhadra or Udaya, but their order is uncertain. The existence of the Darsaka of the *Purānas*, who is not mentioned by Buddhist tradition, is confirmed from his appearance as king of Magadha and brother of one of the queens of Udayana, king of Avantī, in the drama *Svapnavāsavadattā*, written over a thousand years later. Of Udaya we know that he built a new capital, Kusumapura, afterwards known as Pātaliputra, destined to be for centuries the most important city in India. The dynasty lasted several generations longer; nothing is known of the history of the period and the names of the rulers vary in Buddhist and Purānic tradition. According to the Buddhists every king of this line came to the throne by murdering his father. Finally a popular rising took place, so strong was the feeling against the dynasty, and drove the last descendant of Bimbisāra from the throne. A minister named Sisunāga, who had no doubt played a prominent part in the movement, was placed on the throne. He had been the governor of a province. The new ruler went back to the old capital of Girivrāja, whether for strategic reasons, or because of the unpopularity of everything associated with the old dynasty, we do not know. The *Purānas* say that he destroyed the power of the Pradyotas, that is to say, Magadha in his reign was powerful enough to dispose of its old rival, Avantī. His son and successor was the Kākavarna of the *Purānas*, called Kālāsoka by Buddhist writers. He restored Pātaliputra to its place as capital, and the second Buddhist council was held in his reign. Bāna records the fact that he was assassinated. On his death the kingdom was inherited by his sons, from whom it passed as an easy prey to the founder of the Nanda dynasty, who was probably connected with the former dynasty in some way.

The last ruler of the line of Sisunāga was murdered about the beginning of the fourth century B.C. by a king whom the *Purānas* call Mahāpadma, the founder of the Nanda dynasty, who is described as the destroyer of all the Kshatriyas and as sole monarch, terms which suggest that he brought many neighbouring kingdoms under his rule. Stories of the rise to power of the first Nanda have survived in Greek sources. Curtius says that the founder of the Nanda power, whom he calls Agrammes, was a barber in humble circumstances, whose handsome figure attracted the queen through whom he gained an important place at court. He finally murdered his sovereign, seized the throne and murdered the king's children. This king must have been Kālāsoka, the Kākavarna of the Saisunāga line, whom Bāna mentions as having been murdered near his own city. Jain tradition also records that Nanda was the son of a barber; the *Purānas* on the other hand describe him as a son of a Saisunāga by a Sudra mother, so that he may have had some claim to the throne through his father. The corrupt form, Agrammes or Xandrames, under which classical texts preserve the name of his son, has not been satisfactorily identified in Indian sources. Ceylon tradition gives him the name of Ugrasena, and it has been suggested that this or a patronymic from it is the original of Agrammes, but the form Xandrames looks more like some other Indian word. The Greek references to the power of the kingdom of the Gangaridae show that there is some truth in the Purānic statement that he was a great conqueror, and the great power inherited by Chandragupta is further evidence of this.

He probably reigned for twenty-eight years. He is said to have been succeeded by his eight sons who ruled in succession, but their reigns covered very few years. The last of them, Dhana Nanda, the Agrammes of the Greeks, was detested by his subjects because he had inherited the plebeian character of his father and none of the virtues of a king. The wealth of the Nandas was proverbial, and it is probable that the extortions by which it was acquired increased their unpopularity. The country seemed to be ripe for the revolution which put the Maurya Chandragupta on the throne; it was organised by the Nanda's former minister Kautilya, to whom the credit of its success is given by various Indian sources. That the revolution was not by any means bloodless is seen from a curious reference in the *Milindapanha* to a haunted battlefield. This had been the scene of the last stand of the Nanda general, Bhaddasāla, against Chandagutta (Chandragupta) in which many thousands had been slain. With the accession of the Mauryas the history of Magadha becomes the history of India; there is little doubt that Chandragupta Maurya owed a great deal to his predecessors, who had gradually consolidated the power of Magadha, accumulated wealth, and trained great forces, which he soon led successfully into the field and probably improved through his knowledge of the Greek armies.

CHAPTER II

Alexander

In the fourth century B.C. it is at last possible to give a more or less connected account of a short period in the history of India, or at least of the Indus valley; this we owe to the classical records of Alexander's Indian campaign. In 330 B.C. Alexander routed Darius, occupied Persepolis and then set about the subjugation of the eastern provinces of the Achaemenid empire. Early in the spring of the following year he marched from Seistan to the site of the modern Kandahār, where he built the city of Alexandria-in-Arachosia. Thence he pushed on to the Kābul valley, where the army encamped until the passes of the Hindu Kush were opened in the following spring. To the north lay the still unconquered Persian province of Bactria, which constituted a threat to Alexander's communications and prevented any further advance westward. At the foot of the Hindu Kush, at a point guarding the entrance to the roads to Bactria, another Alexandria was built, with smaller settlements like Cartana and Nicaea within reach of it. This Alexandria is identified with the modern Charikar. In the following year, the Greeks engaged in the campaign which brought the whole of eastern Irān under their power, and it was not till early in 327 B.C. that Alexander again turned southwards and eastwards. News of his successes had gone before him, and there seems to have been some hesitation among the Indian rulers whom he was likely to encounter first whether they should offer him peace or war. One of the more prominent among them, Ambhi (Omphis), son of the king of Taxila, had little doubt as to the advisability of making a friend of Alexander, and, while the latter was still in Bactria, had sent messengers to offer him assistance in invading India. His father seems on reflection to have come to the same conclusion, probably hoping thus to gain an ally able to crush his powerful rival, whom the Greeks call Porus (Paurava?), whose kingdom lay on the other side of the Hydaspes. Porus had for some years been engaged in subjugating his neighbours and now felt strong enough to threaten the kingdom of Taxila, hitherto apparently paramount in these regions.

In the summer of 327 B.C., the Greeks returned to Charikar, which was enlarged and strengthened and organised as a base of operations. Nicanor, son of Alexander's old friend Parmenion, was put in charge of this important depôt. Alexander went on with the bulk of his army to Nicaea, whence he sent envoys to ask the Indian rulers of the Indus to meet him in the Kābul valley. That some had already joined him we know from the mention of a certain Sisikottos (Sasigupta) as attached to his army. This summons finally decided the king of Taxila to join the invader, and his example was followed by other less powerful princes. The hill-tops, however, were still held by numerous tribes, as independent then as they are to-day, who declined to sacrifice the opportunity of harassing an army passing through the valley. Alexander had therefore to take steps to secure his route. He sent one half of his army direct to the Indus, probably following the Kābul river all the way and avoiding the Khaibar pass. On reaching the Indus, they were to make ready to cross immediately on Alexander's arrival after coming through the hills. It is impossible to trace the route followed by Alexander himself, but, from the incidents recorded, it is clear that his advance involved a series of attacks on mountain strongholds, which were frequently taken only after fierce fighting; at one town Alexander was wounded by an arrow, which filled his followers with such fury that the town was razed to the ground and all prisoners slain. The strongest opposition was offered by a people called the Assakenoi whose capital was Massaga, a very strong fortress, the natural advantages of which had been improved by all the engineering devices of the time. But the Greek artillery proved equal to the task, and the capture of the stronghold was facilitated by a chance shot which killed Assakenos (Asvaka), the king of the region. His mother and daughter, or, according to another version, his wife and son, were taken prisoner The garrison of this city included a large body of mercenaries from the south, who agreed to join Alexander on condition that their lives were spared. They changed their mind, however, and, rather than fight against their countrymen, resolved to escape under cover of night. But their plans were discovered and the Greeks, catching them unawares, slew them all, despite their desperate resistance; their number is said to have been 7000. Thus severely did Alexander punish this breach of faith, for he could take no risks so far from his base in the midst of an enemy country. The reception of the Macedonians, however, was not always hostile. At one town, called Nysa by the Greeks, the inhabitants claimed kinship with them and said they were descendants of followers of Dionysus who had settled there during his campaign in the east. The profuse growth in the neighbourhood of the vine and ivy, plants sacred to Dionysus, and certain place-names like Nysa and Meru (Meros), lent support to the story, and for a few days the Greeks made holiday with their long-lost kinsmen. When Alexander left the Nysans, 300 of their horsemen went with him and accompanied his army right through his Indian campaign. Probably the greatest exploit of this campaign was the siege and capture of Aornos, a mountain stronghold on the Indus, accessible only by a single path. The story ran that even Hercules on his Indian campaign had failed to capture it. Elaborate preparations were made to ensure success, Alexander himself working with his men to fill in a ravine which cut off the approach to the summit. Finally the Greeks secured a position commanding the fortress, and the garrison began to negotiate for surrender. In the darkness of the night, however, they endeavoured to escape; but the movement was seen, and Alexander himself led an attack in which many of the defenders were slain. The capture of this fortress was a source of particular pride to the Greeks, and special sacrifices were offered to celebrate their victory. Various attempts have been made to locate the place, but the descriptions preserved by the classical authors, who no doubt exaggerate the difficulties of its position, are not sufficient to identify it with certainty. Sisikottos (Sasigupta), an Indian who had long been in Alexander's service, was left in charge of the garrison. In the meanwhile, the other army under Hephaistion and Perdikkas had reached the Indus and had duly made preparations to cross. They had met with little opposition on their march; only the overthrow of a chief named Astes (Hasti) is recorded. The site of the bridge of boats which they built has been identified as Ohind, some sixteen miles above Attock. Alexander marked his arrival at the river by great sacrifices and other celebrations, and gave his troops a month's rest and relaxation. Here he was joined by Ambhi, who had succeeded to the throne of Taxila on his father's death, and who brought him large presents of sheep, oxen and money. Early in 326 B.C., on a day when the omens had been declared favourable, the army crossed the Indus and marched in the direction of Taxila, the king of which came out a few miles with his whole army to meet them. The display of military force was such that Alexander feared treachery until Ambhi rode out and put his army at his disposal. The Greeks were entertained most hospitably, and lavish gifts were exchanged between the allies. Alexander's generosity indeed was such as to arouse the jealousy of some of his own officers. The Greeks found much to interest them in the great Indian city, and anecdotes of the curious things that impressed them have come down to us—notably of naked ascetics, one of whom, called Kalanos by the Greeks, joined Alexander and accompanied him till his departure from India.

In the meanwhile Porus, the great rival of the king of Taxila and the leader of the opposition to Alexander, was preparing to resist the invader whom new Indian allies were daily joining. When Alexander summoned him to Taxila, he haughtily answered that they would meet in arms upon his frontier. Although Abhisara, a powerful chief and former ally of Porus, now submitted to Alexander, Porus gathered all his available forces and those of his remaining allies and vassals on the banks of the Hydaspes, towards which Alexander advanced rapidly in spite of the heat of summer, having sent with his advance guard the boats which had been used to cross the Indus. The Indian horsemen whom Porus sent to harass the advance were easily disposed of, and soon the two armies were facing one another, on opposite sides of the river. For some time the Greeks sought in vain a possible landing-place on the other side, while the Indians vigilantly guarded against any attempt to cross. The river was rising, the rains had begun, and it looked as if the Greeks would have to postpone their attack till the waters had sunk again to their low level in the autumn. Alexander indeed seems to have encouraged this belief by collecting great stores. But at the same time his reconnaissances along the river-bank kept the Indian host in a state of considerable tension.

At last one morning, after a night of unusual storm, the Indian sentries reported that the Greeks were crossing some sixteen miles above the camp. Alexander had made all his preparations : a place where a wooded island hid his movements; he led a picked force by night to this point, and pushed off into the flooded river under cover of the island so that his men were within reach of the further bank before they became visible. The Macedonians thus could land, though with great difficulty, and draw up their forces before any serious opposition could be offered. Porus had at once sent his son with a force of cavalry and chariots to hinder their landing, but it was too late. The force proved no match for the Macedonian cavalry; it was routed with heavy losses; and the shattered remnants returned to tell Porus that Alexander was fully arrayed to meet him. Porus then drew up his army; in the centre were 200 elephants, with 30,000 infantry in rear, while on each wing were 150 chariots and 2000 cavalry; the infantry were armed with the powerful Indian bow which required to be rested on the ground; but the wet weather which had soaked the soil interfered with the proper adjustment of the weapon and caused valuable time to be wasted.

Alexander's mounted archers attacked the Indian left wing and were followed by the heavier cavalry, whose pressure forced Porus to bring supports round from his right wing. A body of Macedonian horse rode round the Indian army, and caused further confusion by attacking them in the rear. Alexander now drove home his attack on the wings, which fled to the shelter of the elephants in the centre. At first the elephants had some success against the Macedonian infantry, but the discipline of the latter held good, and ultimately confusion began to prevail in the Indian ranks. The Indian cavalry were no match for the heavy Macedonian cavalry, whose charges did great execution in their now broken ranks. The elephants then began to stampede. This wrought havoc among the crowded Indians, while the Macedonians had plenty of room to evade their rushes. The whole enemy line was finally surrounded, and cavalry and infantry alike cut to pieces. Any who could find a gap through which to escape, fled, only to meet the remainder of the Greek army under Krateros, who had crossed opposite the camp in readiness to receive the fugitives. The Indian losses were enormous, and included two sons of Porus and many of his high officers. The Greek losses were about 1000 and the Indian 15,000 killed with 9000 taken prisoners. Porus himself fought nobly on an elephant of gigantic size, and was always to be found in the forefront of the battle. The king of Taxila galloped up to him with a message from Alexander, but the proud Indian refused to listen to one whom he regarded as a renegade and hurled a spear at him.

Ambhi then returned to Alexander, and a detachment of horsemen was sent who were able to persuade Porus that he had done
his duty and that there was no shame in surrender. The king, a
man of unusual physique, now completely exhausted and bleeding
from a number of wounds, was led to Alexander, who greeted
his noble antagonist with honour and readily agreed to recognise
his kingly rank. Porus was restored to his kingdom, to which
Alexander added considerable territory; and he became a valuable
ally of the Macedonians. The victory is commemorated on a
remarkable medallion struck by Alexander, on one side of which
he is being crowned by Victory, while on the other the battle
is symbolised by a combat between a Macedonian horseman and
an Indian elephant-rider.

To commemorate his victory Alexander built on the battlefield
the city of Nicaea, and on the site of his camp on the other side
of the river arose another town, Bucephala, named after his
celebrated steed, which had succumbed after accompanying his
master so far. Bucephala became a place of considerable importance, and its successor is the modern Jhélum.

The funeral rites of the dead were performed, sacrifices offered
and games celebrated, and the army allowed a brief relaxation.

Alexander then led a force into the country of the Glausai,
who submitted. He gave the conquered territory to Porus, and
crossed the Chināb into the lands of another Porus, who had
previously made overtures to the invaders but had changed his
mind. On the approach of the Greeks Porus fled and his territory
was easily subjugated. Leaving Hephaistion to consolidate his
conquests, Alexander advanced to the Rāvi (Hydraotes), where
he met with a more vigorous resistance, notably at a town called
Sangala which was stormed, 17,000 of the defenders being slain
and 70,000 taken prisoner. Alexander's losses were not great and
the conquered town was razed to the ground. Friendly relations
were established with a king named Sopeithes (Sophytes, Saub-
huti) who entertained Alexander royally; his hunting parties and
his dogs particularly impressed the Greeks. The Hyphasis (Beās)
was reached, and Alexander, nearing the eastern limit of the Indus
valley, had already begun to hear of the splendours of the kingdoms of the Ganges. But his exhausted army could go no farther.
In reply to his appeal to it to follow him, Koinos, who was one
of his most trusted officers and had commanded the cavalry in

the battle with Porus, acted as spokesman and emphasised the fact that only the exhausted remnants of Alexander's once great army remained. Arrian, who gives a full account of the proceedings, contrasts the silence that followed Alexander's appeal with the applause that greeted the words of Koinos. Alexander retired to his tent and, after a three days' struggle with himself, admitted the necessity of turning back. He therefore built twelve great altars of stone on the banks of the river to commemorate his progress. This was in the late summer of 326 B.C. Classical writers record that these altars, dedicated to the gods of Greece, were long held in veneration by the kings of India, who came to offer sacrifices at them.

Alexander returned to the Hydaspes to make preparations for his return journey down the Indus to the sea; here he received reinforcements from Babylon. Porus was appointed ruler of the lands between the Hydaspes and the Hyphasis, and Ambhi, king of Taxila, was given the lands between the Hydaspes and the Indus, while Philip was appointed satrap of the lands west of the Indus. A fleet was prepared to take the horses and part of the army down the river, while the remainder, under Hephaistion and Krateros, was ordered to march down either bank.

Philip followed in command of the rearguard. In a few days the junction of the Jhelum and Chināb (Hydaspes and Akesines) was reached without opposition, but two boats were lost in the whirlpools. Farther south, however, opposition was being prepared. The Siboi submitted, but the Agalassoi, who resisted, were severely punished for the losses they inflicted on the Greeks. The Malloi (Mālavas) and the Oxydrakai (Kshudrakas), two powerful tribes on the lower Rāvi, combined with other warlike tribes to offer strong resistance to the invaders. Alexander's sudden attacks took them individually by surprise, and the Malloi were routed, in spite of their superior numbers, before their allies could join them. The towns, however, offered some resistance. At one of these Alexander, needlessly exposing himself, was struck by an arrow and apparently seriously wounded. His troops, maddened at their leader's fall, sacked the town and massacred the inhabitants. The wounded Alexander was taken by boat to his base, and on his recovery received the submission of the Malloi, while the Kshudrakas, to avoid a similar fate, came in of their own accord to pay homage to the victor. Other tribes also submitted, and some supplied boats for the Greek army, which continued its progress till the junction of the Chināb and Indus was reached, where a halt was made and a city founded. Farther south, at the city of Sogdi, another Alexandria was planned, which was to be the great port of the upper Indus. The next great ruler whose territory was to be entered was one known to the Greeks as Mousikanos, who had so far made no overtures to the advancing conqueror; on the approach of Alexander, however, he hastened to offer presents and to pay homage, which Alexander readily accepted, and left him on his throne. The Greeks found much to interest them in his kingdom, the customs of which reminded them of Sparta. At this moment Mousikanos's rival and enemy, Sambos (Sambhu), who had previously joined Alexander, rebelled but was quickly disposed of. In the meanwhile, however, the philosophers (i.e. the Brāhmans) had been urging Mousikanos to withdraw his submission, and, when he openly rebelled, Peithon, the new governor of the lower Indus territory, was sent against him. The monarch was captured and executed along with many of the Brāhmans, who were everywhere stirring up the people against the Greeks. The enormous slaughter recorded among the natives of this region shows that Alexander could not afford to take risks and was determined to strike terror into the lands through which he was passing.

Krateros was then sent with nearly half the army to return by the route through the mountains over which they had come. Alexander continued down the river with the fleet, while Peithon replaced Krateros on one bank, and Hephaistion remained in charge on the other. In the summer of 325 B.C. the joint forces reached Patala, an important city standing at a place where the Indus divided into two arms, probably somewhere south-east of the modern Hyderabad in Sind. Hephaistion was ordered to build new walls for the city, and to do everything necessary to make it a great port and naval base. Alexander himself explored the two arms of the Indus and reached the sea, where he sacrificed to Poseidon. On returning to Patala, he made preparations for his departure from India. While Alexander marched through Gedrosia along the northern coast of the Indian Ocean and the Persian Gulf, Nearchos was to remain in charge of the fleet, keeping within touch of the coast and the army. Alexander set out on his hazardous march through the land of the Aritai, which he left Apollophanes to govern. Heavy fighting followed his departure, in which Apollophanes was slain. Entering the deserts of Gedrosia, Alexander found it impossible to keep in touch with the fleet as he had intended, and had to go inland round the mountains. The soldiers suffered terribly from the heat and scarcity of water, and were obliged to abandon the booty which they had taken in India and carried so far; ultimately the survivors reached Carmania, where their troubles were over. Nearchos left an account of his voyage, for he had been asked by Alexander to make observations of the countries along which he coasted, and portions of his narrative have been preserved by later writers. The fleet kept close to the coast, anchoring from time to time to await favourable winds or to get in touch with the garrisons and depôts left by Alexander. After seeing many strange and wild peoples, and enduring great privations, this portion of the expedition finally reached Ormuz, where they found Greeks who told them Alexander was not far away. Nearchos at once went to report to the king. With their meeting the story of Alexander's expedition to India ends; it had lasted three years, 327–324 B.C. His death in the following year prevented the consolidation of his Indian conquests, and a few years after his death not a single Greek officer was left in India. He had, however, proved, as the Muslims were to do in later centuries, the tremendous superiority of a trained army over the vast and unwieldy Hindu armies fighting according to the text-book. He had found routes to India by land and sea which he could have used again, had he survived to do so. He had completely altered the balance of power and the political complexion of north-western India; this was probably the main result of his expedition, but we cannot trace the results in detail. Of the cities he founded none has as yet been excavated, and the majority are unidentified; something of them and of his roads must have remained to facilitate the advance of his successors from Bactria a century later. To us the most important thing is the light thrown on Indian history by the records that survive in the classical historians of an achievement which rightly made a great impression on the ancient world. Alexander is not mentioned in Indian records until the Muslim period; but the Greek historians have preserved the name of one great Indian, Porus, unknown in his own land, as well as others of less note.

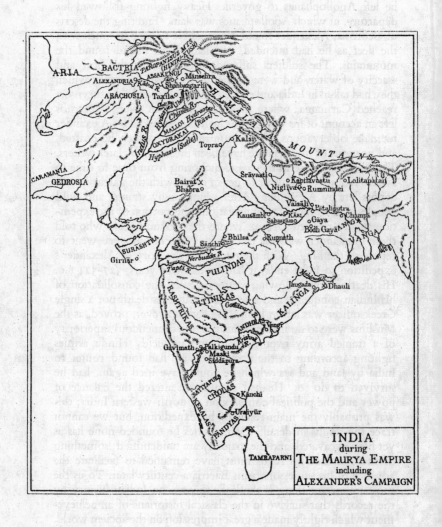

INDIA
during
THE MAURYA EMPIRE
including
ALEXANDER'S CAMPAIGN

CHAPTER III

The Early Mauryas

Very soon after Alexander's departure from India the slightness of the Macedonian hold on the territory which had acknowledged his suzerainty became apparent. Philip, whom he had left as satrap of the north-western provinces, was treacherously assassinated, and Alexander appointed his two Indian allies, Porus and the king of Taxila, to administer these provinces under the general supervision of Eudemos, whose own command lay farther south. The latter was able to maintain his authority, probably more or less nominal, for some six years, when he left India to assist Eumenes in his struggle against Antigonos; he had previously put to death, probably through treachery, one of his Indian colleagues, possibly the great Porus. The lands on the lower Indus, at least those west of the river, remained under Peithon. Little strength was required to shake off the precarious hold of the Greek garrisons in India when the news of Alexander's death reached the lands beyond the Indus.

For the history of the events that followed we are entirely dependent on scattered references in classical literature and a Sanskrit play, the *Mudrārākshasa*, which is of a much later date. When Alexander made enquiries about the lands of the Ganges valley, he was told that there were two great kingdoms there, the Prasii and the Gangaridae. "Prasii" is identified as the Sanskrit *Prachyās*, the "Easterns", and, as we know the Gangaridae lived around the delta of the Ganges, it must be a general term for the states under the suzerainty of Magadha, then the most important kingdom of northern India. The king, Agrammes or Xandrames, was said to be a man of low character, the son of a barber and the paramour of the queen of his predecessor whom he had murdered in order to seize the throne. He is identified as the Dhana Nanda of the *Purānas*. The Indian leader who, according to Justin, liberated India from the yoke of Greek servitude, was Sandracottos, or Chandragupta, a young man whose ambitions had early attracted the interest of the Nanda house. It is generally agreed that Chandragupta was of humble origin on the maternal side, and the family name, Maurya, borne by his dynasty, suggests that her name was Murā. Through his father, however, he was connected with the royal house of Magadha. Buddhist tradition asserts that the Mauryas were descended from an ancient noble family, the Moriyas, who play a prominent part in the time of Buddha. By his arrogant behaviour Chandragupta had aroused the wrath of his master, the Nanda king of Magadha, in whose army he held a high command, and his execution had been ordered. He fled northwards, and during his exile met Alexander, whom, according to Plutarch, he advised to continue his advance into the Ganges valley, where the incompetence and unpopularity of the reigning monarch would make the conquest of Magadha an easy task, thus corroborating what Alexander had already been told by his Indian allies. The text of Justin has *Alexandrum* as the name of the monarch from whom Chandragupta fled, and it is usual to emend this to *Nandrum* (*i.e.* Nanda), as in the above story. If we reject this emendation, however, then it was Alexander himself whom Chandragupta had offended so seriously that he had to seek safety in flight. It is very likely, in any case, that he, like many other Indian rajas, visited Alexander to seek his help against a rival, and that he hoped to persuade the Macedonian to aid him to the throne of Magadha. He was certainly able to raise a sufficient force to return to Magadha and overthrow the son of the usurper, who now ruled in his father's place. Chandragupta seated himself on the throne to which, through his father, he had some claim, and set about the organisation and extension of the vast army which his predecessor had commanded. The troubles that followed the death of Alexander found Chandragupta strong enough to overrun northern India and drive the Macedonian garrisons everywhere back across the Indus, so that his frontier became coterminous with that of Seleucus, then ruler of the eastern part of Alexander's dominions. Throughout his career, Chandragupta was assisted and advised by a very able Brāhman named Vishnugupta Chānakya, who plays a Machiavellian part in the *Mudrārākshasa*. According to the play, Chānakya disposed of Parvataka and his brother Vairodhaka, who had been Chandragupta's chief allies. It is just possible that this Parvataka is the king whom the Greeks call Porus, and that we have here further evidence that he came to an untimely end. After disposing of the Greeks, Chandragupta was able to conquer all northern India, but we have no details of his campaigns.

In the twenty years following Alexander's death, the struggle for his dominions in Asia was finally settled in favour of Seleucus Nikator. About 304 B.C. Seleucus had sufficiently consolidated his hold on his empire to think of resuming Alexander's campaign in India, and with this object he crossed the Indus. Whether Chandragupta and Seleucus ever came into direct conflict is not evident from the sources, but it is probable that they did not. It is certain that Seleucus found the Indians much too strong for him. Chandragupta had learned something of military matters from the Macedonians, and his army was no longer a mere unwieldy mass. We do know that Seleucus, who was probably anxious about events far away in Asia Minor where Antigonos was again preparing for a final bid for power, concluded a treaty with Chandragupta, the terms of which suggest that the latter was victorious, if not in the field, at least in the negotiations. The Indian monarch presented Seleucus with 500 elephants, which were destined to play an important part in the final conflict with Antigonos at Ipsus, and in return received the satrapies of Parapanisadae, Aria and Arachosia, and the eastern part of Gedrosia, that is to say the southern half of modern Afghanistan and Balūchistan. Seleucus withdrew to the west of the Hindu Kush, thus leaving the Indian emperor a natural frontier. It is not quite clear whether a matrimonial alliance formed part of this treaty, or whether the right of marriage between the two families was simply recognised. If the usual oriental practice was followed and if we regard Chandragupta as the victor, then it would mean that a daughter or other female relative of Seleucus was given to the Indian ruler or to one of his sons, so that Asoka may have had Greek blood in his veins. Seleucus sent an ambassador, Megasthenes, to the Maurya court, who left a valuable record of his sojourn in India. We know little of the details of Chandragupta's reign, but from a classical source we learn that by his tyrannical rule he forfeited the name of liberator which his campaigns against the Macedonians had earned him. This may mean no more than that he saw the necessity of ruling with a firm hand his vast empire, much of which would have slipped away from him on the slightest display of weakness; in his younger days he had seen too many kings lose their lives and thrones not to take every precaution against possible rivals and assassins. His interest in public works is shown by his construction of the great lake

Sudarsana, near Junāgarh, which was improved for his grandson Asoka by a Yavana governor named Tushāspha. Jain tradition, which is neither corroborated nor contradicted elsewhere, says that Chandragupta was, or became, a Jain and abdicated to spend the remainder of his life as an ascetic. There is nothing improbable in the story.

In any case, after a reign of twenty-four years he was succeeded in the early years of the third century B.C. by his son Bindusāra, whose epithet Amitraghāta, "the slayer of his foes", has been preserved by the Greeks in the form "Amitrochates". Of his reign we know little; a rebellion which broke out in Taxila was easily suppressed by his son Asoka, who found that the discontent of the people was with the local governor and not with the king. Bindusāra kept his father's empire intact and may even have extended it in the south, for Asoka succeeded to a vast empire. He maintained friendly relations with Seleucus, who sent an ambassador to his court. It is to a chance incident in their relations that we owe the preservation of his name in Greek literature, for he was the hero of the anecdote of the monarch who asked Seleucus to procure him figs, wine and a philosopher, but was told that sophists were not for sale among the Greeks. The interest of the anecdote lies in its suggesting that the two monarchs kept up a regular correspondence.

Seleucus sent an ambassador named Megasthenes to the court of Chandragupta, where he spent a number of years; he had previously been on the staff of Sibyrtios, satrap of Arachosia, and had several times visited the Maurya capital. He was therefore chosen for this new post as familiar with Indian courts and likely to be *persona grata* with Chandragupta himself. Megasthenes compiled an account of India, its geography, social life and political institutions, which formed the principal source upon which later classical writers drew for their knowledge of India. The book survives only in the fragments preserved by later writers, yet it tells us more about India than any other foreign account before the time of al-Bīrūnī. There is no reason to doubt the general accuracy of Megasthenes on matters which came under his own observation, or for which he could readily have secured trustworthy informants. The few travellers' tales which he records do not in any way justify suspicion of the more sober parts of his book.

The capital of the kingdom of the Prasii, or Magadha, was, he tells us, Palibothra, i.e. Pātaliputra; it stood where a large tributary (the Sōn) joins the Ganges, and occupied a narrow parallelogram, eight miles in length and one and a half in breadth. It was surrounded by a wall defended by 570 towers and pierced by a number of gates. Around the city was a ditch 600 feet broad and 30 cubits deep. The king, we are told, was also known by the name of his capital.

Elaborate precautions were taken to secure the safety of the king's person. He was continually surrounded by a bodyguard of women who were probably, if we may judge from the yavanīs of Sanskrit literature, of foreign origin. The casual statement of Megasthenes, that a woman who kills a king when he is drunk becomes the wife of his successor, suggests the dangers that threatened the throne in India, and is probably a memory of the means by which the Nanda had gained the throne of Magadha. The king was in constant terror of his life and regularly changed his sleeping apartment lest plotters should come upon him in the night. That this was one of the dangers that did threaten an Indian king we know from the author of the Mudrārākshasa, who tells us how Chānakya saved Chandragupta, not only from being poisoned, but also from a plot to assassinate him at midnight in his chamber. The king was not entirely confined to his palace, however. He used to leave it to administer justice in the court, a part of his duties in which he showed great energy, sometimes spending the whole day there if necessary. When the hour came for his daily massage, a very popular exercise among the Indians, he did not allow it to interrupt the business of the court, but continued to hear cases while four attendants massaged him. Sometimes he left the palace to offer sacrifice or to go hunting. On the latter occasions his route was marked off by ropes and he was surrounded by his bodyguard of Amazons, who were in turn escorted by spearmen. It was death for any one to attempt to enter within the ropes, and drums and gongs were beaten to herald the king's approach. When hunting in his grounds he shot from a platform to which the game was driven; in the open country he rode an elephant. His women-guards were armed with every variety of weapons, and rode on elephants or horses, or drove in chariots, just like men.

Besides his body-guard of women, Chandragupta had considerable military forces; he is said to have had at his disposal 600,000 infantry, 30,000 cavalry and 9000 elephants, in addition to chariots and camp followers. Similar figures are given for the Āndhra kingdom a century or two later, and Muslim writers fifteen hundred years afterwards report equally huge and unwieldy armies in the Hindu kingdoms of the south.

The army was administered by a board of thirty officials divided into six groups of five each, in charge of departments; one department with its council of five was responsible for co-operation between the army and the admiral of the fleet, while a second dealt with transport and commissariat of all kinds, the provision of bullocks, the transport of artillery, food for the soldiers and fodder for the cattle; it was their duty also to supply drummers and gong-beaters, grooms and grass-cutters for the horses, and all the technical service required. The other four departments controlled the fighting-men, who were divided into the four traditional arms of India, infantry, cavalry, chariots and elephants. The king maintained stables for the horses and elephants and depôts for the arms; the soldiers had to return their mounts to the one and their arms to the other. The foot-soldiers carried a bow of a man's height, which shot an arrow three yards long, and was so large and powerful that it had to be rested on the ground and a foot used to draw it. All were armed with a long, narrow shield and a long sword, and some carried javelins also. The cavalry bore a lance, sword and buckler. The soldiers, who were maintained at the king's expense, spent their time drinking in idleness when not fighting, but they were always ready to take the field, for they had to provide nothing of their own.

Megasthenes also gives an outline of the civil administration of the country and of the capital. The latter was ruled by six boards each consisting of five members. The first board dealt with everything relating to industry. The second was responsible for the control of foreigners, it allotted lodgings to them during their stay in the country, and maintained a staff whose duty it was to supervise their movements and to escort them until they left. They were looked after if they fell ill, buried if they died, and in the latter case their estates were administered on behalf of their heirs. The third board corresponded to our registrars of births and deaths. It is interesting to note that Megasthenes was struck by the fact that the object of this office was not the purely utilitarian one of gathering statistics for taxation purposes, but that it existed on the general ground that births and deaths among all classes of the community were a matter of concern to the government. The fourth board dealt with trade and commerce in all their aspects. It had its inspectors of weights and measures, and saw to it that all produce was duly sold in the public markets as it came into season. A tax was levied on the seller of each commodity, and if a merchant wished to deal in more than one he had to pay additional taxes. New and second-hand articles had to be kept separate, any breach of this rule being a punishable offence. The sixth board collected the taxes, the tithes on articles sold in the markets. Any attempt to evade this tax was punished by death. In their collective capacity the boards dealt with matters of general public interest, such as the maintenance of public buildings and the upkeep of market-places and temples.

Megasthenes gives no details of the provincial administration of the empire, of which, however, we are able to learn something a generation later from the inscriptions of Asoka. The former describes the seventh and highest class of the population as that of the king's ministers, who held the chief government posts and the legal offices. Another class, the sixth, consisted of the inspectors, who watched all that went on and reported secretly to the king. These offices were given only to very reliable men, who obtained much of their information through the courtesans of the cities and camps. They were believed never to make false reports, and indeed there are other ancient testimonies to the high reputation of Indians for truthfulness. Asoka seems to have increased considerably the number of these inspectors and to have extended their duties.

Megasthenes divides the people of India into seven classes, three of which have already been mentioned. One he calls the "philosophers", *i.e.* the Brāhmans, who are employed privately to offer sacrifices or publicly by the king. At the new year they were assembled by the king to make suggestions for improving the country and furthering public interests generally; good advice was rewarded by exemption from taxation.

The second class, the agriculturists, formed the bulk of the population. They were exempt from military service, and the remarkable spectacle is presented to us of peasants carrying on their labours undisturbed with a battle raging close at hand. The land was the property of the king, who received one-fourth of the produce from the tiller of the soil.

Megasthenes' next class comprised herdsmen and hunters, who alone were allowed to deal in animals. For their services in protecting the tilled fields from birds and beasts they received an allowance of grain from the king.

The fourth class included all those who worked at trades, or sold goods, or performed any manual labour. Some, like the armourers and shipbuilders, were employed directly by the king, and were not allowed to work for private individuals. The soldiers were provided with weapons by the state. The admiral of the king's navy hired out ships to private individuals for the transport of goods and passengers. The soldiers, the fifth class, have already been mentioned. It will thus be seen that Megasthenes had grasped the general principle of the caste system.

Other officials were in charge of the rivers and of the irrigation system, measuring the land and seeing that every one had his share of water. Of the Maurya interest in irrigation schemes we know from an inscription of Rudradāman, which tells how he restored the irrigation system of the Sudarsana lake, first planned by Pushyamitra, the governor for the Maurya Chandragupta, and afterwards improved, as already stated, by Asoka's governor, Tushāspha. Other officials built roads and set up mile-stones with distances engraved on them. This, taken in conjunction with the statement of Megasthenes that the Brāhmans made their suggestions to the king in writing, are early indications of the general literacy suggested by Asoka's inscriptions.

In 1905 the manuscript of a work on politics (*Arthasāstra*) was discovered in south India, professing to be composed by Vishnugupta, or Chānakya, or Kautilya, the celebrated minister of Chandragupta, conqueror of the Nandas. Nothing is elsewhere recorded of his having written a book on the subject of which he was a practical master. The work has been much discussed since its discovery, and many distinguished scholars maintain that it is the work of the famous Maurya minister. References to works on politics are not uncommon in Sanskrit literature, but such as had survived were of late date. With the *dharmasāstra* we are familiar; it deals with law and morality: the *Arthasāstra* is not concerned with morality, but with profit and expediency. It assumes that the end justifies the means. In view of the importance of the *Kautilīya Arthasāstra*, however, as a work dealing largely with practical affairs, we may here give a brief sketch of its contents. Its practical aspect must not be overestimated. Many of its details and regulations are probably quite theoretical and appear to be the outcome of the Indian love of systematisation. The only form of government it conceives is an absolute monarchy. Book I therefore deals with the education and training of a king; he should study religion, philosophy and economics in every aspect that may affect the lives of his subjects, and should himself practise self-control. The selection of ministers and means of testing them are then discussed, together with the employment of spies and other agents at home and abroad. In conclusion, the king's private life is dealt with and the precautions that should be taken to protect him in the palace, in the harem and from his sons. Book II particularises the duties of the vast army of inspectors who control every sphere of the citizen's life, from the collection of taxes to the prevention of fire. The third and fourth books treat of civil and criminal law, the punishment of crime and the methods of extorting confessions. They also deal with the means of averting and relieving such natural calamities as famine and flood. Book V treats of ministers, and how to get rid of those who are not trusted. It also deals with the replenishment of the treasury, and gives an elaborate scale of salaries for servants of the state. The sixth book sets forth the proper qualities of a king and the nature of his foreign relations. In the seventh the six forms of state policy are discussed. According to some Indian writers there are only two, war and peace; but Kautilya distinguishes six, by the addition of degrees of neutrality or alliance, and discusses at length the question whether the stronger or weaker enemy should be attacked first. The eighth book investigates the vices of a king, and the calamities which may threaten a kingdom. The ninth and tenth deal with war, when and how to make it, how to avoid it if possible, but how to prosecute it whole-heartedly once it has been begun. The eleventh book expounds the various ways of weakening an enemy by sowing dissension in his camp, while the twelfth tells how to reduce a foe too strong to be met in the field by the use of spies, assassins, poison and women. The thirteenth book is similar, and describes the art of capturing an enemy fortress by provoking dissension within, frightening the garrison by apparently supernatural means, luring out and capturing its king by stratagem, or in the last resort by direct attack; in conclusion the pacification of conquered territory is dealt with. The fourteenth book deals with secret means of injuring an enemy. The concluding book contains the scheme of the whole work, which it attributes to Kautilya.

Great ingenuity has been displayed, but with little real success, in finding in the *Arthasāstra* passages to prove its Maurya date by comparison with statements of Megasthenes. Coincidences indeed occur, but many of them are repeated in other ages of Indian history, and the differences are much more striking. Megasthenes finds more corroboration in Manu than in Kautilya. There is no reference to the boards of five described by Megasthenes; indeed, the author of the *Arthasāstra* distinctly states that three or four is as large a number as can be trusted to form a council. The writer makes no reference to a navy or to the elaborate passport regulations and rules for the care of strangers recorded by Megasthenes. It may be noted, also, in passing that allusions to natural products in the text suggest familiarity with south rather than north India. In so far as Megasthenes can be accepted as an authority, the *Arthasāstra* describes a much more complicated system of taxation and a more highly developed industrial and commercial life than existed under Maurya rule. The frequent references to gold coins for example must refer to a period in the Christian era.

In dealing with the date of the *Arthasāstra* it is very necessary not to lay too much emphasis on detail. It does not read like the work of a minister of a great empire, but presupposes a small kingdom surrounded by enemies of equal or greater strength. There is nothing in it to suggest that the author played a very active part in politics. It is incredible that Chānakya could have written a work of this kind without revealing a personal touch. The opinions of a certain Kautilya are frequently quoted in a way which shows that the compiler followed him and his school. It is possible that the great Kautilya compiled a book of political aphorisms which are quoted by the author along with other writers but with more approval. But there is no means of proving that the Kautilya in question is the Maurya minister. In declining to credit Chānakya with the authorship of the *Kautilīya Arthasāstra*, we are not diminishing his reputation. It is not by any means a work to be compared with Aristotle's *Politics*. There is no internal evidence as to the date of the work; that must be sought elsewhere. It was known to Bāna and Dandin, and probably to Kālidāsa, so that it was in existence in the sixth or fifth century A.D. From the literary point of view it does not appear to be a work of the third century B.C., a period in which no work of a like form is known to have been written. The book indeed describes itself correctly as "a compendium of all the *Arthasāstras* that have been written by ancient teachers for the guidance of kings in acquiring and holding the earth". It is thus one of those encyclopaedic works compiled in the third or fourth century A.D., when the codification of knowledge was fashionable. The *Purānas*, the *Mānavadharmasāstra*, and the *Kāmasūtra*, a book with which the *Arthasāstra* has many affinities in style, are other works of this date, a period when scholars were at work codifying and systematising the various branches of knowledge. The attribution to Chānakya is late, and was probably encouraged by the tradition that he had written an *Arthasāstra*.

CHAPTER IV

Asoka, the Sungas and the Āndhras

After a reign of some twenty-five years, Bindusāra was succeeded about 274 B.C. by his son, Asokavardhana, usually known as Asoka, whose importance in the eyes of Buddhists has given him a place in Indian history to which, from a political point of view, his grandfather is much more entitled. He is called Asokavardhana in the *Purānas*, and in Buddhist literature Asoka; in the only one of his inscriptions in which he refers to himself by name he is Asoka. In all his other inscriptions he is called Devānāmpriya, usually with the epithet Priyadarsin. The term Devānāmpriya, "dear to the gods", may be translated as "His Majesty"; from one of the rock edicts we learn that it was also used by his predecessors, and we find it in an inscription of his grandson, Dasaratha; in the *Mudrārākshasa* it is applied to his grandfather, Chandragupta. One other reference to Asoka is found, that in the Girnar inscription of the satrap Rudradāman, which calls him Asoka Maurya. It hardly required the recently discovered Maski inscription to confirm the identity of the Asoka of Buddhist tradition with the Priyadarsin or Piyadasi of the inscriptions. It is to these inscriptions, engraved on rock in various parts of his vast empire, that we owe the fact that we have a picture of Asoka such as we possess of no other character in early Indian history. But although they throw some valuable light on the history of his reign, these inscriptions were not intended as historical documents.

For the events attending Asoka's accession our only source of information is Buddhist tradition, but there is no serious reason to doubt its statement that he had served with success as governor of Taxila and was acting in the same capacity at the still more important centre of Ujjain when he succeeded to the throne, to which in the usual Indian manner he had been designated by Bindusāra as the most worthy of his sons. That his elder brother Susima disputed his claim and was vanquished is probably true, but it is not necessary to believe that Asoka had ninety-nine brothers and disposed of them all to make his throne secure.

We know that his coronation took place four years after his accession; the reasons for the delay are unknown, but the fact gives support to the tradition that his claim to the throne was disputed. Moreover, his inscriptions are dated not from his accession, but from his solemn coronation, the anniversary of which was always celebrated with particular ceremony.

Asoka inherited a vast empire which two able rulers had been organising and pacifying for half a century, and he seems to have had little cause for wars of offence or defence. In the ninth year after his coronation, however, he states that he waged war on the Kalinga country, which adjoined his empire on the southeast, cutting it off from access to the Indian Ocean. This campaign was probably similar to that of Samudragupta six hundred years later. The kingdom of Kalinga in those days was very powerful, and the severity of the campaign and the miseries it inflicted on both sides made a deep impression on the victor, who records that 100,000 men were slain, 150,000 taken prisoners, and many times that number perished of disease and hardship. He became filled with remorse when he saw the losses by slaughter, disease and capture which the war had entailed, and, looking back in later years, said that he would then regret deeply even a thousandth part of such losses in war. The Kalinga war marks the close of the Maurya era of conquest begun by Chandragupta. From the distribution of Asoka's inscriptions and other sources we have a good idea of the extent of his empire; the inscriptions mention his governors of Taxila in the Panjab, Tosali in Kalinga, Ujjain in central India, and Suvarnagiri in the south; while he himself ruled in Pātaliputra, the ancient centre of Magadhan culture, and occasionally called himself king of Magadha. The location of his pillar inscriptions at Delhi (Topra and Meerut), Allāhābād, Lauriya and Rāmpūrva in northern Bihar, and at Sanchi in Bhopāl, adds little to our geographical knowledge, but those at Niglīva and Rumnindei show that the Nepalese Terai was within his dominions. Nepalese tradition records that he founded the city of Lalitapatan, where he built five stupas. His daughter Charumati settled in Nepāl in a convent built by her. We have it on Kalhana's authority, late it is true, that Asoka ruled Kashmīr, where he built Srīnagar.

The inscriptions engraved on rocks are more widely distributed. The most northerly is at Shahbazgarhi, 40 miles north-east of

Peshawar, and there is another to the east of this at Mānsehra in the Hazāra district of the Panjab. On the borders of the empire, in the lower Himalaya, are the Kalsi edicts, 15 miles west of Mussoorie. In western India are edicts at Girnar in Kāthiāwār and at Sopāra in the Thāna district of Bombay, and in the east, in the conquered Kalinga country, at Dhauli, to the north of Puri and Jaugada, in the Ganjam district of Madras. In the centre of the empire are the Bhabra edict, found near Bairat in Jaipur, and others at Sahasrām in Bengal and Rupnath in the north of the Central Provinces. The south has the Maski edict, in the Rāichūr district of Hyderabad, and edicts at Gavimath and Palkigundu in the Koppal district of Hyderabad, and at Siddapura in Mysore. It is evident then, from the testimony of the epigraphic records, that Asoka ruled the whole of India except the extreme south, which was in the hands of the Cholas and Pāndyas. The inscriptions refer also to the nations on the borders of the empire. There were in the south, as already mentioned, the Cholas and Pāndyas, whose lands stretched as far as Tamraparni, *i.e.* Ceylon; while one edict adds two smaller border chiefs, the Keralaputra, *i.e.* the king of Kerāla or Malabar, and the Satiyaputra, not yet satisfactorily identified, but probably connected with the Āndhras. Mentioned along with these independent kingdoms of the south are the Yavana king, Antiyaka, that is the Seleucid Antiochos Theos, whose lands marched with the Maurya empire on the north-west, and the other Greek kings who were his neighbours. On the outer fringe of the empire, but within the king's territory, were the Yonas, the Greeks in the lands ceded by Seleucus to Chandragupta; other Yavanàs are named, along with the Gandhāras, apparently as independent; they were probably the rulers of southern Afghanistan and the land west of the upper Indus. The Kambojas, mentioned with them and located north-west of Gandhāra in the Hindu Kush, spoke a semi-Iranian language and were regarded by Hindus as only half-civilised. Another group of frontier peoples living within the king's territory but probably retaining some vestiges of autonomy, belonged to the south. The Pulindas or Parindas and the Āndhras were peoples of the Deccan, the latter of which rose to great power on the break-up of the Maurya empire. The Bhojas, Pitinikàs and Rashtrikas are other peoples of the centre or south who cannot be identified with certainty. Independent evidence of Maurya suzerainty in

Kāthiāwār is found in Rudradāman's inscription. Kashmīr tradition need not be doubted when it says that Kashmīr was included in Asoka's dominions, and that he built the first Srīnagar as its capital.

One of the most important pieces of information contained in the inscriptions of Asoka is chronological. The thirteenth rock edict refers to the realms of his contemporaries, Antiyaka, king of the Yavanas, and beyond him Turamaya, Maga, Antekina and Alikasadara; these are identified as the kings of the Greek world at this time, Antiochos (Theos) the Seleucid king of Syria (265–246 B.C.), Ptolemy (Philadelphos) king of Egypt (285–247 B.C.), Magas, king of Cyrene (285–258 B.C.), Antigonos of Macedon (277–239 B.C.), and Alexander, probably Alexander king of Epirus (272–255 B.C.). The latest period at which all these were ruling together may be put at 258–257 B.C., which may be regarded as the thirteenth and fourteenth years after Asoka's coronation, in which the inscription was cut. His coronation may therefore be dated about 270 B.C., and his accession 274 or 273 B.C. This date, which, it should be remembered, is only the latest possible, fits in very well with the traditional lengths of the reigns of Chandragupta and Bindusāra, for the former of which we have points fixed within narrow limits by the death of Alexander the Great and the treaty with Seleucus. It is of course possible that Bindusāra may have reigned for a shorter period than the twenty-five years with which he is credited in the *Purānas*, in which case Asoka's accession must be put a little earlier.

A certain amount of information regarding the administration of the empire can be gleaned from the inscriptions of Asoka, for officials of various ranks are mentioned with hints as to the scope of their duties. The great provinces were ruled by governors, several of whom were members of the royal family; these were the north-western province, which Asoka himself had ruled in his youth, with its capital at Taxila; the important western province administered from Ujjain; the recently conquered lands of the Kalingas in the east, the capital of which was Tosali; and the southern province, the governor of which resided at Suvarna-giri, identified as the modern Kanakagiri.

A later record already mentioned has preserved the name of a local governor of Girnar who is described as a Yavana raja; his name, Tushāspha, seems to be Persian and certainly is not Greek.

Next to the provincial governors were the district commissioners, the *mahāmātras* or *pradesikas*, of whom there seem to have been several grades, for sometimes *mahāmātras* received orders from other officials of the same name. Thus the *mahāmātras* of the district of Isila were subordinate to the prince and *mahāmātras* of Suvarna-giri, who had authority over the whole province. Some districts seem to have preserved an old republican constitution, for they were administered by a *parishad* or group of *mahāmātras*, to whom Asoka gave his orders direct. *Mahāmātras* were also appointed for other than purely administrative purposes. The *anta-mahā-mātras* supervising the border tribes must have had duties of a semi-military character, while the *dharma-mahāmātras* were inspectors of religion and morals. Another important class of officers were the *rājukas*, a word which originally meant a land-surveyor, one who measured land with a rope (*rajju*) to assess the tax upon it. But in Asoka's time the *rājukas* were officials of great power, controlling hundreds of thousands of men, with full discretion to punish or reward. Megasthenes calls them *archons*. Minor officials were the *yutas* or *yuktas*, who acted as secretaries to the council. Light is perhaps thrown on Asoka's foreign relations by a reference to his *dūtas* in a context which implies that he sent them to the lands of the Greek princes mentioned above. The reference may be only to special envoys who were missionaries rather than political representatives; but when we remember that Seleucus and Chandragupta maintained representatives at one another's courts, we are justified in taking the word *dūta* in its usual meaning and in assuming that Asoka was diplomatically represented at the courts of the great kings of the Greek world of his day.

After the Kalinga war, Asoka decided to employ his position and power not, in the traditional manner, in military conquests and the extension of his dominions, but to promote the cultivation of the virtues by the system of ethics, which he calls *dhamma* (*dharma*), duty, the law of right living, morality. His system was based on Buddhism, by which he had then become deeply influenced. In the seventeenth year of his reign he laid down the new principles by which the empire was to be ruled and the lives of the people guided. These were published in a series of edicts engraved on rocks or on specially prepared pillars in various parts of the country, and composed in the particular form of Prākrit

which was the vernacular of the district. They were, as the seventh
pillar edict says, inscribed wherever there were rocks or pillars,
so that they might be permanent. Their contents were intended
to be made known to every citizen. It is impossible to say how
far we ought to assume widespread literacy from the dissemination of these inscriptions. The fact that they are called *sravanas*,
proclamations, suggests that they were read aloud by officers appointed for the purpose and that, like proclamations in medieval
Europe, it was through the ear rather than the eye that their
contents were promulgated, although they were afterwards set
as reminders in a public place for all to see. The inscriptions of
the north-west are in the local script of Gandhāra, Kharoshthi,
which runs from right to left, while those elsewhere are in the
Brāhmī alphabet, the ancestor of the Devanāgarī alphabets, which,
like the Kharoshthi, can be traced back to a Phoenician original.
But whereas Kharoshthi is a natural evolution from an Aramaic
original, Brāhmī is a learned and artificial adaptation of a foreign
alphabet to the phonetic system of the Indian grammarians. It is
of interest to note that the writers of some of the Brāhmī inscriptions, even in the far south, give their signatures in Kharoshthi,
which suggests that they were brought from the north-west to
do the work. There is no reason to doubt that the idea of in-
scribing these edicts on stone was suggested by the Persian custom,
and the very formula with which they open, "Thus speaks king
Devānāmpriya Priyadarsin", seems to be modelled on the corresponding Achaemenid formula. The word *lipi* or *dipi*, meaning
an inscription, is also Persian. The Kharoshthi alphabet had been
in use in the provinces of the north-west, which had been under
Persian rule; and the fact that the words *lip* and *pish*, signifying
to write, are both Persian loan-words, suggests that the art of
writing thus came to India.

It is customary to classify Asoka's inscriptions as follows, in
what may, with considerable certainty, be described as their
chronological order.

I. The minor rock edicts inscribed in nine different places,
dating from about 257 B.C. In these Asoka appeals to all earnestly
to exert themselves to obtain true happiness, and gives a brief
summary of the law of right living.

II. The unique Bhabra edict addressed to the clergy of Magadha
is of special value for the history of the Buddhist canon, as in it

the king commends seven texts, which can all be identified, as specially worthy of attention.

III. The fourteen rock edicts found in seven different places, and dated in the seventeenth and eighteenth regnal years, or about 257–256 B.C. These tell the story of the change in Asoka's outlook on life and expound the principles he wished to be observed.

IV. The two Kalinga edicts, which are specially concerned with the conquered province and are therefore not duplicated elsewhere. These take the place of certain edicts in the general series.

V. The dedications in the Barābar caves near Gāya of the seventeenth and twenty-fourth regnal years. These are quite brief but are of interest as showing that Asoka did, as he claimed, honour all sects, for the Ajīvikas, a very strict order of ascetics, for whom, possibly, he even had the caves excavated, had little or nothing in common with Buddhists.

VI. The two pillar inscriptions in the Terai are important as corroborating the literary tradition that Asoka performed a pilgrimage to the sites associated with Buddha. That at Rumnindei fixes the position of the Lumbinī garden where Buddha was born. The Niglīva pillar tells us incidentally that Asoka also reverenced the former Buddhas.

VII. The seven pillar edicts, found in six places, were published about 243 B.C. and supplement the rock edicts.

VIII. The last records of Asoka's reign are the minor pillar edicts, which relate to the government of the Buddhist church.

The most marked feature of Asoka's preaching was its exaggerated insistence on the sanctity of life, especially of animal life. In his youth he had been devoted to war and to hunting. Tradition indeed says that he used to be known as the "cruel Asoka". He tells us himself that thousands of animals used to be killed daily to supply the needs of the royal household. The revulsion of feeling he experienced after the Kalinga war, and his gradual adoption of Buddhist teaching, facilitated by the old Indian doctrine of successive rebirths, not only made him cease from war, but also led him to prevent the slaughter of animals as far as possible. He says that he had reduced the daily allowance of flesh in his household to two peacocks and a deer, and even this was later abolished. As Megasthenes tells us, hunting had always been the sport of Indian kings; Asoka says that kings in the past had been fond of hunting expeditions and similar amusements, but that he no longer cared for such frivolous entertainments and had ordered them to be replaced by tours of inspection, varied with visits to holy men and the discussion of ethical problems (Rock Edict VIII). Fifteen years later, in the thirtieth year of his reign, the fifth pillar edict laid down a code of regulations for the protection of animal life throughout the kingdom. A large variety of animals was not to be killed under any circumstances, including parrots, wild geese, bats, ants, tortoises, squirrels, porcupines, lizards, rhinoceroses, pigeons, and all quadrupeds which were neither useful nor edible. This last qualification applied to most of the animals on the list. There was little economic or other advantage in preserving most of the animals mentioned, so that it was probably their very uselessness that made their slaughter seem so needless to Asoka. It should be noted that the list shows that Asoka did not restrict the liberty of his subjects to eat animal food nearly as much as he did that of the royal household. Goats, ewes and sows, with young or in milk, were not to be slaughtered, nor their young till they were six months old. On certain days of the year, fifty-six in number, fish were not to be caught or sold, and on the same days no animals might be killed in the royal game-preserves. These regulations can be justified as easily on economic as on humanitarian or religious grounds. The object was to introduce a close time for semi-domesticated animals, like the game in the royal preserves and the fish in artificial ponds. The branding of horses was forbidden on certain days as was also the castration of animals. The humanitarian motive underlying these measures is probably indicated by the fact that the edict concludes with the statement that the king was accustomed to release a number of prisoners on each anniversary of his coronation. With the slaughter of living creatures and cruelty to them, Asoka classed disrespect to relatives, Brāhmans and ascetics, and he therefore urged the cultivation of such virtues as obedience to parents, kindness to servants, generous treatment of friends, and respect for holy men. He emphasised the need of speaking the truth, an interesting commentary on the classical stories of the truthfulness of Indians. All sects were to be honoured equally, and in this the king himself set an example to his subjects. A man who disparages other sects from pride in his own really injures his own sect; it is essentials that matter and not external forms.

Asoka highly commended charity, but he pointed out that no charity excels the gift of right living. He himself displayed his benevolence in highly practical fashion; special officials were appointed to supervise the distribution of his charities and those of his queens and other members of the royal family. Travellers in particular were well cared for. Along the roads banyan trees were planted to give shade to man and beast; at each half *kōs*, wells were dug; and rest-houses were built and watering-places made for the comfort of wayfarers. Medical services were provided for man and beast, and healing herbs were imported and planted in districts to which they were not native.

We give one of Asoka's edicts (Pillar Edict VII as translated by Hultsch), as a specimen of the style and matter of these documents:

King Devānāmpriya Priyadarsin speaks thus:

The kings who were in times past, had this desire, that men might (be made to) progress by the promotion of morality; but men were not made to progress by an adequate promotion of morality.

Concerning this, King Devānāmpriya Priyadarsin speaks thus:

The following occurred to me. On one hand, in times past kings had this desire, that men might (be made to) progress by an adequate promotion of morality; (but) on the other hand, men were not made to progress by an adequate promotion of morality. How then might men (be made to) conform to (morality)? How might men (be made to) progress by an adequate promotion of morality? How could I elevate them by the promotion of morality? Concerning this, King Devānāmpriya Priyadarsin speaks thus:

The following occurred to me. I shall issue proclamations on morality, (and) shall order instruction in morality (to be given). Hearing this, men will conform to (it), will be elevated, and will (be made to) progress considerably by the promotion of morality. For this purpose proclamations on morality were issued by me, (and) manifold instruction in morality was ordered (to be given), (in order that those agents) (of mine) too who are occupied with many people, will exhort (them) and will explain (morality to them) in detail. The *rājukas* also, who are occupied with many hundred thousands of men,—these too were ordered by me: "In such and such a manner exhort ye the people who are devoted to morality".

Devānāmpriya Priyadarsin speaks thus:

Having in view this very (matter), I have set up pillars of morality, appointed *mahāmātras* of morality, (and) issued (proclamations) on morality.

King Devānāmpriya Priyadarsin speaks thus:

On the roads banyan-trees were caused to be planted by me (in order that) they might afford shade to cattle and men, (and) (mango-groves) were caused to be planted. And (at intervals) of eight kōs wells were caused to be dug by me, and flights of steps (for descending into the water) were caused to be built. Numerous drinking-places were caused to be established by me, here and there, for the enjoyment of cattle and men. (But) this so-called enjoyment (is) (of little consequence). For with various comforts have the people been blessed both by former kings and by myself. But by me this has been done for the following purpose: that they might conform to that practice of morality.

Devānāmpriya Priyadarsin speaks thus:

Those my *mahāmātras* of morality too are occupied with affairs of many kinds which are beneficial to ascetics as well as to house-holders, and they are occupied also with all sects. Some (*mahāmātras*) were ordered by me to busy themselves with the affairs of the *samgha*; likewise others were ordered by me to busy themselves also with the Brāhmanas (and) Ajīvikas, others were ordered by me to busy themselves also with the Nirgranthas; others were ordered by me to busy themselves also with various (other) sects; (thus) different *mahāmātras* (are busying themselves) specially with different (congregations). But my *mahāmātras* of morality are occupied with these (congregations) as well as with all other sects.

King Devānāmpriya Priyadarsin speaks thus:

Both these and many other chief (officers) are occupied with the delivery of the gifts of myself as well as of the queens, and among my whole harem (they are reporting) in divers ways different worthy recipients of charity both here and in the provinces. And others were ordered by me to busy themselves also with the delivery of the gifts of (my) sons and of other queens' sons, in order (to promote) noble deeds of morality (and) the practice of morality. For noble deeds of morality and the practice of morality (consist in) this, that (morality), *viz.* compassion, liberality, truthfulness, purity, gentleness, and goodness, will thus be promoted among men.

King Devānāmpriya Priyadarsin speaks thus.

Whatever good deeds have been performed by me, those the people have imitated, and to those they are conforming. Thereby they have been made to progress and will (be made to) progress in obedience to mother and father, in obedience to elders, in courtesy to the aged, in courtesy to Brāhmanas and Sramanas, to the poor and distressed, (and) even to slaves and servants.

King Devānāmpriya Priyadarsin speaks thus:

Now this progress of morality among men has been promoted (by me) only in two ways, (*viz.*) by moral restrictions and by conversion. But among these (two), those moral restrictions are of little consequence; by conversion, however, (morality is promoted) more considerably. Now moral restrictions indeed are these, that I have ordered this, (that) certain animals are inviolable. But there are also many other moral restrictions which have been imposed by me. By conversion, however, the progress of morality among men has been promoted more considerably, (because it leads) to abstention from hurting living beings (and) to abstention from killing animals. Now for the following purpose has this been ordered, that it may last as long as (my) sons and great-grand-sons (shall reign and) as long as the moon and the sun (shall shine), and in order that (men) may conform to it. For if one conforms to this, (happiness) in this (world) and in the other (world) will be attained. This rescript on morality was caused to be written by me (when I had been) anointed twenty-seven years.

Concerning this, Devānāmpriya says:

This rescript on morality must be engraved there, where either stone pillars or stone slabs are (available), in order that this may be of long duration.

From the inscriptions we also learn that Asoka became a lay-brother (*upasaka*) for more than two and a half years after his adoption of Buddhism. That he actually became a monk is possible, but the precise significance of the passages in question is still disputed. In any case we know from his own records that he did go on a pilgrimage to the holy places of Buddhism. His road to Nepāl is marked by pillars with inscriptions at Bakhira, Lauriya and Rāmpūrva. Thence he went to visit the Lumbinī garden, and set up a pillar to mark the spot where Buddha was born. At Niglīva he set up a pillar to commemorate his enlargement of the stupa of the Buddha Kanakamuni. It is related that he was accompanied by the famous saint Upagupta who at the king's request acted as his guide.

Buddhist tradition records that Asoka convened a great Buddhist council to deal with various abuses that had grown up in the church. According to Asoka's own statement, he sent envoys all over India and to the lands of his Greek neighbours; though in the latter case it is not clear whether they were religious or diplomatic representatives, or possibly both. Singalese tradition traces the introduction of Buddhism into Ceylon to Asoka's brother, Mahendra, who went at the head of a mission and settled there. It has even preserved a list of missionaries sent to other parts of the world.

Of the family life of Asoka we know little. The name of one of his queens, Kāruvākī, survives in an edict relating to her charities. She was the mother of his son Tīvara. Another son's name, Jalauka, is known from Kashmīr tradition, which describes him as no Buddhist, but an able king who defended Kashmīr well and extended its territory. The name of Kunāla, another son, is also recorded.

There is little doubt that Asoka's pacific tendencies resulted in the Maurya empire collapsing with more than usual rapidity. He died about 232 B.C., after a reign of some forty years, and little is known of the remainder of his dynasty. His grandson, Dasaratha, is known from an inscription recording an endowment given to the Ajīvikas. The number of persons mentioned in the *Purānas* as his successors may mean that the dynasty broke up into several branches. The last of the line was certainly Brihadratha, who was killed by Pushyamitra, the founder of the Sunga dynasty, about 185 B.C.; various minor dynasties continued, however, for centuries, to claim Maurya blood. Hiuen Tsang records one such in the seventh century A.D. The southern dominions of the Mauryas passed to the Āndhras and Kalingas, and, in the northwest, the Greeks from Bactria began to retake territory that had for a brief period owned the rule of Alexander.

About 185 B.C. the last Maurya, Brihadratha, ruling over a much diminished empire, was assassinated by his commander-in-chief, Pushyamitra, who seized the throne. The story related in the *Harshacharita* of Bāna, who has preserved a number of "sad stories of the deaths of kings", is no doubt reliable, although written eight centuries later than the event to which it refers. According to this author, Pushyamitra assembled the entire Maurya army on the pretext that he wished his sovereign to see what a fine force could be put into the field, and then assassinated him at the review. The army was, apparently, devoted to Pushyamitra, who knew, therefore, that he could successfully carry through his *coup d'état*. He was a member of the Sunga family, and the *Purānas* apply the name Sunga to the ten sovereigns constituting the dynasty which he founded. The Sungas were a very old family, claiming descent from Bharadvaja, the family priest of the great Vedic hero, Divodāsa, king of the Tritsus. They were presumably vassals or feudatories of the Mauryas, and in literature are particularly associated with Vidisa, the modern Besnagar, an ancient centre of culture, in the neighbourhood of which, at Bhārhut, Rupnath, and Kausāmbī, are still found extensive remains of the Sunga period. At Bhārhut occurs the only epigraphic reference to the dynasty of the Sungas that has survived. An inscription there states that two gateways were erected "in the reign of the Sungas". Pātaliputra, however, remained the capital of the empire, although it is improbable that Magadha continued to play a predominant part. Only the centre of the vast empire of Asoka passed to the Sungas. In the south and south-east the Āndhras and Kalingas were at the same time establishing themselves securely in independent kingdoms, while evidence that the north-west had already passed from the Mauryas is found in the account of the Indian campaign of Antiochos the Great. The "Sophagasenus" (Saubhāgasena), whom Polybius calls king of the Indians, and who exchanged gifts with Antiochos, was evidently a great king and not a petty chief, for Antiochos treated him as an equal. His territory must at one time have formed part of Chandragupta's empire, and this casual reference is valuable as showing that the process of disintegration, which we know to have begun in the south at the beginning of the second century B.C., had begun even earlier in the north-west. Saubhāgesena, or rather the founder of his line, must have declared his independence very soon after the death of Asoka. Kashmīr tradition records that, on his father's death, one of Asoka's sons made himself independent in Kashmīr and the adjoining territory. The Sungas therefore inherited only the central parts of the old Maurya empire.

It is possible to make certain deductions about Pushyamitra's reign from Kālidāsa's *Mālavikāgnimitra*, although the play was written five hundred years after the event with which it deals. Its hero, Agnimitra, the ruler of Vidisa, and son and viceroy of Pushyamitra, is in love with Mālavikā, the daughter of the king of Vidarbha. The reference to the war between Pushyamitra and Yajnasena of Vidarbha, suggests that the apportionment of Maurya territory between the Sungas and Āndhras was not completed without bloodshed, if we assume that the ruler of Vidarbha was a feudatory of the Āndhras, as seems likely. It has also been suggested that Khāravela, the famous Kalinga king, was the enemy of Pushyamitra, and the Hathigumpha inscription has been interpreted to make Khāravela claim a victory over him. The two must in any case have been contemporaries and rivals, although it is difficult to say whether they came into actual conflict. The play also contains a reference to a horse-sacrifice performed by Pushyamitra; in the course of its wanderings the body of troops escorting the horse under the leadership of Pushyamitra's grandson, Vasumitra, encountered a body of Yavanas (Greeks) on the south bank of the Indus; a fierce fight resulted in a victory for the Indians, and the prince brought his charge safely home. There is no doubt that Kālidāsa is right in saying that there were encounters between the Greeks and Indians in Pushyamitra's reign. We learn from another source that this was the period in which the Bactrian Greeks were making great inroads into India. Patanjali, the grammarian, a contemporary of Pushyamitra, has preserved some important fragments of history in his grammatical examples. Thus, to illustrate the use of the present tense to indicate an incomplete action, he takes the sentence "We are sacrificing for Pushyamitra", a probable allusion to the Sunga king's horse-sacrifice, and proof that the grammarian was his contemporary. As examples of the use of the imperfect to indicate events not witnessed by the speaker but recent enough to have been seen by him, he gives the examples: "The Greek was besieging Madhyamikā", and "The Greek was besieging Sāketa". These are almost the only records in Indian literature of the great Greek invasion which reached Madhyamikā near Chitor in Rājputāna and Sāketa in Oudh. An additional allusion to this campaign occurs in the *Gargī Samhitā*. This *Purāna* says that "the wicked and valiant Greeks" occupied Sāketa, Panchāla, and Mathura, and advanced as far as Kusūmadhvaja (*i.e.* Pātaliputra). These references to the campaigns probably of Eucratides and certainly of Menander, show that, although much harassed by the Greeks, Pushyamitra ultimately drove them out of Magadha. Buddhist legend, which represents Pushyamitra as a great persecutor of the Buddhists, states that he went to Sākala (Sialkot) and exterminated the monks there. But, as the *Milinda-panha* refers to Sākala as Menander's capital it is possible that Menander, or an earlier ruler like Demetrius, had taken this important city from Pushyamitra. So far as can be judged from

the evidence available, Buddhist tradition is unjust to the memory
of Pushyamitra. Buddhist architecture unquestionably flourished
in the Sunga period, and, while Pushyamitra, a member of an old
Brāhman family which had adopted the profession of arms, did
a great deal to revive Brahmanical ritual, which had been neglected
for a century, there is no real reason to think that he actually
persecuted Buddhists.

Agnimitra succeeded his father in 148 B.C.; according to
Kālidāsa, he had previously governed the southern provinces of
the kingdom. Of his successor, Sujyeshta, nothing is known. The
fourth king, Vasumitra, had, as we learn from Kālidāsa, been in
command on the north-west frontier in his grandfather's reign.
According to Bāna, he was killed while engaged in amateur
theatricals by one Mitradeva, perhaps a member of the powerful
family of Brāhman ministers which ultimately supplanted the
Sungas. An inscription recording the excavation of a cave at
Pabhosā is dated in the tenth year of a king whose name has been
read as Udaka, identified with the fifth Sunga king, whose name
is recorded in the Purānas as "Antaka", "Odruka", and
"Andraka". An inscription at Besnagar records the erection of a
Garuda pillar by Heliodoros, a native of Taxila, who had been
sent as ambassador by the Greek king, Antalkidas, to Bhāga;
bhadra Kasīputra in the fourteenth year of his reign. Bhāgabhadra
has been identified with the fifth Sunga king, but, more probably,
with the ninth—Bhāga, Bhadaka, or Bhāgavata. The latter may
also be the Bhāgavata of another Garuda pillar at Besnagar dated
in his twelfth regnal year, but the Bhāgabhadra of one pillar can
hardly be the Bhāgavata of the other.

The last Sunga king, Devabhūti, or Devabhūmi, was murdered
about 80 B.C. at the instigation of his minister, Vasudeva, by a
slave-girl disguised as his queen. Such checks as we can apply
to the Purānic chronology of the Sunga period suggest that this
date is approximately correct. We have already mentioned the
epigraphic and classical references to the Sungas. It seems impossible to attribute to the Sungas the extensive series of coins
issued by a dynasty whose rulers' names all ended in -mitra. Like
other series of the period, it must have been struck by contemporaries or feudatories.

From the Purānas, confirmed by Bāna's story, we learn of the
foundation of the Kānva dynasty by Vasudeva. Of this short-

lived dynasty we know only the names of its four kings, who are said to have ruled for forty-five years, after which the last of them was dispossessed by the Āndhras, then the paramount power in the Deccan. It is impossible to identify the Āndhra king who destroyed Susarma, the last member of the Kānva dynasty, about 28 B.C.

A little light is thrown on the history of Kalinga in the second century B.C. by the celebrated and much discussed Hathigumpha inscription of Khāravela. The Kalingas had early taken advantage of the decline of the Maurya power to regain the independence they had lost under Asoka. Of their history we know nothing till the time of Khāravela, the third ruler of the Cheta dynasty, from whose inscription, unfortunately very badly preserved, we derive certain information. He had become crown prince at the age of fifteen and king at twenty-four. In the eighth year of his reign he had attacked and put to flight the king of Rājagriha (Magadha), and sacked the fortress of Goradha. In his tenth year he had sent troops into Bharatavarsha, and two years later had filled the kings of northern India (Uttarapatha) with terror and bathed his elephants in the Ganges. He conquered Brihaspati-mitra, king of Magadha. In defiance of Sātakarni, lord of the west, he sent an army into the Āndhra country. He conquered the Rashtrikas and Bhojakas. Even making allowance for the enthusiasm of his panegyrist, Khāravela was evidently a powerful ruler, but no record of his name or of his dynasty is found in any Purānic list. The Hathigumpha inscription is believed to be dated in the year 165 of the Maurya era, or about 160 B.C.; this would support the proposed identification of Brihaspatimitra with the Sunga Pushyamitra, Pushya being a synonym of Brihas-pati. In any case, if Khāravela's arms did reach Magadha and the Ganges, it must have been at the expense of the Sungas. Nothing is known of the fate of Khāravela or of his dynasty, if indeed he had any successors on his throne. It is most probable that they were destroyed when the final day of reckoning came with the Āndhras, and that the latter more than avenged them-selves for the Kalinga ruler's early successes.

The Āndhras, whose modern representatives, the Telugu people, still occupy the region between the Godāvarī and the Krishnā, on the east coast of India, are mentioned very early in Indian

literature. The *Aitareya Brāhmana* describes them as a people outside the sphere of Āryan influence. From a reference in Pliny,
we learn that some centuries before his time, presumably in the
early Maurya period, they were a powerful people with a large
army and some thirty fortified towns—next to the kingdom of
Magadha the strongest state in India. Their capital was first
Srikākula, on the Krishnā, and later Dhanyakataka, higher up
the same river. Asoka mentions them among the peoples who
had adopted his teaching; thus, while there is no evidence that
they were his vassals, he presumably exercised a nominal suzerainty
over them. Like other peoples, the Āndhras certainly took
advantage of the decline of the Maurya empire to extend their
dominion. Towards the end of the third century B.C. they were
rapidly expanding their territory under a king named Simuka,
who founded the Sātavāhana or Sātakarni dynasty, which ruled
the Telugu country for nearly 500 years. The meaning of the
title Sātakarni is uncertain. It has presumably been given a
Sanskrit popular etymology, and the first component is probably
connected with the *Sata* in Sātavāhana (whose badge is the *sata*).
In the reigns of Simuka and his younger brother and successor,
Krishna, the power of the Āndhras extended almost across the
whole width of India, as the inscriptions at Nasik and Nānaghāt
show. The third member of the dynasty, Sātakarni, is mentioned
as lord of the west in the inscription of Khāravela, king of the
Kalingas, dated in the 165th year of the Maurya era (157 B.C.),
and the 13th of Khāravela's reign. Khāravela was also the third
ruler of his house, so that both dynasties must have arisen about
the same time, *i.e.* during the decline of the Mauryas. The relations of the two powers are not clearly defined in the inscription,
but we are told that Khāravela was in contact with the Sātavāhana king in the second year of his reign (168 B.C.), which
gives a fixed point in Āndhra chronology. Khāravela says that
he sent an army to the west, disregarding Sātakarni, "the protector of the west". About the same time the Āndhras came into
conflict with the Sungas of Magadha, over whom they were
ultimately victorious, for in the latter part of the second century
the Āndhras were issuing coins in western Mālwā, and there is
an Āndhra inscription of a century later from eastern Mālwā
which shows that this region had also passed under their rule.
It was probably Khāravela who dealt the final blow to the power

of Magadha. About 28 B.C. an Āndhra king slew the last of the short-lived Kānva dynasty which had ousted the declining Sungas, and this is all that is known of Āndhra history till the beginning of the second century A.D., by which time there had risen to power on the western coast of India the Saka dynasty of the Kshaharātas, whose territory marched on the south with that of the Āndhras.

An inscription at Nasik of the Āndhra queen, Balā Srī, dated in the reign of her grandson, Vāsishthīputra Srī Pulumāvī, records the conquests of her son, Gautamīputra Srī Sātakarni, probably the greatest of the Āndhra kings. He is said by his mother to have destroyed the Sakas, Yavanas and Pallavas, to have uprooted the Kshaharātas, and restored the glories of the Sātavāhanas. A list of the lands he conquered is given in considerable detail; they correspond to the modern Gujarāt (Surāshtra), Mālwā, portions of central India, Berar (Vidarbha), and the country around Nasik and Poona. That is to say, he claimed to have conquered much of the land which had been ruled by the Kshaharāta Nahapāna, and which at a later date, again fell under the rule of the western Kshatrapas. Gautamīputra's claim to have uprooted the Kshaharātas and to have conquered large portions of their territory is confirmed in a remarkable fashion by his coins. A great find of over 13,000 silver coins was made at Joghalthembi, in the Nasik district, in 1906; it consisted of 4000 silver coins of Nahapāna and 9000 of the same pieces restruck by Gautamīputra. From this it may be deduced that the Āndhra king conquered country belonging to Nahapāna, called in the local currency, and counter-marked it with his own types, a proceeding paralleled in other lands and periods. Of Gautamīputra's reign, which may be dated A.D. 90–120, there survives an inscription issued from his victorious camp at Vaijayantī (Banavāsī) in his eighteenth regnal year, probably on his return from his campaign against Nahapāna. He was succeeded by his son Vāsishthīputra Srī Pulumāvī, who is identified with the Sātakarni, lord of the Deccan, whom Rudradāman twice routed but did not destroy because of their relationship, which, as we learn from the inscription of the Āndhra queen, Balā Srī, was the result of the marriage of Rudradāman's daughter to the Āndhra king. The Kshatrapa ruler seems to have regained much of the land that had been conquered by Gautamīputra. Srī Pulumāvī is identified with the *Siroptolemaiou* of Ptolemy, who calls him king of Paithan (Pratisthāna?).

Vāsishthīputra reigned till about A.D. 155. Some fifteen years later we have records of another powerful Āndhra monarch in Gautamīputra Srī Yajna Sātakarni, who ruled from about A.D. 165 to 195. The distribution of his inscriptions and his coins, and specially the fact that he struck silver coins in the style of those of the western Kshatrapas, suggests that he extended the Āndhra dominions, and did something to revive the glories of Gautamīputra Srī Sātakarni's reign. In the third century the Āndhra dominions were broken up between two dynasties, branches of the Sātakarni family, the line of Sātavāhana and the line of Chutu, under circumstances of which we know nothing, and at last the five hundred years of Āndhra rule came to an end about the middle of the third century A.D., after which we find their territory shared by the Ābhīras, Pallavas and Kadambas.

The inscriptions of the Āndhra period are of disappointingly little value for the political history of the time, but they throw some light on the social life of the period. Buddhism and Brahmanism flourished side by side. To the former we owe the many rock-cut caves of the period which were excavated by pious donors as homes for *bhikshus*, for whose maintenance provision was also made. Of Brahmanism we learn that while most of the old Brahmanical sacrifices, including the *asvamedha*, were performed by the Sātakarni kings, this did not prevent them from endowing charities for Buddhist monks. During this period foreigners of various origins, Sakas and Yavanas, were penetrating into all ranks of Hindu society and adopting Hinduism and Buddhism. An illustration of this is seen in the marriage of the Āndhra king, Gautamīputra, to the daughter of the Saka Rudradāman. If we may judge by the numerous endowments and the sums spent on sacrifices, the country was very wealthy. Trade and commerce flourished, especially with the western world. It is mainly to the Āndhra kingdom that the account of eastern trade in the *Periplus* refers. Ptolemy also had heard of the fame of the Āndhra kings of his time. The Āndhras have left us an extensive series of coins, mainly of lead. Their attribution to definite rulers is occasionally a matter of difficulty, but their distribution and types throw some light on the history and extent of the Āndhra dominions. The legends are always in Prākrit, never in Sanskrit. The titles on coins and in inscriptions show that the Āndhra kings bore matronymics; these are characteristic of this dynasty. An Āndhra queen, in addition to her personal name, e.g. Balā Srī, had a religious surname, e.g. Gautamī, and her son was Gautamīputra, i.e. son of the lady of the gotra of Gotama. These religious titles are explained as having been given in honour of the family priest, but it should not be forgotten that in the Nasik inscription Gautamīputra is called a Brāhman, and we are also told that he destroyed the pride of the Kshatriyas. There may therefore be some foundation for the tradition that the Sātavāhanas were of mixed Brāhman origin.

While the western Kshatrapas in the second century A.D. use Sanskrit in their inscriptions, and Rudradāman proudly records his ability to compose according to the canons of Sanskrit rhetoric, the Āndhras used only Prākrit; and it is interesting to note that they are the traditional patrons of Prākrit literature. Hāla (i.e. in Dravidian Prākrit, Sāta[vāhana], the seventeenth king in the Purānic lists, but unknown from inscriptions) is credited with having compiled the Sattasai (Saptasataka), an anthology in the Prākrit of Mahārāshtra; while Gunādhya, one of his ministers, wrote the original Brihatkathā in Prākrit. Sarvavarman is said to have composed his Sanskrit grammar, the Kātantra, for an Āndhra king who was ashamed of his ignorance of Sanskrit and found Pānini too difficult. None of these traditions will bear the test of detailed criticism; but they seem to enshrine the fact that Prākrit, to the exclusion of Sanskrit, literature, flourished at the court of the Sātavāhanas.

CHAPTER V

Foreign Invaders of North-West India

With the rapid disintegration of the Maurya empire at the end of the third and the beginning of the second century B.C., the north-west of India began to pass into the hands of Greeks from Bactria where they had been established since the time of Alexander the Great. The history of India in the second and first centuries B.C. is therefore largely concerned with a limited area, some of which is now the modern Afghanistan and Baluchistan, and politically not part of modern India. The reason for this is the relative wealth of material, numismatic and epigraphic, left by the successive waves of invasion, Greek, Scythian and Kushān. The Greeks are known to Indian literature as Yavanas or Ionians, a name which came to India through Persia, and owes its origin to the fact that the Persians, as they became acquainted with Greeks other than those of Ionia, extended the term Ionian to all Hellenes. The earliest occurrence of the word in India is in Pānini, which shows that the word had passed into Sanskrit before the time of Alexander the Great. In its Prākrit form, Yona, we find it in the inscriptions of Asoka as the name of his Hellenistic neighbours. The word survived in India long after its original application was forgotten, and came to mean foreigners in general —indeed there are signs that it was quite early applied, not only to the Greeks, but also to the Sakas; so that in later times it was regularly applied to the Muhammadans.

Of the history of the Greeks in the Seleucid province of Bactria in the third century B.C. we know very little. Some time in the reign of Antiochos I (280–261 B.C.), Diodotos was appointed satrap of Bactria, then a great and wealthy province, which had grown up around cities founded by Alexander to maintain his political hold and to disseminate Greek culture. Diodotos gradually strengthened his position, and may even have declared his independence. More probably, however, full independence was achieved only by his son Diodotos II. About the same time, the middle of the third century B.C., Parthia also became independent. Diodotos II came to terms with the Parthian monarch, and was thus able to defy his Seleucid suzerain without fear of attack from Parthia. Diodotos II probably reigned from about 250–230 B.C. Of his end we know nothing, but when, in 212 B.C., Antiochos III came to the east hoping to regain the allegiance of the Parthian and Bactrian rebels, he found a certain Euthydemos, a native of Magnesia, on the throne of Bactria. Having brought the Parthian ruler, Arsaces III, to terms, Antiochos III then attacked Euthydemos in spite of the latter's protest that he was no rebel but had become king by putting the children of rebels to death. This suggests that Diodotos II had been slain by Euthydemos, and that Diodotos I had rebelled against the Seleucids. Fierce fighting followed, and Euthydemos sustained a long siege in Balkh, his capital. When negotiations for peace at last began, they were conducted on behalf of Euthydemos by his son Demetrios. Antiochos recognised the independence of Bactria, and was so much impressed by Demetrios that he gave him his daughter in marriage. Antiochos then proceeded to cross the Hindu Kush. In the Kābul valley he received the homage of a king named Saubhāgasena, who, or one of whose immediate ancestors, had set up an independent kingdom there on the decline of the Maurya power. The fact that he is described by Strabo as king of the Indians suggests that he was a considerable ruler; and the same writer's statement that the two kings renewed their friendship shows that he had been ruling for some time and had already had diplomatic relations with Antiochos. He may have been a grandson of Asoka, as Prof. F. W. Thomas suggests, quoting the statement of Tāranāth, the Tibetan historian, that Asoka's son, Vīrasena, was the king of Gandhāra, and observing how names in -sena run in families.

This Indian ruler gave Antiochos supplies for his army and war-elephants, and promised him a large treasure, which Antiochos left Androsthenes to collect. He himself had to turn his back on India and hurry to the west where he was urgently required. On his departure Euthydemos appears to have extended his authority over Arachosia and the lands through which the Seleucid had passed. His coinage is extensive, and the variety of monograms on it indicates the existence of numerous mints. The provenance of his coins suggests that his rule was wide-spread, while the change in its portraiture from youth to old age is evidence of a long reign. He probably died about 190 B.C., leaving his son a Bactrian empire which included modern

Afghanistan. Demetrios, whose ability had been early recognised by his father's appointing him to negotiate with Antiochos III, extended his power into India, that is to say, over the Hindu Kush. While he was engaged in India a rising, headed by Eucratides, took place in Bactria about 175 B.C., leading to the establishment of a separate kingdom. We do not know what became of Demetrios, but Bactria and most of his Indian conquests seem to have passed to his rival, since the latter had assumed the title "Great" before 162 B.C., a date fixed by the rebellion of the Seleucid Timarchus who copies the coins of Eucratides; the conquest of India must therefore have taken place earlier. Justin says that Demetrios was ruling in India when Eucratides was king of Bactria and Mithridates of Parthia, and that these two began to rule about the same time, that is about 170 B.C.

Of the family of Demetrios several kings are known, but only from their coins. These include Euthydemos II, certainly his son, named after his grandfather, and Demetrios II, to whom, rather than to Demetrios I, are to be attributed the bilingual coins showing that this family occupied lands where a form of Prākrit was spoken. A fine series of coins serves to connect its issuers, of whom nothing else is known, with the family. These are the coins of Agathocles, Pantaleon and Antimachos, who must have ruled about the middle of the second century. Two of them, Agathocles and Pantaleon, struck coins in India, imitating the local types of Taxila. Agathocles also issued a remarkable series of commemo tive pieces in honour of Alexander the Great, Antiochos II, Diodotos and Euthydemos I. Antiochos and Agathocles were probably grandsons of Euthydemos I. About the middle of the second century then, the old kingdom of Bactria, together with the Indian conquests, was divided between the houses of Eucratides and Euthydemos. The former held Bactria, Kābul, Gandhāra, and Taxila, while the latter ruled the Panjab from Sākala (Sialkot). It is possible through the coin-types to connect with one or other of these houses a number of kings, otherwise unknown to history. The latest historical reference to the Bactrian Greeks is Justin's account of the end of Eucratides, who "conquered India and became lord of a thousand cities". While returning to Bactria from his successful Indian campaign, he was murdered by his son and colleague, probably about 155 B.C. The parricide was probably Heliocles.

Of the members of the house of Euthydemos only two, Apollodotos and Menander, are mentioned in literature. According to the author of the *Periplus*, their coins were still in circulation at Broach in the first century A.D. The fact that coins have been found with the types of Eucratides re-struck on those of Apollodotos shows that the latter was of a slightly earlier date than the former and Demetrios. Menander is the most celebrated of the Yavanas. He is the Milinda, king of Sākala, who plays the leading part in the *Milindapanha*, "the Questions of Milinda", a Buddhist philosophical treatise in the form of a dialogue between the king and the Buddhist sage, Nāgasena, who ultimately converts the king, who had been notorious for his skill in puzzling the sages with heretical questions. The Pāli texts have preserved in Indianised form the names of some of his Greek courtiers, such as Anantakāya, *i.e.* Antiochos. The fame of Menander survived till the time of Plutarch, who records that his ashes were distributed among a number of cities which disputed the honour of preserving them. His coins are still exceedingly numerous and indicate a prolonged rule over an extensive kingdom. Menander was probably the Yavana who invaded Magadha, as recorded by Patanjali. His queen was possibly Agathocleia, who issued coins first in her own name, and later in conjunction with her young son Strato I. Strato's coins evidence the length of his reign, for the latest depict him as an old man dividing the rule with his grandson, Strato II. The family of Apollodotos I is represented during this period by Apollodotos II, Apollophanes, Dionysos, Zoilos and Hippostratos. By the end of the reign of Strato, the debased and crude nature of the coins suggests that the fortunes of the Greek kings had sunk to a low ebb, and towards the close of the first century B.C., Sakas, like Ranjubula, were issuing coins copied from Greek types in regions where Greeks once had ruled.

Eucratides was succeeded in Bactria and in his Indian territories by Heliocles, his son, and possibly also his murderer. The latter was the last of the Greeks to rule in Bactria, which afterwards passed to the Sakas. He probably extended his father's conquests in India. Members of his house known from their coins are Philoxenos, Artemidoros, Epander, Amyntas, Peucolaos, Lysias and Antalkidas. The last-named is mentioned in an inscription at Besnagar, near Bhīlsa, which records the erection of a column in honour of Krishna by the Yavana ambassador, Heliodoros of Taxila, who had been sent by the Greek king, Antalkidas, to the local rāja, Kāsīputra Bhāgabhadra. The inscription shows incidentally that the Yavanas had adopted Indian religions, for Heliodoros describes himself as *bhāgavata*. Of the other kings whose names are known from their coins little can be told. There is evidence to show that their lands gradually passed to the Sakas, who rapidly reduced the territory held by the Greeks until they were confined to the mountain-valleys of Afghanistan. Hermaeus was the last of the Greek kings of the Indian border-land. His coins are numerous but not varied. They were widely imitated by the Kushāns when they invaded the Kābul valley, just as those of Heliocles had been copied by the barbarians in Bactria half a century earlier. Hermaeus may have survived till the middle of the first century, but not much later. Some of his coins bear the bust of his queen, Calliope, who is otherwise unknown.

In the first century B.C., under a pressure similar to that which, about a century earlier, had destroyed the last vestiges of Hellenic rule in Bactria, the Greeks began to be driven from their remaining possessions in India by the Sakas and Pahlavas. These two ethnics, Saka and Pahlava, are regularly associated with each other and frequently with the Yavanas, in Indian literature and inscriptions. Even the earliest epigraphic references show that the two were inextricably confused, at least so far as can be judged from their names. "Saka" is the Indian term for Scythian, and "Pahlava" for Parthian. For centuries the nomad Scythians of central Asia had owned more or less allegiance to the Persian empire, that is to say, to the settled and more highly cultured peoples of Irān. The degree of suzerainty admitted, and the area it covered, varied with the power of the reigning Persian monarch. It is with the Scythian tribes of Bactria and Seistān, who had migrated thither and settled in the centuries immediately before the Christian era, that we are here concerned. The young Parthian empire had to maintain a severe struggle with the then powerful Scythian tribes, who had long forgotten the allegiance they had once owned to the Achaemenids. Phraates II was killed in a war with the Scythians in 128 B.C., and Artabanus in 123 B.C. Mithridates II, however, in his long and successful reign, once again asserted the supremacy of the settled heirs of an ancient culture over the nomads, and it was probably during this period that the intermingling of Sakas and Parthians took place, the Sakas becoming more or less settled in Drangiana, Arachosia, and the border provinces of the old Achaemenid empire. After the reign of Mithridates II, these Scythian or Scytho-Parthian vassals of the Parthians began to reassert themselves and invade India. The stimulus to this invasion came ultimately from the movements of central Asian tribes in the second century B.C., which will be described later in connection with the rise of the Kushāns. When the Yueh-chi conquerors of Bactria were themselves thrust southward by the Hiung-nu, they exerted a pressure on the semi-settled Scythians which set the latter in motion again. The strength of the Parthian kingdom naturally deflected them eastwards, through Seistān, southern Afghanistan (Kandahār), and Balūchistan, into the lower Indus valley. They did not enter India through the Hindu Kush, as the Greeks had done, but fol-lowed·ancient routes to the south, such as that used by Krateros when Alexander sent him home with a portion of his army. It was from these new settlers that the lower Indus valley became known to the classical geographers as Scythia. It must be re-membered also that in ancient times the natural frontier between Irān and India in this region was the Indus. It was so under the Achaemenids and under the Parthian Mithridates II in historic times, while the links between the early Indus valley and Sumerian cultures suggest that this natural frontier was very old.

The distinction made between the Saka and Pahlava dynasties in India is somewhat artificial. Nomenclature is of little assistance. Persian names were used in Saka families and *vice versa*. Their coinages were similar, and the system of government by satraps was common to Sakas and Pahlavas, and was taken over from them by the Kushāns. It is, however, the usual practice to call the line of Maues, with its predominantly Scythian names, Sakas, and to apply the term Pahlava or Parthian to the later group of rulers with distinctively Persian names, belonging to the line of Gondophares. But, as will be shown, they were closely con-nected.

The empire of Mithridates II stretched as far as the southern Indus valley, and it must have been when Parthiaɴ power began to decline after his death in 88 B.C. that his Saka and Pahlava satraps began to assert their independence, and use the forces under them for their own advancement. The earliest Saka king of India is the Maues of the coins, who is identified with the Moga of the Taxila plate of Patika, the son of Liaka Kusūlaka, Moga's satrap of Chukhsa and Chhahara. The name Moga is the same as Mauakes, the name of the leader of the Sakas at Gaugamela, which is formed from the stem of Maues and the derivative suffix -ka. The provenance of his coins and their types suggest that Moga ruled Gandhāra and the western Panjab. Taxila certainly owned his sway, for he had a satrap there. It is probable that the conquests made in his advance northwards thrust a wedge between the Greeks in the Kābul valley and those left in the eastern Panjab. He used the Iranian title "king of kings" on his coins, while his satrap called him the "great king". The Taxila copper plate of the latter is dated in a Parthian month of the year 78, but the era is unknown. Several dated inscriptions of the Sakas and Pahlavas survive, but they appear to be in local eras, probably in more than one. Maues must have flourished in the third quarter of the first century B.C., or even a little later. His title, "king of kings", could only have been assumed after the death of Mithridates II, at a period when the Parthian power was very weak. The period of civil war in Parthia in the third quarter of the century was a time when a powerful satrap might well have asserted a virtual independence, and set out to extend his power in a direction which would not bring him into direct conflict with his nominal suzerain.

Maues was succeeded by Azes, who continued his predecessor's coin-types, adding to them others which show that the Sakas were ruling the lands once held by the descendants of Apollodotos and Menander. Thus by the time of Azes, Saka rule had been extended over the eastern Panjab also. The coins of this family afford a certain amount of genealogical information, but it is not always clear. On Maues' coins his name appears alone with the title "king of kings". But the coins of his successors, Azes King of Kings, of Spalahores his brother, and of Spalagadames his nephew, sometimes also bear on the obverse Greek legends, with the name Vonones King of Kings—a Parthian, as distinct from a Scythian name. Azes sometimes struck coins, like Maues, in his own name alone, but also sometimes with Azilises King of Kings as well as with the strategos Aspavarman, son of Indra-

varman. Azilises, likewise, issued coins both in his sole name and
with Azes King of Kings on the reverse. Spalirises issued coins
alone as king's brother, as king of kings, and as great king with
Azes as king. Herzfeld is probably justified in asserting that
Vonones, whose suzerainty Azes, Spalahores, and Spalagadames
all recognised by putting his titles on the obverse of their coins,
and who struck no Saka coins of his own, was the Arsacid
Vonones who reigned from A.D. 8–14. This gives a fixed point
in the series. In Dr Herzfeld's view Spalirises was the brother of
Maues, and Azes his son; Spalahores was the brother of Azes,
and Spalagadames his son, while the Azes who struck coins jointly
with the strategos Aspavarman, with whom Gondophares also
struck coins, was Azes, the successor of Maues. There are on this
theory only two kings before Gondophares—Maues and Azes.
The other names which appear on coins are those of vassals and
governors, and Azilises is simply another form of the name Azes.

But, on the view that Vonones is not the Arsacid, but an independent contemporary of Maues, ruling in Arachosia and issuing
coins in imitation of the types of the house of Eucratides, Spalirises
and Spalahores were brothers of Vonones, and Spalagadames was
his nephew; while in the other line Azilises would be the successor of Azes I and be succeeded by Azes II, another nephew of
Vonones; thus there would be a connection between the two
families. Azes must have reigned from about 20 B.C. to A.D. 20
and, if Azes I, Azilises and Azes II are three rulers, they must
occupy about the same period.

Besides Liaka Kusūlaka and his son Patika, inscriptions have
preserved the names of various satrap families of the period of the
great kings Maues and Azes. Zeionises, also known from his
coins, was the son of Manigula, satrap of Chukhsa, previously
ruled by Liaka Kusūlaka. The celebrated "Lion-capital" from
Mathura, the capital of a pillar in Persian style consisting of two
lions back to back, completely covered with inscriptions, gives
genealogical information about the satraps of Mathura. The inscription records a donation by the chief queen of the great satrap
Rājūla (the Rājuvula and Ranjubula of the coins) who is also
known by his copies of the coins of Strato I, and, presumably,
put an end to the rule of that family. He also copied the coins of
the local rajas of Mathura, as also did his predecessors, the satraps
Hagāna and Hagāmasha. Other coins bear the name of his son,

Sodāsa, who succeeded him as great satrap. From another inscription we know that Sodāsa was a satrap when Padika, perhaps
the Patika of the Taxila inscription, was great satrap. Another
member of the family known to us by his coins is Kharaosta,
son of Arta, the son of a daughter of Ranjubula. The names and
periods of two other satraps, the strategos Indravarman and his
son Aspavarman, are preserved by their coins. The latter was
governing in the reigns of Azes (or Azes II) and Gondophares,
the third of the great kings of the Sakas and Pahlavas. The family
of Gondophares is usually distinguished as Pahlava, for all its
members bear Iranian names. His name is the old Persian *Vinda-
pharna*, "winner of glory", and appears in the Greek legends on
his coins as *Undopherros* or *Gondopharos*, and in the Kharoshthi
as *Gudaphara* or *Gandaphara*.

The coins of Gondophares, all of very base silver and copper,
are exceedingly numerous, and indicate a long reign over a wide
area. In addition to the coins issued in his own name and those
already mentioned as also bearing the name of the strategos, Aspavarman, he issued others conjointly with Sasas, with Guda the
king's brother, and with Abdagases son of his brother, and as king
of kings with Orthagnes as king of kings. The name of Orthagnes,
like that of Vonones, occurs only in the Greek inscriptions on the
obverse, and, if we admit that Vonones is the name of a Parthian
suzerain, Orthagnes must also be that of a Parthian suzerain. In
this case Herzfeld would identify Orthagnes with that unnamed
son of Vardanes, mentioned by Tacitus, who claimed the throne
against Volagases I about A.D. 55. In any case the striking similarity of the Orthagnes coins to the coins of Pacorus makes it
unlikely that Orthagnes was a predecessor of Gondophares. He
may, like the strategos Sasas, the king's brother Guda, and his
son Abdagases, have been a governor for Gondophares, but in
this case he would hardly have borne the suzerain title of king
of kings. The other members of the family who strike coins in
their own name alone are Pacorus, already mentioned, and
Sanabares, who probably ruled kingdoms of their own on the
break-up of the empire of Gondophares. Sasas, Abdagases, Guda,
Sapedanes and Satavastra were local governors—the last two in
the region of Taxila. The coins of Sanabares are purely Parthian
in type and not Indian, showing that he secured the western part
of the kingdom. Gondophares reigned from about A.D. 20–60

and his successors can hardly have ruled more than twenty years before the Kushān conquest. Much of the territory of the Saka empire was recovered by the slightly more stable Parthia. The date A.D. 78 may therefore be taken as marking the end of Pahlava rule. One family of Persian origin, the so-called western satraps, however, continued for nearly 300 years.

Classical references to this period are scanty. According to Philostratos, Apollonios of Tyana visited India about A.D. 44, and found a Parthian king, Phraates, ruling at Taxila independently of Vardanes, the king of Parthia. Phraates has not been identified with any of the rulers known from coins. The author of the *Periplus* in the last decades of the first century A.D. says that at that time the lower Indus valley was under the rule of Parthian chiefs, who were constantly deposing one another. The Saka empire was clearly in a state of dissolution. We have an inscription from Takht-i Bahi, dated in the twenty-sixth year of the reign of Gondophares (*Gudufara*), in the fifth day of the month Vaisākha of the year 103. If this is dated in the Vikrama era, and the use of a Hindu month suggests an Indian era, the inscription was composed in A.D. 45, which would give A.D. 19 as the year of accession of Gondophares, a very probable date, as we have already seen.

The names of Gondophares and of some of his family have survived in the apocryphal *Acts of St Thomas*. Gondophares appears under the form Gudnaphara; and Gad, the king's brother, also mentioned in the *Acts*, must be the Guda or Gudaya of the coins. St Thomas, who had been sent to convert India, undertook to build Gondophares a palace, but spent the money in charity, and told the king he was building him a palace in heaven. For this he was thrown into prison along with Abanes, the merchant who had brought him to India. Gad, the king's brother, then died, and, being carried to heaven, saw the palace which St Thomas had built by his good deeds. He was then restored to life and was converted along with Gondophares. This story exists in various forms, all of which end in the martyrdom of St Thomas in another Indian kingdom. These legends are important, not so much as regards the life of St Thomas, as because they show that in the first century A.D., in the milieu in which they arose, there was a certain amount of knowledge of India. No one doubts that Gudnaphar is Gondophares, who, through the Armenian

form of his name Gathaspar, becomes Caspar, one of the Three
Magi; Gad, the king's brother, is the Guda of the coins; while
Labdanes or Abdan, may, though with less certainty, be identified
as the Abdagases of the coins. Misdaios, the king in whose land
St Thomas was martyred, is simply the "Mazdaean" and is not
mentioned by name. His general, Siphor or Sifur, is Shāpūr or
Sapor, and his capital, Quantaria, is Gandhāra (Kandahār). The
son of Misdaios is Ouzanes, a name which may conceal Kushān
in its form Gusana. The question whether St Thomas really
visited India is still unsettled, in spite of all that has been written
on the subject, and, although the south Indian tradition is also
very old, it does not provide sufficient proof. Nevertheless there
is not enough evidence on the other side for us to deny the
possibility. It is interesting to note that the legend seems to refer
to the Kushāns as powerful Zoroastrian neighbours of the Pahlavas.

To trace the rise of the Kushān dynasty, it is necessary to go
back to central Asia in the second century B.C., regarding which
Chinese historians have preserved a few scraps of information.
Towards the middle of the second quarter of the second century
B.C.—the date usually given is 165—a central Asian tribe, called
by the Chinese the Hiung-nu, won a crushing victory over their
neighbours, the Yueh-chi, and compelled them to abandon the
pastures on which they lived and to move westwards. The king
of the Yueh-chi was killed defending his land, and it is recorded
that his skull was fashioned into a drinking-cup for the victorious
chief of the Hiung-nu. His widow assumed control of the tribe,
or rather people, for they numbered several hundred thousands.
In their search for new lands, the Yueh-chi came into conflict
in the valley of the Ili with the Wu-sun, whose numbers were
not sufficient to prevent the invaders from sweeping through the
country and killing their king, whose son escaped to a friendly
kingdom. One body of the Yueh-chi now turned southwards,
and became distinguished from the main body by the name Little
Yueh-chi. The main body continued to advance until they reached
the lands of the Sakas, who failed completely to defend themselves against the Yueh-chi hordes. The Sakas were forced to
abandon their lands north of the Syr Darya and seek a new home,
which they found in the territory of the Greek kings in what is

now southern Afghanistan, while the Yueh-chi then settled in Bactria.

Some twenty years later, the infant son of the slain Wu-sun king, having reached manhood, sought, with the assistance of the Hiung-nu among whom he had found a home, to avenge his father's death. He attacked the Yueh-chi, driving them out of the lands they had taken from the Sakas, and forcing them to move on to the Oxus valley, where they easily reduced the prosperous, unwarlike inhabitants, called by the Chinese the Ta-Hia. Here, in course of time, the Yueh-chi, having passed from a nomadic to a settled mode of life, prospered and gradually covered Bactria and Soghdiana. In this connection the Chinese historians inform us that there were five clans or tribes of the Yueh-chi, of which the Kushāns were one.

Our chronological data are, unfortunately, very scanty. It was probably about 140 B.C. that the son of the Wu-sun king avenged his father's death, so that it must have been towards the beginning of the first century B.C. that the Yueh-chi, having abandoned their nomadic habits, had begun to lead a settled existence in Bactria. The Chinese historian next tells us that over a hundred years after the partition of the land of the Ta-hia among the Yueh-chi, the chief of the Kushāns conquered and deposed the chiefs of the other four sections and declared himself king of the five tribes. This event must have taken place early in the first century A.D., probably about 25 or 30, when Kadphises was in the early thirties. This king, known to the Chinese as Kieu Tsiu K'io, is identified with the Kujala Kadaphes or Kujala-Kadphises of the coins, for convenience called Kadphises I. In his conquests he repeated the achievements of the Bactrian Greeks of two centuries earlier, and occupied the lands south of the Hindu Kush, southern Afghanistan and the provinces of Kābul and Kandahār. He is also said to have invaded Parthia. The Kushān empire of Kadphises I thus stretched from the Parthian frontier to the Indus, covering modern Afghanistan and much of the plains to the north of it (Bukhāra). The advance across the Hindu Kush involved the extinction of the Greek and Parthian dynasties still reigning in the Kābul valley. Kujala-Kadphises is the first member of his family whose coins are known. These still exist in enormous numbers, but are of copper only. One group with the name Kujala-Kasa inscribed in Kharoshthi, and Kozoulo-Kadphises in

Greek, falls into two classes: those which also bear the names of Hermaeus, the last Greek king, and those which bear the name of Kadphises alone. We are probably hardly justified in continuing to assume that the first class indicates some kind of alliance between Kadphises and Hermaeus, and that the second class was coined after Kadphises had extinguished his ally. It is more probable that Kadphises simply imitated the coins of Hermaeus which he found current in his new territory, as his ancestors had done with the coins of Euthydemos and Heliocles, and that the two classes indicate stages in the evolution of an independent Kushān coinage. To Kadphises I are, probably, to be attributed the coins bearing the name Kujala-Kaphsa in Kharoshthi and Kozoulo-Kadaphes in Greek. These appear to be copied from Roman coins. The original is usually said from the obverse to be a coin of Augustus, but it is most probably a very common coin of Claudius, as the reverse type is almost certainly borrowed from the type of Constantia on a curule chair. There is no coin of Augustus from which both sides could have been copied. The stratification at Taxila suggests that the coins of Kadphises I are a little later than those of Gondophares, so that they may quite well be as late as the third quarter of the first century A.D. Chinese historians tell us that Kadphises I lived to be over eighty. He must have died about A.D. 80, so that we are tempted to put the date of his death and of the accession of the Kushān conqueror of India in A.D. 78. The Chinese state that his successor was his son, Yen-kao-chen, who, they say, conquered India and there established a chief to govern it. From his time onwards the Yueh-chi became exceedingly powerful, and the name Kushān became synonymous with Yueh-chi, which was forgotten by all except the meticulous Chinese historians. Yen-kao-chen is identified with the Wīma Kadphises (Kadphises II) of the coins. The Chinese statement that he conquered India probably means that he extended Kushān power across the Indus. The coins of Wīma Kadphises are handsome pieces in gold and copper, which give him a string of proud titles, mahārāja, king of kings, son of heaven, mahīsvara, impartially borrowed from Parthia, China and India. His favourite reverse coin-type is Siva and his bull Nandi, and the epithet mahīsvara may also indicate devotion to Siva. The gold double staters are particularly fine pieces, presenting an excellent portrait of the Kushān conqueror. On one type he is represented driving a chariot, a type which may also go back to a Roman original. His gold coins and his large handsome copper pieces are mainly found north-west of the Indus. The obverse legends are in the Greek character and the reverse legends in a fine Kharoshthi. These pieces were probably struck in Gandhāra or even Bactria, and not east of the Indus. The Chinese statement that Kadphises II did not rule India himself but through a viceroy has suggested the theory that to this viceroy should be attributed the enormous numbers of copper coins found in the Panjab, struck for an anonymous "great king". These coins are certainly of about this date and have several links with the coins of Kadphises.

In the last quarter of the first century A.D., Chinese armies under the great general, Pan Chao, carried Chinese power westwards almost to the Caspian, conquering Khotan, Kashgar, and other regions lying on the northern borders of the Kushān empire. The Kushān king, alarmed at the collapse of the bulwarks protecting him from the Chinese, sent an embassy to the Chinese general, who treated it with disrespect. Kadphises therefore sent an army through the Pāmirs to teach the Chinese a lesson. It reached the plains exhausted by the hardships of the journey, and was easily routed by the Chinese. The king of the Kushāns then had to buy peace, and the arrival of his ambassadors bearing tribute to the emperor is recorded by the Chinese historians. The relations of Kadphises II with the west were more fortunate, and a flourishing trade developed between the Kushān kingdom and the Roman empire. The embassies said by Dion Cassius to have been sent to Trajan from India, may have come from the Kushān court. Pliny bears testimony to the enormous sums of money annually sent to India in payment for the luxuries imported thence to Rome, and the institution of a gold coinage by Kadphises II, in a region which had been without a gold currency since the days of the Achaemenids, is probably to be connected with this influx of the precious metal. Certain small copper coins attributed to Kadphises I bear a remarkable resemblance to Roman *denarii*; but there is no agreement about the original from which they were taken; as already mentioned, we are inclined to find it in the common Constantia type of the Emperor Claudius (A.D. 41–54); if the Kadphises who struck them is Kadphises I, he must be even later than is generally supposed. The fine coins of Wīma Kadphises II form a curiously isolated group, in types as well as in style.

Kadphises II was followed by a ruler named Kanishka, a name famous in Buddhist tradition. The connection between Kanishka and the Kadphises family is quite unknown, if indeed there was any. It is not certain that Kanishka was the immediate successor of Kadphises II; there may have been a gap between them; the evidence, however, of coin-finds in which the two are continually associated, and the stratification of Taxila, leave little doubt that Kanishka was closely related in time with Kadphises II and indeed succeeded him. His continuation and development of the Kushān gold coins points in this same direction. Further evidence lies in the remarkable similarity in portraiture between the representations of the two monarchs on their coins.

To the Buddhist, Kanishka was as great a figure as Asoka, but unfortunately no early historian mentions him, and his date is very much disputed. Whether he was the founder of the Saka era and came to the throne in A.D. 78, or whether his accession took place forty to sixty years later, is still uncertain, in spite of recent discussions of the evidence. The Chinese were cut off from news of India after A.D. 125, and the fact that Kanishka is not mentioned by Chinese historians thus favours a date not earlier than, say, A.D. 125–50. Moreover two hundred years is ample time for the development from his coinage to that of his successors, which the Guptas copied. It seems impossible that the coins of Kanishka can be, say 300 years earlier than the prototypes of the Gupta coinage. The fact that the Brāhmī script of some of his inscriptions is almost Gupta points in the same direction. We have inscriptions of Kanishka, unfortunately of little historical value, dated in the Kanishkan era, which continued in use under his successors. These show that he cannot have reigned more than twenty-four years, for an inscription of his successor Huvishka is dated in the twenty-fourth year of this era. While Kanishka's inscriptions are in Kharoshthi or Brāhmī, his coins bear legends in the Greek alphabet. Two varieties survive, a regular script in the Greek language, and a more cursive style with inscriptions in the Iranian language of the Kushāns. Like Kadphises on his copper coins he is always depicted as sacrificing at an altar; the bust-type favoured on the gold coins of Kadphises is not used by Kanishka. There is no reason to doubt that the gold coinage of Kanishka was suggested by the Roman solidus; some of the reverses are direct copies of Roman types. These pieces could only have been issued at a time when to the barbarian mind the typical Roman coin had the emperor on one side and a deity on the other with his name. Now it was not till the reign of Titus, or more probably of Trajan at earliest, that this was true. It is therefore hardly possible that Kanishka's coins were issued before the second century A.D. The complete absence of Kharoshthi from his coins is very remarkable when we remember the lengthy and beautifully written inscriptions of Kadphises and the use elsewhere by Kanishka of the Kharoshthi script. The reverse types represent a multitude of deities, Persian and Indian, the former predominating. Greek deities are also found, and include Heracles, Serapis, Helios and Selene. Kanishka's gold coins are not found east of the Indus; which is also true of the gold and the large brass pieces of Kadphises. The countless copper coins found in the Panjab are probably later imitations. Only one gold piece bearing the figure of Buddha is known, so that, to judge from the coins, Buddha played a very insignificant part, compared with Iranian deities, in the mythology of Kanishka's subjects.

Kanishka added Kashmīr to the Kushān empire, and founded a city there called Kanishkapura. Many of its buildings are attributed to him or to his successors. He is said to have invaded India and led his armies as far as Magadha, from which he carried off the learned Buddhist Asvaghosha. His Indian capital was at Peshāwar (Purushapura), where he built an enormous relic-tower, and a monastery which was for centuries a seat of learning. Kanishka is said to have fought successfully against the Parthians. The greatest military achievement of his reign, however, was the successful campaign across the Pāmirs which added Kashgar and Khotan to his dominions. He was thus able to avenge the defeat suffered by the Kushān arms in the preceding reign, and to carry back hostages, though, probably, not from the Chinese empire itself, but from some vassal state. Five centuries later Hiuen Tsang found the memory of those hostages still revered in the monasteries where they had resided, and he relates a curious story about the treasure they had given to one monastery to be used if ever required.

In the case of Kanishka, as in that of Asoka, Buddhist legend emphasises his cruelty and irreligion before his conversion. There exists no corroboration from other sources of the statement that Kanishka, on realising that he had been the cause of the slaughter of some hundreds of thousands of men in war, became penitent and thenceforth devoted himself to good works, but the fact that a similar story is told of Asoka is really no reason for disbelieving it in this case. We should not, however, forget the other story that Kanishka was murdered because his people were tired of his aggressive wars. The fact that he depicts Buddha on his coins along with Zoroastrian, Hellenic and Indian deities throws an interesting sidelight on his conception of Buddha, who in the Hīnayāna system had already become a god. We are told that Kanishka was perplexed in his studies by the diversity of thought in the various schools. He is said therefore to have summoned a conference of learned Buddhists, which was held in Kashmīr and was presided over by the learned Vasumitra and the then aged Asvaghosha. This council of some five hundred members examined the whole of Buddhist literature and prepared exhaustive commentaries. The results of their deliberations are said to have been inscribed on copper plates which were buried in a stupa specially built to receive them. It must be remembered, however, that while there is no doubt about the existence of the Buddhist Council and the work it did, Kanishka's connection with it is not absolutely certain. Paramārtha, for example, who is the earliest and most reliable authority on the subject, does not mention Kanishka, but says that Asvaghosha was sent for from Ayodhyā to superintend the deliberations, thus showing that he did not know the story of Asvaghosha's more or less involuntary sojourn at the court of Kanishka. No record is preserved of the length of Kanishka's reign, but his successor, Huvishka, was reigning in the twenty-fourth year of the Kanishkan era. According to one legend Kanishka, when lying sick, was murdered, by reason of the discontent provoked by his constant wars.

Two tangible relics of Kanishka survive; one is the life-sized statue of him, unfortunately now headless, found at Māt in the Mathura district; the other is the relic casket discovered in 1908 in the Shahjiki Dheri mound at Peshāwar, long ago identified as the stupa of Kanishka mentioned by the Chinese pilgrims. The casket, which contained relics of Buddha, is surmounted by figures of Buddha, Brāhma, and Indra, and includes among the

designs on its side Kanishka standing between the sun and moon.
The inscription on it records that the stupa was built by Agisala,
presumably Agesilaos, a Greek architect.

Kanishka was succeeded by Huvishka, from whose reign survives the most extensive coinage of the Kushān series. Inscriptions are known of a son of Kanishka named Vāsishka, who
evidently ruled in Mathura for some years as his father's viceroy;
but it is unlikely that he lived to succeed his father as sovereign,
as no coins of his seem to have survived. Of Huvishka's reign
we know nothing, but his extensive coinage justifies the assumption that it was of considerable length. The types are even more
numerous than those of Kanishka, but do not include any representation of Buddha. Iranian deities such as Mithra and Mao,
sun and moon gods, and Pharro, god of fire, still predominate,
but Indian deities are more numerous. One of the most remarkable of his coins bears a figure of Roma. The coins bear
excellent portraits; the obverse is a bust and not a standing figure
as in the case of Kanishka. His reign must have occupied the
greater part of the second half of the second century A.D. The
absence of coins indicates that a second Kanishka, whose name
has survived in inscriptions, was not a paramount sovereign but
a viceroy of Huvishka. The latter was succeeded by Vasudeva,
who, if we can judge by the great reduction in the number of
his coin-types, must have ruled a much diminished empire.
Though Vasudeva bore an Indian name—the Bazodeo of the
coins being a reproduction of Vasudeva—he still used the Kushān
or Saka language in his coin legends. Except for a rare type of
the goddess Nanaia, his coins bear the god Siva on their reverse.
It is thus evident that he had lost much of the Iranian territory
which his predecessors had ruled. One is tempted to suggest
that this was due to the rise of the Sassanian empire. This would
necessitate assigning a very late date to Vasudeva, but it may be
remembered that the Chinese historians indicate that the Kushān
(Yueh-chi) empire was still flourishing in the early third century.
The inscriptions in his name show that he ruled about thirty years.
On his death the Kushān empire broke up into numerous little
states, whose rulers imitated the coins of Kanishka and Vasudeva,
adding in the fields their own initials or monograms written perpendicularly in central Asian fashion. The numismatic evidence
shows that these petty dynasties ruled in the third and fourth

centuries, gradually disappearing before the advance of the Sassanians in the west and north, and of the Guptas in India. Such other evidence as we have also points to the recovery of autonomy by Indian dynasties, and republics like the Yaudheyas, and Mādrakas, in the third century A.D., in lands which must have been included in the Kushān empire at its greatest extent. The third century is, however, one of the darkest in Indian history, and it is not till northern India was again united under one great ruler in the next century that fresh light is thrown on its development.

We have already mentioned several families of satraps who ruled in north-western India on behalf of Pahlava suzerains, but probably enjoyed a considerable degree of independence. The most important of these were the northern satraps of Mathura. Further south, in western India, we have records of two important dynasties who call themselves satraps (Kshatrapas), one of which ruled, until its conquest by Chandragupta II, for over three hundred years from the end of Parthian domination. Two families, known to modern historians as the Western Kshatrapas and to Indian literature as the Sakas, must be distinguished. The first, short-lived, is that of the Kshaharātas, of whom two members are known from coins and inscriptions, Bhūmaka and Nahapāna, who were probably father and son. The reverse types of their coins—arrow, thunderbolt, and discus—recall certain coins of Maues, Azes, and Spalirises, and the lion-capital on the reverse of Bhūmaka's coins is a further link with this dynasty. The bust on the obverse of Nahapāna's silver coins resembles that on the coins of Ranjubula (Rājūla), but this may be due to derivation from a common prototype such as the coins of Strato I. The family name Kshaharāta is evidently the same as that mentioned in the Paṭika inscription of Liaka Kusūlaka, who was satrap of the Kshaharas and Chukhsas. A further link with Mathura is found in an inscription from that area which mentions a Kshaharāta satrap called Ghataka. All this suggests a date for these coins in the first century A.D. Bhūmaka calls himself a satrap on his coins, which are of copper only, while Nahapāna uses the Indian title rāja on the reverse and rāja and *kshatrapa* in the very corrupt Greek legend on the obverse, which again suggests a date contemporary with Ranjubula. Both Brāhmī and Kharoshthi legends appear on the reverse.

Nahapāna is known from several inscriptions of his son-in-law, Ushavadāta (Rishabhadatta), husband of his daughter Daksha-mitrā, who bears an Indian name. These inscriptions record charitable endowments, but incidentally one of them states that Ushavadāta was sent by his father-in-law to assist the tribe of Uttamabhadras to repel an invasion of the Mālavas, which he did successfully. The geographical references in the inscriptions show that Nahapāna ruled over a considerable area in western India, around the Gulf of Cambay, much of which Nahapāna could have gained only at the expense of the Āndhras. The inscriptions are dated in the years 41 to 46 of an unspecified era, which is usually supposed to be the Saka era, a theory which would fix the year A.D. 124 as a date in Nahapāna's reign. But his coins cannot be assigned to so late a date in the second century A.D.; this would make the interval between Nahapāna and the Mathura dynasty too great. The Kshatrapas' possession of Āndhra territory was brief, for we know that Gautamīputra destroyed the Sakas, Yavanas and Pahlavas, and, more precisely, "exterminated the race of Kshaharātas". No inscriptions or coins of any successors of Nahapāna are known, and there is no reason to doubt that the Āndhra victory was complete. The Sātakarni king even countermarked the coins of Nahapāna with his own types and inscription, so that the memory of the Saka king might be rooted out; this shows that he conquered the area in which these coins had been current. Somewhere after the middle of the first century, then, Nahapāna swiftly rose to power, and, probably after a long reign, fell before the advancing power of the Sātakarnis. If the name Nahapāna survives in a corrupt form in the *Mambanos* of the *Periplus*, and there is no good reason to doubt this identification, he must have been ruling in the third quarter of the first century A.D. His capital is said to have been Minnagar, which has not been identified. Isidore of Charax knew that *nagara* means "town", for he called the city Minpolis. *Min* is probably a manuscript corruption of some form like *Jun* and "Minnagar" may be a corruption of the original form of Junnār. The centre of Nahapāna's power certainly lay towards the coast, while that of the other line of satraps was in the interior at Ujjain. Ptolemy knew of Tiastanes, whose capital was Ozene, that is Chashtana of Ujjain.

We have seen that the Saka-Pahlava rule came to an end about

A.D. 80, and, working in the other direction, we find from the history of the Kushāns that this date for the establishment of Wīma Kadphises in India fits in very well with their history. It is probable that the exact date was A.D. 78, the starting-point of the Saka era. This era had, however, nothing to do with the more important event, the change from Parthian to Kushān sovereignty in northern India, but dated from the assumption of independence by a family of satraps in western India, who took advantage of the transfer of power in the north to become independent. The era employed by Nahapāna—or rather by his son-in-law—cannot be the Saka era, and must date from an earlier period. It is probably a local one. The Vikrama era is hardly possible as this would be too early.

But the Saka era is undoubtedly that used by the other line of satraps, who traced their descent from Chashtana, so that it is natural to suppose that the era dates from his accession. It is hardly likely that the fall of the Kshaharātas, the rise and fall of the Sātakarni king, the rise of Chashtana, and the secure establishment of his line in the person of Rudradāman took place in the six years between 46 (if we assume Ushavadāta's date is the Saka era) and 52, the date of the Āndhan inscriptions of Rudradāman. These inscriptions from a place in Kachch record the erection of a private monument in the "52nd year of Rudradāman, son of Jayadāman, of Chashtana son of Ysāmotika". There is no "and" in the text yet the expression has been taken to imply a joint rule; this would make Chashtana still alive in the fifty-second year of the Saka era, which makes it improbable but not impossible that the era dates from his accession. It is much more probable that in the inscription we have to supply "grandson", as in the usual formulae later. The inscription as it stands is certainly not lucid. We know that Chashtana was the grandfather of Rudradāman, and the inscription proves that the latter was reigning in A.S. 52. It is therefore not too much to assume that his grandfather began to reign fifty-two years before this. The inscription therefore presents no insuperable difficulty to the assumption that the Saka era of A.D. 78 dates from the accession of Chashtana, the founder of the line which used it and to which it owes its name of *Sakanripakāla, i.e.* the era of the Saka kings.

The second family of satraps, the line founded by Chashtana, was destined to rule for several centuries. A long series of coins,

giving valuable genealogical details and regularly dated, enables
us to date the rulers of this line with an accuracy which is not
reached again till Muhammadan times. They used the Saka era
to which they gave their name, a name by which they were still
known to Bāna, who records that the last of them was killed by
Chandragupta II. The earliest ruler of this line, and the one to
whom later rulers trace their descent, was Chashtana, son of
Ysāmotika. The head on the obverse of his coins closely resembles
that of Nahapāna and comes from the same prototype as does
the corrupt but still recognisable Greek inscription. The obverse
suggests that these coins cannot be very much later than Nahapāna's. The reverse, however, presents a striking difference, for
the types are purely Indian. The "mountain and river" are types
of the Deccan, long familiar on Āndhra coins, to which are
added a crescent and star—probably the sun and moon. A rare
type with crescent and star alone on the reverse is probably
Chashtana's earliest issue, struck before he extended his power
into Mālwā. He undoubtedly extended his territory very considerably at the expense of the Ārdhras, who were too busy
dealing with the other dynasty to interfere with him. The mention
of Chashtana by Ptolemy suggests that he reigned into the second
century, so that his date is probably A.D. 78–110. His son,
Jayadāman, only bore the title Kshatrapa and not Mahākshatrapa,
from which it would appear that the young dynasty suffered some
diminution in territory or influence in his reign (c. A.D. 110–20),
no doubt at the hands of the Āndhras, who, having exterminated
the Kshaharātas, attempted with some success to wipe out the
other family of invaders. This is confirmed by Rudradāman's
boast of his victories over the Āndhras, and by his claim that he
had won for himself the title of "great satrap", corresponding
to the Indian "king of kings" which is never used by the Western
Kshatrapas.

With the reign of Rudradāman we are on surer ground, for
to it belongs one of the most important inscriptions of ancient
India, that of Girnār, which records the repairs made to the dam
of a lake already mentioned in connection with Asoka's reign.
Rudradāman's viceroy in the province of Surāshtra at that
time was the Pahlava, or Parthian, Suvisākha, son of Kulaipa,
whose foreign descent was not forgotten in spite of his Indian
name. The importance of the inscription lies in the information

it gives about Rudradāman. He had conquered the "proud and indomitable" Yaudheyas, who had, presumably, threatened him from the north; in the south he had twice defeated Sātakarni, lord of the Deccan, and on each occasion had restored him to his throne on account of their relationship—the Kshatrapa was the Āndhra's father-in-law. He won for himself the title of "great satrap", and among the lands which owned his sway were Kachch and Kāthiāwār, Sind, eastern and western Mālwā and portions of Rājputāna. The inscription refers to "other territory", not specified, as conquered by his own prowess, and implies that some of the places named had been conquered by him. He was evidently the first great ruler of the dynasty, and must have extended his power mainly at the expense of the Āndhras. The inscription is dated 72 (A.D. 150), and seems to belong to the end of his probably long reign. We know from the Āndhan inscription that he was reigning in 52 (A.D. 130), so that his probable dates are A.D. 120-55. The repairs to the dam were difficult, but the cost was borne by the personal resources of the sovereign, without oppressing the people by extra taxes. Thus the bursting of the dam three centuries after its erection gives us an unexpected glimpse into Indian history. The language of this inscription is good Sanskrit, but the coin legends of Rudradāman and his successors retain Prākrit features. Rudradāman was succeeded by his son Dāmaghsada, whose name was given the Indian form Dāmajada in his lifetime. His successor, Jīvadāman, began to date his coins, a custom continued by his successors to the end of the dynasty. Almost nothing is known of the history of the western satraps for the next two hundred years. A regular series of coins exists, enabling us to trace the succession of rulers with precision, but the few inscriptions of the period contain nothing of historical interest. About A.D. 236-40, the Ābhīra, Īsvaradatta, seems to have conquered a portion at least of Kshatrapa territory, where he issued for a time coins of the local type. The direct line of Chashtana became extinct, in A.D. 304, with the death of Visvasena, son of Bhartridāman. His successor, Rudrasimha II, does not give his father Jīvadāman any important title, but there is no reason to doubt that he was in some way connected with the old family. The dynasty was probably of little importance in the fourth century. The last member of the dynasty known from his coins is Rudrasimha III, whose coins are dated in 31 [Saka] (*c.* A.D. 390). He was no doubt the "Saka" king who was killed by Chandragupta II when he sacked his capital. The Guptas continued the issue of silver coins of Kshatrapa style with their own emblem, the Garuda, replacing the Kshatrapa symbols on the reverse.

A minor dynasty known as the Traikūtakas ruled into the fifth century in the Konkan, a territory that had once belonged to the satraps whose coins they copy. Coins and inscriptions of two kings are known, Dahrasena and his son Vyāghrasena. The name of Dahrasena's father, Indradatta, survives on his coins. The former claims to have performed the horse-sacrifice. The latest known date of Vyāghrasena is A.D. 480.

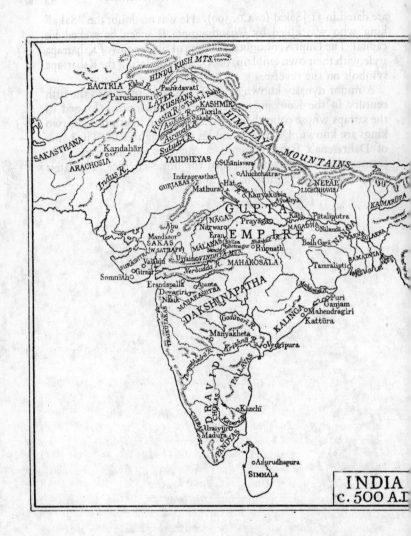

INDIA
c. 500 A.D.

CHAPTER VI

The Gupta Period

In the fourth century a series of important inscriptions again enables us to reconstruct the history of India in its main outlines to a degree not possible since the time of Asoka. The most valuable of these is the Allāhābād inscription of Samudragupta, engraved on one of the stone pillars which Asoka set up and inscribed with his edicts. The substance of Samudragupta's inscription, however, is very different from that of Asoka's, for it details the conquests of one of the greatest rulers India has ever known, but who, before the decipherment of his inscriptions and the correct attribution of his coins, was quite unknown to history.

With Samudragupta himself we shall deal later. We are here concerned first of all with his genealogy as recorded by his inscriptions. He was the son of Mahārājādhirāja Chandragupta and his queen the Mahādevī Kumāradevī of the ancient family of the Lichchhavis; Chandragupta was the son of Ghatotkacha, who was the son of Gupta. Samudragupta's lineage is carried back no farther, nor are the names of his grandmother and great-grandmother given. This genealogy is frequently repeated in the inscriptions of the successors of Chandragupta. Gupta and his son Ghatotkacha bore the simple title mahārāja belonging to a petty dynasty, but Chandragupta and his successors used the title mahārājādhirāja—"king of kings", which indicates paramount sovereignty. The inscriptions are dated in an era beginning from the accession of Chandragupta I; the first year of this era, it has been ascertained, ran from February 26, A.D. 320 to March 15, A.D. 321. The fixing of the date of the beginning of the Gupta era laid the foundation for the chronology of the period. Practically nothing is known of Chandragupta I and his ancestors or of the circumstances which enabled one of the many petty dynasties of the time gradually to triumph over all its neighbours. Gupta's territory presumably lay around Pātaliputra. A single fact about him has been preserved by the Chinese pilgrim I Tsing, who travelled in India in the last quarter of the seventh century, and who states that a mahārāja named Gupta built a temple near Mrigasikhāvana for some Chinese pilgrims whose devoutness had deeply impressed him, and endowed it with twenty-four villages. No serious objection to identifying this king with the grandfather of Chandragupta can be·based on the fact that I Tsing says these events took place five instead of four centuries before his visit. The identification is supported by the fact that the lands in question must have been within Gupta territory. Gupta may be conjectured to have reigned from A.D. 275–300. He was succeeded by his son Ghatotkacha, of whom nothing is known, though his rather uncommon name occurs as a component of the names of later members of the family. Ghatotkacha was succeeded by his son, Chandragupta I, whose queen, Kumāradevī, was the first to be regularly mentioned in the inscriptions. She was a daughter of the Lichchhavi line, an ancient family known to have been ruling at Vaisāli in the early days of Buddhism. The pride with which this ancestry is claimed suggests that the alliance had important results on the fortunes of the Gupta family. Chandragupta's assumption of the title mahārājādhirāja probably indicates that he extended his ancestral dominions by force of arms, and perhaps his marriage with Kumāradevī formed part of the settlement after his conquest of the adjoining kingdom of Vaisāli. But no doubt it was rather the ancient lineage of the Lichchhavis than any material gain resulting from the alliance that impressed the Guptas, who themselves appear to have been of humble birth. We know little of the events of the third century A.D., but the Gupta family was probably one of those that rose with the decline of the power of their Kushān suzerains. It is just possible that Gupta and Ghatotkacha are foreign names, under a Sanskrit guise, and that the Guptas were not of Hindu blood. In any case the name Gupta suggests a humble origin.

We have no records of Chandragupta's reign; his kingdom probably comprised the Ganges valley from Prayāga to Pātaliputra. His importance is evident from the fact that the Gupta era sprang from the custom of reckoning dates from the year of his accession, a custom which was continued mechanically under his successors. Coins exist which commemorate the alliance of Chandragupta and Kumāradevī, but, like several other pieces of a medallic nature, these were struck by Samudragupta. Chandragupta may be assumed to have reigned till about A.D. 335.

Chandragupta was succeeded by his son, Samudragupta, one of the ablest and most versatile rulers India has known. He may not have been Chandragupta's eldest son, for the Allāhābād inscription contains a brief but vivid picture of the scene at court when his father chose him as the worthiest of all his sons to succeed him on the throne. Our knowledge of his reign is derived from his Allāhābād inscription, one of the most important documents of its kind. The other inscription of his reign, at Eran, is very fragmentary, and adds nothing to our knowledge. The Allāhābād inscription, a work of considerable literary merit and interest, gives an account of his conquests in some detail, and, although neither chronologically nor geographically precise, enables us to understand the development of his empire. The inscription is not dated, but must have been set up towards the end of the long career of conquest on which Samudragupta must have set out very soon after his accession, for many campaigns must have been required to achieve the results chronicled. His rivals are divided into four classes according to his treatment of them: kings who were slain by him and whose kingdoms were incorporated into his dominions; kings who were defeated and taken prisoner, but reinstated as tributaries; "frontier kings" who seem voluntarily to have paid some kind of homage to the victor; and kings of more distant monarchies who may, as the inscription asserts, have felt the force of his arms and who certainly seem to have shown some recognition—probably exaggerated by his panegyrist—of his rise to power. The first to suffer were his neighbours of the Ganges valley, for he "violently uprooted" Rudradeva, Matila, Nāgadatta, Chandravarman, Ganapatināga, Nāgasena, Achyuta, Nandi, Balavarman and many kings of Āryāvarta. Of these kings Ganapatināga has been identified as one of the dynasty of Padmavatī or Narwar, while Achyuta is probably a member of the dynasty coins of which are found at Ahichchatra, and of which he may have been king; the others are known only from this inscription. Nāgasena may have been connected with the Narwar dynasty.

Samudragupta's next campaign was directed against all "the kings of the forest country" whom "he made his servants", and the kings of the south, whom he claims to have captured, but whose lives he spared. The place-names mentioned enable us to follow the route of this campaign. Samudragupta was long believed to have reached the Malabar coast. The name Kaurāla in the inscription was emended to Kairala and identified with Kerāla or Keralaputra (*i.e.* Madura), and from this the conclusion was drawn that Samudragupta reached the Chera kingdom of south India. Further support for this theory was secured by identifying Kauttura with Kottūra-Pollāchi in the Coimbatore district, and Palakka with Pālghāt, the headquarters of the district of the same name bordering on Malabar district. Kauttara, however, is now identified with Kothur in Ganjam, and Palakka with a town of that name (Palakollu) in the Kistna district, which in those days lay in Pallava territory. Erandapalla was formerly identified with Erandol in the Khāndesh district of Bombay, and it was supposed that Samudragupta had returned northwards through Bombay, Devarāshtra being identified as Mahārāshtra. But in the inscription Airandapalla is mentioned along with the fortress of Kottūra, which suggests that it also should be sought for in Orissa. The plates of the Ganga king, Devendravarman, of the eleventh century, found at Siddhantam near Chicacole in the Ganjam district, record a gift to a native of Erandapali. This is evidently the Erandapalla of the Allāhābād inscription, and it was therefore in the Ganjam district. Further, Devarāshtra can no longer be equated with the Marātha country, for a copper-plate inscription, found at Kāsimkota in the Vizagapatam district, mentions a gift, made by the eastern Chālukya king, Bhīma I, of a village in Elamancha Kalingadesa, which was part of the province called Devarāshtra, so that Devarāshtra must have been in the Vizagapatam district of Madras. Samudragupta's campaigns therefore covered a more limited area than was at one time thought. All the kingdoms mentioned in the inscription were on the eastern side of the Deccan. The course of his southern expedition was, therefore, somewhat as follows: marching southwards, he conquered Mahendra of Kosala, on the banks of the Mahānadī, in the region of Sirpur and Sombalpur. He then crossed the forest country south of Sonpur, in which only Vyaghrarāja is mentioned by name. Reaching the Orissa coast, he defeated Mantarāja, king of Korala, Mahendra of Pishtapuram, Swāmidatta of Kottūra-on-the-hill, and Damana of Erandapalla. On reaching the banks of the Krishnā, he was met by a confederation of kings led by Vishnugopa, the Pallava king of Kānchī, who is the only one of these kings known from inscriptions. Other rulers of this region who united to check the progress of the invader were Nīlarāja of Avamukta, whose name may perhaps, be preserved in Nilapalli in the Godāvarī district; Hastivarman of Vengī, possibly Vegi, a few miles north of Ellore in the Kistna district; Ugrasena of Palakka, Kubera of Devarāshtra, and Dhanamjaya of Kusthalapura. He may have defeated and released these kings as he claims, but he made no permanent conquests in these regions, and it is very probable that Professor Jouveau-Dubreuil is right in thinking that the last-named rulers formed a confederation which proved too strong for Samudragupta an compelled him to retire.

None of these kingdoms, as Samudragupta himself states, was permanently annexed, but there is no doubt that he exacted a heavy tribute from many, if not all, of them, and carried away enormous wealth, as Malik Kāfūr did nearly a thousand years later.

The next group of states mentioned are those of the frontier kings, who appear voluntarily to have paid tribute and homage. On the east lay Samatata in the Brahmaputra delta, with Davāka to the north of it and Kāmarūpa (Assam) to the north-east; on the north were Nepāl and Kartripura, a clue to the location of which may be given by the modern Kartarpur in the Jalandhar district. With these kings are grouped a number of republican tribes like the Yaudheyas and Mādrakas in the Panjab and the Arjunāyanas, Mālavas and Ābhīras farther south.

With the fourth group, the Daivaputras, Sahis, Sāhānusāhis, Sakas and Murundas, he simply maintained diplomatic relations. The first three words are titles, and the last two ethnic terms. All were representatives of the Sakas and Kushāns who had invaded India nearly four centuries before and gradually conquered all northern India. It is not possible to identify them with certainty, nor even to analyse with precision the compound word of the Sanskrit text. There are various references in literature to the Murundas who may be located in the upper Ganges valley, with the Sakas to the north-east of them. The Daivaputras probably ruled over the remainder of the Panjab, while the Sahis and the Sāhānusāhis, or Sāhisāhanusāhis, should be located in modern Afghanistan.

The fact that Samudragupta's coins are copied from those of the Sakas is evidence of the conquest of a considerable territory in which Saka and late Kushān coins had long been current, just as the silver coinage of the Guptas began with the conquest of the land of the Western Satraps, whose coinage was immediately imitated.

That the people of Sinhāla and all the dwellers in the islands brought gifts to Samudragupta, we learn from other sources. Meghavarman, king of Ceylon (c. A.D. 350–80), sent him gifts, with a request that he would build a monastery at Bodh Gāya for Buddhist pilgrims from Ceylon, and this accordingly was done.

One of the titles given to Samudragupta by his successors is "Restorer of the horse-sacrifice". It was probably at the conclusion of his conquests rather than at the beginning of his career that he celebrated this ancient rite with great splendour. Since it is not mentioned in the Allāhābād inscription, it was probably performed at a date later than that of its incision. A possible allusion to it occurs in the Eran inscription, in the reference to lavish distributions of gold. An interesting memorial of the sacrifice survives in the coins struck to commemorate it, bearing the sacrificial horse on the one side and on the other the queen, who played an important part in the ceremony, with legends relating to the efficacy of the sacrifice.

The inscriptions also tell us that Samudragupta was both poet and musician; the latter statement is corroborated by the existence of coins showing him seated and playing a lyre, while the former accomplishment may explain the existence of metrical legends on his coins. Other coins liken him to Kritānta, the god of death, as do the inscriptions. One of his favourite titles, an allusion to his conquests, was Sarvarājochchettā, "exterminator of all kings", and the use of this epithet on a series of coins bearing the name Kācha proves that they were issued by Samudragupta. Samudragupta probably instituted the Gupta coinage late in his reign, for his coins bear allusions to his conquests, and perhaps owe their profusion to the great quantity of gold which he carried back from his south Indian campaigns. Samudragupta probably lived till about A.D. 385. The name of the queen, who was the mother of his successor, was Dattadevī.

This son, chosen by his father to succeed him, was Chandragupta II, who took the honorific title Vikramāditya. Samudragupta himself is not known to have adopted a title of this form, but may have been called Parākramāditya.

Several inscriptions of Chandragupta II's reign are extant; but all originate from private individuals, and all are of chronological rather than historical importance. The Udayagiri cave inscription records a dedication by a mahārāja of the Sanakānika family, who was a feudatory of Chandragupta, and who dates his inscription in the year G.E. 82. The Sanchi inscription, dated G.E. 93, commemorates a donation made by one of Chandragupta's officers. The Udayagiri inscription is undated, and records the excavation of a cave in honour of Siva by one of Chandragupta's ministers, Vīrasena-Sāba. This inscription is important because it states that the latter was accompanying Chandragupta II, when he was "seeking to conquer the whole world", so that it was probably incised during Chandragupta's campaign against the Western Satraps. The only interest of the Gadhwā inscription is that it is dated G.E. 88. It is from his coins that we learn of the greatest achievement of Chandragupta's reign, the conquest of the Western Satraps. Already the influence of Samudragupta's conquests must have been felt by the Western Satraps, who may perhaps be included among the Sakas of the Allāhābād inscription. The Udayagiri inscription is evidence of the Gupta occupation of eastern Mālwā. The latest coins of the Western Satraps, those of Rudrasimha III, belong to the year 31-, i.e. A.D. 388–97. After his conquest of Surāshtra Chandragupta II instituted a silver coinage which imitates closely that of the Satraps. The earliest date on these is G.E. 90 or 90+, i.e. between A.D. 409 and 413, since Chandragupta died about the latter year. The conquest therefore took place somewhere between A.D. 395 and 400. One of the few references in literature to the Guptas concerns this campaign; according to it Chandragupta slew the last king of the Sakas in his enemy's city while courting another man's wife.

With the westward development of the Gupta empire Ujjain became increasingly important, and probably began to overshadow the ancient capital of Pātaliputra. The inscriptions give Dhruvadevī as the name of Chandragupta's queen, the mother of his successor, Kumāragupta. Bloch's excavations at Basarh (Vaisāli) produced a large number of seals of the period of Chandragupta II, many belonging to officials of the province, and revealing the fact that there existed under the Guptas a highly organised civil service. The most important of these seals is one of Queen Dhruvaswāminī (Dhruvadevī), wife of Chandragupta and mother of the mahārāja Govindagupta, presumably a brother of Kumāragupta, and governor of Vaisāli. The Ghatotkachagupta whose seal was found was probably another son, and certainly was a member of the imperial family. He may be identified with the governor of Eran mentioned in the Tumain inscription. By another queen, Kuberanāgā, Chandragupta had a daughter, Prabhāvatīguptā, who married the Vākātaka, Rudrasena II. The fact that some of her inscriptions refer to her father as Dēvarāja suggests that this was another name or title of Chandragupta.

While Samudragupta's reverses retained traces of their Kushān prototypes, Chandragupta's coins display considerable originality of type and become purely Indian. He was fond of representing himself on horseback, or in combat with a lion. His title was *Vikramāditya*. To his reign belonged the introduction of a silver coinage which became extensive in the reign of his successors; he also issued copper coins, being, most probably, the only member of his dynasty to do so.

The Sanchi inscription shows that Chandragupta was still reigning in G.E. 93 (*i.e.* A.D. 412–13), while the Bilsad inscription of G.E. 96 (*i.e.* A.D. 415–16) is of the reign of Kumāragupta I, whose accession may therefore be dated in A.D. 414. Little is known of the events of his reign, but his extensive coinage and the distribution of the inscriptions of his reign suggest that he retained his father's empire intact. The Bilsad inscription, recording a private dedication, describes his reign as one of "increasing victory". Other inscriptions, the Gadhwā of G.E. 98 (A.D. 417–18), the Udayagiri of 106 (A.D. 425–6), the Tumain of 116 (A.D. 435–6), the Karamadande of 117 (A.D. 436–7), the Mankuwar of 129 (A.D. 448–9), are of importance only by reason of their dates. The long Mandasor inscription of Kumāragupta and Bandhuvarman, his governor at Dāsapura, contains nothing of historical importance. It records the building and repair of a temple in Dāsapura (Mandasor) by the local gild of silk weavers in the Mālava year 493 (A.D. 437–8). Coins are the sole evidence that he, like his grandfather, performed the *asvamedha* sacrifice. He added a number of new types to the coinage, notably one in which Kārttikeya is represented on his vehicle the peacock, and one in which the king appears riding on an elephant. His

silver coinage is very extensive, and during his reign the use of
silver coins spread from the place of their origin in the western
provinces to the home provinces. With Kumāragupta's reign the
period of Gupta greatness closed, and it is evident from his
son's records that his last years were troubled.

Kumāragupta was succeeded in A.D. 455 by Skandagupta, the
son of his queen Anantadevī. From Skandagupta's reign important inscriptions survive, the most valuable being that of
Bhitari, an undated inscription, the primary object of which was
to record the installation by Skandagupta of an image of Vishnu,
and the allotment to it of a village in memory of his father in
order to increase his merit. The value of this inscription lies in
its historical allusions, from which we learn something of the
dangers then threatening the Gupta empire. It contains three
allusions to the restoration of the family fortunes by Skandagupta.
We are told that, preparatory to restoring the fallen fortunes of
his family, Skandagupta slept a night on the bare ground; that
on his father's death he conquered his enemies and re-established
the ruined fortunes of his house; and that with his own armies
he stabilised the tottering lineage of the Guptas. Unfortunately
the precise nature of the catastrophe thus averted is not stated.
There is indeed a reference to his conquest of the Pushyamitras,
tributaries, otherwise unknown, who had developed great power
and wealth. This people seems to have attempted with some success to overthrow the Guptas in the closing years of Kumāragupta, but they were finally crushed by Skandagupta, his father
having died, apparently, while he himself was in the field against
them, for it was to his mother that he announced his victory on
his return, a fact which seems to explain the mention of his
mother in the inscription. The other enemy referred to by name
are the Hūnas, with whom Skandagupta fought a fierce battle
and was victorious. He seems to have had other troubles to face
also. The inscription appears to belong to the early part of his
reign, so that the earliest recorded invasion of India by the Hūnas
must have taken place about A.D. 455. Another long inscription
of his reign is that at Junāgarh, commemorating the restoration,
in 138 (A.D. 457-8), by order of the son of the governor of
Surāshtra, who had been appointed to his office by Skandagupta
himself, of an embankment which had burst two years earlier. The
opening lines are a panegyric of Skandagupta, and we are again

told how, after his father's death, he conquered his enemies and broke the pride of the Mlechchas, who are, presumably, the Hūnas. He appointed governors in all his territories, deliberating with great care before deciding upon whom to confer these important offices. This suggests that the danger which had threatened his frontiers might recur. A Jain inscription, dated G.E. 141 (A.D. 460–1), and recording the dedication of five images at Kakubha, describes Skandagupta's reign as peaceful and calls the monarch lord of a hundred vassal kings, but these are only conventional phrases. The Mathura inscription, of 135 (A.D. 454–5), the Kosam of 139 (A.D. 458–9), and the Indore plate of 146 (A.D. 465–6) are all of his reign, but contain no historical information of importance.

Skandagupta assumed the title *Kramāditya*, although he seems to have used *Vikramāditya* as well. His gold coins are scarce compared with those of his predecessors, and his later gold issues seem to belong only to the east, a fact which suggests a reduction of territory. His extensive silver coinage, however, shows that during the first part of his reign at least he retained his western dominions. His only new type shows the goddess Lakshmī standing beside him, and thus supports the statement of the Bhitarī inscription that he believed himself specially favoured by her.

With the death of Skandagupta about A.D. 470, the glory of the dynasty seems to have passed. The names of a number of his successors are known, chiefly from coins, but the order of their succession is a matter of some uncertainty. On a celebrated seal, found at Bhitari, occurs the genealogy of Kumāragupta II *Kramāditya*, who was the son of Narasimhagupta *Balāditya*, the son of Puragupta *Vikramāditya*, the son of Kumāragupta I. This seal makes no mention of Skandagupta, but traces the Gupta line through his brother Puragupta. Coins are known of all these rulers as well as of Vishnugupta *Chandrāditya*, who seems, from the evidence of coin-finds, to have been the son of Kumāragupta II. Coins are also known of Vainyagupta III *Dvādasāditya*, of Prakāsāditya, whose Gupta name is not known, and of a Ghatot-kachagupta *Kramāditya*. It is possible that these represent the descendants of the line of Skandagupta, and that, the much reduced Gupta empire having been split into two divisions in the last quarter of the fifth century, the family of Skandagupta held the central, and that of Puragupta the eastern, dominions.

The evidence of coin-finds suggests that Prakāsāditya succeeded Skandagupta, but the order of his successors is uncertain. Further evidence of the disruption of the empire is afforded by the existence of dated coins and inscriptions of Budhagupta, who must have reigned about A.D. 480–500, and who was presumably succeeded by Bhānugupta, mentioned in inscriptions of G.E. 191 (A.D. 510–11), which seem to relate to a battle fought against the Hūna invaders. Budhagupta may have been another son of Kumāragupta I, or perhaps a nephew. The coins of Budhagupta and the sites of his inscriptions suggest that this line ruled in the western part of the empire. Of all these rulers only Narasimhagupta (if he is the Balāditya of Hiuen Tsang) is known to have played a part in history. The Chinese pilgrim credits him with building a great temple at Nālandā, the Buddhist university, which he furnished in magnificent style.

Skandagupta's defeat of the Hūnas had only postponed the evil day for the Guptas, and in the last decades of the fifth century, after passing through Persia and sweeping away the petty Kushān and Saka kingdoms of the north-east, they poured into India. Soon the Hūna empire included all the western and central Gupta dominions. The Hūnas produced two great rulers in India, Toramāna and his son Mihirakula. An inscription which mentions the former was found at Eran, and his coins copy the silver pieces of Skandagupta or Budhagupta, while numerous copper coins and an inscription, found at Gwalior, survive from the reign of his son. Toramāna's reign continued into the sixth century; Mihirakula, of whose history more is known, has an unenviable record in Buddhist tradition.

According to Hiuen Tsang, Mihirakula persecuted the Buddhists and invaded the lands of Balāditya, king of Magadha. Balāditya not only routed the invader but captured and afterwards released him. Mihirakula then took refuge in Kashmīr, where he established himself as a ruler. Other evidence exists of Balāditya's interest in Buddhism, but it is difficult to judge how far Hiuen Tsang's story is true. We may probably deduce from it that Balāditya defeated Mihirakula, and was able to check the Hūna advance. The problem is complicated by the existence of two inscriptions of a king named Yasodharman, who claims to have achieved precisely those things which Hiuen Tsang ascribes to Balāditya. Both these inscriptions are at Mandasor.

The first (which is in duplicate) is on a pillar of victory erected to the glory of Yasodharman, who ruled over territory which not even the Guptas had owned, and had invaded lands which not even the Hūnas had penetrated; from the river Lauhitya to Mount Mahendra, and from the Himālaya to the western ocean kings acknowledged him; even Mihirakula paid homage to him after being overthrown. The other inscription mentions Yaso-dharman only incidentally, as having conquered powerful kings of the north and east; it is important because, being dated in the year S.E. 590 (A.D. 533–4), it shows that Mihirakula had a long reign. Nothing more is known of Yasodharman, who, even when due allowance has been made for his panegyrist, must have been a powerful ruler. There is no reason to doubt his claim to have defeated Mihirakula and restored him to liberty. The diffi-culty lies in reconciling his inscription with the statement of the Chinese pilgrim who credits Balāditya with the same achieve-ments. The probability is that Balāditya inflicted some check on the Hūnas, but that their complete rout was due to Yasodharman, and that the Chinese pilgrim gives to the patron of Buddhism more of the credit than was his due. It is probable that in India, as in Europe, the Hūna power declined as rapidly as it rose, and that its collapse was not effected by any individual Indian liberator. In the latter half of the sixth century the Hūnas seem to have broken up into a number of petty tribes of little political im-portance. But the terror which the name of Mihirakula inspired not only is recorded by a contemporary, the Alexandrian monk, Cosmas, who visited India in his time, but finds an echo, nearly six centuries later, in the pages of the Kashmīr Chronicle.

A line of Gupta rulers, whose precise connection with the imperial line is not known, continued to rule in Magadha for two centuries longer. Their genealogy appears from inscriptions, notably those of Ādityasena about A.D. 672, who seems to have somewhat revived the glory of his ancient house and celebrated the horse-sacrifice. Ādityasena traced his descent from a certain Krishnagupta, and claimed Kumāragupta as his ancestor. His son Dāmodragupta overcame the Maukharis. The last known member of the dynasty is Jīvitagupta, the second of that name.

The Chinese pilgrim, Fa Hien, visited India in A.D. 405–11, and has left an account of his travels, which, however, contain dis-appointingly little of interest to the modern reader. One may deduce from his record that the country was prosperous and well-governed, and Pātaliputra seems to have been the capital of the empire. The Buddhist holy places had fallen into neglect, and it is very doubtful if Buddhism was as prominent as the pilgrim would have us believe. The Gupta emperors were Hindus, but some of them are credited with a tolerant interest in other faiths. The Gupta period was, however, one of a great Brahmanical revival. Both Samudragupta and his grandson, for example, celebrated the ancient horse-sacrifice with all its very elaborate ritual.

Seals and inscriptions reveal glimpses of very highly organised civil and military services and elaborate court ceremonial. The ministers were men of wide culture. A dedication informs us that Chandragupta II's war minister, for example, was a poet, logician and rhetorician. The Gupta age was the classical period of Sanskrit literature. The emperors regularly used Sanskrit for their inscriptions, while in the earlier periods pure Sanskrit inscriptions were rare, the language used being generally the local Prākrit. This is the period of great names in Sanskrit literature. The memory of the glories of the court of Chandragupta II, and the men of letters who shed lustre upon it, undoubtedly survives in the old tradition that the "nine gems" of Sanskrit literature flourished at the court of Vikramāditya of Ujjain, although nothing is known of several of the "nine gems", and others cannot possibly be contemporaries. The great Allāhābād inscription of Samudragupta is the work of an otherwise unknown Harisena, who was no mean poet, and forms an important landmark in the chronology of kāvya literature. Kālidāsa, the greatest name in Indian literature, flourished at the court of Chandragupta II, and may have survived until the reign of Skandagupta. Of the other "nine gems" Varāhamihira, the astronomer, and Amarakosa, the lexicographer, lived about a century later. To the Gupta age belong also a number of encyclopaedic works and digests of a theoretical and practical nature like the Purānas, the Laws of Manu, the Arthasāstra of Kautilya, and other works, all revealing a love of codification and systematisation. The Panchatantra also took its present form about the same time. In art and architecture the period was of an importance which can only be appreciated now that excavations have yielded materials for study. The sculpture is characterised by vigour, and evinces a gradual liberation from Gandhāran influence, its technical execution being very fine. All the arts seem to have flourished at the Gupta court in a manner worthy of a great dynasty.

An important dynasty contemporary with the Guptas was that of the Vākāṭakas, whose territory seems originally to have corresponded with modern Berar. The origin of the word Vākāṭaka is unknown but the rulers of the line bear good Sanskrit names. Inscriptions serve to trace the descent of the dynasty from Vindyasakti, who does not appear to have been a ruling sovereign, but whose son, Pravarasena, is referred to as mahārāja, and is said to have performed four horse-sacrifices, thereby earning the title of *samrāj*, or emperor. Pravarasena's son was Gautamīputra, but the second ruler of the line seems to have been Pravarasena's grandson, Rudrasena I. The latter's son Prithivīsena had an unusually long reign and conquered the land of Kuntala (*i.e.* the Kadambas). His son Rudrasena II married Prabhavātī, a daughter of Chandragupta II, who proudly records her Gupta lineage in an inscription. They had a son named Devakarasena who may be the Pravarasena II who succeeded Rudrasena II. In the first half of the fifth century, the Vākāṭaka kingdom, lying between the Gupta empire and the kingdoms of the south, had become the dominant power in the Deccan, and through the Vākāṭakas the culture of northern India began to penetrate into the south. In the last quarter of the century Narendrasena asserted that he was obeyed by the king of Mālwā, a claim which suggests that the Vākāṭaka power had extended northwards with the break up of the Gupta dominions on the death of Skandagupta. Later rulers were Devasena and Harisena, his son, who laid claim to considerable conquests, including Kuntala, Avantī, Kalinga, Trikuta and Āndhra. The dynasty disappeared in the middle of the sixth century, supplanted, apparently, by the Kālachuris. The presence of Vākāṭaka inscriptions in the Ajanta and other sculptured caves is an important factor in the chronology of Indian art. The Nāchnā inscription refers to a certain Vyāghra, feudatory of Prithivīsena I, in central India, and it is not improbable that he is the Vyāghra mentioned in the Allāhābād inscription of Samudragupta, and that at this period the Guptas replaced the Vākāṭakas as the suzerain power in central India, and that the centre of gravity of the latter dynasty was henceforth transferred to the south.

A number of copper-plate inscriptions survive in which some information is preserved concerning a dynasty which ruled at Valabhī, in Surāshtra, from the fifth to the eighth centuries A.D. These contain unusually full genealogical lists, but little historical information. The founder of the dynasty was a certain *senāpati*, Bhātarka, who laid the foundations of the family fortunes by overthrowing a neighbouring tribe called the Maitrakas. The inscriptions of this house are dated in the Gupta era, the use of which was thus continued to the year 447 (*i.e.* A.D. 766). Little is known of the political history of the dynasty, but it may be inferred from the prosperity of Valabhī in the seventh century that its territory had been considerably extended with the decline of Gupta and Hūna power. Harsha defeated a king of Valabhī and drove him from his kingdom to seek refuge with the Gūrjara, Dadda II, who protected him and assisted him to make his peace with Harsha. The latter not only restored him to the throne, but gave him his grand-daughter in marriage. This king seems to have been Dhruvasena II, the nephew of Silāditya. Valabhī rivalled Nālandā as a great school of Buddhist learning, and its memory is enshrined in the pages of Chinese pilgrims.

A line of Gupta rulers, whose connection with the imperial line is not clearly known, continued to rule in Magadha in the sixth and seventh centuries. Our knowledge of them is derived mainly from the inscriptions of two of their number, Ādityasena and Jīvitagupta II. The Aphsad inscription of Ādityasena, whose short Shāpūr inscription is dated 66 (*i.e.* A.D. 672), traces his descent from Krishnagupta, of whose origin nothing is stated. If he were a direct descendant of the imperial Gupta line, we should have expected some reference to the fact. Of Krishnagupta's son and grandson, Harshagupta and Jīvitagupta I, the conventional phrases of the inscription tell us nothing, but the next ruler, Kumāragupta, is stated to have defeated the army of the Maukharī, Isānavarman, whom we know to have been reigning in 611 (*i.e.* A.D. 554). It is also recorded that Kumāragupta died and was buried in Prayāga. His son, Dāmodragupta, fell fighting against the Maukharīs, fresh from their victories over the Hūnas. Of his successor it is recorded that he won a victory over Susthitavarman, king of Kāmarūpa, the memory of which long survived in that region. His son, Mādhavagupta, seems to have acknowledged the suzerainty of Harsha. The Devagupta who had conquered the Maukhari, Grahavarman, and had been in turn easily defeated by Rājyavardhana, Harsha's brother, probably belonged to this dynasty, but as the line was not continued through him he does not appear in the Aphsad inscription. It is probable, since Mādhavagupta was an ally and possibly a vassal of Harsha, that Devagupta was the former's immediate predecessor.

Ādityasena, son of Mādhavagupta, evidently took advantage of the death of Harsha to resume an independent position. The distribution of his inscriptions shows that he ruled in southern and eastern Bihar in the third quarter of the seventh century. As evidence of his sovereign power, he performed the horse-sacrifice, and his inscription claims that his fame extended beyond the seas. To the joint piety of himself, his mother, and his wife we owe the work from which we have our knowledge of the dynasty. The Deo-Baranark inscription of the last known member of the dynasty, Jīvitagupta II, carries on the genealogy from Ādityasena through Devagupta and Vishnugupta, without adding anything definite to our knowledge of the dynasty.

The great rivals of these later Guptas in Magadha were the Maukharis, of whom, again, little is known. They seem to have been of an old family, as a seal survives, inscribed with characters of the third century B.C., and bearing the legend *mokhalinam*, "of the Maukhalis", or Maukharis. The pride with which matrimonial alliance with them is recorded is further evidence of their ancient lineage. Two families of them are known. The more important is that known from the seal of Sarvavarman, which traces his lineage back through Isānavarman, Isvaravarman, and Ādityavarman to Harivarman. From an inscription of his son, Sūryavarman, we learn that Isānavarman was ruling in 611 (*i.e.* A.D. 554), and that he had conquered the land of the Āndhras, defeated the Sulikas, otherwise unknown, and caused the Gaudas to cease their raids and remain within their own territory. We also learn from an inscription of Ādityasena that Isānavarman suffered a reverse at the hands of Kumāragupta. Ādityavarman's queen, Harshaguptā, was probably a sister of Harshagupta of Magadha; and his son, Isvaravarman, seems also to have married a Gupta princess, Upaguptā. A little later Grahavarman, the

Maukhari king, son of Avantivarman, married Rājyasrī, a sister of Harsha, and from Bāna we learn of the end of the dynasty. Grahavarman was slain by the Gupta king of Mālwā, and his queen cast into prison, and it was in seeking to avenge his brother-in-law that Rājyavardhana was lured into the power of the treacherous Gauda king, Sasānka, and slain. With this our knowledge of the main Maukhari line ends. From a Jaunpur inscription, however, we learn of another branch of the family, Ananta-varman, son of Sardulavarman, son of Yajyavarman, probably of minor importance.

CHAPTER VII

Harshavardhana

The sources for the history of Harsha's reign are fuller and more numerous than usual. Epigraphy provides two inscriptions, dated A.D. 628 and 631, and an important seal which records his genealogy. A certain amount of light is also thrown on the history of his reign by the inscriptions of certain of his contemporaries, but the space given to his story in text-books of Indian history, while many equally great rulers are dismissed with a line or two, is the consequence of the preservation of two literary sources, the *Harshacharita* of his court poet, Bāna, and the *Travels* of the Chinese pilgrim, Hiuen Tsang. The *Harshacharita* is not by any means an historical work in the modern sense of the term; it is an exercise in a particular literary genre, with an historical instead of a mythological theme. While it thus leaves much to be desired as an historical source, it is, nevertheless, a great deal more than we possess for many rulers of much greater note. The second work, the memoirs of the celebrated Chinese pilgrim, Hiuen Tsang, is unique of its kind. The author spent sixteen years in India, studying, observing, and taking notes; and his accuracy has frequently been confirmed by archaeological research. As he was primarily interested in religion, he does not deal directly with political history, but he could not live for so long a period in various parts of India without noting much that is now of value to us.

The rapid collapse of the Hūna dominion in northern India, and the failure of the Guptas to recover anything like their former prestige, permitted the appearance of a number of new dynasties, including those of Valabhī, the Chālukyas, the Maukharis, the later Guptas, and especially the Vardhanas of Sthānvi.vara (Thānesar), who were destined to play an important part in history. Thānesar is an ancient site on the Sarasvatī, a river famous even in Vedic times. The city occupied an important strategical position, and had been the scene of the great battle recorded in the epic between the Kauravas and Pāndavas on the field of Kurukshetra. It was there also that the final decisive battle

between Muslims and Hindus was to be fought. Of the kings
who ruled there in the middle of the sixth century little is known.
Their genealogy, so far as it is traceable, goes back only to the
beginning of the sixth century, and there is no reason to think
that the Vardhanas were a ruling family of any importance at
an earlier date. If Bāna is to be believed, Harsha was descended
from a long line of kings; but the inscriptions of the latter, a
much more reliable guide, trace his descent through his father,
Prabhākaravardhana, and grandfather, Ādityavardhana, to Rājyavardhana and Naravardhana. The three last-named receive only
the feudatory title of mahārāja, so that they must have been of
minor importance only. Ādityavardhana's wife, Mahāsenaguptā,
was probably a sister of Mahāsenagupta of Magadha. This alliance
suggests that Ādityavardhana must have considerably extended
his paternal estates. It must also have brought him further advantages, for his son Prabhākaravardhana was no longer a mere
mahārāja, but bore the paramount titles of parāmabhattaraka and
mahārājadhirāja, and numerous feudatories paid him homage.
Little is known of the circumstances attending his rise to supreme
power, but Bāna relates something of his campaigns. He fought
successfully against his northern neighbours the Hūnas, as well
as the Kushān king of Gandhāra, and the ruler of Sind on the
west. He is said also to have been victorious over his neighbours
in the south, the Gurjaras, the Lātas, and the king of Mālwā,
who sent his two sons, Kumāragupta and Mādhavagupta, to the
court of Thānesar as hostages. Towards the end of his reign,
another campaign against the Hūnas became necessary, and the
king put his eldest son, Rājyavardhana, in charge of the operations. The latter's younger brother, Harsha, accompanied him
part of the way. Meanwhile Prabhākaravardhana fell seriously
ill, and the news reaching Harsha first, he returned home. The
king's illness proved fatal, the royal physician committed suicide,
and the queen, Yasomatī, threw herself on the funeral pyre. This
took place in A.D. 605.

Further bad news awaited Rājyavardhana on his return home.
A messenger arrived from Kanauj to say that his brother-in-law,
the Maukhari, Grahavarman, had been killed, and his sister,
Rājyasrī, thrown into prison, by the king of Mālwā who was
on the point of invading Thānesar. Rejecting Harsha's offer to
accompany him, Rājyavardhana at once set out against his

enemy. He was victorious, but very soon afterwards was
treacherously murdered by Sasānka, king of Gauda, who had
invited him to visit him unarmed. Harsha at once determined
to avenge his brother. A general named Bhāndi was sent to
deliver the imprisoned princess. Finding that she had escaped
and had sought refuge in the Vindhya forests, he returned and
rejoined Harsha, who then set him to avenge Rājyavardhana's
murder while he himself went back to seek his sister. Bāna's
work ends with their reunion.

Sasānka may have suffered some reverse at Bhāndi's hands, but
he did not lose his life, for we find an inscription of his as late
as A.D. 620. The main result of this campaign was an alliance with
Bhāskaravarman, king of Kāmarūpa, who thought it advisable
to be on good terms with an enemy of his neighbour the king
of Gauda. But Harsha's campaign was much more important,
ending in the conquest of Mālwā. On his return home, a council
of ministers was held to invite Harsha to assume the royal power.
This he did only after much persuasion and after consulting an
oracle which warned him against formally ascending the throne
and assuming royal titles. For the first part of his reign, therefore, he was known as the *kumārarāja* and took the title of *Silāditya*.
His age on his assumption of power was probably about eighteen.

The kingdoms adjoining the lands of the young ruler on the
south were Mālwā, of which little is recorded, and Valabhī,
somewhat better known. The former seems to have been ruled
by a branch of the Gupta family, if we may judge by the names
of the hostages already mentioned. Still farther south the most
important dynasty was that of the Chālukyas, who ruled Mahārāshtra and waged continual warfare on their southern neighbours. In the east, in Magadha, the Maukharis and Guptas
divided power, and beyond them lay the kingdoms of Kāmarūpa
and Nepāl (both as much under Chinese or Tibetan influence
as Indian), together with Samatata and Gauda.

Harsha's first task seems to have been the thorough reorganisation of his army, and the Chinese pilgrim, Hiuen Tsang, has left
us many details of its size and constitution. For five consecutive
years, he says, the elephants never quitted their harness nor the
soldiers their armour. But details of this prolonged warfare are
lacking.

An obscure reference in an inscription of Mādhavagupta of

Magadha suggests that he had become a feudatory of Harsha, who must therefore have established his ascendancy over Magadha. According to Bāna, he levied tribute on the Tukhāras, inhabitants of inaccessible, snow-clad mountains, a statement which suggests victories in the far north-west. From the same source we learn that he crushed the king of Sind.

We know from an inscription of Dadda II that Harsha conquered Dhruvasena, king of Valabhī, and restored him only on Dadda's intercession. A clue to the date of this campaign lies in Hiuen Tsang's statement that Dhruvasena, whom he met at Harsha's court, had recently adopted Buddhism. The Chinese pilgrim was at Harsha's court in 640, so that the campaign must have been concluded a year or two earlier. When Harsha came to make a trial of strength with his neighbour in the south, the Chālukya Pulakesin II, one of the greatest rulers of that line, he was less successful. The latter had gradually become supreme in the Deccan and if, as he claims, he had conquered the kings of Lāta, Mālwā and Gurjara, was infringing on Harsha's sphere of influence. It may have been this fact that caused Harsha to take the field against him. All that we know is that Pulakesin was victorious, and Harsha failed to cross the Nerbudda.

From scattered references we learn something of Harsha's foreign relations. Tāranāth records that the king of Persia exchanged gifts with the king of Madhyadesa, i.e. with Harsha, and there exists, also, some information about Pulakesin's relations with Persia. Through Hiuen Tsang Harsha established diplomatic relations with China, several embassies being exchanged.

Of the closing years of Harsha we know little, but from the reports of an embassy from China, which arrived in 647, we learn something of the anarchical state of the country immediately after his death. Harsha having died and left no heir, Arjuna, one of his ministers, had seized the throne, and his troops attacked and pillaged the small force accompanying the Chinese ambassador, Wang Hiuen Tse, who escaped to Tibet. There he raised an army of 12,000 men, supported by a contingent of 7000 cavalry from the king of Nepāl, and, returning to India, stormed the usurper's capital, taking it with great slaughter. Arjuna escaped, and, raising a new force, again offered battle, but was captured and carried prisoner to China, whither the victorious Wang Hiuen Tse returned in 648. He is said to have captured 480 towns in India, and the fear inspired by his advance is reflected in the sending of gifts to him by a king named Kumāra of eastern India, and by the king of Kāmarūpa. There was in India no one capable of following in Harsha's footsteps; his empire, which had depended on him alone, crumbled to pieces, and northern India, falling back into its condition of fifty years earlier, split up once more into a number of petty states. Of these the most important was that of the Guptas of Magadha, whose representative, Ādityasena, seems to have seized the occasion to restore something of the glories of his ancient line. He used the era of Harsha dating from A.D. 605-6.

Indian sources throw little light on Harsha's methods of administration, but something of its nature can be gleaned from Hiuen Tsang, who states that the king was continually travelling up and down his wide dominions to see with his own eyes how the people were ruled. Only in the rainy season did he stay at home. He kept continuously in touch by courier with officials in the remoter provinces. Of the details of the administration we know very little, but the Chinese pilgrim was impressed by the benignity of the government. The country was not too heavily taxed; forced labour was paid for; merchants travelled about freely; the tolls levied on roads and ferries were light; officials were paid regularly. Hiuen Tsang found the Indians a law-abiding people; rebels were punished by being thrown into prison, and left to die; heinous crime was punished by mutilation, and trial by ordeal was much in use. The army was divided into four branches, infantry, cavalry, chariots and elephants, and was recruited only from the bravest men of the kingdom, whose profession was also followed by their sons. Special officials were appointed to keep records of the events of the reign, but no trace of such chronicles has survived. Everything seems to indicate that Harsha ruled his empire as an absolute autocrat without the assistance of the usual ministers. When his hand was withdrawn, the structure therefore collapsed.

Harsha was a Buddhist, and in his later years displayed great enthusiasm for both the theory and the practice of his faith. The charge of intolerance, rare in India, has been brought against him, probably with some justice. He favoured the Mahāyānist against the Hīnāyanist school, and for this reason treated the Chinese pilgrim with honour and convened a great assembly at which his guest expounded the law. A vivid account of this conference at Kanauj has been left to us by Hiuen Tsang's biographer.

The king himself attended with his ally, the king of Kāmarūpa, and numbers of his feudatories, including his grandson, the king of Valabhī. A feature of the buildings in which the assembly met was a great tower built to house a golden image of Buddha. This tower was almost destroyed by fire, and immediately afterwards an attempt was made to assassinate the king. The would-be assassin confessed that he was the instrument of a plot hatched by Brāhmans, exasperated at the excessive favour shown to Buddhists. The tower had been set on fire by incendiaries, who had hoped to murder the king in the ensuing confusion. Rigorous steps were taken against the conspirators. This indeed seems to have been a period when sectarian feeling ran high in India, for a little earlier Sasānka, a devout Saivite, had destroyed convents, burned the sacred bodhi tree at Gāya, and broken the footprint of Buddha at Patna. The bodhi tree was later replanted by Pūrnavarman, a local rāja who, according to Hiuen Tsang, was a direct descendant of Asoka, to whom the sacred sites of Buddhism had been objects of special care. Harsha's support seems to have had little permanent effect on Buddhism, which undoubtedly suffered a rapid decline after his death, except in the regions where it had long been dominant. Harsha found time to be a patron of literature as well as religion. Three dramas from his pen survive, of which the best known are the *Nāgānanda* and the *Ratnāvalī*, the third being the *Priyadarsikā*. Although these are not the work of a great poet, they show that Harsha had considerable literary talent and that he was a master of the technique of his subject. He also composed his own inscriptions, one of which bears his autograph. Of the literary men at his court the greatest was Bāna, author of the *Harshacharita* and the *Kādambarī*. Mayūra, Bāna's father-in-law, has a great reputation in Sanskrit literature, but few of his works have survived. To the same period belongs the Jain poet, Merutunga and the great lyric poet, Bhartrihari.

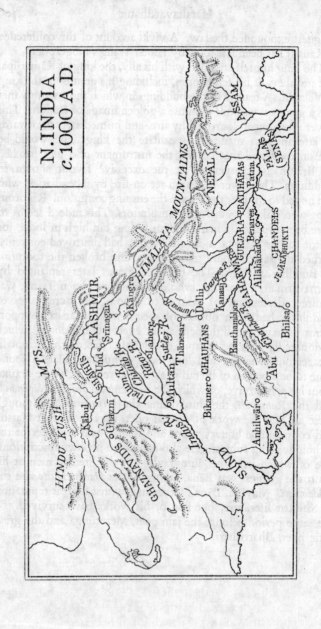

N. INDIA
c. 1000 A.D.

HINDU KUSH
Kabul
Ghazni
GHAZNAVIDS
MTS.
SHAHIS
Und
Srinagar
KASHMIR
Indus R.
Jhelum R.
Chenab R.
Ravi R.
Lahore
Multan
Sutlej R.
Kangra
HIMALAYA MOUNTAINS
J. mount
Thânesar
Delhi
Ganges R.
Kanauj
GURJARA-PRATIHÂRAS
NEPAL
ASSAM
Patna
Benares
Allahabad
PÂLAS
SENS
CHANDELS
BHUKTI
JEJAKA
GAHARWARS
Ranthambhor
CHAUHÂNS
Bikaner
Chambal
Chambal
Abu
Anhilwâro
Bhilsa
SIND

CHAPTER VIII

Northern India in Medieval Times

The secluded kingdom of Kashmīr has so far produced no inscriptions. It is, however, unique in India in that it possesses a chronicle of its own, the *Rājataranginī* of Kalhana, composed in the middle of the twelfth century and continued by later hands down to the sixteenth century. Until it approaches his own time, Kalhana's work has little real historical value. Kashmīr had been under Maurya rule in the time of Asoka, who built a new capital there. His son Jalauka, a somewhat legendary figure, is said to have founded in Kashmīr an independent kingdom, to which he added conquests in the plains. Several hundred years later Kashmīr formed part of the empire of Kanishka. Not till Hiuen Tsang's visit to it in A.D. 631–3 does its continuous history begin. The Chinese pilgrim does not mention the name of the ruler of his day, who treated him with great respect, but he was probably Durlabhavardhana of the Kārkota family, who came to the throne early in the seventh century and, like his son and successor, Durlabhaka, enjoyed a long reign. During the seventh century the power of Kashmīr was considerably extended by Durlabhaka's sons, Chandrapīda and Muktāpīda, who seem to have acknowledged in some way the suzerainty of the Chinese emperor. Muktāpīda, known also as Lalitāditya, extended his rule far beyond the valley of Kashmīr, conquering part of Kanauj, whose ruler, Yasovarman, he defeated and killed about A.D. 740, and gaining territory at the expense of Tibet and others of his neighbours. He built the Mārtānda Temple of the Sun, the ruins of which still exist. His grandson, Jayāpīda Vinayāditya, who ruled in the middle of the eighth century, is a romantic figure in Kashmīr tradition, and marvellous stories are told of his exploits. It is probable that Kashmīr was still a great power in his reign of some thirty years, the later part of which is said to have been marked by great cruelty and extortion. In the middle of the ninth century the exhausted Kārkota dynasty came to an end, being succeeded by the Utpalas, the first of whom was Avantivarman (A.D. 855–83), who devoted himself to restoring peace at home rather than to waging wars of aggression abroad. He was assisted by a very able minister named Sūra, who built new towns and carried out great irrigation works. The name of his great engineer, Suyya, to whose work in draining the marshes and protecting the valley from avalanches, Kashmīr owes its fertility, is preserved in the name of the town of Sōpur (Suyya-pura), which was founded by him. This king was also a great patron of literature. The death of Avantivarman was followed by a civil war in which Sankaravarman, the rightful heir, ulti-mately triumphed over his rivals. But he dissipated the resources of the kingdom in foreign wars, in none of which did he achieve any marked success. In one of these wars he met his death in A.D. 902. To meet the expenses of his army, Sankaravarman introduced an elaborate and oppressive system of taxation, which affected every detail of the life of his subjects. Not content with these extortions, he raided the temple treasures, and it is recorded that his extravagance obliged him to reduce the royal patronage till then enjoyed by men of letters. His young son, Gopālavar-man, succeeded him but, having displayed an excessive curiosity regarding the conduct of his minister, was disposed of, and his mother, Sugandhā, summoned to the throne. After ruling for two years, she also was deposed by the soldiers (tantrins), who were the real power in the land. Her attempt to regain the throne with the help of ekāngas, a kind of military police, who were jealous of the power of the tantrins, ended in her capture and death in A.D. 914. The country, the nominal ruler of which was a young grandson of Sukhavarman and cousin of Sankaravarman named Nirjitavarman and known as Pangu, was reduced to a pitiable condition by corrupt ministers, themselves in the power of the soldiery. A famine, in which thousands perished, was ex-ploited by those in authority, who sold the available supplies at enormous profits. The tantrins placed on the throne whoever would pay them. Finally, in A.D. 936, their power was completely broken by Chakravarman, brother of Nirjitavarman, whose administra-tive ability was unfortunately not equal to his military prowess. His infatuation for a low-caste dancing girl whom he made his chief queen aroused the horror of the aristocrats, and on a night in A.D. 937 he was surprised and murdered in his palace. Another brother was then placed on the throne, but his cruelty and wicked-ness passed all bounds. On his death, at which "even his queens were delighted", in A.D. 939, the Utpala dynasty came to an end, and an assembly of Brāhmans elected a new king, Yasaskara, under whom the land enjoyed a prosperity which it had not known for half a century. On his death in A.D. 948, he was succeeded by his young son, Sangrāmadeva, with a council of ministers as regents. One of these, Parvagupta, murdered the young king and seized the throne. He proved a strong but unpopular ruler, whose short reign was rendered notorious by his extortions. His son, Kshema-gupta, inherited only his vices, and was ruled entirely by his queen, Diddā, or rather by her relations, the powerful Lohara family. Her name even appeared on the coinage, and on his death in A.D. 958, she continued to rule for nearly half a century, at first as regent for the young heir, Abhimanyu. Assisted by an able minister, Naravāhana, she suppressed a great rebellion, led by some of her former ministers. On her son's early death, his mother built numerous religious edifices to his memory, but this fit of piety soon passed and she murdered the next two rulers, her grandsons, Nandigupta and Tribhuvana. Finally, in A.D. 975, her surviving grandson, Bhīmagupta, came to the throne but shared the fate of his predecessors as soon as he was old enough to express horror at his grandmother's profligacy. Diddā's last infatuation was for a young man of humble origin and great ability, Tunga, whose rapid rise to power and favour provoked a rebellion led by the queen's nephew. Tunga suppressed this rising, as he did an even more dangerous one led by Prithivīpāla of Rājapur, a vassal of Kashmīr. The queen died in 1003, leaving the throne to her nephew, Sangrāmarāja, through whom it passed to the Lohara family. She had made the new king and Tunga swear to support one another, but the latter was old and worn-out, and one or two failures, notably the defeat of the army sent to help the Shāhis against Mahmūd of Ghaznī, encouraged his enemies, who succeeded with the king's connivance in murdering him. The country could ill afford to lose him.

A brighter period began with the accession of Ananta in 1028. Early in his reign his extravagance involved him in financial difficulties, but his queen, Sūryamatī, took control, paid his debts, and placed in office a number of able and honest ministers. The country was thus well-governed, and Ananta was tempted to launch out on a career of conquest. At first he met with some success, but the later part of his reign saw defeat abroad and trouble at home, and he was persuaded to abdicate in favour of his son Kalasa, though retaining control through his able minister, Haladhara. Kalasa, however, proved worthless. In spite of his clever mother's devotion to him, he turned against his parents, who were saved only by the loyalty of part of the army. His further acts of cruelty and ingratitude finally drove Ananta to commit suicide and the old queen to join her husband on the funeral pyre. The shock of his parents' death reformed Kalasa, who proceeded to establish order at home and to make the name of Kashmīr respected abroad. In his later years he had trouble with his capable and versatile son, Harsha, who was led by his father's want of generosity to conspire against him. The discovery of this conspiracy was an overwhelming blow to Kalasa. He imprisoned his son, but himself soon lapsed into the bad habits of his youth, thus hastening his end. Before he died in 1089, he appointed as his successor his second son, Utkarsha. Harsha, still in prison, was saved by the rebellion of the new king's half-brother, Vijayamalla. Being released to assist Utkarsha against the rebel, he seized the throne and imprisoned his brother, who terminated his three weeks' reign by committing suicide. Harsha, singularly gifted both physically and mentally, is one of the greatest figures in the history of Kashmīr. A patron of literature and architecture, he was also an innovator and a leader of fashion. He was at first successful both at home and abroad but in the course of time his character deteriorated. His extravagance led him to plunder the temples, which he wantonly desecrated; his foreign policy brought down on him a number of reverses; and the cost of his military enterprises forced him to impose excessive taxation. A rebellion broke out under the leadership of powerful nobles. At first unsuccessful, the rebels then summoned Uchchala, an able general whom Harsha had wrongfully exiled, to return and lead them against the tyrant. Though Uchchala was routed by Harsha, the latter had at once to turn his attention to a new danger, an invasion led by Sussala, Uchchala's brother. In the fighting that followed Harsha's resistance was gradually worn down by the two invaders. His son, Bhoja, who had ably assisted him in the defence, was killed, and Harsha himself met his death in 1101, being discovered, while hiding in a village, by some of Uchchala's men. Thus ended a career which had begun with such splendour and promise. The events of his reign are described with first-hand knowledge by Kalhana, the historian, who was the son of one of his faithful supporters.

Uchchala, having seized the throne of Kashmīr, made his brother, Sussala, ruler of Lohara. He was an able ruler, generous and considerate to the poor. After successfully resisting an attempt by Sussala to dethrone him, he was at last murdered in his palace one evening in 1111 by a certain Radda, who claimed the throne as a descendant of Yasaskara. The death of the usurper after a brief reign brought to the throne Uchchala's step-brother Salhana. But the real power lay in the hands of a noble named Gargachandra, by whose favour and assistance Sussala obtained the throne, Salhana being deposed and imprisoned. After a long struggle, Sussala was driven from Kashmīr by Bhikshāchāra, Harsha's grandson, who had escaped from Uchchala's control and been brought up at the Paramāra court. The new master of Kashmīr gave himself up to voluptuous pleasures, and in six months Sussala easily recovered his capital. Bhikshāchāra was by no means disposed of, however, but remained a thorn in Sussala's side for some six years. The country suffered greatly during these changes, for the horrors of civil war were accentuated by famine. In 1123 Sussala crowned his son, Jayasimha, king, but, on second thoughts, he retained the power in his own hands until, in 1128, he was treacherously murdered. Jayasimha's tact secured such support from the people that he was able to hold the throne for nearly thirty years. But his success was due to his diplomatic, rather than to his military, ability, and he lost for a while the ancestral domain of Lohara through the success of a rebellion led by Salhana's brother, Lothana, who routed the army sent against him. Lothana, though an able ruler, was deposed by a less competent nephew, who proved no match for Jayasimha, and the latter soon regained his lost territory. A few years later, he was also able, by his own diplomacy and the military skill of his generals, to withstand a series of attacks by disaffected vassals aided by large Muhammadan contingents. He died in 1155, having passed his later years in comparative peace. His son, Paramānuka, enjoyed an uneventful reign of ten years, and, with the death in 1172 of Vantideva, his son and successor, the Lohara dynasty came to an end. Among the incompetent rulers who followed, the historian has a word of praise for Jagaddeva (1198–1213). The thirteenth century, of which we have little record, appears to have been a period of civil war and anarchy. A return of peace and prosperity in the reign of Suhadeva (1301–20) was cut short by the invasion of a large Muhammadan army from the east under a leader called Dulucha, who cleared the country of able-bodied men, carrying them off as slaves. Wherever the Muslim army went, it left desolation behind it, while a Tibetan invasion made similar havoc in the north. On Suhadeva's death, Rinchana, the Tibetan leader, seized the throne, and married his daughter, Kotādevī. He ruled the country well and justly until he was murdered in 1323. Sāhamera (Shāh Mīr), an able Muslim who had been in Suhadeva's service and had risen to be Rinchana's trusted adviser, then became the real power in the land. He placed on the throne as a *roi fainéant*, a member of the Tibetan's family, named Udayanadeva, and married him to Rinchana's widow. On her husband's death, the queen endeavoured to snatch the reins of state out of the hand of the powerful Sāhamera. The latter, however, soon discovered her scheme and forced her to marry him and share with him her rights. But no sooner was the ceremony over than he threw her into prison and seized the throne, assuming the title of Shams-ud-dīn. With his accession in 1339 Hindu rule in Kashmīr came to an end, although the kingdom retained its independence until the reign of Akbar.

The ancient kingdom of Nepāl, which comprised only the Nepāl valley and not the extensive mountainous region now known by the name, has always remained independent of India, and in its external relations it has been connected rather with China and Tibet. It has, however, from time to time, made contact with India. Asoka is said to have visited the valley when making his pilgrimage to the holy places of Buddhism. He built there a new capital called Lalitapatan, and his daughter remained in the country as a nun in a convent which she herself built. Stupas and other buildings are still pointed out, the foundation of which is attributed to the great Buddhist emperor and his daughter. More historically precise is the assertion in Samudra-gupta's Allāhābād inscription, that the king of Nepāl was one of the frontier kings who acknowledged his suzerainty and paid him tribute. It is probable that Nepāl did not own his sway in the same degree as some of the other states mentioned in this inscription, but in view of the fact that Samudragupta's mother was a Lichchhavī princess, and that a Lichchhavi dynasty ruled Nepāl at this time, it is not impossible that Chandragupta I had defeated the ruler of Nepāl, and received one of his daughters in marriage, according to Indian custom when peace was made.

Nepāl possesses numerous local chronicles, which are, however, of little historical value for the early period; and their chronology, when it can be checked, is unreliable. About the beginning of the Christian era, the valley was ruled by the Kirāta family, which was succeeded by the Somavansī dynasty. Concerning their successors, the Lichchhavis or Sūryavamsīs, more accurate information is available. Inscriptions of this period survive, dated in an era, the beginning of which, though uncertain, must have been about A.D. 110, the date suggested by Sylvain Lévi. The exact relationship of this Lichchhavi dynasty to the ancient family of the name is not known. In the seventh century A.D. the power of the Lichchhavi ruler, Sivadeva, gradually passed into the hands of Amsuvarman, a powerful and capable minister, whose name is associated, in the inscriptions, with that of Sivadeva and who married the daughter of his master, of whom nothing further is known. Amsuvarman's own inscriptions are dated in a new era, the source of which is disputed. He appears to have acknowledged the suzerainty of Tibet, and is mentioned by the Chinese historians, either on this account or by reason of his great reputation. He is identified with the Nepalese king who had died just before Hiuen Tsang visited India. On his death (c. 645) his successor, Jishnugupta, resumed the use of the old Lichchhavi era, but was apparently not a member of the old family, although his successor certainly was, and the Lichchhavis ruled for at least another century.

Little is known of Nepāl history in the later part of the seventh, and during the eighth, ninth and tenth centuries. Its rulers acknowledged the suzerainty of Tibet till after the middle of the ninth century, and it is probable that the new Nepāl era, which began in A.D. 879, marks the end of foreign domination. From the eleventh century it is possible to establish accurate genealogical lists, although little is known of political events. The country seems to have been prosperous. Lying on the route joining China, Tibet and India, it became the home of rich and prosperous merchants in control of the traffic. Commerce began to play a large part in the life of what had been hitherto a purely agricultural community. Gunakāmadeva, who is reputed to have reigned for sixty years in the ninth century, is said to have been fabulously wealthy.

In the middle of the eleventh century Nepāl was brought into ruder contact with the outside world. The Chālukya, Somesvara II, reckoned Nepāl among his vassals, and other references to successes in Nepāl exist in inscriptions of rulers of the Deccan. How far these references show that Nepāl was directly affected by the expeditions of the Chālukya, Vikramāditya VI, into north-eastern India we do not know; but one of his soldiers seems, like the ancestor of the Senas, to have settled in Bengal, where, a century later, his descendant, Nānyadeva (the name seems to be Canarese), was securely established at Tirhut, whence he extended his power over Nepāl, or a considerable part of it. After his defeat and capture by Vijayasena of Bengal, his descendants continued to rule in Tirhut, but possessed no influence in Nepāl, where, in the first quarter of the twelfth century, a soldier named Sivadeva took advantage of the troubled times to win the country and throne for himself.

In the reign of Tughluk I of Delhi (1320–5), Nepāl came into contact with the Muhammadans, when they destroyed the little kingdom of Tirhut and sacked its capital, Simraon, where a descendant of Nānyadeva still reigned—probably the Harisimha of the Nepalese chroniclers. In the early fifteenth century the Chinese annalists record an exchange of embassies with the king of Nepāl. In the thirteenth century a new dynasty, the Mallas, came to the throne, and their descendants ruled Nepāl until the Gurkha conquest in 1768, despite the division of the kingdom among his heirs by Yakshamalla about 1470.

In early times the modern province of Assam formed the centre of a much larger kingdom, frequently mentioned in the epics and *Purānas*, and known as Kāmarūpa, with its capital of Prāgjyotishapura, one of the great cities of ancient India. Local tradition traces the descent of its kings from the mythical Naraka, who is dated about 2700 B.C. But the first known historical event in the history of Kāmarūpa is its conquest—the completeness of which can only be surmised—by Samudragupta who, in his Allāhābād inscription, numbers its ruler among the frontier kings who paid him homage. The suzerainty of Samudragupta may have been more than nominal, for the king of Assam believed to have been his contemporary called himself Samudravarman, apparently after the great emperor, while their wives were both called Dattadevī. But in any case relations with the Guptas were not always friendly, for Ādityasena's Aphsad inscription records that Mahāsenagupta routed Susthitavarman in a battle fought on the Lauhitya or Brahmaputra. More is known about Susthitavarman's son, Bhāskaravarman, also referred to as Kumāra by the Chinese writers, whom the attacks of Sasānka, king of Gauda, forced to seek an alliance with Harsha. Bāna has preserved an account of the honours with which Harsha welcomed Bhāskaravarman's embassy on that occasion. He evidently enjoyed a long reign, for, while the overtures to Harsha were made quite early in the latter's reign, probably about A.D. 610, he was still reigning when Hiuen Tsang visited his capital in A.D. 643, and five years later he assisted the Chinese general, Wang Hiuen Tse, to destroy Arjuna, who had usurped the throne of Thānesar. The fact that his Nidhanpur copper-plates, tracing his genealogy for some three hundred years back to Pushyavarman, are dated from his camp in Karnasuvarna, once held by Sasānka, suggests that he had been able to take advantage of the deaths of Harsha and the Gauda king to extend his territory. The line of Pushyavarman seems to have been displaced soon after the reign of Bhāskaravarman, which probably ended about A.D. 650, by a certain Sālastambha, whose descendants held power till they in turn were overthrown by a dynasty founded by Prālambha, which became extinct when its last representative Tyāgasinha died childless about the beginning of the eleventh century. The dated inscriptions of this period contain nothing of historical importance and raise, without settling, a number of chronological and genealogical problems. A Pāla inscription, however, states that the king of Prāgjyotisha (Assam) owed some kind of allegiance to Jayapāla.

On Tyāgasinha's death, the throne was filled by the election of a certain Brahmapāla, whose son, Ratnapāla, boasted of many victories. He claims to have triumphed over the Gurjara king, the lord of Gauda (i.e. the Pāla king), the lord of Kerala (t resumably the Chola Rājendra I), the lord of the Deccan (that is, the Chālukya, Vikramāditya VI, who did in fact invade Kāmarūoa in one of his northern expeditions in his father's reign), and the

Bāhikas and Taikas (presumably marauding bands of Muslims). He was succeeded by his grandson Indrapāla, of whom, as of the later members of this dynasty, little is known.

Assam became involved in Muhammadan expansion in the thirteenth century. The disastrous expedition of Muhammad ibn Bakhtiyār to Tibet in 1205 was undertaken against the advice of the "Rai of Kāmrūd", *i.e.* king of Kāmarūpa. The Muslims insisted on advancing into Tibet at an unsuitable season of the year. They reached Tibet exhausted, and were at once expelled by superior forces. In the meantime the Assamese had destroyed a bridge on the only route of return, and there attacked the Muslims who were either killed or driven into the river. Only a hundred escaped of the 10,000 who had set out. Assam itself was invaded by the Muslims in 1258, but after some initial success, the attempt ended in disaster. Equally unsuccessful was the great expedition of Mīr Jumla in the middle of the seventeenth century. In the thirteenth century the line founded by Brahmapāla was brought to an end by the Āhom conquest, which established a powerful kingdom lasting till the beginning of the nineteenth century.

Of the history of the Kābul valley and the old province of Gandhāra little is known from the decline of the great Kushān empire in the third century A.D. Al-Bīrūnī states that it was governed by a dynasty of sixty rulers who bore the title *Shāhi*, a word which is related to the old Kushān form, *Shao*, king. He calls them Turks, or Turushkas, so that they probably traced their descent from the Kushāns. The Chinese pilgrim, Hiuen Tsang, notes that this region was ruled by a *kshatriya*, whom the Arab historians of the wars of the seventh and eighth centuries call *ratbīl*, a title which has not yet been explained. Nothing is recorded of the history of this long line of *Shāhis* until the last of them, Lagatūrmān, who reigned at the end of the ninth century. He was thrown into prison by his minister, a Brāhman named Kallār, who usurped the throne, and founded a new dynasty, the names of whose members are recorded by al-Bīrūnī, as Sāmand (Sāmanta), Kamalū, Bhīm (Bhīma), Jaipāl (Jayapāla), Ānandapāla, Tarojanapāla (Trilochanapāla) and Bhīmapāla. Coins of some of these survive to corroborate the Arab chronologist's account.

The Kashmīr chronicler, Kalhana, throws some additional light on the history of this dynasty of Brāhman Shāhis. Sankaravar-man, ruler of Kashmīr in the last quarter of the ninth century, sent against "Alakhāna, king of Gurjara", an expedition which was victorious in spite of the support given to his enemy by Lalliya Shāhi. A few years later Prabhākaradeva, minister of Gopāla-varman, deposed the Shāhi ruler of Udabhāndapura (Wahind, Ohind, Und), and set up the latter's son, Toramāna, in his stead, giving him the new name of Kamaluka—the Kamalū of al-Bīrūnī. Lalliya is apparently to be identified with the Kallār of al-Bīrūnī, and the difference in form has been explained as a copyist's error in the text of the unique Arabic manuscript of the *Indica*; the Arab writer's Sāmand is the Sāmantadeva of the coins, and he is probably the unnamed father of Toramāna referred to by Kalhana. Bhīma, the next ruler in al-Bīrūnī's list, is known to the Kashmīr chronicler as the grandfather of Queen Diddā of Kashmīr. He was still ruling about A.D. 950, for he built a temple in Kashmīr in the reign of Kshemagupta. The name of the next ruler, Jayapāla, is not mentioned by Kalhana, but we learn from Arabic sources of his struggle against the Ghaznavids. When the pressure of the Muslims drove him out of the Kābul valley, he chose Bhātinda, in the modern Patiāla state, as his capital because it was the best centre from which to organise the defence of the Panjab. The Arabs describe him as "ruler of Hindustan" and a very powerful king. Sabuktigīn conducted several raids into Hindu territory, and finally a great battle was fought on the frontier in which the Muslims had the advantage. A truce was arranged and Jayapāla retired to his own territory. But he soon began to break the terms of the truce and to ill-treat the representatives of the Muslim power. The Muslims then prepared to punish him. Jayapāla appealed for help to his neighbours in the south, and obtained from them large contingents and much money. With a great force he assumed the offensive, but the well-disciplined and ably led Muslim troops of Sabuktigīn routed the unwieldy Hindu army, and Jayapāla was forced to retreat and to cede further territory to the Ghaznavid. In A.D. 998 Mahmūd came to the throne of Ghaznī and soon made plans for an invasion of India. In 1001 he completely routed Jayapāla, taking vast booty and many prisoners, including the king him-self. A huge ransom was paid for him, but after this disgrace he was not restored to the throne. His son, Ānandapāla, succeeded to his much diminished territory and Jayapāla died soon afterwards. The new ruler refused Mahmūd's demand of passage through his territory and resisted valiantly, but in the end Mahmūd forced his way through in spite of the assistance sent to Ānandapāla by the neighbouring Hindu kings. Immense quantities of booty were taken by Mahmūd on this campaign, notably at the sack of Kāngra. About 1014 Ānandapāla was succeeded by his son, Trilochanapāla, who appealed for help against the Muslims to Sangrāmadeva of Kashmīr (1003–28). The Kashmīr general who was sent to his assistance neglected his advice in the encounter which followed, with the result that he was routed and not even the bravery of Trilochanapāla could avert defeat. The Shāhi maintained a hopeless resistance for some time, until finally he fell in 1021, and with him the dynasty came to an end. His son, Bhīmapāla, was killed a few years later, and so thoroughly was the Shāhi house extinguished that thirty years later Kalhana says that men wondered if it had ever really existed. Al-Bīrūnī also remarks on the completeness of the disappearance of the Hindu Shāhis and pays a high tribute to their nobility of character. Younger members of the family took refuge at the court of Kashmīr, where they gained a high reputation as brave soldiers, though with a passion for intrigue.

Indian sources afford no information regarding the history of the lower Indus valley after the Kushān period. From scanty and obscure references in the Arab historians of the early Arab invasions of Sind in the seventh century A.D. we learn that, shortly before the Arabs became interested in the region, there had been a change of dynasty. The Rāī dynasty, which had reigned for 137 years, consisted of five kings, the last of whom was Rāī Sāhasī. On his death his minister, a Brāhman named Chach, married the widowed queen and succeeded to the throne, thus founding a new dynasty. His wide dominions stretched to the borders of Kashmīr. His victory over a king whom the Arabs call Mahrat of Jaipur is recorded. He had a long reign and was succeeded by his brother, Chandra, and then by his son, Dāhir, who met his death in the Arab conquest of Muhammad ibn Kāsim in A.D. 712. Hiuen Tsang, who visited Sind in the reign of Chach, says that its ruler was a Sūdra and a Buddhist, a statement difficult to reconcile with the Arab story of a Brāhman

ruler. The Arabs had been attacking Sind for seventy years before
they finally conquered it. It is probable that many Hindu chiefs
remained as local rulers, acknowledging Arab suzerainty. From
time to time the Arabs undertook campaigns into India from
their base in Sind. The great governor Junaid not only put down
a Hindu rising led by a son of Dāhir, the last Chach ruler, but
carried Arab arms as far as Ujjain and defeated the Gurjaras. The
Lāta Chālukya, Pulakesin, records his defeat of an Arab army
which had reached his lands, and Nāgabhata, the founder of the
Gurjara power, is recorded to have turned back a Mlechcha invader, perhaps the expedition of Junaid already mentioned. The
Gurjaras certainly formed a bulwark against the Arab advance,
and for this reason the Arabs cultivated the friendship of the rival
clan of the Rāshtrakūtas of Mānyakheta (the Balharās). The Arab
rulers of Sind treated the Hindus with a tolerance not shown by
later Muslim conquerors. In the eleventh century Upper Sind
passed into the hands of the Ghaznavids, while Lower Sind seems
to have become independent under a local Sumra dynasty, which
is given an Arab pedigree but is believed to have been Rājput.
The Sumras governed with more or less success for three hundred
years, until they were finally supplanted by the Sammas, who
ruled Sind till its conquest by Akbar. In the thirteenth and early
fourteenth centuries they suffered from occasional attempts of the
Delhi sultans to exert the suzerainty which they claimed over
Sind, but towards the end of that period they became completely
independent. They bore the title of Jām, which still remains in
use in western India.

The sources for the history of the Paramāra dynasty, which
ruled in Mālwā from the ninth to the eleventh century, consist
of an inscription preserved at Udayapur in the Bhīlsa district of
Gwalior State, another at Nāgpur, several land grants, and one
literary source, the *Navasāhasānkacharita* of Padmagupta.

The dynasty claimed descent from Paramāra, "slayer of
enemies", the hero who was created by Vasishta out of the fire-
pit to help him to win back his cow. The first historical king
of the Paramāras, however, was Upendra, also known as Krishna-
rāja. The family belonged to the region of Mount Ābu, where
they held the fortress of Achalgadh, with their capital at Chandra-
vali, a few miles to the south-east. Little is known of Upendra

but he is said to have achieved kingship by valour, from which we may infer that he was the first of the family to enlarge his territory and win renown beyond the original limits of the family estates. He conquered Mālwā early in the ninth century. Of the next three kings, Vairasimha, Sīyaka I, and Vākpati I, nothing is known, and of the next, Vairasimha II, it is recorded only that he was also called Vajratasvāmin. His successor is variously called Srī-Harshadeva, Sīyaka, and Simhabhata. His full name was probably Harshasimha, Sīyaka being a Prākrit corruption of Simhaka. He conquered the land of Radūpātī, and overcame a king of the Hūnas, then a Kshatriya tribe, though they may formerly have been Huns. He also carried off by force the wealth of King Khottiga, presumably a Rāshtrakūta king of Mānyakheta. Further evidence of the hostility between these dynasties is found in Dhanapāla's *Paiyalachchi*, which states that Mānyakheta was "plundered by the lord of Mālwā" in A.D. 972. Harshasimha's son was Vākpati II, known as Munja, Amoghavarsha, or Prithivī-vallabha, who is celebrated as a poet and patron of literature. His panegyrist describes him as a great soldier also, and claims that he conquered the Karnātas, Lātas, Keralas and Cholas, and defeated Yuvarāja, the Kālachuri king of Chedi. He can hardly have come into contact with either the Keralas or the Cholas, but that he won a victory over the Lātas of central Gujarāt is not improbable. Victorious in six campaigns against the Chālukya king, Tailapa II, in a seventh, against the advice of his minister, he crossed the Godāvarī into Chālukya territory, where he was captured and ultimately put to death, after an unsuccessful attempt to escape, about A.D. 995; Chālukya inscriptions also record this success of the Chālukya arms. Vākpati II Munja was succeeded by his younger brother, Sindhurāja, called Navasāhasānka, whose exploits are recorded by his court poet, Padmagupta. He defeated a king of the Hūnas, and his biographer claims for him victories over Kosala, Vagada, Lāta and the Muralas. If the last name is used definitely for the Keralas in particular, and not vaguely for the Dravidian kingdoms in general, the statement can hardly be correct. It probably implies little more than that hostilities continued between Mālwā and the Chālukyas of Kalyāni. Sindhurāja was succeeded by his son, Bhoja, the best known member of the dynasty, who reigned for forty years. The sources emphasise his literary versatility, and many of his works still survive. These include writings on politics and architecture, and he is said to have been an extensive builder. Extravagant claims are made in the Udayapur inscription regarding the extent of his kingdom, which, far from extending from the Himālāya to Malabar, as is asserted, can scarcely have exceeded the limits of modern Mālwā. He is further alleged to have conquered the land of Chedi, Bhīma king of the Gurjaras, the land of Lāta, the Karnātas and the Turushkas. But with regard to his war with the Karnātas, that is, the old enemy of the Paramāras, the Chālukyas of Kalyāni, an inscription of the Chālukya Jayasimha III, of the year 1019-20, asserts that he defeated Bhoja and put to flight the confederacy of Mālwā, and it is certain that the Chālukyas suffered no serious reverse during this reign. Any victory won by Bhoja must therefore have been greatly magnified by his panegyrist. We also learn from Bilhana of a later defeat of Bhoja by Jayasimha's successor, Somesvara II, who stormed Dhārā and forced Bhoja to seek safety in flight. Bhoja's victory over the Chaulukya of Anhilwār, Bhīma I, is recorded by Merutunga. While Bhīma was away fighting in Sind, Bhoja sent an army which succeeded in capturing his capital. Of his other campaigns nothing is known. Two were waged with old enemies of the dynasty, while the Turushkas were presumably a raiding force of Muhammadans sent out by Mahmūd of Ghaznī on one of his Indian campaigns. Bhoja seems to have been involved in fighting to the end of his reign for, according to Merutunga, he was either slain or else he died during a combined attack on him by Karna, king of Chedi, and Bhīma I, a statement which does not find the corroboration which might be expected from the panegyrists of these two rulers. He reigned from about 1010 to 1065. Of his successor Udayāditya the panegyrist tells us that he freed his country from the enemies who had conquered it, or had been threatening it, at the time of his predecessor's death. It was presumably after him that the dynasty began to sink into the insignificant position it seems to have occupied in the twelfth century.

With the rise of the kingdom of Anhilwār (Anahilavāda) in the eighth century, it becomes possible to give a fairly continuous account of the history of Gujarāt, relating to which a number of writings of an historical nature are available. In the early part

of the century a line of petty chiefs, known as the Chāvadās of
Panchāsar in Vadhiār, began to come to the front. The stories
told of Jayasekhara, the father of Vanarāja and founder of the
dynasty, are more or less mythical. Vanarāja, a posthumous child
brought up in exile by an uncle, collected enough men and
money by brigandage to establish himself securely in the spot
which afterwards became the great town of Anhilwār. He was
installed as a sovereign ruler about A.D. 765. A statue at Sidhpur
probably represents him. Of his successors little is known, but
the throne remained in the family till the tenth century, the last
Chāvadā being slain in A.D. 961 by his nephew and son-in-law,
Mūlarāja, who seized the little kingdom of Anhilwār. Mūlarāja
belonged to the Chaulukya or Solanki family; the former is a
learned and the latter a popular variant of the well known name
Chālukya, but the connection between the Chaulukyas and the
great Deccan family of the name is not known. Mūlarāja soon
began to expand his power and, according to the Jain historians,
became the greatest figure of the dynasty. He conquered Kachch
and Kāthiāwār in the south, and won victories over the kings
of Lāta in southern Gujarāt and Ajmir in the north. Bārappa,
the king of Lāta, was killed in the course of the war with
Mūlarāja, but the campaign against the king of Ajmir seems to
have been less successful. Mūlarāja also attacked an Ābhīra ruler
who had been interfering with pilgrims to the shrine of Somnāth
at Prabhāsa, and took this "cow-eating barbarian" prisoner.
Another of his victims was Lākha, a son of the king of Kachch,
whom he finally slew, after having been defeated by him several
times. After a life of fighting and conquest, Mūlarāja devoted
his last years to good works. He built numerous temples, and
gathered at his court learned men from other lands. He is said
to have voluntarily ended his life on the funeral pyre; in any
case he died about A.D. 996, and was succeeded by his son,
Chāmunda, who had distinguished himself in his father's wars,
but of whom as king nothing is known except that he reigned
until 1010. The success of his son, Durlabha, at a *svayamvara*
attracted the enmity of the rejected suitors, but he was as successful in the field as in love. Durlabha's nephew, Bhīma I, succeeded him in 1022, and seems to have further extended the power
of the dynasty. He conducted a successful campaign against the
king of Sind, but, while he was thus engaged, Kulachandra, a

general of the Paramāra king, Bhoja, pillaged Anhilwār so thoroughly that the phrase "the sack of Anhilwār" became proverbial.

The great event of this reign was the destruction of the great temple of Somnāth (Somanātha) in Prabhāsa, by Mahmūd of Ghaznī in 1024, recorded in detail by the Muslim historians. The idol, Somnāth, was said to be the most revered of all the idols of India, and its shrines had been enriched for centuries by the Hindu rulers of the surrounding country. In 1024, on his tenth raid into India, Mahmūd set out for Anhilwār. At his approach Bhīma fled, and Mahmūd pushed on through the desert until he reached the coast and the strong fortifications of the sacred city. The first onslaught of the Muslims lasted a whole day but was unsuccessful, and the attack was renewed next morning. Finally they forced their way into the town, and the Hindus made their final stand before the temple, which they defended valiantly till they fell, the few who tried to escape by sea being pursued and put to the sword or drowned. Mahmūd burned part of the great idol, and carried part to Ghaznī, where he made of it a step at the entrance to the principal mosque. Fifty thousand Hindus were slain in the storming of the town, and booty valued at over two million dinars was taken.

After taking Somnāth, Mahmūd marched against Bhīma, who had taken refuge in the fortress of Khandahat, some 250 miles away, and drove him from his stronghold. After the conqueror's return to Ghaznī, Bhīma began to rebuild the temple of Somnāth. It is recorded that he defeated the Paramāra ruler of Ābu, who surrendered Chitrakūta to him. He died in 1064 and was succeeded by Karna, who devoted his energies mainly to public works. After a troubled reign of thirty years, he was succeeded by his son, Siddharāja, who was still a minor, the real power being exercised by his mother, Miyānanadevī. On reaching manhood, Siddharāja made a state pilgrimage to Somnāth, commemorating it by remitting the taxes levied on the pilgrims, an act which must have involved a considerable loss of revenue. He was a great builder, and local tradition ascribes to him everything of architectural importance in the country. After a successful campaign in Surāshtra, he became involved in a great war with the Paramāra, Naravarman, which dragged on for twenty years. The Paramāra capital was finally taken, and Yasovarman,

who had succeeded his father on the Paramāra throne, was taken
to Anhilwār and imprisoned in a cage. To celebrate his conquest
of Mālwā, Siddharāja assumed the title "lord of Avanti". His
next war was with the famous king, Madanavarman, of the
Chandel dynasty, but against him he does not seem to have
gained any remarkable success. Siddharāja died in 1143, leaving
no heir, and the throne passed from this branch of the family
to another descendant of Bhīma I, named Kumārapāla. During
Siddharāja's reign, he had been obliged to flee the country to
avoid the king's alleged designs against him leaving his brother-
in-law, Krishnadeva, to watch over his interets during his exile.
On succeeding to the throne, Kumārapāla proved himself a
capable ruler. He was uniformly successful in his campaigns
against his neighbours, notably over Mallikarjuna, king of the
Konkan, and the king of Surāshtra. He found time to restore
much of the great shrine of Somnāth, where the remains of his
work can still be seen. He was also a patron of learning and a
great benefactor of the Jains. His chief minister was the celebrated Hemachandra, the most learned man of his time. Kumārapāla died in 1174 at a great age, and was succeeded by his nephew,
Ajayapāla, whose cruelties were soon brought to an end by his
assassination in 1177. Of his successors, Mūlarāja II and Bhīma-
rāja, little is recorded, but it is clear that the power of the dynasty
declined, and that the government of the country gradually
passed into the hands of the Vāghelas, who had been ministers
of the Chaulukyas and traced their descent from Anaka, the son
of a sister of the Solankī, Kumārapāla.

Anaka's son, Lavanaprasāda, a minister of Bhīmadeva II, extended the estates of the Vāghela family and gradually became
independent of his sovereign, whose reign over the northern
portion of the Chaulukya kingdom lasted till 1242. Lavanaprasāda's ambitions were opposed by Yādava Singhana of Devagiri. But the latter was completely routed, and forced to conclude a treaty which rendered the Vāghela ruler free from
aggression on the south. In 1232 Lavanaprasāda abdicated in
favour of his son, Vīradhavala, who, in the course of his six years'
reign, conducted a number of successful campaigns, and won a
great victory over a Muslim force led by the Ghūrid sultān
Bahrām Shāh of Delhi. Vīradhavala's son, Vīsaladeva (1243–61),
boasted himself a great warrior, devouring the armies of the

Yādavas like fire. His good administration did much to alleviate the miseries of a three years' famine which afflicted the country in his reign. He completed the establishment of Vāghela rule throughout Gujarāt, but the power of the dynasty seems to have weakened in the next two reigns, until, in the time of Karnadeva (1296–1304), the Muslims made an easy conquest of the country. A Muslim army under Nasrat Khān occupied Anhilwār in 1287, and Karnadeva, abandoning his wives, his children, and all his wealth, took refuge with the Yādava king of Devagiri. The Muslims continued their successes, taking Cambay and once more destroying the temple of Somnāth. In this campaign there was captured in Cambay a slave named Malik Kāfūr, who afterwards became a great general of the sultans of Delhi. The fate of Karnadeva is unknown, but Gujarāt remained thenceforth under Muslim rule.

Though the Hūnas founded no lasting kingdoms, another invading people was destined to prosper and for five centuries to play a considerable part in the history of northern India. These were the Gurjaras, a people of central Asian origin, whose name still survives in such place-names as Gujarāt. The Gurjaras probably invaded India soon after the Hūnas, in conjunction with whom they are mentioned, although always distinguished from them in early references. But as the name is not included in Skandagupta's references to the Hūnas, the inference is that they arrived a little later. They seem to have settled first in the Panjab, although detailed information regarding them begins only after they reached Rājputāna. The earliest specific reference to the Gurjaras is found in Bāna's *Harshacharita*, in which it is stated that Harsha's father, Prabhākaravardhana, was a terror to the Hūnas, Gurjaras, Lātas and Mālavas. The Aihole inscription (A.D. 634) of the great Chālukya, Pulakesin II, records his triumphs over the Lātas, Mālavas and Gurjaras, so that the Gurjara kingdom must have lain in the same region as those of the Lātas and Mālavas. A few years later Hiuen Tsang visited the kingdom, the capital of which is identified as the modern Bhilmal.

The history of the Gurjaras has been traced, however, mainly from their own inscriptions and only since these inscriptions have been fully understood has the greatness of the Gurjaras been realised. The inscriptions deal mainly with one clan, the Prati-hāras, who seem early to have taken the lead among their fellows.

We have already seen that hostility existed between the Gur-jaras and the kings of Thānesar, and that Harsha and his father were apparently able to frustrate all their attempts at expansion. But, with the complete collapse of Harsha's empire after his death, this obstacle to their southward progress disappeared.

Their first great leader was Harichandra, and from him and his Kshatrya queen, Bhadra, the Pratihāra dynasty traced its descent. From another wife, an unnamed Brāhman woman, were descended the Parihāra Brāhmans, and medieval genealogists found an ancestor for the family in Lakshmana, who had acted as door-keeper (pratihāra) to his brother Rāma. By the time of Harichandra the Gurjaras must have adopted Hinduism in its entirety, for he is said to have lived at first the quiet, rural life of the learned Brāhman teacher. But, when the opportunity came, presumably in the turmoil following on the death of Harsha, he displayed and developed the remarkable military talents till then latent in him. Details of Harichandra's conquests are wanting, but he evidently occupied considerable territory in Rājputāna. Five of his sons are mentioned in inscriptions. They conquered Mandyapura (Mandor), and built a stronghold there. Harichandra's successor was Rajjila. Two generations later the family divided into two ruling branches. The main Bhāndi or Jodhpur stock retained its former possessions, while Rajjila's grandson, Nāgabhata I, settled at Medantaka and established the Avantī branch of kings.

In Broach and other parts of southern Gujarāt Harichandra's younger brother, Dadda I, set up a subordinate state, of which the most famous ruler was Dadda II. A number of inscriptions survive relating to this branch of the family. The territory which it ruled seems to have been gained at the expense of the Kālachuris, and its further advance into the Lāta country probably brought it into conflict with Pulakesin II, as has already been mentioned. In view of Harsha's designs on the south, Pulakesin probably came to some agreement with the Gurjaras in order to prevent them from lending their support to the invader; and this under-standing between Pulakesin and the Gurjaras perhaps explains why the king of Valabhī, Dharasena IV, fled for protection from

Harsha to the Gurjara of Broach, Dadda II, and why the latter was able to negotiate terms with Harsha on his behalf. After the collapse of Harsha's empire, Dadda III is stated to have fought "the kings of east and west", and an inscription of Jayabhata III, the last of this southern branch, claims a victory in A.D. 730 over the king of Valabhī. Originally a viceroyalty of the main branch, and probably never completely separated from it, the line of Broach could always rely on the support of the Gurjaras in Rājputāna, and therefore enjoyed a power and prestige out of proportion to the size of its dominions.

The history of the main branch of the family is obscure. Of Tata, Yasovardhana, and Chanduka, nothing is known. Probably in the reign of the ninth king, Siluka, the Arab invasion led by Junaid swept over all the Gurjara territories (c. A.D. 725–35). The Nausari grants of A.D. 738 record that the Arabs were ultimately defeated and driven back by the Lāta Chālukya, Pulakesin, while the Arab historian, Balādhurī, states that the invaders conquered Jurz (Gurjara) and Barus (Broach), but were less successful against Uzain (Ujjain) and Maliba (Mālwā). The power that checked the eastward advance of the Arabs was the Avantī dynasty of Rājputāna and western Mālwā, whose descendants were destined to play a great part in the history of northern India. That Ujjain in the eighth century was the centre of the Pratihāra power we know from various sources. The Jain *Harivamsa*, for example, was finished in A.D. 783–4, when Vatsarāja, who must be the Gurjara of that name, was reigning at Avantī; the Sanjan plates of the Rāshtrakūta, Amoghavarsha, of A.D. 871 mention a Gurjara Pratihāra, king of Ujjain; and the Gwalior inscription of Bhoja traces the foundation of his dynasty's greatness to Nāgabhata, who defeated the Mlecchas, *i.e.* the Arabs. It is thus evident that one clan of the Gurjaras successfully withstood the Arab invasion which overwhelmed much of the territory of the other branch which had hitherto been predominant. The leader of the successful clan was Nāgabhata, to the inscriptions of whose successors we owe most of our knowledge of the dynasty. He was ruler of Avantī, and may be dated about A.D. 725–40.

Meanwhile the older Jodhpur or Bhāndi family was less successful. The statement that Siluka "fixed the boundaries" of Stravani and Valla means that he was able to preserve these two provinces from the Arabs. Thus, although his power was not annihilated, it must have been greatly reduced. Nāgabhata, of the Avantī line, was succeeded by Kakkuka, whose successor, Devarāja, seems to have attacked his weakened relative of Jodhpur. But Siluka defeated Devarāja and so, for the moment, contrived to retain, as the inscription has it, "the badge of the umbrella", *i.e.* suzerainty over all the Gurjaras. Devarāja's son, Vatsarāja, however, again assumed the offensive, and at last wrested the supremacy of the Gurjara clans from the Bhāndis, *i.e.* Siluka or his sons, whose family had held it for two hundred years from the time of Harichandra. Thereafter the political importance of the Gurjaras centres round the newer line, the Avantī family. The fourth king of this line was Vatsarāja (*c.* A.D. 775–800), the son of Devarāja and Bhuyikā. His reign is recorded with more than usual fulness, for at that time began the three-cornered struggle of the Gurjaras, Pālas and Rāshtrakūtas for the hegemony of northern India. The eighth century had seen the rise to power of the Rāshtrakūtas of Mālkhed in the south, and the Sanjan plates of the Rāshtrakūta, Amoghavarsha, record that the founder of that line conquered Avantī and forced its king to serve as door-keeper at a sacrifice. The king thus humiliated was presumably Devarāja. But civil war in the Rāshtrakūta kingdom gave to Devarāja's son, Vatsarāja, an opportunity which he at once seized. He attacked his eastern neighbour the king of Vanga (western Bengal), presumably Gopāla, founder of the Pāla dynasty, and defeated him together with his vassal, the king of Gauda (eastern Bengal). Soon afterwards, however, Vatsarāja was routed in his turn and driven into the desert by the Rāshtrakūta, Dhruvasena, as the latter's son records, but he must have recovered from this reverse, for at a later date, as we have seen, he secured the head-ship of the Gurjara clans. Vatsarāja was succeeded by Nāgabhata II (*c.* A.D. 800–25), son of his queen Sundarī. The new king seems to have formed an alliance with the rulers of Sind, Āndhra, Vidarbha, and Kalinga, thus driving a wedge between the Pālas and Rāshtrakūtas. He then attacked and overthrew Chakrāyudha, whom the Pāla ruler had seated on the throne of his recent conquest, Kanauj. War followed upon this direct challenge to the Pālas, and Dharmapāla's numerous army was scattered by Nāgabhata at Monghyr. That Nāgabhata, too, had gathered a great following is evident from the fact that several of his feudatories proudly recorded their share in the battle. Among them was Kakka, the representative of the older Pratihāra line. Further successes are claimed for Nāgabhata. He is said to have captured fortresses in Anartta (Kāthiāwār), Mālwā, Kirāta, Turushka, Vatsa and Matsya (Rājputāna). The Turushkas were the Arabs, established in Sind, who probably still retained some hold on Gurjara territory in Gujarāt. We learn from Rāshtrakūta records, however, that Nāgabhata II was not more successful against the Rāshtrakūta power than his father, Devarāja, had been, and they claim that he fled at the approach of Govinda III, who advanced northwards as far as the Himālāyas, receiving the homage of Dharmapāla on the way, and defeating Nāgabhata, who lost some part of his territory in Mālwā. Nāgabhata was succeeded in A.D. 832 by his son, Ranabhadra, of whose reign little is known. It appears, however, from the Gwalior inscription, that although he suffered severe reverses he recovered his prestige by driving out invaders, who cannot be identified with certainty but were probably the Pālas. He was succeeded, probably after a short reign, by his more talented son, Mihira, known as Bhoja, a son of Queen Appadevī. Bhoja's first success seems to have been won over his relatives of the main branch of Harichandra's family, two able members of which, Bauka and Kakkuka, had conquered territory from the Avantī line after it had been weakened by the Rāshtrakūta invasions. Bhoja recovered this land, but it seems to have been taken once again by Kakkuka about the middle of the ninth century. In the first half of this century Devapāla, the king of Bengal, claimed that he had made all northern India tributary, and that he had humbled the pride of the king of the Gurjaras [Bhoja], who had been puffed up by his early successes.

-The Rāshtrakūtas also claim to have defeated Bhoja about this time, but in spite of these reverses he was still resolved, as the inscription has it, to "conquer the three worlds". His opportunity came with the death of the great Devapāla, who left no worthy successor. With the assistance of two Chedi rulers, Bhoja routed the Bengal army, and about the same time internal dissensions among the Rāshtrakūtas relieved him from trouble in the south. He lived to a great age, reigning for nearly fifty years over a wide empire, which he ruled from Kanauj, and which included practically all northern India except Sind and Kashmīr. An Arab traveller comments on the size of Bhoja's army and the magnificence of his cavalry, and adds that he was no friend of the Arabs. His country must have been well governed, for no other Indian kingdom was so free from robbers. Bhoja added Magadha to the Pratihāra empire, an extension to the east for which his predecessors had fought in vain. The empire thus stretched from the source of the Ganges to that of the Reva, and from the eastern to the western ocean. The Pratihāra dynasty had reached its zenith, and thereafter its glories waned. The poet Rajasekhara held a position at the court of Bhoja.

He was succeeded about A.D. 890 by Mahendrapāla, his son by Queen Chandrabhattarikā. Bhoja II succeeded his father, Mahendrapāla, and after a brief reign was himself followed by his half-brother, Mahīpāla (c. A.D. 914-40). Early in this reign, the Rāshtrakūta, Indra III, must have occupied Kanauj, for his inscription claims that he devastated "Mahodaya, celebrated as Kusasthala", both of which are names of Kanyakubja. This defeat proved, however, only a temporary blow to the Pratihāra power, which, taking advantage of the troubles in the Rāshtra-kūta kingdom, soon began to recover. Mahīpāla was loyally aided to recover his throne by the Chandel king, Harsha, but the latter's son, Yasovarman, displayed a more independent temper, and his allegiance to his Pratihāra suzerain must have been only nominal. Mahīpāla died about A.D. 940, leaving his kingdom, so far as can be judged, more prosperous than he had found it. He was succeeded by his son, Mahendrapāla II. From an inscription of the Chandel, Yasovarman, we learn that in A.D. 954 he forced Devapāla to surrender to him a highly prized image of Vishnu, a fact which reveals the inferiority of the Gurjaras to the rising power of the Chandels. Devapāla was succeeded by his brother, Vijayapāla, under whom the weakness of the empire became increasingly apparent. Yasovar-man's successor, Dhanga, won "royal power by defeating the king of Kanauj", and we know that in the course of a long reign he took Gwalior from the Pratihāras and extended his frontiers as far as Benares. About the same time the Chaulukya, Mūlarāja, founded the kingdom of Anhilwār in Gujarāt and southern Rājputāna, and much of the land where the Gurjaras had ruled longest thus passed from their possession. The Paramāras esta-blished themselves in Mālwā at the same time, and in the middle of the tenth century the Chedi king claimed a victory over the

Gurjaras, so that the Pratihāra empire was threatened on all sides. Vijayapāla succeeded to a much diminished empire at a time when the threat from the Muslims had become more serious than it had been since the days of his great ancestor, Nāgabhata. While the Rāshtrakūta king was on good terms with the Muhammadans, the Gurjara rulers had always been their enemies. In A.D. 991 the king of Kanauj (Rājyapāla or his father) assisted Jayapāla in the great battle of the Kurram valley, and shared in the Hindu defeat which opened India to the Muslims. In the battle of Peshāwar, in 1008, the Gurjara kingdom again played its part under Ānandapāla. Ten years later the Muslims reached Rājyapāla's territory, at a time when he was engaged in defending himself against the Chandels in the south. Mahmūd of Ghaznī occupied Baran and Mathura and advanced on Kanauj. Rājyapāla, unable to defend it, abandoned it, and Mahmūd, after sacking the city, returned home. Though he met with more resistance on his next invasion, he was equally successful and received the submission of Rājyapāla. An alliance of Hindu states led by the Chandels then fell upon this much-tried ruler whom they regarded as a traitor to the Hindu cause for his submission. He died defending himself against them, and was succeeded by his son Trilochanapāla, who survived till about A.D. 1030. Mahmūd himself came to avenge the death of Rājyapāla, whom he regarded as his vassal, and the Hindu army fled, leaving vast quantities of booty. Trilochanapāla made a feeble stand and then fled, abandoning his capital to the invader, and retiring to Allāhābād, where seven years later (1027) he still exercised some little royal power. We know nothing of his successors, if indeed he had any. About the end of the eleventh century Kanauj passed to the Gāhadavālas who held it for a century till the Muslim conquest.

In the twelfth century a line of petty chiefs who had long ruled over Sāmbhar in Rājputāna attained to greater power. These were the Chāhumānas (Chauhāns), whose ancestors claimed to have assisted in checking the advance of the Arabs of Sind in the eighth century. At the end of the eleventh century Ajayadeva extended the power of the dynasty and founded Ajmir. Vigraharāja still further increased its territories, and interesting memorials of his reign survive in two dramas, one written in his honour and the other said to have been composed by him, which were discovered on stone tablets in Ajmir. Prithivīrāja, the Rāī Pithora of the Muslims, a nephew of Vigraharāja and son of his brother Somesvara, is the most celebrated of the Chauhān kings, and is a great figure in the popular literature of Rājputāna, particularly in the Chand-rāisā, the Hindī epic attributed to his court poet. Prithivīrāja's most romantic exploit was the abduction of the daughter of Jayachandra of Kanauj, and his greatest military achievement was his invasion of Chandel terri-tory and his defeat of its king, Paramardi. He successfully re-pelled the onslaught of Muhammad ibn Sām in the first battle of Tarāorī (1191), but in the next year the vast army which he and his allies had assembled was easily routed by the carefully trained and disciplined, though much smaller, Muslim forces. Prithivīrāja was captured and put to death, his capital Ajmir sacked, and its inhabitants carried off into slavery. Delhi, not long founded, was taken in the next year. Govindarāja, an illegitimate son of the dead king, was appointed by the Muslims to govern the conquered territory, but, being deposed by his uncle, Harirāja, he fled to Ranthambhor, where the dynasty sur-vived for nearly a century.

After some minor successes against the Muslims, Harirāja was defeated by Kutb-ud-dīn Aibak and retired to Ajmir, where he mounted the funeral pyre, and Ajmir thus passed finally under the Muslims. Vīra Narāyana, Govindarāja's grandson, the repre-sentative of the Chauhān line at Ranthambor, was then enticed to Delhi and poisoned by Īltutmish, who had failed to take Ranthambhor by direct attack. Vīra Narāyana's uncle, Vāgbhata, was able, however, to maintain the Chauhān possession of Ranthambhor and to ward off the attacks of the sultans of Delhi. The next Chauhān ruler of note was Hamīra, grandson of Vāg-bhata, who came to power about 1282. He won victories over his Hindu neighbours, notably over Bhojà, king of Mālwā, and recovered Ajmir and Sāmbhar. These successes made him so dangerous that the Delhi sultan decided to send an army against him. On its defeat, 'Alā-ud-dīn Muhammad undertook the com-mand of the campaign in person. In 1301, after a long siege in which the defence suffered from the desertion of some leading Hindus, the fortress of Ranthambhor was stormed, and Hamīra with most of his chief officers was slain. Thus, after an exceptionally long and vigorous resistance, the Chauhān dynasty fell before the Muslims.

In the Jumna-Ganges doab, on the collapse of the Gurjara-Pratihāra empire with the death of Rājyapāla early in the eleventh century, power seems to have passed for a while into the hands of various petty dynasties of which little is known. By the end of the century, however, the new and powerful line of the Gāhadavālas (Gaharwārs) had established itself securely in this territory. The first member of the family to rise to fame and fortune was the successful soldier, Chandradeva, son of Mahī-chandra. Details of his career are not known, but an allusion in one of his grandson's inscriptions suggests that he took advantage of the troubles following on the death of the Kālachuri king, Karnadeva, to set himself up at Kanauj. The capital of the dynasty was, however, Benares, and Kanauj seems rather to have been the residence of a vassal dynasty of Rāshtrakūtas. The dated inscriptions of Chandradeva cover the period 1090–1100, so that he reigned approximately from 1085 to 1102. He was succeeded by his son, Madanapāla, whose earliest known date is 1104, and latest 1109. His reign may therefore be fixed at 1102–12. He was the first of the dynasty to issue coins. The greatest of the Gaharwārs was Madanapāla's son, Govindachandra, whose numerous inscriptions cover the forty years 1114–54, so that his dates may be given as 1112–55. The frequency with which his coins are still found suggests a long and prosperous reign. He had already distinguished himself in his father's reign as a soldier, not only defeating the Pāla king of Bengal "in spite of his irresistible elephants", but also repelling a Muslim invasion.

Unfortunately the inscriptions of his reign contain little information of historical value. They allude, however, to his successful defence of Benares against the Muslims, from which it is clear that the Hindus suffered no loss of prestige in his reign. The distribution of his inscriptions shows that his arms reached Patna, which was taken from the Pālas. There are also indications that his power had been extended to the south at the expense of the Kālachuris, and perhaps this explains the friendly relations which Madanapāla established with the Cholas. He was succeeded by his son, Vijayachandra; two other sons are mentioned in his inscriptions, the *yuvarāja* Ashphotachandra and another unnamed; but we do not know what became of them, and Vijayachandra's reign, though it lasted some fifteen years (1155–70), is itself obscure. According to an inscription of his son he routed a Muslim invader. More is known of this son, Jayachandra, who reigned for some twenty years (1170–90). He came into conflict with the Senas, and is probably the king whom Lakshmanasena claims to have defeated. He was on friendly terms with the Chandels, and assisted them against the Chāhumānas (Chauhāns). The Muhammadans describe him as very powerful. His daughter, Samyogitā, was the heroine of the romantic episode in which the Chāhumāna Prithivīrāja played the part of young Lochinvar at her *svayamvara*, resulting in that feud between the two powerful Hindu rulers which proved disastrous when the Muslim invasion began in earnest.

In the last decade but one of the twelfth century, power in the north-west passed from the last of the Ghaznavids to the young and vigorous Ghūrids, and Muhammad ibn Sām soon proved an enemy to be dreaded. In 1191, after some early successes, he was defeated in the first battle of Tarāorī by a powerful Hindu coalition led by Prithivīrāja, and retired to Ghaznī, where he spent the winter organising his next advance into India. In 1192, in the second battle of Tarāorī, he completely routed the Hindus and slew Prithivīrāja. It is said that the latter's father-in-law, Jayachandra, not only failed to assist him on this occasion, but was in league with the Muslims. Northern India thus passed into Muhammad's hands and he next attacked Jayachandra, who thus found cause to regret his contribution to the Muslim successes. In the battle of Chandwār, in 1193, he stubbornly resisted Muhammad's general, Aibak, but was slain by a chance arrow and his army then fled in disorder. The Muslims took immense quantities of plunder; they occupied Benares; they destroyed its temples and built mosques upon the ruins. Thus the Hindu king perished, and a Muslim governor ruled in his stead; but the Gaharwār family survived for some time longer, for an inscription dated 1197 of Harichandra, son of Jayachandra, suggests that the former still ruled in the eastern corner of his grandfather's great kingdom.

Another dynasty which rose to power at the expense of the Pratihāras was that of the Chandels of Jejākabhukti, the modern

Bundelkhand, which takes its name from the Bundelas, a clan
which only appeared there in the fourteenth century. Early in
the ninth century, a Chandel chief named Nannuka overthrew
the local Pratihāra ruler at Mau-Sahaniya, near Chattarpur, and
became the founder of the Chandel dynasty. The Chandels, who
were probably of Gond origin, gradually extended their power
till they reached the Jumna which formed their frontier on the
Kanauj side. They may at first have acknowledged the suzerainty
of the Gurjara-Pratihāras, but the sixth king, Harshadeva, was a
powerful and independent ruler in the second decade of the tenth
century. He claims to have replaced on the throne of Kanauj
a king whom he calls Kshitipāla, who is evidently Mahīpāla.
The circumstances in which the latter lost his kingdom are not
known, but the Rāshtrakūta, Indra III, claims to have defeated
the king of Kanauj, and Harsha's restoration of the latter must
be connected with these events. But whether Harsha interceded
with the victorious Rāshtrakūta, or whether he drove him out
of Kanauj, on behalf of the deposed ruler, we do not know. In
any case the success of the Rāshtrakūtas was only transitory.
Harsha's son, Yasovarman (c. A.D. 930–50), conquered Kālinjar
and generally enlarged and consolidated the power of his dynasty.
He built the great temple of Vishnu at Khajurāho, and was
powerful enough to extort for it from Devapāla of Kanauj a
famous image of the god. In an inscription of his son he is said
to have waged successful wars with the Gaudas, Kosalas, Mālavas,
Chedis, Gurjaras and others, that is to say, with all his neighbours.
There is no reason to doubt that he raised the Chandels to a
position of acknowledged power. The most famous member of
the dynasty was Yasovarman's son, Dhanga, who reigned for
nearly fifty years (A.D. 950–99), and, like others of his family,
was a great builder. As one of the leading Hindu rulers of the
time, he was summoned by Jayapāla to join the confederation
against Sabuktigīn and shared in the disastrous defeat of the Hindu
coalition. Dhanga lived to be a hundred, and was succeeded by
his son, Ganda (999–1025). Enraged at the submission of his
neighbour, Rājyapāla of Kanauj, to Mahmūd of Ghaznī, Ganda
despatched a force under Vidyadhara, who captured the Gurjara
capital and slew Rājyapāla in 1019. The wrath of the great Muslim
leader was roused by this treatment of his vassal, and he advanced
against the Chandel kingdoms. But though Ganda assembled an

army, huge in comparison with Mahmūd's force, he fled by night, not daring to strike a blow. The Muslims collected a vast quantity of booty with which they returned to Ghaznī. A second campaign in 1023 was equally successful. Ganda again refused to fight, surrendering to the invader the stronghold of Kālinjar and its vast treasures. Mahmūd gave him back part of his territory, including Kālinjar, and returned home, and for nearly two hundred years no Muslim force again entered this region. Little is known of Ganda's successors until Kīrtivarman (1060–1100), who, after losing his throne for a short time in a long and bitter struggle with the Kālachuri, Karna, at last completely overcame his enemy. These events are recorded not only in his own inscriptions, but also in the prologue to a Sanskrit drama, the *Prabodhachandrodaya*, which was performed before the king by command of his general, Gopāla, to celebrate his success against the Kālachuris. His great-grandson, Madanavarman (1128–65), was the next distinguished member of the dynasty. He defeated his neighbour, the Kālachuri king of Chedi, slew the "Mālava" (i.e. Paramāra) king, and was on friendly terms with the Gāhadavāla king of Benares. His successor was Paramardi (Parmāl), who ruled for nearly forty years (1165–1203). His defeat by the celebrated Chauhān, Prithivīrāja, at the battle of Sirswagarh in 1182 is another of the great exploits of that romantic hero. The Chauhāns occupied Mahobā, the capital, but were forced to retire later. Twenty years afterwards the Chandels had completely recovered from this reverse. When the Muslim general, Kutb-uddīn Aibak, invaded their territory, Parmāl was able to offer a vigorous resistance. He finally retired into the fortress of Kālinjar which he defended until he was granted honourable terms of surrender. But the Hindu king having died before these terms could be carried out, his minister, Ājadeva, continued the defence until he was forced by lack of water to surrender unconditionally. Thus fell one of the most celebrated strongholds of medieval India. Its temples were turned into mosques, and Aibak carried off its vast treasures and thousands of Hindu slaves. He then occupied the capital, Mahobā, and, having appointed a governor to rule the conquered territory, returned northwards. The Chandel dynasty thus ceased to be a power in India, although members of the family survived as local chieftains till the end of the sixteenth century. In spite of the destruction wrought by the Muslim invaders, many splendid temples still stand as memorials of the dynasty.

To the south of the lands of the Chandels lay the territory of their rivals, the Kālachuris, or Haihayas, of Chedi, in central India. The Kālachuri line is probably ancient, for they use an era of their own dating from A.D. 249. Haihayas are mentioned in Chālukya records of the sixth and seventh centuries. The Kālachuris of the ninth to the twelfth century trace their descent back to Kokalla I, who reigned in the last quarter of the ninth century. He fought with Bhoja I (Mihira) of Kanauj, and with the Rāshtrakūta, Krishna II. Little is known of his successors, Mughdatunga and Keyuravansha or Yuvarāja. The next ruler, Lakshmana (c. A.D. 950–75), invaded Orissa and carried off a famous image of the serpent, Kaliya, which he placed in the temple of Somnāth. His daughter married the Chālukya, Vikramāditya IV. Of his successors, Yuvarāja and Kokalla II, nothing of importance is recorded.

In the eleventh century Kokalla II's son, Gangeyadeva (1015–40), considerably extended the power of the dynasty. His son and successor, Karna (1040–70), seems to have had some initial successes; he was at first victorious over the Pālas and contributed to the overthrow of Bhoja of Mālwā. The Pālas, however, claim to have defeated him in the end, and the fact that Vigrahapāla III married one of his daughters suggests that Karna was the conquered party. Kīrtivarman, the Chandel king, defeated him, while the Chālukya, Somesvara I, declares that he "utterly destroyed" the power of Karna. The Kālachuri power must therefore have been much diminished in his reign. When Lakshmīdhara of Mālwā invaded Chedi in the reign of Karna's successor, Yasahkarna, he records that his progress was like a "pleasure excursion", so little opposition did he meet. In the course of the twelfth century the dynasty divided into two unimportant lines, that of Dāhāla with its capital at Tripura in the west, and an eastern line established at Ratanpur.

From the death of Harshavardhana to the rise of the Pāla dynasty the history of Bengal is almost unknown. That part of it was under the rule of the later Guptas of Magadha, may be assumed from the distribution of their inscriptions, but their records comprise little more than a list of names preserved in the inscription of Jīvitagupta II. The end of the ancient Gupta line is obscure, but there is a certain amount of evidence to show that the seventh and eighth centuries were very troubled times in Bengal. It was overrun by Yasovarman of Kanauj in the early part of the eighth century, and invaded from Kāmarūpa (Assam). Finally, it seems to have been conquered by the Gurjaras and Rāshtrakūtas. When the Avantī Gurjara, Vatsarāja, having over-thrówn the main Gurjara dynasty of Bhāndi, was in turn defeated by the Rāshtrakūta, Dhruvarāja, an inscription states that "the two umbrellas of Bengal", *i.e.* the sovereignty of Gauda and Vanga, passed from the Gurjaras to the Rāshtrakūtas. The Gurjara conquest must therefore have been short-lived; and probably the Rāshtrakūta triumph also was temporary, but no evidence exists to determine the length of the Rāshtrakūta occupa-tion. Presumably the new invaders were soon forced to with-draw, and local dynasties recovered their lost authority. During this period of invasion, anarchy, and misrule, the old Gupta dynasty disappeared, and the need of a strong ruler became in-creasingly evident. At a formal election, the details of which are wanting, Gopāla was chosen to save the country from anarchy (*matsyanyāyam*, the law of the fishes, by which the great devour the small). The choice seems to have been based entirely upon ability, for Gopāla was probably neither a Kshatriya nor a Brāhman, though he is said to have sprung from a cultured family. Unlike most dynastic founders of the period, his descent is not traced back in inscriptions to any mythical or epic hero. His father, Vapyata, had been an able soldier, and probably he, or some earlier ancestor, had succeeded in founding a petty kingdom by force of arms in the troubled period of the eighth century. Later writers invent for the Pālas the usual mythical descent, from the sea or from the solar race.

Of the events of Gopāla's reign little is recorded. The consolida-tion of his power must have absorbed all his energies, but, on his death, his son was able to set out at once on military expeditions, so that Gopāla must have left the kingdom in a strong and settled condition. Tibetan records state that Gopāla reigned for forty-five years, but this can hardly refer to the period of his full power. His dates are probably *c.* A.D. 765–70. His son, Dharmapāla, whose mother was Deddadevī, a daughter of the King of Bhadra, was, however, the real founder of the greatness

of the dynasty. He became the leading figure in northern India
in the second half of the eighth century, and his influence survived far into the ninth. He seems to have thought the position
which he had inherited from his father strong enough to warrant
attacks upon his neighbours. From the Bhāgalpur grant of
Narāyanapāla we learn that Dharmapāla conquered Indrarāja
and others and bestowed their lands on the "humble suppliant",
Chakrāyudha. This may be interpreted to mean that Dharmapāla
dethroned Indrarāja, king of Kanauj, and installed Chakrāyudha
in his place. If, as is probable, Indrarāja is to be identified with
the Indrāyudha of the Jain *Harivamsa*, Dharmapāla must have
achieved considerable military success in. northern India. References in the contemporary inscriptions of other dynasties
suggest that after the fall of the Chandel, Yasovarman, no effective government survived in the Ganges valley. Dharmapāla
therefore invaded Kanauj and placed his own nominee on the
throne of Indrāyudha, the third successive member of the Kanauj
dynasty to perish at the hands of an invader. Here, however,
Dharmapāla was obliged soon to meet other rivals in the persons
of the Gurjara kings, Vatsarāja and Nāgabhata II, and the Rāshtrakūtas Dhruva and Govinda III, and Pāla success seems to have
been short-lived. Dharmapāla quickly lost his dominant position
and was forced to seek alliance with Govinda III against Nāgabhata, thus encouraging Rāshtrakūta ambitions and endangering
Pāla supremacy. Dharmapāla was a Buddhist, and built a celebrated monastery at Vikramasila, on the bank of the Ganges. He
seems to have enjoyed a very long reign, probably of forty-five
years (A.D. 770–815).

He was succeeded by Devapāla, who is stated to have been a
great conqueror. His elephants, we are told, reached the Vindhyas,
and his cavalry scoured the Kamboja country. Though these
claims are undoubtedly exaggerated, they must be based upon
some military success. The panegyrist's phrases probably mean
that Devapāla had more than held his own against his Gurjara
and Rāshtrakūta rivals. An inscription belonging to his reign,
and throwing light on the foreign relations of India at this period,
is a grant to a Buddhist monastery made by a king of Java and
Sumatra, which indicates that there must have been a regular
pilgrim traffic by sea between Bengal and the Farther East.
Devapāla probably reigned from *c.* A.D. 815 to 854. There is a

reference in an inscription to the *yuvarāja*, Rājyapāla, who, however, presumably died before him, for Devapāla's successor was his cousin Vigrahapāla I, the son of Jayapāla, the general to whom much of the military success of Devapāla's reign is attributed. Vigrahapāla seems also to have been known as Sūrapāla. Nothing is known which corroborates the claims of his inscription that as a destroyer of enemies he resembled Indra. On the contrary, he seems to have been of an unwarlike and ascetic disposition, and there is a hint that he abdicated in favour of his son, Nārāyana-pāla (*c.* A.D. 845–97), whose reign was long and by no means uneventful, although the course of events is not at all clear. His inscriptions suggest that he ruled over a considerable portion of Bihar. Those were troubled times, and northern India was beginning to pass under the rule of the Gurjaras, whose representative, Bhoja I, had been advancing his boundaries northwards from the ancestral lands of the Gurjaras. He had established his capital at Kanauj, which he may have taken from the Pālas; and in any case Pāla territory suffered considerable diminution during this period. Bhoja invaded Bengal, and inflicted a disastrous defeat on its king. Other epigraphical evidence confirms our belief in a great war between Bhoja and the Pālas, and it is clear that for a time Magadha also was added to the Pratihāra empire.

Nārāyanapāla was succeeded by his son, Rājyapāla, another great builder. The distribution of his inscriptions shows that the Pālas still held the Patna district, but the Gurjaras had by then crossed the Sōn and occupied the Gāya district, while in the north they had overrun Tīrabhukti (Tirhut). There is reason to believe, however, that these Gurjara successes were short-lived, and that the Pāla power began to revive in the reign of Rājya-pāla's successor, Gopāla II, who ruled for nearly sixty-six years. His reign coincided with the beginning of the decline of the Gurjara power, and he recovered the Gāya district. Bhoja II was defeated by the Rāshtrakūta, Krishna II, and the latter's grandson, Indra III, crossed the Jumna and sacked the city of Mahodaya. The Rāshtrakūtas claimed that they had bathed their horses where the Ganges enters the sea, and had put Mahīpāla to headlong flight. The Gurjaras were overwhelmed by their southern foes, and though later they rallied a little, they had suffered a blow from which they never fully recovered, and the Pālas presumably seized this occasion to regain some of their lost territory.

But other misfortunes awaited them. An inscription of Mahī-pāla I, son of Vigrahapāla II and grandson of Gopāla II, states that he won back his ancestral kingdom from those who had unjustly seized it. The nature of this disaster is not clear, but probably the rulers of Kamboja were coming to the front and extending their territory at the expense of the Pālas. Mahīpāla I reigned for fifty years (c. 992–1040), and was clearly a successful king. He ruled over the Gāya, Patna, and Muzaffarpur districts of Bihar, and possibly over the Tippera district also. He restored the failing fortunes of the Pālas, and for that reason soon came into conflict with other rising powers. There is some evidence of a struggle between him and the Kālachuris and Karnātas, but more is known about the Chola invasion of his country. Rājendra Chola I earned the title of *Gangavijayī* by reaching the Ganges in a northward thrust, and his campaign is recorded in the Tirumalai rock inscription. Passing through Orissa, and Kosala, he subdued Dandabhukti, which is identified with the modern province of Bihar. He then moved on, and, after conquering eastern Bengal (Vangāladesa), attacked and defeated Mahīpāla I and reached the Ganges. This was the northern limit of his conquests, and Mahīpāla seems to have recovered from this reverse and to have been able to check the further advance of the conqueror about 1020.

About the same time Benares seems to have passed from the Pālas to the Kālachuris of Chedi. Mahīpāla I was succeeded by Nayapāla, also called Nyāyapāla, of whom we know only that he ruled for some fifteen years and held portions of Bihar. He was succeeded by his son, Vigrahapāla III, who early came into conflict with the Chedi ruler, the Kālachuri Lakshmīkarna, who had already given the Pālas trouble, and who, though he enjoyed a long and successful reign, suffered many reverses in his old age. In his last war with the Pālas, Karna was defeated and had to sue for peace. Vigrahapāla married his daughter Yauvanasrī, and refrained from completely depriving his father-in-law of power. There is also a record of a Chālukya invasion in the reign of Somesvara I (c. 1044–68), led by his son, Vikramāditya, who defeated the kings of Gauda and Kāmarūpa. This raid of the Karnāta ruler brought bodies of his countrymen into Bengal, where they afterwards formed small principalities, and this pro-bably explains the origin of the Sena dynasty. The history of the reigns of Vigrahapāla's successors, Mahīpāla and his brothers, is derived from the *Rāmacharita* of Sandhyākara Nandi. According to this work Mahīpāla on his accession imprisoned his two brothers and eventual successors, Sūrapāla and Rāmapāla. Divvoka, chief of the Kaivartas, and a vassal of the Pālas, rebelled and conquered a considerable portion of northern Bengal. Mahīpāla II, neglecting the advice of his minister, hurriedly advanced against him, and began a disastrous campaign which ended in his defeat and death.

Sūrapāla II succeeded for a brief period, after which the third brother, Rāmapāla, took his place. Divvoka's throne was then occupied by his nephew, Bhīma, who harassed what was left of Pāla territory. Rāmapāla, having first convinced himself that he could rely on the support of his feudatories, then took the field against Bhīma, his army being led by Sivarāja. The latter seems to have driven the intruders out of the ancestral lands of the Pālas, but his success was only temporary, and Rāmapāla soon had to lead a larger army into northern Bengal. He next carried hostilities into the south, against Dandabhukti, Vālavalabhī, and other places, many of which are difficult to identify. After consolidating his conquests he began to wage war farther afield in Utkala, Kalinga and Kāmarūpa, the last campaign being conducted by his feudatory, Mayana. One of the Yādavas of eastern Bengal also appealed for his assistance, probably on account of an invasion by Sāmantasena, then rising to power. Rāmapāla was succeeded by his son, Kumārapāla, under whose weaker rule the forces of disruption, which had been checked by Rāmapāla, began to break forth again. His reign was short, and his able minister, Vaidyadeva, seems to have been a more important figure than his master, for he claims the credit of a naval victory, probably on the lower course of the Ganges. Kumārapāla was succeeded and probably murdered by his uncle, Madanapāla, who ruled for some twenty years from about 1130. Down to his reign the Pāla dominions still included eastern Magadha and northern Bengal, but the dynasty was nearing its close. Vijayasena, the first important ruler of the Sena dynasty, seems to have gained power in eastern and western Bengal, and, encouraged by the weakness of Madanapāla, invaded northern Bengal and captured the southern part of Varendra. He himself states that he attacked the king of Gauda, *i.e.*, Madanapāla, with a great force, and captured the king of Mithilā. Nothing is known of Madanapāla's sons or successors, but the Gāhadavāla kings of Kanauj, notably Govindachandra, were certainly advancing eastward, thus reducing still further the territory of the Pālas.

In 1160 a king named Govindapāla is mentioned, whose name and Buddhist title suggest that the Pālas were still a ruling family. He seems to have survived till 1199, when Chauhāns, Pālas, and Senas were all swept away by the Muslims.

The Pāla dynasty thus ruled for an unusually prolonged period. Dharmapāla and Devapāla made Bengal one of the great Indian powers, and their successes were by no means despicable; but the rise of the Kamboja family about the middle of the tenth century was a shock from which they never quite recovered. Their rule formed a period of beneficent and artistic activity. Numerous tanks still testify to their zeal for public works, and they proved the sincerity of their Buddhist faith by their generous patronage of learned men and famous monasteries.

By the middle of the twelfth century, at the end of Madanapāla's reign, the dynasty retained very little territory in Bengal, and Pāla rule was confined to a part of Magadha. It had in fact been supplanted by the Senas, who had been gradually gaining power since the middle of the preceding century. The origin of this dynasty is not definitely known, but there is evidence to show that it came from the south. Its founder was Sāmantasena, who flourished in the third quarter of the eleventh century. In his inscriptions he is designated a Kshatriya of Karnāta, "born in a family which was the glory of Rādha", in western Bengal, and again, "born in a family of Brāhma-Kshatriyas". His ancestry is traced back to Vīrasena, a monarch of the south belonging to the lunar line. The family had, therefore, come originally from the south, and had settled at Rādhā. The epithet 'Brāhma-Kshatriya' suggests that Sāmantasena was a Brāhman who had taken to the profession of arms, and indeed the epithet 'Brāhma' disappears from the later inscriptions. Of Sāmantasena we know very little. An allusion to his slaying the robbers of Karnāta suggests that he fought in the south, and another statement seems to indicate that he retired to a hermitage in his old age. Of his son, Hemantasena, nothing precise is recorded; but the fact that his queen is called 'Mahārājnī' (i.e. Mahādevī) suggests that he claimed to be a ruler of some importance, for this title was usually given only to queens of independent sovereigns.

The real founder of the Sena kingdom was Hemantasena's son, Vijayasena, who reigned from about 1100 to 1165. His wife was a member of the Sūra family, and this alliance may have increased his prestige. In his Deopara inscription, he claims that he defeated Navya and Vīra, attacked the lord of Gauda, humbled the king of Kāmarūpa, protected the king of Kalinga, made many lesser rulers captive, and sailed his fleet up the Ganges. Of these the lord of Gauda has been identified as Madanapāla, who was driven out of Bengal by the Senas; but the chief importance of the inscription lies in its proof that Vijayasena found Pāla territory divided up among a number of petty dynasties, of which till his time the Senas had themselves been one.

The find-spots of his inscriptions show that Vijayasena ruled over considerable territory and to this extent his claims are corroborated. He is said to have amassed great wealth and to have distributed it lavishly to the pious. His son was Ballālasena, "lord of Gauda". He was celebrated for his learning, several compilations being attributed to him. He reigned from about 1165 to 1185. His son and successor was Lakshmanasena, to whom the inscriptions give imposing titles which suggest great military achievements. A literary source states that he reached the hills of Malaya (Travancore) in his "conquest of the world". Inscriptions also record that he erected pillars of victory at Puri, Benares, and Prayāga, to mark the limits of his conquests, and that he overcame Kāmarūpa. He seems to have swept away the last remnants of Pāla power, and so to have come into contact with the Gāhadavālas, who, in the twelfth century, had been advancing gradually into Magadha.

In the meanwhile, however, the Muhammadans were progressing steadily down the Ganges. In 1192 Muhammad ibn Sām had avenged Prithivīrāja's defeat of the Muslims in the previous year, and had crushed the Chāhumāna opposition to his advance. In 1193 Delhi had fallen, and in 1194 Kanauj, and in the same year Muhammad ibn Bakhtiyār, one of Kutb-ud-dīn Aibak's generals, advanced rapidly, conquered Bihar, took Nadiya and overthrew Lakshmanasena who escaped with his life. If the Muhammadan historians are to be believed, the invaders met with no organised opposition, and their conquest was extraordinarily easy. The Gāhadavālas seem to have withdrawn and left open the way through Magadha. In Bihar itself there were no armed men, and the capital, Nadiya (afterwards Lakhnautī), was taken by only eighteen horsemen. Lakshmanasena escaped across the river into eastern Bengal, where early in the thirteenth century his sons succeeded him. Literature seems to have flourished at his court, the most notable names being those of Jayadeva, author of the *Gitagovinda*, Halāyudha, and Dhoyī, author of the *Pavanadūta*, an imitation of the celebrated *Meghadūta*. Inscriptions surviving from the reigns of his sons, Visvarūpasena and Kesavasena, tell us only that these kings granted certain lands in the Vanga region and ruled for about fourteen and three years respectively. But, although the progress of the Muhammadans was slower in eastern than in western Bengal, by the middle of the thirteenth century all trace of Hindu rule had disappeared.

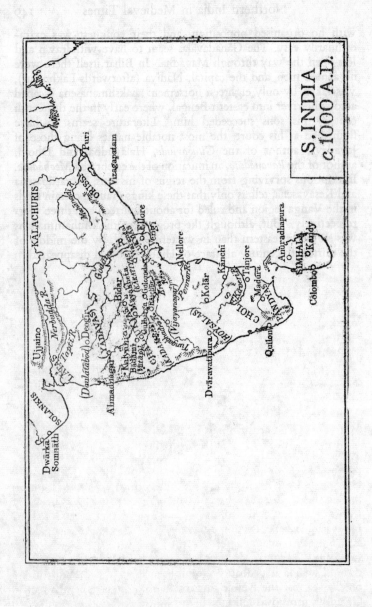

S. INDIA
c. 1000 A.D.

CHAPTER IX

The Deccan

In the sixth century the Chālukya inscriptions provide a series of records which enable us to give a consecutive account of the history of the Deccan and south India for two hundred years. The history of the Western Chālukyas falls into two periods. The Western Chālukyas of Bādāmi (Vātāpi) established a kingdom corresponding to the modern Bombay Presidency with additions to the south and east, but without Kāthiāwār and Gujarāt, and held this territory from the middle of the sixth to the middle of the eighth century, when they disappeared before the Rāshtrakūtas. About a hundred years later Taila II, who claimed descent from the old Chālukya family, overthrew the Rāshtrakūtas and founded the line of the Western Chālukyas of Kalyāni, which survived for two centuries more. The Eastern Chālukyas, an offshoot of the Western branch, ruled at Vengī for nearly five hundred years from the beginning of the seventh century.

The inscriptions trace the descent of the family back to a certain Jayasimha and his son Ranarāga. Nothing is known of either, but they were, presumably, not independent princes. The first sovereign ruler of the dynasty was Ranarāga's son, Pulakesin I Satyāsraya, who bore the title mahārāja. He rose to power about A.D. 550, and established himself at Vātāpi, the modern town of Bādāmi in the Bījāpur district, from which he conquered a little kingdom at the expense of the Kadambas. He was succeeded about A.D. 566 by his eldest son Kīrtivarman I, called Pururana-parākrama, who further extended the family territory at the expense of the Kadambas, taking their capital, Banavasī. Extravagant claims are made for him in later inscriptions, but he cannot, for example, have conquered kings of Magadha and Vanga. He was succeeded about A.D. 597 by his brother, Mangalesa Ranavikrānta, who gained considerable territory to the north from the Kālachuris. He also conquered a region named Revatīdvīpa, which is probably the modern Redi and certainly was on the sea, for the Aihole inscription records that the attacking Chālukya army was reflected in the waters of the ocean. Mangalesa died about A.D. 608, during a civil war between himself and his nephew Pulakesin II Satyāsraya, son of Kīrtivarman I. His death was followed by a period of great confusion and strife, out of which Pulakesin finally emerged triumphant. He had, however, to repel invaders who thought to take advantage of the weakened state of the kingdom, and to reconquer Banavasī. By a series of campaigns he quickly re-established Chālukya power and extended it north, east and south. The Lātas and Gurjaras were routed, and an attempt by Harshavardhana of Thānesar, then the greatest king of northern India, to extend his power southwards was checked on the Nerbudda. In the east the Kalingas were defeated, and the fortress of Pishtapuram, mentioned two hundred years earlier in the record of Samudragupta's campaign, was reduced. In the south the Pallavas were attacked and their king driven to take refuge within the walls of Kānchī, his capital. Pallava records claim a victory for Mahendravarman I over the Chālukyas at Pollilūr, a town near Kānchī, and so confirm the claim made by the Chālukyas that they almost reached the walls of the Pallava capital. Farther south the Chola country was invaded, but an alliance was then formed by the Chālukyas with the Cholas, Pāndyas and Kerālas. This account of Pulakesin's reassertion of the power of the Chālukyas, which is recorded in the Aihole inscription of A.D. 634, has in it nothing improbable. On the conclusion of his campaign he returned to his capital, Vātāpi, from which he ruled his dominions "as if they were one city". His formal coronation took place in A.D. 609, some time after the death of his predecessor. Pulakesin adopted the *biruda* of Satyāsraya, by which name he is commonly referred to in the records of the family. He is the first member of his dynasty to assume the titles of *mahārājādhirāja* and *paramesvara*. The latter title he is said to have acquired by defeating Harshavardhana. His dominion became so extensive that he appointed his younger brother, Vishnuvardhana I, to govern the eastern territories from Vengī. Either with or without the consent of his brother, Vishnuvardhana soon established himself as an independent sovereign, becoming the founder of the Eastern Chālukyas who ruled in Vengī for five hundred years.

Towards the end of the reign of Pulakesin, the Pallavas avenged their early reverses. Narasimhavarman I, having won a series of victories over his immediate neighbours, proceeded to attack the

Chālukyas. He routed Pulakesin in a series of battles and destroyed his capital, in memory of which achievement he assumed the title "Vātāpikonde", "taker of Vātāpi". After the downfall of Pulakesin II about 642; there seems to have been an interregnum of some ten years.

From Arabic sources we learn that Pulakesin exchanged embassies and presents with Khusraw II of Persia, and one of the Ajanta paintings depicts the presentation of a letter from the Persian king to Pulakesin. The Chinese pilgrim, Hiuen Tsang, has left an account of the kingdom of Pu-lo-ki-she, i.e. Pulakesin, one of whose cities he visited, probably Nasik. He describes Pulakesin's subjects as submissive and well behaved. In the Chālukya army the custom prevailed of giving wine not only to the men, but to the elephants, to make their onrush irresistible. Harsha conquered his enemies in the east and west but had been unable, even with the help of many kingdoms, to subdue the Chālukyas in the south.

The fortunes of the Chālukyas were restored by Vikramāditya I Satyāsraya, a son of Pulakesin. In a series of campaigns he reconquered the lands of his ancestors and recovered his inheritance. He cast down the glory of the three kings who had seized his father's lands, and restored to the gods and the Brāhmans the grants which the invaders had confiscated. The three usurpers were the Pallava kings, Narasimhavarman, conqueror of Bādāmi, and his successors, Mahendravarman and Paramesvaravarman I. The struggle with the Pallavas must have been long and severe, for Pallava records of the early part of the reign of Paramesvaravarman state that he won a great victory over the Chālukyas and that Bādāmi was again destroyed. But then fortune turned. Paramesvaravarman was routed, and the Pallava capital, Kānchī, taken by Vikramāditya, who, ably assisted by his son, Vinayāditya, and his grandson, Vijayāditya, re-established Chālukya superiority and made the Cholas, Pāndyas and Kerālas feel his power. This restoration of Chālukya authority was completed about A.D. 655, and the distribution of the records of this reign goes to prove that the whole of his father's territory was recovered by Vikramāditya. Records also survive of two of his brothers, Chandrāditya and Ādityavarman, who on his behalf governed provinces of his kingdom.

In A.D. 680 Vikramāditya was succeeded by his son, Vinayāditya Satyāsraya, who had distinguished himself, as already mentioned, in his father's campaigns in the south and east. He had also fought in the north, as did his son, Vijayāditya Satyāsraya, who came to the throne in A.D. 696, after long experience both as a commander in the field and as an administrator under his father and grandfather. He was a great builder, the most famous of his temples being the Samgamesvara at Pattadakal. He was succeeded about A.D. 733 by his son, Vikramāditya II, likewise a great builder and benefactor of temples. He made war on the Pallavas, routed their king, Nandipotavarman, entered Kānchī, and in a temple there set up an inscription recording his victory. He continued his advance towards the south, commemorating his defeat of the Pāndyas and Cholas by setting up a pillar of victory on the shore of the southern ocean. His son, Kīrtivarman II, who succeeded him in A.D. 746, and who had conducted a successful campaign against the Pallavas in his father's reign, was destined to be the last of his line. Half a century later the whole of the Western Chālukya empire was in the possession of the Rāshtrakūtas. In the middle of the eighth century the Rāshtrakūta, Dantidurga, had acquired sovereign power by conquering Vallabha (i.e. Kīrtivarman II), and routing the Karnātaka (i.e. Chālukya) army, despite its long experience in wars with the Pallavas and Cholas. Kīrtivarman seems to have made an attempt to regain his territory in the reign of Krishna I, the second Rāshtrakūta ruler, but he was completely routed and thereafter for two centuries the Rāshtrakūtas remained supreme. Taila II, who restored the fortunes of the family and founded the line of Kalyāni, traced his descent back to a cousin of Kīrtivarman II.

As has already been stated, Pulakesin II appointed his younger brother, Vishnuvardhana, viceroy of his eastern dominions in the Vengī country, which lay between the Godāvarī and the Krishnā and was bounded on the west by the Eastern Ghauts. About A.D. 630 Vishnuvardhana established himself as an independent ruler, and his dynasty remained distinct for nearly five centuries. He reigned from A.D. 615 to 633 and dated his regnal years from his installation as governor. All the rulers of the dynasty are known, and the chronology is unusually accurate, but the inscriptions do not yield much precise historical information. Vijavāditya II called Narendramrigarāja, who reigned from A.D. 799 to 843, fought many battles with the Gangas and Rāshtras, and b   l

numerous temples in honour of Sambhu (Siva). He is probably
that lord of Vengī whom the Rāshtrakūta, Govinda III, claims to
have summoned to his presence, and ordered to help in the fortifying of one of his cities, presumably his new capital; so that on
this occasion at least the Rāshtrakūta armies were triumphant. Of
Vijayāditya III Gunaka (A.D. 844–88) we know that he routed the
Rāshtrakūta, Krishna II (c. A.D. 888–915), and destroyed his capital,
Mālkhed, and that he won a victory over the Gangas. He also
slew in battle a certain Mangi, who may have been a Chola king.
The claim of the Rāshtrakūta, Amoghavarsha (c. A.D. 814–77),
that the lord of Vengī paid homage to him must refer to some
Chālukya reverse earlier in Vijayāditya's reign. Some time after
his death the Rāshtrakūtas gained a series of successes and overran
the Vengī country, which had to be reconquered by Bhīma I
(A.D. 888–918) from Krishna II. The former's successor, Amma
Vishnuvardhana VI, had to fight for his throne against a number
of his relatives and feudatories who conspired against him with
his hereditary enemies, the Rāshtrakūtas. The throne changed
hands by a series of usurpations until Bhīma II, who slew his
predecessor Yuddhamalla and reigned from A.D. 934 to 945. He
won a series of victories over his neighbours, notably Govinda V.

Bhīma's son, Vijayāditya VI (A.D. 948–70), was able to succeed
him and thereafter the succession continued in the direct line.
For the thirty years from A.D. 973 to 1003 the land of Vengī "was
without a leader". Nothing is known of the dynasty during this
period, but the probability is that the country was conquered and
occupied by the Cholas. Of Saktivarman, who reigned from
1003 to 1015, coins survive. His nephew Rājarāja I (called after
his Chola grandfather) Vishnuvardhana VIII had a long reign,
(1022–63) as had his son, Kulottunga Chodadeva I (1063–112), who
also had a Chola mother. These intermarriages with the Chola
royal family made this king more Chola than Chālukya by blood,
and gave him a strong claim to the Chola throne, which trouble
in the Chola country enabled him to enforce. Inscriptions state
that he preferred the Chola throne, and made his uncle, Vijayāditya VII, viceroy of Vengī, and that he did this because he was
desirous of devoting himself to further conquests. His first campaign seems to have been that directed against his Chola neighbour, and a literary source, the *Vikramānkadevacharita*, primarily
concerned with the Western Chālukyas, throws some light on the

circumstances in which the Eastern Chālukya became lord of the Chola country. Vikramāditya VI, of the former dynasty, in his father's lifetime, had, we are told, repeatedly defeated the Cholas, and had sacked Kānchī, as his father had done before him. On the accession of his brother, Somesvara II, Vikramāditya VI was planning yet another campaign against the Cholas when the Chola king begged for peace and a treaty between the two kingdoms was cemented by the marriage of his daughter with Vikramāditya. The Chola king died soon afterwards and the troubles which followed brought Vikramāditya back to restore order. He set his Chola brother-in-law on the throne, but had scarcely reached the frontier on his homeward journey when he received news that the Chola had been slain in a new rebellion, and that Rajiga, lord of Vengī, had seized the throne of Kānchī. According to the Chālukya poet, Vikramāditya routed Rajiga, though Rajiga had won over to his side the reigning Western Chālukya, the former's brother, Somesvara II. Later mentions of Vikramāditya's campaigns against the Cholas probably refer to wars with the Eastern Chālukyas, who, despite Rajiga's defeat, maintained their hold upon Kānchī. The name Rajiga is a popular form of Rājendra Chola, which was the name of the Chālukya ruler before he seized the Chola throne, after which he became Kulottunga Chodadeva. It is clear then that the Eastern Chālukya profited by troubles in the Chola kingdom to seize the power there and to place in the old home of the dynasty viceroys, among whom were three of his sons. A Tamil poem celebrates the campaign of Kulottunga's minister, Karunākara, against Anantavarma Chodagangadeva, the ruler of Kalinga, who had refused to pay tribute. With Kulottunga the Eastern Chālukyas merge into the Cholas, although his grandson, Kulottunga Chodadeva II, in 1132 still claims a Chālukya genealogy. This mixed dynasty lasted a century and a half.

In the sixth decade of the eighth century the sovereignty over the lands roughly corresponding with the modern Bombay Presidency passed from the Western Chālukyas to the most powerful branch of the Rāshtrakūta family, later known as of Mānyakheta or Mālkhed, from their capital. For a time another branch of this family held the northern part of the Western Chālukya empire, but it was soon ousted by its more powerful relatives in the south. Only the names of the earliest members of the dynasty, Dantivarman I, Indra I, Govinda I, Kakka I, and Indra II, who flourished in the latter half of the seventh and first half of the eighth century, are known from later records. The first important member, and the real founder, of the dynasty was Dantidurga Khadgāvaloka, who was reigning in A.D. 753. He was the first to assume titles indicating paramount sovereignty. He defeated the Western Chālukya, Kīrtivarman II, routing his great army, despite its previous victories over the Cholas and Pāndyas. Dantidurga seems to have held all the Chālukya dominions except some lands in the south and north, the latter being occupied by another branch of the family, which was represented about this time by Kakkarāja II. Dantidurga was succeeded by his uncle, Krishna I, known as Akālavarsha or Subhatunga who dethroned his nephew because he had lapsed into evil ways. By finally overthrowing his nephew's enemy, Kīrtivarman II, Krishna I firmly established Rāshtrakūta supremacy or, as the inscriptions put it, he snatched the goddess of fortune from the Chālukya family and made the boar (the badge of the Chālukyas) flee like a timid deer. The records also lay great stress on his victory over a certain powerful ruler, otherwise unknown, named Rāhappa, who, it has been suggested, may have been Kakkarāja II of the northern branch of the Rāshtrakūta family.

Krishna I was succeeded by his younger son, Dhruva Dhārāvarsha, the elder son, Govinda II, having reigned, if at all, only for a very brief period. Dhruva defeated the Gangas and Pallavas, and, somewhere about A.D. 780, routed Vatsarāja of Ujjain, who had conquered Gauda. His son, Govinda III, called Prabhūtavarsha and Jagattunga, whom we know to have been chosen as yuvarāja in his father's lifetime from among several brothers, reigned from about A.D. 783 to 815. It is clear that he established the position of the dynasty on an even broader basis than his predecessors had done. In his various campaigns he secured the submission of the Gurjara king and of the lord of Mālwā and won much wealth from the Pallavas. It was in his reign that the new capital, Mānyakheta, was built, and the fact that he was able to compel Vijayāditya of Vengī to assist in its construction is evidence of the strength of Govinda's position. He waged continual warfare with the Eastern Chālukyas. The records of his conquests suggest that his kingdom extended from the west coast far inland to the east, and from the Vindhyas down to the Tungabhadrā.

In view of the extent of his dominions he appointed to govern the Lāta country in the north his brother, Indrarāja, who quickly disposed of the Gurjara leader opposing him. Govinda III was succeeded by his son called Amoghavarsha, but whose real name is not known. The succession was disputed but, with the assistance of Kakkarāja, son of Indrarāja, just mentioned, Amoghavarsha finally prevailed. His reign, which lasted from A.D. 815 to 877, witnessed no diminution of the empire he had inherited from his father, although some of the claims made in his inscriptions, such as that the king of Magadha paid homage to him, are undoubtedly exaggerated. The wars with the Eastern Chālukyas continued. Amoghavarsha completed the fortification of Mānyakheta. In his old age he abdicated in favour of his son, Krishna II, who reigned till A.D. 912 and was known as Akālavarsha or Subhatunga. In his reign the Eastern Chālukya, Vijayāditya III, claims to have defeated him and burned his capital. Later records, however, admit a successful counter-thrust by Krishna II, who overran the land of Vengī, which had to be reconquered by Bhīma I. Krishna II's son, called Jagattunga, did not come to the throne, the next occupant of which was Krishna's grandson Indra III Nityavarsha. Indra's successor, Govinda IV Prabhūtavarsha, seems to have suffered reverses at the hands of the Eastern Chālukyas, and in the end to have lost the affections of his people. He was succeeded about A.D. 933 by his uncle, Vaddiga Amoghavarsha. The next ruler was the latter's son, Krishna III Akālavarsha, who reigned from A.D. 940 to 970. The great event of his reign was the war with the Chola king, Rājāditya, who was treacherously killed at Takkola by a Ganga prince, Būtuga, who was handsomely rewarded for the murder by Krishna III. The Gangas and Pallavas were overcome, and he seems also to have held his own in the north against the Gurjaras, but his younger brother and successor, Khottiga Nityavarsha, was defeated by the Paramāra king, Sīyaka, and his capital plundered. He was succeeded in A.D. 972 by his nephew, Kakka II Amoghavarsha, for whom are claimed successes over his neighbours the Gurjaras, Cholas and Pāndyas. In A.D. 973 he was overthrown by the Western Chālukya, Taila II; the dynasty came to an end; and the lands everted to their former holders, the Chālukyas. The Rāshtrakūta family survived however, and various members of it played a part in the history of the next two centuries.

With the overthrow of Kakka II in A.D. 973 by Taila, who was descended from the old Bādāmi Chālukya line, the two hundred years of Rāshtrakūta usurpation came to an end, and the Chālukya dynasty was restored. The new line is known from its capital as the dynasty of the Western Chālukyas of Kalyāni, a town, now in the Nizam's dominions, founded by Somesvara I.

Taila or Tailapa II, called Ahavamalla, ruled for twenty-four years (A.D. 973–97), and regained most of the lands which his family had formerly ruled. He bore the titles of *mahārājādhirāja* and *paramesvara*, evidence of paramount sovereignty, and in one inscription he is given the title of *chakravartin*. His capital may still have been the Rāshtrakūtas' capital of Mānyakheta. He does not seem to have ruled in Gujarāt; there the Chaulukya kings of Anhilwār still reigned, and they also held the Lāta country. While it can hardly be true that he conquered Chedi, Orissa, and Nepāl, his claim to have subjugated the Kuntala country is borne out by the distribution of Chālukya inscriptions; moreover the Western Chālukyas call themselves lords of Kuntala. The limits of this region are not clear, but it corresponds roughly with the whole of the Kanarese districts. Another of his military successes, the capture and execution of Munja, the Paramāra king of Mālwā, has already been mentioned.

In A.D. 997 Taila was succeeded by his son, Satyāsraya, also called Solliga or Sallina, but no records from his reign survive. From Chola sources, however, we learn that he had to defend himself against Rājarāja Rājakerarivarman, who overran his country and claimed considerable success. On the other hand, a later Chālukya inscription (Haltur), while admitting the initial Chola successes, asserts that the Chālukya ultimately drove out the enemy, captured great stores of wealth, and conquered the southern country. Of the next few kings, Dasavarman, Vikramāditya V, Jayasimha I and Jayadekamala, we know little more than their names. The last-named claims to have overthrown Bhoja, the Paramāra, defeated the Chola and Chedi monarchs, and put to flight the confederacy of Mālwā. Other records refer to his victory over the Chola king, Rājendra, who, however, claimed successes himself.

The next king, Somesvara I Trailokyamalla-Ahavamalla, was a ruler of considerable importance. The inscriptions of his reign show that numerous feudatories owned his sway. Bilhana tells us that he made Kalyānapura his capital, a statement supported by the fact that the inscription of 1053 in which the town is first mentioned, calls it the settled residence of the king. During this reign the war with the Cholas continued, but while the Chola records represent Rājendra as conquering Somesvara at a place named Koppam, on the Perara river, a Western Chālukya inscription of 1071, while admitting the invasion and the damage done by the Cholas, adds that the Chola king lost his life later in the campaign, and that the Chola succession was thus broken, for he left no direct heir. An inscription recording a donation by Somesvara on his return from a conquest of the southern countries and of the Cholas serves to fix the date of this Chālukya victory at about 1060. Bilhana also tells us that the Chālukya king carried the war into the enemy territory and penetrated as far as the capital, Kānchī, the ruler of which had to flee to the jungle. He also credits Somesvara with the capture of Dhārā, the Paramāra capital, and with the destruction of the power of Karna, the Kālachuri ruler of Chedi.

Of his three sons the second, Vikramāditya VI, showed such promise that Somesvara proposed to appoint him to succeed to the throne, but, as he refused to usurp his elder brother's right, the latter, Somesvara II, was appointed yuvarāja, while Vikramāditya set out on a series of military expeditions. He repeatedly defeated the Cholas and assisted the king of Mālwā to regain his kingdom. He is also said to have reached Bengal and Assam, to have attacked the king of Ceylon, and slain the lord of Kerāla. Finally, we are told, he captured Gangaikonda from the Cholas, Vengī, the capital of the Eastern Chālukyas, and Chakrakotra, a fortress of the Paramāras. On his way home he heard that his father, who had fallen very ill, on learning that his disease was incurable, had solemnly committed suicide by drowning himself in the Tungabhadrā. Vikramāditya thereupon hurried home to console his elder brother, who succeeded to the throne in 1068. His reign was uneventful, but when he became intoxicated with pride and neglected his subjects, Vikramāditya deposed him about 1075 and reigned in his stead. Bilhana tells a more elaborate story of these events. According to him the two brothers remained on good terms until Somesvara began to fall into evil ways and tried to injure Vikramāditya, who therefore left the capital with his men, taking his younger brother with him. In spite of the king's efforts to bring him back, Vikramāditya led his army to the Tungabhadrā, where he rested it in preparation for an invasion of the Chola country. He seems however to have turned first to the south-west, for he received the homage of Jayakesin, lord of the Konkan, and of the king of Kerāla. He then opened hostilities against the Cholas, but was stopped by the overtures of the Chola king, Vīra Rājendradeva I, and they parted on good terms, sealing their friendship by Vikramāditya's marriage with the daughter of the Chola king. But the death of the latter plunged the kingdom into a state of anarchy. Vikramāditya hurried to Kānchī, put down the rebellion, established his brother-in-law on the throne, and returned to the Tungabhadrā. There he heard that his brother-in-law had lost his life in a new rebellion and that the throne had been seized by the Eastern Chālukya, Kottuṅga (Rajiga). Vikramāditya and Somesvara II then set out, the one to expel, and the other to assist, the usurper, and when Vikramāditya at last came up with Rajiga's forces, Somesvara's army was not far behind. In the conflict that ensued, Vikramāditya seems to have received valuable assistance from the Yādava prince, Seunachandra II. Rajiga fled and Somesvara was taken prisoner. The latter's fate is not known, for although Vikramāditya at first proposed to restore his brother to the Chālukya throne, he finally proclaimed himself king and appointed Jayasimha III viceroy at Banavasī. These events took place in 1076, from which year Vikramāditya began a new era, the *Chālukya-Vikrama-kāla*. He probably reigned for nearly half a century, and numerous epi-graphical records survive, the distribution of which frequently confirms Bilhana's statements, while the many feudatories men-tioned show that the authority which Vikramāditya claimed was real. His reign was, on the whole, peaceful, disturbed at home only by an attempted rebellion of his younger brother and abroad by a campaign against the new Chālukya family of Chola kings, whose arrogance demanded chastisement. About 1117, the Hoy-salas claim to have invaded the Belvola country and advanced as far as the Krishnā. From Sinda records we learn of the defeat and pursuit of an invading Hoysala army by Achgi III, a loyal feudatory and devoted supporter of the Chālukyas.

Vikramāditya VI's younger brother presumably died before him and about 1126 Somesvara III succeeded to the throne. His numerous records indicate that he enjoyed a peaceful reign, with leisure to follow literary pursuits. He was succeeded by Jagade-kamala II, in whose reign Hoysala invaders reappeared, but were again driven back by the Sindas, although Hoysala records claim considerable successes in the field. Of his successor, Taila III, little is known, but it is evident that the power of the Chālukyas was beginning to decline, and some time during his reign a severe blow seems to have been dealt to them by the Kākatiya prince, Prola, who captured Taila, but afterwards released him. Internal troubles were a further source of weakness. Bijjala, the powerful commander-in-chief, incited the army to rebel and finally usurped the throne. Claiming descent from the Kālachuri kings of central India, Bijjala appears first about 1140 as a feudatory of Jaga-dekamala II, and later as governor of Banavasī and a devoted servant of the Chālukyas. He is mentioned in a Bījāpur inscription of the third year of Taila, without any special titles, and in 1155, although he was then *mahāmandalesvara*, he still recognised Taila as his sovereign. But in the next year he threw off his allegiance and declared himself independent, assuming, among other im-portant titles, that of Kālachurya *chakravartin*. In 1162 he adopted the titles of a paramount sovereign, and rapidly annexed all the Western Chālukya dominions, apparently with the assistance of the Silāhāra Vijayāditya of Karad, for a record of this family claims that Vijayāditya's help enabled Bijjala to become a *chakra-vartin*. A few years later, in 1168, while his dominions still re-mained intact, he abdicated and transferred the throne to his son, Sovideva (Somesvara), whose inscriptions dwell on his wife's accomplishments rather than on his own achievements. Sankama, Vīra Narāyana and Singhana followed. In 1183 the Chālukyas' sovereignty was restored through the efforts of the *dandanāyaka* Brāhma, in the person of Somesvara IV, son of Taila III. Bijjala having been assassinated in revenge for cruelty to two Jains, and none of his sons and successors possessing his ability, the Chālukyas found it easy to re-establish their authority. Brāhma's services are commemorated by a variety of epithets. He is called "the establisher of Chālukya sovereignty", and the "death-fire to the Kālachuryas". A Hoysala inscription also records his exploits, and mentions that his father, Kavana, was the leader of the Kālachurya forces. But the restoration was short-lived. The Yādavas of Devagiri seem to have been encroaching from the west, while the Hoysalas, under Vīra Ballāla I, were advancing from the south,

and a Hoysaia inscription expressly mentions a victory over the
Chālukya general, Brāhma. Between these two enemies Somesvara was gradually driven into the south-west corner of his kingdom, where he maintained his authority over a remnant of his
feudatories, and on his death about 1190 the dynasty ended. A few
references to the Chālukyas occur in the thirteenth and fourteenth
centuries, and now and then individuals appeared who claimed
Chālukya blood, but none of them seems to have been a direct
descendant.

The Yādava dynasty of Devagiri is credited with a long pedigree by Hemādri in his *Vratakhanda*, but their epigraphical records
begin only in A.D. 1000, with a grant of Bhillama II, a vassal of
the Western Chālukyas, and not till the second half of the eleventh
century did an outstanding figure emerge in Seunachandra II, who
claims to have rendered signal service to the Chālukya, Vikramāditya VI. The first member of the family to assume the titles
of paramount sovereignty was Bhillama III, who, about 1187,
seized the northern and eastern portions of the lands of his
Chālukya suzerain, Somesvara IV, and who was killed in battle
by the Hoysalas. Bhillama founded the city of Devagiri, with
which the dynasty was thenceforth associated. His son was
Jaitugi I, who claims to have slain in battle the Tailanga king,
identified with the Kākatiya, Rudradeva. Numerous records
exist of his son, Singhana, who succeeded about 1210, but they
contain little precise information, though, from their distribution,
it is evident that he ruled over all the lands that had belonged to
the Western Chālukyas. References to his successes against the
Hoysalas are frequent. His claims are very exaggerated, and, taken
literally, imply a dominion extending over India. He certainly
won some successes in the north, crossing the Taptī and reaching
the Mahī, and ravaging the country round Broach. About 1247
he was succeeded by his grandson, Krishna, who seems to have
been able to keep the kingdom intact, but little definite information about his reign is available. His brother, Mahādeva, succeeded in 1260, and, while the dynasty suffered no loss of prestige
in his reign, its end drew near under his successor, Rāmachandra
(1271–1310). He was victorious over the Hoysalas, taking their
capital and building a temple there in honour of his victory. At
the end of the thirteenth century local record cease, but the

Muslim historians record the conquest of the kingdom. In 1294, during the Muslim invasion, 'Alā-ud-dīn Muhammad defeated Rāmachandra outside his capital, which was taken and plundered. Peace was made on payment of a large indemnity and a promise of tribute to the victor, who then withdrew. In 1306, Rāmachandra being in arrears with his tribute, Malik Kāfūr laid siege to Devagiri in the course of his Deccan campaign. New terms were made. Rāmachandra was treated with honour and restored to his throne, and thereafter he paid homage to the Delhi sultan. His son, Sankara, who succeeded in 1310, was less well disposed to the Muslims, and in 1312 was seized and put to death in the course of Malik Kāfūr's fourth campaign in the Deccan. Devagiri then became Malik Kāfūr's headquarters until his return to Delhi. Harapāla, a brother-in-law of Sankara, then raised a rebellion in the Deccan which spread rapidly until Mubārak took the field against him, when he was captured and executed, and the Yādava dynasty was brought to an end.

The Hoysalas (Poysalas), like the Rāshtrakūtas and other great families, claimed descent from the line of Yadu, i.e. the lunar race. The town first associated with their rule is Velāpura (Bellore) in Mysore, but, at a later date, the centre of their government was transferred to Dorasamudra, the modern Halebid. Various legends associated with the rise of the dynasty suggest that they were originally Jains, and later became Vaishnavas. The earliest reference to the Hoysalas is in an inscription of 1006, which mentions that an officer of the Chola king, Rājarāja, had defeated a Hoysala minister named Naganna. The records of the Hoysala dynasty, however, do not trace it beyond Vinayāditya, who is known to have flourished about 1048 as a feudatory of the Cholas. Of his son, Ereyanga, we have no records, but we are told in a later inscription that he conducted a campaign into the north, in which he destroyed Dharā, the capital of the kings of Mālwā, and that he was equally successful against the Cholas and in Kalinga. How much of this is true we have no means of telling, but his successes were presumably won on behalf of his Chālukya suzerain, and not as an independent monarch. His son, Ballāla I, succeeded him early in the twelfth century and was soon afterwards followed by his younger brother Vishnuvardhana who was reigning in 1117. From a land grant one learns that he was the first to establish his family in a position of independent authority, by conquering the lands at one time held by the Gangas, which he took from the Chola king.

By 1117 Vishnuvardhana had defeated the Pāndyas and Tulus, subdued a number of petty chiefs, conquered considerable territory, and even threatened Kānchī. Fourteen years later even greater claims are made on his behalf; he is then said to have humbled the Cholas, Pāndyas, and Kerālas, and to have slain the king of the Āndhras. An inscription of a later reign says that he was strong enough to be treated as an equal by the Chālukya, Vikramāditya VI. But his boast of having washed his horses in the Krishnā is unconfirmed. This region owned the suzerainty of Vikramāditya, and records of the latter's devoted Sinda feudatories assert that they routed the Hoysalas, besieging Dorasamudra and driving the king from his capital. This is the more probable version and any distant conquests which Vishnuvardhana made cannot have been permanent. Frequent mention is made of a member of the Ganga family, Gangarāja, whose support enabled him to secure extensive territory. But though Vishnuvardhana evidently exercised considerable freedom of action, he still bore only the titles of a feudatory.

His son, Narasimha, seems to have done nothing to extend the power of the family, but his grandson, Vīra Ballāla I, established himself as an independent king and signalised the event by establishing about 1191–2 an era of his own. He had already defeated Bŕahma, the general of Somesvara IV, the Western Chālukya, and Bhillama, the Yādava king of Devagiri; but his assertion that he became the ruler of all the lands that had belonged to the Western Chālukyas must be accepted with reserve. His final struggle with his Yādava rivals probably took place in the last decade of the twelfth century, for an inscription dated 1202 records that he defeated and slew Bhillama in the vicinity of Gadag. Vīra Ballāla thus became master of most of the territory which the Yādavas had conquered from the Chālukya, Somesvara IV, and reigned over his extended dominions till about 1212. Narasimha II seems to have lost some of his father's territory, but claims victories over the Pāndyas and Kadambas. After a reign of some twenty years he was succeeded by Vīra-Somesvara whose son, Narasimha III, was reigning in 1254. One of his inscriptions, dated 1279, contains an interesting reference to the fact that natives of the Kanarese country resident in Benares paid a tax to the Turushkas, *i.e.*, the Muhammadan sultan of Delhi. The last ruler of the Hoysala dynasty was Vīra Ballāla III, whose inscriptions are dated from 1292 to 1317. In 1310 'Alā-ud-dīn Muhammad, having completed the conquest of the Yādavas, sent an army under Malik Kāfūr and Khvāja Hājjī against the Hoysalas. Crossing the Godāvarī, the invaders laid waste the Hoysala kingdom, captured the king, and sacked his capital. After being detained in Delhi for three years, Ballāla was released, and, on his return, set about organising the defences of his country against further Muslim attacks. In the course of this he founded the impregnable city of Vijayanagar, whence Hindu leaders long continued to defend the south against their enemies. Thus arose out of the Hoysala empire the kingdom known by the name of its great fortress and capital.

With the decline of the Āndhras the western part of the southern Deccan, like the eastern, passed to the Chutus, of whom little is known. Not till this region, known as the Karnātaka, came into the possession of their successors, the Kadambas, does its history begin. The story of the rise of the Kadamba dynasty is told in the Talgund inscription of Kākusthavarman (*c.* A.D. 425–50). Its founder was a Brāhman named Mayūrasarman, who went to study in Kānchī, for centuries a famous centre of learning. There he quarrelled with a Kshatriya and was humiliated to find that those who followed the profession of arms held students in contempt. Determining, therefore, "to exchange the implements of sacrifice for the sword", he set up as a freebooter, gathered a following in his native district, and soon grew powerful. He became a thorn in the side of the Pallavas, then suffering under Samudragupta's invasion. Deeming it advisable to come to terms, they recognised Mayūrasarman as lord of considerable territory in the west, with Banavasī as his capital, and in return he acknowledged Pallava suzerainty. His date may be put at A.D. 340–60. Of his successors little is known. Of Kangavarman, Bhagīratha and Raghu only conventional records survive in the inscriptions, from which one gathers they were not left in peace by their neighbours. One of them was the king of Kuntala over whom the Vākātaka Prithivīsena I claimed a victory. Raghu was succeeded by his brother, Kākusthavarman, in whose reign the country seems to have enjoyed unusual prosperity. He was probably the greatest of the early Kadambas. His daughters made distinguished marriages, from which we may deduce that his neighbours were anxious to have him as an ally. One of them married a "Gupta" king, *i.e.* one of the Vākātakas, who were exceedingly proud of their descent from the daughter of Chandragupta II. Sāntivarman, son and successor of Kākustha, ruled with equal success and added to the Kadamba dominions, which became so extensive that he appointed his brother, Krishnavarman, to rule the southern portion as viceroy. The next ruler, Mrigesavarman, came to the throne in A.D. 472. During his reign the southern province, under his uncle, Krishnavarman, seceded and became independent, while another member of the family, Kumāravarman, established himself in the east, where he was succeeded by his son, Mandhata. Mrigesavarman fought successfully against the Gangas and Pallavas. His uncle, Krishnavarman, was less fortunate. Though apparently so successful at first that he is said to have performed the horse-sacrifice, he suffered a severe defeat in a war with the Pallavas, and probably became a Pallava vassal, for his son in disgust became a hermit. Another son, Vishnuvarman, was set on the throne by the Pallavas but neither he nor his son, Simhavarman, appears to have been in any way distinguished.

On the death of Mrigesavarman, both Mandhata and Vishnuvarman, the representatives of the younger lines, tried to seize Banavasī and the lands of the older branch, but Ravivarman, the youthful heir, finally routed Mandhata and slew Vishnuvarman. He became one of the great rulers of the Kadambas. Not only did he defeat all claimants to the throne and unite all the Kadamba territory, but he waged successful war on his neighbours, the Gangas and Pallavas. He overthrew the Pallava whom he calls Chandadanda, presumably Skandavarman V. The distribution of his inscriptions shows that he did extend his territory. He made a new capital at Palāsikā (Halsi). Ravivarman's long reign probably covered the first four decades of the sixth century. His son, Harivarman, was the last of the main line and was succeeded, whether peacefully or otherwise cannot be determined with certainty, by Krishnavarman II of the southern branch. This reign was marked by the loss to the Chālukyas of the northern portion of Kadamba territory, where Pulakesin I made Vātāpi his capital. Krishnavarman II is stated to have ruled his diminished territory with sufficient success to justify his performing the horse-sacrifice, but his son, Ajavarman, was reduced to the position of a vassal of the Chālukyas. Ajavarman's son, Bhogivarman, took advantage of Pulakesin II's engagements elsewhere to regain a short-lived independence, but, as soon as the Chālukya was free, he crushed his rebellious vassal and the dynasty thus came to an end, its lands passing to the Chālukyas. About this time Hiuen Tsang visited Banavasī. For over two centuries, the Karnātaka shared the history of the Chālukyas—for whom it was ruled by their vassals, the Alūpas—and the Rāshtrakūtas.

The Kadamba family however was not extinct, and when Tailapa II succeeded in overthrowing the Rāshtrakūtas and re-establishing the Chālukyas, he rewarded a Kadamba named Irivabedanga who had assisted him, by restoring to him, about A.D. 975, the old kingdom of Banavasī. Irivabedanga's son, Chattadeva, proved a valiant supporter of the Chālukyas. His kingdom formed a bulwark against the Cholas and must have suffered much from their invasions. He played a prominent part in the war between the Chālukyas and Paramāras, assisting considerably in the rout of the latter. Chattadeva enjoyed a long reign which lasted till 1031 at least, and those of his immediate successors were uneventful except for occasional Chola raids. A dispute regarding the succession, which arose between Taila's grandson, Sāntivarman, and the latter's nephew, Kīrtivarman, was amicably settled by a partition of territory. The latter made an unsuccessful attempt to cast off his allegiance to the Chālukyas. Early in the twelfth century the Kadambas began to suffer from the ambition of the Hoysala, Vishnuvardhana, who, after defeating the Pāndyas, turned his attention to the Carnatic. He sacked Banavasī and proceeded to lay siege to Hangāl, the capital, which was finally reduced in spite of the valiant defence of Taila II, who was taken prisoner and put to death in 1130. Tailapa's son and eventual successor, Mallikarjuna, was more fortunate, for during his reign the Hoysalas were fully occupied in resisting the Sinda general dispatched by the Chālukyas to curb their rapidly increasing power. Mallikarjuna's nephew, Kīrtideva, succeeded, probably with the help of the Kālachuris, who had replaced the Chālukyas as overlords of the Kadambas, in regaining all that had been lost to the Hoysalas. Kāmadeva, son of Kīrtideva, not only successfully resisted Hoysala aggression, but turned the tables on them by invading their territory. During his reign (1180–1217) Kadamba independence, so seriously threatened fifty years before, was firmly re-established, and he left to his successor, Mallideva, a considerable kingdom which remained, for a time, unmolested by its exhausted enemies. Towards the end of his reign, however, Mallideva seems to have acknowledged the suzerainty of the Yādavas, who helped him to avenge a defeat which he suffered at the hands of the Hoysalas. Kāmádeva, who succeeded to the throne about 1260, and who was probably a son of Mallideva, seems to have assisted his Yādava suzerain against the Hoysalas and to have been suitably rewarded. Towards the end of the century, however, the Yādavas were weakened by the Muhammadan invasion, and the Hoysalas who, under the able Vīra Ballāla III, had settled their domestic troubles and were seeking to regain their former position in the Deccan, invaded Kadamba territory, at first with considerable success, but in 1300 they were completely routed at Sirsi by a combined Kadamba and Chālukya force. In 1310 Malik Kāfūr sacked Dorasamudra and took the Hoysala king prisoner. The Kadambas also must have suffered, as the Muslim army passed through their country, but, like the Hoysalas, they recovered. The final destruction of the Hoysalas and the death of Vīra Ballāla III did not however restore the Kadambas to power, for Vīra Ballāla had securely laid the foundations of the great Vijayanagar empire, and Purandara, the last Kadamba ruler, was one of the first victims of Harihara, or rather of his brother, Mārapa, and the Banavasī and Hangāl territory, with which the Kadambas had been associated for a century, passed from them.

In the tenth century another branch of the Kadamba family began to rise to prominence with the decline of the Rāshtrakūtas. Their capital was at first Chandūr (Chandrapura), and their original territory was a strip of coast between the sea and the mountains to the south of Goa, which was still in the possession of the Silāhāras. Later inscriptions trace the foundation of this kingdom to a certain Shashtha and his son, Chaturbhuja. The latter's son, Guhalladeva, extended his power at the expense of his neighbours and claims to have assisted a Pallava king, presumably against the Cholas. The next ruler, Shashtadeva, reduced the Southern Silāhāras, his neighbours on the north, and added the Konkan to his ancestral lands. His capture of Goa is compared by his panegyrists to Rāma's conquest of Ceylon. He died, after a long reign, about 1050, leaving a considerable and well-established kingdom to his son, Jayakesin I, who moved his capital to the city of Goa, already embellished by his father. In the north he extended his power still further by slaying the last Silāhāra king, Mammuri, and adding Kāpardika to his territory. Thence he led a successful expedition into the Lāta country. In the south he claimed a success against the Cholas, presumably won on behalf of his Chālukya overlord, for he seems to have acted as intermediary in the peace negotiations that followed. A few years later, in connection with the struggle between the two Chālukyas, Somesvara II, and his brother, Vikramāditya VI, Jayakesin claims to have helped to set the latter on the throne. He also brought under his rule the other branch of the Kadambas, that of Hangāl and Banavasī, thus for a time uniting all the Kadamba lands under one ruler. The next two kings were undistinguished, but Jayakesin II, who came to the throne in 1104, was one of the greatest of the dynasty. Early in his reign, taking advantage of Chālukya preoccupation with a Hoysala invasion, he cast off his allegiance. But, having been speedily reduced to obedience by force, he was conciliated by diplomacy, and the Chālukya further attached his powerful feudatory to him by giving him his daughter in marriage. Towards the end of his reign Jayakesin, like his relative in Hangāl, lost territory to the Hoysala, Vishnuvardhana. In 1148 he was succeeded by his son, Permādi, who remained faithful to the Chālukyas until their overthrow in 1186, when he proclaimed himself independent as emperor of the Konkan. In the reign of his brother and successor, Vijayāditya (Vishnuchitta), the Kālachuryas made an unsuccessful attempt to extort allegiance from the Kadambas. The Hoysalas were more successful, however, for Vijayāditya paid tribute to Vīra Ballāla III, and about the same time Kāmadeva of the Hangāl branch also claimed that Vijayāditya was his feudatory. The next ruler, Jayakesin III, had a long and uneventful reign, for the Hoysalas and Yādavas were too busily engaged with each other to be able to interfere elsewhere; but, when the struggle was decided in favour of the Yādavas, one of their first victims was the next Kadamba ruler, Tribhuvanamalla, who was slain in a crushing defeat about 1236. The Yādavas then ruled the Kadamba country for ten years until its recovery by Tribhuvanamalla's son, Shashtadeva. After his victories over the Yādavas, Malik Kāfūr marched on Goa and destroyed it, the old city of Chandūr becoming the capital of Kāmadeva, who had succeeded his brother-in-law about 1260 and who ruled till 1310. The last blow to the Kadambas was the invasion of Muhammad ibn Tughluk in 1327, when Chandūr was destroyed. The sultans of Delhi did not again invade the Konkan, but a Muslim force finally sacked Chandūr and destroyed the last vestiges of Kadamba power. According to Ibn Battūta the Muslims attacked Chandūr by invitation of a rebel son of the Kadamba king, and after a long siege took the town. It never was regained by the Kadambas, who disappear from history.

At the beginning of the fourteenth century, when the Muslims were preparing to extend their conquests southwards, the Deccan and south India were divided into four kingdoms, two in the Deccan and two in the peninsula. The western half of the Deccan formed the territory of the Yādavas of Devagiri (Deogīr); to the south and east lay the Hoysala kingdom, with the Kākatiyas of Warangal to the north and to the south the Pāndyas, who had enlarged their territory at the expense of the Cholas, after the latter had been reduced by the Hoysalas. The Hoysalas lay therefore in a central position, and had to be on their guard against their neighbours in all directions. The relative geographical positions of these four powers and their divided interests formed the main reason for their taking no concerted steps against the Muslim invaders. The serious nature of the threat from the north was not at first realised, as the early Muslim invasions were little more than raiding expeditions with plunder as their chief object. Not until Malik Kāfūr was sent with definite orders to conquer southern India were the eyes of the Hindu rulers of the south opened to the danger that threatened them, but the danger of one kingdom evoked neither sympathy nor cooperation from the others. Deogīr fell, and Warangal became a base for further advance southwards. The Hoysala capital was the next to fall, and its ruler also became a Muslim feudatory. Finally a pretext was found for Muhammadan intervention in the far south. Vīra and Sundara, the two sons of Māravarman, disputed the Pāndyan succession, and the latter is said to have appealed for help to the Muslims, who invaded the Pāndyan territory, set Sundara on the throne, and collected vast booty. Malik Kāfūr then returned to Delhi, where he was detained by the troubles that broke out on the death of 'Alā-ud-dīn. South India then recovered so much of its independence that when Mubārak came to power he was obliged to reconquer it. In a vigorous campaign he extinguished the Yādava dynasty, made Deogīr a Muslim province, and constructed a series of forts in strategical positions on his southern frontier. While the Hoysala ruler, Vīra Ballāla, recognised his danger and made counter preparations, the Kākatiyas shared the fate of the Yādavas. Muhammad ibn Tughluk advanced southwards as far as Madura and Cannanore in 1328. But the Hoysala monarch, continuing his defensive preparations and moving his capital to a more suitable centre, prevented the Muslims from conquering Madura. The governor there declared himself independent. Vīra Ballāla gradually extended his territory southwards and himself seriously threatened Madura; but in a battle fought at Trichinopoly in 1342 he was taken prisoner and put to death, and, a few years later, his son and successor met a similar fate. The Hoysala monarch's work was, however, continued by competent officers. Prominent among these were three brothers. The eldest / Harihara, governed the southern Marātha country, with his headquarters at Bankapur, while Kampa held Nellore and Udayagiri, and Bukka Hampi and Dorasamudra. Their two younger brothers also held minor posts, while farther south was Bukka's able son Kampana, doorkeeper to the Hoysala king. These five brothers and their nephew were the founders of the kingdom of Vijayanagar, and the protagonists of a Hindu movement seeking to defend its threatened culture in the south. A learned Brāhman, Vidyaranya, is credited with sharing in their councils. The great stronghold of Vijayanagar was built by Vīra Ballāla III, soon after Muhammad ibn Tughluk's destruction of Kampli and the Muslim conquest of Dorasamudra. In the meanwhile the Bahmanīs had established their power in the Deccan, and were watching Delhi as anxiously as the Hindus. Harihara is last mentioned about the time that Bahman Shāh declared his independence. By the time of the latter's death, Bukka seems to have been the sole surviving representative of the five brothers, who had inherited the Hoysala traditions of hostility to Islam. When Fīrūz Shāh III announced that he would not attempt to bring the south again under the rule of Delhi, the Hindus of Vijayanagar and the Muhammadans of Gulbarga, freed from this anxiety, were able to undertake hostilities on their own account. As soon as Bukka had destroyed the kingdom of Madura, and was free from danger on the south, a pretext for a quarrel was soon found. Bahman Shāh prohibited the gold coins of Vijayanagar from circulating in his kingdom. Bukka resented this and was supported by the Hindu bankers of the Deccan, who melted down the coins of their Muslim sovereign. Repeated warnings were diregarded, till in 1360 all Hindu bankers and money-changers in Muslim territory were put to death and for the next forty years their descendants were not allowed to resume business. The king of Vijayanagar arrogantly protested against the Muslim claim to issue gold coin as an assertion of sovereignty, demanding that the Rāichūr Doāb should be surrendered to him, and threatening to join the sultan of Delhi in an attack on the Deccan. The Bahmanī sultan, Muhammad I, delayed his reply to this ultimatum until his preparations were complete. He then demanded why his vassal of Vijayanagar had not sent him gifts on his accession and required that they should be sent at once. A joint Hindu force from Warangal and Vijayanagar then took the field against him, but the Bahmanīs were victorious and, marching to Warangal, levied a great indemnity before returning to Gulbarga. Hostilities continued, and in 1362 on the complaint of some horse-dealers that on their way through Vināyak Deva's country they had been compelled to sell him their best horses, Muhammad raided Warangal, captured Vināyak Deva, and put him to a cruel death. In the course of his withdrawal, Muhammad was much harassed by the Hindus, losing a considerable number of men and all his baggage. In 1365 Muhammad, in a fit of drunken humour, demanded that a troupe of dancers, who had been entertaining him, should be paid from the Vijayanagar treasury. This order infuriated Bukka, who sent the messenger back with contumely, and, rapidly crossing the Tungabhadra at the head of an army, captured Mudgal and massacred the garrison. Muhammad swore revenge, and the vigour with which he began to put his threats into action so alarmed Bukka that he fled with his cavalry, leaving the rest of his numerous army to follow as best it could. The Muhammadans captured a vast quantity of booty, and slew 70,000 Hindus regardless of age, rank, or sex. After the rainy season they again took the field, and in 1367 a fierce battle was fought at Kauthal, the first great conflict between Hindus and Muslims in the Deccan. At first victory inclined to the Hindus, but when the Muslim reserves came up, with the king himself in command, the tide began to turn, and the superiority of the Muslim artillery with its European and Turkish gunners determined the issue. The Hindu forces fled, pursued by the victors, who gave no quarter. Bukka shut himself up in Vijayanagar which was besieged by the

Muslims without success, until, feigning a retreat, they tempted
out the defenders, who were taken by surprise and routed. Bukka
fled back to his stronghold, and Muhammad began a general
massacre, which continued until Bukka sued for peace. This was
granted only when Bukka consented to honour Muhammad's
draft on his treasury. More than 400,000 Hindus had been slain,
and it was agreed that in future non-combatants should be spared.

In 1377 Mujāhid succeeded to the Bahmanī throne and demanded the cession of large tracts of lands from Bukka, whose
refusal was reinforced by a counter-claim. Mujāhid thereupon
took the field against Bukka, who evaded battle for six months
and finally shut himself in his capital. After some minor successes
the invaders withdrew, taking with them a large number of
prisoners. They then besieged Adoni for some months without
success, after which peace was made, the Muslims returned home,
and for the next twenty years the two kingdoms refrained from
war. In 1379 Bukka was succeeded by Harihara II, who, taking
advantage of local risings against the Muslims which were then
engaging the shah's attention, invaded Bahmanī territory in 1398
at the head of an enormous army. With the comparatively small
force left at his disposal to meet this new threat, Fīrūz Shāh advanced to the Krishnā, on the other bank of which the Hindu army,
numbering over 900,000, was encamped. In view of the overwhelming odds, direct attack was hopeless, but a certain Surāj-ud-
dīn, who occupied a minor judicial post in the Bahmanī service,
obtained Fīrūz's sanction of a bold stratagem which proved entirely
successful. Surāj-ud-dīn, who was an expert conjurer, crossed the
river with a small company of players and gave exhibitions of
skill in the Hindu camp. The performers' fame quickly spread,
and they were invited to the tent of Harihara's son. After displaying their more peaceful arts, they proceeded to give a
marvellous demonstration of sword-play, in the course of which
they fell suddenly upon the prince and his retinue, slew them and
their guards, and escaped in the darkness. The Hindu camp was
thrown into great disorder, confusion turning to panic as rumours
grew and spread. In the meanwhile the passage of the Muslim
army across the river was covered by a small force which had been
sent over in readiness for this purpose. The panic-stricken Hindus
could offer no ordered resistance, and Harihara fled, leaving his
army to its fate. The Bahmanīs chased the fugitives into Vijaya-

nagar, where peace was made—on payment of a large indemnity to ransom the prisoners taken in the campaign, and Fīrūz Shāh withdrew in triumph.

Harihara died in 1406 and was succeeded by his son, Bukka II, who very soon broke the peace with the Bahmanīs. Hearing of the beauty of a goldsmith's daughter of Mudgal, he sent to her parents to demand her, but the girl herself declined the honour, and when Bukka, at the head of a small force, crossed the Tunga-bhadrā to seize her, she fled. The Hindus then pillaged the country, until they were defeated and expelled by the governor of the province. At the end of the year Fīrūz headed an expedition to avenge this insult, but could effect nothing against the defences of Vijayanagar. He therefore withdrew, but took up a strong posi-tion at some distance from the capital, where he defied Bukka's efforts to dislodge him. In the meanwhile the shah's brother, Ahmad Khān, was plundering the country, seizing vast quantities of treasure and taking numerous prisoners. Peace was at last secured only when Bukka appealed for it in person, and agreed to accept humiliating terms. In addition to satisfying exorbitant demands for money, jewels, elephants and slaves, he was forced to give a daughter in marriage to Fīrūz, whose son then married the goldsmith's beautiful daughter. Bukka died in 1408, and was succeeded by his brother, whose son, Vīra Vijaya, followed him after a short reign of five years. Some initial successes won by the latter over the old and enfeebled Fīrūz were vigorously avenged by the new Muslim ruler, Ahmad Shāh. Vīra Vijaya defended the south bank of the Tungabhadrā with a huge but unwieldy army until Ahmad assumed the offensive. He sent a force across by night which, while preparing to attack the Hindu army in the rear, actually captured Vīra Vijaya himself, who, though he es-caped, was too late to rally his men, and they were quickly scattered by the main Muslim force, which had already crossed the river. Ahmad then marched his army through the country, plundering and slaughtering in revenge for the Hindu atrocities of the earlier part of the campaign. Everything possible was done to wound the religious and natural feelings of the Hindus, until at length Vīra Vijaya sued for peace, which was again purchased at a heavy price. On Vīra Vijaya's death, Devarāya II, his successor, re-organised the Vijayanagar army. Like the Bahmanīs, he recog-nised the value of Turkish mounted archers, and enlisted 2000 of them, giving them a mosque, and taking every precaution against offending their religious scruples. In due time the force of 60,000 men trained by these mercenaries made its influence felt. When Devarāya II died in 1449, he left a powerful army and a kingdom with an excellent administrative system, and his successor, Mallikarjuna, who ruled till about 1468, was able to repel the Muslim attacks. In circumstances which are not quite clear, Mallikarjuna was succeeded by his brother, Virupāksha, who put to death all possible claimants to the throne, and proceeded to rule both incompetently and cruelly, until Sāluva Narasimha, the viceroy of the eastern provinces, intervened, deposed the king, and himself ruled for six years, during which he restored order in the provinces that had seceded from Virupāksha. Sāluva Narasimha was succeeded by his two sons, one after the other, the second being deposed by Vīra Narasimha, a son of that Narasa who had been Sāluva Narasimha's trusted general and adviser. On Vīra Narasimha's death in 1509 his minister secured the throne for the king's youngest brother, Krishnadevarāya, destined to be Vijayanagar's greatest ruler. By the beginning of the sixteenth century the Bahmanīs had given place to the five Muslim kingdoms of Bījāpur, Ahmadnagar, Bīdar, Berar, and Golconda, while the Portuguese, who had by that time established themselves at Goa, introduced a new element into south Indian politics. Krishna employed the early years of his reign in consolidating his northern and western frontiers. He then turned to the east, where the kings of Orissa still held sway as far south as Udayagiri, which he took in 1513. In the following year he resumed his campaign and reduced other strongholds of the king of Orissa, the most important being that of Kondavīr. After these and other victories of the Vijayanagar arms, peace was made, and Orissa ceded all the land south of the Krishnā. On his return home from his campaigns, Krishnadevarāya devoted himself to restoring the buildings that had been damaged or destroyed in the Muslim invasions. His next warlike act was the seizure of the Rāichūr Doāb, long coveted by his predecessors, and he was able to resist the efforts of the 'Ādil Shāhīs to recover it. His later years were troubled by illness, as well as by the rebellions of his relatives and trusted officials. Achyutarāya succeeded him in 1530, and was obliged, immediately after his accession, to take the field against Sellappa, a rebel governor who had taken refuge with the king of Travancore.

After thus successfully inaugurating his reign, Achyuta returned home and gave himself up to a life of leisure, allowing the real power to pass into the hands of his brothers-in-law, the Tirumalas. But their exercise of the royal authority was resented by three brothers, one of whom was connected by marriage with Krishnadevaraya, and they took up arms against the usurpers. At first the latter were successful, but later were forced to seek the assistance of Ibrāhīm 'Ādil of Bījāpur and in the end the three brothers triumphed. In the meanwhile Achyuta had died and been succeeded by his son, Venkataraya, who was killed by one of the Tirumalas. In 1542 the three brothers placed on the throne Sadāsivarāya, one of whose first acts was to invade Bījāpur in concert with the rulers of Golconda, Ahmadnagar and Bīdar. Ibrāhīm, however, withstood this assault and won over the ruler of Bīdar, 'Alī Barīd, from his unnatural alliance. In 1547 a new alliance between Burhān Shāh of Ahmadnagar and Sadāsivarāya led to a number of victories over Bījāpur, the most notable being the capture of the stronghold of Sholapur, which was retained by Burhān Nizām Shāh. On the death of Ibrāhīm 'Ādil Shāh in 1558, his successor, 'Alī 'Ādil Shāh, formed a confederation against his powerful rival, Ahmadnagar. Having won over Sadāsivarāya to his side, and secured the help of Ibrāhīm Kutb Shāh of Golconda, he felt strong enough to demand the return of Sholapur, and when this was refused, the allied armies invaded Ahmadnagar, where the Hindus were guilty of great excesses against the Muslim inhabitants. Although deserted by their Golconda ally, and harassed by a Berar army under Jahāngīr Khān, the invaders were victorious, and dictated humiliating terms to Husain. In these events Sadāsiva had taken the lead, and began to treat his ally, 'Alī 'Ādil Shāh, as a vassal. Husain at once began to plan his revenge, and with Ibrāhīm Kutb Shāh laid siege to Kalyāni in 1561. On the approach of 'Alī and Sadāsivarāya to the relief of the town, they turned to meet them. But Husain lost most of his artillery in country made impassable by floods, while his ally fled at the first attack. He was therefore forced to retire, leaving his camp and artillery in the hands of the Vijayanagar army. The victory of the Hindus was marked by further atrocities against Muslim noncombatants, from which their Muslim ally was unable to restrain them. Sadāsivarāya proceeded to lay siege to Ahmadnagar, but, having lost a large part of his army in a sudden flood, was forced to return home, whence he sent demands for the cession of territory by friend and foe alike. It soon became apparent that, unless he were checked, he would become paramount in south India. The differences between the Muslim rulers were therefore composed; an alliance was formed by the kings of Ahmadnagar, Bījāpur, Golconda and Bīdar; and, at the end of 1564, the combined forces met at Sholapur, which had been handed back by Husain to 'Alī as his daughter's dowry. From Sholapur the allies advanced to Talikota, on a tributary of the Krishnā. The Hindus in the meanwhile had not been idle, and, while a large force guarded the fords of the Krishnā, Sadāsiva, with the main army of nearly a million, took up his position a few miles to the south. The Muslims, finding the fords guarded, marched for three days up stream, the Hindus following on the opposite side. They then turned suddenly, and, covering in one day the whole distance, crossed by the unguarded fords. A fierce encounter took place on January 5, 1565. On the Hindu side, the king of Vijayanagar commanded the centre, with his brothers on right and left, while Husain, with the artillery, commanded the Muslim centre. The first charge of the Hindu cavalry almost won the day, but Husain was able to hold his ground until his army had recovered from the shock, and the Muslim artillery quickly wrought havoc in the close ranks of the Hindus. A cavalry charge increased the confusion, and Sadāsiva, who had refused a horse and directed the battle from a throne, sought to escape in a litter. He was captured, by accident rather than design, and was immediately executed by Husain Shāh. The loss of their leader ended the resistance of the Hindus. Besides taking vast quantities of plunder, the victorious Muslims, aided, no doubt, by Muslim mercenaries in the garrison who had been disgusted by Sadāsiva's atrocities against their coreligionists, captured Vijayanagar, till then believed to be impregnable. The battle of Talikota marked the end of Hindu dominion in south India, which a year or two earlier had seemed to be passing, state by state, under Vijayanagar control. A comparatively small, but well-trained and disciplined force had triumphed over a huge, but unwieldy and ill-trained army. One of Sadāsiva's brothers became a vassal of Bījāpur, while the other continued to hold a portion of the country in the south; but Krishnadevarāya's great Hindu kingdom had become only a memory.

CHAPTER X

South India

The southern extremity of the Indian peninsula has always had a history and character of its own. This is the Tamil country, *Tamilakam*, the northern boundary of which is roughly a line drawn from Mahé in the west to Venkata, about a hundred miles north of Madras, in the east. Tamil was originally the language of the whole area, Malayalam, the language of the Malabar coast, having branched off from it in the historical period. The name *Tamilakam* was known to Ptolemy in the readily recognisable form of *Damirike*. Tamil is really the same word as Dravidian (*Dravida*), but it has come to have a more limited application.

Early references to the extreme south are rare in the Sanskrit literature of northern India. There is no mention of it in Pānini, but his commentator, Kātyāyana, who lived in the fourth century A.D., knew of the Cholas and Pāndyas. The epics show some knowledge of the place-names of the south, while the *Arthasāstra's* fuller acquaintance with southern products has provoked the suggestion that it is the work of a southern author; but this fact should rather be regarded as evidence of a late date. Although dynasties like the Pāndyas later claimed descent from the Pāndus and other epic heroes, it is quite clear from the early Tamil literature that the Tamils were not Āryans, and that between the two there existed a great breach and a hereditary enmity similar to that between the Āryans and Dasyus in the north.

South India was traditionally divided into three kingdoms, Chola, Pāndya and Chera (or Kerāla). In the interior were also a number of tribes or petty principalities, none of whose chiefs ever attained recognition as a "crowned king". Tamil literature depicts the early rulers of southern India as continually engaged in war, a state of affairs equally true of the historical period. The kingdoms of the south were extremely wealthy. Their land grew spices, especially pepper, much sought after in the western world; their elephants gave ivory, also highly prized; the sea yielded pearls, and their mines precious stones. They manufactured muslins and silks. From early times they traded with Egypt and

Arabia on the one side, and with the Malay archipelago and thence with China on the other. Their seaports were great commercial centres, sending forth the valuable products of their own lands in return for those of foreign regions. This trade was ancient. It was ultimately, if not directly, from south India that the ships of Tarshish brought to Solomon ivory, apes and peacocks. The Hebrew word for "peacock" is clearly a Tamil loan-word, and the English "pea-" can be traced through Latin and Greek to the same Tamil source. Other Tamil words which early came into Greek with exports from the south were the words for rice, ginger, cinnamon, and other articles. A Greek play discovered on a papyrus in Egypt contains passages which have been identified as Tamil. The Greeks of Egypt under the Ptolemies of the last three centuries B.C. traded regularly with India, and, when Egypt became a Roman province, this commerce was still further developed. By Pliny's time men had discovered how to take advantage of the monsoons and use the shortest sea-route, instead of hugging the coast as they had done in the earliest days of this trade. Pliny gives a brief account of the trade with India, and the author of the *Periplus* gives further details. The former laments the wealth of Roman gold poured into India in payment for luxuries, and this is corroborated by the extensive finds in southern India of Roman coins, both gold and silver, of the first two and a half centuries A.D. The Pāndyan king sent embassies to Augustus, and the fact that there were colonies of Roman merchants in the seaports of southern India suggests that their position was regulated by diplomatic agreements. An elaborate customs-system existed. Tamil sources corroborate the Roman writers. They tell us of wine, lamps and vases imported by the 'Yavanas' and gold brought in exchange for pepper. Both Greeks and Romans are known to the southern literature as 'Yavanas', a word which must have come from the north through the Sanskrit. The Sanskrit *mlechcha*, 'barbarian', is also applied to them. There is no trace of any name which might have been used by these Greeks or Romans of themselves—but it could not have been Ionians'. Tamil poets describe the fine ships of the 'Yavanas', while Pliny tells us of the archers they carried as a protection against pirates. The discipline of the Roman veterans seems to have impressed the Tamil kings, for they employed bodyguards of Roman soldiers, whose habit of wearing long coats was as remarkable to the southern poets as the comparative nudity of the Tamils has been to strangers at all periods. These Romans are described as dumb because they could only communicate with their fellow-retainers by gestures, and they seem to have kept to themselves. The earliest copper coins of south India and Ceylon are copies of Roman coins of the Constantinian period, by which time, however, regular trade had ceased. It is just possible that they were issued in some of the Roman settlements which are believed to have existed.

The Romans are said to have had two cohorts stationed at Muziris (Cranganore) in the Chera country to protect their interests, and even to have built a temple of Augustus. The great Chola port of Kāverīpattanam (Puhār) also had a quarter for foreign merchants. How far it is true that southern Indian, and particularly Pallava, architecture shows Roman influence is a question still to be settled. Ptolemy's geographical knowledge of southern India is much more detailed and accurate than of the north. Classical sources, however, tell us nothing of political history; for that we are dependent on Tamil literature and inscriptions. The history of the south is the history of the three kingdoms, each of which had its day, with a period in which the intruding Pallavas were predominant.

The earliest reference to the Pāndyas and their territory is found in Megasthenes, who mentions the kingdom of *Pandaiē*, celebrated for its pearls. It was, he says, called after the daughter of the Indian Hercules, *i.e.* Siva, which is probably an echo of some myth connecting Pāndya with the Pāndus. In the inscriptions of Asoka the Pāndyas are mentioned among the southern neighbours of the Mauryas. Pliny refers to the *Pandae* who, he says, were ruled by women, a statement which no doubt owes its origin to inaccurate stories of the matriarchal institutions of southern India. The *Mahāvamsa* records a Pāndyan occupation of Ceylon from 43 to 29 B.C. The 'Pandion' who sent an embassy to Augustus must have been a Pāndyan king. The cotton and pearls of the Pāndya country are mentioned in the *Arthasāstra*.

It is not till the early centuries of the Christian era, with the rise of the literature of the Tamil academies (*sangam*), that we have any regular record of the Pāndya territory as forming an important kingdom in southern India, occupying the most southerly and the south-eastern part of the peninsula, roughly corresponding with the modern districts of Tinnevelly, Rāmnād and Madura, with its capital at Madura, the 'southern Mathura'.

The references to Pāndya rulers which occur in the *sangam* literature are quite incidental, and it is not possible to reconstruct from them any consecutive history. Mudukudumi Peruvaludi is mentioned as a celebrated conqueror, and there are references to a great battle at Talaiyālangānam, in which a young king named Nedunjeliyan finally triumphed over a confederation of adversaries who at first seemed likely to crush him. The *sangam* literature, however, tells more of the social life of the Pāndyas than of their political history. The country was wealthy and prosperous, and already completely under the influence of Brāhmanism. The Pāndya kings performed the Vedic sacrifices.

For the period from the fourth to the sixth century no records exist. Not till the eighth and ninth centuries do dated inscriptions set the chronology on certain ground. It is probable that during the earlier period Pāndya power suffered an eclipse, but a revival began in the seventh century under a king named Kadungon and his son, Māravarman. The latter's grandson, Arikesari Māravarman, a more authentic figure, destroyed the Paravas, and won a great victory over the Kerāla (Chera) king at the battle of Nelveli. He seems to have enlarged considerably the Pāndya kingdom. His son, Kochchadaiyan Ranadhīra, was also a great conqueror, and won numerous titles of honour on the battlefield. He carried the Pāndya arms as far as Mangalore in the west where he defeated the 'Mahāratha' probably the Western Chālukya Vikramāditya I. His son, Rājasimha I, consolidated his father's conquests in the west, and routed the Pallava king, Pallavamalla. Jatila Parāntaka, the son and successor of Rājasimha I, ascended the throne about 760. During his long reign of nearly fifty years, he continued his father's campaigns, winning particular successes in the north and west. The Kongu king was captured and thrown into prison, and his land passed definitely under Pāndya rule. A similar fate befel the king of Venād in the south. Parāntaka was one of the greatest of the earlier Pāndya kings, and his rule extended far beyond that of any of his predecessors. An equally successful reign is claimed for his son Srīmāra Srīvallabha, who took the title *Parachakrakotapala*, and who is said to have conquered Ceylon. His success in Ceylon is admitted by Singhalese sources, but it is difficult to reconcile with the Indian evidence their story of a great counter-offensive which ended in the death of the Pāndya king, the sack of his capital, and the placing of a Singhalese nominee on the throne. Srīmāra's victory over the Pallavas at Kudamūkku seems to be admitted by the Pallavas, but was later avenged by Nripatunga at Arichit. The next Pāndya king, Varagunavarman, reigned from A.D. 860 till about 880. At first he held his own with some success against the Pallavas and the rising power of the Cholas, but towards the end of his reign he suffered a severe reverse at the hands of Aparājita, son of Nripatunga. Passing over the brief reign of Varaguna's brother, we come to that of his nephew, Rājasimha II, which is well documented from Pāndya and Chola records. By this time the power of the Cholas constituted a serious threat to the older kingdom; Rājasimha II therefore looked around for allies, and, with the help of a force sent by the king of Ceylon, invaded the lands of the Chola king, Parāntaka. In a great battle fought at Velūr the invaders were completely routed. The Pāndya king escaped with his regalia to his ally in Ceylon, leaving his capital to be occupied by the Chola king. The Chola success was complete, and the half-hearted efforts of Rājasimha to restore his fortunes were of no avail. The Pāndya kingdom was thus deprived of its independence for some three centuries, from about A.D. 920 until the end of the twelfth century.

The Pāndya line, however, was not extinct, and the lot of the Chola governors was difficult. The weakening of Chola power in the middle of the tenth century after the great victory of the Rāshtrakūta, Krishna III, gave to Vīra Pāndya, a member of the old ruling family, an opportunity which he hastened to seize. He seems to have killed the Chola governor, but, when the Cholas had recovered from the shock inflicted on them in the north, he was overcome and executed. Rājarāja, the great Chola, seems to have found it necessary to reconquer the Pāndya country, but he finally established his power there, as is evident from the fact that he used it as a base for his invasion of Ceylon. His son, Rājendra, still had a firm hold on the conquered territory at the time of his invasion of Ceylon in 1017, but a year or two later he had to remove his rebellious Pāndya vassal, whom he replaced by his own son. The new viceroy was given the name or title 'Chola-Pāndya', and for some generations afterwards the country was ruled by a succession of Chola princes who bore this name. Pāndya princes of the old family still gave occasional trouble, and regularly received assistance from Ceylon. With the weakening of Chola power occasioned by the troubles following the accession of Kulottunga I, the Pāndyas again began to raise their heads. Towards the end of the eleventh century the records of local rulers became fuller. So completely had Chola suzerainty disappeared by the middle of the twelfth century that a civil war broke out in the Pāndya kingdom between two Pāndya princes, Kulasekhara and Parākrama. The latter held Madura, but the former appears to have had the better claim to represent the ancient line. Parākrama was offered the assistance of the king of Ceylon, but, before Singhalese reinforcements, under a general named Lankāpura, could arrive, Kulasekhara captured Madura and put his opponent to death. According to the *Mahāvamsa*, the Singhalese pursued the victorious Pāndya, and, after various successes, drove him out of the Pāndya lands and set Vīra Pāndya, a son of Parākrama, on the throne, and, in spite of Chola assistance, again defeated Kulasekhara. However, it is more probable that the Chola troops turned the scale, for Lankāpura retired to Ceylon and Kulasekhara was restored to the throne. The Cholas had occasionally to protect him and his successor, Vikrama, against Vīra Pāndya and his Singhalese allies, but, in 1182, this opposition was finally crushed, and Vikrama's rights to Madura and the throne were recognised. Kulottunga III assumed the title of *Pāndyari* after this victory. Though this was the last occasion on which Cholas actively interfered in Pāndyan affairs, Kulottunga remained the suzerain of Vikrama Pāndya for whom he had done so much.

With the accession of Jātavarman Kulasekhara, at the end of the eleventh century, and the rapid decline of Chola power after the death of Kulottunga III, the relationship rapidly changed and the Pāndyas recovered much of their former eminence. Unfortunately, in spite of the numerous records that we possess for this period, the lack of precise chronological and genealogical data makes it difficult to give a clear account of the period. The matter is further complicated by the existence of numerous Pānaya rulers who seem at times to have shared the powers of the king with whom they acted as co-regents. But a great revival of Pāndya power began with the next ruler, Māravarman Sūndara Pāndya, who ascended the throne in 1216. He extended his kingdom by conquering Chola territory in an expedition in the course of which he destroyed Tanjore and put to flight the Chola ruler, who was restored to his throne only when he and his heir had done homage to the Pāndyas—thus rapidly had the relative fortunes of the two kingdoms changed. A few years later the Chola, Rājarāja III, rebelled but was easily defeated. Nevertheless he was still permitted to continue on his throne. Perhaps this was due to the influence of the Hoysalas, who about this time began to interfere in the affairs of the south. The Hoysala, Narasimha II, styles himself "restorer of the Chola kingdom". It is therefore probable that the Chola owed his restoration and maintenance to the influence of his powerful neighbour on the north, who had no wish to see the Pāndyas incorporate the Chola kingdom. We have, however, no precise details of the negotiations.

Māravarman Sundara Pāndya was succeeded in 1238 by the second ruler of this name, who maintained Pāndya prestige in southern India in spite of the increasing aggressiveness of the Hoysalas. He was succeeded in 1251 by Jātavarman Sundara Pāndya, the greatest of the later Pāndya dynasty, who ruled over the whole of the peninsula. The Cholas had by then sunk into oblivion, and the Hoysalas, who had taken their place, were not strong enough to interfere in the south. Chera had become a Pāndya province, as also had Ceylon. Sundara Pāndya's rout of the Hoysalas and capture of their fortress of Kannanūr-Koppam was a serious check which they evidently tried to avenge, for a few years later the Pāndya records another victory over a Hoysala force at Perambalūr. He also defeated the Kākatiya ruler of Warangal, who had gone to the assistance of one of the southern princes. Thus Pāndya arms were successful in every direction, and Sundara was able to assume the title of a paramount sovereign, and style himself *mahārājādhirāja*. The records of his buildings and lavish endowments show that he had accumulated vast wealth. His reign lasted till about the end of the third quarter of the thirteenth century.

Records also survive of a contemporary Pāndya who assisted him in his campaigns. This was Jātavarman Vīra Pāndya, who took part in the conquest of the Kongu and Chola country, and played a specially prominent part in the occupation of Ceylon. Another late contemporary of Sundara, Māravarman Kulasekhara, became his successor. The existence of this system of co-rulers accounts for references to the "five kings of Ma'bar", and similar stories of foreign travellers, who seem to have supposed that these kings ruled in complete independence of one another. Māravarman appears to have fought with success in Travancore, and to have led an expedition to Ceylon, whence he carried off the sacred tooth, which was only restored when Parākrama Bāhu visited the Pāndya court as a humble suppliant. To this period belong the accounts of southern India written by Wassāf, the Muslim historian, and Marco Polo. Like all foreigners who visited the region, they emphasise the wealth of the country, and in particular its rich stores of pearls and precious stones. According to Wassāf, Māravarman Kulasekhara was murdered by his legitimate son, Jātavarman Sundara Pāndya, because his illegitimate half-brother, Vīra Pāndya, had been designated to succeed to the throne, and civil war resulted. Chronological and other difficulties stand in the way of accepting the story of the parricide, but there is evidence that civil war did break out between the rival claimants to the throne, and that Sundara, being defeated, took refuge with the Muslims shortly before Malik Kāfūr's raid on southern India. It has been suggested that Sundara Pāndya sought help at the Muslim court against his brother, and that this was the cause of Malik Kāfūr's expedition to Madura. There seems, however, to be no authority for this view. Malik Kāfūr's expedition was the natural extension of his previous campaigns, and there is no evidence to prove that he made any distinction between the brothers. The Muslim raid further contributed to disorganise a country already suffering from civil war. Some years after the first Muslim sack of Madura, the sultan of Delhi sent another force under Khusraw Khān in search of further loot. In the meanwhile the ruler of southern Travancore, Ravivarman Kulasekhara, of the old Chera dynasty, who had not been affected by the Muslim advance, sought to turn the plight of his neighbours to his own aggrandisement. In 1315 he defeated Vīra Pāndya and his brother, and made the Pāndyas and the remnant of the Cholas his subjects, though a little later he seems to have been forced to cede some of the conquered territory to the Kākatiyas of Warangal. This last blow hastened the disintegration of the Pāndya dynasty, which then ceased to be a power in the south. The Muhammadan occupation of Madura and the independent sultanate established there in the fourteenth century, surrounded by Hindu foes on all sides, did not last long. It was to the new kingdom of Vijayanagar that the hegemony of southern India passed when the Muslims had been disposed of. The Pāndyas never again recovered their ancient capital of Madura, though minor rulers of the ancient line can be traced in the south in Tinnevelly down to the eighteenth century, more than two thousand years after their first recorded appearance.

The Cholas, like the Pāndyas, are mentioned as ruling in southern India as early as the period of the Asoka inscriptions. Their kingdom (Cholamandalam, *i.e.*, Coromandel) lay to the north-east of that of the Pāndyas, between the Pennār and Velūr rivers. For the earlier history of the dynasty we are again dependent on the *sangam* literature, which preserves only a few anecdotes of early, more or less mythical, kings, usually illustrating their strong sense of justice, such as that of the king who committed suicide because his pet parrot met its death through his negligence. The same story is told at a later date of a Kadamba king, Jayakesin I. The *Mahāvamsa* records the conquest of Ceylon in the middle of the second century B.C. by a Chola named Elāra who ruled it for nearly half a century. The historical period begins only in the middle of the second century A.D., with the reign of Karikāla. Ascending the throne while still a youth, he succeeded his grandfather, who had been killed in battle with the Chera king. The young ruler's first exploit was the rout of a combined force of Cheras and Pāndyas, who were endeavouring to follow up their earlier success and make an end of the Chola kingdom. When peace was made, however, he gave his daughter in marriage to the son of the Chera king. He also raided Ceylon, whence he carried off 12,000 men as slaves to labour at the great irrigation works he began on the Kāveri. His wealth was fabulous and he built the great new capital of Kāverīpattanam on the coast, abandoning Uraiyūr, the ancient residence of his family. The Chola power was certainly greatly extended and consolidated during his reign, though his poets no doubt exaggerate when they say that he carried his standards to the Himālaya. Karikāla's successor was his grandson, Nedumudi-killi, under whom the Chola power rapidly declined. The new capital was overwhelmed by the sea and utterly destroyed; the Cheras and Pāndyas gained ground at the expense of the Cholas, while the attacks of the Pallavas in the north further contributed to reduce the Cholas to insignificance.

Thereafter for some centuries, the Cholas played only a minor part in history, although occasional references show that the dynasty was not extinct. But, after the decline of the Pallavas in the eighth century, they rose once more to power. About the middle of the ninth century, Vijālaya, a member of the old ruling family, took advantage of the troubled state of southern India, and of the war between the Pallavas and Pāndyas in particular, to secure for himself a firm position and regain much of the old Chola territory including Tanjore, which he made his capital. His son, Āditya, who came to the throne about A.D. 880, continued his father's successful policy, and, by his defeat of Aparājita, dealt the final blow to Pallava supremacy. Parāntaka I, Āditya's son, having succeeded in the first decade of the tenth century to a considerable kingdom, turned his attention to the south where, after a successful campaign in Pāndya territory, he sacked its capital, Madura, thus winning the honorific title of 'Maduraikonda', and drove its king, Rājasimha, into exile in Ceylon. An attempt by the latter to restore his fortunes with the aid of a considerable Singhalese force ended in complete disaster, and the Pāndya kingdom, including much that had once been Chola territory, passed to Parāntaka. Towards the end of his prosperous reign of some forty years began the Rāshtrakūta attacks, in one of which his heir, Rājāditya, was killed. The brief reigns of the five rulers who followed were marked by desperate efforts of the Rāshtrakūtas to curb the rising power of the Cholas. On one occasion Kānchī (Conjeeveram) was occupied and Tanjore besieged. To Parāntaka's reign belong the famous group of inscriptions from Uttaramerur which throw so much light on the organisation of communities in the Tamil country. When the great Chola king, Rājarāja, came to the throne in A.D. 985, the menace from the north had been removed through the overthrow of the Rāshtrakūtas by the Chālukyas. The golden age of the Chola dynasty then began. During the first ten years of his reign, Rājarāja consolidated his hold on the old Pāndya kingdom in the south and added the Chera territory in the west to his dominions. He had already won fame in his youth by a naval exploit in which he destroyed the Chera fleet off the Malabar coast. Having also brought under his sway the Bānas, his immediate neighbours on the north, he carried his campaign of conquest into Kalinga (Orissa), and to the south as far as Travancore. At the beginning of the eleventh century, therefore, the Cholas ruled the whole of southern India, and Rājarāja was then able to add Ceylon to his already extensive dominions. The last years of his reign were spent in fighting the. Chālukyas, who then held the position in the southern Deccan formerly occupied by the Pallavas. In the twentieth year of his reign (1012) Rājarāja built the great Rāja-rājesvāra temple at Tanjore, on which the record of his achievements can still be read, and endowed it with treasure taken by him in his campaigns.

In 1012 Rājarāja was succeeded by his son, Rājendra Utta-machola, a man in every way worthy of the throne. He had already distinguished himself as a warrior in his father's campaigns, and as a ruler he displayed great administrative talent. It is not always possible to decide from the inscriptions which of his conquests belong to the period of his father's reign and which to his own. He ravaged the country round Dharwar with an enormous army, but does not seem to have effected any permanent conquest. A similar raid some years later ended in a victory for the Chālukya king, Satyāsraya, who seems on this occasion to have been better prepared to meet the invader.

From an expedition to Ceylon he brought back the heirlooms of the royal treasury, and kept the Singhalese king a prisoner for life in the Chola capital. He also added to his treasury the crown of the Chera kings, reputed to have belonged to Parasurāma. In the north Rājendra was equally successful. After defeating the Chālukya king, Jayasimha III, in 1020, he continued his advance northwards, leaving as he went records of victories in Orissa and Kosala, reached Bengal, where he put to flight Govindachandra and Mahīpāla, and came at last to the banks of the Ganges. In memory of this exploit he took the title of 'Gangaikonda'. He sent a naval expedition across the Bay of Bengal, which occupied Kādara (variously identified with the capital of Pegu, and with Kedah, and other places in the Malay peninsula), and returned with considerable booty. His campaigns, however, were not permitted to distract his attention from home affairs. He built a new capital, Cholapuram, with a remarkable irrigation system and handsome palaces and temples, whose deserted ruins still convey an idea of its former grandeur. Rājendra ruled till 1042, but the inscriptions of his son, Rājādhirāja, are dated from 1018 when, in accordance with Chola custom, he was first associated with his father as joint ruler. His period of sole rule was filled with fighting neighbouring princes, who strove to avenge the humiliation they had suffered at the hands of Rājendra. After overcoming his rebel vassals in the Pāndya and Chera country, Rājādhirāja curbed Chālukya aggression, and then invaded Ceylon where he defeated and slew four kings. At the end of these campaigns he performed the horse-sacrifice, and assumed the well-merited title of 'Jayamkondachola'. War with the Chālukyas soon broke out again, and in the great battle of Koppam, on the Tungabhadrā river, the Chola king was slain in 1052. His brother, Rājendra, however, took command and saved the day for the southern power. Chola and Chālukya records flatly contradict one another as to subsequent events, so that it is probable that their relative positions, if changed at all, were changed but slightly in favour of the Cholas. Bilhana says that the Chālukyas occupied Kānchī, the Chola capital; while Chola records say that Rājendra advanced as far as Kolhapur, where he erected a column to commemorate his victory. Under the new king, Rājendra, a great famine is recorded in 1055. The chief military exploit of this reign was an expedition to Ceylon in 1054, in the course of which the Singhalese were routed and their king, Vijayabāhu, driven to take refuge in a mountain-fortress. The distribution of Rājendra's inscriptions shows that the Chola empire suffered no loss of territory in his reign. He died in 1063, and was succeeded by his brother, Vīra Rājendra. The new ruler was at once involved in a war with the Western Chālukya king, Somesvara I, whose forces had crossed the Tungabhadrā and invaded Chola territory. They were driven back and pursued by the Cholas, who won a great victory in a pitched battle at Kūdal-sangaman. A few years later the Chālukya king challenged the victor to meet him again at the same place. The Chola accepted and for a month waited in vain at the rendezvous for the Chālukya to appear. The latter died soon afterwards and was succeeded by his elder son, Somesvara II, while the second son, Vikramāditya, fled to the Chola court where he was well received by the king, who himself records that he recognised him as king of the Western Chalukyas. It was presumably then arranged between them that Vikramāditya VI, who had married a daughter of Rājendra, should receive Chola support to dethrone Somesvara. Meanwhile the Singhalese king, Vijayabāhu, took advantage of the Chola engagements in the north to organise a rebellion, by which the Chola garrison was driven out of Ceylon. On the death of Vīra Rājendra in 1070 the succession was disputed and the heir, Ādhirājendra, only succeeded to the throne by the help of his brother-in-law, the Western Chālukya, Vikramāditya VI. Ādhirājendra's reign was brief, and with his murder in 1074 the direct Chola line seems to have become extinct.

The Eastern Chālukya, Rājendra II, viceroy of Vengī, was a grandson through his mother of the Chola, Rājendra Gangaikonda; indeed he was three-quarters Chola by blood, for his grandmother also had been a Chola princess. Whether he seized or succeeded to the Chola throne is uncertain; he may have been brought up as a Chola prince, while his uncle, Vijayāditya, was allowed to succeed at Vengī as viceroy of the Western family. In any case Rājendra disposed of the latter, and united the Eastern Chālukya and Chola kingdoms under one rule, assuming soon afterwards the name Kulottunga Chola, by which he is best known. But before he could be crowned, he had to repel an attempt by the Western Chālukya prince, Vikramāditya VI, to avenge his Chola brother-in-law with the ostensible help of Somesvara II. By a secret arrangement, however, with Rājendra, Somesvara, who had his own reasons for wanting to rid himself of his ambitious younger brother, had ordered his own troops to turn on those of Vikramāditya in the course of the battle. Vikramāditya was thus caught between two fires, but escaped unhurt, and later took his brother prisoner and seized the Western Chālukyan throne in 1076. This is Bilhana's story, his 'Rajiga' being Rājendra. Kulottunga claims his indecisive action with Vikramāditya as a victory for the Chola arms. The new king took up his residence in the Chola capital, while one of his sons acted as governor of the old Chālukya province of Vengī. In addition to victories nearer home, Kulottunga's inscriptions record an expedition into Kalinga about the end of the eleventh century, and a more successful one in 1111 led by the general, Karunākara Tondamān. Kulottunga's reign of forty-nine years came to an end in 1112, when he was succeeded by his son, Vikrama Chola, viceroy of Vengī. To Kulottunga's reign belongs the great and elaborate (though not the first) survey of the country for taxation purposes, a kind of Domesday Book. The numerous inscriptions of the period throw a great deal of light on the highly organised systems of administration and taxation in force under the Cholas. The later years of this reign were marked by the rise of the Hoysalas in southern and western Mysore. Nominally governing for the Western Chālukyas, on the death of the aged Vikramāditya VI, the Hoysala, Vishnuvardhana, asserted the independence for which he had long been preparing, and the Hoysala power rapidly expanded with the decline of that of the Chālukyas and Cholas. Vikrama Chola seems to have lost the province of Vengī as soon as he left it to assume the crown in the capital, but on the other hand the Chola ancestral dominions suffered no diminution during his reign of fifteen years. He died in 1133, the year in which the Hoysala, Vishnuvardhana, who had been gradually increasing his power at the expense of the Chālukyas, claims to have "shaken the pride of the Cholas". Kulottunga II, who succeeded Vikrama, is best known as a patron of literature. His successor in 1146 was Rājarāja II, whose reign of fifteen years left Chola power on the verge of collapse. The Hoysalas had become independent and powerful, and in the south the Chola hold was sufficiently relaxed for two claimants to the ancient Pāndya throne to engage in civil war. The Singhalese strongly supported one claimant, Parākrama, and when he was murdered by his rival, they put his son, Vīra Pāndya, on the throne. The Chola, Rājādhirāja II, son of Rājarāja II, then intervened on behalf of the other pretender, Kulasekhara, drove out the Singhalese, and installed his protégé. A generation later a Chola king, Kulottunga II, again intervened successfully in a civil war in the Pāndya kingdom. When this Chola king ceased to reign in 1216 and was succeeded by Rājarāja III, the Pāndyas were once more powerful and were steadily encroaching on Chola territory. In the course of one campaign Tanjore was destroyed and the Chola was forced to become a vassal of the Pāndya king. The representative of the once great Chola empire had finally to call for the assistance of the Hoysala, Narasimha II, in order to regain his independence. On all sides the vassals of the Cholas were beginning to cast off their allegiance. Among them was Ko-Perunjinga, a chief of Pallava descent, whose headquarters were at Sendamangalam in the modern South Arcot district. He had tried to make himself independent while the Chola king was involved with the Pāndya invasion, but had been suppressed by the strong hand of Narasimha II. Ten years later, however, in 1232, he captured and imprisoned the Chola king. But a strong Hoysala force sent to secure his release outmanœuvred Perunjinga and forced him to surrender his prisoner, who was restored to his throne and occupied it for some ten years in comparative peace. In 1243, however, Perunjinga's son, who bore the same name as his father, rebelled and assumed the royal titles. At the same time the Kākatiyas were advancing from the north to share with the Hoysalas in the partition of the Chola empire, while in the south the Pāndyas were vigorously striving to regain at the expense of the Cholas their old position. Rājarāja III, who survived till about 1252, was obliged from 1246 to share his diminished kingdom with a rival, Rājendra III, who maintained his authority in Tanjore till 1267, when Chola rule came to an end.

The third of the traditional divisions of the Tamil country was Kerāla or Chera, the king of which, the Keralaputra, is mentioned in the Asoka inscriptions and three hundred years later by Pliny and the *Periplus*. The Chera country lay to the west and north of that of the Pāndyas, and comprised the narrow strip of land between the mountains and the sea, the southern half of it being the modern state of Travancore. Of its political history, for which we are mainly dependent on incidental references in early Tamil literature and the inscriptions of the Cholas and Pāndyas, we know little compared with its two more important neighbours in the east. The great days of the Chera country seem to have been the early centuries of the Christian era, when it ranked with the two other southern kingdoms of the period. With the cessation of trade between its ports and the west, its wealth, and consequently its power, declined. Its documented history begins in the middle of the second century A.D., with the great battle fought between Cheras and Cholas, in which the father of Karikāla was slain and the Chera king, Ādan I, also lost his life. But for a time at least peace must have reigned between the two kingdoms, for Ādan II later on became the son-in-law of Karikāla. The Chera king next allied himself with the Pāndya, Nedunjeliyan, against the powerful Chola. At the battle of Vennil the latter was victorious over the allies, and the Chera king committed suicide from shame, so tradition has it, at having been wounded in the back. In the troubles that broke out after the death of Karikāla, Ādan II's successor Senguttuvan, the 'Red Chera', came to the rescue of the hard pressed heir, Nedumudi-killi, routing his rivals and establishing his cousin securely on the throne. Chera poets claim many successes for this new king, and there is probably a substratum of fact in their exaggerated account of his expedition to the north, in the course of which, they assert, he crossed the Ganges. He was succeeded early in the second century by the equally warlike Sey, called Yānaikkan, who fought with the Cholas and Pāndyas. In a battle with the latter he was taken prisoner, but succeeded in escaping and regaining his power. This is the last recorded event in the history of the Chera country till the beginning of the eighth century, when the Pallava Paramesvara Potavarman claims to have twice defeated the Chera king. In A.D. 783 the Pāndya, Jatila Parākrama, records his conquest of Venād, the southern part of the Chera country (Travancore), then, apparently, a separate kingdom, and the destruction of the fortress of Vilinam. Within the next ten years, however, the Chera king succeeded in regaining his lost territory, and a document exists, signed at the beginning of the tenth century by the Chera king, Sthanu-Ravi, and the Chola, Āditya, with whom he was evidently on good terms. It was to the Chera country that the Pāndya, Rājasimha, fled before Parāntaka I about 918. We know that Parāntaka married a Chera princess, and it is probable that this was part of a treaty by which the Chola secured Chera support, or at least neutrality, for his southern campaigns. Later in his reign the Chera king seems to have recognised the Chola as his overlord, and Parāntaka II also married a Chera princess. About this time the Chera king, Bhāskara Ravivarman, granted a charter to the Jewish colony at Cranganore (Muziris). This colony was certainly of great antiquity and claimed to have come to south India after the Roman conquest of Palestine in the first century A.D. Towards the end of the century harmonious relations with the Cholas ceased, for one of the earliest exploits of Rājarāja I was the destruction of the Chera fleet, and before he had been long on the throne he had conquered the "lords of the Chera country". A similar claim is made by his grandson, Rājādhirāja, in his famous Manimangalam inscription, and it is evident from occasional references that the Cholas held at least the southern Chera country until the beginning of their decline in the twelfth century, when, in the second quarter of the century, a king named Vīrakerāla again established its independence. His successor was Vīra-Ravivarman, who acknowledged the suzerainty of the growing Pāndya power. Towards the end of the century the Chera king joined Vīra Pāndya against Kulottunga III and shared his defeat, but was restored to his throne. From the thirteenth century a few records survive of Chera kings in Travancore. The most important of these was Ravivarman Kulasekhara, who came to the throne in 1299. So skilfully did he turn to advantage the weakening of his neighbours by civil wars and Muslim raids, that in 1315 he claims to have conquered both the Chola and Pāndya kingdoms. But he was later driven out of Chola territory by the Kākatiya, Rudra II, and his successor, Mārttandavarman, seems to have ruled only in Travancore, where he was established in 1317. Little is known of the history of the Chera country between that date and the rise of the modern kingdom of Travancore.

The Pallava dynasty played a great part in the history of south India, where it was the dominant power from the fifth to the ninth century, during the period between the two Chola empires. At its greatest extent the Pallava empire included most of the Chola territory along the Coromandel coast on the east, and to the north portions of the old Āndhra-Sātavāhana empire, comprising the Telugu country round the lower Krishnā, and the lands to the south of it, with its capital at Kānchī (Kānchīpuram, i.e., Conjeeveram). The origin of the Pallavas was for long a matter of conjecture but that they were foreigners has now been established with as much certainty as is possible in the circumstances. Kānchī was, of course, one of the great cities of ancient India, and is mentioned by the grammarian, Patanjali, in the second century B.C. But there is no such early reference to the Pallavas, nor do they find a place among the traditional kingdoms of the Tamil country. They were a dynasty or family, and not a people.

A number of Pallava records survive, which fall into several groups. The earliest of these consists of a small series of copperplate grants of the third century A.D., written in Prākrit. Of the fifth and sixth centuries there remain a few inscriptions and a further series of grants written in Sanskrit. Of the seventh, eighth and ninth centuries we have a wealth of documents on copper and stone, also in Sanskrit, but usually accompanied by a Tamil version or summary. A fixed point in the early history of the Pallava dynasty is the mention of Vishnugopa of Kānchī in the Allāhābād inscription of Samudragupta. There is no reason to

doubt that the former was a Pallava, for the Pallavas held Kāñchī
at that time; and indeed Vishnugopa is mentioned in the genealogical lists of later inscriptions. He must have been reigning
about A.D. 350, and it is very probable that with his allies he was
powerful enough to check Samudragupta's advance to the south.

The Pallavas were a family of foreign origin, the name Pallava
or Palava being equivalent to Pahlava (Parthava) or Parthian.
There is some evidence that, as might be expected, families of
Persian origin had come from the north-west and west into the
Deccan in the early centuries of the Christian era and taken service there. By the time of the inscription of the Āndhra queen,
Balā Śrī, the Pahlavas had penetrated far enough south to come
into conflict with Gautamīputra. They were then probably vassals
or allies of the Western Kshatrapas. The Junāgarh inscription of
Rudradāman of the middle of the second century states that his
minister was a Pahlava named Suvisākha. It is not improbable
that nobles of Pahlava origin were in the service of the Āndhras.
Some, no doubt, came in the train of the daughter of Rudradāman,
who married the Āndhra king. In any case the etymological
identity of 'Pallava' and 'Pahlava' is obvious, and presents no
difficulty. That 'Pallava' should later have been given a popular
etymology and derived from a word meaning 'sprig', is natural
enough. The founder of the Pallava family must have been a local
governor of Pahlava origin, who, with the decline of Āndhra
power in the beginning of the third century A.D., made himself
independent in the Telugu country on the lower Krishnā. Whether
he directly succeeded the much reduced Āndhra-Sātavāhanas or
whether, as is more probable, he gained his territory at the expense of the Chutu-Sātakarnis or the Nāgas, who shared the old
Āndhra empire for a time, is not certain. The origin of the little-
known dynasty of the Salankāyanas may have been similar.

Of this early dynasty a few grants survive. From these, which
are, it should be noted, like the Āndhra inscriptions, in Prākrit,
we learn that the founder of the dynasty whose real name is not
given was known as Bappadeva and that he was succeeded by
Sivaskandavarman, Buddhyankura and Visvavarman. If we take
the fifth ruler to be Vishnugopa, whose dates must have been
about A.D. 325-50, and assume as a fair average that the reigns of
his four predecessors covered a century, then Bappadeva must
have reigned about A.D. 225-50, very likely dates for the rise of

a new power in this region. It is probable that Bappadeva's head-quarters were still at Amarāvatī, the old capital of the Telugu country. Who extended Pallava power to the south at the expense of the Cholas is uncertain, but it was probably the second ruler, Sivaskandavarman. He is said to have performed the horse-sacrifice, which indicates a career of conquest as does also the title 'Vijayaskandavarman', by which he was known. No inscriptions of Bappadeva survive, but we have one of his son as crown-prince, dated in the tenth year of Bappa's reign. A much later inscription tells us that the founder of the dynasty was Vīrakurcha, who married a daughter of the Nāga king, and became the father of Skandavarman or Skandasishya. It is thus very likely that Bappadeva's name was Vīrakurcha, and his marriage with a Nāga princess suggests victories won over the Nāga supplanters of the Āndhras; but of them, no more is known than of their neighbours, the Chutus.

The second group of Pallava inscriptions belongs to the fifth and sixth centuries. These, like the inscriptions of the Guptas, are written in Sanskrit. There is no reason to doubt that the kings whose names are thus preserved were the successors of those already mentioned. The records are mainly of a private nature, commemorating pious donations, and containing little to enable us to reconstruct the history of the period. It is not even possible with certainty to arrange the rulers in chronological order, nor do we know that all the members of the family named as bene-factors or mentioned in other connections, were independent rulers. Some, probably, were only princes. The names of some thirteen rulers are known between Skandavarman, who probably succeeded Vishnugopa about A.D. 350-75, and Simhavishnu, who reigned in the last quarter of the sixth century. With the latter the great period of Pallava history begins, and our material becomes more plentiful. That the Pallava power was considerable in the middle of the fourth century is evident from the fact that they came into contact with the Kadambas in the west and were able to exercise a nominal suzerainty over this rising power. There is some evidence that for a time the dynasty had two branches, one of which ruled the older Telugu province in the north and the other the Tamil province (Tondaimandalam), with its capital at Kānchī. What little is known of the history of this period is de-rived from the records of other dynasties. With the help of their feudatories, the Gangas, the Pallavas conquered the Bānas. In the middle of the fifth century a Pallava king, called in the Kadamba record Nanakkāsa, inflicted a disastrous defeat on the Kadamba king, Krishnavarman, and laid his country waste, so that his son, Sivānanda, retired from the world to become a hermit. Later on, however, the Pallavas restored to power Sivānanda's son, Vishnu-varman, and the Kadambas recovered rapidly, for fifty years later Ravivarman claimed to have "uprooted the lord of Kānchī", that is, to have won a victory over the Pallavas. There is evidence of a breach between the Pallavas and Gangas at the beginning of the sixth century, when Dūrvinīta recounts, among other exploits, the capture of the Pallava king.

The great period of Pallava history begins towards the end of the sixth century with the reign of Simhavishnu Potarāja, also called Avanisimha in allusion to his conquests. Records become more numerous, for the Pallavas of this epoch were great builders. They brought from their northern province and original home the art of hewing shrines out of rock and transforming caves into temples. They also built largely in stone, instead of wood which had till then been the building-material of the south. To the Pallavas and to the stimulus given by them, we owe the great series of temples, most of which still stand in southern India. Simhavishnu's successors speak of him as a great conqueror, who extended Pallava territory southward at the expense of the Cholas. The Pāndyas and even Ceylon are said to have felt the force of his arms. He was succeeded about A.D. 600 by his son, Mahendra-varman, the first great builder of the dynasty. His foundation in-scriptions show that he ruled a wide territory, most of which he must have inherited from his father, for no particular conquests are recorded of him. One of the most interesting memorials of his reign is found in the reliefs in Ādivarāha temple at Mahā-balipuram (built by his grandson), which represents both himself and two of his wives and his father, also with two of his wives. In his reign began the conflict with the Chālukyas, then very powerful under Pulakesin II, the vanquisher of Harsha. About A.D. 610 the Chālukya deprived Mahendravarman of the province of Vengī, over which he set his brother as viceroy. The Pallavas never regained this province, which later became the Eastern Chālukya kingdom. In his Aihole inscription Pulakesin claims to have driven the Pallava king to seek refuge behind the walls of

Kānchī, while Mahendra claims to have routed the Chālukyas at Pollilūr near Kānchī. It appears then that the Chālukyas advanced with success far into Pallava territory but were finally driven back again. In any case the growth of the Chālukyas forced the Pallavas to seek expansion southward. Mahendravarman was a patron of arts and letters and a musician. He wrote a comedy, the *Mattavilāsaprahasana*, which is of unexpected value for the history of the obscure sect of the Kāpālikas.

His successor was Narasimhavarman (A.D. 625–60), known as Mahamalla. Early in his reign he repelled a Chālukya invasion and inflicted defeat on Pulakesin in three successive battles. He followed up these victories by invading Chālukya territory, taking and sacking the capital, Bādāmi (Vātāpi), and returning to Kānchī with vast booty. In memory of this exploit he took the title Vātāpikonda. The general who led the victorious army was Paramjoti. Pulakesin may have been killed in this campaign, for the Chālukyas themselves record that their capital was without a ruler for thirteen years after its destruction by the Pallavas. Manavamma, a claimant to the throne of Ceylon, took refuge at the Pallava court and apparently distinguished himself there, for the Pallava king sent an expedition to Ceylon to put him on the throne. The Singhalese, however, were more than a match for him. A second and stronger force was then sent, which achieved its object. This success had a considerable moral effect on the kingdoms of south India and is compared in the inscriptions to Rāma's exploit.

Narasimha also was a great builder; the city of Mamallapuram (Mahamallapuram) which bears his name was founded by him, and the great rock-temples there are his work. It was in his reign that Hiuen Tsang visited Kānchī. He calls the country Dravida. The capital, he says, was still largely Buddhist, but various forms of Hinduism also flourished there. The Buddhist teacher, Dharmapāla, was a native of Kānchī. Asoka was credited with the building of *stupas* in the vicinity.

On his death Mahamalla left a great and prosperous country to his successor, Mahendravarman II, who seems to have had a short but peaceful reign (A.D. 660–70). The next ruler, Paramesvaravarman, was again involved in war with the Chālukyas, and both sides claim success. Vikramāditya I asserts that he conquered Kānchī but spared it; Paramesvara, on the other hand, took a

Chālukya town, as yet unidentified, which he calls Ranarasika. Vikramāditya was able at least to advance far south, but, in the vicinity of Trichinopoly, was met by a combined Pallava and Pāndya force and defeated in three battles. The last of these, Peruvalanallūr, ended most disastrously, for the Chālukya king had to flee "with only a rag to cover him". The Kurram plates give a vivid description of the battle, but unfortunately lack the details which a modern historian would like to have. The severe fighting of this reign was followed by a period of peace which enabled Narasimhavarman II (Rājasimha), who ruled in the last quarter of the century, to devote himself to building. His most notable temple is the Kailāsanātha in Conjeeveram. The next ruler, Paramesvaravarman, reigned only for a short time, probably A.D. 715–17, his successor being Nandivarman II Pallavamalla, a son of Hiranyavarman, who himself perhaps never reigned. The death of Paramesvaravarman seems to have been followed by civil war. There was at least one other claimant to the throne, Chitramaya, who was supported by the Pāndyas. The war lasted some time with alternating fortune until finally Nandivarman's general, Udayachandra, inflicted a severe defeat on the Pāndyas and slew the pretender with his own hand. Whether Chitramaya was a son of Paramesvaravarman or had in some way a better claim to the throne than Nandivarman, we do not know. It is probable that the direct line had become extinct and that there were several claimants. Nandivarman was descended from a younger son of Simhavishnu. His succession seems to have been popular, for it is recorded that he was chosen by his subjects. He must have been quite young at his accession for he reigned for sixty-five years. One notable event of his reign, recorded in Chālukya inscriptions, was a Chālukya invasion, in which Vikramāditya II soon after his accession (A.D. 733) occupied Kānchī, spared the city, and even generously gave to the Rājesvara temple gifts which an inscription still commemorates. He had defeated the Pallava king's attempt to turn him back and took much booty from him before entering the undefended capital. Later on Nandivarman regained his capital and waged war against the Tamil kings. On one occasion he was shut in his fortress of Nandipura by the Tamil army, but the besiegers were scattered by a relieving force led by Udayachandra, who followed up this exploit by other successes in the south and north. Nandivarman in the course of his long reign had wars with all his neighbours, Tamil, Chālukya and Ganga. A new power, the Rāshtrakūtas, had risen in the Deccan with the end of the Chālukyas; Dantidurga in the middle of the century swept through Chālukya territory and invaded the land of the Pallavas, for a time occupying Kānchī itself; this exploit was repeated half a century later, in the reign of Govinda III.

Of the next reign, that of Pallavamalla's son, Dantivarman (c. A.D. 780–830), little is known; he was the son of a Rāshtrakūta princess and married a Kadamba princess. Towards the end of his reign he seems to have lost territory to the Pāndyas. Nandivarman III (c. A.D. 830–50) was the son of his predecessor. He checked the Pāndya advance in the battle of Tellaru and is credited with other victories over the retreating invaders. The next ruler, Nripatungavarman (A.D. 850–75), still found the southern kingdom a menace, but won a great victory over it at Arichit. Aparājita (A.D. 875–85) with Ganga help dealt a heavy blow to the Pāndyas in the battle of Perambiyam. But he was not destined to enjoy his success for long. The Chola, Āditya I, was then rapidly restoring the fortunes of his ancient line, and was soon powerful enough to attack the failing Pallava kingdom, and, having conquered Aparājita, regained the territory of Tondaimandalam for its former rulers. With Aparājita the Pallava dynasty may be said to have come to an end. The family survived for some centuries and one member of it, Perunjinga, played a part at the break-up of the Chola empire. Though most of the deeds of the Pallavas are forgotten, they have left us an unsurpassed series of monuments, which show that the arts flourished under their rule to a degree that can hardly be paralleled elsewhere in India.

Part II

MUSLIM INDIA

CHAPTER I

Early Muslim Conquests and the Foundation of the Kingdom of Delhi

India lay above the high water-mark of the flood of Arab conquest which, in the later part of the seventh and the early part of the eighth centuries of the Christian era, swept over Syria, Egypt, Persia, Transoxiana, Asia Minor, Northern Africa, and Spain; but in A.D. 711 Sind was invaded by an Arab force under Muhammad ibn Kāsim. The invasion is said to have been provoked by an act of piracy or brigandage for which Dāhir, the Brāhman raja of Sind, was unable or unwilling to make reparation, and was sanctioned by the Caliph al-Walid at the instance of al-Hajjāj, viceroy of the eastern provinces of the caliphate. Dāhir was slain and Sind was conquered, and became an Arab province, remaining so until A.D. 871, when, as the authority of the 'Abbāsids declined, two Arab chiefs established independent principalities, one in Upper Sind, with its capital at Multān, and the other in Lower Sind. The two states retained the fiction of allegiance to the caliphate, and early in the eleventh century, when Mahmūd of Ghaznī was wasting northern India with fire and sword, the Muslim governor of Upper Sind professed to be the caliph's vassal.

The conquest of Sind had no far-reaching effects and the religion which was destined to dominate India for nearly five centuries did not penetrate beyond the frontier tract annexed by the Arabs. The governor of Sind invaded Kachch, but the expedition was a mere raid, and no settlement was made. For the most part, the Arab governors of Sind maintained friendly relations with the Maitrakas of Valabhī in Gujarāt, and with the Chāvadās and Chālukyas who succeeded them; the states of Rājasthān were protected from aggression by the Thar or Indian Desert; and the Muslim rulers of Multān seem never to have made any serious attempt to subdue the Upper Panjab.

As the power of the 'Abbāsid caliphs declined, national spirit revived in the peoples conquered and converted to Islam by the

Arabs. Among the earliest dynasties which became virtually independent in the eastern provinces of the caliphate was a Persian house, the Sāmānids, who had their capital at Bukhāra. Very soon after the rise of such independent dynasties, the Turks became one of the most prominent peoples in the eastern caliphate. Originally rude and uncivilised nomads, they were as remarkable for the beauty of their women as for the bravery and fidelity of their men, and they were employed as royal slaves, the men chiefly in military service, at the courts of Muslim rulers. They "embraced Islam with all the fervour of their uncouth souls", and absorbed much of the culture of their masters. Alptigīn, a Turk in high office under the Sāmānids, having been deprived of his place, left the court, and in A.D. 962 established an independent principality with its capital at Ghaznī. He was followed, after his death, by his son Ishāk and he by three of his father's slaves, the third of whom, Sabuktigīn, founded in A.D. 976 a dynasty which endured for more than two centuries.

Northern India was parcelled out at this time among a number of Hindu dynasties, none of which was predominant; Solankīs in Gujarat, Chauhāns in Ajmir, Tomāras in Delhi, Pawārs in Mālwā, Kachhwāhas in Gwalior, Chandels in Bundelkhand, Parihāras in Kanauj, and Pālas in Bengal. The Hindu prince with whom Sabuktigīn came into contact was Jayapāla, raja of the Panjab, probably a Jāt by race, whose capital was Bhātinda, and whose dominions extended on the west to Kābul. In the course of four campaigns, Jayapāla lost all his territory west of the Indus, and Peshāwar was occupied by the Muslims. In A.D. 998 Mahmūd, the eldest son of Sabuktigīn, succeeded his father on the throne of Ghaznī, after a brief contest with his younger brother, Ismā'il.

Mahmūd is one of the most prominent figures in the history of Islam. During a reign of thirty-two years he extended his empire over the whole of the country now known as Afghanistan, the greater part of Persia and Transoxiana, and the Panjab. He is said to have made a vow to wage every year a holy war against the misbelievers of India, and he invaded the country no fewer than seventeen times, extinguished the ruling house of the Panjab, crossed the Ganges, penetrated into Bundelkhand, and reached the western sea. The caliph, al-Kādir, on receiving the dispatch announcing one of his victorious raids, caused it to be publicly proclaimed that "what the Companions of the Blessed Prophet had done in Arabia, Persia, Syria, and 'Irak, Mahmūd had achieved in Hindūstan'', an empty vaunt, for in India Mahmūd was a raider rather than a conqueror. He plundered temples, acquiring immense booty, destroyed ancient monuments, and slew and enslaved vast numbers of the inhabitants, but it was not until 1022, when he annexed the Panjab, which ultimately became the last refuge of his house, that he effected a permanent conquest and became an Indian ruler. He was opposed on some of his expeditions by individual Indian rulers, such as Jayapāla, Ānandapāla, and Nidar Bhīm of the Panjab, and Ganda of Kālinjar, and on others by confederacies of Hindu princes. But no single Indian prince was strong enough to withstand him, and, owing to mutual jealousies and animosities, one defeat sufficed to dissolve any confederacy.

The most famous of all Mahmūd's expeditions was that to Somnāth, on the coast of Kāthiāwār, undertaken in 1020, ostensibly for the purpose of destroying the idol worshipped at that shrine, but in fact with the object of plundering its wealth. The idol was destroyed, and Mahmūd returned to Ghaznī with much spoil, harassed on his retreat by the Jāts of the Panjab, whom he punished in 1027, when he led his army into India for the last time. The remaining years of his life were occupied with the western affairs of his empire, with the Saljuk Turks, already a menace, whom he had allowed to settle in Khurāsān, and with the Buwayhids, from whom he wrested the kingdom of Rayy. On April 21, 1030, he died. It would be unjust to judge him by his Indian raids alone. There he was a ruthless marauder, but his court at Ghaznī was in his age the chief centre of art, literature, and science. "Like many a great soldier he loved the society of educated men; after sweeping like a pestilence for hundreds of miles across India, or pouncing like a hawk upon Khvārazm beside the Sea of Aral, and then coursing south to Hamasān, almost within call of Baghdād itself, he would settle down to listen to the songs of poets and the wise conversation of divines."

Mahmūd was succeeded, after a fratricidal struggle, by his second son, Mas'ūd, during whose reign the Saljuks began their attacks on the great empire which his father had founded. He was well served by Hindus, who contributed to his army a large corps of cavalry under a Hindu officer, Tilak, a man of humble origin who was advanced to the dignity of a noble of his court; but the

Saljuks gradually expelled from Persia the descendants of Mahmūd, who continued, however, until 1161 to rule their eastern dominions, including the Panjab, from Ghaznī. They were sometimes troubled by rebellions in the Panjab, and they occasionally led or dispatched raiding expeditions into Indian states, but none of them made any serious attempt to extend his Indian dominions, and the Hindu states of northern India were left free to pursue their internecine strife. The Gaharwār Rājputs superseded the Parihāras in Kanauj, Benares, and Ayodhyā, and reduced the Tomāras of Delhi to vassalage. The Kālachuris of Chedi extended their authority over Magadha and Bihar, broke the power of the Pawārs of Mālwā, and nearly succeeded in becoming the paramount power in northern India, but, falling on evil days, were supplanted by the Vāghela chief of Rewa. Neither the Gahlot state of southern Rājasthān, nor the Pāla kings of Bengal and Bihar, attempted to oppose Mahmūd's raids, and the latter dynasty, the members of which were devout Buddhists, was ousted from its kingdom by the Senas of Bengal, who were Brahmanical Hindus. In the middle of the twelfth century the Chauhān prince of Sāmbhar and Ajmir expelled the Tomāras from Delhi, and added their dominions to his own. His nephew and successor, Prithivīrāja, became the most powerful Hindu prince in northern India, but jeopardised the cause of national unity by a domestic dispute with the Gaharwār raja of Kanauj, and by stripping the powerful Chandel raja Parmāl of Bundelkhand of much of his territory, including the important fortress of Mahobā.

In Mahmūd's reign the district of Ghūr, on the southern slopes of the Safid Kish range, had been ruled by a petty prince whom he reduced to vassalage. As the power of the Ghaznavids declined, that of the Shansabānids, the descendants of this prince, grew. One of them was poisoned by Bahrām, the fifteenth of the Ghaznavids, whose sister he had married; and his brother expelled Bahrām from Ghaznī, but was afterwards defeated by him and treacherously put to death. 'Alā-ud-dīn Husain, another brother, who became ruler of Ghūr, avenged their deaths by capturing and burning Ghaznī, from which act of vandalism he became known as Jahānsūz or 'the World-Burner'. He was afterwards defeated and imprisoned by Sultan Sanjar the Saljuk, and was succeeded in Ghūr by two nephews, Ghiyās-ud-dīn Muhammad and Shihāb-ud-dīn (afterwards Mu'izz-ud-dīn) Muhammad, who ruled jointly and, strangely enough, amicably.

Bahrām returned to Ghaznī, but his son and successor, Khusraw Shāh, was driven from the city by the Ghuzz Turkmāns, and retired to Lahore, which then became the capital of the Ghaznavids. He died there in 1160 and was succeeded by his son Khusraw Malik, the last of the line.

The two brothers of Ghūr founded an extensive but ephemeral empire, with which we are not here concerned; and while the elder occupied himself with extending this empire westward, he left the affairs of its eastern provinces in the hands of the younger, usually styled Muhammad Ghūrī, who established himself in Ghaznī.

Muhammad Ghūrī, unlike Mahmūd, who had been content with plundering raids into India, resolved to extend the rule of Islam over the idolators, and to conquer their land. His first expedition, in 1175, was against Multān, where the Ismā'īlī heretics had established their rule. Wresting the city from them, he appointed an orthodox governor, and next captured the strong fortress of Uch, betrayed into his hands by the wife of its Hindu governor. Three years later he led a disastrous expedition across the Indian desert into Gujarāt, where his exhausted army was defeated by Bhīma, the young Vāghela raja of the country, and suffered so much during its retreat across the inhospitable desert that only a remnant reached Ghaznī. In 1181 he invaded the Panjab and there left a garrison which was attacked by Khusraw Malik. But this degenerate descendant of Mahmūd sued for peace when Muhammad, in 1186, again appeared before the gates of Lahore, and was treacherously seized and sent to Ghūr, where he was afterwards put to death as a dangerous incumbrance. Thus ended the line of Mahmūd of Ghaznī.

The annexation of the Panjab carried Muhammad's frontier eastward to the Sutlej, and provided him with an advanced base of operations. In 1190 he crossed the Sutlej and took Bhātinda, then in the dominions of Prithivīrāja of Delhi, whom the Muslim historians style 'Rāi Pithaura'. Prithivīrāja marched to meet him and came up with him at Tarāorī, near Karnāl, where Muhammad was wounded and defeated, but in 1192 he returned at the head of 12,000 horse, again met Prithivīrāja at Tarāorī, and defeated and dispersed the Hindu army, both Prithivīrāja and his brother being slain. After the battle various fortresses surrendered, and Muhammad marched to Ajmir, plundered the city, carried off numbers of its inhabitants as slaves, and appointed as his tributary governor a son of Prithivīrāja.

These successes had given Muhammad northern India almost to the gates of Delhi, and, on departing for Ghaznī, he left as governor of his Indian dominions Kutb-ud-dīn Aibak, the most trusty of his Turkish officers, not only to administer the new conquests, but also at his discretion to extend them. Henceforward Aibak was the Muslim ruler of northern India, for his master, who retained Ghaznī as his capital, was so occupied with the affairs of Khurāsān that he only twice again marched into India, once in 1193, when he defeated and slew Jayachandra, raja of Kanauj and Benares, and again in 1205, to crush a dangerous rebellion of the Khokhars in the Salt Range of the Panjab.

Aibak subjugated the Gangetic doāb, crushed a rebellion in Ajmir and appointed a Muslim governor of the province, avenged a former defeat of Muhammad by twice invading the dominions of Bhīma, raja of Gujarāt, and sacking his capital, defeated Parmāl, the Chandel raja of Kālinjar, whose ancestor had paid tribute to Mahmūd, surpassed Mahmūd by capturing his two greatest fortresses, Kālinjar and Mahobā, and established a port to the east of the Ganges by capturing the important city of Budaun.

Meanwhile another Turkish officer, subordinate to Aibak, had been carrying the banner of Islam further afield. Muhammad Khaljī, son of Bakhtiyār, had invaded Bihar, taken its capital, Odantapuri, slain the Buddhist monks in its great monastery, and returned to Delhi with his plunder, which included the monastery library. He was dismissed with honours, received as a fief his past and future conquests, and returned to Bihar, whence, in 1202, he invaded Bengal, drove its sovereign from Nadiya, his capital, and annexed that rich kingdom, making Gaur, or Lakhnāwati, his provincial capital.

The Khokhars, already mentioned, had been encouraged to rebel by the news that Muhammad Ghūrī, whose elder brother had died, had suffered a severe defeat at the hands of 'Alā-ud-dīn, king of Khvārazm. Aibak was unable to crush the rebellion, and in October, 1205, Muhammad left Ghaznī for India. The rising was crushed with appalling severity, great numbers of Khokhars being slain, or captured and sold into slavery; but Muhammad, while on his way back to Ghaznī, was assassinated, on March 15, 1206, on the banks of the Indus, by fanatical heretics of the

Ismā'īli sect. He left no son, and though, on his death, two puppet princes were successively raised to the throne in Ghaznī, the viceroys of his provinces, Aibak in India and Tāj-ud-dīn Yildiz in Kirmān, assumed the insignia of royalty. Aibak thus became the first Muslim sultan of Delhi. One of his earliest tasks as a sovereign was the appointment of a governor in Bengal. Muhammad Khaljī had rashly led an expedition from the plains into the Himālāya, with the result that his army had been almost annihilated. On his return to Lakhnāwati, he took to his bed, and was murdered by an ambitious kinsman, 'Ali Mardān, who, concealing his guilt, persuaded Aibak to appoint him governor. His advancement profited him little, for his high rank disturbed the balance of his mind. He assumed the royal title, and behaved with such arrogance and cruelty that his officers conspired and slew him.

Aibak's military activity was confined chiefly to the period of his viceroyalty, but after his master's death he embarked on one foolish adventure which has left a blot on his reputation as a soldier. Having defeated Tāj-ud-dīn Yildiz, viceroy of Kirmān, who claimed the sovereignty of the Panjab, he drove him from Ghaznī and occupied that city, but permitted his troops to treat its citizens as enemies and to plunder them, with the consequence that they secretly summoned Yildiz to their aid, and he, returning when Aibak was celebrating his success with wine and revelry, surprised him so completely that he fled to Lahore without striking a blow. The victory of Yildiz confined Aibak to India, so that he became a purely Indian sovereign, founding the dynasty known as the Slave Kings of Delhi. He died in November 1210, as the result of an accident at polo.

The designation of this dynasty will appear to many a contradiction in terms; but in an eastern monarchy, where the sovereign was the heir of all his subjects, who held both life and property at his pleasure, to be the personal slave of the ruler was a distinction rather than a disgrace. The Ghaznavids were sprung from a Turkish slave; the Mamelukes, at a later period, were the Circassian slaves of Egyptian rulers. Loyal service earned for a slave a regard and esteem sometimes withheld from a son born in the purple, and corrupted from his cradle by flattery and luxury. A favourite slave often received the hand of his master's daughter in marriage; and Muhammad Ghūrī, when a courtier condoled with him on having no son, is said to have replied that in his

14-2

Turkish slaves he had thousands of sons, who would succeed him and carry on his name. So it happened on the death of Aibak. A worthless son, Ārām, succeeded him, but Nāsir-ud-dīn Kabācha, his son-in-law and governor of the Panjab, withheld his allegiance from Ārām. Bengal was already independent, and the attitude of the Hindus was so menacing that within a year Shams-ud-dīn Īltutmish, the foremost slave and the son-in-law of Aibak, deposed the weakling and ascended the throne, but succeeded to no more than a remnant of Aibak's wide dominions. Kabācha claimed Lahore, but that city was occupied in 1214 by Yildiz, who had been driven from Ghaznī by 'Alā-ud-dīn Khvārazmshāh. Īltutmish defeated and captured Yildiz, and shortly afterwards put him to death, and in 1217 recovered the Panjab from Kabācha.

In 1220 the heathen Mongols under Chingīz Khān swept over Khvārazm and Persia, expelling 'Alā-ud-dīn from his great empire. India lay beyond the range of their conquests, as it had lain beyond the range of those of the Arabs five and a half centuries earlier, but not beyond the reach of their raids, and the foreign affairs of the Muslims of India, for more than a century after this time, were confined chiefly to the repulse of those raids and to their relations with the Mongol Īl-khāns of Persia. It was now that Jalāl-ud-dīn Mangobarni, heir to 'Alā-ud-dīn, fled before Chingīz into India and took refuge in Lahore, where he allied himself with the Khokhars, and then, having humiliated Kabācha in Multān and plundered his territory, returned to Persia.

Meanwhile Īltutmish had reduced 'Iwāz Khān, the rebellious governor of Bengal, to obedience, recovered from the Rājputs the fortress of Ranthambhor, and, after the return of Mangobarni to Persia, was free to deal with Kabācha, who was defeated, and afterwards accidentally drowned in the Indus. The officers of Īltutmish completed their task of conquering Lower Sind, and thus extending his dominions to the sea. Bengal again rebelled, but the rebellion was crushed by Īltutmish's eldest son, Mahmūd, who governed the province for his father till his early death, after which Īltutmish was obliged to suppress yet another rebellion. Later on he recovered Gwalior, his earliest fief, which had been seized by the Hindus, and slaughtered 700 of its garrison. He had then established his authority throughout the dominions which Aibak had ruled, and in 1234 carried the arms of Islam for the first time into Mālwā, captured Bhīlsa, and sacked Ujjain, destroying all the temples in that ancient city. His last campaign was undertaken with the object of subjugating the turbulent Khokhars of the Salt Range, whose hostility still menaced the peace of the realm; but, on his way thither, he fell sick, and, having been borne back to Delhi in a litter, died on April 29, 1236.

Īltutmish was the greatest of the Slave Kings. To the dominions of Aibak he added Lower Sind and part of Mālwā, besides restoring and maintaining order in the loose congeries of fiefs of which those dominions were composed. He was a builder as well as a conqueror and an administrator, and left monuments both at Delhi and Ajmīr displaying his taste in architecture. On his death his son Fīrūz, a weak and licentious prince, was raised to the throne. The royal slaves had by then formed themselves into a college or council of forty, which divided among its members all the great fiefs of the kingdom and the highest offices in the state. Īltutmish had preserved the royal dignity intact, but the Forty would not endure a *roi fainéant*, and after a reign of six months Fīrūz was deposed and put to death. The choice of the Forty next fell upon Raziyya, the daughter of Īltutmish, whom he had named as his successor, but whose sex was at first considered an insuperable bar to her elevation, though her dying father had assured his advisers that they would find her a better man than any of her brothers. She suppressed, by subtle intrigue rather than by force of arms, a serious rebellion of those of the Forty who hesitated to acknowledge her, and a rising in Delhi of the Ismā'īli heretics, whom Īltutmish had already once been obliged to punish for revolting and attempting his life, and the fanatics were now annihilated. Raziyya offended the Forty by promoting to the important place of master of the horse an African named Yākūt. There appears to have been no impropriety in her relations with him, but the proud Turks would not endure her preference for a negro, and rebelled, slew Yākūt, and deposed and imprisoned Raziyya, raising to the throne her brother, Bahrām. Altūniya, the leading rebel, disappointed of what he conceived to be his just share of the spoils, released her, married her, and attempted to restore her, but was defeated, and both lost their lives.

During the reign of Bahrām the Mongols invaded the Panjab, sacked Lahore, and laid the city waste. The king was too feeble to take any steps against them, and gradually estranged the Turkish nobles by mistimed and futile attempts to assert his authority over them. The Forty besieged him in the White Fort at Delhi, which fell on May 10, 1242, when Bahrām was seized and put to death. After an abortive attempt by one of the Forty to seize the crown, the rest of that body raised to the throne Mas'ūd, the son of Fīrūz, during whose short reign the country was disturbed by a rebellion in Bengal, by the invasion of the same province by the Hindus of Cuttack, by a Hindu rebellion in Bihar, and by an invasion of the Panjab by the Mongols. On June 10, 1246, Mas'ūd was deposed and thrown into prison, where he perished shortly afterwards, and his uncle, Nāsir-ud-dīn Mahmūd, the youngest son of Iltutmish, was raised to the throne.

Mahmūd was an amiable and unassuming prince, possessing the virtues of continence, frugality, and practical piety, and a taste for caligraphy, which led him to employ his leisure in making copies of the Koran. For the greater part of his reign he was under the influence of Ghiyās-ud-dīn Balban, a Turkish slave whom Iltutmish had purchased and married to one of his daughters, and who had given a daughter in marriage to Mahmūd. During the brief and troubled reigns of Mahmūd's predecessors, the kingdom had fallen into disorder. The Mongols had not only sacked Lahore and levelled its buildings with the ground, but had so devastated the country west of the Jhelum that no cultivation remained, but in the neighbourhood of the Salt Range. The turbulent Hindus of the doāb were in rebellion, as were also the Meos of Mewāt, the region now nearly covered by the Alwar state. On the advice of Balban, who held the office of lord chamberlain, Mahmūd first set out to recover the Panjab. The Khokhars were subdued, and a marauding force of Mongols fled when it found itself confronted by Balban's army. The doāb was reduced to obedience, a Hindu raja who had occupied the country on both banks of the Jumna above Allāhābād was driven back into Bundelkhand, and the Meos were severely chastised. Balban's reward for these services was promotion to the post of lieutenant of the kingdom, his brother, Kashli Khān, succeeding him as lord chamberlain; and he next led a successful expedition into eastern Mālwā, but on his return to court discovered that he had become the victim of a plot. The queen-mother, who, it was afterwards discovered, had been secretly married to Kutlugh Khān, one of the Forty, a eunuch named Raihān, and some of the Forty who were jealous of his influence, had conspired against him, Raihān being the leader of the conspiracy, and persuaded the king that his power was dangerous. He was dismissed from court to his fief, and immediately afterwards transferred to a less valuable fief, in order to provoke him into rebellion, but he remained quiet until a majority of the Forty, weary of the eunuch's arrogance, joined him, and took the field against Mahmūd and Raihān. The rebels hesitated to strike a blow against their sovereign, and Mahmūd secretly longed for the aid and support of his father-in-law. Private communications emboldened him to dismiss the eunuch from court to the fief of Budaun, and to restore Balban to his former place. Henceforward he was supreme in the kingdom. Kutlugh Khān was transferred from Bayāna to Oudh, and afterwards, when Raihān was put to death, joined a formidable band of rebels led by Kishlū Khān, governor of Multān, who had transferred his allegiance from Mahmūd to Hulāgū, the Mongol Īl-khān of Persia. Balban marched against these rebels, but they eluded him and appeared before Delhi, only to find the city in a state of defence. Most of their followers deserted them, and made their peace with the king, and the leaders fled into the Siwālik hills. Later in the year Kishlū Khān joined a predatory host of Mongols who invaded the Panjab, but hastily retreated on learning that Mahmūd was about to march against them. Their retreat was fortunate, for the kingdom was in such disorder that no army could safely have marched against an invader. The Hindus of the doāb and the Meos of Mewāt were again in revolt, two great fief-holders were virtually in rebellion, and Bengal had ceased to remit revenue to Delhi. Balban dealt effectively with all these rebels, and barbarously with the Meos, who had given most provocation; while a welcome mission from Hulāgū assured Mahmūd that no Mongol raids on India would in future be permitted. Mahmūd died, without an heir, on February 18, 1266, having designated as his successor his father-in-law, Balban, who in any case would probably have ascended the throne.

But his position was not free from embarrassment, for the hereditary principle had then been established for fifty years, and the Forty were inclined to resent the predominance of one of themselves. Balban, on the other hand, was resolved to found a new dynasty, and, perceiving that success would be doubtful until the power of the Forty had been crushed, set himself to crush it. For the easy manners of Mahmūd's court, where the mild and unassuming king had been content with but little outward deference, he substituted a rigid ceremonial. His court was an austere assembly, where jest and laughter were seldom heard. Offenders among the Forty were punished with the utmost severity. One, who had caused the death of a slave, was flogged to death; another for a similar offence received 500 stripes and redeemed his life with a great sum; another, who had been defeated by rebels, was hanged over the gate of the city which he had ruled. Yet he allowed aged, inefficient, and dishonest fiefholders to retain their fiefs without performing the services for which they had been granted. The royal diversions were hunting, conversing with theologians, and listening to sermons, at which Balban wept copiously, though he could remain unmoved at the sight of cruel tortures.

In spite of his severity his reign was disturbed by rebellions and by Mongol invasions, but Lahore was rebuilt, and provincial government was restored in the Panjab; the Meos, who during Mahmūd's last years had plundered the country to the gates of the capital, suffered severely for their offences; and rebellions of the Hindus of the doāb and of Katehr, the region east of the Ganges, were crushed, and in Katehr such numbers were slaughtered that the air was polluted for miles with the stench of the corpses. But the most formidable rebellion was that headed by Tughril, whom Balban had appointed to the government of Bengal. This man defeated successively two royal armies sent against him, and induced numbers of officers and men of the defeated forces to transfer to him their allegiance. The news of these reverses so enraged Balban that he gnawed his own flesh in his fury, and set out in person to crush the rebel, his army being accompanied by a large fleet of boats collected on the Jumna and the Ganges. Tughril long eluded him, and the army despaired of ever seeing their homes again, for Balban had sworn not to turn back until Tughril had been taken or slain. At length a troop of horse came upon the rebel force encamped in a forest, and took it completely by surprise. Tughril was slain, his head was carried to Balban, and the army withdrew, with a great number of prisoners, to Lakhnāwati, where those who belonged to that city were punished by impalement upon rows of stakes. Balban appointed his second son, Bughrā Khān, governor of Bengal, and adjured him to take warning against rebellion from the dreadful spectacle which he had just witnessed. Those who had deserted to the rebels from the royal armies were reserved for punishment at Delhi, and a double row of stakes more than seven miles in length had been set up for their impalement, but, before the army reached the capital, its *kāzī* induced Balban to abandon his design, and the deserters suffered very little for their crime.

Balban, then eighty years of age, was at the height of his prosperity and glory. His elder son, Muhammad Khān, a most promising prince who had been designated his heir, had been appointed governor of Multān, in order that he might repel Mongol raids into India. On March 9, 1285, after defeating a large force of Mongols, he fell into an ambush, and was slain. The old king continued to hold his court, and in public no change in his demeanour was visible, but in his chamber he rent his clothes, cast dust upon his head, and mourned his son as David mourned Absalom. The dead prince was henceforth styled *Shahīd*, "the Martyr", and his son was designated heir to the throne.

When Balban died, in 1287, his nobles disregarded his wishes, and raised to the throne Kaikubād, son of the worthless Bughrā, who was in Bengal at the time of his father's death. Kaikubād's reign was brief and evil. He had been brought up by his grandfather in the straitest paths of virtue and under the most rigid discipline. On ascending the throne at the age of seventeen or eighteen, he burst his bonds, neglected all business, and abandoned himself to the satisfaction of his appetites. His example set the fashion, and the reaction from Balban's stern rule produced a general outburst of licentiousness. The son of the martyr prince was put to death, and one Nizām-ud-dīn, son of the aged magistrate of Delhi, acquired absolute control of the debauched youth and of all public business. Even the slothful and self-indulgent Bughrā wrote to his son, warning him of the inevitable consequences of this neglect of public business, and of permitting a subject to usurp his authority. After a Mongol force had been defeated at Lahore, and a large number of the raiders publicly executed at Delhi, Kaikubād learned that his father was leading his army from Lakhnāwati towards Delhi. His object could hardly be doubted, and in March, 1288, Kaikubād marched from Delhi to meet him. The two armies met on the Gogra, and Bughrā, after sending some menacing messages to his son, changed his tone, and even consented to do homage to him as sovereign of Delhi. The meeting between father and son was affecting. Bughrā advanced to do homage, but Kaikubād, overcome by natural feelings, descended from his throne and received him with the respect due to a father. Friendly meetings, not devoid of conviviality, continued for some days, and Bughrā found an opportunity of secretly warning his son against the designs of Nizām-ud-dīn. They parted with tokens of affection, and returned, each to his own capital. "Alas!" cried Bughrā, as he set out, "I have seen the last of my son, and the last of Delhi." Kaikubād, on his return, dismissed Nizām-ud-dīn to Multān, and, on his hesitating to obey, caused him to be poisoned. His removal dislocated the machinery of the administration, and Kaikubād appointed to the fief of Baran and the command of the army Jalāl-ud-dīn Fīrūz Khaljī. His appointment gave great offence to the Turkish nobles, and to the people of the capital, who affected to despise his tribe and feared both his power and his ambition. As soon as Fīrūz had taken possession of his fief, Kaikubād, as a result of his incontinence and intemperance, was stricken with paralysis and lay a helpless wreck in his palace. Fīrūz marched on Delhi, and the Turkish nobles enthroned Kayūmars, the three-year old son of Kaikubād; but the sons of Fīrūz dashed into the city, carried off the child-king, and defeated a force sent in pursuit of them. Most of the Turkish nobles now submitted to Fīrūz, while the populace maintained an attitude of sullen aloofness. The wretched Kaikubād was put to death; his corpse was thrown into the Jumna; and on June 13, 1290, Fīrūz was enthroned in the palace of Kīlūgharī as Jalāl-ud-dīn Fīrūz Shāh. Thus ended the line of the Slave Kings.

The Muhammadan kingdom of Delhi was not a homogeneous political entity. The government was feudal, but differed from the feudal systems of Europe in that the fief-holders had no hereditary, or even personal, title to their fiefs, but might be, and often were transferred from one fief to another. The great fiefs, to which the fief-holders discharged most of the functions of provincial governors, were centres of Muslim influence, but the subordinate machinery of government and the agency for the ordinary collection of the revenue were largely Hindu, and the tiller of the soil probably found very little difference between Muslim and Hindu rule, since under neither was he usually allowed to retain more of the fruits of his labour than sufficed to satisfy the most frugal needs of himself and his family. When, owing to the weakness of the central government, or of a local administration, he withheld his land-rent, or followed a rebellious Hindu chieftain into the field, he was often barbarously treated, but he was punished for contumacy or rebellion, not, as the rhapsodies of pious Muslim historians might lead us to believe, for idolatry. Nor was Muslim rule firmly established throughout the area within its geographical limits. The north-western frontier districts were constantly devastated by Mongol inroads; the Khokhars were only occasionally in subjection; the fortresses of Gwalior, Ranthambhor, and Nāgaur changed hands more than once; the great fiefs were interspersed with lands held by the Hindu chieftains, whose subjection was as fitful as that of the Khokhars; Mewāt had been harassed, but never subdued; the Hindus of the doāb were frequently in revolt; those of Katehr harried the eastern frontier; and the great fiefs in the west were merely outposts against the chiefs of Rājasthān. What enabled a comparatively small foreign garrison to maintain its supremacy over Hindūstan, the Panjab, and Bengal, was its religious homogeneity and the impossibility of any union among the Hindus. From them the spirit of caste has for ages ousted the sentiment of nationality. Caste despises caste, or resents in caste the assumption of superiority. The Brāhman contemns the cultivator; the cultivator resents the attitude of the Brāhman; both despise the menial. Each Rājput clan deems itself superior to any other, and there has never been an Indian nation. Another factor in the stability of Muslim rule was the gradual Indianisation of the ruling class. The original invaders had nothing in common with India, but they made it their home, and their descendants knew no other. Many Hindus accepted the religion of their conquerors, and thus made inter-marriage possible, and Hindu concubines taken in war introduced Hindu blood into Muslim families. Even from the works of bigoted Muslim historians much evidence of the gradual Indianisation of the invaders may be gathered. But even as to-day, to the Muslim the Hindu was ever an idolatrous misbeliever, and to the Hindu the Muslim was ever an unclean Mlechchha.

CHAPTER II

The First Muslim Empire: The Khaljīs and the Tughluks

The Khalj were a Turkish tribe, but, having been long domiciled in the country now known as Afghanistan, had adopted some Afghan habits and customs, and the opposition to Fīrūz of the Turkish nobles and of the citizens, interesting as evidence of the existence of a body of public opinion, was based on the belief that he was an Afghan, and therefore a barbarian. So bitter was this opposition that for some time he dwelt in the suburb of Kīlūgharī, and did not enter the city. It was soon discovered that he had been misjudged, for no milder king had ever sat upon the throne of Delhi. Whatever violence he had committed in his younger days, he was then an old man, engaged in making his peace with Heaven, and his foolish tenderness to rebels and other criminals subjected him to rebukes from a blunt and outspoken kinsman, Ahmad Chap, who was one of his chief courtiers. His position was difficult. The remnant of the Turkish nobles had opposed his ascent of the throne, but their power was broken, and he allowed most of them to retain their places. His tribesmen, though by no means neglected, resented his generosity, and murmured that he knew neither how to punish his foes nor reward his friends.

Among the old nobles allowed to retain their fiefs was 'Abdullāh, known as Chhajjū, who enjoyed the rich fief of Kara, on the Ganges, about forty miles above Allāhābād. He was a nephew of Balban, and, rising in rebellion, assumed the royal title and marched on Delhi. But he was defeated near Budaun by Arkali Khān, the second son of Fīrūz. When Chhajjū and his associates were brought before Fīrūz he not only pardoned them, but entertained them at a wine party, to the indignation of Ahmad Chap and his other courtiers. Chhajjū was not, however, restored to his fief, which was bestowed upon 'Alā-ud-dīn, the nephew and son-in-law of Fīrūz.

The worst instance of the leniency of Fīrūz to criminals was his treatment of some *thags*, now mentioned for the first time in history. A few of the assassins, seized at Delhi, gave information which led to the arrest of over a thousand. Not one was punished, but the whole gang was sent down the river and set free in Bengal. Certain courtiers, disgusted with the king's misgovernment, freely discussed over their wine his deposition and removal. Their conversation was reported, but the only punishment inflicted on them was a year's banishment from court.

Once only did Fīrūz depart from his policy of leniency, and this was in the case of a religious leader named Sīdī Maulā, suspected by reason of his mode of life and the unknown source of his wealth. He failed to satisfy Fīrūz, and was put to death in his presence. The darkening of the sun by a dust-storm, and a famine which followed, were attributed by the superstitious to divine wrath with the slayer of the holy man; but it is not improbable that Sīdī Maulā was associated in some way with the *thags*.

Fīrūz once more enraged the worthy Ahmad Chap by abandoning an expedition which he had undertaken for the recovery of Ranthambhor. A hundred such fortresses, he said, were not worth a single hair on a true believer's head; but he might have reached this decision without leaving Delhi, and without openly displaying his fear of the Rājputs. 'Alā-ud-dīn, who had received the fief of Kara, was treated by Fīrūz more as a son than a nephew, and his uncle would believe no ill of him; but he was unhappily married, and his wife and his mother-in-law, the principal wife of Fīrūz, may have suspected his designs, for he was both ambitious and unscrupulous, and they gave him no peace. He undertook, with his uncle's leave, an expedition into Mālwā, and, as a reward for the spoils of Bhīlsa, which he laid at the sultan's feet, received, in addition to Kara, the great fief of Oudh. At Bhīlsa he heard of the wealthy Marātha kingdom in the western Deccan, the capital of which was Deogīr, the modern Daulatābād, and, on his return from Delhi to Kara, began secretly to equip a force for a descent on this kingdom, then ruled by Rāmachandra, the seventh of the Yādava dynasty. He set out in 1294 at the head of seven or eight thousand horse, and after marching for two months by unfrequented routes, arrived at Ellichpur in Berar, the northern province of the kingdom. He explained his presence, and secured himself from molestation, by giving out that he was a discontented noble of Delhi, seeking service in southern India. He then pressed on to Deogīr, where he took Rāmachandra completely by surprise.

The greater part of the army was absent with the raja's wife and eldest son, Sankara, who were perforr ting a pilgrimage, and 'Alā-ud-dīn defeated Rāmachandra and drove him into his citadel, which was not provisioned. The Muslims plundered the city, and the raja sued for peace, which was granted on condition that they were allowed to retire with their plunder, and with what they could extort from the citizens. Sankara then returned, and, though begged by his father not to break faith with the invaders, attacked them, and was defeated.

News of 'Alā-ud-dīn's return reached Fīrūz while he was on a hunting tour at Gwalior; and he was urged to punish him for having ventured on such an enterprise without permission, but he rebuked his courtiers for their unworthy suspicions, and decided to return to Delhi and await his nephew's arrival. "If you return to Delhi", cried Ahmad Chap, striking his hands together, ".you slay us with your own hand!" Pretending that he feared to meet his uncle after his presumption, 'Alā-ud-dīn lingered at Kara until the old king, urged thereto by Ulugh Khān, 'Alā-ud-dīn's brother, decided to visit him there. Despite the warnings of his counsellors, he travelled to Kara by boat. 'Alā-ud-dīn knelt before him on the river bank, and, as his uncle kindly raised him, two of his companions, at a signal, cut the old man down, and severed his head from his body, raising it aloft on a spear, while 'Alā-ud-dīn, causing an umbrella to be raised over his head, was proclaimed king.

The royal army was hurriedly led back to Delhi, while 'Alā-ud-dīn marched in more leisurely fashion towards the capital, scattering largesse on his way. As he approached the city, his cousin Ibrāhīm Khān, who had been proclaimed king, fled with his mother and was pursued to Multān, where both were captured, together with Arkali Khān, Ibrāhīm's elder brother. The two princes were blinded, and their mother was imprisoned. On October 3, 1296, 'Alā-ud-dīn was enthroned in the Red Palace of Balban, and those who were disgusted by his ingratitude and treachery were silenced by the gold of the Deccan.

With the reign of 'Alā-ud-dīn begins what may be called the imperial period of the sultanate, during which the kings of Delhi extended their authority, either directly or indirectly, over the whole of the Indian peninsula. This period lasted for about half a century

The first state doomed to extinction was Gujarāt. This kingdom had been ravaged and plundered once by Mahmūd and twice by Aibak, but had never owned a Muslim sovereign. It was now ruled by Rāja Karan, the Vāghela. 'Alā-ud-dīn sent from Delhi an army under his brother, Ulugh Khān, and his minister, Nusrat Khān. The country was overrun, the capital was occupied, and Karan was forced to flee, first to Deogīr, and later into Baglāna: A mutiny broke out in the army during its return from Gujarāt, but was suppressed, those of the mutineers who escaped taking refuge with Hamīr Singh in Ranthambhor. 'Alā-ud-dīn's successes turned his head, and he pondered two extravagant schemes; to emulate Alexander the Great as a world-conqueror, and to emulate Muhammad as a prophet and the preacher of a new faith. Like Alexander, he had hitherto succeeded in everything which he had undertaken, and like Muhammad he had, he said, four faithful companions to propagate his faith. He was brought to his senses by his faithful old servant, 'Alā-ul-mulk, formerly his lieutenant in Kara, and now *kotwāl* of Delhi. To his first scheme it was objected that he had not yet conquered India, and that, should he conquer it, he would require a regent as trusty as Aristotle to rule it while he fared forth into the world. As to the second, the *kotwāl* said, prophecy and religion were not based on temporal power, but on revelation. The old man concluded by warning him against excess in wine, which bred extravagant fancies. 'Alā-ud-dīn acknowledged the justice of the rebuke, commended his adviser, and abandoned his projects, but nevertheless described himself on his coins as "the Second Alexander".

Ranthambhor had been in the hands of the Hindus since the reign of Raziyya, and was now held by Hamīr Singh, who had offended 'Alā-ud-dīn by harbouring the deserters from the army. An army was sent to reduce the fortress, and, when Nusrat Khān was killed, the king led a second army from Delhi. At Tilpat, on his way to the fortress, he was benighted in the hunting field, and in the morning his nephew Ākat Khān, who was in search of him, tempted by his apparently defenceless condition, attacked and wounded him, and, believing that he had killed him, returned to the camp and demanded to be recognised as king. But the officers were cautious, and would not believe that the king was dead until they saw his head; and in the meantime 'Alā-ud-dīn, who had been joined by other troops, and whose wound had been dressed, approached the camp with the royal umbrella over his head. Ākat Khān fled, but was overtaken and beheaded, and 'Alā-ud-dīn, on his recovery, continued his march to Ranthambhor and infused new life into the siege.

While he was yet before Ranthambhor two serious rebellions broke out. His sister's sons rose in Budaun and Oudh, but were captured and sent to him, and their eyes were cut out in his presence; and Hājjī Maulā, an old officer who had been disappointed of succeeding 'Alā-ul-mulk as kotwāl, rose in Delhi, murdered the kotwāl, headed a mob which plundered the treasury, and enthroned a Sayyid, said to be descended, through his mother, from Īltutmish, with the suggestive name of Shāhinshāh. The city was in the hands of the rebels for a week, but they were at length overpowered, Hājjī Maulā was slain, and the unfortunate Sayyid was beheaded. Ranthambhor was betrayed into the hands of 'Alā-ud-dīn, Hamīr Singh was put to death, a Muslim governor was appointed to the fortress, and 'Alā-ud-dīn returned to Delhi. He now set himself to discover the reasons for the rebellions which had broken out in the short period since his accession, and decided that they were due to lack of information regarding discontent, the use of wine, intermarriages between and social gatherings among the families of the great nobles, and the general prosperity, which relieved many of the necessity for working for their bread, and left them leisure for idle thoughts and mischievous plots. To remedy the irregularities arising from these causes he issued four ordinances. By the first he abolished the feudal system, substituting direct payments from the treasury for the granting of fiefs, resumed all rent-free grants of land and religious endowments, and directed the tax-gatherers to exact from the people all that they could pay. The second ordinance established an army of spies, who were to report not only breaches of the ordinances, but all that passed in the houses of the nobles. The third prohibited the manufacture and use of wine, and offences against this ordinance were punished with great barbarity, but 'Alā-ud-dīn discovered, as has lately been discovered by others, that such an ordinance could not be enforced, and was obliged to permit the sale of wine under certain conditions. The fourth ordinance prohibited, except with special leave, social gatherings in the houses of the nobles, and marriages between the members of their families; and finally a special code of laws against Hindus was framed. The

most burdensome taxes were imposed upon them, in order that
to none might be left sufficient to enable him to ride a horse, to
carry arms, to wear rich clothes, or to enjoy any other luxuries.
This law was rigorously enforced.

In 1302 'Alā-ud-dīn marched to Chitor, the chief fortress of the
Gahlot Rājputs, and is said to have entrapped the regent, Bhīma
Singh, and to have refused to release him until he should surrender
his beautiful wife, but the regent was rescued by a stratagem, and
the king returned to the siege of Chitor, which he captured and
sacked after the garrison had performed the awful rite of *jauhar*,
immolating their wives and daughters to save them from dishonour, and then rushing on the foe and sacrificing their own
lives.

During the king's absence from his capital an army of 120,000
Mughuls[1] invaded his dominions, on this occasion with the object
of conquest. They advanced rapidly on Delhi. The Kara contingent, which had just returned from a disastrous expedition into
the Deccan by the east coast route, could not march to its relief,
and the Mughuls closed the other approaches to the capital, so
that 'Alā-ud-dīn, on his return, was obliged to take refuge in the
fortress of Sirī, where he was beleaguered for two months. The
Mughuls, who had devastated all the surrounding country, and
were alarmed by the approach of reinforcements, then vanished
as suddenly as they had appeared. This humiliating experience
caused 'Alā-ud-dīn to improve the defences of his kingdom. All
the fortresses between Delhi and the frontier were thoroughly repaired, and were garrisoned, but in 1304 the Mughuls again invaded the country in force.

During the campaign in Gujarāt a eunuch named Kāfūr had
been captured and presented to 'Alā-ud-dīn under the name of
Hazārdīnārī, or "the thousand dīnār slave", that being the price
for which his former master had bought him. He first won the
king's regard by his beauty, and became his vile favourite, but
he was an efficient soldier, and was sent with Ghiyās-ud-dīn
Tughluk, master of the horse, against the Mughuls who invaded
the country in 1304. They came up with them on their retreat,

[1] This people is usually described as Mongols before and as Mughuls
after its conversion to Islam. Mughul is the Arabic form of Mongol,
and the Mughuls of Persia and Transoxiana were now Muslims.

laden with booty, and inflicted on them a crushing defeat, bearing back to Delhi their leaders and 8000 others, all of whom were publicly executed. For this service the eunuch was made lieutenant of the kingdom, with the title of Malik Nāib, and Tughluk was made governor of the Panjab.

'Alā-ud-dīn's designs of conquest, and the liability of his realm to Mughul raids, required the maintenance of a great standing army, but, owing to the influx of treasure from the south, the value of money had fallen, and prices had so risen that the soldier could not live on his pay. This the king was not disposed to augment. Instead, he issued an edict arbitrarily fixing the prices of all the necessaries and most of the luxuries of life, on such a scale that the soldier was able to support himself in moderate comfort. This device would not commend itself to a modern economist, but the tariff was calculated with care, for, after a few initial difficulties with obstinate merchants and traders, it was enforced, and though prices rose when it was rescinded after 'Alā-ud-dīn's death, they fell a few years later to a level not much above the prices fixed by him.

Mālwā had hitherto been little molested by the Muslims. Iltutmish had advanced as far as Chanderī, and 'Alā-ud-dīn had sacked Bhīlsa, but these were mere raids. The country was now invaded with a view to its conquest, and an army under 'Ain-ul-mulk, governor of Multān, defeated on December 9, 1305, a great Hindu force under Koka, or Haranand, a raja of the Paramāra tribe of Rājputs, and the Muslims became masters of Ujjain, Māndū, Dhār, and Chanderī. Kāner Dev, the Chauhān raja of Jālor, submitted to 'Alā-ud-dīn and became his vassal, though he rebelled two years later, and was put to death.

After 1304 the Mughuls only twice again invaded India in force, once in 1306, to avenge their late defeat, and again in 1307. On both occasions they were defeated by Tughluk, now known as Ghāzī Malik, and large numbers of captives were sent to Delhi for execution; but there was never peace on the frontier, and Tughluk declared in an inscription that he had defeated them on twenty-nine occasions, and hence was entitled Ghāzī.

Rāmachandra of Deogīr had been remiss in the payment of tribute and the eunuch Malik Nāib was sent to call him to account, and also to capture the daughter of Karan of Gujarāt, whom her mother, now a member of the royal harem, wished to see again.

The princess, having been betrothed to Sankara, son of Rāmachandra, was on her way to Deogīr and was captured, not by Malik Nāib's troops, but by those of Alp Khān, governor of Gujarāt, and was sent to Delhi. Rāmachandra submitted, paid all arrears due from him, and was sent to Delhi, whence he was allowed to return to Deogīr as governor on the king's behalf, but the province of Berar was annexed.

The Deccan and the peninsula were then divided between three great Hindu kingdoms, that of Deogīr on the west, that of Telingāna in the east, and the Hoysala kingdom to the south of the Krishnā and Tungabhadrā. The ruler of Telingāna, Pratāparudra II, had his capital at Warangal, and in the southern kingdom Vīra Ballāla III reigned at Dvāravatīpura, the ruins of which are yet to be seen at Halebid in Mysore. Malik Nāib learned much of the wealth of the eastern and southern kingdoms while he was at Deogīr, and 'Alā-ud-dīn, who had but recently returned from a victorious campaign in Mārwār, sent him in 1308 to make a second attempt to establish his authority in Telingāna. Aided by Rāmachandra of Deogīr, he invaded Telingāna by way of Indūr, and besieged Warangal. On his carrying the outer line of defence, a high earthen rampart, Pratāparudra sued for peace, tendering an enormous indemnity and promising to pay an annual tribute. These terms were accepted, and the eunuch returned to Delhi with his spoil, and with further accounts of the wealth of the Hoysala kingdom. In 1310 he was again sent southwards to deal with this kingdom as he had dealt with Telingāna.

Meanwhile Rāmachandra of Deogīr had, in the words of a Muslim historian, "gone to Hell", and the loyalty of his son Sankara, who had succeeded him, was so doubtful that Malik Nāib, before continuing his southward march, was obliged to consider the protection of his line of communications. He marched on Dvāravatīpura with such rapidity as to take the Hindus entirely by surprise. Vīra Ballāla in the first attack on his capital was captured and compelled to submit, and much plunder was taken. Malik Nāib then marched on to the extreme south of the peninsula, defeated and plundered the rajas ruling the small kingdoms of the Pāndyas and the Kerālas, plundered the great temple of Madura, and, marching to the Palk Strait, built at Rameswaram, on the island of Pāmban, a mosque which he named after his master.

'Alā-ud-dīn's power had reached its zenith. With the exception of a very few remote regions, the whole of the Indian peninsula owned his sway, and his wealth certainly exceeded that of any prince then living; but his bodily and mental powers were failing, his temper was embittered and his intellect clouded by ill health, and his declining years were darkened by rebellion and disorder.

Of the various hordes of Mongols who had invaded India, many had accepted Islam, had been allowed to settle in the country, and had been provided for in the royal service, where they were known as New Muslims. They were discontented and turbulent and had been a continual source of trouble. The mutineers in the army returning from Gujarāt, the followers of Ākat Khān, and many other rebels, had been New Muslims; and the king therefore dismissed the whole community from his service. The malcontents hatched a plot to assassinate him as he was hawking in the neighbourhood of Delhi, but it was discovered, and a decree for the massacre of all the New Muslims was issued, obedience being ensured by a promise that the slayer of a New Muslim should become the owner of all that his victim had possessed. Between twenty and thirty thousand were slaughtered, and their wives, children, and property were seized by their murderers.

In 1312 Khizr Khān, the king's eldest son, who had married Deval Devi, the princess of Gujarāt, was designated heir apparent, and Malik Nāib, who hated him, so resented this action that at his own request he was sent back to the Deccan. There he collected all arrears of tribute, put to death Sankara, who had defied the royal authority, assumed the government of Deogīr, captured Gulbarga, annexed the doāb between the Krishnā and the Tungabhadrā, invaded and plundered Telingāna and the Hoysala kingdom, and took the sea-ports of Dābhol and Chaul. 'Alā-ud-dīn, who had been obliged to take to his bed, and was neglected by his family, recalled the eunuch to Delhi, where he was able to take revenge on all his enemies by persuading the king that they were conspiring against his life. Alp Khān was put to death, and the two elder princes, Khizr Khān and Shādī Khān, with their mother, were imprisoned. The eunuch's malevolent activity enraged all, and rebellions broke out in Gujarāt, Rājasthān, and Deogīr, where Rāmachandra's son-in-law, Harpāl, proclaimed himself independent. On January 2, 1316, 'Alā-ud-dīn died, and his favourite produced a will disinheriting the three eldest sons, and leaving the crown to the fourth, Shihāb-ud-dīn 'Umar, a child of five or six. The two eldest sons were blinded, and soldiers were sent to blind the third, Mubārak, but he bribed them to slay the monster who had employed them.

Mubārak at first assumed office as regent for his young brother, but two months later deposed him and ascended the throne as Kutb-ud-dīn Mubārak Shāh, and soon afterwards caused the child and his two elder brothers to be put to death.

Mubārak at first gained much popularity by the rescission of all his father's harsher edicts. The abolition of the feudal system had been much resented, as had also a regulation requiring that all horses produced for service in the army should be branded, for more profit could be made from fiefs than from fixed salaries, and the production of borrowed horses for muster parades was far less costly than the maintenance of horses fit for service. The feudal system was restored; grants of rent-free land were made; and the branding regulation and the tariff of fixed prices were withdrawn. The sudden removal of all restraints produced an outburst of licentiousness similar to that which had disgraced the reign of Kaikubād, and once again the king's example encouraged his subjects, for his morals were no better than his father's, and from the earliest days of his reign he was under the influence of a vile favourite who had belonged to one of the scavenger castes of western India, but had nominally accepted Islam, and had been entitled Khusraw Khān. The old nobles were disgusted by the ribaldry and the foul obscenities which Mubārak not only permitted, but encouraged at his court, and by the appearance of their ruler, decked out with female finery and jewels.

The restoration of order was the new king's first serious task. He sent to Gujarāt 'Ain-ul-mulk of Multān, who quelled the rebellion there, and, in 1317, himself set out for the Deccan. Harpāl fled from Deogīr, but was pursued, captured, and flayed alive; and Mahārāshtra was once more parcelled out among Muslim officers. He remained at Deogīr for a year, during which time he built the great mosque still standing there, and in the autumn of 1318 he dispatched Khusraw, now lieutenant of the kingdom, on an expedition to Madura. During his march to Delhi he narrowly escaped death as the result of a plot in which some of his own relatives, the descendants of his grand-uncle Yaghrush Khān, were implicated. On reaching Delhi he put to death all Yaghrush Khān's descendants, twenty-nine in number, some of whom were mere infants. Mubārak then, in the midst of his debauchery, ventured on an act but little less impudent than that which his father had contemplated. The 'Abbāsid caliphate of Baghdād had been extinguished by Hulāgū in 1258, and there was no caliph in the eastern Islamic world. The drunken young libertine arrogated to himself the titles of Commander of the Faithful and *al-Wāthik billāh*.

His insane behaviour disgusted his friends and encouraged his enemies; his favourite's half-brother rebelled in Gujarāt, but was captured and pardoned; Malik Yaklakī, governor of Deogīr, rebelled in that city, and lost his nose and ears; and Khusraw was meditating treason in the south when he was recalled to Delhi, and those who had revealed his designs were punished. Surrounding his infatuated master with his own creatures, he put him to death on the night of April 14, 1320, and in the morning the courtiers, who had assembled in ignorance of what had happened, saw the outcast on the throne, and heard him proclaimed as Nāsir-ud-dīn Khusraw Shāh. The royal treasure was dissipated in an attempt to secure the support of the nobles and the army; but Khusraw soon betrayed the nature of his conversion to Islam, and Muslim historians record with indignation the open celebration of idolatrous worship at court, and the gross insults offered to their faith. Mosques were defiled and destroyed, and copies of the scriptures of Islam were used as seats and stools.

The eyes of all Muslims then turned towards Tughluk, the old warden of the marches. Khusraw was deserted by 'Ain-ul-mulk of Multān, and Tughluk, marching on Delhi, encountered the usurper on September 5, defeated him, and put him to death. He then sought for a scion of the royal house whom he might enthrone, but none survived, and all acclaimed him as king.

The new king was of mixed blood, the son of a Turkish father and an Indian mother. Though old, he was full of vigour; within a week he had pacified the capital, and within forty days his sovereignty was everywhere acknowledged. He enforced some of the more salutary laws of 'Alā-ud-dīn, and, as a natural consequence of recent events, Hindus were subjected to some repressive legislation. He pursued and punished all who had participated in Khusraw's offences, and recovered most of the public money which the usurper had lavished on his creatures and supporters. He devoted himself to the improvement of the administration and restored a most efficient postal service, but his chief care was the encouragement and extension of agriculture, to which end he reduced the demand for land revenue.

Only one vassal, Pratāparudra of Warangal, appeared to believe that his fealty to Delhi was dissolved by the extinction of the Khaljīs, and in 1321 Tughluk sent his eldest son, Muhammad Jauna, entitled Ulugh Khān, to reduce him again to obedience. Pratāparudra, after enduring a siege for some time, attempted to purchase peace, as before, by submission, but his offer was rejected, and the siege continued. The Hindus, however, interrupted the postal service of the army, so that for some time no news was received from Delhi, and Ulugh Khān, misled by evil counsellors, announced the death of his father, and tried to persuade the army to acknowledge him as king. But Tughluk's officers refused to rebel against their old master, and the dissensions in the army necessitated the raising of the siege. Ulugh Khān succeeded in silencing for ever some of his opponents, and returned by forced marches to Delhi, with his personal contingent of horse. There, by some means or other, he persuaded his father either of his innocence or of his penitence, and in 1323 he was permitted to lead another expedition into Telingāna, and on this occasion he was entirely successful. Pratāparudra surrendered; he, his family, and his principal nobles were sent to Delhi with a great quantity of treasure; and Telingāna was annexed, and administered by Muslim officers as a province of the empire. Ulugh Khān, after establishing a Muslim government in the country, led a raid into a Hindu kingdom in Orissa.

The kingdom of Bengal, ruled by the descendants of Bughrā Khān, the younger son of Balban, had been left in peace during the brief period of Khaljī rule at Delhi. But Bughrā's grandsons were now disputing the succession; and the eldest, having been worsted by his younger brother, Bahādur, appealed to Tughluk for aid. Tughluk, welcoming this opportunity for intervention, recalled Ulugh Khān from Telingāna, installed him as regent in Delhi, and marched into Bengal, annexing on the way the Hindu province of Tirhut, and driving its raja into Nepāl. Nāsir-ud-dīn, one of Bughrā's grandsons, was established as a vassal ruler in Lakhnāwati, and Bahādur was carried off, a prisoner.

Meanwhile Ulugh Khān's conduct at Delhi had aroused his father's suspicion, for he appeared to be preparing to usurp the throne. His father warned him, but Ulugh Khān apparently succeeded in allaying his suspicions, for on his return from Bengal he was received ceremoniously in a temporary pavilion at some miles distance from Delhi, before his triumphal entry into the city. This pavilion was so ingeniously constructed that it could be caused to collapse in a moment, and it fell on the old king, killing him.

It was in February or March, 1325, that Ulugh Khān succeeded his father under the title of Sultān Muhammad ibn Tughluk. He was a genius, with a share of that madness to which great wit is nearly allied, and his character was a strange medley of the most contradictory qualities. It is described by two contemporary writers, one native, fettered by the bonds of official reticence, and one foreign, untrammelled by any such bonds. Both are lost in astonishment at his arrogance, his piety, his disregard for the sacred law, his humility, his pride, his lavish generosity, his rapacity, his care for and his hostility to his people, his preference for foreigners, his love of justice, and his ferocious cruelty, and can find no better description of him than that he was a freak of creation.

The imperial policy of Tughluk, and of his son after him, differed widely from that of 'Alā-ud-dīn, who had been content to leave native rulers in possession of their ancestral domains, provided that they acknowledged him as their overlord and paid tribute. Under the new dynasty "local feudatories were superseded by governors appointed by the head of the state, and the selection of fitting and trustworthy representatives was attended by far greater risks than of old, now that the national bond, so effective among the ruling classes under the dynasty of the Turks, had disappeared amid the dissensions of Turk and Khaljī, both of whom had to bow to an alien sultan of curiously mixed breed. In the Muhammadan distrust of unconverted Hindus, all manner of foreign adventurers were installed in divisional posts; these men, having little or no interest in the stability of the throne, were ever ready to aid any projected rising, or to join, with their combined forces, any of the more influential rebels. The annals of the period present a mere succession of outbreaks—no sooner was one section of the empire brought back to its allegiance than another would seek to assert its independence".[1]

This brief view of the difficulties and defects of the administration would be incomplete without some mention of the pernicious system adopted by Muhammad in the later part of his reign of farming out the revenues, not of small areas, but of great provinces and even of groups of provinces, to men of base origin and bad principles, usually to the highest bidder. Under this system outbreaks of disorder became almost inevitable. Either the exactions of the farmer of the revenues drove the cultivators into revolt; or the farmer himself, unable to raise the sum which he had bid, found no course open to him but rebellion.

Muhammad's first measure was to assemble at Delhi officials from all the twenty-four provinces of the empire for the compilation of a register of the lands, and of the revenue assessed on them, his object being to establish a uniform system of land revenue throughout the empire, and to ensure that no village escaped taxation. Of this register, unfortunately, no vestige remains.

In the second year of his reign the series of rebellions against his authority began. His cousin Gurshāsp, the son of Tughluk's sister, rebelled in Sāgar, in the Deccan, but was defeated as he was marching on Deogīr, and took refuge with the raja of Kampli, near the Tungabhadrā. The raja refused to surrender him, and, having sent him to Vīra Ballāla III, met the Muslim troops in the field, and was defeated and slain. Vīra Ballāla surrendered the refugee, who was carried to Deogīr, and there flayed alive, his skin, stuffed with straw, being sent to the principal cities in the empire for exhibition. Kishlū Khān, governor of Multān, refused to exhibit the miserable relic, and buried it. He then rose in rebellion, whereupon Muhammad marched against him, and slew him.

It was, perhaps, the rebellion of Gurshāsp in the Deccan that suggested to Muhammad the desirability of a more central position than Delhi for his capital; and in 1327 he decreed that Deogīr, which he renamed Daulatābād, should supersede Delhi. The city was much beautified and the courtiers and officials were required to build houses there, and make it their home. The

[1] Thomas, *Chronicles*, pp. 204, 205.

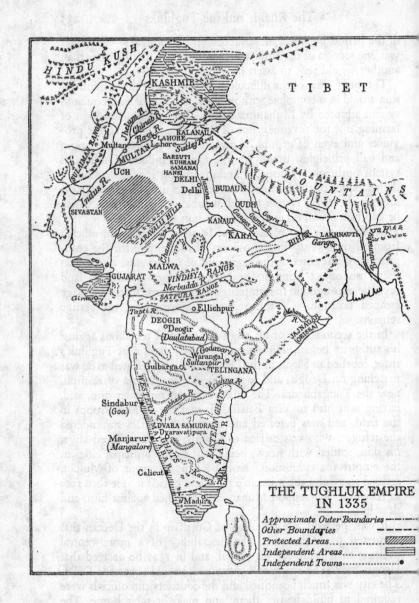

THE TUGHLUK EMPIRE
IN 1335

Approximate Outer Boundaries ----
Other Boundaries - - - -
Protected Areas
Independent Areas
Independent Towns ....•

citizens of Delhi also were encouraged to migrate to Daulatābād, and, elaborate arrangements having been made for their comfort on the way thither, many did so, but it was not until two years later, when Muhammad, having repelled and pursued into the Panjab a raiding force of Mughuls under the Chaghatāy Khān, 'Alā-ud-dīn Tirmāshīrīn, returned to Delhi and found the citizens bitterly resentful of the depopulation and impoverishment of the city, that he deported them wholesale to his new capital. He attempted, but with little success, to repopulate Delhi from other cities in northern India. The traveller Ibn Battūta, who arrived there five years later, writes, "When I entered Delhi it was almost a desert".

At about the same time the assessment of the land revenue in the Gangetic doāb was greatly enhanced. The extent of the enhancement is uncertain, but was evidently extravagant, for the Hindus of this region were still disaffected and turbulent, and it was devised as a punitive measure. It failed of its object, for most of the cultivators, unable to meet the increased demand, abandoned their holdings and took to brigandage, and one of the richest and most fertile tracts in the empire became the seat of war between the people and the royal troops.

To replenish his treasury, Muhammad had recourse to his famous device of a fictitious currency. He must have heard of the paper currency of Kublai Khān in China, and of the parchment currency attempted by the Īl-Khāns in Persia, but the failure of the latter did not discourage him. His subsequent action proves that he understood the principles of a managed currency, and that he did not believe, as is suggested by some historians ignorant of those principles, that his command could raise the value of the baser to that of the precious metals. He issued brass or copper tokens, to pass current for the silver *tanga* of 140 grains. Success might have been possible had the measure been efficiently supervised, but no steps were taken to prevent fraud. "There was no special machinery to mark the difference of the fabric of the royal mint and the handiwork of the moderately skilled artisan. Unlike the precautions taken to prevent the imitation of the Chinese paper notes, there was positively no check on the authenticity of the copper tokens and no limit to the power of production of the masses at large."[1]

[1] Thomas, *Chronicles*, pp. 245, 246.

In the three years during which the tokens were current, the country was flooded with counterfeits, but Muhammad boldly faced the situation, called in the tokens, and redeemed all, both genuine and counterfeit. The loss must have been enormous, and the remains of the mountains of base metal which arose at the treasuries were to be seen a century later.

In 1333 and 1334, during which time the Moorish traveller, Ibn Battūta, whose record of his travels is one of the best authorities for this reign, arrived at Delhi, Muhammad was engaged in attempting to restore order in the doāb, but succeeded only in devastating the country. His lavish treatment of Ibn Battūta after his return to Delhi is a fair example of his indiscriminate liberality to foreigners, though the traveller was not, as were some wandering mendicants, unworthy of his bounty. A worthless descendant of one of the caliphs of Baghdād, who visited his court some years later, received such extravagant gifts and allowances that Muhammad's treatment of him cannot be reconciled with sanity, for its recipient was merely a well-born beggar, mean and miserly almost beyond belief, and grossly dishonest.

Muhammad was called away from Delhi by the news of a serious rebellion in the peninsula. Ahsan, the governor of Ma'bar, the most southerly province of the empire, had raised the standard of revolt at Madura, and had assumed the royal title. Muhammad marched against him by way of Daulatābād and Warangal, but, in Telingāna, his troops were smitten with pestilence, and his advance was arrested. He was obliged to halt in order that the plague might be stamped out, and that his army might rest. When the disease abated, he led the rest of his army back to Bīdar, and never had another opportunity of recovering his southern province, where Ahsan Shāh founded a Muslim dynasty, which was overthrown in 1378, by the third ruler of the newly established Hindu kingdom of Vijayanagar.

The treasury had been depleted by lavish expenditure, and, above all, by the currency experiment, and Muhammad, in order to refill it, introduced the farming system, to which reference has already been made. The government of the province of Bīdar was bestowed upon Nusrat Khān, in consideration of his undertaking to pay annually into the treasury the sum of ten millions of *tangas*.

During Muhammad's absence in Warangal a report had spread that he had himself succumbed to the plague. This encouraged Malik Hūshang, a noble with whom he had been on terms of peculiar affection and intimacy, to rebel in Daulatābād. On learning that Muhammad yet lived, the rebel fled and took refuge with a petty Hindu chieftain, but was surrendered to Muhammad, and Muhammad, strange to say, pardoned him.

One of the objects in welcoming foreigners to India had been Muhammad's hope that they would help him to accomplish one of his extravagant designs, the conquest of Khurāsān. For this purpose he had raised an enormous army, which was such a drain on the treasury that in the second year of its existence no funds remained for its payment, and it melted away. The beggarly scion of the caliphs, already mentioned, had lived before his arrival under the protection of Tirmāshīrīn, in Transoxiana, and Muhammad was doubtless counting on his assistance when he welcomed him so bounteously. Another immigrant who had been received with the same object was a Mughul chieftain named Hulāgū, who had received a fief at Lahore. He rebelled, but his revolt was suppressed by the minister, Khvāja Jahān, who had been advanced to his high place at the beginning of the reign as a reward for having been the architect of the pavilion which had buried the king's father beneath its ruins.

On leaving Daulatābād for Delhi, Muhammad granted to those who had been deported eight years before a general permit to return to their old homes, and most of them joyfully accepted the concession, but some had become attached to the land of their exile and remained.

During the king's protracted absence from Delhi a heavy calamity had befallen northern India, and famine was sore in the land. For seven years the rainfall had been deficient, and the severity of the famine had been increased by the havoc which the king's punitive measures had wrought in the doāb. As he marched through Mālwā the effects of famine appalled him. Towns and whole districts of that fertile province were depopulated. On reaching Delhi he issued for six months regular rations of grain to all the citizens, and cooked food was distributed daily at various shrines in the city. Large sums were advanced to enable husbandmen to buy seed and plough-cattle, to sink wells, and to improve and extend their holdings; but those tempted by hunger to apply these advances to the satisfaction of even more pressing needs were punished with such rigour that the tale of executions shocked and disgusted even those accustomed to Muhammad's barbarous severity. He then decreed a fresh evacuation of Delhi, moved on this occasion by a desire for the welfare of his people. The fertile province of Oudh had for years prospered under the beneficent rule of its governor, 'Ain-ul-mulk, and as the king dared not transport corn from its over-flowing granaries across the sorely-vexed doāb, he built on the Ganges, near the ancient city of Kara, a town of booths to which he gave the Sanskrit name of Sargadvārī (Swarga-dwāra) or "the Gate of Paradise", and which he made his headquarters for the next six years. To this town he brought the citizens of Delhi, and there they were fed on the corn of Oudh, and lived in moderate comfort.

After the foundation of Sargadvārī he committed an act of folly for which he has been blamed to an unmerited degree. It has been represented as an attempt to conquer China, or at least Tibet, but was in fact no more than a punitive expedition on a large scale against a refractory chieftain in the Himālāya, but even so it was foolish enough. An army of 100,000 horse and a large number of foot was sent into the mountains by way of Nagarkot, or Kāngra, which it captured, and then advanced into the territories of the hill-chieftain. It was overtaken by the heavy rains of the mountains, and began to retire with its plunder, but the mountaineers cut off its retreat, and destroyed it almost to a man. Only two officers and ten men returned to Delhi. The loss of the troops and treasure was far from being the most injurious effect of the disaster. The king's prestige received such a blow that provinces smouldering with discontent under his tyranny were ready at any moment to blaze into rebellion. Nusrat Khān, unable to pay even a quarter of the vast price which he had promised for the government of Bīdar, had already risen in rebellion, but had been defeated and captured and sent to Delhi by Kutlugh Khān, governor of Daulatābād. In Gulbarga 'Ali Shāh Kar rose in rebellion, marched to Bīdar, slew the governor, and occupied that town, but he also was captured and sent to Delhi by Kutlugh Khān. He was banished from India, and after-wards, on returning without leave, was put to death. On the death of the governor of eastern Bengal in 1339 one of his

officers assumed independence in that province, and western
Bengal was shortly afterwards severed from the empire by
rebellion. 'Ain-ul-mulk, governor of Oudh, had for years ruled
that province with justice and clemency, and the victualling of
Sargadvārī had been entirely due to his prudence and foresight,
and to his arrangements for the transport of grain. He had
demurred to the surrender of some refugees whom Muhammad
had stigmatised as criminals, and was deeply perturbed by the
announcement of the king's design to transfer him from Oudh
to the government of the Deccan. He rebelled, and seized the
royal elephants, horses, pack-animals, and cattle, which were
grazing in Oudh. He assumed the title of Sultān 'Alā-ud-dīn;
his troops, numbering 50,000, attacked Muhammad, marching
to take refuge in the fortified city of Kanauj, but were defeated,
and the rebel, having been captured, was carried before Muhammad, who had the grace to remember his long and faithful service,
and, after keeping him in confinement for some months, released
and reinstated him. Malik Shāhū Lodī, an Afghan, next rose
at Multān, slew the governor, and seized the city, but fled beyond
the Indus on learning that the king was marching against him.
The subsequent rebellions in Gujarāt and the Deccan were partly
due to the galling restrictions placed on Afghan officers in consequence of Shāhū's revolt. When Muhammad returned to
Delhi, the famine was at its height, and the people were eating
human flesh. Theorist as he was, he had for some time been
pondering a code of regulations to restore prosperity to the
country, and these were immediately issued. The first divided
the empire into administrative districts measuring thirty by thirty
leagues, or about 8100 square miles, in none of which was a
span of land to be left uncultivated. No allowance was made
for forest, pasture, or uncultivable land. A fixed rotation of
crops, which was ordained, displayed complete ignorance of the
principles of agriculture. Each district was placed under the
control of an officer whose title may be translated 'undertaker',
in the sense in which that term is used in Anglo-Irish history;
but it was found to be difficult to bribe even irresponsible adventurers to undertake the execution of the regulation. Seventy
million *tangas* were thus expended, and at last some persons were
induced to undertake to re-people the land and to see that every
square mile maintained a fixed number of horsemen. The bribes

are described by one historian as the blood-money of the under-takers, who, when they perceived the impossibility of carrying out their agreements, appropriated to their own use all that they had collected, trusting to events to enable them to escape their merited fate. At the end of the stipulated term of three years, says Baranī, not one-hundredth, nay not one-thousandth, part of the undertakings had been fulfilled, and, had not Muhammad died when he did, not one of the undertakers would have sur-vived his resentment.

The second regulation encouraged the Mughuls to settle in India, and great sums were expended in inducing these foreigners to make India their home. The third regulation was framed with a view to the development and expansion of the resources of the state, but these were already taxed to the utmost, and we are not told how Muhammad proposed to exact any more from a starving and harassed people. The fourth enhanced the severity of the penal code, already sufficiently barbarous. "The king", says Ibn Battūta, "slew both small and great, and spared not the learned, the pious, or the noble. Daily there were brought to the council-hall men in chains, fetters, and bonds, and they were led away, some to execution, some to torture, some to scourging. May God preserve us from such calamities!"

Ibn Battūta left Delhi in July, 1342, the king taking advantage of his departure to entrust him with a mission to China. This had no result, but the traveller's account of his journey through India discloses the deplorable state of the country. The doāb was in rebellion, and not even an escort of a thousand horse sufficed to save him from being captured by Hindu rebels. He escaped, and eventually reached the Muslim court of Madura.

In 1343 Muhammad was occupied in the regions between the Jumna and the Sutlej, where many Hindus had abandoned agriculture for brigandage, dispersing the gangs of bandits and capturing their leaders. On his return to Delhi he received with the most extravagant honours the envoy of the puppet 'Abbāsīd caliph in Cairo, al-Hākim II, his self-abasement before the astonished Egyptian verging on the grotesque. As Baranī says, "Without the caliph's command the king scarcely ventured to drink a cup of water".

Rebellions continued. The caliph's envoy was yet at Delhi when Nizām-ul-mulk, a worthless debauchee to whom the district of Kara had been farmed for an immense sum, finding that he could not pay one-tenth of the price, rose in rebellion, styling himself Sultān 'Alā-ud-dīn. Muhammad was preparing to march against him when he received the rebel's skin, sent him by 'Ain-ul-mulk of Oudh.

The revenue of the Deccan had fallen by ninety per cent. owing to the introduction of the farming system and consequent rebellions. Grave apprehensions were aroused by the recall of the mild and pious Kutlugh Khān, who had governed the province benevolently throughout the reign, and by the announcement of the king's intention to divide the Deccan and Mālwā into four *shikks*, or revenue divisions, from which he proposed to collect annually 670 million *tangas*. Alarm was increased by the selection of the collecting agency, at the head of which was placed 'Azīz Khammār ("the Vintner"), a low-born, unscrupulous, and extortionate adventurer. Those who were chiefly blamed for the trouble in Mālwā, Gujarāt, and the Deccan were the "centurions", military officers who, in a civil capacity, were responsible for the maintenance of order and the collection of the revenue in *parganas*, or groups of villages. Regarding these officials 'Azīz had received special instructions, and, summoning eighty-nine of them before him, he had them executed before his official residence at Dhār. The horror of the centurions of Gujarāt and the Deccan at this atrocious act was increased by the king's openly avowed approval of it, and those of Gujarāt rose in rebellion and plundered a large consignment of revenue, leaving that province for the capital. The king marched from Delhi, and on his way towards Gujarāt was incensed, but not surprised, by the news that 'Azīz, having marched against the rebels, had been defeated and taken by them, and put to death with torture. He continued his march in the spring of 1345, and a force detached by him defeated the centurions near Baroda. They fled towards the Deccan, and the king, marching to Broach, sent a force to intercept them. This force came up with them on the Nerbudda, and again defeated them. Some fugitives reached Daulatābād, and a few took refuge in Baglāna, where the raja imprisoned them. Those centurions of Broach, who had shown their loyalty by marching with the royal army against their fellows, were put to death by Muhammad's order, and the news of this ferocious act added fuel to the fire of sedition in the Deccan. Muhammad remained at Broach, collecting arrears of revenue with great severity, and putting to death all suspected of having sympathised with the rebellion. He sent orders to the governor of Daulatābād, directing him to send the centurions of that province to Broach under escort. Of his intention there could be no doubt, and the centurions, having been dispatched as ordered, turned on their escort at the end of the first day's march, slew its leaders, and returned to Daulatābād. There they imprisoned the governor, seized the treasure, and proclaimed Ismā'il Mukh the Afghan, one of their number, king of the Deccan, under the title of Nāsir-ud-dīn Ismā'il Shāh. Muhammad marched to Daulatābād, and the rebels went forth to meet him, but were defeated and driven into the citadel, while the centurions of Bīdar under Hasan, entitled Zafar Khān, fell back on Gulbarga in order to recruit their forces. Sartīz, governor of Ellichpur, was sent against them, and Muhammad opened the siege of Daulatābād. He was thus engaged when he received news of another serious rising in Gujarāt under the leadership of Taghī, a man of humble origin. Leaving a force to continue the siege of Daulatābād, he marched back into Gujarāt, and for more than three years was engaged in pursuing the elusive Taghī, and in bringing into the Muslim obedience, for the first time, the raja of Girnār, now Junāgarh, in Kāthiāwār, who had harboured the rebel. When Girnār fell, both its ruler and the raja of Kachch, his ally, made their submission to Muhammad; but Taghī had fled into Sind before the leaguer of Girnār had been completed; and Muhammad, having spent the rainy season of 1350 in Gondal, prostrated by an attack of fever, set out in the autumn for Sind, in pursuit of Taghī, having summoned to his assistance a contingent of four or five thousand Mughuls, under a chieftain named Ultūn Bahādur. He marched on Tatta, but, when within thirty leagues of that town, again fell sick, and continued his journey by boat. Within fourteen leagues of Tatta he was obliged to rest, and great fear fell upon his army, which was held together by his personal authority alone. Far from home, encumbered with their wives and families, within reach of the enemy, and attended by allies whom they feared, they knew not what would befall them on the death of their leader. On March 20, 1351, the event they dreaded came to pass, "and so", says Budaunī, "the king was freed of his people, and they of their king".

The great empire founded by 'Alā-ud-dīn and ruled by Muhammad at the beginning of his reign had for some time been in the course of dissolution. First the peninsula and then Bengal had fallen away from it. Shortly after Muhammad had left Daulatābād to deal with Taghī in Gujarāt, Zafar Khān had advanced from Gulbarga to Bīdar, and, having there defeated and slain Sartīz, had marched to the relief of Daulatābād. On his approach the royal troops had raised the siege and had beaten a hasty retreat into Mālwā. Ismā'il Shāh, descending from the citadel, had welcomed his deliverer and abdicated in his favour, and on August 3, 1347, Zafar Khān was proclaimed king of the Deccan under the title of 'Alā-ud-dīn Bahman Shāh, and the great tract of country, lying between the Nerbudda on the north and the Krishnā and the Tungabhadrā on the south, was cut off from the kingdom of Delhi for two and a half centuries. Thus ended the first Muslim empire in India.

CHAPTER III

The Fall of the Tughluks

In an Oriental monarchy the demise of the crown, unless the throne is at once filled, throws the state into anarchy, for the king is the state, and if there is no king there is no state. The death of Muhammad occurred in peculiarly unfortunate circumstances, and, while anarchy at Delhi was probable, anarchy in the army, leaderless and beset by dangers, was immediate. With the army at the time was Muhammad's cousin-german, Fīrūz, entitled Malik Rajab. It is said by his court historians that Muhammad had bequeathed the crown to him, but this is uncertain, and Fīrūz was most unwilling to assume it. The army, having already begun to retreat in a straggling and disorderly fashion, was attacked in rear by the people of Sind and in flank by its recent allies, the Mughuls, and was plundered by both; yet it was two days before Fīrūz yielded to the importunity of its officers, and assumed the royal title. Having done so he drove off the enemy and led the army towards Delhi.

The aged minister, Khvājā Jahān, had meanwhile attempted to ensure peace in the capital by proclaiming a child whom he alleged to be the son of Muhammad, but whom the panegyrists of Fīrūz represent to be supposititious. The child's paternity, as alleged by the minister, was no recommendation to the people, who declined to be ruled by the son of the tyrant, and, as Fīrūz approached, the minister's position became hopeless, and he was obliged to seek the royal camp as a suppliant. Fīrūz punished him only with banishment to Sāmāna, but the nobles, who had from the first insisted that he should be put to death, caused him to be assassinated on his way thither. Fīrūz was a contrast to his cousin. He made no serious attempt to recover either Bengal or the Deccan, and was an administrator rather than a soldier. He did his best to repair the errors of Muhammad, whose memory he respected, though he trembled for the fate of his soul, and imposed upon himself the duty of vicarious atonement. All those who had been tortured or mutilated, and the heirs of all who had been unjustly put to death, received compensation, and were

required to execute deeds, attested by witnesses, declaring themselves to be satisfied. These deeds were laid in a chest, placed in
Muhammad's tomb, to enable him to meet any charges which
might be brought against him beyond the grave.

The first administrative measure adopted was the appointment
of an assessor of the land revenue, who, within six years, completed a tour of the kingdom and submitted his report. The
demand on account of land revenue was so reduced as to leave
ample provision for the cultivator's needs, and one result of this
and other beneficent measures was an enormous expansion of
the cultivated area. In fertile tracts thriving villages inhabited
by a contented peasantry dotted the country at intervals of about
two miles, and in the neighbourhood of Delhi alone there were
1200 garden villages in which fruit was grown, and which contributed £15,000 a year to the treasury. The annual revenue from
the doāb, nearly depopulated during the last reign, soon amounted
to £65,000, and that of the crown lands of the whole kingdom
to over five and a half millions. At a later period Fīrūz abolished
some twenty-five vexatious cesses, chiefly of the nature of octroi
duties, at a loss to the exchequer of about a quarter of a million,
but the result was a fall in prices which brought them to the
level of 'Alā-ud-dīn's tariff. Nor was it only by lightening the
burdens of the people that he encouraged agriculture and trade,
for he is still remembered as the author of schemes of irrigation,
and traces of his canals yet remain. He also sank 150 wells for
the purposes of irrigation and the relief of travellers, and indulged
a passion for building which equalled, if it did not surpass, that
of the Roman emperor, Augustus. He built many villages and
towns, among them Fīrūzābād or New Delhi, Fathābād, Hissār,
Fīrūzpūr near Budaun, and Jaunpur; four mosques, thirty palaces,
two hundred caravanserais, five reservoirs, five hospitals, a hundred
tombs, ten baths, ten memorial pillars, and a hundred bridges.

He was pious, and mild and indulgent to those of his own faith,
for whom he abolished capital punishment, but he was a rigid
Muslim, and the harsher side of his piety was displayed in his
persecution of heretics, sectaries, and Hindus. He burned to
death a Brāhman accused of attempting to propagate his faith;
and he insisted on Brāhmans paying the *jizya*, or poll-tax on
non-Muslims, which they had long evaded. Towards the end
of his reign Kharkir, the raja of Katehr, treacherously put to

death the Sayyid governor of Budaun and his two brothers. The powers of Fīrūz were beginning to fail, and he had become slothful; but this insult to his faith aroused him from his lethargy, and his vengeance was worthy of his cousin. In the spring of 1380 he marched into Katehr, and there commanded a massacre of the Hindus so general and so indiscriminate that, as one historian says, "the spirits of the murdered Sayyids themselves arose to intercede". The raja fled into the hills, leaving his subjects to the mercy of Fīrūz, who slew vast numbers and enslaved 23,000, and on his departure left an Afghan governor, with orders to devastate Katehr annually with fire and sword. For five successive years he visited the province, and so supplemented the Afghan's bloody work that in these years "not an acre of land was cultivated, no man slept in his house, and the death of the three Sayyids was avenged by that of countless thousands of Hindus".

In 1352 one Hājjī Iliyās had established his authority over both eastern and western Bengal, and styled himself Shams-ud-dīn Iliyās Shāh. He invaded Tirhut with the object of annexing the province, but Fīrūz, though he had acquiesced in the independence of Bengal, was not prepared to suffer its ruler to encroach on his own dominions, and marched against him with an army of 70,000 horse. Iliyās retired to Ikdāla, a village situated on islands in the Brahmaputra, and protected by the dense jungle which clothed the river's banks. Fīrūz was unable to reduce this stronghold, and was obliged to retreat before the rainy season began. Iliyās followed him, and is said to have been defeated in the field, but Fīrūz was obliged to continue his retreat.

Four years later an envoy from al-Mu'tadid, the puppet caliph in Egypt, reached Delhi with a commission recognising Fīrūz as the sultan of Delhi, but bearing also a letter announcing that the caliph had recognised Bahman Shāh as king of the Deccan. Three years later Fīrūz again invaded Bengal. Iliyās had died in 1357, and had been succeeded by his son, Sikandar Shāh, a pretext for attacking whom was furnished by the Persian, Zafar Khān. He had married the daughter of Mubārak Shāh, who had established his independence in eastern Bengal in 1338. Zafar Khān's hopes of succeeding his father-in-law had been shattered by the conquest of eastern Bengal by Iliyās in 1352, and he had taken refuge at the court of Fīrūz, where he had been favourably received and generously treated. The flimsy pretext of vindicating his rights served Firūz, who marched from Delhi in the spring of 1359 and halted for six months, until the end of the rainy season, on the Gumti, where he founded the city of Jaunpur. In the autumn he continued his march, and Sikandar, like his father, retired to Ikdāla. The second siege was no more successful than the first, and Sikandar obtained peace on very favourable terms. The historians of Firūz say that Sikandar agreed to pay an annual tribute of forty elephants, and to surrender Sonārgāon, the capital of eastern Bengal, to Zafar Khān, but the tribute was seldom, if ever, remitted to Delhi, and Zafar Khān preferred the security and emoluments of his place at Delhi to the precarious tenure of a vassal throne. On the other hand Firūz presented to Sikandar a jewelled crown and 5000 fine horses, and recognised his royal title.

Firūz retired to Jaunpur and, in the autumn of 1360, led an expedition into Orissa, his objective being Puri, famous for the great temple of Jagannāth. He reached Puri, occupied the raja's palace, and is said to have sent the great idol to Delhi, to be trodden underfoot by the faithful, and the raja, who had fled into Telingāna, made his peace with a promise to send an annual tribute of twenty elephants. Firūz then attempted to reach Kara, which he had made his base, by the direct route through the hills and forests of Jhārkhand, or Chota Nāgpur. Here the army lost its way, and wandered for six months in an unknown country. Supplies were not to be had, and numbers perished from the hardships and privations which they suffered. Meanwhile the absence of news from the army caused grave unrest at Delhi, and the minister, a Brāhman of Telingāna who had received the name of Makbūl when he accepted Islam, and was now entitled Khānjahān, had much difficulty in maintaining order; but the news that the army had emerged into the plains of Bihar allayed the excitement of the populace, and the king was received with great joy on his return.

In 1351, before the caliph's recognition of Bahman Shāh of the Deccan, Firūz had marched from Delhi with the object of recovering Daulatābād, but, his progress having been arrested by reports that the raja of Kāngra had ventured to invade his kingdom and plunder some of the districts at the foot of the mountains, he turned against him by way of Sirhind, visited the temple of

Jwāla-Mukhi, some of the books in the library of which he caused to be translated into Persian, and, on the surrender and submission of the raja, generously allowed him to retain his state as a fief of Delhi.

The enforced retreat from Sind, and the insolence of its people had rankled in the memory of Fīrūz, ever since his accession, and in 1362 he set out for that country with an army of 90,000 horse and 480 elephants, accompanied by a great fleet of boats which he had assembled on the Indus; but when he reached Tatta, the capital, the crops had been reaped and stored in the city, which was resolutely defended by its ruler, Jām Mālī, and his nephew Bābaniya. The besiegers were famine-stricken, and three-fourths of their horses were carried off or disabled by disease. The fleet was captured, and Fīrūz decided to retire into Gujarāt to enable his troops to recruit their strength and replace their horses. During the retreat the sufferings of the army were terrible. Famine still prevailed, and starving men fell out by the wayside and died. They were treacherously guided across the Rann of Kachch, where there was no fresh water, and thirst was added to their other sufferings. Once again no news of the army reached Delhi for some months, and the minister was reduced to the expedient of forging a dispatch to allay the excitement of the people. At length the army debouched into the fertile plains of Gujarāt, and there gradually recovered its strength. During the rainy season of 1363 Fīrūz led it again into Sind. His return was unexpected, and he arrived before Tatta while the crops were yet green. After an unsuccessful attack on the city he sent to Delhi for reinforcements, and his troops cut the crops, which afforded them ample supplies, while the garrison began to feel the pinch of famine, and were so distressed that even before the reinforcements arrived the jām sent envoys to sue for peace. He was allowed to retain his kingdom on undertaking to pay annually 400,000 *tangas* as tribute, but for the time being both he and his nephew were required to accompany Fīrūz to Delhi as hostages. The sufferings of the army during its retreat into Gujarāt had so affected Fīrūz that he swore never again to make war, but for the suppression of rebellion. Thus it was that when, in 1366, envoys came from Bahrām Khān Māzandārāni, who was in rebellion against his brother-in-law, Muhammad Shāh Bahmanī I of the Deccan, and offered, should Fīrūz aid him, to hold the

Deccan as a fief of Delhi, they were told that their employer
and his friends were suffering the just punishment of rebellion,
and were summarily dismissed.

Death now began to deprive Fīrūz of his best and dearest.
In 1372 his faithful minister, Makbūl Khānjahān, died, and was
succeeded in his office and his title by his son, and in 1374
Fīrūz's favourite son died. The gradual impairment of his
faculties, which then first became evident in his neglect of public
business, may be attributed to his grief at his loss. A few years
later the failure of his powers kindled the ambition of the new
minister, who succeeded in persuading him that his eldest surviving son, Muhammad, was conspiring to remove him, and
to usurp the throne. The prince was summoned to a durbar, at
which he was to have been arrested, but evaded attendance on
the plea of ill-health, and a little later forced his way into his
father's presence and convinced him that it was Khānjahān, not
he, who was harbouring ambitious designs, and, with his permission, led the household troops in an attack on the minister's
house. Khānjahān was defeated and wounded, and fled into
Mewāt, but Koka the Chauhān, the Rājput chief with whom he
took refuge, surrendered him to one of the prince's officers, and
his head was sent to Muhammad in Delhi.

Fīrūz, no longer capable of ruling, associated his son with himself in the government, and even in the royal title, causing him
to be proclaimed as Nāsir-ud-dīn Muhammad Shāh. Muhammad, believing his succession to be assured, neglected all public
business and devoted himself entirely to pleasure. For five months
the administrative machinery, which had been reformed by
Fīrūz in the early years of his reign, worked automatically, until
the apathy and incompetency of Muhammad threw it out of
order. Many of the old servants of the crown rose against him
in the interests of Fīrūz, and, when hard pressed by his troops,
forced their way into the palace and brought the old king forth
in a litter. Muhammad's troops, finding themselves arrayed
against Fīrūz, deserted their master, and he fled into Sirmūr with
but a few retainers. Fīrūz then promoted his grandson, Tughluk,
son of the deceased Fath Khān, to the position recently held by
Muhammad, and conferred on him the royal title. On September
20, 1388, Fīrūz died, at the age of eighty-three, after a reign of
thirty-seven years.

The great empire of India had begun to dissolve before the
death of Muhammad ibn Tughluk, and before the death of Fīrūz
even the kingdom of Delhi was already dissolving. As his bodily
and mental powers decayed, power fell more and more into the
hands of the nobles and officers of state, and on his death he left
a disputed succession, one of the worst legacies which the subjects
of an oriental ruler can inherit, even when the result of the
contest is reasonably certain; but there now remained none of
the royal house worthy of the throne. His grandson, Ghiyās-ud-
dīn Tughluk II, succeeded him at Delhi, while his son Muhammad
was preparing in the Sirmūr hills to assert his title to the throne.
Tughluk, before he could come to grips with his uncle, was
driven from the throne, and put to death by his cousin, Abu
Bakr. The details of the contest are too complicated and confusing to be followed minutely here. On August 31, 1390,
Muhammad established himself in Delhi, and Abu Bakr fled into
Mewāt, where he was shortly afterwards captured. Muhammad's
brief reign was troubled, for the Hindus of the doāb and Bahādur
Nāhir, the chief of Mewāt, were again in rebellion. On January
30, 1394, Muhammad died, and was succeeded by his son
Humāyūn, who ascended the throne as ʿAlā-ud-dīn Sikandar
Shāh, but died within two months.

A eunuch, Malik Sarvar, had risen to power during Muhammad's reign, and had been left as regent at Delhi during
the king's absence from the capital. He persuaded the provincial
governors, who were assembled at Delhi to consult about restoring order in the Panjab, to enthrone, under the title of
Nāsir-ud-dīn Mahmūd, Humāyūn's brother, the younger son of
Muhammad. The new king was feeble-minded, and throughout
his reign was a puppet in the hands of one or other of the great
nobles. The kingdom was in a deplorable condition. The Khokhars
were in rebellion in the Panjab; in the eastern provinces the
Hindus, who had long ceased to contribute anything to the
exchequer, threw off all semblance of obedience, and Sarvar
induced or compelled the young king to bestow upon him the
lofty title of *Sultān-ush-shark*, or "King of the East", and to
commit to him the duty of crushing the rebellion and restoring
order. He left Delhi in May, 1394, reduced to obedience the rebels
in the doāb, and occupied Jaunpur, where he established himself
as an independent ruler. The day on which he left Delhi may be

reckoned as the date of the foundation of the dynasty of "the Kings of the East", or Jaunpur. Meanwhile Sārang Khān, governor of Dīpālpur, had defeated the Khokhars and established his own authority in the Panjab, and at the same time the two great provinces of Mālwā and Gujarāt were severed from the kingdom. Dilāvar Khān, governor of Mālwā, never assumed the royal title, but from 1392 onwards he neither remitted tribute nor paid any heed to the affairs of Delhi. Zafar Khān of Gujarāt assumed the royal title in 1396, as Muzaffar Shāh, but for some time before that year he had ceased to hold communication with the capital.

In the miserable remnant of the kingdom factious nobles were contending with each other for the possession of the person of a puppet king. One Saʿādat Khān prevailed for some time, but the king wearied of his control, and, fleeing from him, took refuge in Delhi with Mukarrab Khān, while Saʿādat Khān, enraged by his desertion, proclaimed as king in Fīrūzābād Nusrat Khān, the younger son of Fath Khān, eldest son of Fīrūz. There were thus two kings in adjoining cities, each a puppet in the hands of a powerful noble. The affairs of the kingdom were in this condition when Pīr Muhammad crossed the Indus, and, in May 1398, occupied Multān.

To this portent the factious nobles of Delhi paid no heed. One Mallū, who had received the title of Ikbāl Khān, murdered Mukarrab Khān, gained possession of the person of Mahmūd, and drove Nusrat Shāh as a fugitive into the doāb.

The continuance of squabbles for precedence, in a kingdom but a shred of its former self, in face of the deadly peril which now menaced India, betrays the ignorance and parochial outlook of those in whose hands it remained. The terrible amir of Samarkand, Tīmūr, conqueror of Persia and Mesopotamia, had announced his intention of invading the country, and Pīr Muhammad, his forerunner, had already occupied a frontier province. Tīmūr seldom required either a pretext or a stimulus for his aggressions, but India supplied him with both. The pretext was the toleration of idolatry by its Muslim rulers, and the stimulus was the disintegration of the kingdom, unparalleled in its history. Tīmūr joined his grandson at Multān and marched on Delhi. He massacred the people of Talamba, defeated Jasrat the Khokhar on the Sutlej, captured Bhatnair and massacred its inhabitants, and then marched on towards the capital, plundering and massacring and enslaving those of the villagers and townsfolk who failed to make their escape. On December 10, 1398, having crossed the Jumna, he occupied Lonī, and, having massacred its Hindu inhabitants, made it his headquarters. Two days later his captives exhibited some signs of joy when a reconnaissance, led across the river by Tīmūr himself, was attacked by Mallū. The poor wretches, to the number of 100,000, paid for their indiscretion with their lives. On December 17, Tīmūr, crossing the river, fell upon and defeated the army which Mallū and Mahmūd led out from Delhi. Mallū concealed himself in Baran, but Mahmūd made the best of his way to Gujarāt, and sought an asylum with Sultān Muzaffar. Tīmūr granted an amnesty to the people of Delhi, but the licence of his troops provoked a rising which was punished by a general massacre, and for several days his army sacked the city, slaying many thousands of its inhabitants, whose "bodies were given as food to the birds and the beasts, their souls being sent to the depths of hell". So many captives were taken that in the army "there was none so humble but he had at least twenty slaves". On January 1, 1399, Tīmūr retired, and after taking Meerut by storm and massacring its Hindu inhabitants, followed the line of the lower slopes of the Himālāyas, marking his track by the almost daily slaughter of great numbers of Hindus.

At Delhi Khizr Khān, the Sayyid, who had been expelled from the province of Multān by Mallū's brother, Sārang Khān, made his submission to Tīmūr, and accompanied him on his retreat as far as Kashmīr, where Tīmūr dismissed him, after appointing him to the government of the Panjab. Some historians say that he was also appointed Tīmūr's viceroy in Delhi, but this addition was perhaps suggested by later events.

After the invader's departure the whole of northern India was in indescribable disorder and confusion. As a result of the wholesale destruction of stores of grain and standing crops, famine was rife in the land, and the thousands of putrefying corpses polluted the air and the water, and bred a pestilence. "Delhi was utterly ruined, and those of its people who were left died, while for two whole months not a bird moved wing in the city." Of the kingdom hardly a trace remained. The Panjab and Upper Sind were ruled by Khizr Khān as Tīmūr's viceroy; Ghālib Khān was independent in Sāmāna, and Shams Khān Auhadī in Bayāna; Kālpī and Mahobā formed a principality under Nāsir-ud-dīn Mahmūd, and Mewār another under Bahādur Nāhir; Gwalior had been recovered by the Tonwār Rājput, Har Singh, and a Rājput clan had established its independence in Etāwah. Nusrat Shāh occupied Delhi, but was driven thence by Mallū who, after an abortive campaign against Jaunpur, where Sarvar had been succeeded by his adopted son, Mubārak, returned in 1401 to Delhi, and invited Mahmūd to return to his capital. The wanderer's experiences had been bitterly humiliating. Muzaffar Shāh of Gujarāt had been at no pains to conceal from him that his presence was distasteful, and he had fled from Gujarāt to Mālwā, where Dilāvar Khān had treated him more courteously, and housed him in comfort; but he could not refuse to return to his kingdom, and, on his reaching Delhi, Mallū interned him in his palace and governed the remnant of his kingdom without even feigning to consult him. In 1402, on the death of Mubārak Shāh in Jaunpur, Mallū marched to attack his successor, Ibrāhīm, in the hope of recovering Jaunpur, but, on coming face to face with Ibrāhīm's army, dared not attack it. Mahmūd, whom he had carried with him to Kanauj, attempted to take refuge with Ibrāhīm, but was so ill received that he again fled, and established himself in the strongly fortified city of Kanauj, while Mallū, much weakened by his defection, returned to Delhi. During the next three years Mallū attempted, but without success, to recover Gwalior, Etāwah, and Kanauj, and in 1405 marched against Khizr Khān, who was then established in Dīpālpur. On November 12 Khizr Khān defeated and slew him near Pāk Pattan. On his death the direction of affairs at Delhi fell into the hands of a body of officers headed by Daulat Khān Lodī and Ikhtiyār Khān, at whose invitation Mahmūd returned to his capital. Daulat Khān succeeded in recovering Sāmāna, which had been captured and held by one of Khizr Khān's officers, and then a year was wasted in languid and inconclusive warfare with Jaunpur, while Khizr Khān began to close in on Delhi. He twice besieged the city, but on each occasion was obliged to retire owing to the scarcity of supplies. In February 1413, Mahmūd died at Kaithal, after a nominal reign of twenty years, and the Tughluk dynasty came to an end. On his death the local officers transferred their allegiance to Daulat Khān Lodī, but in March 1414 Khizr Khān opened the siege of Delhi, and captured it after four months. He had for some years ruled the Panjab, and the acquisition of Delhi added little to his territories, for the authority of those from whom he took it extended hardly beyond the neighbourhood of the city walls.

CHAPTER IV

The Sayyid and the Lodī Dynasties, and the Kingdom of Jaunpur

Khizr Khān founded the Sayyid dynasty, of which four kings reigned for thirty-seven years. Their territory consisted of Delhi and the country round its walls, and the history of the period is a record of raids to collect revenue or tribute, and of futile campaigns against the more powerful kingdom of Jaunpur. Khizr Khān, during the seven years of his reign, was constantly in the field, engaged, according to Muslim historians, in quelling rebellions, but there was little active rebellion, for there was no need for it. Fief-holders and Hindu chieftains lived ordinarily at peace in their strongholds, disturbed occasionally by Khizr Khān who, when he was in need, attacked them. He could not reduce their strongholds, but he could cut off supplies and harass the wretched cultivators until their rulers bought him off by meeting his demands, and by promises, never kept or intended to be kept, of regular payments in future. In his short reign he thus harried the raja of Etāwah four times, those of Katehr and Gwalior three times, the feudatories of Chandwār (Fīrūzābād), Koīl, Bayāna and Sirhind twice, and those of five other districts once. Throughout his reign and those of his successors the territories nominally subject to Delhi were frequently raided from the north-west by Jasrat the Khokhar, who was independent in the northern Panjab, declining to acknowledge the sovereignty of the Sayyids, and would have seized the throne of Delhi but that the powerful feudatories who withheld their allegiance from that throne would have actively combined against him. Khizr Khān died on May 20, 1421. He never assumed the royal title, but was content to be styled *Rāyāt-i-aʿlā* or the 'Sublime Banners', a title which embodied a profession of vassalage of Tīmūr and his son Shāhrukh. His elder son, who succeeded him as Muʿizz-ud-dīn Mubārak Shāh, assumed the royal title and owed no allegiance to the Timurids. His reign, like that of his father, was spent largely in a series of raids on those whose allegiance he claimed, but who would never acknowledge his sovereignty until compelled by force to make some material contribution to his treasury.

Khizr Khān, though no statesman, was an active and energetic soldier, and the same, in a less degree, may be said of his son. Gradual degeneracy is a marked characteristic of oriental dynasties, but in this dynasty the degeneracy was rapid, not gradual. Four generations of the house sat upon the throne, and each of the last three rulers was more contemptible than his predecessor. Mubārak, though inferior to his father both as a soldier and as a statesman, was not so slothful or mean-spirited as his successors. He led expeditions into the districts which his father had invaded, and into some others; he drove Jasrat out of his kingdom, and with the help of Bhīm, raja of Jammū, whom Jasrat afterwards defeated and slew, attacked and destroyed his principal stronghold; he fortified and garrisoned Lahore, which had been in ruins since Tīmūr's invasion, and he dealt vigorously with a new enemy. This was Shaikh 'Alī, lieutenant of Suyūrghātmish, fourth son of Shāhrukh and governor, on behalf of his father, of Kābul. It may be that his raids into India were attempts to punish Mubārak for having repudiated allegiance to Shāhrukh. He occupied Multān and plundered its inhabitants until driven out by one of Mubārak's officers, and he received a yearly sum as blackmail from the governor of Lahore. He marched to Bhātinda, then held by a rebel, compelled Mubārak's troops to raise the siege of the town, and received a great sum as the price of his assistance, but was defeated, on his retreat, by the governor of Multān. He continued, however, to raid the Panjab, and occupied the fortress of Shorkot. He defeated and slew Islām Khān Lodī, one of Mubārak's best officers, and governor of the important district of Sirhind; but two years later his nephew, Amīr Muzaffar, was attacked by Mubārak in Shorkot, and was obliged to purchase a safe retreat by giving his daughter in marriage to Muhammad, Mubārak's nephew and adopted son.

On discovering that his powerful minister, Sarvar-ul-mulk, whom he dared not dismiss, had long been neglecting his duty, Mubārak appointed a coadjutor, and Sarvar-ul-mulk, resenting what he regarded as supersession, formed a conspiracy against his master. Mubārak, unconscious of his danger, was employing himself in building Mubārakābād, a town on the Jumna, until he was called away by the welcome news that Bhātinda had at last fallen, and that Fūlād, the leader of the rebellion, had perished. He marched to Bhātinda, and was there extinguishing the embers of disaffection when he learned that Ibrāhīm Shāh of Jaunpur and Hūshang Shāh of Mālwā had claimed the sovereignty of the district of Kālpī, and were marching to decide the question by an appeal to arms. He could not permit two independent rulers to dispute the sovereignty of a district which had always, at least nominally, belonged to the kingdom of Delhi, and he returned to Delhi to assemble his forces. On his way to Kālpī, he turned aside to visit Mubārakābād, and there, on February 19, 1434, Sarvar-ul-mulk caused him to be assassinated.

He left no son, and the nobles at Delhi enthroned Muhammad, the son of his deceased brother, Farīd. Sarvar-ul-mulk's guilt was known to all, but he held possession of the royal treasury, armoury and elephants, and Muhammad dared not dismiss him. In order to intimidate the loyal nobles, the minister executed one of their number, and distributed such fiefs as were vacant to his own partisans, but the great fief-holders of the kingdom, well aware that he aspired to the throne, assembled their forces and marched on Delhi. Here the regicide was besieged for three months, and, on discovering that Muhammad, as was not surprising, was in sympathy with the besiegers, attempted to assassinate him, but the king's attendants were prepared for the attempt, and slew him and some of his chief accomplices. The nobles who were besieging the city, led by Malik Ilāhdād Lodī, governor of Sambhal, and Kamāl-ud-dīn, formerly Sarvar-ul-mulk's coadjutor, were admitted and the remaining conspirators were seized and executed. Muhammad was again enthroned, and Kamāl-ud-dīn became his minister.

The king had hitherto been the victim of circumstances, but, as soon as he had an opportunity of displaying his fitness for rule, he so abused it as to lose both the affection and the confidence of those who had freed him from his enemies. He made a pilgrimage to Multān, to visit the shrines of saints, but so lightly was his authority regarded there that little more than three years after his departure the people of the city elected their own governor, a pious man named Shaikh Yūsuf.

Muhammad's predecessors had fitfully maintained a measure of authority by a constant series of forays against those who refused or neglected to acknowledge it, but he remained in his capital, sunk in indolence and vice, until his nobles perceived that, if the ancient pre-eminence of Delhi were to be preserved, they must seek some other ruler. Mention has already been made of the Lodī tribe of Afghans. Islām Khān of that tribe had held for some years the important fief of Sirhind, until he was defeated and slain by Shaikh 'Alī; Ilāhdād, governor of Sambhal, had been one of those who freed the king from the treacherous faction of Sarvar-ul-mulk; but the foremost member of the clan was Buhlūl, nephew and adopted son of Islām Khān, whom he had succeeded in the fief of Sirhind. As the king's weakness and meanness of spirit became more apparent, Buhlūl gradually extended his authority over the Panjab, and withheld the revenue due to the royal treasury. Muhammad's authority did not extend beyond Pānīpat to the north; on the south-east the raja of Gwalior no longer made any pretence of fealty, and Mahmūd Shāh of Jaunpur annexed the lower doāb. The Hindus elsewhere in the doāb ignored with impunity an authority which was never asserted, and the tribesmen of Mewāt plundered the country almost to the gates of the capital. Buhlūl Lodī was obviously the coming man, but the nobles would not submit to one of their own number, and a faction appealed in 1440 to Mahmūd I of Mālwā, an active and warlike prince, who in 1436 had seized the throne of that kingdom, and implored him to restore the former glories of Delhi. Muhammad, on learning that Mahmūd was responding to their appeal, assembled such troops as he could muster and begged Buhlūl to hasten to his aid. Buhlūl responded readily, not in loyalty to Muhammad, but in order to save the kingdom for himself, and the armies met between Delhi and Tughlukābād. A battle which began at noon lasted without decisive advantage to either side until nightfall, when each army retired to its camp, and Muhammad, who had lurked in his palace, too pusillanimous to lead his troops, made undignified proposals for peace. These would probably have been rejected with contempt, had not Mahmūd learned that a mob had risen in his capital and proclaimed a pretender. He accordingly accepted the proffered terms, and the next day began his retreat, but Buhlūl, violating the condition that he should be allowed to retire unmolested, followed him, gaining a trivial success over his rearguard, and some plunder. He was received on his return with extravagant demonstrations of joy; his petty triumph was magnified into a great victory; and Muhammad distinguished him by styling him his son and conferring on him the title of Khānkhānān. He now feigned loyalty to Muhammad, who in the following year visited him at Sāmāna, and bestowed on him the fiefs of Dīpālpur and Lahore, which were no longer his to give. He also desired him to crush Jasrat, but Buhlūl, on discovering that Jasrat was not opposed to his designs on Delhi, left him in peace, and enlisted large numbers of Afghans, largely of his own tribe. He then picked a quarrel, on trivial grounds, with Muhammad, and besieged him in Delhi, but was bought off and returned, unmolested, to his fiefs, where he styled himself Sultān Buhlūl

After the siege of the capital the disorders of the kingdom increased daily, and when Muhammad died, in 1444, no point on his frontier was more than forty miles distant from Delhi, and the kingdom inherited by his son, who took the title of 'Ālam Shāh, or 'World-King', comprised little more than the city and the neighbouring villages. He was more feeble-minded and mean-spirited than even his father had been, and in 1447, when he marched to Budaun, he found that city so attractive that he decided, in spite of the protests of his advisers, to reside there rather than at Delhi, and in 1448 he retired thither, leaving the control of affairs at the capital in the hands of his two brothers-in-law. They quarrelled, and one killed the other in a faction fight; but the mob rose against the survivor and put him to death. Hamīd Khān, who had been 'Ālam Shāh's minister, and Hisām Khān, another noble, became arbiters of the destinies of Delhi, and sought a ruler. 'Ālam Shāh refused to leave Budaun, and they would gladly have found another puppet in whose name they could rule, but none was to be found, and they were obliged to have recourse to Buhlūl, lest he should seize the throne by force. He came, and on April 19, 1451, ascended the throne, having written to 'Ālam Shāh a letter, explaining that he was actuated solely by jealousy for the royal authority, which had been set at nought. 'Ālam Shāh, content with ease, replied that he cheerfully resigned his throne to Buhlūl, whom his father had styled his son, as to an elder brother; and he remained contentedly in Budaun, where the revenue of the small territory which he was permitted to retain sufficed to provide his pleasures.

The condition of the kingdom which Buhlūl was called to govern has been described, but he was already, before he ascended the throne of Delhi, a powerful ruler. Most of the Panjab owned his sway, and his kinsman, Daryā Khān, was ruler of the upper doāb and of most of the province now known as Rohilkhand.

The new king was active and warlike, and was resolved to restore the kingdom to its former pre-eminence. He would be a puppet in the hands of none, and one of his earliest acts was to imprison Hamīd Khān, at whose invitation he had ascended the throne. On the other hand, his relations with members of his own tribe differed from those of former kings of Delhi with their courtiers. The rude Afghans, many of whom were his own kinsmen, would not abase themselves before a leader whom they regarded as no more than *primus inter pares*; but he knew how to control them, and was content to forgo courtly obeisance while he could command military obedience. Shaikh Yūsuf, the popularly-elected governor of Multān, having been expelled from that city by a Balūch chief, now begged Buhlūl to recover the lost province, and late in 1451 Buhlūl left Delhi for Multān, but was almost immediately recalled by the news that Mahmūd Shāh of Jaunpur had invaded his kingdom. He was never able to recover the province of Multān, where the Langāhs, as the descendants of the Balūch chief were called, reigned until after Bābur had conquered Hindūstān.

Some of the old nobles of the Sayyids, finding the energetic rule of the new king little to their taste, had invited Mahmūd to attack the city and expel the Afghans, and Mahmūd, responding to the appeal, had been joined, during his advance, by Buhlūl's kinsman, Daryā Khān Lodī, whose adherence was, however, a matter rather of necessity than of choice. Buhlūl hastened back, attacked the invaders, who were deserted by Daryā Khān at a critical moment, and put them to flight. Mahmūd thereupon raised the siege of Delhi, and retired to Jaunpur; but this action marked but the opening of a period of hostilities with Jaunpur which endured until 1479, when Husain, the last of the Sharkī dynasty, was overthrown, and Jaunpur was annexed.

A detailed account of these campaigns would be neither interesting nor instructive. Jaunpur had been, ever since Tīmūr's invasion, a more powerful kingdom than Delhi, and Buhlūl judged aright when he decided that the first step to be taken was the restoration of Delhi's power by the subjugation of Mewāt and the fief-holders and Hindu chieftains of the doāb. This action necessarily brought him into conflict with Jaunpur, and he was twice reduced to such straits, by the approach to Delhi of an army superior in numbers to his own, as to offer to submit and hold Delhi as a fief of Jaunpur. Fortunately for him, these offers were rejected, and on each occasion he contrived to defeat his enemy. In 1458, when he compelled the raja of Etāwah to swear allegiance to him, he was attacked by Mahmūd of Jaunpur; but Mahmūd died suddenly, as the armies drew within striking distance, and his place was taken by his son Muhammad. Buhlūl then attacked Muhammad; but, while hostilities were yet in progress, Muhammad learned that his brother, Husain, had been proclaimed king in Jaunpur, and he was shortly afterwards put to death by those of his officers who favoured Husain's cause. Although the accession of Husain introduced a new element of strife, for his wife Jalīla, a sister of 'Ālam Shāh, constantly urged him to avenge her brother's wrongs, and to restore him to the throne of Delhi, it was followed by nearly five years of peace, which gave Buhlūl time to continue his task of establishing order throughout his kingdom, and of reducing the great fief-holders to obedience. In 1473, Husain, stirred at length to action, marched on Delhi and rejected Buhlūl's offer of submission, but was defeated, his women falling into the hands of Buhlūl, who magnanimously sent them unmolested to Jaunpur. A truce of three years, accepted by both kings, was broken by Husain, and a series of campaigns followed, in which the advantage lay, on the whole, with Buhlūl. In March, 1479, Husain marched on Delhi for the last time. His prospects of success were better than on any previous occasion, but he was induced to make peace on receiving the cession of all the territory to the east of the Ganges. As he was retiring, in leisurely fashion, Buhlūl perfidiously attacked him, defeated his army, and pursued it. This victory marked the turn of the tide in favour of Delhi. Husain, in attempting to redeem his losses, was more crushingly defeated then ever before; and Buhlūl then took the offensive. Husain was again defeated, and driven to Gwalior, where the raja, Kirat Singh, still faithful to him, enabled him again to take the field; but he suffered a series of defeats at the hand of Buhlūl, who, after capturing Jaunpur and placing an officer named Mubārak

Khān in command of the city, marched to Budaun, which had been nominally subject to Jaunpur since the death of 'Ālam Shāh in 1478. Husain re-assembled his forces, and expelled Mubārak Khān from Jaunpur, but Buhlūl returned and drove him from his kingdom into Bihar, where he thenceforth lived as a refugee. Buhlūl then, in 1486, placed his eldest surviving son, Bārbak, in Jaunpur, and, though he permitted him to use the royal title and to coin money in his own name, the independence of Jaunpur had come to an end.

The history of this kingdom, founded by Malik Sarvar in 1394, is chiefly limited to its wars with Delhi, of which some account has already been given. The dynasty which ruled it is known as the Sharkī dynasty, partly from the title bestowed on Sarvar, and partly because it was established in the eastern provinces of the kingdom of Delhi. Sarvar extended his authority not only over Oudh, but also over the doāb, as far as Koïl, and on the east into Tirhut and Bihar. He sent no aid to Delhi when it was attacked by Tīmūr, and paid no heed to the invader. He died in 1399, and was succeeded by his adopted son, Malik Karanful, who assumed the title of Mubārak Shāh; Mubārak was succeeded in 1402 by his younger brother, who ascended the throne as Shams-ud-dīn Ibrāhīm. He was persuaded by the saint, Kutb-ul-'Ālam, to invade Bengal for the purpose of punishing Rāja Ganesh, who, having acquired in that kingdom more power than its nominal ruler, was persecuting Islam. Ganesh, unable to cope with the foes whom his policy had raised against him, promised to desist, and permitted Kutb-ul-'Ālam to convert his son, Jaimal, to Islam; and the saint, satisfied with his success, induced Ibrāhīm to retire. In 1433, the idea of annexing the district of Kālpī, now ruled by Sādir Khān, occurred simultaneously to Ibrāhīm and to Hūshang Shāh of Mālwā, and both marched on Kālpī, but before they met, Ibrāhīm was recalled by the news that Mubārak Shāh of Delhi was marching on Jaunpur. He was relieved of his apprehensions by the assassination of Mubārak, but Hūshang had profited by his absence to annex Kālpī, and Ibrāhīm was obliged to acquiesce.

Ibrāhīm was a cultured prince, a liberal patron of learning, and a builder. Some of the monuments of architecture raised by him or under his encouragement were destroyed when Buhlūl took Jaunpur, but the Atala Mosque, the earliest and finest example of the Jaunpur style, yet remains. Ibrāhīm died in 1436, and was succeeded by his son, Mahmūd Shāh.

Meanwhile Kālpī had again, owing to disputes regarding the succession in Mālwā, become independent, and its governor, Nasīr Khān, or Nasīr Shāh, as he styled himself, had been grossly violating the sacred law of Islam. His treatment of Muslim women gave great offence to Mahmūd of Jaunpur, and he complained to Mahmūd I, then reigning in Mālwā. Some correspondence ensued, and in November, 1444, the two kings marched to Īrij, and after desultory and indecisive hostilities which lasted for some months, both agreed that Nasīr, who had been expelled from Kālpī, and was held to have been sufficiently punished, should be reinstated on promising amendment.

Mahmūd died in 1457, and was succeeded by his son, Muhammad, whose barbarous cruelty led to his death and to the enthronement of his brother Husain. Husain was the most warlike, but not the most fortunate of his line. His wars with Delhi were not his only military enterprises. During a four years' truce with Buhlūl, he led a great army on a foray into Orissa, first plundering and devastating Tirhut, and then extorting from the raja of Orissa vast treasure, which Muslim vanity represents as the first instalment of an annual tribute. In 1466 he sent an army to reduce the fortress of Gwalior, and, though the fortress was not captured, the raja, Mān Singh, paid a heavy indemnity, and he and his successor, Kirat Singh, remained faithful to Husain until he was finally driven from his kingdom.

The dynasty reigned in Jaunpur for rather more than eighty years, and left very creditable memorials in their public buildings. Ibrāhīm was the most enlightened monarch of the line, and in his reign his capital earned the title of "the Shīrāz of India". The character of Husain, the last of the line, is perplexing and disappointing. He was a man of ideas, with wide opportunities and commensurate resources, ever on the point of realising some great scheme of aggrandisement, and ever missing his opportunity through carelessness, folly, and perhaps physical cowardice. He lived in Bengal under the protection of Shams-ud-dīn Yūsuf Shāh and his successors until 1500, but hardly made any attempt to recover his throne, except by futile intrigue.

After the conquest of Jaunpur, Buhlūl marched to Dholpur, and was content to extort from the raja, Vināyak Deo, as earnest of submission, a large sum in gold, and from Kirāt Singh of Gwalior, whom he also visited, eight million *tangas*; he reduced some refractory fief-holders to obedience, but on his way to Delhi fell mortally sick at Saket. His illness produced a crop of intrigues regarding the succession. Some favoured the eldest surviving son, Bārbak Shāh; others held that Bārbak had been provided for at Jaunpur and supported the claims of A'zam-i-Humāyūn, son of Khvāja Bāyazīd, Buhlūl's eldest son; others, again, considered Nizām Khān, the second surviving son, the fittest successor to his father, but the Afghan nobles generally objected to Nizām Khān, whose mother was the daughter of a Hindu goldsmith. Nizām Khān was summoned to the camp, but remained at Delhi, mistrusting his father's intentions. On Buhlūl's death, however, he joined the camp at Jalālī, and on July 17, 1489, ascended the throne as Sikandar Shāh.

The early days of his reign were disturbed; for those who had opposed his elevation, principally of his own kin, were not disposed to submit to him, and he was obliged to have recourse to arms. Some he deprived of their fiefs, which he bestowed on his adherents, and some he conciliated. Among his opponents was his brother, Bārbak, whom he defeated, and generously reappointed to Jaunpur, taking, however, the precaution of bestowing the great fiefs in that province upon his own partisans. But Bārbak failed to deal effectively with a serious rebellion of the Hindu land-holders of the province, instigated by Husain, the former king, and contented himself with coquetting with the rebels, and with Husain. Sikandar suppressed the rebellion, and removed his brother from the government of the province. He also recovered the important fiefs of Kotala, Kālpī, and Bayāna, and bestowed them on men whom he could trust, and he reduced Kirāt Singh of Gwalior to obedience.

The rebels, though defeated by Sikandar, had not been crushed, and a number remained in arms under Bhīl, raja of Phāphāman. For some years Sikandar was engaged in extensive operations against them in Jaunpur, and in the districts of Kara, Chunār, Benares, Tirhut, and Bihar. Husain was once encouraged by the rebels to attack him, but suffered a crushing defeat and fled into Bengal. 'Alā-ud-dīn Husain Shāh of Bengal, resenting the invasion of Bihar and the pursuit of his *protégé*, sent a column against the pursuing force, but neither party had anything to gain by active hostilities, and a treaty was concluded. Its terms were vague, but the peace was not broken and Sikandar retained possession of Bihar. He retired from Bihar to Jaunpur, where he discovered that some of his courtiers had entered into a conspiracy to depose him, and raise to the throne his younger brother, Fath Khān. He treated them leniently, and their only punishment was banishment from court. In 1499 he left Jaunpur for Sambhal, and remained there for four years, being the first sovereign of Delhi to place the administration of the trans-Gangetic province of Katehr on an entirely satisfactory footing, subject, however, to the bigotry which was a prominent feature of his character. A Brāhman of Bengal had aroused the indignation of orthodox Muslims by publicly maintaining that Islam and Hinduism were both true religions, and were but different roads by which God might be approached. The governor of Bihar was directed to send the offender to court, where Sikandar asked the jurists whether it was permissible thus to preach. They decided that, since the Brāhman had admitted the truth of Islam, he should be invited to embrace it, with death as the alternative. The decision commended itself to Sikandar, and the penalty was exacted from the Brāhman, who refused to change his faith.

In 1500 Mān Singh of Gwalior gave offence by harbouring some disaffected nobles, and two years later, when Sikandar attacked Vināyak of Dholpur and annexed his state, the latter, also, took refuge with Mān Singh. Sikandar marched towards Gwalior with the intention of annexing the state once more to the kingdom of Delhi, but on his way thither his army was smitten with a pestilence, and suffered so severely that he was obliged to abandon for the time all thought of pursuing the campaign. He restored Vināyak in Dholpur, and made peace with Mān Singh, but with no intention of keeping it, for, instead of returning to Delhi, he transferred his capital to Āgra. This was the first occasion on which this city, which acquired such importance under the Timurids, came prominently into notice. It had merely been a dependency of the more important fortress of Bayāna.

The nature of Sikandar's subsequent operations indicates the strength of Mān Singh and the extent of his territory, for the king did not venture to attack him in Gwalior, but only attempted the systematic reduction of fortresses and conquest of

districts subject or tributary to him. In March, 1505, he captured
Mandrāel,[1] destroyed Hindu temples in the town, erected mosques
on their sites, and plundered and laid waste the country round the
fortress. On his way back to Āgra he removed Vināyak from
Dholpur, and appointed a Muslim governor to the state. After
the rainy season he again took the field, and devastated a large
area of the Gwalior country, slaying or enslaving those of the
inhabitants who failed to save themselves by flight. On his return
he met and defeated Mān Singh's army on the banks of the
Chambal, and, after the rainy season of 1506, carried the fortress
of Utgīr[2] by assault, treated its temples as he had treated those
of Mandrāel, and appointed a Muslim governor to the fortress.
Early in 1508 he marched on Narwar, usually included in the
kingdom of Mālwā, but then subject to Gwalior. This fortress
was reduced by famine, and Sikandar, after his custom, destroyed
its temples and on their sites raised mosques, which he endowed
with lands in the district. He then after some successful operations against the Hindus of the Athghāt district, returned, in the
summer of 1509, to Āgra. After the rainy season of that year,
while he was in Dholpur, fortune added another province to his
kingdom. The brother of Muhammad Khān, ruler of the small
but independent state of Nāgaur, having rebelled against him,
fled to Sikandar and sought his aid, but Muhammad Khān forestalled attack by sending gifts to Sikandar and acknowledging
him as his sovereign.

Troubles in Mālwā next provided him with an excuse for
interfering in the domestic affairs of that kingdom. Sāhib Khān,
elder brother of Mahmūd II, was proclaimed king by a faction,
and held the districts of Chanderī, Rāisen and Bhīlsa, but distrusted his partisans and fled to Sikandar, who willingly befriended
him, and, early in 1514, sent five nobles to govern the territory,
nominally on the pretender's behalf, but in fact as a fief of Delhi.

Sikandar was then led to believe that Daulat Khān, who held
the fortress of Ranthambhor for Mahmūd II of Mālwā, was prepared to surrender it to him, and marched to Bayāna to receive
his submission, but there discovered that his informant had been
playing a double game, and had secretly urged Daulat not to
surrender the place. On his return to Āgra, Sikandar fell sick

[1] Situated in 77° 18′ E. and 26° 18′ N.
[2] Situated in 76° 57′ E. and 26° 7′ N.

of fever and of a quinsy, but struggled against his malady, and continued to attend to the business of state until, on November 21, 1517, he was choked while trying to swallow a morsel of food, and died.

He was the greatest of the three kings of his house, and completed with success the task left unfinished by his father. We hear little of the Panjab during his reign, and he drew no troops from it to aid him in his eastern campaigns, but it was more tranquil and obedient than it had been in his father's reign. His vigorous rule amply justified the choice of the minority which, in the face of strong opposition, raised him to the throne, and his firmness saved the kingdom from becoming the plaything of an oligarchy of turbulent, ignorant, and haughty Afghans. He showed weakness only in his support of his incompetent brother, Bārbak, for whom he had a sincere affection, strengthened by compunction for having supplanted him in his birthright; but, when he discovered that leniency was a mistaken policy, he dealt fittingly with him.

The greatest blot on his character was his bigotry. The accounts of his conquests, doubtless exaggerated by pious historians, resemble those of the raids of the protagonists of Islam in India. The wholesale destruction of temples was not the best method of conciliating the Hindus of a conquered area, and the murder of a Brāhman, whose only offence was a desire for an accommodation between the religions of the conquerors and the conquered, was not a politic act; but Sikandar's mind was warped by habitual association with theologians.

The Lodī nobles at Āgra raised to the throne his eldest son, Ibrāhīm, but a faction, for its own ends, advocated the partition of the kingdom, and carried off to Jaunpur, and there enthroned, Jalāl Khān, who was either a younger brother of Ibrāhīm, or his uncle, the youngest son of Buhlūl. This prince's partisans were gradually seduced from their allegiance, and he retired from Jaunpur to Kālpī. There he gained a powerful adherent, and attempted to recover Jaunpur, but his new friend quarrelled with him on the way thither, and in his absence the royal troops captured Kālpī. He then marched on Āgra, but the governor of that city, who took the field against him, persuaded him to make his submission, promising to induce Ibrāhīm to pardon him and reinstate him in Kālpī. On Ibrāhīm's refusal, he fled and took refuge with Bikramājīt, who had succeeded his father, Mān Singh, in Gwalior. Ibrāhīm therefore decided to carry out his father's design of expelling the Tonwār Rājputs from that state and of re-annexing it to the kingdom of Delhi. Before his army reached Gwalior, Jalāl had fled and taken refuge with Mahmūd II of Mālwā, but the siege was opened vigorously, and Jalāl later fell into Ibrāhīm's hands. He had fled from Mālwā into the Gond principality of Garha-Katanka, and the Gonds sent him as a prisoner to Ibrāhīm, who ordered his confinement in the state prison of Hānsī, but he was murdered on the way thither. In 1518 the fortress of Gwalior was surrendered to Ibrāhīm, and the state became once more part of the kingdom of Delhi.

The remainder of the reign was passed in strife with the great nobles of the kingdom. These Afghans were insubordinate and unruly, preferring their own interests and those of their clans to the public good. Buhlūl had controlled them by conciliating their prejudices, indulging their vanity, and playing off one against another. Sikandar had dealt more sternly with them, but rightly estimated the sentiments and the predilections of each, and had known when to be severe and when to be lenient; but Ibrāhīm, by nature suspicious and timid, feared them, and having detected some in disloyal schemes, distrusted all, and dealt harshly even with those who were loyal. Some were deprived of their fiefs, some were imprisoned, and many, apprehensive of a similar fate, rose in rebellion. Those sent against them were injudiciously warned that unless they crushed them they would themselves be treated as rebels, so that failure, or even apprehension of failure, left open no course but rebellion. The king mistrusted and feared his nobles, and they mistrusted and feared him. Matters stood thus when Ghāzī Khān, son of the governor of the Panjab, visited Delhi. The control of the Lodīs over this great province had been feeble ever since Buhlūl, having seized the throne of Delhi, had been obliged to confine his attention to the recovery of those provinces which were near at hand, and in order to retain the allegiance of the governor of the Panjab had found it necessary to treat him with consideration. The province was ruled by Daulat Khān Lodī, who had been much perturbed by reports of the state of affairs at Delhi, and had sent his son to ascertain how matters stood. Ghāzī Khān found them even worse than he expected. Daryā Khān, of the Lohānī tribe of Afghans, had asserted his independence in Bihar, and on his death his son, Bahādur Khān, having been proclaimed king, had annexed Oudh and Katehr. Disaffection was rife at court, and the king suspected all. Ghāzī Khān returned to the Panjab with the lowest opinion of Ibrāhīm, and warned his father that he would not be left long in possession of Lahore, should the king be successful in his campaigns against the rebels in Hindūstān and Bihar. From this moment date Daulat Khān's virtual assumption of independence and his intrigues with Bābur, which led to Ibrāhīm's overthrow and to the establishment of yet another foreign dynasty on the throne of Delhi.

Daulat.Khān died while Bābur was yet on the way to his great conquest, and at the same time died Bahādur, or Sultān Muhammad, king of Bihar; but on April 18, 1526, after a reign of nine years, Ibrāhīm was defeated and slain by Bābur at Pānīpat.

CHAPTER 7

The Kingdom of Bengal

The allegiance of the Muslim governors of Bengal to Delhi depended chiefly on the personality and activity of the sultan. Remittances of revenue or tribute were seldom regular, and sometimes ceased altogether, and its capital, Gaur, or Lakhnāwati, was known in Delhi as Balghākpur, "the City of Rebellion". Officers settled in Bengal became acclimatised; but the hot, moist climate which stimulated its productiveness was disliked by those accustomed to the drier atmosphere of Hindūstān. They described the province as "a hell filled with good things"; and their distaste for service in Bengal, the impossibility of military movements in the rainy season over its sodden soil, and the succession of Mongol raids which for a century kept the sultans of Delhi occupied on their north-western frontier, encouraged rebellion in Bengal and helped to ensure its success.

Bughrā, the second son of Balban, became independent in Bengal when his son Kaikubād ascended the throne in Delhi, and his successors retained their independence until two of his grandsons quarrelled over the succession, when the elder invoked the aid of Tughluk, who invaded Bengal and carried off the younger, Bahādur, as a prisoner. He was afterwards allowed to return to eastern Bengal, but rebelled and was put to death. In 1339 'Alī Shāh, who had established himself as ruler of western Bengal, rebelled, and Muhammad ibn Tughluk never had leisure to attempt the reconquest of the province. In 1345, 'Alī was assassinated at the instigation of his foster-brother, Shams-ud-dīn Iliyās, who annexed eastern Bengal in 1352, and thus became sovereign of all Bengal. The two campaigns of Fīrūz Shāh against Iliyās and his son Sikandar were the last attempts of a sultan of Delhi to assert his authority over Bengal until Humāyūn overran the country in 1538, and Bengal remained an independent kingdom until it was annexed by Akbar.

Bengal, whether as a province of Delhi or as an independent kingdom, was not a homogeneous Muslim state. Great Hindu land-holders held estates which were, in fact, principalities, and

their allegiance to a Muslim ruler, like his to a sultan of Delhi,
depended on the ruler's personality. The chief of these states was
Bishnupur, governed by a Hindu dynasty which was founded
in the eighth century and endured until the eighteenth, when it
was ruined by the ravages of Marāthas and by the famine of 1770,
which depopulated its territory. Another state was Dīnājpur,
which early in the fifteenth century produced a powerful chieftain who dominated the Muslim sultan, and eventually usurped
his throne.

Sikandar Shāh, who succeeded his father Iliyās in 1357, had
seventeen sons by his first wife, and by his second but one,
Ghiyās-ud-dīn A'zam, the ablest and most promising of them
all. A'zam's stepmother, by traducing him to his father, in the
hope of securing the throne for one of her own sons, drove him
into rebellion, and in 1389 his father marched against him, and
their armies met at Goālpāra, where Sikandar was defeated and
slain. A'zam ascended the throne, put out the eyes of his seventeen half-brothers, and sent them as a gift to their mother. He is
more pleasantly remembered by an interesting correspondence
with the great Persian poet, Hāfiz, and by his regard for the law
of Islam. He died in 1396, and, though he was succeeded by his
son, Hamza, the actual ruler of Bengal during Hamza's reign and
that of his successor, Bāyazīd, was Rāja Ganesh of Dīnājpur,
styled Kāns by Muslim historians. Ganesh persecuted Muslims,
and Kutb-ul-'Ālam, a Muslim saint, summoned to the aid of the
faithful Ibrāhīm Shāh of Jaunpur. Ganesh besought the saint to
persuade Ibrāhīm to retire, but he refused to intercede for an
infidel, and Ganesh delivered to him his son, in order that he
might be converted to Islam and proclaimed king. The saint
agreed, and induced the invader to retire, whereupon Ganesh
seized his son, compelled him to undergo an elaborate ceremony
of purification, in order that he might be re-admitted to the
Hindu fold, and persecuted the Muslims more severely than
before, but died in 1414, and his son, whose conversion had been
genuine, and who had been imprisoned for refusing to abjure
Islam, was raised to the throne as Jalāl-ud-dīn Muhammad, and
persecuted the Hindus more severely than his father had persecuted Muslims, compelling great numbers of them to accept
Islam.

The general attitude of the Muslim rulers of Bengal to their

Hindu subjects was tolerant, but it is evident, from the numerical superiority in eastern Bengal of Muslims who are certainly not the descendants of dominant invaders, that from time to time waves of proselytism swept over the country. Such was the case during the reign of Jalāl-ud-dīn, who had a convert's zeal as well as good reason to hate the faith of his fathers.

He was succeeded in 1431 by his son, Shams-ud-dīn Ahmad, whose tyranny in the later days of his reign became so unbearable that in 1442 he was put to death by two of his officers, one of whom, Nāsir Khān, claimed descent from Iliyās, and succeeded, as Nāsir-ud-dīn Mahmūd, to the throne, thus restoring the old line. He was a builder, and besides restoring and beautifying Gaur, built a mosque at Satgām. His son Rukn-ud-dīn Bārbak, who succeeded him in 1459, was the first king in India to raise African slaves in large numbers to high rank. He had no fewer than 8000 of these slaves, and they afterwards became a curse to the state. He died in 1474, and his son and successor, Yūsuf, caused much discontent and disaffection by insisting on the strict observance of the Islamic law and forbidding the use of wine. He died in 1481, and his son, Sikandar, was discovered, after he had been enthroned, to be a maniac, and was deposed in favour of his grand-uncle, Jalāl-ud-dīn Fath Shāh, a son of Muhammad. Fath Shāh attempted to cope with the African menace, and sternly curbed the insolence and punished the excesses of the slaves who thronged the court. The Africans resented his repressive measures, and in 1486 their leader, a eunuch named Sultān Shāhzāda, caused him to be assassinated and usurped the throne, under the title of Bārbak Shāh. Another African, Indīl Khān, had been loyal to his master, and, on returning to the capital after an expedition, took advantage of the usurper's condition after a drinking bout to put him to death. Fath Shāh's widow, whose son was but two years old, begged the avenger of her husband's murder to ascend the throne, and Indīl, after a decent display of reluctance, was proclaimed under the title of Saif-ud-dīn Fīrūz. During his short reign of three years he restored order in the kingdom, and discipline in the army, but historians have justly observed that his elevation established an evil precedent, and that it became an accepted rule in Bengal that the slayer of a king's murderer was entitled to the throne. On the death of Fīrūz in 1489, the young son of Fath Shāh was proclaimed as Nāsir-ud-dīn Mahmūd II, but the regent, an African named Habash Khān, was almost immediately murdered by another African, Sīdī Badr the Madman, who, not content with the regency, put the young king to death and ascended the throne as Shams-ud-dīn Muzaffar Shāh. This bloodthirsty monster, during a reign of three years, put to death most of the leading men in the kingdom, and alienated both his people and his army by extorting exorbitant taxes from the former, and reducing the emoluments of the latter, so that when his minister, 'Alā-ud-dīn Husain, a Sayyid of Tirmiz, retired from his service in disgust, the army placed him at its head and rose against the usurper, who was besieged for four months in Gaur, and at last slain in a *sortie* which he led from the city. Those of the old nobles who still remained alive raised Sayyid Husain to the throne in 1493, on receiving from him guarantees which bore some resemblance to a European constitution of 1848.

During the brief period which intervened between the death of the negro and the establishment of the Sayyid's authority, the scum of the populace rose in Gaur, and indulged in an orgy of rapine. Husain Shāh's orders that it should cease were not at once obeyed, and his punishment of the refractory was both prompt and severe. He is said to have put to death 12,000 of the robbers, and to have enriched the treasury with the booty taken from them, and, in his disgust at the lawlessness of the capital, he transferred his residence to Ikdāla.

Husain was, with the exception of Iliyās, the greatest of the Muslim kings of Bengal. He enriched the capital and other owns with fine buildings, and he restored security by breaking up two dangerous corporations. The first was the large force of *pāiks*, or Hindu infantry, which had long been employed as guards of the palace and of the king's person, and had gradually attained to a position resembling that of the Praetorian Guards at Rome; and the second was the great body of Africans. A great part of the force of the *pāiks* was disbanded; the remainder were employed at a distance from the capital; and duties at the palace were entrusted to Muslim troops. The Africans were expelled from the country, and most of the exiles, after vainly seeking an asylum in Delhi and Jaunpur, where their record in Bengal was well known, drifted to the Deccan and Gujarāt, where men of their race had for some time been largely employed.

Husain also recovered the territory which had, during the six preceding reigns, fallen away from a trunk too feeble to support its branches, and extended his dominions to the borders of Orissa. In 1498 he invaded the kingdom of Assam, but this attempt at foreign conquest was unfortunate. Assam was occupied, but the raja and his troops merely retired into the hills, and, during the rainy season, when the dispatch of reinforcements into the country was impossible, fell upon the Muslim garrisons and put them to the sword. After this experience Husain confined his military activities to securing his frontiers. He died in 1518, and was succeeded by his eldest son, Nusrat Shāh, who was a prince of gentle and amiable disposition, and, instead of following the barbarous eastern custom of slaying, mutilating, or imprisoning his brothers, doubled the provision which his father had made for them. Early in his reign he annexed Tirhut, and, after the defeat and death of Ibrāhīm Lodī of Delhi, he welcomed to Bengal the Afghan refugees who fled thither rather than serve the conqueror, and he married a daughter of Ibrāhīm. He made a demonstration against Bābur by sending a force to invade Oudh, but withdrew it, and after Bābur had captured Jaunpur, attempted to conciliate him with gifts.

In his reign the Portuguese made their first appearance in Bengal. Martim Affonso, who had been sent in charge of a trading expedition into the Bay of Bengal, established himself in Chittagong, and, though he had attempted to conciliate Nusrat by sending to him a mission bearing gifts, the misconduct and arrogance of the Portuguese so incensed the king that he ordered their arrest and the confiscation of their property. The governor of Chittagong treacherously seized their leaders at a banquet to which he had invited them, slew such of the community as had not time to escape to their ships, confiscated property worth about £100,000, and sent his prisoners to Gaur. The Portuguese retaliated by burning Chittagong.

Nusrat's character deteriorated as a result of his debauchery, and in 1533 he was murdered by some of the palace eunuchs whom he had threatened with punishment. His son, Fīrūz, was murdered after reign of a few months by his uncle, Mahmūd, who was almost immediately involved in troubles by the rebellion of Makhdūm-i-'ālam, who held the fief of Hājīpur in Bihar, and had entered into an alliance with Shīr Khān of Sasarām, afterwards Shīr Shāh of Delhi. The two rebels defeated and slew the governor of Monghyr, and were greatly enriched by their spoils, but Makhdūm was at last defeated and slain by Mahmūd's troops. Shīr Khān, marching to avenge his death, was held up for a month at Teliyāgarhi, on the Ganges, the 'Gate of Bengal', but ultimately forced the defile, defeated the main body of Mahmūd's army between Teliyāgarhi and Gaur, and then besieged Gaur. He was recalled by a rising in Bihar, but left his son, Jalāl Khān, and an officer named Khavāss Khān, to continue the siege, and the garrison was reduced to such straits by famine that on April 6, 1538, Mahmūd led it forth against the besiegers. He was defeated and put to flight, his sons were captured, and Gaur was sacked and occupied by Jalāl Khān.

Shīr Khān returned to Bengal, pursued Mahmūd, and again defeated him. He fled for protection to Humāyūn, who, taking advantage of Shīr Khān's absence in Bengal, had taken Chunār and advanced into Bihar. Shīr Khān sent Jalāl Khān and Khavāss Khān to hold the Gate of Bengal, and there they defeated the advanced guard of Humāyūn's army, but retired on the approach of his main body, and, as Humāyūn advanced on Gaur, Shīr Khān fled into Chota Nāgpur; but Humāyūn, instead of pursuing him, lingered aimlessly at Gaur, which he renamed Jannātābād; or the 'Abode of Paradise', while his officers occupied Sonārgāon, Chittagong, and other ports in his name, until the climate bred sickness in his army and destroyed many of his horses and camels. Meanwhile Shīr Khān had occupied the fortress of Rohtās, from which he menaced Humāyūn's line of communications by descending on Monghyr, and putting his officers there to the sword. At the same time, in 1539, Humāyūn received the news of the rebellion of his brother, Hindāl Mīrzā, in Delhi, and, overwhelmed by this accumulation of misfortunes, hastened back towards Āgra, leaving Jahāngīr Kulī Beg behind him as governor of Bengal. Shīr Khān intercepted his retreat at Chausa, on the Ganges, and after holding him there for three months, fell upon his army, defeating and dispersing it. He afterwards disposed of Jahāngīr Kulī Beg by causing him to be assassinated. Having thus become supreme in Bengal, he assumed the royal title, and the increasing confusion in the newly established empire of Delhi enabled him to oust Humāyūn and to ascend the imperial throne.

When he marched from Bengal in 1540 to attack Humāyūn, he left Khizr Khān as governor of the province. Khizr Khān's head was turned by his elevation. He married a daughter of Mahmūd Shāh, and assumed so many of the airs of royalty that Shīr Shāh, when he was established on the imperial throne, returned to Bengal to nip his ambition in the bud. Khizr Khān, not strong enough to try conclusions with the conqueror of Delhi, welcomed him submissively, but, being unable to justify his recent presumption, was imprisoned. Shīr Shāh obviated a recurrence of his offence by dividing Bengal into a number of small prefectures, the governors of which were responsible to a central controller of the revenues.

Thus, for a time, ended the independence of Bengal. It revived under an Afghan dynasty after Shīr Shāh's death, but was finally extinguished by Akbar's army in 1576.

The annals of Bengal are stained with blood; the long list of Muslim kings contains the names of some monsters of cruelty; but it would be unjust to condemn them all. Some certainly reciprocated the attitude of the lower classes of their Hindu subjects, who welcomed them as their deliverers from the priestly yoke, and even described them in popular poetry as the gods, come down to earth to punish the wicked Brāhmans. Others were enlightened patrons of literature. At the courts of Hindu rajas priestly influence maintained Sanskrit as the literary language, and there was a tendency to despise the vulgar tongue as a literary vehicle, but Muslim kings, who could not be expected to learn Sanskrit, could both understand and appreciate the writings of those who condescended to use the tongue in which they themselves communicated with their subjects, and it was the Muslim sultan rather than the Hindu raja who was the patron of vernacular literature. Nusrat Shāh, anticipating Akbar, caused the *Mahābhārata* to be translated from Sanskrit into Bengali, and of two earlier versions of the poem one possibly owed something to Muslim patronage, and the other was made to the order of Husain Shāh, Nusrat's father, who is mentioned in Bengali literature with affection and respect.

CHAPTER VI

The Kingdoms of the Deccan
and of Vijayanagar

In 1347, after the army left in the Deccan by Muhammad ibn
Tughluk had been driven from Daulatābād, Ismāʿil, who had
been elected king, abdicated in favour of Hasan, who had relieved
the fortress. Hasan claimed descent from Bahman, son of
Isfandiyār, known in the west as Artaxerxes Longimanus, and
assumed the royal title of Bahman Shāh. Of the dynasty which
he founded, known as the Bahmanids, eighteen kings ascended
the throne, of whom fourteen ruled the Deccan until 1490, when
the provincial governors assumed independence, and the great
kingdom was divided into five separate states.

While the Muslims in the Deccan were in revolt against Delhi,
and the power of the Hoysala dynasty of Dvāravatīpura was
declining in the peninsula, three brothers who governed its
northern provinces founded a great Hindu kingdom, with its
capital at Vijayanagar on the Krishnā. This kingdom gradually
spread over the whole of the south of the peninsula; and Kānhayya, a scion of the Kākatiyas, established himself in their
kingdom.

Bahman made Gulbarga his capital, and divided his kingdom
into four provinces (*taraf*), Gulbarga, Daulatābād, Berar and
Bīdar. The provincial governors, or *tarafdars*, had great power.
Each commanded the army of his province, and was solely
responsible for its administration and for the collection of the
revenue. The system worked tolerably well under a king powerful
enough to keep the governors under control, but its dangers
became apparent even in the reign of Bahman's successor, and
it was the power of the *tarafdars* that ultimately led to the dismemberment of the kingdom.

For the greater part of his reign of eleven years Bahman was
engaged in quelling the unruly in his kingdom and in establishing
order. The recognition of his sovereignty in the Deccan by
al-Muʿtadid, the puppet caliph in Egypt, contributed perhaps to

his success in this task, which by 1357 was so far completed that he was able to lead an expedition into Gujarāt with a view to the conquest of that province, which was still subject to Delhi; but he fell sick at Navsārī, and was obliged to return to Gulbarga, where he died on February 11, 1358.

He was succeeded by his eldest son, Muhammad I, the early part of whose reign was devoted to the organisation of his government. His system is worthy of record, for it was imitated first in the five states which rose on the ruins of the kingdom, and, later, by Sīvajī, the founder of the Marātha power. He appointed eight ministers of state: (1) *vakīl-us-saltana*, or lieutenant of the kingdom, who was the immediate subordinate of the sovereign, and held the regency when he was absent from the capital; (2) *wazir-i-kull*, who supervised the work of all other ministers; (3) *amīr-i-jumla*, minister of finance; (4) *wazir-i-ashrāf*, minister of foreign affairs and master of the ceremonies; (5) *nāzir*, assistant minister of finance; (6) *pēshwā*, who was associated with the lieutenant of the kingdom, and whose office was, in later times, almost always amalgamated with his; (7) *kotwāl*, or chief of police and city magistrate in the capital; and (8) *sadr-i-jahān*, or chief justice and minister of religious affairs and endowments.

The royal bodyguard consisted of 200 esquires to the king and 4000 gentleman-troopers, divided into four reliefs, each of 50 esquires and 1000 troopers, commanded by one of the great nobles at the capital. The tour of duty of each relief was four days, and the whole force was commanded by one of the ministers, who, however, performed his routine military duties by deputy.

Muhammad I soon became involved in war with Kānhayya of Warangal, and with Vijayanagar, now ruled by Bukka I. The Hindu bankers and money-changers in the Deccan were in the habit of retaining and hoarding, or selling to the mints of Vijayanagar and Warangal, Muhammad's gold coins, which were finer than those of the Hindu mints, so that the Hindu coins became the ordinary gold currency of the kingdom. Muhammad naturally objected to this practice, and, after repeatedly warning the offenders, in 1360 put them all to death, their place being taken by more amenable Hindus who had accompanied the armies from northern India. It was not until the reign of Fīrūz the eighth king of the dynasty, that the descendants of the slaughtered men were able to purchase from the crown the right to resume the occupation of their fathers. Bukka and Kānhayya regarded this measure as an assertion of suzerainty, and addressed to Muhammad arrogant and provocative messages. He detained their envoys for eighteen months, and then demanded, with an effrontery exceeding theirs, the payment of vast sums as tribute. Kānhayya's son Vināyak then attacked the fortress of Kaulās, but was driven thence by the armies of Berar and Bīdar under Bahādur Khān, who marched on Warangal and compelled Kānhayya to ransom his capital with a great sum. A year later Muhammad, angered by another insult, marched on Vailam-pallam, the appanage of Vināyak, captured Vināyak, and hurled him from a *balista* on the ramparts into a fire which had been kindled beneath. Muhammad suffered severely during his re-treat, and avenged his losses by laying waste Kānhayya's country in two successive years. Kānhayya ultimately purchased peace by paying a huge indemnity and surrendering the important fortress of Golconda. Henceforth the Hindu ruler of Telingāna was a vassal of the Muslim kingdom of the Deccan.

Bahman had appointed as governor of Daulatābād his sister's son, Bahrām Khān Māzandārāni, who, pretending that his uncle had promised to leave him a share of the kingdom, sent two missions to Fīrūz Shāh of Delhi, imploring aid, the reply to which was that, if the rebels of the Deccan were suffering under a tyrant, they had only themselves to thank. But one member of the mission, Ahmad Fārūki, obtained from Fīrūz the small fief of Thālner, on the Taptī, and, having assumed independence there in 1382, founded the dynasty which ruled Khāndesh until nearly the end of Akbar's reign. Before Muhammad I could seriously attempt the suppression of his cousin's rebellion, he was involved in war with Vijayanagar. On March 21, 1365, while merry with wine after a banquet held to celebrate his victories in Telingāna, he rewarded the singers and dancers who had entertained him with a draft on the treasury of Vijayanagar. Bukka, having treated with contumely the envoy who pre-sented the draft, crossed the Tungabhadrā and put to the sword the garrison of Mudgal. Muhammad then crossed the Krishnā and avenged the garrison by slaughtering 70,000 Hindus. After spending the rainy season in Mudgal, he took the field, and met

Bukka's army at Kauthal. Here, early in 1367, was fought the first of many great battles between the Muslims of the Deccan and the Hindus of the peninsula. It was fiercely contested, but the Hindus were routed. In the course of three months, during which Muhammad pursued Bukka through his dominions, no fewer than 400,000 Hindus, including 10,000 Brāhmans, were slaughtered. The garrison of Mudgal was now avenged and Muhammad's draft was honoured. The Hindus, horrified by the bloodshed, proposed that both parties should agree to spare non-combatants in future. Muhammad consented, and the pact, though twice violated, mitigated to some extent the horrors of the long period of intermittent warfare between the two states.

The history of the foreign affairs of the kingdom of the Deccan is largely that of its warfare with Vijayanagar. It was occasionally involved in conflicts with Gujarāt, Mālwā and Khāndesh, with the Gonds, and with the Hindus of Telingāna, but Vijayanagar was the real enemy, and between this campaign, in which the Muslims inflicted such terrible punishment on the Hindus, and the disruption of the Bahmanī kingdom in 1490, the two kingdoms were involved in no fewer than six great wars. The advantage lay chiefly with the Muslims, whose troops were vastly superior to the masses of half-trained men whom the Hindus placed in the field; but, when fortune favoured the Hindus, they were as ruthless as their foes. After a time the Hindus perceived where their defect lay, and remedied it by the employment of Muslim mercenaries, who were superior to any troops which their own dominions could supply.

In 1377 Mujāhid, the son and successor of Muhammad I, demanded of Bukka I the cession of the territory between the Rāichūr doāb and the Arabian Sea, and, on receiving an insolent reply, invaded the Hindu kingdom, pursued Bukka for some months through the Carnatic, and besieged both Adoni and Vijayanagar, but failed to reduce either. On his return to Gulbarga Mujāhid was assassinated at the instance of his uncle, Dāūd, and, during the confusion which followed his death, Bukka invaded the doāb and besieged Rāichūr; but when Muhammad II, Dāūd's nephew, was enthroned in 1378, and order was restored, the Hindus raised the siege and retired to Vijayanagar. Muhammad II, who reigned until 1397, was a pacific ruler, and during his reign the peace between the Deccan and Vijayanagar was not broken. On his death two puppets were successively raised to the throne, but were deposed within a year, and were followed by Fīrūz, the eighth of his line. On Muhammad's death Harihara II, the third raja of the first dynasty of Vijayanagar, invaded the doāb with a vast army, but he had underestimated his enemy, and Fīrūz, though beset by difficulties, marched against him with 12,000 horse. Harihara then retired to the south of the Krishnā, where his great army was widely distributed in order to obtain supplies. A small band from the Muslim army entered the Hindu camp disguised as minstrels and obtained admission to the tents of Harihara's son, who was entertaining a party to drink and music. In the course of their performance, they suddenly fell upon the inebriated Hindus, stabbed the prince, extinguished the lights, and escaped in the darkness. In the panic which ensued, different bodies of the Hindu army turned their arms against each other, and Fīrūz crossed the river during the confusion, and at dawn fell upon the terrified host and pursued it, with great slaughter, to the gates of Vijayanagar. Non-combatants were not slain, but large numbers were enslaved, and, as these included 10,000 Brāhmans, the members of the priestly caste in the city insisted on their being ransomed, and Harihara obtained peace by the payment of a heavy indemnity.

In 1406 the 'War of the Goldsmith's Daughter' broke out. A poor goldsmith of Mudgal had a beautiful and accomplished daughter, and Bukka II, who had succeeded his father, Harihara, in Vijayanagar, inflamed by the accounts which he had heard of the girl's beauty, sent a body of 5000 horse to Mudgal to seize her. These troops, finding that the girl and her parents had fled, plundered Mudgal, but, after they had been joined by Bukka, were driven back to Vijayanagar by Fūlād Khān, governor of the doāb. Later in the year Fīrūz avenged the invasion of his territory by again marching to Vijayanagar. Though he failed to take the city, and was repulsed and wounded, two forces of his troops plundered the country to the south of the capital, taking 60,000 captives, and subduing the country to the west of the doāb. Bukka obtained peace by the cession of this tract, by paying a heavy indemnity, and by giving a daughter in marriage to Fīrūz, but the marriage failed to promote goodwill between the two monarchs.

The important fortress of Pāngul, about twenty-five miles to the north of the confluence of the Krishnā and the Tungabhadrā, lay in the Golconda territory, which had been ceded by Kānhayya to Muhammad I. After 1413 it was occupied by the troops of Vīra Vijaya, who had succeeded his brother, Devarāya I, in Vijayanagar in that year; and in 1418 Fīrūz, though his powers were then failing, marched to recover it. The siege was prolonged for two years, during which time disease among men and beasts bred disorder and panic in his army. Vīra Vijaya marched to the relief of the town, routed and pursued the army of Fīrūz, and occupied the southern and eastern districts of his kingdom, where the Hindus repaid with interest the treatment which they had so often received at the hands of the Muslims. Ahmad Khān, the brother of Fīrūz, then drove them beyond the frontier, and in September, 1422, succeeded his brother on the throne.

At the end of the year Ahmad Shāh led an army to avenge the disaster of Pāngul, for the Hindus had violated the old treaty by slaughtering non-combatants. Vīra Vijaya, with a vast army, held the southern bank of the Tungabhadrā, but a division of the Muslims crossed the river above his left, and, while marching eastwards to take the Hindu army in rear, came at dawn upon the garden in which Vīra Vijaya was lodged. The raja, surprised, hid himself in a standing crop of sugar-cane, and the troopers who discovered him, taking him for the gardener, drove him on before them with their whips, bearing a sheaf of sugar-cane for their refreshment. Meanwhile the main body of the Muslim army had begun to cross the river, and the leaderless host of Hindus, already attacked in rear by the division which had captured the raja, broke and fled. While the Muslims were plundering the camp, the raja made his escape, and, being too exhausted and too broken in spirit to attempt to rally his army, joined it in its flight to Vijayanagar.

The Hindus then had reason to repent of their breach of the humane treaty, for never in the course of the wars between the two kingdoms did either army display such ferocity as did Ahmad's, marching through the kingdom, slaughtering men, and enslaving women and children. An account of the butchery was kept, and, whenever the tale of the victims reached 20,000, Ahmad halted and celebrated the event. On one of these occasions, while he was hunting, a party of the enemy surprised him.

His bodyguard held its ground until relief arrived, and the Hindus were driven off. The defence made by the foreign archers of his guard so impressed Ahmad that he ordered the principal foreign officer in his service, entitled Malik-ut-tujjār, to raise a corps of three thousand of them, a measure which was destined to have a deep and lasting effect on the history of the Muslims in the Deccan.

As Ahmad approached Vijayanagar, Vīra Vijaya, appalled by the sufferings of his people, sued for peace. The long arrears of tribute were borne to the Muslim camp, and the Muslims retained their captives, of whom two Brāhman boys, after conversion to Islam, were to attain to the highest rank in the service of the state, and eventually to found dynasties of kings.

After this severe blow Devarāya II, who succeeded his brother in 1424, perceived the inferiority of his troops to those of his enemy and reorganised his army, which had hitherto consisted of 200,000 inferior cavalry and nearly a million of worse infantry. He enlisted Muslims freely, and employed them both in the ranks and as instructors of his Hindu troops. His army, after its reorganisation, consisted of 10,000 mounted foreign archers, 60,000 Hindu horse, also trained to the use of the bow, and 300,000 tolerably well-trained infantry. But even with this army, it was not until twenty years had passed that Devarāya attempted reprisals for the misery which Ahmad Shāh had inflicted on his people. In 1443 he invaded the doāb, captured Mudgal and laid waste the country, while his two sons besieged Rāichūr and Bankāpuram. 'Alā-ud-dīn, who had succeeded his father on the throne of the Deccan in 1436, marched into the doāb, and met Devarāya at Mudgal. Devarāya's elder son was killed in battle, and the Hindus were obliged to sue for peace, which was granted on Devarāya's promise to make no further default in the payment of tribute. This was the last war between Vijayanagar and the Bahmanī kings, and this brief record of it closes the account of the relations of the kingdom of the Deccan with its southern neighbour.

During the successful campaign of Muhammad I against Vijayanagar, his cousin Bahrām had been in rebellion in Daulatābād. He had been virtually independent for some years; he had gained the support of a Marātha chieftain named Kondbā, of some of the fief-holders in Berar, and of a local saint named Zain-ud-dīn; he had entered into an alliance with the raja of Baglāna; and he was enriched by the accumulation of several years' revenue of his province. Muhammad I, in appointing Khān Muhammad to Daulatābād with instructions to crush the rebel, underestimated his strength, for Khān Muhammad, approaching the rebel forces at Paithan, on the Godāvarī, begged the king to come to his assistance. Muhammad, who was hunting in the neighbourhood, marched on Paithan, and the rebels, on learning of his approach, dispersed and fled, and were pursued to the frontier of Gujarāt, in which province they took refuge.

From Daulatābād Muhammad returned to Gulbarga. Brigandage was rife in the kingdom, and he dealt with it so drastically that within six months the heads of 20,000 bandits were sent to the capital. Otherwise the kingdom was at peace for the rest of his reign, and he was occupied in public business and in building. He built two mosques at Gulbarga. One, the great mosque, completed in 1367, measures 216 by 176 feet, and, unlike other mosques in India, has a roofed courtyard. Of this building Sir John Marshall writes: "To single out for praise any particular feature of the mosque would be difficult; yet there is about the whole a dignified simplicity and grandeur that place it in the first rank of such buildings".

Muhammad died in the spring of 1377, and was succeeded by his elder son, Mujāhid, remarkable for his personal beauty, his great bodily strength, and his headstrong disposition. During his expedition to Vijayanagar he gave great offence to his uncle Dāūd, by publicly rebuking him for neglect of duty, and on April 15, 1378, while the army was returning to the capital, some assassins entered the king's tent at night and slew him, and Dāūd was proclaimed king.

Dāūd's action was generally condemned. The provincial governors returned to their provinces without tendering their allegiance to him, and the aged Saif-ud-dīn Ghūrī, lieutenant of the kingdom, refused to serve him, and retired into private life. Mujāhid's sister employed an assassin who, on May 30, 1378, slew the usurper while he was at public prayers in the great mosque, forestalled an attempt to proclaim his young son by blinding the child, and raised to the throne Muhammad,[1] son of Mahmūd Khān, the fourth son of Bahman Shāh.

[1] Wrongly styled Mahmūd by Firishta, who ridicules those historians who give him his correct name, but is refuted by inscriptions and legends on coins. English historians have blindly followed Firishta.

Peace was restored. Muhammad II punished the partisans of the late usurper, and the provincial governors returned to their allegiance, and Saif-ud-dīn to his duties.

Muhammad II was a man of peace, devoted to learning, and his reign of nineteen years was undisturbed by foreign wars. His love of learning was encouraged by Mir Fazlullāh Injū of Shīrāz, a Sayyid who held the office of *sadr-i-jahān*, at whose instance the great poet Hāfiz was invited to Gulbarga, and embarked, but a storm in the Persian Gulf so unnerved him that he landed and returned to Shīrāz, excusing himself in a well-known ode. During this reign the Deccan was visited by a terrible famine, to relieve the distress caused by which large quantities of grain were imported from Gujarāt and Mālwā, and orphanages were established, but these benefits were restricted to Muslims, and were probably used as a means of propaganda. In the last year of the reign a rebellion at Sāgar was suppressed; and on April 20, 1397, Muhammad II died of a fever. On the following day Saif-ud-dīn Ghūrī, the faithful old servant of his house, passed away at the great age of 104 and was buried beside his master.

Muhammad was succeeded by his elder son, Ghiyās-ud-dīn, a youth of seventeen, who angered Tughalchīn, the chief of the Turkish slaves, by refusing to appoint him *vakīl-us-saltana*, and afterwards indiscreetly placed himself in his power, lured on by an infatuation for his daughter. Tughalchīn blinded him, caused the principal nobles of the court to be assassinated, and on the same day, June 14, 1397, raised to the throne Shams-ud-dīn Dāūd, the younger half-brother of the blinded king, and assumed the place which Ghiyās-ud-dīn had denied him.

This treatment of the royal family was resented by two of the king's cousins, Fīrūz and Ahmad, who had been brought up by Muhammad II, and married to two of his daughters. They were the sons of Ahmad Khān, the third son of Bahman Shāh. They withdrew from the capital, assembled their forces, and attacked Tughalchīn, but were defeated and put to flight. They then feigned penitence, and were allowed to return to Gulbarga. On November 15, 1397, they gained admission to the palace on the pretext of paying their respects to the king, and there they and their adherents overpowered both him and Tughalchīn. The elder brother ascended the throne as Tāj-ud-dīn Fīrūz Shāh, and the young king was blinded. The blind Ghiyās-ud-dīn was brought from Sāgar, a sword was placed in his hand, and Tughalchīn, who was compelled to sit before him, was cut to pieces by his former victim. Ahmad Khān was then appointed chief minister and Fazlullāh *vakīl-us-saltana*.

Fīrūz Shāh's war with Vijayanagar has been mentioned. It was with difficulty that he defended his southern frontier, for he had first to crush a rebellion of Kolis north of the Krishnā, and then to detach from his force the armies of Daulatābād and Berar, for his kingdom had been invaded on the north by Narasingha, the Gond raja of Kherla, who had ravaged the eastern districts of Berar. On returning from his campaign against Harihara II, he learned that these armies had not been able either to restore order in Berar or to punish Narasingha, whose acts of aggression had been instigated by Dilāvar Khān of Mālwā and Nasīr Khān of Khāndesh. He therefore again took the field, and, in the winter of 1398, compelled the governor of Māhūr, who had declared for Narasingha, to surrender that fortress. He then marched on to Ellichpur and sent Ahmad and Fazlullāh against Narasingha. After a hotly contested battle they defeated the Gonds and drove them into Kherla, capturing Kosal, Narasingha's son. Narasingha, after a siege of two months, made his submission, waited on Fīrūz at Ellichpur, paid tribute, and surrendered a daughter to Fīrūz.

On his return to Gulbarga Fīrūz built for himself the town of Fīrūzābād, on the Bhīma. In 1401 he is said to have sent a submissive message to Tīmūr, then in Āzarbāyjān, and to have received in reply a grant of the kingdoms of the Deccan, Gujarāt, and Mālwā, the report of which so alarmed Muzaffar I of Gujarāt and Dilāvar Khān of Mālwā that, after warning Fīrūz to keep the peace, they entered into an alliance with Harihara II of Vijayanagar. It was this alliance which emboldened him to withhold payment of tribute and his son, Bukka II, to attempt to abduct the goldsmith's daughter of Mudgal. Fīrūz, after returning from Vijayanagar, sent for the girl and gave her in marriage to his son, Hasan Khān. Her parents received gifts of money and a grant of their native village, and it was probably on this occasion that Fīrūz restored to the money-changers of the Deccan the right of following their ancestral calling.

Fīrūz, a man of twenty-seven at the time of his accession, had been an amiable, generous, accomplished, and tolerant prince, possessed of a vigorous constitution and understanding, but these had been undermined by excesses, and he became slothful and lethargic. In 1412 he led an expedition to Māhūr, but failed to reduce its rebellious governor to obedience, and, after a raid into Gondwāna, returned to Gulbarga and gradually abandoned all public business, leaving it in the hands of two manumitted slaves, Hūshiyār and Bīdar. In 1417 he so far roused himself as to re-cover arrears of tribute from the raja of Telingāna, and then set out on the disastrous expedition to Pāngul, already described. Its failure was largely due to his lethargy. After his return to Gul-barga he fell sick, and Hūshiyār and Bīdar, in order to secure the succession to his weak and voluptuous son, induced him to order that his brother, Ahmad, should be blinded. Ahmad fled from the capital and was pursued by Hūshiyār and Bīdar, but defeated them, and drove them back to Gulbarga. Here they brought into the field in a litter Fīrūz, now grievously sick, and ventured another battle, but the king swooned, and a rumour that he was dead caused most of his army to transfer its allegiance to Ahmad. The citadel was surrendered, and in an affecting interview Ahmad accepted his brother's abdication, and took charge of his two sons.

Ahmad ascended the throne on September 22, 1422, and ten days later his brother died, his death being probably accelerated by Ahmad. Ahmad owed his success very largely to Khalaf Hasan, a rich merchant from Basra, whom he rewarded with the title of Malik-ut-tujjār and the place of lieutenant of the kingdom, and then occupied himself with setting affairs in order. The status and powers of its chief officers were more precisely determined, and Ahmad was then at leisure to avenge the disasters of the Pāngul campaign, in the manner already described. On his return from Vijayanagar in the summer of 1423, the rains failed, causing a famine, and in the following year it appeared that they were about to fail again. Ahmad ascended a hill beyond the city-wall, and, in the sight of the multitude, prayed for rain. Fortune favoured him, clouds gathered, and rain fell. The drenched and shivering multitude hailed him as a saint, and henceforward he proudly bore the title of *walī*.

He then extinguished the semi-independence of Telingāna. In 1424 he invaded the country, captured the raja, put him to death, and extended the eastern frontier of his kingdom to the sea.

The raja who held Māhūr was still in rebellion, and late in

1425 Ahmad marched against him, induced him by promises of pardon to surrender, and then put him to death, with five or six thousand of his followers. He then marched northwards to Kalam, captured the place from a Gond rebel, and led a foray into Gondwāna.

The foreign policy of the Bahmanids had hitherto been restricted to their relations with the great Hindu kingdom in the south, to which they might well have confined their attention; but Tīmūr's empty grant of the kingdoms of Gujarāt and Mālwā turned their eyes towards the north, and Ahmad conceived the vain project of converting that grant into a reality. Hūshang of Mālwā had, in 1422, furnished him with a *casus belli* by compelling his vassal, Narasingha, to swear allegiance to Mālwā, and, in 1428, while Ahmad, at Ellichpur, was strengthening the defences of his northern frontier by rebuilding the fortresses of Gāwīl and Narnāla in the Sātpuras, Hūshang marched on Khetla in order to enforce the payment of arrears of tribute. Ahmad protested against this molestation of his vassal, but retired, and Hūshang, attributing to fear a retreat which was in fact due to religious scruples, followed him, but suffered a crushing defeat and was driven back into Mālwā. Ahmad, returning to Gulbarga, was so attracted by the climate and situation, and perhaps by the legendary glories, of the ancient city of Bīdar, that he decided to adopt it as his capital, instead of Gulbarga, and in 1429, when his new city had risen, continued his designs against the northern kingdoms by entering into a close alliance with Nasīr Khān of Khāndesh, who gave a daughter in marriage to 'Alā-ud-dīn, Ahmad's son. Ahmad then attacked Gujarāt, which was ruled by a king of his own name. Between 1430 and 1432 his troops were defeated in four campaigns at various points on his northern frontier. The final battle, fought near Bhaul,[1] on the Girna, between armies led by the two kings in person, is described as indecisive, but Ahmad of the Deccan, dismayed by his losses, retreated at once to Bīdar. The state was so exhausted by this disastrous war that Hūshang of Mālwā retrieved his late discomfiture by capturing Kherla and putting Narasingha to death. Ahmad marched against him, but was so ill-prepared that he submitted to a composition of the quarrel by Nasīr Khān of

[1] Situated in 20° 36' N. and 75° 5' E.

Khāndesh on terms disgraceful to himself. He admitted that Kherla was a fief of Mālwā, and accepted the insolent concession that the rest of Berar should remain a province of the Deccan.

After this humiliating treaty the bodily and mental powers of Ahmad gradually decayed, and he died in 1435. His character was simpler than that of his versatile and accomplished brother, Fīrūz, for whose learning, with its taint of scepticism, he substituted a simple faith, tinged by superstition. He was at first a follower of Jamāl-ud-dīn Husainī, Gīsū Daraz ("Long Locks"), a zealot from Delhi who settled at Gulbarga; but he later transferred his devotion to the famous saint Ni'matullāh of Māhān, near Kirmān, in Persia, whose son, Khalīlullāh, visited the Deccan and converted Ahmad, as is clear from the inscriptions in his tomb, to the faith of the Shiah. However to him religion was a personal matter, and he wisely refrained from interfering with that of his subjects. The first militant Shiah ruler in India was Yūsuf 'Ādil Shāh of Bījāpur. Ahmad's preference for foreign troops was a cause of bitter strife in his kingdom. Foreigners had been employed from the earliest days of the rule of the Bahmanids in the Deccan, but, with the growth of the foreign legion, they became numerous enough to form a political party. The natives of the Deccan were less energetic and enterprising than those of more northern latitudes, and, being unable to compete with the hardy Arab, the intellectual Persian, and the virile Turk, were obliged to give place to them at court as well as in camp. The feud was complicated by religious differences. The Deccanis were Sunnis, and, though all the Foreigners[1] were not Shiahs, a sufficient number of them belonged to that sect to brand the party with heterodoxy. But one class of foreigners, afterwards largely employed, stood apart from the rest. These were the Africans, whom attachment to the Sunni faith, and the contemptuous attitude adopted towards them by other foreigners, threw into the arms of the Deccanis. Thus, in this disastrous strife, the Foreign party consisted of Turks, Arabs, Mughuls and Persians, and the Deccani party of natives of the Deccan and negroes. War between the two parties was openly declared when Khalaf Hasan of Basra attributed a defeat suffered by him in one of the campaigns against Gujarāt to the cowardice of the Deccanis, and the feud thus begun was

[1] This word, when used of the political party, will be spelt with a capital letter.

not confined to intrigues for place and power, but frequently found expression in pitched battles and bloody massacres, of which last the Foreigners were usually the victims. Thenceforward the history of the domestic affairs of the Deccan is mainly a record of this strife, which contributed in no small measure to the disintegration of the kingdom, and afterwards to the weakness of the states which rose on its ruins. When Ahmad died, Miyān Mahmūd Nizām-ul-mulk, a Deccani, was lieutenant of the kingdom and Khalaf Hasan governor of Daulatābād.

Ahmad was succeeded by his eldest son, 'Alā-ud-dīn, who, after quelling a rebellion headed by his brother, Muhammad, was involved in hostilities with Khāndesh. His wife, daughter of Nasīr Khān of Khāndesh, complained to her father of 'Alā-ud-dīn's neglect of her for a younger Hindu wife, and Nasīr Khān invaded Berar. Khalaf Hasan undertook to expel him, but enraged the native party by insisting that he should not be hampered by the inclusion of Deccani troops in his army. He drove Nasīr Khān out of Berar, invaded Khāndesh, there again defeated Nasīr Khān, and returned in triumph to Bīdar, laden with spoil. His success assured the supremacy of his party, and gained for it the place of honour at court, on the right of the throne, the Deccanis and Africans being relegated to the left.

'Alā-ud-dīn, after his campaign in the Rāichūr doāb in 1443, already described, devoted himself for some time to the administration of his government, to the destruction of Hindu temples, the punishment of wine-bibbers, and works of benevolence, but gradually retired into the seclusion of the harem, so neglecting business as to hold a public audience no oftener than once in four or five months. During this period the Deccanis regained much of the power which they had lost, and their leader, Miyān Mīnullāh, organised a campaign for the subjugation of the northern Konkan, the command of which was given to Khalaf Hasan. The climate of this tract proved deadly to the foreign troops; they were betrayed and misled by a raja whom they trusted, and the powerful raja of Sangameshwar took the demoralised army by surprise, defeating it, and slaying Khalaf Hasan with the greater part of his troops. The remnant made its way back to Chākan, which Khalaf Hasan had made his base; and the Deccani officers there, who had refused to accompany the force, secretly reported that the disaster had been due to the rashness of Khalaf Hasan and the treachery of his troops. The report was purposely delivered to the king when he was drunk, and he was persuaded to allow the Deccanis to punish the remnant of the Foreigners in their own way. They lured them from the fortress of Chākan, murdered their officers at a banquet, and slaughtered the rest, among them many Sayyids. The wives and children of the murdered men were taken by their murderers. One, Kāsim Beg, and two other foreign officers contrived, with great difficulty, to escape, and to lay before the king a true account of the whole affair. He was overcome by remorse, executed the leaders of the Deccani party, dismissed the lesser members of the party from the places which they held, and forswore the use of wine. Kāsim Beg was appointed to the vacant government of Daulatābād, and his two companions were promoted to high rank.

In 1453 'Alā-ud-dīn's confinement to his palace as the result of an injury led to rumours of his death, which encouraged Jalāl Khān, governor of Bālkonda, and his son, Sikandar, to rebel. Jalāl Khān had married a sister of the king, and his son aspired to a share in the kingdom. They persuaded Mahmūd I of Mālwā to aid them, but he retired in dudgeon on discovering that 'Alā-ud-dīn still lived. The rebels were besieged in Bālkonda by Khvāja Mahmūd Gāvān of Gīlān, a foreign officer who afterwards rose to the highest rank in the state. They surrendered, and the king pardoned them, and injudiciously allowed them to retain Bālkonda.

'Alā-ud-dīn died in 1458. Shortly before his death an Arab merchant, who had been unable to obtain payment for some horses which he had sold to courtiers, heard the king's titles recited in the khūtba, and am ng them al-'Ādil ("the Just") on which he prided himself. The Arab sprang up and cried, "No, by God! Thou art not just, gen rous, clement, or compassionate. O tyrant and liar! Thou hast slain the pure seed of the prophet, and in the pulpit of the Muslims takest to thyself such titles as these!" The king retired to his chamber, and left it no more until he was borne forth to the grave.

He was succeeded by his eldest son, Humāyūn, whose reputation was so bad that a party attempted to enthrone one of his younger brothers, Hasan; but Humāyūn fought his way into the palace and seized the throne, imprisoning Hasan. He favoured the Foreign party, but the Deccanis were not entirely excluded from office.

The short reign of this monster was marked by a series of rebellions. Jalāl Khān and Sikandar-again rose; the Hindus of Telingāna rebelled; and, during the king's absence at Warangal, the populace at the capital released his two brothers and other political prisoners. These risings were punished with revolting cruelty. The *kotwāl* of Bīdar, though he had done his best to suppress the populace, was confined in a cage and exhibited daily in the city for the rest of his life, which soon came to an end, for he was allowed no food but portions of his own body, which were cut off and offered to him. The troops who had failed to suppress the rising were massacred. Hasan Khān, who had assumed the royal title, was thrown to a tiger. Others were thrown to beasts, tortured, boiled to death, or slowly cut to pieces, joint by joint. He unjustly executed, without inquiry, a high official, Nizām-ul-mulk Ghūrī, who was related to the royal house of Mālwā, and whose family fled thither and placed themselves under the protection of the king, Mahmūd I. After these atrocities Humāyūn, known as *Zālim*, or "the tyrant", became a homicidal maniac. "The torch-bearer of his wrath ever consumed both Hindu and Muslim alike; the broker of his fury sold at one price the guilty and the innocent; and the executioner of his punishments slew whole families for a single fault." Nobles summoned to court made their wills and bade their families farewell; the inmates of the harem were butchered in mere sportive brutality; and from the families of his subjects, high and low, he exacted the *droit du seigneur*. He fell sick, and an African girl, at the instigation of others, stabbed him lest he should recover. He died on September 4, 1461.

He was succeeded by his infant son, Nizām Shāh. The Hindus of Orissa and Telingāna then invaded the kingdom and advanced to within twenty miles of Bīdar before they were defeated and driven back; but they returned when it became known that Mahmūd I of Mālwā was invading the kingdom to avenge the death of his kinsman. The child-king was borne out with his army, which met Mahmūd near Kandhār, but was defeated, and the boy was carried off by his mother to Fīrūzābād, while Mahmūd I captured the city of Bīdar and besieged the citadel, but retired on learning that Mahmūd Begarha of Gujarāt and Mahmūd Gāvān had taken the field to cut off his retreat. Though he suffered considerable loss during his withdrawal, he reappeared in the following year and reached Daulatābād, but returned in haste on hearing that Mahmūd Begarha was again threatening his territories.

The youthful Nizām Shāh died on July 30, 1463, and was succeeded by his brother, Muhammad III, aged nine. The Foreign party retained its predominance in the state, which was governed by the queen-mother and Mahmūd Gāvān until Muhammad reached the age of fifteen, when his mother retired from the regency. Muhammad reigned for nineteen years, for eighteen years of which the lieutenant of the kingdom was Mahmūd Gāvān, the greatest statesman who ever served a Muslim ruler of the Deccan. During the king's minority he avenged Khalaf Hasan's death by conquering the Konkan, and another noble, Malik Hasan, reduced to obedience all Hindu chiefs in Telingāna, and was rewarded with the government of that province. The kingdom of the Bahmanids, for the first time, stretched from sea to sea, its coast-line extending on the west from Bombay to Goa, and on the east from Coconada to the mouth of the Krishnā.

Mahmūd Gāvān, though a foreigner, refused to identify himself with either party in the state, and divided the honours evenly between the two factions. He held the governments of Gulbarga and Bījāpur, and Yūsuf 'Ādil Khān, a Turk who was the leader of the Foreign party, that of Daulatābād. Berar was bestowed on Fathullāh 'Imād-ul-mulk, and Telingāna, as has been said, on Malik Hasan. These last two were Brāhmans by birth. Fathullāh was a Brāhman of Vijayanagar, and Hasan was the son of Bhairav, a Brāhman of Pāthri on the Godāvarī, who had fled to Vijayanagar. Both had been captured as boys during Ahmad Shāh's campaign in Vijayanagar, and had been brought up as Muslims, but neither forgot his origin. The Foreigners were well-disposed towards the Deccanis, and Fathullāh was a lifelong friend of Yūsuf, the leader of the Foreign party, but Hasan, crafty, ambitious and unscrupulous, was ill content that a foreigner should hold the first place in the state, and never rested until he had destroyed Mahmūd Gāvān.

At the end of 1472 Muhammad marched with Mahmūd Gāvān against the rajas of Bankāpuram and Belgaum, defeated them, and added Bankāpuram to Mahmūd's fief of Bījāpur. Further military operations were checked by a terrible famine, following the failure of the rains for two successive years, which devastated the Deccan, and was followed by an epidemic of cholera. Little or nothing was done for the wretched sufferers. When this calamity was passed, the king and Mahmūd Gāvān were obliged to march into Telingāna, to suppress a rebellion in Kondavīr, which had been abetted by a raja in Orissa. The rebellion was quelled; the raja was punished; and Muhammad, after completely tranquillising Telingāna, made Rājahmundry his headquarters for nearly three years, and there took, by the advice of Mahmūd Gāvān, the first step in the reform of the provincial administration of his kingdom by dividing the great province of Telingāna into two, with Rājahmundry as the capital of the eastern, and Warangal as that of the western province. The measure was necessary, but Hasan bitterly resented the dismemberment of the great province which he had governed. For some time after this Muhammad was engaged in an expedition into the eastern Carnatic, which formed part of the kingdom of Vijayanagar, and after his return the division of the four great provinces of the kingdom was completed. Berar was divided into the provinces of Gāwīl, or northern, and Māhūr, or southern Berar; Daulatābād into those of Daulatābād on the east, and Junnār on the west; and Gulbarga into those of Gulbarga on the east and Belgaum on the west. At the same time the powers of the provincial governors were curtailed in many ways.

The new provincial governments were fairly divided between the two parties of the state, but the reforms were most unpopular, and Hasan, who had been the first to suffer by them, formed a conspiracy against the life of their author. The conspirators, taking advantage of the absence of Yūsuf with an expeditionary force, induced the keeper of Mahmūd's seals, an African, to affix his private seal to a blank sheet of paper, on which they afterwards wrote a treasonable letter to the raja in Orissa who had instigated the rebellion at Kondavīr. The letter was read and shown to the king when he was drunk. Without making any inquiries, he sent for Mahmūd and roughly demanded of him what was the punishment meet for a traitor. "Death by the sword", replied he, confident in his innocence. The letter was then shown to him, and he exclaimed, "By God, this is a manifest forgery! The seal is mine, but the writing is none of mine, and I know nothing of the matter". The king made no reply, but, as he rose to leave the hall, ordered the executioner to put Mahmūd to death. The minister knelt, recited the short creed of his faith, and, as the sword fell, cried, "Praise be to God for the blessing of martyrdom!" He was seventy-eight years of age when, on April 5, 1481, he was murdered, and he had well and faithfully served the Bahmanids for thirty-five years. He was learned, accomplished, generous, charitable, and blameless in his private life. He had endeavoured to heal the disastrous feud between the Deccanis and the Foreigners, and, but for the rancour of the Brāhman, Hasan, might have succeeded. The king found that his murdered minister had left no hoards, having distributed his income, as he received it, in charity; and his treasurer, when examined, demanded proof of his master's guilt, and openly charged the king, who could produce none, with murder. The whole camp was in confusion. The Foreigners and the respectable members of the Deccani party joined Yūsuf 'Ādil Khān, and refused even to see the king. The wretched man, deserted by all but the conspirators, was thrown into their arms, and was obliged to accede to their demands. Hasan became lieutenant of the kingdom, with the title of Malik Nāib, and his son Ahmad received the province of Daulatābād, vacated by Yūsuf when he took possession of Mahmūd's fiefs of Bījāpur and Belgaum. Muhammad returned to Bīdar, accompanied by the Malik Nāib and his friends, the rest of the nobles marching apart, and avoiding all intercourse with him. From Bīdar they returned to their provinces without taking leave of him, and, when summoned to attend him on a progress to Belgaum, where he hoped to conciliate Yūsuf, marched at a distance from the royal troops, and again returned to their provinces without leave. Muhammad attempted to drown his remorse in drink, and after his return to Bīdar he died from its effects on March 22, 1482, crying out with his latest breath that Mahmūd Gāvān was slaying him. He was but twenty-eight years of age, an accomplished and high-spirited prince, who was better served than any of his predecessors, and might well have been the greatest of his line, but for his love of strong liquor, which destroyed first his authority and then his life. It was the curse of his race, and of the long line of eighteen kings there were few who were not habitual drunkards. The massacre of the Foreigners at Chākan, and the murders of Nizām-ul-mulk Ghūrī and Mahmūd Gāvān, all factors in the ruin of the dynasty, were due to orders issued by kings under the influence of drink.

On Muhammad's death his son, Mahmūd, a boy twelve years of age, was enthroned by the Malik Nāib. Mahmūd, who soon became a slave to the vice of his house, was never king but in name, being always under the influence of one dominant minister or another. The gathering of the provincial governors to swear allegiance to the young king led to street-fighting between the two factions, lasting for twenty days, and costing 4000 lives before peace was restored. In 1486 the Malik Nāib carried Mahmūd on an expedition to suppress a rebellion in Telingāna, but discovered a conspiracy against his own life, and fled to Bīdar, where Dilpasand Khān, one of his own creatures, played the Malik Nāib false, strangled him, and sent his head to the king. Mahmūd then favoured the Foreigners, and the Deccanis, in 1487, conspired to dethrone him, and might have succeeded, had not his Turkish guards stood by him until the foreign troops could be assembled. They put the conspirators to death, but meanwhile, in their absence, the city mob plundered their houses, until the king at sunrise took his seat on the throne, and ordered a general massacre of the Deccanis and Africans. The carnage continued for three days, and was not checked till a Turk named Kāsim, and entitled *Barīd-ul-mamālik*, assumed the lieutenancy of the kingdom and the guardianship of the king. The provincial governors were not disposed to obey the behests of Kāsim, who issued his commands in the king's name, and whose policy was to maintain his own supremacy by setting them at variance; and in 1490 the late Malik Nāib's son, Ahmad Nizām-ul-mulk, governor of Daulatābād, sent envoys to Yūsuf 'Ādil Khān of Bījāpur and Fathullāh 'Imād-ul-mulk of Berar, inviting them to join in asserting their independence of Bīdar. They agreed, and from this may be dated the appearance of the smaller sultanates. Later, in 1512, Sultān Kulī Kutb-ul-mulk of Golconda and, on the death of the last of the Bahmanids in 1527, Amīr 'Alī Barīd in Bīdar, also assumed independence. These were the founders of the five independent houses of the Deccan, known from their titles as the Nizām Shāhī, the 'Ādil Shāhī, the Kutb Shāhī, the 'Imād Shāhī, and the Barīd Shāhī dynasties.

Meanwhile Kāsim Barīd incited Ahmad Nizām Shāh and the

regent of Vijayanagar to join him in attacking Yūsuf 'Ādil Shāh. Ahmad stood aloof; but though the Hindus captured Rāichūr and Mudgal, Yūsuf defeated Kāsim. Once more, for a time, the powers of the Deccan were united. On the death of Najm-ud-dīn Gīlānī, governor of Goa, in 1485, his servant, Bahādur Gīlānī, had seized Goa and opened business as a pirate. He enjoyed a successful and profitable career, till in 1493 Mahmūd Begarha of Gujarāt complained that his trading vessels and ports had been plundered. All then united to suppress the pirate, lest the powerful king of Gujarāt should have a pretext for invading the Deccan. The pirate long held the Konkan and much of the country above the ghāts against all his enemies, but was at length driven from the fortress of Panhāla, captured, and slain. It is impossible to unravel here the tangled skein of intrigues among the powers of the Deccan after the suppression of Bahādur. In 1504 Kāsim died, and was succeeded by his son, Amīr 'Alī Barīd, and Fathullāh died, and was succeeded by his son, 'Alā-ud-dīn, who reigned in Berar until 1529. In 1504, too, Yūsuf 'Ādil Shāh established the Shiah faith in his dominions, and attempted to suppress all Sunni observances. This step was important, for it was the first attempt to establish in any part of India the Shiah religion, which ultimately became the established faith in the Deccan. But it raised a storm of opposition. All the powers of the Deccan united against Yūsuf, who took refuge first with 'Alā-ud-dīn in Berar and afterwards with Dāūd Khān of Khāndesh. By sowing the seeds of discord among his enemies, he succeeded in separating them, so that Amīr 'Alī and the puppet king, Mahmūd, were left alone. Yūsuf then emerged from Khāndesh, defeated Amīr 'Alī, and returned to his kingdom.

In 1509 Ahmad Nizām Shāh died, and was succeeded at Ahmadnagar, the new capital which he had built for himself, by his son, Burhān, and in the following year Yūsuf died, and was succeeded by his son, Ismā'il. Shortly after this time Amīr 'Alī appointed a governor to Gulbarga, which was included in the dominions of Bījāpur. In the war which followed this act of aggression, he was defeated by Ismā'il 'Ādil Shāh, who captured the puppet Mahmūd Shāh, and sent him back to Bīdar with an escort of cavalry; but the weakling again fell into the hands of Amīr 'Alī, and remained a prisoner until his death, in 1518, when his son, Ahmad, was enthroned by Amīr 'Alī. Ahmad died in 1521. and his brother, 'Alā-ud-dīn II, was then set on the throne.

The new king attempted to rid himself of his master, but his plans were detected, and he was deposed. His brother, Valī-ullāh, who succeeded him, likewise attempted to rid himself of the *maire du palais*, and was put to death; and his brother, Kalī-mullāh, the last of the Bahmanids, was placed on the throne. For a time he patiently bore his yoke, but, on learning of Bābur's conquest of northern India, secretly wrote to him, offering to cede to him the provinces of Berar and Daulatābād in return for his aid in establishing his authority over the rest of the Deccan. The letter was intercepted by Amīr 'Alī, and Kalīmullāh fled to Bījāpur, and, on being ill received there, to Ahmadnagar, where Burhān Nizām Shāh received him at first with extravagant demonstrations of respect, but, fearing to compromise his own status as a sovereign prince, suddenly changed his attitude, and Kalīmullāh shortly afterwards died, not without suspicion of poison. With him ended the line of Bahman Shāh.

The rule of the Bahmanids had been harsh, and they showed little regard for the welfare of their Hindu subjects. The Russian merchant, Athanasius Nikitin, describes the poverty and misery of the children of the soil, and the wealth and luxury of the ruling class, and describes Muhammad III, even in 1474, as being in the power of his nobles, who maintained large forces. It was from this thraldom that Mahmūd Gāvān attempted to free him, with the result already recorded. Some of the line were bigots, but their neglect of the welfare of their Hindu subjects is to be attributed neither to their bigotry nor to the apathy bred of habitual drunkenness, for the peasantry of the Hindu kingdom of Vijayanagar was equally neglected and equally miserable. The tiller of the soil existed for the maintenance of the state, and it was seldom that he was allowed to retain of the fruits of his labour much more than would suffice to keep body and soul together.

In 1565 the allied kingdoms of Bījāpur, Ahmadnagar, Golconda, and Bīdar finally overthrew the great Hindu kingdom of Vijaya-nagar. In 1574 the kingdom of Ahmadnagar absorbed that of Berar, and in 1619 the kingdom of Bījāpur that of Bīdar. Between 1596 and 1600 Akbar annexed the greater part of the kingdom of Ahmadnagar, and after thirty years of intermittent warfare his grandson, Shāhjāhān, finally extinguished it in 1633, leaving the two kingdoms of Bījāpur and Golconda, which were annexed by Aurangzīb, the first in 1686 and the second in 1687.

CHAPTER VII

Gujarāt, Mālwā and Khāndesh

The Deccan had fallen away from the empire of Delhi in 1347, but it was not until the complete disruption of that empire after the death of Fīrūz Tughluk in 1388 that the great provinces of Gujarāt and Mālwā were severed from.it. The small state of Khāndesh had ceased after 1382 to hold any communication with the capital, and in 1392 the governor of Mālwā, and in 1396 the governor of Gujarāt assumed independence. No revolt was necessary, for the empire was crumbling away.

The governor of Gujarāt, Zafar Khān, son of Vajīh-ul-mulk of Dīdvāna, a Rājput convert to Islam, assumed in 1396 the title of Muzaffar Shāh, and in 1400 reduced to vassalage the Rājput state of Īdar. In 1399 Mahmūd Shāh of Delhi and his retinue, fleeing from Tīmūr, arrived in Gujarāt, but Mahmūd, finding Muzaffar Shāh unwilling to treat him with the deference due from a subject to his sovereign, retired to Mālwā.

Dilāvar Khān Ghūrī, who claimed descent from the princes of Ghūr, had been appointed governor of Mālwā by Fīrūz. He never assumed the royal title, but after 1392 he behaved as an independent ruler. Nevertheless he received Mahmūd as his sovereign, and entertained him with princely hospitality at Dhār until his guest was able, in 1401, to return to his own capital. Dilāvar's son, Alp Khān, disapproved of his deference to Mahmūd and withdrew to Māndū, where he occupied himself in perfecting the defences of the great fortress-city. He had long been impatient for his inheritance, and in 1406 he removed his father by poison, and ascended the throne of Mālwā, adopting the title of Hūshang Shāh. But he did not long enjoy his throne in peace, for Muzaffar of Gujarāt, resenting the murder of his old friend, invaded Mālwā to punish the parricide. He besieged Hūshang in Dhār, captured him, and carried him off as a prisoner into Gujarāt, leaving his own brother, Nusrat Khān, in Dhār as governor of Mālwā. His rule was so oppressive and extortionate that the army rose against him, expelled him, and elected as their ruler Mūsa Khān, a cousin of Hūshang. Hūshang now protested his innocence of his father's death, and implored Muzaffar to restore him to his throne. Muzaffar sent with him into Mālwā his own grandson, Ahmad, who established Hūshang at Dhār, but did not attempt to oust Mūsa from Māndū. On his return to Gujarāt Ahmad was designated heir to his grandfather, who died in 1411, when Ahmad was confronted with a formidable rebellion, headed by his four uncles. Hūshang, instead of aiding his bene-factor, twice invaded Gujarāt in support of the rebels, but they were defeated on each occasion, and Hūshang was obliged to retire.

The relations between Gujarāt and Mālwā were at first com-plicated by the rise of the small state of Khāndesh, founded in 1382 by Rāja Ahmad, otherwise styled Malik Rāja. He had established himself at Thālner, on the Taptī, as capital of the fief granted to him by Fīrūz, and by 1382 had conquered the sur-rounding country and ruled his small territory as an independent prince; but he and his successors for some generations were content with the title of khān from which their state became known as Khāndesh, "the Country of the Khāns". His dynasty was dis-tinguished by the patronymic Fārūki, from the title of the second caliph, 'Umar al-Fārūk or "the Discriminator", from whom Ahmad claimed descent.

Ahmad died in 1399, leaving two sons, Nasīr and Hasan, to inherit his dominions. Nasīr took the eastern and Hasan the western districts, and Nasīr founded in 1400 the city of Burhānpur, and captured from a Hindu chieftain the strong fortress of Asīr, while Hasan retained Thālner, his father's capital. In 1417 Nasīr, with the aid of Hūshang of Mālwā who had married his sister, captured Thālner and imprisoned Hasan, and then, fearing the intervention of Ahmad I of Gujarāt, forestalled him by marching on Nandurbār. A force from Gujarāt drove him from Nandurbār to Asīr, and there besieged him until he sued for peace. This was granted on his promising to refrain from aggression in future, and on his swearing allegiance to Ahmad I, who recognised his title to Khāndesh. Hasan retired to Gujarāt, where he and his descendants found a home and intermarried with the royal house.

Nasīr resented Hūshang's failure to aid him against Ahmad, and the alliance between Khāndesh and Mālwā came to an end. In 1429 Nasīr entered into an alliance with the Deccan, and gave his daughter in marriage to 'Alā-ud-dīn, later the ninth of the Bahmanids, but the union engendered strife, and Khāndesh, after a disastrous war with its powerful neighbours, was at length driven into the arms of Gujarāt.

In 1419 Ahmad of Gujarāt, provoked by aggressions, invaded Mālwā, defeated Hūshang in a fiercely-contested battle, drove him into Māndū, and laid waste the country, but retired before the rainy season began, and was dissuaded from returning in the following year only by Hūshang's submissive attitude and promises of amendment.

In 1422 Hūshang, attributing his military inferiority to lack of elephants, undertook a most daring raid. He led a party of only a thousand horse across India, through the forests of Gondwāna, into Orissa, and at Jājpur posed as a merchant and induced the *kēsari* raja of that state to visit his camp in order to inspect his goods. There he seized him and demanded seventy-five elephants as his ransom; and, having received these, returned to Mālwā. On his way to Māndū he surprised Kherla, and carried off its Gond raja, Narasingha, as a prisoner. As he approached Māndū, he found that Ahmad I of Gujarāt was besieging the fortress, but he eluded his troops and succeeded in entering the city. Ahmad then retired into the Sārangpur district, but, being followed by Hūshang, retreated into Gujarāt. After his departure Hūshang captured Gāgraun, and then marched on Gwalior, but retired when Mubārak Shāh of Delhi advanced to the relief of the fortress.

Hūshang's defeat in 1428 by Ahmad Shāh Bahmanī of the Deccan has been mentioned in the preceding chapter. In 1433 he annexed Kālpī, on the Jumna, and, shortly before his death in 1435, founded Hūshangābād on the Nerbudda.

His eldest son, Ghaznī Khān, who succeeded him under the title of Muhammad Shāh, was a confirmed drunkard, and the only part which he took in the government of his kingdom was to put his three brothers to death. His barbarity so disgusted his cousin, Mahmūd Khaljī, that he poisoned him, drove his son, Mas'ūd, to take refuge in Gujarāt, and, after offering the throne to his own father, who declined, occupied it himself.

Mughīs, the father of Mahmūd, was the son of Dilāvar Khān's sister, married to an officer named 'Alī Shīr Khaljī, who claimed descent from Nāsir-ud-dīn, the eldest brother of Jalāl-ud-dīn Fīrūz Shāh Khaljī of Delhi. Mughīs was thus a first cousin of Hūshang, and Mahmūd was a second cousin of Muhammad

Shāh. Mahmūd founded the Khaljī dynasty of Mālwā, of which four kings reigned, before Mālwā was annexed in 1531 by Bahādur Shāh of Gujarāt.

Soon after the defeat of Hūshang by Ahmad Shāh Bahmanī, Ahmad I of Gujarāt also became involved in hostilities with the Deccan. The aggressor was Ahmad Shāh Bahmanī, who had conceived the design of annexing both Gujarāt and Mālwā. It is needless to attempt to follow the course of the campaigns and the engagements between the armies of the two states, extending over a period of nearly two years. The advantage lay almost wholly on the side of Gujarāt, and after the last battle, in 1431, Ahmad Shāh Bahmanī retreated to Bīdar, and was obliged to abandon his insane design.

Nasīr Khān of Khāndesh died in 1437, and was succeeded by his son, 'Ādil Khān I, who died in 1441, and was succeeded by his son, Mubārak Khān I, and in 1442 Ahmad I of Gujarāt, having failed to restore Mas'ūd to the throne of Mālwā, died, and was succeeded by his son Muhammad I, known as Karīm. Ahmad had built, on the site of Asāwal, a city which he named Ahmadābād, and which took the place of Anhilwār as the capital of Gujarāt.

In 1440 Mahmūd I of Mālwā, as has been mentioned in chapter IV, responded to the appeal of a party among the nobles of Delhi who had invited him to ascend the throne, disgusted with the worthlessness of the ruling king, Muhammad Sayyid. He failed to overcome the party which was loyal to Muhammad, and his return was accelerated by the news that a mob in Māndū had torn the gilded umbrella from the tomb of Hūshang and raised it over the head of a pretender; but on his return he found that the rising had been crushed by his father. Ever since his ascent of the throne, he had been obliged to contend with disaffection, for the other nobles had resented its usurpation by one of themselves. Domestic disaffection had gradually subsided, as Mahmūd proved himself worthy of his station, but his usurpation had served foreign enemies as a pretext for helping those whom he had ousted. Ahmad I had disappointed the elder son of Muhammad of Mālwā, but Kumbha, rāna of Mewār, who had harboured his younger son, 'Umar Khān, was prepared to attempt his restoration by armed force.

The rāna had aroused the hostility of the rulers of both Mālwā and Gujarāt. His support of a pretender and his relations with Rājput chiefs within the borders of Mālwā were a menace to Mahmūd's tenure of the throne which he had usurped; his pretension to the allegiance of the lesser Rājput states on his south-western border, claimed by the sultan of Gujarāt, and his intervention in the affairs of the small state of Nāgaur, ruled by that sultan's kinsmen, more than once led to war. Had the two Muslim rulers acted together, the consequences would have been serious to the rāna, but, though in 1456 they concluded a treaty binding each to abstain from hostilities against the other in order that both might be free to attack the common enemy, they acted independently against him. Each was frequently at war with him, and according to Muslim historians inflicted on him several defeats and extorted from him heavy indemnities, but he never suffered at their hands any reverse which placed either his independence or his authority in jeopardy. It was not until nearly eighty years after this time that their troops fought in alliance, with a result disastrous to the sultan of Mālwā, and it was not until that kingdom had been absorbed by Gujarāt that Bahādur Shāh, for the second time in the history of the Muslims in India, captured the great fortress of Chitor.

A detailed account of the series of campaigns between Mālwā and Gujarāt on the one hand and Mewār on the other would be out of place here, but two may be mentioned. In 1453 Kumbha defeated and nearly destroyed, near Nāgaur, the army of Kutb-ud-dīn of Gujarāt; and in 1455 Mahmūd I of Mālwā, in the course of a long and successful campaign, recovered the city of Ajmīr, with the shrine of the Muslim saint, Shaikh Mu'īn-ud-dīn Chishtī, captured Būndī, and extorted heavy indemnities from the rāna and from other chiefs.

One of the expeditions of Mahmūd I of Mālwā against the rāna was interrupted by a difference with Mahmūd of Jaunpur in connection with Kālpī, but Nasīr Khān, who pretended to independence in that small principality, was reinstated under the protection of Mālwā, and the question of his status was, for the time, settled.

In 1449 Muhammad I of Gujarāt attempted to annex the small state of Chāmpāner. He defeated the raja, Gangadās, in the field, and drove him into his fortress, whence he sent an appeal for aid to Mahmūd I. Mahmūd responded, but, on learning that

Muhammad had advanced to Godhra to meet him, hastily retreated. Muhammad, having contracted a severe illness before Chāmpāner, was unable to continue the siege, and returned to Ahmadābād, where, on February 10, 1451, he died, and his son, Kutb-ud-dīn Ahmad, succeeded him. His death was regarded by Mahmūd as an opportunity for humbling, and possibly annexing, Gujarāt, and he invaded the country; but near Ahmadābād the army of Gujarāt inflicted a crushing defeat on him, capturing eighty elephants and all his camp equipage, and he returned to Māndū in sorry plight.

On May 18, 1458, Kutb-ud-dīn of Gujarāt died, after a short illness, and the nobles raised to the throne his uncle, Dāūd, but the depravity of this prince was such as to indicate a disordered mind, and after a reign of twenty-seven days he was deposed, and his younger brother, Mahmūd, was enthroned in his stead. Mahmūd, a mere youth, was involved on his accession in the meshes of a formidable conspiracy, but, with a courage and acumen worthy of a mature and experienced ruler, detected the carefully concealed design of the conspirators, boldly withstood them, and put them to death. Later in his reign Mahmūd was known as Begarha, an appellation which will be explained later, but which it will be convenient to use now, in order to distinguish him from contemporaries of the same name.

Mention has already been made of the assassination of Nizām-ul-mulk Ghūrī, at the instance of the tyrant, Humāyūn, of the Deccan. The murdered man's wife and family fled to the court of Mālwā, and begged Mahmūd I to avenge his death. In 1461 Humāyūn was dead, and his son, Nizām Shāh, who had succeeded him, was an infant. Mahmūd I, welcoming an opportunity of conquering the Deccan, marched on Bīdar, defeated the army of the Deccan in the field, occupied the city, and opened the siege of its citadel. Meanwhile the child's guardians had appealed for aid to the young Begarha, who marched to Nandurbār, near the northern frontier of the Deccan, and ordered Mahmūd I to desist from the disgraceful act of waging war on a child. The invader, finding his line of retreat threatened, began to retire, and was so harassed by a combined force of the armies of Gujarāt and the Deccan that he abandoned his elephants and his heavy baggage, and attempted to elude his pursuers by plunging into the forests of the Melghāt, where his army was nearly destroyed. Large numbers died of thirst, and the Korkus fell upon the remainder, of whom very few reached Māndū.

Untaught by this disaster, Mahmūd I again invaded the Deccan in the following year, but found the young king's army drawn up to meet him at Daulatābād, and learned that Begarha was again marching on Nandurbār. On this occasion he retired before it was too late.

In 1465 Mahmūd I was gratified by the arrival at Māndū of an envoy from the puppet caliph in Egypt, al-Mustanjid Yūsuf, bearing for him a patent of sovereignty, an empty but highly prized honour. Three years later he received another mission, on this occasion from Tīmūr's great-grandson, Abu Saʿīd, king of Transoxiana, Khurāsān and Balkh. The mission was gratifying as a recognition of sovereignty, and he sent an envoy in return to Saʿīd, destined to be the grandfather of Bābur.

After Mahmūd's second discomfiture in the Deccan, an army from that kingdom had captured Kherla. In 1466 a treaty of peace between Mālwā and the Deccan was concluded, and Kherla was surrendered to Mahmūd, in consideration of his agreeing to refrain from future acts of aggression. Muhammad III of the Deccan, who succeeded Nizām Shāh, violated this treaty, and induced Mahmūd's governor of Kherla to transfer his allegiance, but Mahmūd recovered the fortress and thenceforward Kherla was included in the dominion of Mālwā.

In 1468, after an expedition against some predatory Rājputs, Mahmūd I marched to Chanderī, and thence sent a force to besiege Karera, nearly sixty miles to the north of that town. Karera was burned by means of fireballs thrown into it from the trenches, and, when it fell, 7000 prisoners were taken. Having received a mission from Buhlūl Lodī of Delhi, he returned from Chanderī to Māndū. He was sixty-eight years of age, and during a reign of more than thirty-three years hardly a year had passed without his having taken the field. Exhausted by almost unceasing warfare, he suffered severely during the march from the fierce heat of an Indian summer, and on June 1, 1469, shortly after his arrival at his capital, he expired. Almost at the same time died his enemy, Rāna Kumbha, assassinated by his son Ūda, who succeeded him and reigned for five years, but whose name, like that of the treacherous doge in Venice, is blank in the annals of Mewār. In 1473 he was driven from the throne by the rāna,

Raimal, who carried on the line of the Gahlots. Mahmūd I was the greatest of the Muslim kings of Mālwā. He had, indeed, failed to conquer Delhi, Gujarāt, Chitor and the Deccan, all of which he had attempted to annex, but against these failures must be set many successes against the rāna and minor Rājput chieftains, and the kings of the Deccan, and his enlargement of the frontiers of his kingdom. His recognition by the phantom caliph and by Abu Sa'īd proved that his fame had reached Egypt and Samarkand. He was a builder as well as a soldier, and among his many works at Māndū is the Tower of Victory, raised to commemorate his successes over Kumbha. The more famous Tower of Victory at Chitor is said to commemorate Kumbha's victories over Begarha and Mahmūd I, but the successes of the Gahlots were gained by Sangrama Singh against Mahmūd. II, not by Kumbha against Mahmūd I.

Mahmūd I was succeeded by his eldest son, Ghiyās-ud-dīn, a most peaceful prince, whose avowed policy was to rest content with the wide dominions which his father had left him, and to live in peace with his neighbours; and to this policy he adhered throughout his reign. He once set out from Māndū in response to an appeal for aid from the raja of Chāmpāner, whose fortress was besieged by Begarha, but withdrew on being advised that it was unlawful to aid a misbeliever against a brother Muslim. He most scrupulously observed all the rites of his faith, and abstained from strong drink and from wearing garments of materials not sanctioned by the sacred law. He was the dupe of every rogue who feigned piety, and at his court beggars of all classes abounded, and the taxes wrung from an industrious and thrifty people were squandered upon vagabonds and idlers. He left his brothers in possession of the fiefs which they had held in his father's reign, and conferred on his eldest son, 'Abd-ul-kādir, the royal title of Nāsir-ud-dīn Sultān, and left affairs of state almost entirely in his hands, while he amused himself with the administration of his vast harem, organised as a miniature state, and wasted in this futile pursuit the time and energy which should have been employed in the government of his kingdom.

The internal peace of the kingdom was disturbed only shortly before his death by a violent quarrel between his two sons, the cause of the younger being adopted by his mother, who desired that he should succeed to the throne. The feeble-minded king vacillated between his designated heir and his wife's favourite until the elder having left the capital in dudgeon returned, put his brother to death, imprisoned his mother, and on October 22, 1500, ascended the throne with his father's consent. Four months later Ghiyās-ud-dīn died of poison, administered, as was generally believed, by his son's orders. Many of the nobles in the provinces refused to believe that the old king had abdicated voluntarily, and rose in rebellion, but Nāsir-ud-dīn defeated them twice and crushed the rising. Later he led a foray into the dominions of the rāna, Raimal, and sent a force into Khāndesh to the assistance of Dāūd Khān Fārūki, whose territory had been invaded by Ahmad Nizām Shāh of Ahmadnagar.

Nāsir-ud-dīn aggravated by deep drinking the natural ferocity of his disposition, and by his violent temper so incensed his nobles, that when, in 1510, his elder son, Shihāb-ud-dīn, rose in rebellion, many supported him. Nāsir-ud-dīn marched out to Dhār, where his son was encouraged by his numerical superiority to attack him, but was defeated and fled, first to Chanderī and then to Siprī, near Narwar, and his father, after vainly endeavouring to persuade him to return to his allegiance, set out for Māndū. On his way thither he died, according to some authorities of fever, and according to others of poison administered by his nobles, and on May 2, 1511, his third son, who was in the camp, was raised to the throne as Mahmūd II.

Shihāb-ud-dīn, on hearing of his father's death, hastened towards Māndū, but his brother outstripped him, and shut the gates in his face. He retired into Khāndesh and there resided at Asīr as the guest of 'Ādil Khān III.

It is now time to revert to Gujarāt. The state of Girnār, in Sorath or Kāthiāwār, had remained unmolested since Muhammad ibn Tughluk had captured the fortress and punished the raja for harbouring the rebel Taghī. Mandulak Chudāsama was the reigning raja, and in 1466 Mahmūd Begarha invaded his dominions with the object of reducing him to vassalage. The country was pillaged, temples were sacked, Mandulak agreed to pay tribute, and Begarha retired, but in the following year, learning that Mandulak was in the habit of using the insignia of royalty, commanded him to desist, and Mandulak, fearing another invasion, obeyed him. His submission gained him little, for late in 1469 Mahmūd led a great army into Sorath, and, to Mandulak's protest that he had committed no offence and had regularly paid tribute, replied that he had come neither for tribute nor for plunder, but to establish the true faith in Sorath, and offered Mandulak the choice between Islam and death. The unfortunate raja retired to his citadel, Ūparkot, and was there closely besieged. He attempted to purchase peace by the offer of an enormous indemnity, and, when this was refused, fled to his hill-fort in the Girnār mountains, whither Mahmūd followed him. He was again closely besieged, and on December 4, 1470, surrendered and accepted Islam, receiving the title of Khānjahān. With him the long line of Chudāsama rajas of Girnār came to an end, and Mahmūd incorporated the state with his dominions, and at the foot of the hills founded the city of Mustafā-ābād, which became one of his capitals.

The mother of Mahmūd had been a princess of Sind, daughter of Jām Nizām-ud-dīn, and during the next two years he was occupied in Sind, where, as was reported to him, Muslims were persecuted by Hindus. He crossed the Rann with a very small force, and found a large body of men drawn up to receive him, but not to oppose him, for it was composed of Sumras, Sodas, and Kalhoras, who were professing Muslims, but knew little of their faith. They were probably the descendants of Rājputs who had been forced to accept Islam, and who, though excluded from the fellowship of their unconverted brethren, had been neglected by the leaders of their adopted faith, and allowed to lapse into ignorance. Mahmūd invited those who would to enter his service, and many accepted and received grants of land in Sorath, where teachers were appointed to instruct them in the faith.

In 1472 Mahmūd marched to the assistance of his father-in-law, the jām, who was beset by rebels. These dispersed on his approach, and Mahmūd received from the jām valuable gifts, and also one of his daughters, whom he married to Kaisar Khān, of the Fārūki house of Khāndesh. On his return, in 1473, Mahmūd marched to Dwārkā, the Hindus of which town had plundered a Muslim merchant who had been driven ashore. He plundered and destroyed the famous temple, building a mosque in its place, pursued Rāja Bhīm to Bet Shankhodhar, defeated him in a sea-fight, and forced him to surrender. The merchant recovered all that he had lost, and much more, and Bhīm was sent to Ahmadābād, where he was impaled.

In 1482 Mahmūd was able to prosecute an enterprise on which he had long set his heart—the annexation of Chāmpāner. On December 4, he set out from Ahmadābād, and the raja was driven into his strong hill-fortress of Pāvāgarh. Mahmūd occupied Chāmpāner, at the foot of the hill, and began, even before the fort had fallen, to beautify it with buildings. The siege lasted for a year and nine months, and at length the Rājputs, reduced to extremities, resolved to perform the dreadful rite of *jauhar*. The women were burnt, and the men, arrayed in yellow garments, went forth to die. The Muslims met them in the gate, and slew nearly all of the seven thousand who rushed forth; but the raja and two of his ministers were wounded and captured, and having obstinately refused during five months of captivity to accept Islam, were then put to death. Patāi's son accepted Islam, and in the next reign received the government of Īdar, with the title of Nizām-ul-mulk, but scions of the family fled to Chota Udaipur and Deogarh Bāriya, where their descendants still rule.

It was after the fall of Chāmpāner that Mahmūd received the cognomen of Begarha (*be garha*, "of two forts") as the conqueror of the two great Hindu strongholds of Girnār and Chāmpāner. Chāmpāner was named Muhammadābād, and became one of his chief places of residence.

The Portuguese, who had first appeared on the Malabar coast in 1498, at this time became a factor in the foreign politics of Gujarāt. They had established a great trading centre at Cochin, and in 1507 they formed a settlement on Socotra, near the entrance to the Red Sea. In less than a decade they had diverted the greater part of the lucrative spice trade from the Red Sea and Egypt to the direct sea-route between India and Europe, thus depriving the Mameluke sultans of the heavy dues which they levied, both at Jeddah and Alexandria, on goods in transit. This diversion of the trade affected not only the Mamlūks, but also the Muslim merchants of Indian ports, and the Portuguese, who, with memories of the Moors in their minds, loathed all Muslims, also interfered with the pilgrim traffic between the Indian ports and Jeddah, and thus became obnoxious to all the Muslim powers surrounding the Arabian Sea, who determined to make a combined effort to oust them. It was agreed by Kansauh al-Ghaurī, sultan of Egypt, Mahmūd Begarha, other local Muhammadan rulers, and a Hindu, the Zamorin of Calicut, that a fleet should be equipped at Suez and dispatched to India, where it would be reinforced by local squadrons, and would attack the Portuguese. The Portuguese viceroy, Francisco de Almeida, unaware of the fleet having left the Red Sea, sent his son Lourenço, with a small squadron, to explore the ports on the western coast of India, north of Cochin; and in January, 1508, Lourenço encountered the great allied fleet at Chaul. His small squadron was overwhelmed, and he died a hero's death. The allies, however, had no lasting cause of joy in having thus provoked the Portuguese. After the victory Mahmūd Begarha returned to Chāmpāner.

We must now revert to the history of Khāndesh, in the affairs of which state Begarha became, not unwillingly, involved. Since Khāndesh had been overrun, shortly before the death of Nasīr Khān, by the troops of the Deccan, the rulers of Khāndesh had regarded the sultan of Gujarāt as their protector, and had paid him tribute. Nasīr Khān had died in 1437, and had been succeeded by his son, 'Ādil Khān I, who was succeeded in 1441 by his son, Mubārak Khān, an active and warlike prince who had extended his rule over part of Gondwāna and carried his arms as far afield as the region now known as Chota Nāgpur. His son 'Ādil Khān II, who succeeded him in 1457, for a time withheld payment of tribute to Gujarāt, but a demonstration by Mahmūd Begarha sufficed to bring him to his senses and he remained on good terms with his overlord until his death in 1501, when he was succeeded by his brother, Dāūd Khān. When Rāja Ahmad Khān, the founder of the dynasty, died, his younger son, Hasan Khān, on being ousted by his brother, Nasīr Khān, had made his home at the court of Gujarāt, where he was well received, and where he and his descendants were honoured guests. His son, Ghaznī Khān, had married a daughter of Ahmad I of Gujarāt, and their son Kaisar Khān, already mentioned, a daughter of Jām Nizām-ud-dīn of Sind. Kaisar's son, Ahsan Khān, married a daughter of Mahmūd Begarha, and their son, 'Ālam Khān, married a daughter of Muzaffar II, Mahmūd's son. When Mahmūd had marched into Khāndesh to compel 'Ādil Khān II to pay tribute, the latter submitted, and a friendly interview took place. Mahmūd had taken advantage of this interview to persuade 'Ādil to nominate as his heir 'Ālam Khān, who, besides being a direct descendant of Rāja Ahmad, was Mahmūd's grandson, and had married his grand-daughter. At the time of the death of 'Ādil Khān II, Mahmūd was not in a position to press his grandson's claim, and 'Ādil Khān's brother, Dāūd, succeeded without opposition. He was a feeble but reckless prince, and embroiled himself with Ahmad Nizām Shāh of Ahmadnagar, who invaded Khāndesh, and could not be expelled until Dāūd purchased the aid of Nāsir-ud-dīn of Mālwā by causing the *khūtba* to be recited in his name. Dāūd's death in 1508 ended an inglorious reign, and his son Ghaznī Khān, who succeeded him, was poisoned only eight days later. Ahmad Nizām Shāh then invaded Khāndesh with the object of enthroning another scion of the Fārūki house, also named 'Ālam Khān, but Mahmūd Begarha drove him from the country and enthroned his own client, 'Ālam Khān, under the title of 'Ādil Khān III. His reign was not marked by any noteworthy event, and on his death in August, 1520, he was succeeded by his son, Muhammad I, usually styled Muhammad Shāh, from his having been summoned to the throne of Gujarāt, which, however, he never lived to occupy. Some time after Mahmūd's return to Gujarāt, an envoy from Shāh Ismā'il Safavī of Persia arrived at Ahmadābād to invite Mahmūd to embrace the faith of the Shiah, but, being rejected as a heretic, he proceeded to Mālwā, where he was more favourably received, but failed to gain a single convert.

Mahmūd's health was failing, and on November 23, 1511, he died, and was succeeded by his son, Muzaffar II. Mahmūd was not only the greatest of the sultans of Gujarāt, but holds an honourable place among the warrior princes of India. He was a prodigy of precocity. Though little more than a child at his accession, he coped successfully with a formidable conspiracy, and thereafter ruled his kingdom himself. In his manhood his appearance was striking. Tall and robust, with a beard which descended to his waist and a heavy moustache, twisted and curled upwards, he struck awe into his courtiers. His brother had died of poison, and of him it is said that he gradually absorbed poisons into his system until he became immune from the effects of any that might be administered to him. This is, of course, a fable, but a convenient fable, belief in which he probably fostered. Lack of space forbids a description of his normal diet, but he is said to have eaten between twenty and thirty pounds' weight of food a day.

The naval victory at Chaul had no lasting results, and before his death Mahmūd offered to the Portuguese a site for a factory at Diū, but Muzaffar II refused to allow them to fortify it.

The reign of Mahmūd II, which marks the rapid decline of Mālwā, began in widespread rebellion, and ended in disaster. His first minister was a Hindu, who was murdered by jealous Muslim nobles, after which Muhāfiz Khān, governor of Māndū, became dictator, and so angered the nobles that a party of them repaired to Asīr and invited Shihāb-ud-dīn to return to Mālwā and ascend the throne. He died on his way thither, and his partisans proclaimed his son king under the title of Hūshang II, and carried him, after suffering a defeat, to Sihor, whence they sent a message to Mahmūd, assuring him that they were loyal at heart but would not endure the rule of Muhāfiz Khān.

Meanwhile Muhāfiz Khān, unable to bend the king to his will, had rebelled, and proclaimed the eldest brother, Sāhib Khān, under the title of Muhammad II. Thus there were three kings in Mālwā. Sāhib Khān held Māndū, Mahmūd II had retired to Ujjain, and Hūshang II remained in Sihor, but was gradually deserted by his followers, who joined Mahmūd, since he was opposed to Muhāfiz Khān. Mahmūd secured the adherence of Mednī Rāi, a Rājput who held the government of Rāisen, and with his help advanced to Māndū. Sāhib Khān fled to Gujarāt, and, being there subjected to disgraceful treatment by the Persian envoy, fled in his shame to Berar, where he became the guest of 'Alā-ud-dīn 'Imād Shāh.

In Māndū Mahmūd II was the servant rather than the master of the Rājputs who had restored him. Mednī Rāi caused many of the old Muslim nobles to be put to death, and the rest left the capital. The Rājputs scandalised all Muslims by their treatment of those professing Islam, and Mahmūd, having twice failed to master them, eluded his custodians while on a hunting tour, and fled to the frontier of Gujarāt where he was honourably received, for Muzaffar II had long been preparing to intervene in the affairs of Mālwā, and, joining him with a large army, marched on Māndū.

On Mahmūd's escape Mednī Rāi had gone to Chitor to enlist the aid of Sangrama Singh, the rāna who had succeeded his father, Raimal, in 1508, but the Rājput garrison had remained in Māndū, and was twice defeated before the walls of the city. In the siege which followed, the garrison attempted to hold out until the rāna and Mednī Rāi could relieve them, but on February 23, 1518, Māndū was carried by escalade, the garrison performed the rite of *jauhar*, and the Muslims then massacred all who remained; 19,000 were put to the sword, and the streets ran with their blood.

Muzaffar then turned against the rāna and Mednī Rāi, who had reached Ujjain, but who, on hearing of the massacre in Māndū, had hastily retreated to Chitor. He therefore returned to Gujarāt where he was occupied in a campaign against the Rājputs of Īdar, but left a force of 10,000 horse, under Āsaf Khān in Māndū, to assist Mahmūd against his enemies. Mahmūd and Āsaf Khān marched on Gāgraun, held by Hemkaran, a Rājput, captured the town and put Hemkaran to death, and then turned against the rāna, who was marching to attack them. The armies met when the Muslims were exhausted and in disorder after a forced march, and the Rājputs cut their force to pieces. Mahmūd was captured and carried before Sangrama Singh, who received him courteously and sent him back to Māndū with an escort which replaced him on his throne, but the rāna compelled him to surrender his crown-jewels.

After this battle, which, owing to Āsaf Khān's presence, is always represented in Hindu annals as a victory over the combined armies of Mālwā and Gujarāt, Sangrama Singh invaded Gujarāt, plundered some of its towns, and returned to Chitor. In 1521, Muzaffar retaliated by sending a large army into Mewār which ravaged the rāna's country.

Muzaffar II had designated his eldest son, Sikandar, as his heir, and his second son, Bahādur, left Gujarāt in dudgeon and visited Chitor and Delhi, in both of which cities he was well received. He reached Delhi shortly before Bābur's invasion, and is said to have been present at the battle of Pānīpat, but not to have taken part in it. Shortly afterwards he received a message urging him to return. His father had died on April 7, 1526, and Sikandar had been enthroned, but had almost immediately proved his unfitness for sovereign power. The nobles were divided into three factions, supporting the claims of Sikandar, Bahādur, and Latīf, Muzaffar's third son, who was assembling his forces at Nandurbār. Meanwhile 'Imād-ul-mulk Khushkadam, the leading noble, caused Sikandar to be assassinated and raised to the throne Mahmūd, Muzaffar's youngest son, a mere infant, in whose name he intended to rule. On Bahādur's arrival most of the nobles transferred their allegiance to him, and on July 11, 1526, he was acclaimed king in Ahmadābād. Khushkadam had retired, with the child, Mahmūd II, to Chāmpāner, and Bahādur, pursuing him thither, captured him, and put him to death. Latīf, who was lurking in the town, fled towards Nandurbār, but the governor of that district defeated and wounded him, and he died a prisoner on the way to Chāmpāner. There remained one other candidate for the throne, Muzaffar's fourth son, Chānd Khān, who fled and took refuge with Mahmūd II of Mālwā, who encouraged him to hope for his support.

Late in 1527 Bahādur marched to the assistance of 'Alā-ud-dīn 'Imād Shāh of Berar and Muhammad I of Khāndesh, who had succeeded his father, 'Ādil Khān III, in 1520. Burhān I of Ahmadnagar had annexed the district of Pāthrī, on the Godāvarī, which had belonged to Berar, and 'Alā-ud-dīn, with the help of Muhammad I, had attempted to recover it, but had been defeated and driven from his kingdom into Khāndesh. Bahādur marched through Berar on Ahmadnagar, occupied the city, drove Burhān Nizām Shāh and his ally, Amīr 'Alī Barīd Shāh of Bīdar, into the hills, and then formed the siege of Daulatābād. The siege was protracted, and, as the rainy season of 1529 was approaching, Muhammad I entered into negotiations with the enemy, and peace was concluded. The kings of Ahmadnagar and Berar were to cause the khūtba to be recited in their capitals in Bahādur's name, Pāthrī and Māhūr were to be ceded to Berar, and all elephants taken by Burhān I were to be returned. These terms were never satisfactorily fulfilled, but Bahādur returned to Gujarāt.

In 1530 the Portuguese captured the port of Damān, and in 1531 failed to capture Diū, but left a fleet in the Gulf of Cambay to harass the trade and shipping of Gujarāt.

The authority of Mahmūd II of Mālwā, after his defeat by the rāna, extended little beyond the neighbourhood of his capital, but the rāna's state, Mewār, fell into disorder after the death of Sangrama Singh in 1527. Mahmūd's treatment of his Muslim nobles drove many of them into Gujarāt, where they were received at the court of Bahādur, who was justly incensed by Mahmūd's foolish support of the claims of the pretender, Chānd Khān. Bahādur, with Muhammad I of Khāndesh, then invaded

Mālwā. Mahmūd II was in grave difficulties, for the new rāna, Ratan Singh, was menacing Ujjain. On receiving Bahādur's message, summoning him to his camp, he retired into his seraglio, and told his advisers that all was over, and that he would spend his remaining days in pleasure. Troops could hardly be expected to fight well for such a chief, and on March 17, 1531, Bahādur entered Māndū. Mahmūd and his officers appeared before him, the *khūtba* was recited in his name, and Mālwā was annexed to Gujarāt. Mahmūd and his sons were sent towards Chāmpāner, but on the way, the camp was attacked by tribesmen from the hills, and the escort, fearing a rescue, put Mahmūd to death.

Bahādur and Muhammad I retired from Māndū to Burhānpur, where Bahādur compelled Burhān I of Ahmadnagar to wait on him, and during the next eighteen months their troops were engaged in establishing order in Mālwā, and in expelling Rājputs who had occupied much territory in the north of the kingdom. In 1533 the Muslims appeared before Chitor, and the queen-mother, Jawāhir Bai, purchased peace by surrendering what remained of the spoil taken by her husband, Sangrama, from Mahmūd II, including the jewelled crown of Mālwā.

In 1534 Bahādur again advanced upon Chitor. He defeated the rāna, Vikramāditya, in the field, and proceeded to besiege the capital. He had favourably received in his camp Muhammad Zamān Mīrzā, a rebellious prince of the house of Tīmūr; Humāyūn had written, protesting against such conduct, and Bahādur, when drunk, had dictated a most insolent reply. Humāyūn, much enraged, answered that he was on the point of marching to punish him, but that he would not molest him until the holy war against the misbelievers was ended. Meanwhile Bahādur completed the investment of Chitor. After three months his artillery opened a practicable breach in its defence, and Jawāhir Bai led a *sortie* from the fortress, and was slain at the head of her warriors. The infant heir, Udai Singh, was conveyed to a place of safety, and the surviving Rā puts performed the rite of *jauhar*. Thirteen thousand women, headed by the mother of the young prince, are said to have voluntarily perished in an immense conflagration, and the survivors of the garrison rushed on the Muslims and were exterminated. Bahādur appointed a Muslim governor to Chitor and began his retreat.

He then found reason to repent the folly of which he had been guilty in insulting Humāyūn. The emperor was awaiting him in Mandasor, and Bahādur, who dared not attack, entrenched his camp. His troops, beleaguered for two months, suffered grievously from famine, and he basely deserted them and fled to Māndū. Humāyūn followed, and captured Māndū; but Bahādur escaped and fled to Chāmpāner. Humāyūn again pursued him, and he fled to Cambay, and thence to Diū. But when Humāyūn reached Cambay, he was recalled by the news of disturbance in Ahmadābād, and, returning to Chāmpāner, captured that fortress. He then foolishly began to organise the administration of Gujarāt as though it were a settled province of his empire, despite the need of his presence elsewhere, leading a military promenade through Khāndesh, and then returning to Māndū. But there he received disquieting reports of the activities of Shīr Khān, the Afghan, who eventually drove him from his throne, and he therefore returned with all speed to Āgra. Bahādur returned to Chāmpāner, expelled Humāyūn's governor from the fortress, and on May 25, 1536, took up his residence in the city.

Bahādur, while a fugitive in Diū, had appealed for help to Nunho da Cunha, governor of Portuguese India, and in return for a promise of aid had ceded to him the port of Bassein, and granted him permission to build a fort at Diū. He soon repented of his bargain, and sought to expel the Portuguese from Diū. Da Cunha sailed to Diū, but refused to land, mistrusting Bahādur. Bahadūr lost patience, and, against the advice of all his counsellors, on February 13, 1537, visited da Cunha on board his ship, to inspect the presents said to have been brought. The Portuguese showed some intention of detaining him, whereupon he is said to have lost his temper, and to have cut down a priest. He entered his barge, but the Portuguese boats closed round it, and swords were drawn. Bahādur leaped into the water and was drowned, as were all his attendants except one, who was saved by a friendly Portuguese.

With the exception of Mahmūd Begarha, Bahādur was the greatest of the kings of Gujarāt. He disgraced himself by his desertion of his army at Mandasor, but against this error must be set many successes. He annexed the kingdom of Mālwā, and he was one of the three Muslim sovereigns in India who captured the great Rājput stronghold of Chitor. He left no son, and the nobles of Gujarāt decided to invite Muhammad Shāh of Khāndesh to ascend the throne. He himself, his father, his grandfather, and two more remote ancestors had married princesses of Gujarāt, and, though descent in the female line seldom counts for much in questions of succession in Muslim states, Muhammad had been for years the loyal vassal and brother-in-arms of Bahādur, whose recognition of his title of shah was understood to signify adoption as heir. He obeyed the summons, and set out from Burhānpur, but on May 24 died before he could reach Ahmadābād.

Latīf Khān, Bahādur's brother, had left one son, a boy of eleven, who was then brought from the fortress in Khāndesh where he had been interned, and enthroned as Mahmūd III. For the first nine of the seventeen years of his reign he was no more than a puppet in the hands of one ambitious minister after another. Ikhtiyār Khān, who had raised him to the throne, was assassinated, but a recital of the feuds, intrigues, and crimes which continued until 1546 would be tedious and unprofitable.

The Ottoman sultan, Sulaimān I, who had made himself master of Egypt in 1517, had learned with indignation of the death of Bahādur and the subsequent growth of the power of the Portuguese in the eastern seas, from which he resolved to expel them; but it was not until 1538 that he took the first step to this end by sending from Suez a large fleet under Sulaimān Pasha to aid the sultan of Gujarāt in wresting Diū from the Christians. The pasha announced that he was setting forth on a holy war against the misbelievers, but the treachery and cruelty with which he treated his fellow-Muslims at Aden rendered him an object of suspicion to Khvāja Safar, appointed by Mahmūd III to the command of his land-forces. Diū was attacked and the Portuguese were reduced to great straits, but the co-operation between the land- and sea-forces was incomplete, and Khvāja Safar, perceiving that the expulsion of the Portuguese would place Diū in the hands of Sulaimān Pasha, a less desirable tenant, falsely assured the pasha that a large fleet was on its way from Goa to the relief of the beleaguered garrison. The Turks therefore sailed away, but left behind several officers who entered the service of Gujarāt. The land-forces, having set fire to the town of Diū, then retired.

In 1546 Mahmūd III, freed at length from the domination of selfish ministers, made another determined attempt to recover

Diū. The Portuguese were again reduced to great straits, but at length a fleet of nearly one hundred sail under João de Castro, governor of Portuguese India, enabled the garrison to take the offensive, and with the loss of no more than one hundred men they captured nearly all the besiegers' artillery and utterly defeated them. In the field 1500 were killed, 2000 wounded, and many taken. On receiving the news of this disaster Mahmūd wept with rage and mortification, and caused twenty-eight Portuguese prisoners to be torn to pieces in his presence. In the following year the Portuguese burned the fort and city of Broach, and massacred the inhabitants, and also plundered and destroyed other ports on the coasts of Kāthiāwār and the Konkan, and in 1548 Mahmūd was obliged to conclude a treaty most advantageous to them.

In 1549 he retired to Mahmūdābād, where he lived in splendour and luxury for the rest of his reign. There he was joined by Kādir Khān, driven from Mālwā by Shujā'at Khān, the governor appointed by Shīr Shāh. His death was due to an act of clemency. He had sentenced one of his attendants, Burhān-ud-dīn, to death by being immured, but, before the man died, relented and had him released. His victim remembered only his sufferings, and on February 15, 1554, slew the king as he lay on his bed, stupefied with drink and drugs. The leading nobles were then summoned to the palace in the king's name, ten of them were assassinated, and Burhān was proclaimed king, but the surviving nobles led their troops against him and he was slain.

Mahmūd III had had a morbid dread of the possibility of a son being set up as his rival, and took the barbarous measure of procuring an abortion whenever a woman in his harem became pregnant. It was therefore no easy matter to find an heir, but the nobles, headed by I'timād Khān, raised to the throne, under the title of Ahmad II, a scion of the royal house named Razī-ul-mulk, a great-grandson of Shakar Khān, who was a younger son of Ahmad I. The great nobles of the state became virtually independent, and the young king remained a prisoner in the hands of I'timād Khān, who was regent. He made one unsuccessful attempt to escape, and, after being recaptured, consoled himself by foolishly boasting to the officers who had access to him his determination to destroy I'timād Khān. The regent knew that he was incapable of any desperate deed, but, fearing lest he might find a capable confederate, caused him to be assassinated in 1562.

I'timād solved the question of the succession by producing a child named Nathū, who, he solemnly swore, was the son of Mahmūd. He said that Mahmūd had handed over to him a pregnant concubine, with orders that an abortion was to be procured, but that he, finding that the girl was in the sixth month of her pregnancy, had not the heart to subject her to an almost certainly fatal operation, and having left matters to take their course, had secretly brought up her son. The story was improbable enough, but any heir was better than none, and the child was proclaimed as Muzaffar III. The story of his ten years' reign is a record of perpetual strife between the independent nobles of the kingdom, while I'timād Khān retained the regency.

In 1568 I'timād Khān, having been ousted from the regency by another noble, Chingīz Khān, invited Akbar, who was then before Chitor, to invade Gujarāt. Chingīz Khān bestowed extensive fiefs on the Mīrzās, Akbar's rebellious kinsmen, and maintained his position as regent until he was murdered by another noble, Jhujhār Khān, who invited I'timād Khān to return. But the king had fallen into the hands of another noble, Shīr Khān Fūlādī, to whom I'timād Khān wrote, impudently repudiating his own solemn oath, and adding that as Muzaffar was not the son of Mahmūd III he had deposed him, and had invited the Mīrzās from Broach, in order that one of them might ascend the throne.

Shīr Khān was besieging Ahmadābād when Akbar's army reached Pātan, and fled carrying with him Muzaffar III. The Mīrzās fled to Baroda and Broach, and the nobles in Ahmadābād submitted to Akbar and entered his service.

In 1572 Muzaffar III escaped from Shīr Khān, who had not treated him well, and, being found by some imperial officers, was brought to Akbar. Akbar detained him as a political prisoner and annexed Gujarāt to the empire.

Muzaffar was later permitted to live in retirement in Kāthiāwār, and when, in 1583, a rebellion appeared to offer him a chance of recovering his throne, he joined the rebels. After ten years of hopeless adventure, during most of which time he was a fugitive, he fell into the hands of the imperial troops, and committed suicide by cutting his throat.

Bābur, who defeated and slew Ibrāhīm Lodī in the spring of 1526, and reigned in Delhi and Āgra until 1530, had no leisure to attempt the conquest of Mālwā. Humāyūn's rapid expedition through Mālwā to Gujarāt can hardly be described as a conquest of either country. But Shīr Shāh the Afghan, who in 1539 drove Humāyūn from his throne and from India, conquered the province and appointed Shujā'at Khān to its government. When Humāyūn recovered his throne in 1555, Shujā'at Khān refrained from acknowledging him, but died within a year. It was not until 1561 that Akbar's troops wrested Mālwā from Shujā'at Khān's son Bayāzid, known as Bāz Bahādur, and it became a province of the Mughal Empire.

CHAPTER VIII

Bābur, Humāyūn and the Afghans

After Tīmūr's death in 1404 his son Shāhrukh retained much of
his father's power and dignity until 1447, but on his death the
numerous scions of his great house, beset by many enemies, contended for the fragments of his empire. Tīmūr's great-grandson
ruled Khurāsān and Transoxiana until his death in 1467, and
'Umar Shaikh, the fifth of his nine sons, received as his appanage
the small principality of Farghāna, in the mountains of Turkistān,
east of Samarkand, and, dying there in 1494, left as his successor
his eldest son, Bābur, a boy of twelve. With the young prince's
twelve years of strife, with little success and much misery, we
are not here concerned. At last, driven from his home by the
Uzbegs, he retired in 1504 to Kābul, and there made for himself
a small kingdom, and, after one more fruitless attempt to recover
his great ancestor's capital, turned his eyes towards India.

We know Bābur more intimately than we know any other
eastern ruler, for he has left us in his diary a charmingly frank
and human record of the life of a soldier, a poet, a man of letters,
a leader of men, an acute observer, and a lover of good cheer.

In 1519 he conquered Bajaur and led a raid into India, but it
was not until he had been twenty years on the throne of Kābul
that he made a serious attempt at conquest. He was well aware
of the disaffection at the court of Ibrāhīm Lodī. The latter's insistence on vexatious etiquette, humiliating to the chiefs and
tribesmen of his court, and his degradation of those who resented
it in favour of men not of Afghan blood, bred discontent, and
his severity to the malcontents bred rebellion. Oudh, Jaunpur,
and Bihar were severed from his kingdom under Daryā Khān
of the Lohānī tribe of Afghans. Daulat Khān Lodī, governor of
the Panjab, was independent, and 'Alam Khān fled to Kābul and
sought Bābur's help against his nephew, Ibrāhīm. His appeal was
Bābur's opportunity. No longer content with raiding India,
he resolved to conquer it. His counsellors, like those of Tīmūr,
opposed the enterprise. They had no objection to enriching
themselves by for: ys, but they had no desire to exchange the cool

and pleasant air of Kābul for the burning plains of India. Bābur paid no heed to them, but rated them for their meanness of spirit and set forth.

He found the city of Lahore occupied by Ibrāhīm's troops, who had expelled the rebel, Daulat Khān, but Bābur fell upon them, drove them from the city, and plundered and burned its shops. From Lahore he marched on Dīpālpur, carried the fortified city by assault, sacked it, and put many of its inhabitants to the sword. There, for the time being, he established Ibrāhīm's uncle as Sultān 'Alā-ud-dīn, and, having placed both the province and its nominal sovereign under the charge of trusty officers of his own, retired to Kābul to assemble his army for the conquest of India. His eldest son, Humāyūn, brought a force from his province of Badakhshān, and Khvāja Kalān another from Ghaznī, but the army which Bābur led into India in November, 1525, numbered no more than 12,000, of whom it has been estimated that 10,000 were fighting men. He had received two invitations to invade India, one from Daulat Khān, and one from the rāna, Sangrama Singh, who wished to engage the rival Muslim powers in a struggle so exhausting as to enable him to restore Hindu supremacy. He had promised Bābur his support, but stood aloof and watched events. Daulat Khān, disappointed by Bābur's establishment of the puppet, 'Alā-ud-dīn, and convinced that he intended to seize the throne for himself, not only withheld his support, but assembled an army of 40,000 horse and took the field against him, girding himself with two swords as a symbol of his resolve to conquer or die. But India had broken the Afghan spirit; Daulat Khān's great force dissolved and fled before the attack of Bābur's hardy warriors; and the old man himself was captured, and shortly afterwards died.

Bābur did not diverge towards Dīpālpur, but marched directly on Delhi, and at Pānīpat, that "historic site" where the fate of India has been thrice decided, came into contact with Ibrāhīm's great army of 100,000 horse and 100 elephants. Of his gun-carriages and baggage-waggons, of which he had collected a great number, Bābur formed a laager, lashing them together with thongs of bull's hide, but leaving gaps through which squadrons of horse could charge. His artillery and his matchlock-men were in the centre of the laager, and behind it his army was drawn up: centre, right and left wings, and reserve. His right was

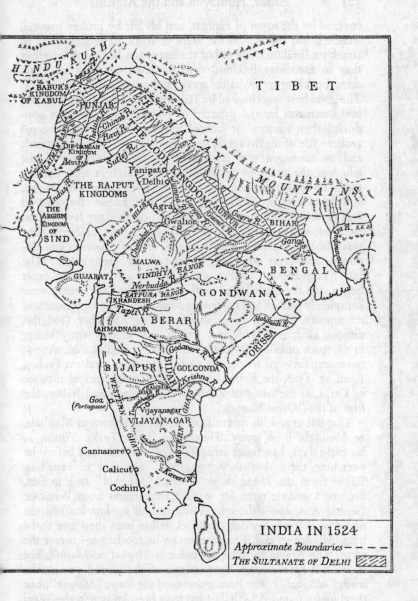

INDIA IN 1524

Approximate Boundaries — — —

THE SULTANATE OF DELHI

covered by the town of Pānīpat, and his left by broken ground, trenches, and *abattis*. On the night of April 20 he attempted an attack on Ibrāhīm's camp, but the operation had no other effect than to encourage Ibrāhīm, who, at dawn on April 26, 1526, drew up his army in battle array, and advanced to the attack. The great host was checked by Bābur's defences, and was thrown into confusion by the pressure of the troops in the rear continuing their advance. It suffered terribly from the well-directed artillery fire of the invaders; its languid charges were ineffectual; and its confusion was completed by the manœuvre of the *tulughma*, the attack by bodies of mounted archers who, circling round its flanks, attacked it in rear, first with showers of arrows, and then by vigorous charges, pressed well home. By noon all was over. Ibrāhīm and fifteen thousand of his army lay dead on the field, and the rest were in headlong flight. Ibrāhīm's head was laid before Bābur, and an endless line of prisoners and elephants, and great quantities of booty were brought in. "The sun", says Bābur, "had mounted spear-high when the onset began, and the battle lasted until midday, when the enemy were completely broken and routed, and my men were victorious and triumphant. By the grace and mercy of Almighty God this difficult affair was made easy to me, that mighty army being, in the space of half a day, laid in the dust." Small forces were at once sent forward to occupy Delhi and Āgra, and on Friday, April 27, 1526, the *khūtba* was recited, in the principal mosque of Delhi, in the name of Zahīr-ud-dīn Muhammad Bābur, the first of the "Great Moguls".

That Bābur and his descendants should be known as Mughals, or Mongols, is an irony. They were Barlas Turks. Tīmūr, in his early days, had fierce struggles with the Mughuls before he overcame them, but they eventually succeeded in expelling Bābur from the home of his fathers. "Mughul" had, in fact, become a generic term for warlike adventurers from Persia or Central Asia, and although Tīmūr and all his line loathed the name, as that of their bitterest foes, it has been their fate to be branded with it, and it now seems to be too late to correct the error. The Arabic form of the name is *Mughul* or *Mughūl*, but in India it has assumed, by a change of the second vowel, the form "Mughal". The Portuguese used the form "Mogor", but the dynasty founded by Bābur has long been known in the West as that of the Great Moguls.

Bābur distributed the great spoils of Delhi and Āgra with a bounteous hand, his eldest son receiving the lion's share, but none, even of the traders and camp-followers of the army, was disappointed and to every man and woman in Kābul a silver coin was sent as a token of their sovereign's victory. Humāyūn's greatest prize was the diamond now known as the Kūh-i-nūr, or "Mountain of Light". This he received as a gift from the family of Rāna Vikramāditya, whom he had protected from the spoiler, and offered to his father, who generously returned it to him.

The defeat of Ibrāhīm's army was but the beginning of Bābur's task. He was master of Delhi and Āgra, but of little more. The populace was hostile, the fortresses of the doāb and Mewār were closed against him, a scion of the Lodīs had taken refuge with the rāna, who was preparing to attack the invaders, and the Afghans held Oudh, Bihar, and the country to the south and east of Āgra in force. The summer heat was unusually fierce, the roads were impassable, and almost every village was a hostile camp, so that the conquerors, laden with treasure, were famishing. Nor were these the only difficulties with which Bābur had to contend. Discontent was rife in the army; both officers and men were murmuring. Was it for this that they had left the cool and pleasant air of Kābul? Of what use was treasure which would buy nothing? Why might they not return and enjoy the plunder which their toil had won? But their leader was to be baulked neither by the hostility of the people nor by mutiny in his own army. Calling his officers before him, he reminded them of all that they, and he no less, had suffered and accomplished. "A mighty enemy has been overcome, and a rich and powerful kingdom is at our feet. And now, having attained our goal and won our game, are we to forsake all that we have gained and flee to Kābul like beaten men? Let no man who calls himself my friend ever again mention such a thing; but if any one of you fears to stay, let him go." The malcontents were silenced. "There are few acts more splendidly heroic in Bābur's career than this bold resolve to stay where he was—in the middle of India, among hostile nations and a discontented soldiery—and the reward of his firmness soon appeared." Not only was his army pacified, but many of his enemies, convinced of his determination to remain, and conciliated by his clemency and generosity, were won over.

More than one Afghan leader joined him with his troops. His eldest son, more active than at any other period of his life, served him well. Sambhal was taken, and Humāyūn attacked a large army of Afghans which had invaded the doāb from the east, dispersed it, and pursued it. He captured Jaunpur and Ghāzīpur, and returned by way of Kālpī to Āgra, in response to a summons from his father, who urgently needed his help.

The rāna, Sangrama Singh, disappointed by Bābur's complete success and the failure of his own scheme, attempted nevertheless to realise his dream of a Hindu empire. Summoning to his standard all the chiefs who acknowledged his right to lead, he took the field. The old hero, bearing the scars of eighty wounds, and wanting an eye and an arm, was able to allay for the moment the feuds of the Rājputs and to place in the field 80,000 horse and 500 elephants, led to his standard by the chiefs of Mārwār, Amber, Gwalior, Ajmir, Chanderī, Kotah and many another. He marched on Bayāna, and Bābur, sending forward a small force to harass, so far as it could, the Hindu host, assembled his army in Āgra, and on February 11, 1527, set forth, for the first time in his life of warfare, on a *jihād*, or holy war against the misbelievers. He encamped at Sīkrī and, having been joined by the garrison of Bayāna, moved forward towards Khānua, and, as at Pānīpat, covered his front with his gun-carriages and baggage-waggons, but here also with trenches. For twenty-five days his position was thus strengthened, and Bābur set himself to inspire his troops, demoralised by reports of the valour and numbers of the Rājputs, with a courage equal to his own. Brushing aside the warnings of his foolish astrologer, he addressed his officers, adjuring them by their faith to quit themselves like men against the misbelievers, and reminding them that every one who should fall would attain the blessings of martyrdom. He then declared his repentance of the sin of drinking wine, to which he had been addicted all his life, and renounced it, breaking all his drinking vessels, and pouring out his stores of strong drink on the ground. All, inflamed with zeal, solemnly swore on the Koran to conquer or to die. The army then moved forward, and, re-forming the laager, on March 16 met the Hindu host at Khānua. His artillery and matchlock-men did fearful execution, but failed to check repeated charges of the gallant Rājputs, and after several hours of close fighting he repeated the manœuvre of the *tulughma*, sending

his mounted archers round the enemy's flanks to attack in rear.
At the same time his matchlock-men advanced firing, and his
bodyguard charged the enemy in front. The *tulughma* threw the
Rājputs into confusion, and "nothing but their indomitable
gallantry prolonged a battle which was fast becoming a massacre".
The fire of the artillery mowed them down, and at length they
broke, forced their way through the Muslims surrounding them,
and fled leaving thousands, including several chiefs, dead on the
field. Sangrama, once more severely wounded, escaped, but
died soon afterwards, and Bābur commemorated his victory by
raising a tower of the heads of the slain. But he had not yet
finished with the Rājputs. His next expedition was to Chanderī,
the stronghold of the powerful chieftain Mednī Rāi, who dominated the Muslim kingdom of Mālwā. The fortress was taken
by storm, and its garrison performed the rite of *jauhar*, first
slaughtering their wives and daughters, and then rushing forth
on the enemy and fighting until they fell. The power of the
Rājputs was crushed, but the Afghans of Bihar, who had assumed
the offensive while Bābur was engaged with the Rājputs, yet
remained, and in February, 1528, he marched against them. They
had invaded the doāb, and were encamped at Kanauj, but retired
across the Ganges. Bābur crossed the river by a temporary
bridge, the construction of which excited their ridicule, but his
artillery and matchlock-men covered both the construction of
the bridge and the passage of the river, and after a well-contested
battle the Afghans retired towards Ayodhyā. But Bābur, pursuing them, inflicted heavy losses, captured their families and
baggage, and dispersed their army. He then retired for a brief
season of repose to Āgra. Having spent the rainy season in the
delightful gardens which he had laid out in the suburbs of that
city, he marched to Dholpur, where he was assembling his forces
for the purpose of subduing the province of Sind, when he
learned, in January, 1529, that the Afghans of Bihar, having
recovered from the effects of their disastrous campaign in Oudh,
had temporarily composed their feuds, and had assembled, to
the number of 100,000, under the leadership of Mahmūd Lodī,
the brother of Ibrāhīm, whose authority was acknowledged
throughout Bihar and eastern Oudh, and who was besieging a
Mughal garrison in the fortress of Chunār. Bābur at once
returned to Āgra and marched on Chunār. On his approach

Mahmūd raised the siege and retired, while the great Afghan army dissolved. Bābur marched on to Buxar, and many of the Afghan leaders joined him with their contingents and made their submission, while Mahmūd fled and took refuge with Nusrat Shāh of Bengal, who warmly supported him, less from love of the Lodī dynasty than from fear lest Bābur, having secured Bihar, should invade Bengal as well. The Bengal army assembled on its western frontier, just above the confluence of the Gogra and the Ganges. Bābur could not suffer this great force to remain, menacing his eastern frontier, and, crossing the Ganges, advanced to the Gogra, reinforced by his son 'Askarī, who joined him from Jaunpur with 20,000 horse. Bābur's artillery and matchlock-men maintained a heavy fire on the front and the left flank of the enemy army and on the flotilla which accompanied it, while 'Askarī crossed the Gogra unmolested, above its right flank, and wheeled round to attack it in rear. The greater part of the army of Bengal turned to face him, but a considerable force remained to oppose Bābur's passage of the river. Under cover of the guns and matchlocks he crossed, in spite of the resistance which he met, and the enemy, attacked at once in front and rear and on the flanks, broke and fled, and the Afghan rebellion was crushed. A treaty of peace was concluded with Nusrat Shāh of Bengal, and thus "in three battles Bābur had reduced northern India to submission".

He returned to Āgra, and the brief remainder of his reign was spent in organising the administration of the provinces which formed his new kingdom. His system was purely feudal, and the greater part of his territory was parcelled out into fiefs among his officers, who were responsible, each within the limits of his fief, for the collection of the revenue and for all branches of the civil administration. Much of his territory remained in the hands of native landholders, Hindu as well as Muslim, whose obedience depended on his ability and readiness to punish contumacy. From the provinces "west to east from Bhēra and Lahore to Bahraich and Bihar, and north and south from Sialkot to Ranthambhor" Bābur received the equivalent of £2,600,000 as land rent. He has left us an interesting description of his kingdom of Hindūstān, which he loved little better than those mutinous officers who, after the victory of Pānīpat, had clamoured to be led back to Kābul. He found it uninteresting and monotonous, with few pleasures to recommend it. Its people were ugly and unsociable, without genius, intellect, politeness, ingenuity, or artistic sense. They had "no good horses, no good flesh-meat, no grapes or melons, no good fruits, no ice or cold water, no good food or bread, no baths or colleges". His strictures are harsh, but his standard was high.

Of his end a touching story is told. His favourite son Humāyūn lay sick unto death, as it was feared, and Bābur, performing a well-known ceremony, walked round his couch, and prayed that his son's malady might be transferred to him. From that moment, it is said, Humāyūn began to recover, while his father sickened, and, on December 26, 1530, breathed his last. We need not believe that he did, in fact, give his life for his son, but that was his desire. He was no more than forty-eight at the time of his death, but he was "a king of thirty-six years, crowded with hardship, tumult, and strenuous energy", and the sufferings of his boyhood and early manhood would have destroyed any constitution less robust than his. His method of alleviating them, by merry drinking bouts and the use of opium, failed, perhaps, to improve his power of resistance to disease. He had probably suffered intermittently from malaria for the greater part of his life, and from this complaint India grants no relief, and his overstrained constitution suddenly broke down. His body, in accordance with his will, was carried to Kābul, and "there lies at peace in his grave in the garden on the hill, surrounded by those he loved, by the sweet-smelling flowers of his choice, and the cool running stream; and the people still flock to the tomb and offer prayers at the simple mosque which an august descendant built in memory of the founder of the Indian Empire".

Humāyūn, at the time of his accession to his father's throne, was no more than twenty-three years of age, but had already had much experience. He had governed the province of Badakhshān, and had been second in command, under his father, in the Indian campaigns. He was courteous, brave, accomplished, and capable, on occasion, of displaying great energy, but not of sustained effort, or of such severity as was necessary to make his throne secure. He was too ready to indulge in opium and enjoy prolonged intervals of relaxation, and he almost invariably chose the wrong time for such indulgence, and was thus incapable of dealing with the numerous hostile forces by which he was surrounded. The Afghans of Bihar, led at first by Mahmūd Lodī, but later by a more formidable enemy, Shīr Khān, whose genius and ambition he failed, until too late, to reckon at their true value; the neighbouring kingdoms of Gujarāt and Bengal; and disaffected landowners within his own dominions were not his only enemies. Of his three brothers Kāmrān, the eldest, held the government of Kābul and annexed the Panjab, offering vain professions of allegiance, while he thus cut off the ruler of India from the natural recruiting grounds for his army, and obliged him to rely for his defences on the ever diminishing remnants of the forces which his father had led. The other two, 'Askarī and Hindāl, were weak and vain, without the ability to be personally formidable, but dangerous tools in the hands of ambitious and disaffected officers. Two cousins, Muhammad Zamān and Muhammad Sultān, known as the Mīrzās, put forth claims to the throne. Humāyūn should have crushed them all as dangerous rivals, but he amiably and foolishly tolerated them. Bahādur Shāh of Gujarāt, without the serious designs on Delhi and Āgra with which some historians have credited him, was nevertheless a menace, for he had recently extended his power by the annexation of the neighbouring kingdom of Mālwā, which marched with Humāyūn's dominions, and by more than one victory over the Rājputs, and shortly afterwards gave grave offence to Humāyūn by harbouring the Mīrzās and returning a most insolent reply to a demand for their surrender. With all these foes Humāyūn should have dealt in order, crushing each one before he turned to the next; but this he failed to do. He suppressed a rising under Mahmūd Lodī in Bihar, but before crushing the Afghan revolt withdrew in order to deal with Bahādur of Gujarāt, and wasted a year in successful but futile campaigns against him. Believing that he had established his authority over that kingdom, he left his treacherous brother as governor of Gujarāt, and retired into Mālwā, where he celebrated his success with carousals and feasts, while 'Askarī assumed the airs of royalty and caroused at Ahmadābād. Humāyūn was suddenly aroused from his slothful ease by the news that Shīr Khān, having established himself in Bihar, was engaged in bringing Bengal under his sway, and that Muhammad Lodī had been proclaimed king at Kanauj. The retreat was sounded; 'Askarī was recalled from Ahmadābād; and Humāyūn returned to Āgra, followed by his brother, and leaving both Gujarāt and Mālwā to Bahādur.

The grave perils which had suddenly recalled him from the kingdom which he had conquered should have aroused him from his lethargy, but he lingered at Āgra, indulging in dreams begotten of opium, broken by an occasional carousal, and unable to determine whether he should first attempt to recover Mālwā at least, if not Gujarāt, or deal with the peril which menaced his eastern frontier. A year passed before he reached the right decision, and in July, 1537, he led his whole army towards Bihar. His first task was to reduce the strong fortress of Chunār, held for Shīr Khān, who was engaged in the conquest of Bengal. Chunār was taken, and those of the garrison who fell into his hands were most barbarously treated, the hands of the gunners being lopped off. Shīr Khān's troops had meanwhile captured Gaur, the capital of Bengal, but, on learning of the fall of Chunār, he carried his family, his treasure, his artillery and his plunder into the fortress of Rohtās, which he made his stronghold, and sent his son, Jalāl Khān, to hold the defile of Teliyāgarhi, "the Gate of Bengal". Humāyūn, moved by one of his occasional spasms of energy, pressed on from Chunār, and Jalāl Khān, having defeated his advanced guard, and held the defile for so long as was necessary, retired as the main body of the imperial army came up. Humāyūn advanced and, early in 1538, occupied Gaur. The conquest of a second kingdom was then celebrated, and Humāyūn spent six months in merriment and idleness while his troops and their horses were succumbing to a pestilence bred of the noxious air of Gaur, and Shīr Khān was preparing to cut off his retreat. The capture of Monghyr, and the assumption of the royal title by Shīr Khān, whose troops were besieging Chunār and Jaunpur, and whose authority was acknowledged in the country between these fortresses, aroused him too late, and, with an army no longer fit to take the field, he began his retreat towards Āgra. His movements were slow, and he was not at first harassed by Shīr Khān; but the rebellion of his brother, Hindāl, roused him and the retreat was accelerated until, at Chausa on the Ganges, he found himself confronted by the army of Shīr Khān. The two forces encamped on the opposite banks of an affluent of the Ganges for two months, neither daring to attack the other, and Humāyūn's situation became so desperate that he opened negotia-

tions. The terms to which Shīr Khān agreed were that he should
retain Bengal and most of Bihar, and should bear the royal title,
while acknowledging Humāyūn as his overlord. The conclusion
of the treaty lulled Humāyūn's army into security until, as they
were preparing before dawn to move their camp, the Afghans
suddenly fell upon them. They were taken completely by surprise, and nearly the whole force was destroyed, but Humāyūn
with difficulty made his escape, and in May, 1539, arrived at
Āgra with a few followers.

For a year both he and Shīr Shāh were engaged in assembling
and preparing their forces for the decisive contest. Shīr Shāh,
in Bengal and Bihar, was, as ever, indefatigable, but Humāyūn's
efforts were interrupted by fits of lethargy and by vain endeavours
to gain the whole-hearted support of his worthless brothers.
Hindāl was pardoned, and retained the government of Āgra, but
Kāmrān stood aloof, hoping that Humāyūn and Shīr Shāh would
exhaust themselves and allow the imperial crown to fall into his
grasp. He little knew Shīr Shāh. The rivals at length took the
field. Humāyūn had succeeded in collecting 100,000 horse, but
they were of poor quality, ill-officered, and hampered by an
unwarlike host of camp-followers, whose tendency to panic was
a grave danger to such a force. Shīr Shāh advanced westward,
and encamped at a short distance from the Ganges, opposite
Kanauj. Humāyūn foolishly ventured to cross the river, and on
May 17, 1540, the two armies met. Humāyūn's tactics little
resembled Bābur's. The artillery was hardly employed at all, and
the vigorous charges of the Afghans overwhelmed his wretched
troops. First his left wing, then his right wing, and lastly his
centre gave way, and the disorderly host attempted to flee across
the Ganges. Their weight broke the flimsy bridge, and large
numbers were drowned. Humāyūn again escaped with difficulty,
and fled, with but a remnant of his army, to Āgra. There he
could not maintain himself, and, as Shīr Shāh approached, retired
on Delhi, but the pursuit was continued, and he was driven first
from Delhi and then from Lahore. Kāmrān offered no help, and
the unfortunate Humāyūn retired into Sind, where he lived for
some time the life of a fugitive, and where, on November 23,
1542, his son Akbar was born at the small town of 'Umarkot.
Humāyūn next attempted to occupy Kandahār, then held by his
brother 'Askarī for Kāmrān. 'Askarī refused either to admit or

to assist the fugitive, but his wife received and kindly treated
the infant boy, and Humāyūn, continuing his flight, took refuge
at the court of Shāh Tahmāsp I of Persia, with whose aid he,
in September, 1547, captured Kandahār and received the surrender of 'Askarī, whom he pardoned. Two months later he
drove Kāmrān from Kābul and occupied that city, where his
position was much the same as that of his father when he first
turned his eyes towards India.

In the reign of Buhlūl Lodī many Afghans had left their country
and entered his service; among them was Ibrāhīm Khān, of the
Sūr tribe, who received fiefs in the neighbourhood of Nāgaur.
His son, Hasan Khān, placed himself under the patronage of one
of his own nation who governed Jaunpur, and himself received
Sasarām and other small districts in fee. He neglected his two
eldest sons, Farīd and Nizām, in favour of younger sons by a
concubine with whom he was infatuated, and Farīd escaped as
a boy to Jaunpur, and there, with a zeal for learning rare among
Afghans, applied himself to study. His father afterwards placed
him in charge of some of his fiefs, and Farīd applying to his task
the knowledge which he had acquired, was so successful in the
management of the estates, and in suppressing brigandage and
maintaining order, as to win the confidence of all; but he again
quarrelled with his father, and, fleeing to Āgra, placed himself
under the protection of an Afghan noble who obtained for him,
on his father's death, a grant of the family fiefs. He returned to
Bihar and entered the service of the Lohānī Afghan who assumed
independence in that province, and, having slain a tiger in his
presence in the hunting field, received from him the title of
Shīr Khān. Afterwards, falling into disfavour owing to the
intrigues of the Lohānī Afghans, he again visited Āgra, and
entered the service of Bābur, but an indiscreet remark on the
defects of his system of administration aroused the conqueror's
suspicion, and Shīr Khān fled once more to Bihar, regained the
favour of his former master and was left by him the guardian
of his minor son, Jalāl Shāh. The Lohānīs, impatient of submission to one not of their own tribe, persuaded Mahmūd Shāh
of Bengal to attack him, and Jalāl to take refuge in Mahmūd's
camp. Shīr Khān defeated Mahmūd's army, and, since Jalāl
could not return to Bihar, became the ruler of the province, and
acquired the fortress of Chunār by marrying the widow of its

governor. He aided Humāyūn in suppressing the Lodī pretender, but during the expedition into Mālwā and Gujarāt utilised the period of Humāyūn's absence from his capital, and of his lethargy after his return, to extend and consolidate his own power.

After these vicissitudes of fortune Shīr Shāh found himself ruler of an empire far greater than Bābur's, for he had already subdued Bengal, and shortly after driving Humāyūn from India, added to his dominions the kingdom of Mālwā, by expelling thence the governor appointed by Bahādur of Gujarāt, and appointed to the government of the great province a valiant and capable Afghan on whom he had conferred the title of Shujā'at Khān.

The governor whom he had left in Bengal, having married the daughter of its deposed king, showed symptoms of pretending to independence, but Shīr Shāh fell upon him before his plans were ripe, imprisoned him, and reformed the administration of the province by parcelling it out into fiefs, and appointing to their supervision a controller of the revenues, retaining all executive power in his own hands.

Shīr Shāh has received scant justice at the hands of some historians of India, who have relied largely on the records left by the court annalists of the Mughal Empire, to whom he was no more than Shīr Khān, the Afghan rebel. He was, in truth, one of the greatest rulers who ever sat upon the throne of Delhi. No other, from Aibak to Aurangzīb, possessed such intimate knowledge of the details of administration, or was able to examine and control public business so minutely and effectively as he. He restrained the turbulence and quelled the tribal jealousies of the Afghan chiefs, he reformed the land-revenue administration, he introduced a system of great trunk-roads, furnished with caravanserais, wells and every convenience for the comfort and safety of the traveller, and he maintained throughout his dominions such order that "none dared to turn the eye of dishonesty upon another's goods. An old woman with a pot of gold might securely lay herself down to rest beside her burden, even in the desert, and a cripple was not afraid of a Rustam". Himself a pious Muslim, he suffered none to be persecuted in the name of religion, and, far wiser than Akbar, made no attempt to assume spiritual power, but left each to seek God after his own fashion. Budaunī, the orthodox Muslim historian, thanks God that he was born in the reign of so just a king. Of his wise and judicious measures of administration many were adopted or imitated by Akbar without acknowledgement, and he was far more successful than any who followed him in checking corruption, peculation, and frauds on the public treasury. "It behoves the great", he said, "to be always active", and throughout his life he allowed himself no more rest than was necessary for his health and the preservation of his bodily and mental powers. "All this", says Mr Keene, "has an importance beyond the immediate time. After the Mughal restoration, Shīr Shāh's officials passed into Akbar's service; the faults imputed by the shah to what he called Mughal administration—but which are common to all Turks— were prevented; and this far-sighted man, even after his death and the subversion of his dynasty, remained the originator of all that was done by mediaeval Indian rulers for the good of the people."

Shīr Shāh, like Bābur, found it necessary to curb the pride of the Rājputs, of whom the most powerful was now the Rāthor ruler of Mārwār. Shīr Shāh advanced against him with great caution and overcame the difficulty of entrenching his camp in the desert by filling empty meal-sacks with sand, a device said to have been suggested to him by his small grandson, who may thus be regarded as the inventor of sandbags. The decisive battle was fiercely contested, and though the Rājputs were finally defeated with great slaughter, Shīr Shāh was sensible of the risk which he had run, and, observing the barrenness of the land, remarked, "I had wellnigh lost the empire of India for a handful of millet".

The Rājputs of Mednī Rāi, led by his son Silahdī, had recovered from the crushing defeat inflicted on them by Bābur, and held Rāisen, where they gave great offence to all Muslims by keeping, as dancing girls and concubines, Muslim women whose husbands and fathers they had slain. Shīr Shāh attacked the Rājputs, and induced them to surrender by promising them their lives, but, instigated by their victims, and by the jurists of Islam, fell upon them and put them to death. This breach of faith, the one blot on his character, was excusable in the eyes of orthodox Muslims, owing to the heinousness of the offence of the misbelievers. From Rāisen he marched to Kālinjar, held by a Rājput chief, and opened the siege of the fortress. On May 22, 1545, while standing

by a store of powder which was accidentally ignited, he was so
severely burned that he lived only until the evening, but before
breathing his last was cheered by the news that the fortress had
fallen. His death was the ruin of his house, for he left none fit
to succeed him.

The Afghan nobles raised to the throne his second son, who
assumed the title of Islām Shāh; but his brief fratricidal contest
with his elder brother revived the embers of strife among the
factious Afghans, and Islām Shāh not only failed to extinguish
them, but, by his foolish conduct, allowed them to burst into
flame. The Niyāzīs, a powerful tribe, rose in rebellion against
him; his behaviour alienated the powerful Shujā'at Khān of
Mālwā and the feudatories of Bengal; and throughout his seven
years' reign he and the chieftains who, despite his injudicious
treatment, remained loyal to him, were occupied in repressing
rebellions. On his death, in 1552, his son, a boy of twelve, was
murdered by his uncle, a nephew of Shīr Shāh, whose sister was
married to Islām Shāh, and the murderer usurped the throne
under the title of Muhammad 'Ādil Shāh. Islām Shāh had been
repeatedly urged by his counsellors to secure his son's succession
by removing 'Ādil, but the prince feigned imbecility, and his
sister's intercession saved his life. But she had occasion bitterly
to repent her regard for him. The new king, contemptuously
nicknamed 'Adlī, was a worthless debauchee, and to the indignation of the Afghan nobles, gradually entrusted all power in the
state to a Hindu adviser, Hīmū, a *baniya* of Rawārī, who, having
been appointed inspector of the market of that town, gradually
rose in the royal service, and, displaying considerable political
acumen and military ability, became 'Adlī's right hand. Muhammad, a member of the Sūr tribe, proclaimed himself independent
in Bengal; 'Adlī spent his time chiefly at Chunār and Gwalior;
and two of his cousins, rising against him, assumed royal titles.
Ibrāhīm Sūr seized Delhi and Āgra, and Sikandar Sūr, having
failed to persuade his brother to divide the kingdom with him,
established himself in the Panjab, and then drove him from
Delhi and Āgra. Thus, at the close of 1554, there were four
Afghan kings in northern India, Muhammad in Bengal, 'Adlī
in Bihar, Sikandar in the Panjab and the doāb, and Ibrāhīm,
temporarily worsted, but still in the field.

Humāyūn had long been forming vague designs for the recovery of his Indian throne, and this was an opportunity such as even he could hardly neglect. Leaving Kābul in November, 1554, at the head of 15,000 horse, he occupied Lahore without striking a blow, and lingered there while his troops, nominally under the command of the young Akbar, on June 22, 1555, gained a decisive victory over those of Sikandar Sūr at Sirhind. Sikandar fled eastward towards the Himālāya, and in July Humāyūn once more entered Delhi, and Akbar, under the guardianship of Bairam Khān Khānkhānān, was appointed to the government of the Panjab and sent in pursuit of Sikandar.

Humāyūn did not long enjoy the throne which he had recovered. On January 24, 1556, overcome by drowsiness as he was about to descend the steep stair from the roof of his palace in response to the call to prayer, he leaned upon his staff, which slipped, and, tripping on the skirt of his robe, he fell to the foot of the stairs, fractured the base of his skull, and died after three days, during which time it is doubtful whether he recovered consciousness.

"His end was of a piece with his character. If there was a possibility of falling, Humāyūn was not the man to miss it. He tumbled through life, and he tumbled out of it." In order to prevent disturbances his death was concealed, false news of his recovery was disseminated, and a man dressed in his robes personated him in public. But the news of his death was sent confidentially to the young prince and Bairam Khān, then engaged in operations against Sikandar, and on February 14, 1556, Jalāl-ud-dīn Muhammad Akbar was enthroned at Kalānaur, in the Gurdāspur district.

CHAPTER IX

Akbar

Akbar, at the time of his accession little more than thirteen years old, remained under the guidance of Bairam Khān until 1560, when, in his eighteenth year, he shook off the trammels of tutelage. He was a precocious and self-assertive lad, and neither his tutors nor his father ever persuaded him to learn to read or write; but his intellectual development suffered little from his ignorance of the ordinary apparatus of learning, for he employed readers, and listened always with attention to works on history, philosophy, ethics, and theology, and his memory was so retentive that he could repeat long passages of poetry after hearing them read, and forgot little of what he heard. He loved horses, elephants, and all animals, and was devoted to sport and to bodily exercise of every kind, none the less if it were spiced with danger, and as he grew to manhood he acquired great agility and physical strength.

He remained with the regent at Kalānaur while his troops hunted Sikandar into the mountains, and then moved to Jalandhar, where he remained for some months. Tardī Beg, who had proclaimed him at Delhi, and other officers held Āgra and the intervening territory, but meanwhile Hīmū, who had been too late to arrest Humāyūn's progress, had assembled a great army, with 1500 war elephants, to oppose Akbar's occupation of his capital. Advancing from Gwalior, he drove the Mughal officers from Āgra, and near Tughlukābād routed their forces, capturing elephants, horses, and much booty. They fled, with Tardī Beg, who had failed to support them, and joined Akbar's camp at Sirhind, where Bairam Khān caused Tardī Beg to be put to death for his disgraceful neglect of duty.

Hīmū, who now held Delhi and Āgra, was so intoxicated with his success that he assumed the style of royalty, and the title of Rāja Vikramāditya, conciliating the Afghans of his army by a liberal distribution of spoils, and concealing his usurpation from his master. Meanwhile Akbar had reached the neighbourhood of Pānīpat, and his advanced guard captured Hīmū's artillery;

but even after this loss Hīmū's superiority was so great that on November 5, 1556, he advanced with confidence to the attack. The young emperor was retained by Bairam Khān with the reserves, and Hīmū, having defeated the right and left wings of the army, was advancing, with every prospect of success, against the centre, commanded by the Uzbeg, Khānzamān, when he was pierced in the eye by an arrow. His elephant fled, and his army broke and dispersed in every direction. The elephant was captured, and the unconscious Hīmū was brought before Akbar, who, at the suggestion of Bairam Khān, earned the title of *Ghāzī* by striking the unconscious misbeliever on the neck with his sword,[1] after which the officers with him dispatched the dying man. A tower was built of the heads of the slain, and the fleeing host was pursued with great slaughter. On the following day Akbar entered Delhi, Hīmū's family was captured, his vast treasure was taken, and his aged father was put to death. A month later Akbar and Bairam Khān returned from Delhi to Lahore in pursuit of Sikandar, who was driven into the fortress of Mānkot, in Jammū, where, in May, 1557, he surrendered, and was generously treated, receiving a fief in Bihar, where he died two years later. 'Adlī died at about the same time, and Akbar was left without a rival. From Lahore Akbar returned to Delhi, and in October moved to Āgra, which became his principal place of residence. He devoted his time to sport, while his officers, during the next two years, received the surrender of Gwalior, annexed Jaunpur, which had been in the hands of the Afghans, and extended his authority over the reconquered empire. As he grew towards manhood the regent's control irked him. Bairam Khān was haughty and arrogant, obnoxious to the orthodox as an adherent of the Shiah sect, the members of which he indiscreetly favoured, advancing one of them, Shaikh Gadā'ī, to the office of *sadr-us-sudūr*, the highest judicial and ecclesiastical position in the empire; his execution of Tardī Beg had offended many; Akbar himself was kept short of funds, while Bairam's servants grew rich; and the ladies of the imperial harem were impatient of an authority which baulked their ambition to make

---

[1] According to a later and more courtly version of the incident Akbar magnanimously refused to strike a wounded foe, but this story seems to be an invention, and there is little doubt that the boy fleshed his maiden sword on the dying Hindu.

the youthful sovereign their own instrument. Early in 1560 the court was at Āgra, but the ladies were at Delhi, and Akbar, while out hunting, was induced to ride to Delhi to visit his mother without advising the regent of his intention. The governor of Delhi prepared to hold the city, if necessary, against the regent, and Akbar, at the instance of the ladies, sent an order to Bairam Khān, informing him that he had decided to take the reins of government into his own hands, directing him to make the pilgrimage to Mecca, an honourable form of banishment, and assuring him that a suitable fief should be assigned to him for his maintenance.

Bairam Khān hesitated whether to rebel, as many of his partisans advised, or to submit, but finally bowed to his young master's orders, and set off towards Gujarāt. Akbar, probably at the instance of the ladies, subjected him to a further unmerited humiliation by deputing Pīr Muhammad Khān, a former servant of his, who had incurred his master's displeasure, to follow him and see that he left the imperial dominions without delay. The insult goaded him into rebellion, and he turned back into the Panjab. A force sent against him defeated him near Jalandhar, and he retired into the hills, but was almost immediately captured and brought before Akbar, who pardoned him and allowed him once more to set out for Mecca. He reached Pātan, or Anhilwār, in Gujarāt, but was there assassinated by an Afghan whose father had fallen in a battle fought by Bairam against Sikandar's forces. Bairam's infant son, 'Abdur Rahīm, was brought to court and educated under Akbar's care, and eventually received his father's title and became the first noble in the empire. The post of minister and the title of Khānkhānān were conferred on Mun'im Khān, the guardian of Akbar's younger brother, Muhammad Hakīm, who had been summoned from Kābul when Bairam was dismissed.

Akbar was not yet his own master. He had shaken off Bairam Khān, but was still loth to allow his duties to interfere with his pleasures, and the regent's administration was followed by the "monstrous regiment of women", the most influential and unscrupulous of the ladies of the harem being Māham Anaga, one of Akbar's foster-mothers.

During the reign of Islām Shāh, Shujā'at Khān had become independent in Mālwā, and, on his death in 1555, had been suc-

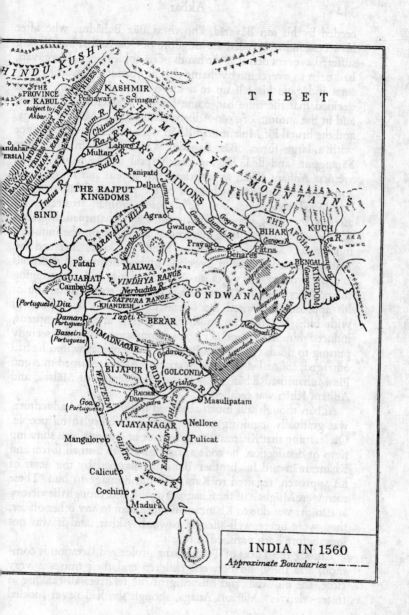

ceeded by his son Bāyazīd, known as Bāz Bahādur, who after his accession had invaded the kingdom of Gondwāna, but, having suffered a severe defeat at the hands of its noble queen, Durgāvatī, had been so overcome by shame that he abandoned warlike pursuits and gave himself up to a life of sensual pleasure. Akbar decided that the time had come for the annexation of Mālwā, and in the autumn of 1560 Adham Khān, son of Māham Anaga, and the brutal Pīr Muhammad Khān were sent into that province with a large force. Bāz Bahādur was defeated in 1561 near Sārangpur, and fled, leaving much spoil in the hands of the victors. Adham Khān appropriated his harem and his treasure, and attempted to possess himself of the person of Rūpmatī, his best-loved concubine, but the devoted woman frustrated his attempt by taking poison; and he and Pīr Muhammad disgraced themselves by committing the foulest atrocities on the innocent inhabitants, Muslim as well as Hindu. Akbar, incensed by Adham's misconduct, but especially by his retention of the spoils and the women, left Āgra on April 27, 1561, and, outstripping the couriers whom Māham Anaga had sent to warn her son of his approach, surprised the offender. It would have gone ill with him, but that his mother, hastening after the emperor, induced him to accept her son's submission, and, by secretly putting to death two of Bāz Bahādur's concubines whom he had outraged, concealed some of his crimes. Akbar returned to Āgra, Pīr Muhammad Khān was appointed governor of Mālwā, and Adham Khān was recalled.

Akbar, though still much absorbed in hunting and adventure, was gradually acquiring a sense of responsibility to his people. On learning that Khānzamān, governor of Jaunpur, was showing signs of disaffection, he rode against him with a small force, and Khānzamān and his brother Bahādur, alarmed by the news of his approach, repaired to Kara, and did homage to him. These men were Mughals of the Chaghatāy tribe, and, though the victory at Pānīpat was due to Khānzamān more than to any other officer, they were never well-affected towards Akbar, and it was not long before both perished as rebels.

Among the Turks of Transoxiana prolonged lactation is common, and the bond between children and their nurses is very close, the husbands and offspring of the relatives all ranking as foster-relatives. Māham Anaga, though she had never suckled

Akbar, had been the superintendent of his nurses, and ranked as a foster-mother. The most influential of those who had actually suckled him was Jījī Anaga, whose husband, Shams-ud-dīn Muhammad, had saved Humāyūn from drowning after the battle of Kanauj, and was entitled Ataga ("foster-father") Khān. He was the head of the group of foster-relatives known as the *Ataga Khail*, or "foster-father battalion". Their influence, not always for good, was very great until Akbar felt strong enough to break it.

In November, 1561, Ataga Khān was summoned from Kābul and was made minister. His appointment was resented by Mun'im Khān, whom he superseded, and by Māham Anaga, who regarded herself as prime minister *de facto*. Māham Anaga's resentment was increased by the recall of her son, Adham, from Mālwā. Pīr Muhammad, who succeeded him, was not a fortunate selection, for he was rough, brutal, and arrogant. Bāz Bahādur had taken refuge in Khāndesh, and Pīr Muhammad, invading that state in pursuit of him, committed horrible atrocities, destroying towns and villages by fire, and massacring or enslaving their inhabitants. Bāz Bahādur fled before him across the Nerbudda, and Pīr Muhammad pursued him. While he was rashly attempting to cross the river by a dangerous ford, his horse came into contact with some pack-animals, and its rider was thrown, carried away by the current, and drowned. "Thus", says Budaunī, "he went by water to fire; his cruelty, insolence, and severity were punished; and the sighs of the orphans, the captives, and the helpless were avenged." As a result of this monster's death Bāz Bahādur recovered Mālwā, but not for long, for in the following year 'Abdullāh Khān Uzbeg, who was appointed to the government of the province, expelled him, and again incorporated it in Akbar's dominions. For eight years Bāz Bahādur wandered as a refugee from one court to another, but at length made his submission to Akbar, and entered his service, in which he held, at the time of his death, the rank of commander of 2000 horse, but he was chiefly distinguished as "a singer without rival".

Early in 1562 Akbar, having heard minstrels sing of the sanctity of Mu'īn-ud-dīn Chishtī, the saint whose shrine is at Ajmir, vowed to make a yearly pilgrimage to his tomb, and set out on his first journey thither. The occasion was memorable, for on his way thither he received Rāja Bihar Mal of Amber, who came forth to do him homage and offered him his eldest daughter in marriage. This may be regarded as the first step in Akbar's attempt to weld the Hindus and Muslims of India into one people. The Hindu princess afterwards became the mother of Jahāngīr, and Bihar Mal's heir, Bhagwān Dās, and Bhagwān's nephew and adopted son, Mān Singh, attained to the highest rank in the imperial service.

In the same year the strong fortress of Mertha was taken from the raja of Mārwār, and the discontent of Māham Anaga, Mun'im Khān, and the harem party culminated in the murder of Ataga Khān, who was slain in his apartments in the palace by Adham Khān and his attendants. Akbar, asleep in an inner room, was roused by the uproar which followed the crime, and coming forth, met the murderer. Infuriated at his threatening air, Akbar felled him with a blow of his fist, and commanded the attendants to throw him from the parapet into the ditch. Being seen to move in the ditch he was brought up and thrown down a second time, and his brains were dashed out. Akbar then retired and told Māham Anaga what he had done. She replied that he had done well, but, already ailing, never recovered, and died forty days later. Mun'im Khān and others implicated in the plot fled, but were captured and brought before Akbar, who did not punish them, but again appointed Mun'im Khān minister. Akbar afterwards confessed that at this period of his life he "experienced an internal bitterness", which may be attributed to the discovery that none in whom he had placed his trust was worthy. Mun'im Khān was re-appointed owing to his experience of the routine duties of office. He was again minister, but he was never again trusted. Akbar was henceforth his own minister, and, though he consulted others, always reserved for himself the final decision of every case. The control of the finances, which had been corruptly managed by Māham Anaga, was taken from Mun'im Khān and entrusted to an able eunuch entitled I'timād Khān, who prevented peculation and introduced a sound system of administration; and, lest the peace should be disturbed by the naturally vengeful feelings of the "foster-father battalion", he dispatched its members on an expedition against the Gakkhars of the Salt Range.

Akbar's liberal views and his leanings towards Hinduism are

commonly attributed to the influence of the free-thinking Shaikh Mubārak and his two sons, Faizī, afterwards poet-laureate, and Abul Fazl, who became the emperor's secretary and historian. But Mubārak does not appear to have come forward at court until 1573; his sons were not presented until a year later; and Akbar had inaugurated his policy of conciliation more than ten years earlier, first in 1562, by marrying the Amber princess and admitting Mān Singh to high office, and in 1563 and again in 1564 by two very great pecuniary sacrifices, the remission of the tax on Hindu pilgrims visiting their sacred places, and the remission of the *jizya*, or poll-tax on Hindus. These measures were most obnoxious to bigoted Muslims, but, with the exception of the marriage, which was regarded with mixed feelings, were most welcome to Hindus of all classes; and it is greatly to Akbar's credit that "the main lines of his policy, directed to obliterating all difference in treatment between Muslims and Hindus, were fixed as political principles while he was still to all outward appearance an orthodox and zealous Muslim and long before his open breach with Islam" in 1582.

Humāyūn had left his younger son, Muhammad Hakīm, nominal governor of the province of Kābul, with Mun'im Khān as his tutor and guardian. When Mun'im Khān was summoned to India, his place was taken by his son, Ghanī Khān, who quarrelled with the prince's mother, and was by her shut out of Kābul. She defeated Mun'im Khān, who was sent to restore peace, and Shāh Abul Ma'ālī, a turbulent noble who had been banished to Mecca for political offences, returned to Kābul from his pilgrimage, married the young prince's sister, and put his mother to death. Hakīm would have been his next victim had not his cousin, Sulaimān Mīrzā of Badakhshān, come to his rescue, and defeated and executed Abul Ma'ālī.

The death of Adham and his mother had broken the power of the harem faction, and, in 1564, another act of violence entirely freed Akbar from its influence. Being warned that Khvāja Mu'azzam, his mother's half-brother, a maniac who had already committed more than one violent crime, was meditating the murder of his wife, Akbar rode out to his country house, in the hope of preventing the crime, but arrived too late, for the bloody knife with which it had been committed was thrown at his feet by the murderer. He threw his uncle into the Jumna, and, as he did not drown, sent him to the state-prison at Gwalior, where he afterwards died. Thereafter Akbar treated his mother with respect, but no longer permitted her to interfere in matters of state, and his emancipation from harem influence was complete. He now began his career of conquest, interrupted occasionally by serious rebellions.

Āsaf Khān, governor of Kara, had already conquered Panna in Bundelkhand, and in 1564 was ordered to invade Gondwāna. The raja of that country was Bīr Narāyan, but its real ruler was his mother, Durgāvatī, a daughter of the Chandel house of Mahobā, whose father had been obliged by poverty to give her in marriage to the Gond raja. The warlike lady had ruled the Gond kingdom well, and had defeated both Bāz Bahādur of Mālwā and the Afghans. She had never molested Akbar, but the Gond kingdom was both extensive and wealthy, and the attack was an act of unprovoked aggression. Durgāvatī gallantly withstood the invaders more than once, but her troops were no match for those of Āsaf Khān, and in the last battle she was wounded while leading a charge, and "choosing death rather than dishonour, stabbed herself to the heart". Āsaf Khān then besieged Chaurāgarh, the principal fortress of the Gonds, which was gallantly defended by the young raja, who performed the rite of *jauhar* before he fell. Much treasure and many elephants fell into the hands of Āsaf Khān, and Akbar, not being prepared to deal with him, was obliged to leave them in his hands.

The disaffection of Akbar's officers of the Chaghatāy or Uzbeg tribe, led by Khānzamān, has already been noticed. They were, in a sense, his natural enemies, for it was their tribe which had driven his house from its ancestral domains in Transoxiana, now ruled by their chief, 'Abdullāh Khān. They were orthodox and bigoted Sunnis, and resented the leaning which Akbar evinced towards the Shiah heresy, the favour which he showed to his Persian officers and, above all, his conciliatory treatment of the Hindus. They were in communication with his brother, Hakīm, understood to be more orthodox than he, and also, probably, with their own chief in Bukhārā. An Uzbeg officer also named 'Abdullāh Khān, whom Akbar had appointed to the government of Mālwā, was the first to rebel, and Akbar marched rapidly on Mandū, defeated him, and drove him into Gujarāt; but 'Abdullāh escaped from that kingdom, and joined Khānzamān in Jaunpur.

Early in 1565 the Uzbegs rose in Jaunpur and drove the imperial troops into the northern districts of Oudh. Akbar marched against them and, having been joined by Āsaf Khān of Kara, drove them into Bihar and occupied Jaunpur, but was embarrassed by the defection of Āsaf Khān, who, fearing lest he should be called to account for the treasure of Gondwāna, deserted him, and left him hardly strong enough to attempt to crush the rebels. He opened negotiations with them, and Khānzamān, having expressed contrition, was readmitted to Jaunpur, and Akbar, in March, 1566, returned to Āgra. There he amused himself by founding at Kakrālī, seven miles south of the city, a palatial hunting-lodge. A town sprang up round it, and was named by him Nagarchain, or the "Abode of Ease", and there he enjoyed the chase, and the game of polo, for which he invented a ball of the wood of the *dhāk* or *palās* tree, which when ignited, made it possible to continue the game at night.

These amusements were interrupted by the news that Hakīm had invaded the Panjab and that Khānzamān had recited the *khūtba* in his name at Jaunpur. Akbar was furious, and, in November, 1566, set forth to deal with his brother, but, on reaching Lahore three months later, found that Hakīm, not daring to await him, had fled back to Kābul. Near Lahore he amused himself with a great slaughter of game. For a month hosts of beaters, having encircled a large tract of country, gradually closed inwards, driving all the game into a small area, where Akbar and his favoured courtiers slaughtered incessantly for five days. He was recalled eastward by the news of the rebellion of his cousins, "the Mīrzās", who, having risen in Sambhal, had been driven thence into Mālwā, and, on his way, had an opportunity of enjoying some "sport" even more entertaining than the *battue* at Lahore. Two gangs of *sannyāsīs*, or religious mendicants whose business was the extortion of money from the pilgrims at the holy fair of Thānesar, had quarrelled, one of them having occupied and refused to vacate the more profitable "pitch" of the other. Feeling ran so high that they sought leave to decide their difference by combat, and Akbar granted permission and witnessed the fight. One party, five hundred strong, was pressing the other, numbering only three hundred, very hard, when Akbar permitted some of his troops to help the weaker body. The tables were turned, and "many of the wretches were sent to annihilation. The emperor greatly enjoyed the sight". His spiritual awakening was, as yet, incomplete.

Early in May, 1567, he left Āgra in order to crush the rebellion of the Uzbegs, who had been in revolt ever since Hakīm's invasion of the Panjab, and had lately marched on Kālpī. He surprised them when the leaders were drunk and their troops in disorder, and in a battle near Allāhābād defeated them, Khānzamān being slain and his brother, Bahādur, captured and executed. Several of the leaders taken were trampled to death by elephants, and a reward of a gold coin was paid for every Uzbeg's head. He then marched to Allāhābād, and thence to Benares, which closed its gates against him, and in order to punish the citizens the troops were allowed to sack the city.

From Benares he marched to Jaunpur, and conferred all the fiefs of Khānzamān on Mun'im Khān. 'Abdullāh Khān having died a natural death, and an Uzbeg force under Sikandar Khān having been driven from Oudh, the whole faction was thus stamped out. In July, 1567, he returned to Āgra, and in the following September set out to humble the rāna of Mewār. He had cause of offence against the rāna, who had proudly refrained from attending his court, had condemned those princes of his race who had besmirched their honour by giving daughters in marriage to the unclean Turk, and had granted an asylum to Bāz Bahādur and to a rebellious chief of Narwar. His son, Sakat Singh, resenting a tactless gibe, had left the imperial camp without permission. Leaving officers to deal with the rebellious Mīrzās in Mālwā, Akbar marched on Chitor.

Sangrama Singh, Bābur's opponent, had died in 1530, and two of his sons succeeded him in turn. There remained a third, Udai Singh, a posthumous child, whose life was saved by the fidelity of a nurse when a bastard relative, having usurped the throne, sought to destroy the heir. In 1542 the Rājput nobles expelled the bastard and enthroned the boy. Udai Singh, says Tod, "had not one quality of a sovereign; and, wanting martial virtue, the common heritage of his race, he was destitute of all". He was then thirty-seven years of age, and when, in October, 1567, Akbar opened the siege of Chitor, its ruler was not within its walls. He had fled and concealed himself in a small palace around which Udaipur, the modern capital of Mewār, has grown up,

and the defence of his fortress was left to the gallant Jaimal, the
Rāthor, of Bednor, and the young Patta of Kailwa. The investment of the fortress was completed within a month, and Akbar
many times attempted to carry it by assault, but without success.
Mines were no more efficacious, but the approach was gradually
made by means of a covered way, and Akbar, within musket-
shot of the fortress, amused himself by picking off any of the
garrison who exposed themselves, and, on February 23, brought
down an officer who was directing the defence. Within an hour
it was learned that the Rājputs had withdrawn from the ramparts.
Fire then broke out in the fort, and Bhagwān Dās, who was with
Akbar, assured him that the Rājputs were beginning to perform
the rite of *jauhar*, and that the fires were those in which the
women were being burned. Early the next morning it was
ascertained that Bhagwān had spoken truly and that Akbar's
victim had been Jaimal. Akbar's troops then entered the fortress.
The eight thousand Rājputs of the garrison came forth, and,
fighting desperately, were slain to a man. Among them fell
Patta, who was trampled to death by an elephant. About three
hundred ladies had perished in the flames. A corps of a thousand
musketeers from Kālpī, who had most efficiently aided the gallant
Rājputs in the defence, escaped by passing themselves off as part
of Akbar's forces carrying off female captives, the captives being
their own wives and daughters; and it was well for them that
they succeeded, for Akbar, incensed by the obstinacy of the
defence, disgraced himself by the most revolting barbarity. Of
40,000 peasants, who had assisted the garrison in defending the
fortress, 20,000 were massacred and the remainder enslaved.
"From that day Chitor has been held accursed, no successor of
Udai Singh has entered it, and 'the sin of the slaughter of
Chitor', like 'the curse of Cromwell' in Ireland, has become
proverbial."

Chitor had already been twice taken by Muslim monarchs,
'Alā-ud-dīn Khaljī and Bahādur of Gujarāt, neither specially
scrupulous or humane; but it was reserved for Akbar to commit
atrocities which are held to this day to defile the ground on which
the fortress stands. He seems to have repented of his crime, for
he honoured the gallant Jaimal and Patta by erecting statues to
their memory. These were originally set up at the gate of his
palace at Āgra, were removed by his grandson to the gate of his

palace at Delhi, and were destroyed by the bigot Aurangzīb, who held representations of the human form to be unlawful. Some have conjectured that Akbar intended to insult the dead by representing them as his doorkeepers, but this is unjust. He has enough to answer for in the atrocities committed at Chitor, and he had a genuine admiration for his gallant foes. But he fervently desired, to the end of his reign, to crush the rāna, and was baulked only by the unwillingness of his eldest son and his officers to embark on a difficult and dangerous campaign. The rāna was never subdued.

In March, 1568, Akbar returned to Āgra, but the empire was not yet at peace. The Mīrzās were in revolt in Mālwā, and he was obliged to send against them the army which he had assembled for the reduction of Ranthambhor, the third great Rājput stronghold. His foster-relatives, after the death of their leader, had been transferred to the Panjab. Since their extensive fiefs menaced his authority, he broke up the confederacy. He allowed his favourite foster-brother, 'Azīz Koka, entitled Khān-i A'zam, to retain the fief of Dīpālpur, but the other members of the group were dispersed and received fiefs in the provinces to the east of the Ganges, and Akbar was then able, at the end of 1568, to open the siege of Ranthambhor, which was held for the rāna by Surjan Hāra, chief of Būndī.

Surjan transferred his allegiance from the rāna to Akbar, surrendered Ranthambhor, and received in return first a command in Gondwāna, and then, as a reward for good service there, the government of Benares and Chunār, and a residence in the holy city with the privilege of sanctuary, retained by the rajas of Būndī until the nineteenth century. Of the manner in which this surrender was brought about a romantic and not improbable account has been taken by Tod from Rājput annals. After the siege had been formed, Bhagwān Dās of Amber and his adopted son, Mān Singh, undertook to seduce Surjan from his allegiance to the rāna, and Mān Singh, as a brother Rājput, obtained access to the fortress in order to discuss matters with Surjan. While the two chiefs were conversing, Surjan's uncle recognised, in one of Mān Singh's mace-bearers, the features of the emperor, "and with that sudden impulse which arises from respect, took the mace from his hand and placed Akbar on the 'cushion' of the governor of the castle". Akbar then asked what was to be done,

and Mān Singh decided the matter by urging Surjan to enter the
imperial service, offering him the government of fifty-two districts and liberty to name any other terms. Surjan assented, and
the terms which he demanded and obtained were (1) that the
chiefs of Būndī should not be required to surrender a bride to
the imperial harem, (2) that they should be for ever exempt from
the *jizya*, (3) that they should never be compelled to cross the
Indus, (4) that they and their kin should never be required to
send their wives or female relations to the New Year's bazaar
in the imperial palace, (5) that they should be permitted to enter
the hall of audience fully armed, (6) that their temples should
be respected, (7) that they should never be placed under the
command of a Hindu leader, (8) that their horses should not be
branded as state property, (9) that they should not be required
to prostrate themselves before the emperor, and (10) that Būndī
should be to the Hāras what Delhi was to the king, who should
guarantee them from any change of capital.

Meanwhile Majnūn Khān Kākshāl had been sent to besiege
Kālinjar, the fortress before which Shīr Shāh had lost his life,
and which was held by Rāja Rāmchand of Bhatha or Rewa. The
fortress was invested, but Rāmchand, having learned of the fall
of Chitor and the surrender of Ranthambhor, which set Akbar
free to launch all his forces against Kālinjar, surrendered to
Majnūn Khān, and in 1569 received a fief near Allāhābād.

Akbar was thus supreme in northern India. The Panjab, the
territory now known as the United Provinces, Bihar, and Mālwā
owned his sway; the rāna of Mewār and the raja of Mārwār had
been humbled; Mertha, Chitor, Ranthambhor, and Kālinjar had
fallen into his hands; and the rajas of Amber, Būndī and Bundelkhand were his vassals; but his mind was not at peace. He had
many wives, but no child. Children had been born, but had
died, and he had prayed fervently at the shrine at Ajmir for a
son to succeed him. Shaikh Salīm Chishtī, a follower of the
saint of Ajmir, who lived as a hermit at Sīkrī, near the field on
which Bābur had defeated the great Rājput host, had assured him
that his prayers would be answered, and early in 1569 his senior
Hindu wife, the daughter of Bihar Mal of Amber, was found
to be pregnant. She was sent to the shaikh's cell at Sīkrī, in order
that her child might be born under his holy influence, and, on
August 30, 1569, she gave birth to a son whom Akbar, in

gratitude to the shaikh, named Salīm. Two months later a daughter was born of another wife, and early in 1570 Akbar repeated his pilgrimage to Ajmir to offer thanks for the answer to his prayers. On his return he visited Delhi, and inspected there the splendid mausoleum erected by his mother over the grave of his father, one of the finest monuments left to us by the "Great Moguls". On June 8, 1570, Salīma Sultān Begum, Akbar's cousin, whom he had bestowed upon Bairam Khān, and had himself married after Bairam's death, bore a son who was named Murād, and on September 10, 1572, he heard at Bāgor, on his way from Ajmir to Gujarāt, of the birth to him by a concubine whom he had left in the house of Shaikh Dāniyāl, one of the holy men of Ajmir, of a son, whom he named Dāniyāl after the shaikh. These three sons of Akbar all reached manhood.

On a second visit to Ajmir in 1570 Akbar married princesses of the Rājput houses of Bikaner and Jaisalmer, and on his return lodged with Shaikh Salīm at Sīkrī. Thirty years before this time the shaikh had built a hospice and a mosque there, and Akbar had conceived an affection for the spot. He began to erect a town-wall, dwelling-houses, schools, and baths, and to lay out gardens there, and continued to extend and adorn the town for the next fourteen years. Nagarchain was forgotten, and Sīkrī, which received after the conquest of Gujarāt the name of Fathābād or Fathpur, was Akbar's favourite abode until 1585, when he was called away to Kābul.

Gujarāt had been independent of Delhi since the decline of the Tughluks, but the dynasty which ruled it had fallen into decay, and Muzaffar III, its nominal sovereign, was no more than a puppet in the hands of ambitious and turbulent courtiers, while all the great feudatories were virtually independent of the crown. One of these, I'timād Khān, sought Akbar's aid against his rivals, and this invitation, and the presence in Gujarāt of the rebellious Mīrzās, who had retired thither from Mālwā, led Akbar to take measures for the conquest of the kingdom. He left Sīkrī on July 4, 1572, marching in leisurely fashion by way of Ajmir, Bāgor,[1] and Sirohī. His advance was opposed at Sirohī by 150 desperate Rājputs, whom he cut to pieces, and in November Akbar occupied Ahmadābād without difficulty. Muzaffar III,

[1] Not Nāgaur, as suggested by Vincent Smith and other writers.

having been found attempting to hide himself in a cornfield, was carried before him and made his submission. From Ahmadābād Akbar marched to Cambay, where, for the first time in his life, he saw the sea, and where he first made the acquaintance of the Portuguese, receiving some merchants of that nation who paid their respects to him. He appointed 'Azīz Koka to the government of the new province; but the Mīrzās began almost immediately to give trouble. Akbar, with a small body of horse, at once marched against Ibrāhīm Husain Mīrzā, who was encamped at Sarnāl[1] with a much larger force, rashly crossed the Mahī by a difficult ford in the face of the enemy, and fell upon him. Bhūpat, brother of Bhagwān Dās, was killed, and the lives both of Bhagwān Dās and of Akbar himself were for a time in the greatest jeopardy, but the impetuosity of the attack threw the enemy into a panic, and they fled.

Early in 1573 Akbar, while besieging Surat, received a mission from the Portuguese viceroy, Antonio de Noronha, and concluded a treaty which ensured a safe passage across the Indian Ocean for pilgrims to Mecca. Surat fell in February and Akbar caused the tongue of its governor, Hamzabān, who had formerly been in the service of Humāyūn, to be cut out.

After the battle of Sarnāl Ibrāhīm Husain Mīrzā and Mas'ūd Husain Mīrzā had fled into the Panjab, but were defeated and captured by the governor of the province, Husain Kulī Khān. Ibrāhīm Husain died of his wounds but Husain Kulī Khān caused the eyes of Mas'ūd Husain to be sewn up and carried him, with 300 other prisoners, before Akbar at Sīkrī. The stitches in Mas'ūd Husain's eyelids were cut; of the other prisoners many were executed with torture, but some were released. Before defeating the Mīrzās Husain Kulī Khān had compelled Budī Chand of Nagarkot, or Kāngra, to swear allegiance to Akbar, and for his services in the Panjab he received the title of Khānjahān.

But Akbar was not yet finished with the Mīrzās. Within three months of his return to Sīkrī he learned that another of them, Muhammad Husain Mīrzā, had risen in Gujarāt, and with Ikhtiyār-ul-mulk, a local noble, was besieging 'Azīz Koka in Ahmadābād. On this occasion Akbar, a powerful and athletic man in the prime of life, performed the greatest feat of endurance which is recorded of him. On August 23, 1573, he left

[1] Situated in 22° 50′ N. and 73° 10′ E.

Sīkrī with a few selected officers and a small picked force of
cavalry, having sent in advance another small force, including
which his numbers amounted to 3000 in all. Travelling at the
rate of more than fifty miles a day in the melting heat of the
rainy season he appeared before Ahmadābād within eleven days
of his departure. The rebels besieging the city, hearing the blast
of his trumpets, sounded for the purpose of encouraging 'Azīz
Koka to come forth and join him, could not believe that the
emperor, whom their agents had seen in Sīkrī but a fortnight
before, could possibly have reached Gujarāt; but a force was
evidently about to attack them. Ikhtiyār-ul-mulk, with 5000
horse, was left before the gate to prevent 'Azīz from emerging,
and Muhammad Husain Mīrzā, with 15,000, turned against the
relieving force. He was soon convinced that the emperor was
present, for Akbar, with a few followers, crossed the Sabarmati
in the face of his large force, and fell upon him. The advanced
party with Akbar was checked, but as soon as the rest of his small
force had crossed he led a furious charge against the Mīrzā's
army. His horse was wounded, and he, pressing forward almost
alone, was in the gravest danger, and for a short time was believed
to have fallen, but his troops, when they saw that he was yet
unhurt, pressed the attack, and wounded and captured the Mīrzā,
with the natural result that his army broke and fled. Ikhtiyār-ul-
mulk, with his 5000 horse, attempted to retrieve the fortunes of
the day, but his troops, having witnessed the defeat of the Mīrzā's
much larger force, were so panic-stricken that Akbar's men, pursuing and overtaking them, were able to draw the arrows from
their quivers and use them against them. Ikhtiyār-ul-mulk was
cut down, and the Mīrzā was slain by his guards. In one day
(September 2, 1573) within a fortnight of his leaving Sīkrī,
Akbar had crushed a serious rebellion and restored peace to
Gujarāt. The Mīrzās could trouble him no more. There remained
but one, Shāh Mīrzā, who disappeared from the scene. The victor
returned less speedily than he had come, but did not loiter by
the way, for he travelled at the rate of thirty miles a day, and
on October 5, 1573, made his triumphal entry into Sīkrī. He
had taken with him on this expedition the young 'Abdur Rahīm
Khān, the son of his old tutor, Bairam Khān. After his return
to Sīkrī he was occupied with reforms. The assessment and collection of the land-revenue due from Gujarāt, which for many

troubled years had never been paid, was entrusted to Todar Mal, who, within six months, measured the land, divided the province into nine *sarkārs*, or revenue districts, and settled the revenue at a sum which left five millions of rupees yearly for the imperial treasury, after the payment of all expenses. Todar Mal then rejoined his master at Sīkrī, and there assisted him and the revenue minister, Muzaffar Khān Turbatī, in general administrative reforms. These were (1) the introduction of the branding regulation, which had been enforced by 'Alā-ud-dīn and Shīr Shāh, (2) the abolition of the feudal system by resuming fiefs, placing them under the administration of crown officials, and paying both officers and men from the treasury, and (3) the preparation of a graded list of officials, classed as *amīrs* and *mansabdārs*, all, whether civil or military, holding military rank. The first two reforms, intended to remove opportunities for defrauding the state and plundering its subjects, were most unpopular, and Akbar never succeeded in enforcing them on all; but lists of the state officials, with their actual and nominal commands, and the rank of each, are given both in the *Āīn-i Akbarī* and the *Tabakāt-i Akbarī*. Muzaffar Khān, a very able official, did not favour those reforms, and for his wilful neglect of orders was removed from office, but meanwhile the whole scheme of reform was interrupted.

After the death, in 1552, of Islām Shāh, the son and successor of Shīr Shāh, Muhammad Khān Sūr, another member of his tribe, had established his independence in Bengal and had been succeeded, two years later, by his son, Bahādur Shāh, who reigned for six years, and was succeeded, in 1560, by his brother, Jalāl Shāh, whose son and successor was overcome by Tāj Khān, a member of the Kararānī tribe of Afghans, who ascended the throne of Bengal in 1564. His son and successor, Sulaimān, laid siege to the fort of Rohtās, held for Akbar, but retired before a relieving force, and afterwards adopted a conciliatory attitude towards Akbar. On his death in 1572 he was succeeded by his elder son, Bāyazīd, who was murdered, after a reign of a few months, by his cousin and brother-in-law, Hānsū, who aspired to the throne. But Hānsū was put to death, and Lodī Khān, who had been Sulaimān's minister, raised to the throne his master's younger son, Dāūd, a vain and arrogant young debauchee, who foolishly abandoned his father's prudent policy, and, not content with otherwise provoking Akbar, captured and occupied

the small town of Zamānia on the Ganges, which had been built
as a frontier fortress of the empire by Khānzamān. Akbar had
sent orders from Gujarāt to Mun'im Khān, governor of Jaunpur,
to punish Dāūd, but Mun'im Khān was old and sluggish, and
after a few inconclusive actions made peace with Dāūd, through
his minister, Lodī Khān, on very easy terms. Neither Akbar nor
Dāūd was content, for each thought that the other had been let
down too lightly. Dāūd put his minister to death and Akbar
severely censured Mun'im Khān, and, having relieved Todar
Mal of his administrative duties, sent him to Mun'im Khān's
assistance. Mun'im Khān, goaded by Akbar's reproaches, invaded Bihar, and besieged Dāūd in Patna, but, seeing no prospect
of success, begged Akbar to take the field in person. As he, in
March, 1574, was assembling his forces and his flotilla of boats
at Āgra, Shaikh Abul Fazl and the historian Budaunī were presented to him, but neither seems to have made much impression
on him at first.

On June 15, 1574, Akbar left Āgra by boat, his troops marching
by land. Leaving the ladies of the harem in Jaunpur, he continued his voyage, and on August 3, appeared before Patna.
Finding that the city drew its provisions from Hājīpur, the town
opposite to it, on the northern bank of the Ganges, his troops,
after surmounting grave difficulties, took the town by assault,
and Akbar sent the heads of the officers of the garrison to Dāūd,
who, although he had a large force, took fright, escaped from
Patna by night, and fled into Bengal. The garrison, attempting
to follow him, was pursued with heavy slaughter, and on the
next morning Akbar entered the city. He then marched after
the fleeing Afghans for fifty miles, but, failing to overtake them,
returned.

The rainy season, during which military operations in Bengal
are almost impossible, was then at its height, but Akbar would
have no delay, and appointed Mun'im Khān to the government
of Bengal and the command of the army to which the recovery
of the province was entrusted. Todar Mal was appointed second
in command, and Akbar retired to Jaunpur, leaving Mun'im
Khān and Todar Mal to carry on the campaign against Dāūd.
Before returning to Sīkrī, which he reached on January 18, 1575,
he resumed Jaunpur, Benares, Chunār, and other fiefs, placing
their administration in the hands of his own officers.

Meanwhile the campaign in Bengal was progressing. Mun'im Khān captured successively Monghyr, Bhāgalpur, Khalgāon and the Teliyāgarhi defile, and occupied Tānda, then the capital of the province, where he rested, while a force followed Dāūd towards Orissa and occupied Satgāon. Todar Mal also pressed on, but, finding it impossible to induce his officers to persevere in the arduous task of penetrating into Orissa, disturbed Mun'im Khān's repose by calling upon him to join the army in the field and exert his authority. Mun'im Khān joined the army, the road was improved, the advance continued, and on March 3, 1575, the imperial troops met Dāūd's army at Tukaroī, between Midnapur and Jaleswār. Dāūd attacked Mun'im Khān before he was ready to engage, and the old man was so severely wounded that defeat seemed imminent when Gūjar Khān, commanding Dāūd's troops, fell, and his troops broke and fled. In the pursuit many were slain, and all prisoners were slaughtered, eight columns being built of their heads. Dāūd escaped, and Mun'im Khān once more granted him terms, accepting his formal submission to Akbar and allowing him to retain Orissa. Todar Mal, mistrusting the sincerity of Dāūd, refused to sign the treaty, and his mistrust was fully justified by the event. Mun'im Khān retired to Tānda, but the imperial cause in Bengal was weakened by dissensions between him and Muzaffar Khān, who, having regained favour, had been appointed governor of Bihar, his authority extending as far eastwards as Teliyāgarhi.

The Ghorāghāt region, the modern district of Dīnājpur, was in great disorder, and Mun'im Khān, partly in order to be near the troubled district, and partly attracted by the buildings of the old capital, resolved to make Gaur his headquarters. His officers opposed this foolish decision, for the climate of Gaur was known to be deadly. Humāyūn and his army had suffered severely there, and the Afghan kings had found it necessary to move to Tānda, but the obstinate old man insisted, and marched to Gaur. What his officers had feared happened. A pestilence broke out, and according to Budāunī, "things came to such a pass that the living were unable to bury the dead, and threw them into the river". Mun'im Khān fled back to Tānda, but not soon enough to save his life, for in October he died there, and affairs in Bengal fell into the utmost confusion. The army, greatly weakened and thoroughly demoralised, began to retire into Bihar, eager to escape from the pestilential climate of Bengal, and Dāūd, returning from Orissa, recovered his kingdom.

The unwelcome news reached Akbar at Sīkrī, and Khānjahān, governor of the Panjab, was appointed to the government and the command of the troops in Bengal, and set out for that province. At Bhāgalpur he was joined by Todar Mal, who had paid a flying visit to Sīkrī to receive Akbar's orders. Khānjahān and he compelled the troops to return with them, and they recovered Teliyāgarhi and occupied Ākmahal, now Rājmahal, where they were joined by Muzaffar Khān with the army of Bihar, placed at their disposal by Akbar's orders. Dāūd was taken by surprise, but Khānjahān considered the situation so serious that he begged Akbar to come and take command of his army in person. Nevertheless, he and Muzaffar Khān decided to attack Dāūd at once, and on July 12, 1576, the armies met near Rājmahal. Dāūd's two principal officers were his uncle, Junaid, and Kālā Pahār. Junaid died of a gunshot wound which he had received the evening before, and Kālā Pahār was severely wounded. The fight was, for a time, fiercely contested, but at length the army of Bengal gave way, and took to flight. Dāūd's horse was bogged as he was attempting to escape, and he was taken alive and beheaded, his head being sent to court. Akbar, in response to Khānjahān's appeal, set out from Sīkrī on July 22, but he had ridden only one month when Sayyid 'Abdullāh Khān arrived with news of the victory of Rājmahal, gained only eleven days before, and cast down Dāūd's head before him. He then returned to Sīkrī. After nearly two hundred and forty years of independence, interrupted only by the two brief conquests of Humāyūn and Shīr Shāh, Bengal had become part of the great Muslim empire of northern India.

During the conquest of Bengal by his officers Akbar had not been idling in his capital. Almost immediately after his return from Patna and Jaunpur in January, 1575, he had commanded the construction at Sīkrī of his *Ibādat-khāna* or "House of Worship", afterwards the scene of discussions and disputes on questions of religion and philosophy, to which purpose it was devoted, rather than to what we understand by worship. These discussions will be noticed later, in the course of an account of Akbar's spiritual venture. He was still tolerably orthodox. As late as 1581 he encouraged the pilgrimage to Mecca, and even proposed to perform it himself, until he was persuaded that a ruler could not safely leave his kingdom to govern itself. He had not yet plunged deeply into religious speculations and discussions, but during the years 1575 and 1576 was completing the administrative reforms which had been interrupted by the campaign in Bihar. He encountered almost everywhere sullen opposition to and evasion of the branding regulation, which was framed to prevent the production of hired or borrowed horses at musters, and to compel superior officers to maintain the contingents for which they were paid. 'Azīz Koka's opposition to this salutary measure was so determined that Akbar imprisoned him in his garden-house at Āgra.. Another unpopular measure was the abolition of feudal tenure, except in newly-conquered provinces. A fief-holder could, without intolerably oppressing landholders and cultivators, enrich himself by extorting from them much more than was required for the maintenance of his contingent, and, if not required to produce branded horses and men holding certificates of identity, could evade the maintenance of his contingent at its full strength; but on becoming a paid official he could draw from the treasury only his own salary and pay and allowances for men holding descriptive certificates of identity and horses bearing the imperial brand. The reason for the unpopularity of these reforms is thus not far to seek; and they were never fully enforced; but Akbar now, besides attempting to enforce them, introduced his new system of land-revenue administration. Those parts of the empire to which it applied were divided into areas, each of which yielded a crore (*karor*—ten millions) of *dāms*, or a sum of £25,000. To each of these areas was appointed an official styled *karorī*, whose duty it was to collect the revenue and remit it to the treasury. Of these officials 182 were appointed, from which it appears that the settled provinces of the empire were expected to yield forty-five and a half millions of rupees in land-revenue. Abul Fazl says of this measure, "Men's minds were quieted, and cultivation increased, and the path of fraud and falsehood was closed"; but Budaunī says, "A great part of the country was laid waste by the rapacity of the *karorīs*; peasants sold their wives and children and fled away, and the revenue was not collected. But the *karorīs* were called to account by Rāja Todar Mal, and many good men died from the severe beatings which were administered, and from the torture of rack and pincers. So many died from confinement in the prisons of the revenue authorities that there was no need of the executioner, and none heeded to find them grave or shroud". Budauní's standard of morality was not high, his "good men" were doubtless orthodox Muslims who had defrauded the state or oppressed the people, or both, and he was opposed to all reforms; but his criticism, severe as it is, cannot be dismissed as pure invention, and the probability is that it is nearer to the truth than Abul Fazl's adulatory remarks.

The preparation of the graded list of officials, *amīrs* and *mansabdārs*, was a simpler matter. Their rank and precedence were regulated by nominal commands of horse, ranging from five thousand down to ten. These "commands" did not necessarily indicate the number which each was required to maintain. In the case of civil officials, they indicated only their relative rank. The official hierarchy of the empire was easily tabulated, but the other reforms were less successful. So far as they succeeded their tendency was to increase the wealth and exalt the personal power of the monarch, which was the object at which Akbar aimed.

While at Sīkrī at this time, Akbar received his cousin, Sulaimān Mīrzā, who had been expelled from Badakhshān, and ordered Khānjahān, governor of the Panjab, to fit out an expedition for the recovery of Badakhshān. On the death of Mun'im Khān, he offered Sulaimān the government of Bengal, and it was on his refusal of it that he recalled Khānjahān from the Panjab and sent him to Bengal, thus interrupting the preparations for the recovery of Badakhshān, which Akbar never resumed. The final conquest of Bengal was not the only campaign in which the imperial forces were at this time engaged. The pusillanimous Udai Singh of Mewār had died in 1572, and had been succeeded by his heroic son, Pratāp Singh. Akbar earnestly desired to conciliate his Hindu subjects, but could not endure the thought that any Hindu should be loth to become his subject. Pratāp, on the other hand, spurned every overture which had submission for its basis, or the degradation of uniting his family with the Tātār, though "lord of countless multitudes", and "singlehanded, for a quarter of a century did he withstand the combined efforts of the empire; at one time carrying destruction into the plains, at another flying from rock to rock, feeding his family from the fruits of his native hills, and rearing the nursling hero Amar, amidst savage beasts and scarce less savage men, a fit heir to his prowess and revenge". His obdurate pride was sufficient to incense Akbar, and now a deliberate insult so inflamed his wrath as to provoke him to an immediate attack on the dominions of Mewār.

The rāja Mān Singh of Amber visited the rāna, and Pratāp received him courteously, but would not sit at meat with one who was defiled by the union of his sister with the *mlechchha*. This was a personal affront, not only to his brother Rājput, but to the emperor. It was impossible then, as it is to-day, to weld those holding such views into a nation, which was Akbar's aim. Mān Singh was appointed to the command of the imperial forces, which assembled at Māndalgarh and marched on the fortress of Gogūnda, which was their objective. The rāna proposed to hold the pass of Haldīghāt, twelve or fourteen miles from the fortress, and the two armies met in June, 1576, at the entrance to the pass. The historian Budaunī, then *imām*, or leader of the prayers, at court, was present at the battle, being eager to acquire the merit of slaying misbelievers. As the Rājputs in the imperial army and those of the enemy were fighting hand to hand, in a confused mass, the historian, armed with a bow, asked his superior officer how he was to distinguish between friends and enemies, and was advised to shoot into the midst of them. They were all infidels, and whoever fell would be a gain to Islam. The Rājputs fought with desperate valour, but of twenty-two thousand assembled that day for the defence of Haldīghāt, only eight thousand quitted the field alive. Pratāp was wounded, and fled into the hills, but the victors were too exhausted to follow up their victory. On the following day the imperial army marched on to Gogūnda, which it occupied, after slaying a few Rājputs who performed the rite of *jauhar*. Akbar unreasonably blamed Mān Singh for not following up the victory immediately with his exhausted troops, but the displeasure did not last long. The imperial troops followed the rāna and captured most of his strongholds, which, however, he afterwards recovered. The gallant Pratāp lived for several years, and when, in 1597, he died, "worn out in body and mind", left, in the person of his son, Amar Singh, a worthy successor.

In the autumn Akbar marched in person into Rājasthān, visited Gogūnda, and annexed Mount Ābu and the Īdar state. He was

then master of all India north of the Taptī and Mahānadī, and
a force was sent to invade Khāndesh, the northernmost state of
the Deccan, but was almost immediately recalled to aid in the
suppression of disturbances in Gujarāt, to quell which Todar Mal
was appointed to the government of the province. Having restored order, he returned, late in 1577, to the imperial camp, and
was appointed Akbar's chief minister. The camp had moved
towards the Panjab, and in December, near Narnaul, Akbar
reformed the administration of his numerous mints. The local
mints had been under the control of minor officials subject to
no central authority, with the result that the coinage lacked
uniformity. The famous artist 'Abd-us-samad was therefore
made master of the mint, to exercise a general control over all
the mints in the empire, and important officials were appointed
as responsible mint-masters at Tānda, Lahore, Jaunpur, Ahmadābād and Patna. The results of this reform may be seen to-day
in specimens of Akbar's currency. "Akbar deserves high credit
for the excellence of his extremely varied coinage, as regards
purity of metal, fullness of weight, and artistic execution. The
Mughal coinage, when compared with that of Queen Elizabeth
or other contemporary sovereigns in Europe, must be pronounced
far superior on the whole. Akbar and his successors seem never
to have yielded to the temptation of debasing the coinage, either
in weight or purity. The gold in many of Akbar's coins is
believed to be practically pure."

Akbar's spiritual experiences and religious experiments will be
discussed later, but it is necessary to refer here to a mysterious
fit of religious ecstasy which overcame him early in May 1578,
at Nandana, while he was encamped at Bhēra, on the Jhelum.
Preparations had been made for a huge battue, and the beaters
were gradually closing in when Akbar, seated under a tree, fell
into a strange state of ecstasy "and was violently attracted by the
cognition of God, and an unseemly frenzy overcame him in an
inexplicable manner, and every one attributed it to some cause
or another, but what is hidden is known to God alone". What
actually happened is not clear. He may have slept and dreamed,
or he may have had an epileptic fit, but whatever happened he
was deeply affected. The battue was stopped, and orders were
issued that not a bird or a beast was to be molested. He distributed
much in alms, and after his return to Sīkrī filled an empty cistern

with money exceeding ten millions of rupees, and distributed this great sum. He did not at once recover from the effects of his vision, and for a time regarded mundane matters with distaste. But he soon brought his mind back to them. He was, for instance, amused and interested by specimens of Western arts and crafts, among other things an organ and several suits of European clothes, brought to him by Hājjī Habībullāh, an envoy whom he had sent to Goa. Inspired, perhaps, by his vision at Nandana, he indulged freely in his favourite pastime of listening to and directing debates in the "House of Worship". They had originally been confined to members of the different sects and schools of Islam, but these, and especially the two orthodox parties led by Makhdūm-ul-mulk and Shaikh 'Abd-un-nabī, had disgraced themselves by indulging in personal abuse and threats of violence. Their strife had been fomented by Shaikh Mubārak, the father of Faizī and of Abul Fazl, who became Akbar's secretary. Mubārak was a freethinker, content with no religion. Originally a Sunni, he had become a Mahdist, then a Shiah, and then a *sūfī*, seeking for closer union with God. His religious vagaries had incensed the orthodox, who had sought his life, and he was at last enjoying his revenge. Akbar's excellent tutor, a Persian named 'Abd-ul-latif, had early imbued him with the principle of toleration, and his attitude towards the Hindus proves that he was never a bigot. He had, as a youth, been a tolerably orthodox, though not a strict Muslim, but had always been impatient of formalism, and had inclined towards mysticism. This tendency was fostered by Mubārak and his sons, and Mubārak, who had been among those who welcomed him on his triumphal return to Sīkrī after the conquest of Gujarāt, had then suggested that it was his duty to be the spiritual leader as well as the temporal ruler of his people, and the suggestion, not unwelcome to an autocrat, afterwards bore fruit. In June, 1579, supported by Mubārak and his sons, he took the first step towards adopting the status which Mubārak had suggested was his by right, and on the first Friday in the month of *Rabī'-us-sānī*, ascended the pulpit in the chief mosque in Sīkrī and recited the ritual address, or *khūtba*, which had been prepared for him, in metrical form, by Faizī:

> In the name of the Lord who gave us sovereignty,
> Who gave us a wise heart and a strong arm,

Who guided us in equity, and justice,
Who put away from our heart aught but equity,
Whose praise is beyond our understanding,
Exalted be His Majesty! God is most great!

Akbar's attitude towards the orthodox had already aroused some suspicion, and this new step caused much uneasiness among the faithful, some of whom murmured that it was not clear to them whether *Allāhu Akbar* meant "God is great" or "Akbar is God"; but Mubārak lost no time, and, taking as his text a verse of the Koran which runs: "Obey God, and obey the apostle, and those among you invested with authority", drew up a petition beseeching Akbar to assume the functions of the "Just Leader", whose authority in the interpretation of the divine commands and the decision of religious questions is supreme. The petition, accepted and ratified by Akbar, became a decree constituting him pope as well as king of Indian Muslims, and the rival party leaders and other learned jurists "were induced or compelled to set their seals to a pronouncement which their souls abhorred". The pronouncement, known as the "Infallibility Decree", invested Akbar with authority to decide questions in accordance with the Koran. With questionable honesty, he used it as an instrument for discrediting Islam. The leaders of the two orthodox parties were packed off to Mecca. One died on his return, and his wealth was wrested from his sons by torture. The other was murdered, almost certainly at Akbar's instigation. By January, 1580, Akbar had forbidden the use of the name of Muhammad in the public prayers; he afterwards renounced all faith in the Arabian prophet, refused to allow his name to be used at court, and mocked the ordinances of his religion. His supreme folly was a decree forbidding his subjects to spell correctly. Words borrowed from Arabic, the sacred language of Islam, were not to be spelt with letters peculiar to that language. Being illiterate, he probably did not fully understand the folly of his order, but his advisers were scholars, who should have prevented him from making himself ridiculous. A sovereign once claimed to be above grammar. Akbar was above spelling. Afterwards, when policy demanded it, he was guilty of many acts of hypocrisy in ceremonial matters, but he failed to deceive his subjects, who knew that he had renounced Islam.

After the orthodox had disgraced themselves, Akbar had turned his attention to religions other than Islam, and had admitted their professors to debates in the "House of Worship". *Sūfīs*, philosophers, orators, jurists, Sunnis, Shiahs, Brāhmans, Jains of both schools, Chārvākas, Christians, Jews, Sabians, Zoroastrians, and others are mentioned by Abul Fazl as taking part in the debates. Not one of these religions satisfied Akbar. but his attitude towards them alarmed his Muslim subjects. His growing hostility to Islam was not the only cause of discontent. The administration of Bengal and Bihar by Muzaffar Khān produced much dissatisfaction. He attempted to enforce the branding-regulation, instituted an enquiry into the titles of fief-holders, resumed holdings for which titles could not be produced, and reduced the field-service pay of the troops, even demanding the refund of payments regularly made at the old rate. But it was the religious question which underlay the unrest which broke out into open revolt. Early in 1580 Mullā Muhammad Yazdī, *kāzī* of Jaunpur, a bigoted Shiah, delivered an authoritative decree that rebellion against Akbar, as an apostate, was lawful, and at about the same time Wazīr Jamīl and the officers of the Kākshāl tribe rose, and were shortly afterwards joined by Mas'ūm Khān of Kābul, fief-holder of Patna and Mas'ūm Khān Farankhūdī in Bihar. The rebels proclaimed Hakīm, Akbar's half-brother, who was still governor of Kābul. The prince was a cowardly and worthless debauchee, but he had never ventured to question the truth of Islam.

Todar Mal, sent to Bengal by Akbar, failed either to quell the rebellion or to conciliate the malcontents, and Muzaffar retired to the defenceless town of Tānda, which, with all the treasure it contained, was captured by the rebels, and Muzaffar was put to death with a variety of tortures. Akbar's position was critical. His brother might at any moment invade the Panjab, and a party at court, resenting the emperor's attitude to Islam, was in secret correspondence with Kābul. He therefore dared not leave his capital, but he readmitted 'Azīz Koka to favour, bestowed on him the title of Khān-i A'zam, and appointed him to the government of Bengal, recalling Shāhbāz Khān from a campaign in Rājputāna to assist him. Todar Mal was besieged in Monghyr for four months, but held out until the rebel forces melted away for the time. In January, 1581, Shāhbāz Khān defeated the rebels in Oudh, but it was not until 1584 that the

rebellion was finally crushed. Many disaffected ecclesiastics were
put to death without trial. Mas'ūm Kābulī was driven into the
Sundarbans, Mas'ūm Farankhūdī, having been thrice pardoned,
was assassinated under Akbar's instructions, but the other leaders
were pardoned. Akbar, confined to his capital, had leisure to
supervise administrative reforms. The land-revenue settlement,
hitherto made annually, had caused much unnecessary work and
allowed opportunities for fraud. A settlement was therefore prepared on the basis of the previous ten-years average, at first by
Todar Mal and Shāh Mansūr, and, after Todar Mal's departure for
Bengal, by Mansūr alone; and at the same time the empire was
divided into twelve *sūbas* or provinces, Allāhābād, Āgra, Oudh,
Ajmir, Gujarāt, Bihar, Bengal, Delhi, Kābul, the Panjab, Multān
and Mālwā. Later conquests added Kashmīr to the Panjab, Sind
to Multān, and Orissa to Bengal, and towards the close of the reign
three new provinces, Berar, Khāndesh, and Ahmadnagar, were
constituted.

Each province was governed by an officer entitled *sipāhsālār*
(commander-in-chief) and the other provincial officials were a
dīwān (controller of finance); *bakhshī* (paymaster and muster-
master general); *mīr-i 'adl* (doomster, to pronounce sentence on
those condemned by *kāzīs*); *sadr* (controller of ecclesiastical affairs
and grants); *kotwāl* (commissioner of police); *mīr-i bahr* (controller of shipping, ports and ferries); and *wāki'a-nawīs* (news-
writer and record-keeper).

Meanwhile Akbar had detected and frustrated the conspiracy
among his courtiers. Its leader, Mansūr, the minister, was
suspended. After a while he was reinstated, but, on being again
detected in correspondence with Kābul, he was imprisoned.
Early in 1581, after dispatching two unsuccessful forays into the
Panjab, Hakīm invaded that province, but the governor, Mān
Singh, was faithful, and refused him admission to Lahore. Meanwhile Akbar was assembling a great army, and on February 4,
1581, set forth. Mansūr was hanged, as he well deserved to be.
Beyond Sirhind Akbar heard of Hakīm's flight but marched on.
At Lahore he was joined by Mān Singh, whom he sent in advance
with Prince Murād. Murād entered Kābul, Hakīm having fled,
on August 3, and Akbar followed him, arriving six days later. He
appointed to the government of Kābul his sister, the wife of Khvāja
Hasan of Badakhshān, and returned to his capital in December.

But that the embers of rebellion yet smouldered in Bengal, he had then re-established his authority throughout his dominions, and had leisure for his favourite occupation, religious speculation. The Portuguese were firmly established at Goa, Damān, and Diū on the western coast, and were lords of the sea, and able to control the pilgrim traffic between India and Mecca. Akbar bitterly resented their naval supremacy, but, having neither ships nor men able to cope with them, could avenge himself only by instructions to his officers to harass them on land. These were issued secretly, for he depended on the Portuguese for the means of investigating the Christian religion, in which he had begun to take a great interest. A priest from Bengal who had visited his court was a man of greater piety than learning, and, being unable to satisfy his curiosity, had advised him to apply to the viceroy at Goa for the services of more learned ecclesiastics, and in February, 1580, the first of three missions had arrived at Sīkṛī. It consisted of three learned and zealous Jesuits, Rodolfo Acquaviva, Antonio Monserrate, and Francisco Enriquez, the last being a convert from Islam, who acted as interpreter. The honour with which the mission was received and entertained, and the almost extravagant veneration shown by Akbar for the sacred symbols which it bore, kindled the liveliest hopes in the breasts of the priests, who were further encouraged by Akbar's frank admission that he had ceased to be a Muslim. They soon discovered, however, that in spite of his interest in and respect for their religion, there was little hope of converting him. He encouraged them in their debates with the Muslim doctors, and protected them from the violence which their indiscreet zeal tended to provoke; but he professed himself unable to accept the doctrines of the Incarnation and the Trinity, and the moral demands of the church raised difficulties even greater than her doctrines. The Jesuit fathers were perfectly honest, and did not mince matters. When the question of his relations with women was raised, they bluntly told him that he had but one wife, and that the rest were concubines who must be discarded before he could be baptized. He also learned that he could be received only as a humble layman, a position which accorded ill with his views on his own spiritual importance. He could hardly doubt what the effect would be on those proud Rājputs who had done violence to their principles in bestowing daughters and sisters on him in marriage, if those ladies were put away as discarded mistresses. Sadly the fathers realised that the honour of converting the "Great Mogul" would not be theirs; but the favour shown to them, and their intemperate language, which sometimes offended even Akbar, did much to influence zealous Muslims against their protector.

Monserrate accompanied Akbar to Kābul and had much converse with him. In 1582 he was sent with an embassy destined to Spain, which never reached its destination. Acquaviva left Sīkrī in 1582, and two months later was murdered by a fanatical Hindu mob. Before he left the court Akbar had announced his design of promulgating a new, perfect, and universal religion. He had already reduced the great office of sadr-us-sudūr and given its powers to six provincial officials, whose duty it was to control and supervise grants of land for religious purposes, and at the same time he had appointed to each large city a principal kāzī, to supervise the work of lesser judicial officers.

In 1583 Muzaffar III, the ex-king of Gujarāt, escaped from custody in that province, and, having assembled a number of followers, rose in rebellion. In 1584 he suffered two severe defeats and fled into Kachch, but it was not until 1591 that the rebellion was finally suppressed by the capture of Muzaffar, who, after being taken, committed suicide by cutting his throat with a razor. Mīrzā 'Abdur Rahīm, the son of Bairam Khān, who, with the help of the historian, Nizām-ud-dīn Ahmad, restored order in Gujarāt, was rewarded for his services with his father's title of Khānkhānān.

In 1582 Akbar summoned at Sīkrī a general council, attended by "all the masters of learning and the military commandants of the cities round about", to whom he descanted on the evils of discord between the followers of various religions in the empire, and announced his remedy, which was to unite them all in a new faith, the Dīn-i Ilāhī, or "Divine Faith", which he, as their spiritual guide, would propound, "with the great advantage of not losing what was good in any one religion, while gaining what was better in another". He was not prepared with the details of his new religion, and could not answer Bhagwān Dās, who questioned him on the subject, but he sent Shaikh Mubārak on a missionary tour to expound them. The chief tenet of the new faith, which inculcated monotheism, tinged with pantheism, was the acknowledgement of Akbar's supremacy in spiritual as well as in temporal affairs. The creed, so far as there was one, was based largely on Jainism, Zoroastrianism, and Hinduism, and its doctrines and practices were carefully calculated to give as much offence as possible to orthodox Muslims. The building and repairing of mosques, the name of Muhammad, Muslim prayers, the fast of Ramadān, and the pilgrimage to Mecca were forbidden; beards were to be shaven, golden ornaments and silken garments worn at prayers, and the *sijda*, or prostration before the emperor, due, according to Islamic doctrines, to God alone, was commanded. The slaughter of cattle was prohibited, abstinence from flesh was recommended, garlic and onions were not to be eaten, the sun was to be adored, and respect was to be shown to artificial lights. The disciple was required to abjure Islam, or any other religion previously professed by him, and might then proceed to one or more "degrees of devotion", up to four, the four degrees being—readiness to sacrifice to the emperor property, life, honour and religion. Akbar more than once denied that he believed himself to be divine, but many of his practices justify the accusation that he considered himself to be more than man. The references to his names in the salutations *Allāhu Akbar* ("God is most great") and *Jalla jalāluhu* ("May His Majesty be glorified"), which he substituted for the ordinary salutations of Muslims, and his extravagant definitions of the kingly office, aroused the suspicions of many, and later in his reign one of the nobles of Ahmadnagar, resenting the arrogant tone adopted by one of the imperial officers, observed that he knew that Akbar pretended to be God, but had yet to learn that his officers were prophets. "The whole scheme", says Mr Vincent Smith, "was the outcome of ridiculous vanity, a monstrous growth of unrestrained autocracy. Its ignominious failure illustrated the wisdom of the warning addressed by the *kotwāl* to the sultan of Delhi some three centuries earlier, and the folly of kings who seek to assume the rôle of prophets." The movement was a failure. Abul Fazl gives a list of eighteen of its prominent members, only one of whom was a Hindu, and the disciples never numbered more than a few thousands, most of whom professed the faith for a consideration, either in place or cash. They never knew how they stood, for Akbar promulgated from time to time foolish regulations and prohibitions which they were expected to obey, and their zeal

seems soon to have waned. Akbar was not prepared to countenance all Hindu practices, for when he was over forty he rode
a great distance in the hottest season of the year to save the
widow of Jaimal, a cousin of Bhagwān Dās, whose son and other
relatives attempted to compel her to become sati against her will.
The woman was saved, and those who would have murdered
her were punished.

In 1584 the embers of rebellion in Bengal were finally extinguished, and in the autumn of 1585 Akbar marched to Lahore,
which he made his headquarters until 1598, for there was much
to detain him in this part of his dominions. His half-brother,
Muhammad Hakīm, had died at Kābul in July from the effects
of strong drink, leaving the province in some disorder, and it was
feared that 'Abdullāh Khān the Uzbeg, who had already annexed
the province of Badakhshān, might extend his aggressions. On
Hakīm's death Mān Singh had been sent at once to Kābul to
restore order and to defend the province if necessary, and Akbar
had followed him to Lahore. The country between Kābul and
the Indus was in a most disturbed state. To the north of the Kābul
river the Yūsufzai and Mandar tribes preyed upon all caravans
and travellers unprotected by troops, and plundered the lowlands;
and to the south of that river a sect of fanatics had risen under
a prophet named Bāyazīd, who, dying in 1585, was succeeded
by his son Jalāl, who withstood the imperial forces for many
years, and lastly there was the independent kingdom of Kashmīr.
Its ruler, Yūsuf Shāh, when ousted by a usurper, had visited
Akbar at Sīkrī in 1580 and implored his aid. Akbar had sent a
force to reinstate him, but his people, rather than suffer a foreign
invasion, had restored him to his throne, and Yūsuf, though he
had expressed his gratitude by sending his son Ya'kūb with gifts
to Akbar, had declined to appear personally before him as a
vassal. Akbar therefore decided to annex his kingdom, and
operations against the predatory tribesmen and Kashmīr were
undertaken simultaneously, the command of the former being
given to Zain Khān, one of the emperor's foster-brothers, and
that of the latter nominally to his cousin, Shāhrukh Mīrzā, who
was placed under the control and tutelage of Bhagwān Dās.

Zain Khān entered the tribal territory, but, finding his forces
insufficient to cope with the rebels, asked for reinforcements,
whereupon Akbar sent to his assistance two columns, one under

the command of Rāja Bīrbal, the court-poet, wit and jester, and the other under the command of Hakīm Abul Fath, a physician. He soon had reason to repent of the folly of placing men of this sort in military command. The tribesmen having been punished, the force was withdrawn by a pass selected by the two civilians, against the soldiers' advice. The rebels fell on the imperial troops and slew 8000 of them, Bīrbal being cut down as he was attempting to run away, and compelled, in the words of a Muslim historian, "to join the pack of the hounds of hell". Akbar grieved bitterly for him, and for a time refused to see Zain Khān, who was in no way to blame.

In Kashmīr Yūsuf, having failed to dissuade Bhagwān Dās, by concessions, from proceeding to extremities against him, had occupied, and closed to the invaders, a pass from which he could not easily be dislodged. The imperial troops, having advanced far into the country, suffered much from rain, cold, snow, and shortness of supplies, and were disheartened by the news of the disaster in the Yūsufzai country. Bhagwān Dās therefore granted Yūsuf peace on easy terms. The *khūtba* was to be recited and the coinage issued in the name of Akbar, certain departments and monopolies of the government were to be placed in the hands of imperial officers, Yūsuf was to do homage in person, and was to return to Kashmīr as Akbar's vassal. On these terms the troops retired and Yūsuf accompanied them to Akbar's camp. Akbar was much displeased with the terms granted, but ratified the treaty, and, having done so, immediately violated it by detaining Yūsuf as a prisoner. Yūsuf's son, Ya'kūb, had already fled back to Kashmīr, and prepared to hold the kingdom as his father's successor; and Bhagwān Dās, who considered his honour to have been besmirched by Akbar's breach of faith, attempted to commit suicide by stabbing himself, but the wound was not fatal, and he recovered. The imperial army again invaded the country, and occupied the capital, and though Ya'kūb held his own for more than two years in the hills, he finally sub.nitted when Akbar paid a short visit to Kashmīr, and was sent to join his father, then a prisoner in Bihar. Yūsuf was released shortly afterwards, and was appointed commander of 500 horse, in which capacity he served in Bengal under Mān Singh. Akbar's treatment of Yūsuf Shāh and his son is a blot on his character.

At the time of his visit to Kashmīr in 1589 Akbar lost two of his best and most faithful servants, within five days of each other. Todar Mal was the first to die, and was followed by Bhagwān Dās. Abul Fazl censures them both as bigots, but they were no more than orthodox Hindus who refused to follow Akbar in his religious pranks. Mān Singh, who succeeded his adoptive father, Bhagwān Dās, in Amber, was also stigmatised as a bigot. When urged to join the "Divine Faith", he replied that he had already given sufficient proof of his devotion, that he was a Hindu, and was prepared to become a Muslim if so commanded, but knew no religion other than those. The blunt refusal of his best officers and most favoured courtiers to acknowledge him as the prophet of God was a severe blow to Akbar's vanity, and should have convinced him of his folly.

After his visit to Kashmīr Akbar marched to Kābul, where he spent two months, and on his return sent an expedition into Sind. In 1528 Shāh Husain, chief of the Arghūn tribe, had overcome Husain Langāh of Sind, and the Arghūns had since been lords of that land. They had accepted Humāyūn as their overlord, but, since his expulsion from India, had been independent. Akbar resolved, for two reasons, to annex Sind, first because it was traditionally part of the Muslim kingdom of Delhi, and secondly, because its possession was a necessary step to the conquest of Balūchistān and Kandahār. Mīrzā 'Abdur Rahīm, Khānkhānān, had therefore been appointed governor of Multān, with instructions to annex Sind. He defeated Mīrzā Jāni Beg Arghūn in two engagements, compelled him to submit, and in 1593 brought him to Akbar's feet. On his formally renouncing Islam and accepting the "Divine Faith", he was appointed to the command of 3000 horse, and shortly afterwards to the government of Sind. Early in 1601 he died of *delirium tremens* in the Deccan. Akbar thus became master of the whole of northern India, but there still remained the Muslim kingdoms of the Deccan, dissevered from Delhi since the middle of the fourteenth century. They were four in number. A confederacy of the Muslim sultans of the Deccan had, in 1565, overthrown the great Hindu kingdom of Vijayanagar, the lion's share of which had fallen to the kingdom of Bījāpur. In 1574 Murtazā Nizām Shāh I of Ahmadnagar had annexed the kingdom of Berar, partly as a punishment for its not having joined the confederacy against Vijayanagar. In 1565 Burhān-ud-dīn had contested the throne of Ahmadnagar with

his elder brother, Murtazā I, and, having been worsted, had fled,
first to Bījāpur and then, some time later, to the court of Akbar,
who had welcomed him as a useful pawn in the troubled game
of politics in the Deccan. In 1586 Murtazā I was murdered by
his son, Husain II, and the latter, four years later, was deposed
and murdered by his nobles, who enthroned Ismā'īl Nizām Shāh,
the young son of Burhān-ud-dīn. Burhān, seeing his son on the
throne which should have been his, sought leave to gain his
kingdom, which Akbar gladly granted, pressing on him also the
co-operation of imperial troops, which Burhān was wise enough
to decline, for such aid would have made him odious to his
subjects and to his fellow-sovereigns of the Deccan, as binding
him to Akbar. Burhān, after one unsuccessful attempt to invade
Berar and raise his subjects, sought the aid of Rāja 'Alī Khān of
Khāndesh, with his assistance defeated Ismā'īl and his adherents,
and in 1591 ascended the throne of Ahmadnagar as Burhān
Nizām Shāh II. He reigned until his death in 1595, and, when
missions which Akbar had in 1591 sent to the courts of the
Deccan returned to his court in 1593, they reported that Rāja
'Alī Khān of Khāndesh acknowledged his suzerainty, that the
sultans of Bījāpur and Golconda had sent gifts which might be
regarded as tribute, but that Burhān II had sent a gift so paltry
as to be hardly reckoned even as a compliment. Akbar decided
on war. He appointed his youngest son, Dāniyāl, to the command of the army of the Deccan, but afterwards revoked his
commission and appointed the Khānkhānān to the command.
Akbar's second son, Murād, governor of Gujarāt, was ordered
to support and assist him. 'Azīz Koka had been appointed to
Gujarāt after the Khānkhānān's transfer to Multān, but had,
without permission, left the province on a pilgrimage to Mecca,
disgusted with Akbar's religious vagaries. There he was so fleeced
by the holy men of Islam that after his return, in 1594, he was
reconciled to Akbar and embraced the "Divine Faith". But the
invasion of the Deccan was not immediately undertaken.

In 1590, at Akbar's invitation, a second Jesuit mission visited
Lahore. His invitation had led the priests to believe that he was
seriously thinking of embracing Christianity, but after their
arrival they soon discovered that there was no hope of his conversion, and in 1592 the mission returned to Goa. In 1594 Akbar
again invited to his court a mission, which, expecting less than
the others, was less disappointed.

In April, 1595, Muzaffar Husain Mīrzā, the Safavid prince who governed Kandahār, surrendered the city and province to Shāh Beg, one of Akbar's officers. Kandahār was a bone of contention between the Indian and Persian empires. In 1622 the Persians recovered it from Jahāngīr, in 1638 Shāhjahān recovered it from them, and in 1649 the Persians regained it, and it was finally lost to India.

A period of four years of famine and pestilence, which began to devastate Akbar's empire in 1595, did not hinder the outbreak of war in the Deccan at the end of that year. Burhān II had died in 1595, and had been succeeded by his second son, Ibrāhīm, who was almost immediately killed in battle with the troops of Ibrāhīm 'Ādil Shāh II of Bījāpur. He left an infant son named Bahādur. Bahādur was proclaimed by Chānd Sultān, sister of Burhān and widow of 'Alī 'Ādil Shāh I, who had returned to Ahmadnagar after her husband's death, and now took a leading part in the politics of her native land; but the Deccani nobles put forward another candidate, and two factions of the Africans two others, and, while the four factions were quarrelling, Miyān Manjhū, leader of the Deccanis, appealed to the imperial officers to intervene. The Khānkhānān in Mālwā and Sultān Murād in Gujarāt had both been preparing for a campaign in the Deccan, and, on receiving this appeal, both set out, accompanied by Rāja 'Alī Khān, who had sworn allegiance to Akbar, and arrived before Ahmadnagar late in December, 1595. As they approached the city the various factions presented a temporarily united front against them, and were aided by contingents from Bījāpur and Golconda.

The siege of Ahmadnagar was protracted by the quarrels of the prince and the Khānkhānān, by the vigilant defence of Chānd Sultān, and by the secret encouragement from Sultān 'Alī Khān, whose sympathies were with the kingdoms of the Deccan, and in April 1596, Chānd Sultān saved the city by a treaty with the imperial officers, ceding Berar to Akbar.

The peace did not last long. Quarrels regarding the frontiers of Berar and other matters of detail soon led to hostilities, and in 1597 Rāja 'Alī Khān was killed in a bloody battle on the Godāvarī between the Khānkhānān and the troops of Bījāpur and Ahmadnagar, and was succeeded in Khāndesh by his son, Bahādur Khān.

In 1599 Sultān Murād died in Berar, of drink, and Akbar, who had in the preceding year moved his court from Lahore to Āgra, set out for the Deccan, appointing his youngest son, Dāniyāl, with the Khānkhānān, to the command of the army in the field. When Akbar reached Burhānpur, Bahādur Khān refused to do homage to him, and the army, under Akbar, besieged him in his fortress-capital of Asīrgarh, while Dāniyāl and the Khānkhānān marched on to Ahmadnagar. Here conspirators murdered the "noble queen", and in 1600 the imperial troops carried the city by assault, with the usual results, and the young king, Bahādur Nizām Shāh, was sent as a state prisoner to Gwalior. Asīrgarh held out longer, but Akbar, having lured Bahādur Khān into his camp, and, by breach of faith, detained him there, at length succeeded in reducing the fortress by means of bribing the leaders of the garrison. In January, 1601, it fell into his hands, and Khāndesh ceased to exist as a separate state. The greater part of Ahmadnagar yet owned allegiance to Murtazā Nizām Shāh II, set up by the nobles to succeed Bahādur Shāh, but Akbar had occupied enough of the kingdom to form a province of his empire, and Berar, Ahmadnagar and Khāndesh were formed into three additional *sūbas*, the last being re-named Dāndesh in honour of the prince, Dāniyāl, who was appointed to the viceroyalty of the three provinces.

After the reduction of Asīrgarh and the organisation of the administration of the three provinces of the Deccan, Akbar was obliged to set out for Āgra, for his eldest son, Salīm, was in rebellion, and at Allāhābād, of which province he held the government, maintained a court as an independent sovereign. The emperor was in his fifty-ninth year, his health was beginning to fail, and Salīm had every reason to believe that should his father die while he himself was at a distance from the capital he would not gain the crown without a contest. His brother Dāniyāl was yet alive, but he had a more formidable competitor in the person of his own son, Khusraw, who was a favourite of Akbar s, and whose cause was supported by a powerful faction at court, which dreaded Salīm's brutal cruelty and drunken habits. Salīm had therefore declined to leave Allāhābād for the purpose of crushing a serious rebellion in Bengal, and, after Akbar's return from the Deccan, had marched on Āgra with a large force. He hesitated to disobey Akbar's order directing him to return at once to Allāhābād, but he paid no heed to an order appointing him to the government of Bengal and Orissa, and, remaining at Allāhābād, assumed the royal title and struck money in his own name.

Akbar refrained from active measures against his undutiful son, but summoned to court for consultation Abul Fazl, who had been left in the Deccan for the purpose of assisting in the pacification and administration of the new provinces. Abul Fazl both feared and disliked Salīm, and the prince regarded him as his enemy, and feared that he would set his father against him and urge him to disinherit him. He therefore entered into communication with Bīr Singh, the violent and unscrupulous Bundela chief of Orchha, and hired him to murder Abul Fazl on his way to court. In August, 1602, the Bundela waylaid and slew him near Narwar, severed his head from his body, and sent it to Salīm, who "received it with unholy joy and treated it with shameful insult".

The murder of his learned favourite enraged and deeply grieved Akbar, who ordered the pursuit and punishment of Bīr Singh, but the Bundela, though long hunted, escaped and lived to enjoy the favour of the instigator of his crime.

Sultān Salīma Begum, wife of Akbar and mother of Murād, visited Salīm at the end of 1602, and persuaded him to submit. He placed himself under the protection of his grandmother, Akbar's aged mother, and visited Āgra, where a formal reconciliation took place between father and son, and Salīm was deputed to subdue the rāna, Amar Singh, son and successor of Pratāp Singh. He set out, but had no intention of pursuing an arduous campaign, far from the capital, and, when he had reached Sīkrī, made impossible demands for reinforcements and treasure, and, failing to receive them, returned, with Akbar's reluctant assent, to Allāhābād, where he was grievously afflicted by the loss of his favourite wife, Shāh Begum, the adoptive sister of Mān Singh. After a paroxysm of grief, he resumed his evil courses, and so exceeded in the consumption of opium and strong drink as to become a terror to all around him, and a source of great grief to his father.

Early in 1604 Dāniyāl died in the Deccan, from the effects of strong drink, but Khusraw, Salīm's son, still remained as a possible competitor for the crown. Later in the year Akbar announced his intention of visiting Bengal, and prepared to set out from Āgra, his real destination being Allāhābād. Accidents delayed him, and his old mother, who fell ill from grief at the failure of her attempts to dissuade him from proceeding against his first-born, became so feeble that Akbar felt constrained to visit her before leaving, and she died shortly after he had seen her. Akbar then reopened negotiations with his son, and Salīm was persuaded that it would be to his advantage to submit. He set out from Allāhābād for Āgra with a large force, but left it at a distance from the city, and approached the palace with a small personal escort. Akbar received him publicly with distinction and affection, but, when his son fell at his feet, drew him into an inner apartment, struck him in the face, and abused and reproached him. He then placed him under restraint as though he were a dangerous maniac, but, having thus humbled him, gradually relented, and by degrees restored him to favour as his heir. Salīm then settled down in Āgra, where he lived quietly for nearly a year until his father's death.

In September, 1604, Akbar fell sick of diarrhoea, or dysentery, and while he was under treatment a quarrel between the servants of his son and his grandson vexed him and aggravated his complaint. During his father's illness Salīm, who was in the habit of visiting him frequently, discovered a plot of some of the nobles to seize him on the occasion of one of his visits, and to remove him in favour of his son; but, warned in time, he withdrew from the palace before the design could be put into execution, and at a general meeting of the nobles the proposal that he should be excluded from the succession was outvoted, but his adherents afterwards judged it necessary to require from him oaths to protect the Muslim faith. Having satisfied them, he visited his father, now almost past the power of speech. The dying emperor signified his wish that his son should assume the royal turban and gird himself with Humāyūn's sword, and Salīm, leaving the palace, was acclaimed by the multitude as his father's successor. Shortly after his departure his father breathed his last. Muslim writers declare that in his last moments Akbar recanted his errors, and died a good Muslim, but he seems hardly to have recovered consciousness after Salīm had left him, and thus, on October 27, 1605, he died.

Akbar was unquestionably the greatest of all rulers of India of the Muslim period. His age, it has been remarked, was an age of great rulers. His nearest contemporary was Elizabeth of England, but Henry IV of France and 'Abbās the Great of Persia were ruling their kingdoms during a great part of his reign. He was the first, if not the only, Indian monarch to aspire to ruling a united people rather than to leading a dominant race, and his domestic alliances with Rājput families were what is now called a friendly gesture to the subject race, but by degrees he learned that Hinduism and Islam were incompatible, and, though he knew that such alliances as his were regarded by many of the subject race as an indelible disgrace, he laid the blame for this incompatibility chiefly upon the faith of his fathers. Very early in life he adopted and practised the principle of *sulh-i-kull*, or universal toleration, but later there was one creed which he excepted from its benefits, and that one was his own former faith. Many Muslims, eager to claim so great a ruler as one of themselves, contend that Akbar always remained a Muslim, and never went beyond an attempt to reform the faith in the direction of making it less harshly intolerant; but these ignore the undoubted facts that he definitely abjured Islam, and required others to abjure it, and that in the latter part of his life he persecuted its followers and destroyed its places of worship. The exclusiveness and intolerance of Islam was one of the factors in the greatest of his errors, the institution of the "Divine Faith". Another was personal vanity, but the greatest was, perhaps, the idea of founding a faith which all his subjects could accept. This, though an imperial conception, betrayed, besides great vanity, strange ignorance of human nature. Where Zoroastrianism, Buddhism, Jainism, Christianity, and Islam had failed, Akbar's "Divine Faith" was not likely to succeed. It was, in fact, an ignominious failure, and made no appeal to Hindus, Muslims, or Christians; but Akbar never admitted failure, and to the end of his life stood forth as the prophet of his new faith. Far more practical, liberal, and modest was the policy of one of his great predecessors, Shīr Shāh, who, regarding religion as a personal matter, retained his own, and refrained from persecuting others for retaining theirs.

Some uncritical writers have written of Akbar as though he were divine, as his enemies said he pretended to be, and his flatterers almost persuaded him that he was; but he was far from perfect. Aggressive land-hunger, political duplicity, and cruelty were faults of his age and race, and for these it would be unjust to blame one who, though far from guiltless, was not the guiltiest of his line. Incontinence and intemperance, which were among his faults, he attempted to curb, but an attempt on his life in 1564 and one of the conditions attached to the surrender of Ranthambhor indicate that, in early life at least, his fancy ranged sometimes beyond the bounds of his own copious harem; and though he was never, like his sons, a slave to strong drink, and in later life exceeded moderation less often than in his youth, there is evidence enough to prove that he was always what John Evelyn would have styled "a good drinking gentleman".

The fiscal administration for which he and Todar Mal have been so highly praised was based largely on the methods of Shīr Shāh, a born and trained administrator, but Akbar's historians have done scant justice to "Shīr Khān, the Afghan rebel". Its object was the enrichment of the crown rather than the prosperity of the people, and we have no record of effective or widespread measures of relief in the dreadful famines which fell on the land in Akbar's reign.

His illiteracy was no obstacle to his being widely and deeply informed, for he was endowed with prodigious powers of memory, and delighted in listening to readers and disputants; but knowledge acquired in this haphazard fashion was necessarily diffuse and ill-arranged, and left the receptive mind undisciplined. But the Jesuits admit that the range of his knowledge was so wide that none would have suspected his illiteracy.

He was a mystic, and experienced visions which deeply moved him, for he was sincerely religious and devout, and, as his son says, "never for one moment forgot God". As a young man he recited regularly the ritual prayers of Islam, and in later life performed devotions of his own devising, with acts of reverence to the sun, fire and light, as symbols of the divine purity and brilliance. Even when he was not engaged in personal devotions, his chief delight was to listen to discourses on and discussions of religious questions, and to seek the means of closer union with God. His practice fell far short of his precepts but, as Mr Vincent Smith says, "He was a born king of men, with a rightful claim to rank as one of the greatest sovereigns known to history. That claim rests securely on the basis of his extraordinary natural gifts and his magnificent achievements".

CHAPTER X

Jahāngīr

On October 27, 1605, Salīm succeeded his father, assuming the title and throne-name of Nūr-ud-dīn Muhammad Jahāngīr, "the Light of the Faith, Muhammad, the World-Seizer". His personal name, as he explains in his memoirs, was the same as that of an Ottoman emperor, and he therefore changed it from Salīm to Jahāngīr. The change caused him no inconvenience, for his name, Salīm, had seldom been used. His father, "drunk or sober", as he says, had always called him "Shaikhū Bābā". He preferred the more arrogant name of Jahāngīr, but to the Persian court, with which he had much correspondence, he was always "Salīm, the ruler of India".

Jahāngīr, like his brothers and all his father's house, was much addicted to strong drink, and though he was far from being the mere sot that some writers have represented him to be, he habitually exceeded the bounds of moderation. His medical advisers prevailed on him to reduce his allowance of double-distilled spirit, and to cease drinking during the day, but he never went to bed sober, except perhaps on Friday nights, corresponding with our Thursdays. Of his character we glean much from his memoirs, which, though less outspoken than those of Bābur, are sufficiently frank, and from the reports of European travellers. Akbar had received Englishmen. Fitch, Newbery and Leedes, the last of whom died in his service, had visited his court at Sīkrī in 1585. We learn much of him from the Jesuits, and at the end of his reign he received John Mildenhall, bearing a letter from Elizabeth of England; but of Jahāngīr we have portraits from the pen of the bluff sea-captain, William Hawkins, who for some time enjoyed the honour of being his boon companion, and from that of a very different character, the English ambassador, Sir Thomas Roe, who never forgot the dignity of his country, or of his own position as her representative. Observing the favour shown by Jahāngīr to Hawkins, "the Portugalls were like madde dogges", and, though their intrigues did not avail to diminish his personal regard for the English sailor, they pre-

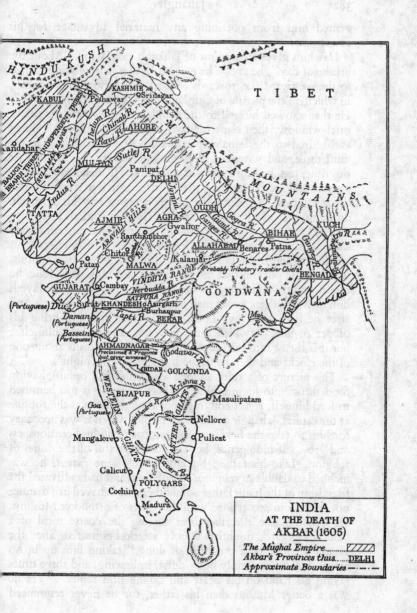

HINDU KUSH

TIBET

KASHMIR
KABUL Peshawar Srinagar

Jhelum R.
Chinab R.
LAHORE
Ravi R.

Indus R.
Sutlej R.
MULTAN
Panipat
DELHI

Jumna R.
AJMIR AGRA
ARAVALI Hills Gwalior
TATTA Ranthambhor
Chitor

OUDH
Gogra R.
Gumti R.
BIHAR
ALLAHABAD Benares Patna
Kalanjar
Probably Tributary Frontier Chiefs

KUCH

Patan
MALWA
GUJARAT Cambay
VINDHYA RANGE
Nerbudda R.
GONDWANA
BENGAL
(Portuguese) Diu
Surat SATPURA RANGE
Daman KHANDESH Asirgarh
(Portuguese) *Tapti R.* Burhanpur
Bassein BERAR
(Portuguese)
ORISSA
Mahanadi R.

AHMADNAGAR
Proclaimed a Province but never annexed
Godavari R.
BIDAR GOLCONDA
BIJAPUR *Krishna R.*
WESTERN GHATS *Tungabhadra R.* Masulipatam
Goa
(Portuguese)
EASTERN GHATS
Nellore
Mangalore Pulicat
Calicut *Kaveri R.*
POLYGARS
Cochin
Madura

INDIA
AT THE DEATH OF
AKBAR (1605)
The Mughal Empire............ //////
Akbar's Provinces thus.....__DELHI__
Approximate Boundaries — · — · —

vented him from obtaining any material advantage for his countrymen.

Hawkins gives an account of Jahāngīr's daily life. "About the breake of day", he says, "he is at his Beades, with his face turned to the westward (*i.e.* towards Mecca) in a private faire room", in which is "the picture of Our Lady and Christ, graven in stone". He then showed himself to the people at the *jharokha*, or palace oriel-window, then slept for two hours, and afterwards dined and retired to the female apartments. At noon he held levees until three, and witnessed elephant fights and other sports. At this time, too, he heard and decided cases. He then again said his prayers and ate his evening meal, of four or five sorts of well-dressed meats, "of which he eateth a bit to stay his stomach, drinking once of his stronge drinke. Then he cometh forth into a private roome (the *ghusl-khāna*), where none can come but such as himself nominateth (for two years I was one of his attendants here). In this place he drinketh other five cupfuls, which is the portion that the physicians alot him. This done, he eateth opium, and being in the height of his drinke he layeth him down to sleep, every man departing to his own home. And after he hath slept two hours they awake him and bring his supper to him, at which time he is not able to feed himselfe; but it is thrust into his mouth by others. And this is about one of the clock; and then he sleepeth the rest of the night".

This picture of a ruler, sodden with drink and opium, having food thrust into his mouth by others when he is too bemused to feed himself, is not edifying; but though this was the routine at the capital, Jahāngīr could rouse himself when it was necessary for him to take the field, and, notwithstanding his licentiousness and gross self-indulgence, he was not neglectful of the duties of religion. Like his father, but not to the same extent, he was inclined to dabble in religious speculation, and had cultivated the friendship of the Jesuit fathers, and otherwise behaved in a manner not entirely in accordance with the views of orthodox Muslims. Sir Thomas Roe describes him sharing the coarse meal of a "filthy beggar", doubtless a holy ascetic besmeared, after the Hindu fashion, with the ashes of dung, "taking him up in his armes, which no cleanly body durst, imbracing, and three times laying his hand on his heart and calling him father". Yet he was a better Muslim than his father, for he never renounced

Islam. His chief fault was cruelty. His was a cruel age, and even Akbar was not free from the taint, though he never gloated, as Jahāngīr did, over the sufferings of men impaled, or flayed alive.

The movement to exclude him from the throne in favour of his son, Khusraw, had been very strong, and Akbar's acknowledgment of him as his heir had not crushed the conspiracy. Khusraw was an amiable young man of great personal charm and of high moral character, but weak and accessible to flatterers. The attempt to oust his father in his favour had inflamed his ambition, and his father, on his accession, had taken necessary precautions for the security of his throne. Khusraw, though not actually in durance, was kept under close surveillance in the fort at Āgra. Chafing under restraint, he succeeded, on April 6, 1606, in effecting his escape from Āgra, and many of the younger nobility, including his kinsman, Hasan Mīrzā, son of Shāhrukh Mīrzā, who were warmly attached to him, gathered round him. He made his way towards Lahore, with a view to seizing that city and establishing himself in the Panjab, and on his way was joined by so many that his followers numbered 12,000 when he arrived there. At Tārn, Taran Arjūn, the *guru* of the Sikhs, provided him with a sum of five thousand rupees, but Dilāvar Khān, the governor of Lahore, was faithful to Jahāngīr, and, though his troops were few they were more than a match, behind defences, for Khusraw's raw levies; and repulsed their assault. Meanwhile Jahāngīr had followed his son with such forces as he could immediately collect, and Khusraw, leaving a small force before Lahore, advanced with ten thousand men to Sultānpur, near the confluence of the Beās and the Sutlej, and near that place offered battle to the advanced guard of the imperial army, under Shaikh Farīd. Jahāngīr sent an envoy to his son to induce him to submit, but the prince, relying on his numerical superiority, was obdurate. In the battle which followed his undisciplined troops were scattered by his father's, many being taken and many slain. Khusraw escaped with his immediate adherents, and against the advice of many endeavoured to reach Kābul. Jahāngīr made Lahore his headquarters, and a force under Abul Kāsim Namakīn, sent by him in pursuit of the fugitives, captured them on the Chināb and carried them into the town of Gujrāt. An escort sent out by Jahāngīr led them before him in Lahore. He, much grieved by his son's conduct, reproached him bitterly, and his two chief adherents, Husain Beg and 'Abdur Rahīm, were sewn up in freshly-flayed hides, the first in that of an ox, and the second in that of an ass, and were paraded through the city on asses face to tail. Husain Beg was crushed to death, but 'Abdur Rahīm, after severe suffering, survived, and was ever afterwards known as 'the ass'. Later, an avenue of stakes was set up between Lahore and a garden without the city, on each stake was impaled one of Khusraw's followers, and Khusraw himself, mounted on an elephant, was led through the avenue, while his father brutally mocked him with the taunt that his followers were making obeisance to him. The prince, overcome with grief, wept almost unceasingly for days, and is said never to have smiled again. Many of those known to have been in sympathy with him were punished by heavy fines. Mān Singh is said to have been amerced in a sum equivalent to ten millions sterling, but the Sikh *guru*, Arjūn, was put to death with torture.

Khusraw's rebellion led to other disturbances. Rai Rai Singh of Bikaner rose in rebellion near Nāgaur, but was defeated, and was later pardoned. A petty chief in Bihar also rose, but was defeated and slain. At the same time a Persian army threatened Kandahār, but withdrew on the approach of a relieving force under Mīrzā Ghāzi, son of Jāni Beg Arghūn.

Jahāngīr marched to Kābul, where he spent the summer, and on his return to Lahore discovered a plot, to which Khusraw was privy, to assassinate him in the hunting-field. Four of the ringleaders were put to death, and Khusraw was blinded, but his sight was not entirely destroyed, and after his return to Āgra Jahāngīr relented, and caused his son's eyes to be treated, so that the sight of one was restored. But the prince's misfortunes endeared him to the people, and in April, 1610, Kutb-ud-dīn, a Muslim youth, rose in rebellion in Bihar, and, by personating him, assembled so many followers that he was able to gain possession of Patna, the provincial capital, and the treasure which it contained, while the two officials in charge of the city fled without striking a blow. The governor, who was on tour, returned and defeated the rebels, whose leader surrendered and was executed, and many of his followers were imprisoned. The two cowardly officials, their heads and beards having been shaved, were paraded through the streets of Āgra in female attire.

In May, 1611, Jahāngīr married Mihr-un-nissā, who received

the title at first of *Nūr Mahal*, 'Light of the Palace', and afterwards that of *Nūr Jahān*, 'Light of the World', by which she
will be described here. Around her name very many romantic
tales, too long and too intricate for repetition, have been woven.
Her true story is as follows. She was the daughter of a Persian
named Ghiyās Beg and his wife, and was born at Kandahār
while her father was on his way from his native land to India.
Ghiyās Beg continued his journey and entered Akbar's service.
He was a learned and cultured man, and in 1595 held the post of
controller of the revenues of the province of Kābul. His daughter
was married to a Persian adventurer, 'Alī Kulī Istājlu, who had
entered the service of 'Abdur Rahīm Khānkhānān and so highly
distinguished himself in the campaign in Sind that he was transferred later to the service of Salīm, the heir-apparent. His dex-
terity and bravery in slaying a tiger gained him the title of Shīr
Afkan Khān ('the Overthrower of the Tiger'), and Jahāngīr,
on his succession, bestowed on him a fief at Bardwān, in Bengal.
Here he fell under suspicion of complicity in the sedition ever
rife in that province, and Kutb-ud-dīn Khān, who had succeeded Mān Singh as governor, was ordered to send him to
court under arrest. The governor accordingly visited Bardwān
with a body of troops, and summoned Shīr Afkan to his camp.
Shīr Afkan obeyed, but, observing that as he approached the
governor he was gradually surrounded, became suspicious, and,
as Kutb-ud-dīn advanced to meet him, drew his sword and
delivered such a cut that the bowels gushed out. Kutb-ud-dīn's
attendants fell on the assassin and cut him down. Mihr-un-nissā
and her daughter were sent to Āgra, where her father now held
high office, and the mother was appointed lady-in-waiting to
Sultān Salīma Begum, Akbar's chief widow, in whose service
Jahāngīr met her, fell in love with her, and in May, 1611,
married her.

The story usually told is that Jahāngīr had fallen in love with
her long before, at his father's court, that Akbar, to prevent a
marriage, caused her to be married to Shīr Afkan, and that
Jahāngīr, thus frustrated, afterwards compassed her husband's
death, after which she for four years repelled the advances of
his murderer, but at last relented. From the best contemporary
evidence it appears that this story is a fabrication. Shīr Afkan
suffered death as any other assassin would have suffered in like

circumstances, not because the emperor loved his wife, and his widow was not unkind to her imperial wooer.

Nūr Jahān was an extraordinary woman. Nearly thirty-four, an age at which most oriental women are in the sere and yellow leaf, her great beauty inflamed the emperor's passion, and her physical charms were the least of her merits. With a commanding intellect, she was most highly educated in her mother-tongue, the most beautiful in the East, and was no mean poetess. She was mistress of most feminine accomplishments, and had great taste in art, which inspired her even to introduce a change in the fashion of female dress. She was well acquainted with public affairs, and her ruling passion was ambition and the love of power, in acquiring and in wielding which she was hindered by few scruples.

After her marriage to Jahāngīr, Nūr Jahān formed a party, which virtually ruled the empire until, in 1622, Khurram's revolt against his father separated him from it, and it was enfeebled by the death of some of its leading members; but Nūr Jahān retained her influence over her husband until his death. The party consisted of her father, Ghiyās Beg, now entitled I'timād-ud-daula, her brother, Āsaf Khān, and Jahāngīr's third son, Khurram, generally regarded as heir apparent, who married her daughter, Arjumand Bānū Begum, and whose claim to the succession she strongly supported.

Jahāngīr was not at first a mere tool of this clique, for they were acquainted with his designs and his policy, and were careful not to thwart him, but as a result of years of self-indulgence he became slothful, and impatient of the tedium of public business. He knew, he said, that his wife was well able to rule, and for his own part he was well content with a bottle and a piece of meat. As for Nūr Jahān, she brushed aside the convention of feminine seclusion, accompanied her husband in the hunting field, showed herself to the public at the *jharokha*, or palace window, issued *farmāns*, and alone among the wives of Indian rulers was allowed the honour of the impression of her name upon the coin of the realm, with that of her husband.

The palace party of Nūr Jahān was not unopposed. The opposition comprised many of the old nobles, headed by Mahābat Khān. The Khānkhānān would have been its natural leader, but he lacked the spirit, and perhaps the disinterestedness, to set

himself in opposition to a clique so powerful. The view of the
opposition was that the empire was virtually ruled by a woman,
and that Jahāngīr was disgracefully subservient to his wife.
Mahābat Khān, though he sacrificed his own advancement, persistently ventilated this view. The bug-bear of the palace party
was the much-loved Khusraw, whose sight was not so impaired
as to disqualify him for the throne, and whose claim to the succession was strenuously advocated by the opposition. The palace
party's dread was Jahāngīr's inconquerable affection for his son
in spite of his delinquencies, and no efforts were spared to alienate
him from the prince. For a long time Nūr Jahān found her
husband inexorable on this point, and in 1613 Khusraw was
allowed considerable liberty, and was favourably received at
court, but a year later Nūr Jahān succeeded in obtaining the
revocation of the orders in his favour, and, late in 1616, persuaded Jahāngīr to commit the unfortunate prince to the custody
of her brother, Āsaf Khān. His fate will be noticed later. The
palace party was later to be disappointed in its own candidate
for the throne, Khurram, the third of Jahāngīr's sons, and the
ablest.

Between Khusraw's rebellion, suppressed in 1605, and Khurram's near the end of the reign, the internal peace of the empire
was disturbed by various wars and rebellions, of which only
the principal need be noticed, the subjection of Mewār, the
pacification of the Deccan, and the subjection of the important
state of Kishtwār, in Kashmīr. But in 1613 the Portuguese
seized off Surat four of Jahāngīr's ships, containing much treasure.
The Portuguese, owing to the superiority of their arms and discipline, were usually successful against the imperial troops on land,
and on the sea there was no power but the English which could
compete with them, for the Muslims were neither seamen nor
warriors when afloat. Early in 1615 Mukarrab Khān, the governor
of Surat, was gratified by the defeat of the Portuguese fleet under
the viceroy, de Azevedo, which was driven from the coasts of
Gujarāt by four English ships under Nicholas Downton, but the
English were ill-rewarded by the conclusion of a treaty in June,
1615, between the Portuguese and Jahāngīr, the avowed object
of which was to keep the English and the Dutch out of India.
Its only result, however, was that Jahāngīr remained at peace
with the Portuguese for the rest of his life.

Bengal was in confusion during the greater part of the reign. 'Usmān, an Afghan chief, made a determined attempt to restore Afghan rule in that province, but his rebellion was suppressed by Shujā'at Khān, an officer under Islām Khān, governor of the province, who had transferred the seat of the local government to Dacca, which he renamed Jahāngīrnagar. In March, 1612, Shujā'at Khān defeated 'Usmān, who did not survive the battle. The remaining Afghans submitted, and this was the last Afghan rebellion in Bengal. Further operations against the Maghs of Arakan were less successful. But though the Afghans had been finally subdued in Bengal, matters were otherwise on the north-western frontier, where, in 1611, the fanatical Raushanīs rose once more under a leader named Ahdad, and made a surprise attack on Kābul in the absence of the governor, Khān Daurān. The city held out, but Khān Daurān was degraded for his negligence, and the weakness and the dissensions of the imperial officers in the Kābul province encouraged the fanatics, and their rebellion was not crushed for some years. No sooner had it been suppressed than disturbances arose in the trans-Indus district of Bangash. Late in 1617 Mahābat Khān, who, though obnoxious to the palace party, was one of Jahāngīr's best soldiers, was appointed to the government of Kābul to deal with the rebellion in Bangash, but he, though a native of Kābul, had little success in this affair, and Bangash remained in rebellion for the rest of Jahāngīr's reign.

Since the beginning of the reign there had been much desultory warfare in Mewār, the kingdom of the rāna, but without any decisive result. Amar Singh, who in 1597 had succeeded his father Pratāp Singh, would not acknowledge the emperor's supremacy, and Jahāngīr followed his father's policy of harassing him until he should submit. In 1608 Mahābat Khān conducted a campaign in which he was successful in the field, but was unable to reach the remote fastnesses of the Rājputs, who were thus left unsubdued. In 1609 he was succeeded by 'Abdullāh Khān, who pursued a campaign with similar results. Constant hostilities on the borders of the Deccan long prevented the assembly of an army sufficiently strong to reduce the rāna to obedience, but in 1613 Jahāngīr transferred his court to Ajmīr, and appointed his third son, Khurram, to the command of the army assembled for the conquest of Mewār. Early in 1614 Khurram, with a large reinforcement, took command of the army hitherto commanded by 'Azīz Koka. Their relative positions were not precisely defined, and the prince, resenting the old man's assumption that he was his tutor and guardian, at first complained that 'Azīz Koka, notoriously a partisan of Khusraw, was trying to injure his prospects of success, and finally arrested him. Jahāngīr confirmed this action by confining the old man in Gwalior, under the charge of Āsaf Khān, Khusraw was forbidden the court, and although 'Azīz Koka was shortly afterwards released, the family clique was, for the time, triumphant. Khurram proceeded successfully with the campaign, the open country was devastated and laid waste, and supplies were cut off from the gallant Rājputs in their strongholds in the hills. This method of conducting the war produced famine. Amar Singh saw his subjects dying of hunger; he was deserted by many of his followers; and at length his spirit was broken. He offered to acknowledge the sovereignty of the emperor, to wait on Khurram and make submission to him, and to send his son, Karan Singh, to the imperial court. An imperial *farmān* accepting these terms was dispatched to him, and he came forth, made obeisance to Khurram, and was honourably received. Later in the day his son also made obeisance and accompanied Khurram to Jahāngīr's court at Ajmir. Thus Jahāngīr accomplished a task which had defeated Akbar. The rānas of Mewār remained henceforth loyal to the emperors of Tīmūr's house until Aurang-zīb's bigotry drove them into rebellion.

Jahāngīr received Khurram in a manner befitting his great success, and accorded also a generous reception to the son of his defeated foe, who was appointed to high rank in his service and shortly afterwards permitted to return home.

It was at Ajmir that Jahāngīr received the English ambassador, Sir Thomas Roe, who arrived at his court in January, 1616. Roe's object was a reciprocal treaty, assuring the security and freedom of the English in India, but this he failed to obtain. Jahāngīr's counsellors considered such a treaty beneath his dignity, and thought that Roe should be content to receive imperial rescripts and *farmāns*, but with these he was not content, and in September, 1618, he left the court, having failed in his mission.

Rājasthān having been reduced to obedience, the Deccan next engaged Jahāngīr's attention. After the fall of Ahmadnagar and the deportation to Gwalior of the boy-king, Bahādur Nizām

Shāh, a grandson of Burhān Nizām Shāh I had been raised to the throne under the title of Murtazā Nizām Shāh II, but he was a mere puppet, and the real ruler of the state was Malik 'Ambar, an able, active, and warlike African, who transferred the capital of the state to Khirkī, on the site of which Aurangābād now stands.

Malik 'Ambar was the first to bring against the imperial troops the Marātha light horse, of which he recognised the value against a cumbrous and luxurious army. The Marāthas inhabited the country between the Taptī and a line drawn from Chanda to Goa. They were a dominant tribe of landholders, and a Marātha dynasty had ruled this country from late in the twelfth until the end of the thirteenth century. After the conquest of their country by the Muslims many of them retained their holdings, and those who possessed strongholds in the Western Ghauts and between the mountains and the sea submitted only to the most powerful of the Muslim rulers, and when the central authority weakened enjoyed a rude independence. After the disruption of the king-dom of the Bahmanids, many of the greater Marātha landholders entered the service of the Muslim kingdoms, chiefly those of Bījāpur and Ahmadnagar, and rose to high positions in the service of those states. For their troops, chiefly light cavalry, exceedingly mobile and requiring no transport, the unwieldy armies of the emperors were no match. Besides his arms the Marātha horseman carried a blanket, a flap of bread, and perhaps an onion; he had no cumbrous train of elephants, wagons, and pack-animals, nor did his wife and children accompany him. The tactics of the Marātha leaders consisted in the avoidance of pitched battles, but they hung on the flanks and rear of an army on the march, or on the outskirts of a force in camp, or besieging a city, slew stragglers, intercepted convoys and small parties, cut off supplies until the great host was reduced to distress, and dispersed when any attempt was made to force a battle on them. With such tactics the imperial troops were unable to cope.

Malik 'Ambar introduced into the Ahmadnagar kingdom a land-revenue settlement similar to that introduced by Todar Mal into the empire, organised the forces of the kingdom, and freely employed his Marātha auxiliaries. Since the death of Dāniyāl a state of war had almost continuously prevailed between the remnant of the Ahmadnagar kingdom and the officers holding commands on the southern frontier of the empire. These officers were jealous of one another, quarrelsome, and not always entirely loyal. Military posts in Berar, Khāndesh, and the imperial province of Ahmadnagar often changed hands without apparently sufficient reason, and 'Ambar stoutly held his own. In 1608 the Khānkhānān was appointed to the command of the imperial provinces in the Deccan, but was unable to control the insubordinate local officers, and in 1610 Parvīz, Jahāngīr's second son, then aged twenty, was appointed to the chief command, but contented himself with holding a court at Burhānpur while the Khānkhānān carried on the government. In the same year Pīr Khān Lodī, entitled Khānjahān, was sent to the Deccan with large reinforcements of Rājputs and others, and arrived to find that the Khānkhānān had suffered a severe reverse, and that 'Ambar had recovered Ahmadnagar. The Khānkhānān was recalled to court in disgrace. In 1611 'Abdullāh Khān, recently successful in Mewār, was appointed to the government of Gujarāt, and ordered to co-operate with the troops in the Deccan, but his campaign against Daulatābād was disastrous, and he was obliged to retire into Gujarāt after suffering heavy losses. In 1612 the Khānkhānān, having been re-appointed, captured and burned Khirkī, and to some extent retrieved the disgrace which the imperial arms had suffered, but he again failed to control his insubordinate officers, and was accused, apparently with reason, of receiving gratifications from the enemy. In the autumn of 1616 Parvīz was transferred from the Deccan to Allāhābād, and Khurram, lately successful in Mewār, was appointed to the command in the Deccan, while Jahāngīr moved his court from Ajmir to Māndū, in order to be near the seat of war.

Khurram, after crossing the Nerbudda, sent missions to 'Ambar and his ally, Ibrāhīm 'Ādil Shāh II of Bījāpur, proposing peace on the terms of the retrocession of the imperial territory annexed by 'Ambar, and a promise to pay tribute regularly in future. The approach of Khurram's great army and Jahāngīr's advance to Māndū overawed the allies, each of whom suspected that the other had been corrupted by imperial gold, and in October, 1617, after the conclusion of the treaties, Khurram returned to Māndū. He was then at the height of his fame. He was promoted to the command of 30,000 horse, a rank never before conferred, and received the title of Shāhjahān, or 'King of the World'.

Jahāngīr was thus free to leave Māndū, and set out on a tour through Gujarāt, a province which he had not yet visited. There, like his father, he first saw the sea, but he was not, like Mahmūd of Ghaznī, favourably impressed with the climate of the province, for a severe epidemic of influenza prevailed, and bubonic plague also was rife, and in August, 1617, he set out for Āgra. On October 24, at Dohad, a third son, Aurangzīb, was born to Shāhjahān of his wife, Mumtāz Mahal. Jahāngīr continued his journey by leisurely stages, but, after reaching Āgra, found that the plague was rife there also, and moved his court to Sīkrī until the early autumn of 1619.

The district of Kishtwār, geographically a part of the province of Kashmīr, had retained its independence even after the conquest of the former kingdom by Akbar's officers, and more than one governor had failed in the attempt to reduce its ruler to obedience. Dilāvar Khān was governor of Kashmīr, and in 1620, after an arduous campaign, he brought the raja in chains before Jahāngīr. But later in the year the oppression of the governor again roused the people; the imperial garrison was annihilated, and Jahāngīr was obliged to send an army to quell the revolt. The first officer sent in command of the troops was unable to crush the rebels, and Irādat Khān was appointed governor, and suppressed the rebellion for the time, but two years later the people again rose, and it was not until 1622 that the district was finally pacified and effectively garrisoned.

Jahāngīr had for some time contemplated the reduction of the strong fortress of Kāngra, which Akbar had been unable to capture, but Suraj Mal, to whom the enterprise had been intrusted at the instance of the family clique, played him false. Bikramājīt, however, who had been appointed Suraj Mal's lieutenant, captured both Suraj Mal and the raja of Chamba, with whom he had taken refuge, and on November 16, 1620, after a siege of fourteen months, compelled the garrison of Kāngra to surrender the fortress. In 1621 Jahāngīr visited it, and asserted the supremacy of Islam by causing a bullock to be slaughtered and a mosque built within the fortress.

The family clique was now approaching dissolution. Jahāngīr's health was failing, and Nūr Jahān could not endure the thought of surrendering the reins of government, which she had held for some time, to a masterful successor. Originally she and her brother, Āsaf Khān, had been united in supporting the claims of Shāhjahān, the latter's son-in-law, but the manner of this prince's conduct of the tasks committed to him, the conquest of Rājasthān, and the restoration of peace in the Deccan, had made it perfectly clear that he was not the man to submit to petticoat government, and Nūr Jahān consequently turned her eyes elsewhere. She had a daughter, Lādīlī Begum, by her first husband, whom she was prepared to bestow on the candidate selected by her. She seems to have had some idea at first of choosing Khusraw, but he was a strict monogamist and negotiations never proceeded far with him. Parvīz, the second son, was a hopeless drunkard, without his father's constitution, and it appeared unlikely that he would outlive Jahāngīr. The only son left was the youngest, Shāhryār, a docile and feeble-minded youth of sixteen, just the instrument, in short, that Nūr Jahān needed. This marriage caused a rift in the clique. Āsaf Khān was too astute to quarrel openly with his powerful sister, but he was naturally unwilling, both from personal and loyal motives, to prefer her feeble son-in-law to his own, who had proved his ability to command and rule. Shortly after the marriage the clique was further weakened by the death of 'Ismat Begum and of her husband, the parents of Nūr Jahān and Āsaf Khān.

Three parties thus emerged at court, the partisans of the virtuous Khusraw, still believed to be his father's favourite, those of Shāhjahān, who could count at least on the secret support of the minister, Āsaf Khān, and those of Shāhryār consisting of Nūr Jahān and her personal adherents, who were prepared to sacrifice the interests of the empire to her ambition.

In 1620 the imperial troops were again hard pressed in the Deccan. Ahmadnagar was besieged, and the Khānkhānān was obliged to appeal to court for aid. Shāhjahān was obviously the right man to be sent to restore order, but Jahāngīr was still ailing, and, if he died during the prince's absence in the south, it was almost certain that Khusraw's partisans would succeed in raising him to the throne. Shāhjahān therefore made the delivery of his eldest brother into his charge a condition of his accepting the command. To this Nūr Jahān raised no objection, as compliance with Shāhjahān's demand entailed the absence of her candidate's two rivals; but Jahāngīr must have known that the surrender of Khusraw to his younger brother was almost equivalent to a sentence of death. The crisis in the Deccan, however, was acute, and Shāhjahān, bidding farewell to his father at Lahore, carried his unfortunate brother with him. He drove the troops of Ahmadnagar across the Nerbudda, caused them to raise the siege of Burhānpur and evacuate all the imperial posts which they had occupied, and to retire to Daulatābād, where Malik 'Ambar submitted to him, and the three kingdoms of the Deccan were obliged to pay an indemnity amounting with arrears of tribute to five millions of rupees.

Shāhjahān was occupied for some months in reorganising the administration of the recovered territories, and in August, 1621, on receiving news of his father's serious illness, caused Khusraw to be strangled at Burhānpur, and, after a time, reported to Jahāngīr that he had died of colic. The emperor affected to believe the falsehood, but Nūr Jahān neglected no opportunity of arousing his wrath against the murderer.

At this moment the empire was attacked from without. In 1606 the Persians had failed to capture Kandahār, but in March, 1622, Shāh 'Abbās the Great marched against that fortress and captured it after a siege of forty-five days. Jahāngīr made strenuous efforts at first to relieve and afterwards to recover the fortress. A mighty army with a siege-train was assembled at Multān, and Shāhjahān was bidden to hasten northwards and assume command. He marched as far as Māndū, but there halted, and perceiving that a campaign in Persia would be more arduous than the operations in the Deccan, refused to proceed farther unless the government of the Panjab were conferred upon him. Meanwhile he sent a force to occupy the fief of Dholpur, for which he had applied some time before, and his officers ousted those of Shāhryār, on whom the fief had already been bestowed. Nūr Jahān was furious, insisted that he was already in rebellion, and caused his fiefs in the north to be transferred to Shāhryār, who had already been appointed to the command of the army of Kandahār. Shāhjahān's agent informed him that Nūr Jahān was supreme at court, and the prince, in despair, rose in rebellion, and marched on Āgra with a view to securing the imperial treasury there. The gates of Fathpur Sīkrī were shut against him, but Āgra was plundered.

Nūr Jahān was seriously alarmed. She distrusted her brother, Āsaf Khān, who was Shāhjahān's father-in-law, and caused her

husband to summon from Kābul her old enemy, Mahābat Khān.
The imperial army, numbering, with the contingent from Kābul,
25,000 horse, then marched from Lahore to crush the rebellion,
Jahāngīr and Nūr Jahān accompanying it. Shāhjahān had
marched to Kotala[1] to meet it, and met it at Biloshpur, twenty-nine
miles north-east of that town, on March 29, 1623, and although
'Abdullāh Khān deserted to the prince with 10,000 horse, the
imperial army under Mahābat Khān was victorious, and the
rebels retired towards Māndū. Jahāngīr was joined at Hindaun
by his son Parvīz, who had been summoned from Bihār, but it
was not until May that two imperial forces, one nominally under
the command of Parvīz, but actually under that of Mahābat Khān,
and the other nominally under the command of Bulāki, Khusraw's
son, but actually under that of his grandfather, 'Azīz Koka,
marched, the first against Māndū, where Shāhjahān had taken
refuge, and the second into Gujarāt, to secure that province. At
the same time Jahāngīr moved his court to Ajmīr.

Before Māndū, Shāhjahān was again defeated by Parvīz and
Mahābat Khān, and his lieutenant, 'Abdullāh Khān, was driven
from Gujarāt. The prince fled across the Nerbudda and found an
asylum in the fortress of Asīr, to which he was admitted, but his
army gradually dwindled away, and when Malik 'Ambar refused
him an asylum, and the Khānkhānān, who had supported him,
deserted to Parvīz, he retired into the kingdom of Golconda,
marched eastward, and on November 10 entered Orissa. The
imperial officers in Bengal and Orissa, unaware of his movements,
were unprepared for him, and Ahmad Beg fled from Orissa and
joined Ibrāhīm Khān, brother of Nūr Jahān, in Bengal. The
Portuguese of Hugli refused to assist the rebel; but some of the
landholders and imperial officers joined him; the strong fortress
of Bardwān was surrendered to 'Abdullāh Khān; and Ibrāhīm
Khān, after holding out for some time at Rājmahal, was defeated
and slain. Rāja Bhīm took the fortress of Patna from the deputy
of Parvīz, and the landholders of Bihār, among them the commander of the strong fortress of Rohtās, submitted to the rebel
prince. Shāhjahān, having thus established his authority in Bengal,
Bihār, and Orissa, prepared to annex the provinces of Oudh and
Allāhābād, and 'Abdullāh Khān and Rāja Bhīm proceeded with
a flotilla against the fortress of Allāhābād, while Daryā Khān

[1] Situated 28° N. and 76° 57′ E.

the Afghan led a force to Mānikpur, higher up the river. The prince occupied Jaunpur, and encamped in the forests to the east of that city.

Meanwhile Parvīz and Mahābat Khān had left Burhānpur during the rainy season, had marched rapidly eastwards to deal with the rebels, and had arrived in the doāb. 'Abdullāh Khān raised the siege of Allāhābād, and the flotilla which had been taken to that place at Mahābat Khān's instigation deserted the prince and returned to Bengal, leaving him without supplies and transport. Shāhjahān's numbers had been raised to 10,000 horse by the arrival of Daryā Khān from Patna, but he was in no condition to meet Mahābat Khān, whose force numbered 40,000, and a rapid retreat into Bihar would have been the only wise course to follow. But the prince, misled by his Rājput commander, Bhīm, sanctioned an attack on the imperial forces, and not only was defeated, with the loss of all his artillery, but narrowly escaped capture. He fled to Rohtās, deserted by Daryā Khān, and having recovered his baggage and munitions from Rājmahal, returned to the Deccan by the route by which he had left it.

Ahmadnagar being again at war with Bījāpur, Malik 'Ambar was glad to obtain the aid of Shāhjahān, both in this conflict and in his renewed struggle with the empire. The prince marched to the aid of Ya'kūb Khān the African, who was besieging Burhānpur, but the return of Mahābat Khān from Bengal compelled the allies to raise the siege, and Shāhjahān, sick in mind and body, and no longer able to continue the strife, retired to Rohankhed, and wrote to his father, beseeching him to pardon him. Parvīz, believing that his brother would never recover his former status, and slothfully eager for peace, and Nūr Jahān, alarmed by the increasing power of her old enemy, Mahābat Khān, did not oppose the rebel's petition; and Shāhjahān, having sent two of his sons, Dārā and Aurangzīb, to court as hostages, and caused his agents to surrender to imperial officers the fortresses of Rohtās and Asīr, was permitted to retire to Nasik.

The civil war had lasted for three years, during which the empire was in confusion, many districts in the Deccan had been lost, and no attempt to recover the important province of Kandahār had been possible; the question of the succession still remained unsettled, and yet more trouble was to follow. Jahāngīr's health was breaking, Shāhjahān's disgrace and humiliation had

removed him temporarily from the field, and the credit gained
by Parvīz for the suppression of his brother's rebellion, due really
to Mahābat Khān, had brought him temporarily to the front.
He was a worthless drunkard, but at the age of thirty-six with
much experience of war and administration, he might become,
with Mahābat Khān's support, a formidable rival of the weakling
Shāhryār. Parvīz was ordered to remain at Burhānpur, as nominal
governor of the Deccan, with Khānjahān Lodī as his adviser and
preceptor; and Mahābat Khān was summoned to court to render
an account of the profit which he had made by the suppression
of the rebellion in Bengal. He set out from the Deccan for the
imperial court, well aware of the originator of the insulting
summons, and he reached the court on the southern bank of the
Jhelum, as it was on its way from Lahore to Kābul in the spring
of 1626. With him was his force of four or five thousand Rājputs.
The imperial army and the leading courtiers had been sent across
the river in the daytime, and Jahāngīr, Nūr Jahān, and a small
personal escort remained on the southern bank, intending to
cross in the morning; but Mahābat Khān sent a force to hold
the bridge, and surrounded Jahāngīr with his Rājputs and made
him his prisoner. The enraged emperor had no opportunity of
escape or resistance; but his wife escaped across the river in
disguise, and on the following day drew up the army, and
attempted, with her brother, to lead it across the river to the
rescue of Jahāngīr. The Rājputs, however, had burned the bridge,
the river was in flood, and the attempt failed. The court continued
its march to Kābul, but Jahāngīr was closely guarded by Mahābat
Khān's Rājputs. Āsaf Khān fled to Attock, and attempted to hold
that fortress against Mahābat Khān; but Mahābat Khān had become dictator of the empire, and Āsaf Khān was obliged to
surrender, on the promise that his life should be spared. On
May 18, 1626, the court reached Kābul. Jahāngīr, Nūr Jahān
and Āsaf Khān were prisoners in Mahābat Khān's hands, and the
emperor accepted the situation lest worse should befall him. But
Mahābat Khān's situation was far from secure. A quarrel occurred between some of the royal troops and his Rājputs, and
the royal troops raised the Afghans of the city against the misbelievers. Many of the Rājputs, including their most prominent
leaders, were slain, and many more were captured and sold into
slavery beyond the Hindu Kush. Mahābat Khān, considerably
weakened, was lulled into security by Jahāngīr's assurances that

he was perfectly happy under his charge, and Nūr Jahān intrigued unceasingly for the release of herself and her husband. At Rohtās Jahāngīr ordered Mahābat Khān to precede him by one march, and the dictator did not dare to disobey. From that moment his power was gone, and his brief reign was at an end. After some hesitation he surrendered his prisoners, Āsaf Khān and the sons of Dāniyāl, the emperor's late brother, and, in obedience to Jahāngīr's orders, left Rohtās for Tatta in Sind, then menaced by Shāhjahān, but in fact for Mewār, where he took refuge for some time.

Early in June, 1626, Shāhjahān had left the Deccan with a thousand horse, ostensibly for the purpose of freeing his father, but when Jahāngīr had, with his wife's help, freed himself, he marched on to Tatta, and as he had lost half of his small force on his way, by the death of its leader, he turned his thoughts towards a design of fleeing into Persia and taking refuge with Shāh 'Abbās. He was loth, however, to leave the garrison of Tatta behind him, lest it should pursue him, and therefore made an attempt to reduce that fortress, but its defences had been recently restored, and it was held by a partisan of Nūr Jahān. After a futile attempt to take the fort he retired again to the Deccan by way of Gujarāt and Berar. On his way he learned that his brother, Parvīz, had died of drink, and thus no longer stood in his way. He continued his retreat to the Deccan, and selected Junnār as his residence. There he received from Mahābat Khān, a fugitive in Rājasthān, an offer of support, which he gladly accepted. On receiving this news Nūr Jahān directed Khānjahān Lodī, commanding the imperial troops in the Deccan, to crush the rebellion which she apprehended, but he did nothing.

In March, 1627, the court moved from Lahore to Kashmīr, but Jahāngīr nearly died on the way thither. He recovered for a time, but suffered from asthma, and lost his appetite. At the same time his son, Shāhryār, was attacked by alopecia, and lost all his hair, which rendered him a ridiculous object among men who believed that a man's chief honour lay in the luxuriance of his beard and whiskers. Jahāngīr was advised by his physicians to return to the warm climate of the plains, and set out for Lahore, but grew rapidly feebler, and on November 7, 1627, died near Bhīmbar, in the fifty-eighth year of his age.

The struggle for the throne which then began will be described in the account of Shāhjahān's reign.

CHAPTER XI

Shāhjahān

On the death of Jahāngīr, Āsaf Khān, ever a secret partisan of his own son-in-law, whose claim, he discovered, was supported by nearly all the nobles in the imperial camp, placed his sister under restraint and sent an urgent message to Shāhjahān, but as the prince was in the Deccan, and Shāhryār was certain to have himself proclaimed in Lahore, he was obliged, in order to avoid taking up arms against a titular emperor, to raise to the throne the unfortunate Bulāki, son of Khusraw, and, proclaiming him under the title of Dāvar Bakhsh, used him as a figure-head until he should be able to proclaim Shāhjahān. He then, with Dāvar Bakhsh, marched on Lahore a day's march ahead of Nūr Jahān. Shāhryār, as he had anticipated, had seized the imperial treasure in Lahore, caused himself to be proclaimed emperor, and distributed largesse to his troops, whom he sent immediately against Āsaf Khān. They were defeated, and their master retired into the citadel, but was betrayed by his own followers, dragged forth from the female apartments, compelled to do homage to Dāvar Bakhsh, and then imprisoned and blinded. On December 7, 1627, Shāhjahān set out from Junnār, and on January 9, 1628, was proclaimed emperor in Lahore, while, in accordance with orders received from him, Dāvar Bakhsh,[1] Shāhryār, and Dāniyāl's sons were put to death. On February 2, Shāhjahān entered Lahore in state, acclaimed by all as emperor. Āsaf Khān was made minister, and retained that office until his death in 1641. Nūr Jahān was allowed to live in retirement on a sufficiently liberal pension until her death on December 18, 1645. She had ruled the empire for ten years, but on her husband's death her power ceased.

Shāhjahān, all possible rivals having been removed, left Lahore, and in February took his seat on the throne in Āgra. His position

---

[1] Some years afterwards a man styling himself Bulāki, the son of Khusraw, was generally acknowledged in Persia as the prince who had been enthroned as Dāvar Bakhsh by Āsaf Khān, but there is little doubt that he was an impostor.

was secure and unchallenged, but the affairs of the empire sorely needed attention. The Afghan Pīr Lodī, entitled Khānjahān, who had for some time been governor of the southern provinces of the empire, had displayed hostility to him when he left Junnār on his way northwards to assert his claim to the throne, believing that he would never be able to overcome the opposition of Nūr Jahān. He had since betrayed his trust, in surrendering to Murtazā Nizām Shāh II, for a heavy bribe, the southern highlands of Berar. Shāhjahān had punished him by transferring him from the government of the Deccan to that of Mālwā, appointing Irādat Khān to the Deccan in his place, and summoning the Afghan to court.

Jhujhār Singh of Orchha, too, presuming on the latitude which had been allowed to his father, Bīr Singh, in consideration of the murder of Abul Fazl, had shown a rebellious and turbulent spirit, and had encroached on the domains, not only of his humbler neighbours, but of the emperor himself. He was, after some resistance, subdued, captured, and pardoned. Meanwhile Khānjahān had been detained at Āgra, and, though he had received a formal pardon, he remained conscious of his guilt, and apprehensive of his master's intentions towards him. At length, secretly assembling his Afghan contingent, he fled by night from the capital towards the Deccan. He was pursued, overtaken, and severely defeated on the Chambal, but succeeded in escaping and in making his way, with a considerable part of his force, to the Deccan, where he entered the service of Murtazā Nizām Shāh II, who conferred fiefs upon him and upon his principal followers. This reinforcement enabled Murtazā once more to expel the imperial officers from their posts in the Bālāghāt, and so serious was the situation that Shāhjahān resolved to proceed to the Deccan in person, and, on March 1, 1630, arrived at Burhānpur. Irādat Khān, governor of the Deccan, received the title of A'zam Khān, and under his command the imperial army at once assumed the offensive, and invaded the Bālāghāt in three great columns. Hostilities continued until the rainy season, when they were necessarily suspended, and on their resumption, at the beginning of the cold season, Murtazā, seeing the remnant of his kingdom devastated by the imperial troops, changed his attitude towards Khānjahān, who had brought this misfortune upon him. Khānjahān fled, with his surviving sons, from Daulatābād into Mālwā, hoping to be able to reach the Panjab and to raise trouble there. From Mālwā he turned aside into Bundelkhand. Being driven thence, he was pursued by various imperial officers, and was at length overtaken and slain on the banks of the Sind, the principal affluent of the Chambal.

On June 16, 1631, Shāhjahān suffered the great bereavement of his life, when his dearly-loved wife, Mumtāz Mahal, the mother of nearly all his children, died in childbirth. He mourned her deeply, and, wearying of his sojourn in the Deccan, returned early in the following year to Āgra, and there began the erection of the noblest mausoleum in the world, to which her body was removed, and which now covers his remains as well as hers.

Hostilities still continued in the Deccan. Mahābat Khān, son of the old Khānkhānān, was appointed governor of the imperial province, and early in 1633 appeared before Daulatābād, the siege of which had already been opened by Sayyid Khānjahān, who had received the title formerly held by Pīr Lodī. The fortress was held by Fath Khān, who having put to death the *roi fainéant*, Murtazā, had raised to the throne his younger son, Husain III, and endured a siege of four months, though unable to obtain supplies from the famine-stricken land around it. Attempts were made by the army of Bījāpur and by traitors in the imperial camp to save what had become the frontier-fortress of the independent Deccan by conveying victuals to the garrison, but Fath Khān was compelled to surrender, and on June 28, 1633, came forth with his family and the young king Husain, "and the nine forts of Daulatābād, whereof five are on the plain and four on the slopes of the hill, with many guns and other material of war, lead, powder, grenades, and rockets, fell into the hands of the leaders of the host of the glorious empire". No conqueror till then had been able "to cast the noose of contrivance over the battlement of subjection". The young king Husain was conveyed to Gwalior, where he must have met his kinsman, interned there nearly thirty years earlier by Akbar.

While yet in the Deccan, Shāhjahān had ordered Kāsim Khān to drive the Portuguese from their settlement at Hugli. The Portuguese in Bengal had their chief settlements at Chittagong and Hugli, far removed from the authority of the viceroy at Goa; and their conduct did little credit to their nation. Chittagong was little better than a nest of pirates, and the 200 Portuguese at Hugli owned no fewer than 600 Indian slaves, most of whom they had persuaded or compelled to be baptised into the Christian faith. Over and above these offences, Shāhjahān had personal wrongs to avenge on them. They had refused to aid him when he was in rebellion against his father; they were said to have enticed away two of his wife's serving-maids and converted them to Christianity; and some reverses which his troops had lately suffered from the Bījāpur forces were attributed by him to the assistance of Portuguese gunners from Goa. Kāsim Khān began his preparations in March, 1631, but did not venture to attack the factory until June, 1632. The small body of Portuguese defended themselves valiantly until September 29, when Kāsim Khān carried the place by assault. The survivors of the conflict were sent prisoners to Āgra, to be confined until they accepted Islam; but comparatively few purchased their freedom by apostasy. A few had contrived to escape, and encamped on an island opposite to their old factory. There they remained until 1643, when they were carried away in ships sent by the viceroy from Goa.

In August, 1633, Shāhjahān fell sick at Āgra, and early in the following year left that city for Lahore, visited Kashmīr in the summer, and did not return to Āgra until the spring of 1635, having in the meantime appointed his second son, Sultān Shujāʿ, then seventeen years of age, viceroy of the Deccan, which was divided into the Bālāghāt and Pāʾīnghāt, or highland and lowland divisions. Jhujhār Singh of Orchha, who, having done good service with the imperial troops in the Deccan, had received permission to return to his state, took advantage of Shāhjahān's absence from his capital to attack Rāja Prem Nārāyan of Chaurāgarh, and, disregarding orders sent by the emperor, compelled the raja to surrender, and then treacherously attacked and slew him. Shāhjahān meanly offered him forgiveness in return for the surrender of his plunder, but Jhujhār rejected the offer, and only when the emperor sent a strong force against him was he intimidated into accepting it. But Shāhjahān's terms had then risen. Jhujhār prepared to resist. But, when the imperial forces, under the nominal command of Aurangzīb, Shāhjahān's third son, approached Chaurāgarh, he abandoned the fortress and fled towards the Deccan. Aurangzīb was then recalled to court, but his officers pursued and captured Jhujhār, who escaped, but was slain by the Gonds, his head being sent to court. His sons were

forced to accept Islam; his wives were left to the nobles who
had captured them; his treasures were unearthed and sent to
court; the temples of Bundelkhand were destroyed; and the state
of Orchha ceased for a time to exist. Another campaign during
this year was less successful, when a large force under Najābat
Khān invaded Garhwāl, and was cut off, almost to a man, in
the hills.

Despite the successes of Mahābat Khān, Sayyid Khānjahān,
and Khān Daurān, things were not going well in the Deccan.
The fall of Daulatābād had thoroughly alarmed Muhammad
'Ādil Shāh of Bījāpur and 'Abdullāh Kutb Shāh of Golconda.
The former, who had done his best to relieve the beleaguered
fortress, was still at war with the imperial troops, and much disorder prevailed even in the nominally extinct kingdom of
Ahmadnagar. Malik 'Ambar had given the Marāthas an opportunity of discovering that their old prowess was not dead; and,
on the fall of Daulatābād, Shāhjī Bhonsla, one of the leading
fief-holders, produced a scion of the royal house of Ahmadnagar,
and proclaimed him king. In 1635, therefore, Shāhjahān decided
again to visit the Deccan, arrived at Daulatābād in the spring of
1636, and at once sent envoys bearing letters of warning both to
Muhammad 'Ādil Shāh and to 'Abdullāh Kutb Shāh. The latter
sent a submissive reply, which was regarded as satisfactory; but
the former, who had annexed some of the southern districts of
the kingdom of Ahmadnagar, was less compliant. Four imperial
armies then took the field, two against Shāhjī and two against
Muhammad 'Ādil Shāh. These last two armies devastated the
Bījāpur state, menaced its capital, and compelled Muhammad to
sue for peace, and, shortly after learning of this, Shāhjī, many of
whose forts had been captured, and in one of them his puppet
king, offered to enter the imperial service, but was told that he
might, if he chose, enter that of Bījāpur. The young prince was
sent to join his kinsmen in Gwalior, and Muhammad 'Ādil Shāh,
on accepting the position of a vassal and promising to pay tribute
regularly, was allowed to retain some of the northern districts of
the former kingdom of Ahmadnagar. Peace having been thus
restored in the Deccan, Shāhjahān left the province, and in July,
1636, reached Māndū, where he spent the rainy season. The unwieldy province of the Deccan was divided into four provinces:
(1) Ahmadnagar with Daulatābād, (2) Khāndesh, (3) Berar, and

(4) Telingāna. The viceroyalty of the four provinces was conferred by Shāhjahān on Aurangzīb, then eighteen years of age. After the rainy season the emperor left Māndū for Ajmīr, and in January, 1637, returned to Āgra.

Early in 1638 a stroke of good luck, little merited by one who had refused to obey his father's command to attempt the recovery of the city and the province of Kandahār, befell Shāhjahān. 'Alī Mardān Khān, the Persian governor of Kandahār, had been summoned to court by his bloodthirsty master, Shāh Safī, and, having learned that the shah sought his life, entered into correspondence with the governors of the Indian provinces of Kābul and Multān, and of the city of Ghaznī; and on March 8, 'Iwāz Khān, governor of Ghaznī, was admitted with his troops into Kandahār, and the khūtba was recited in the name of Shāhjahān. Kilīj Khān, governor of Multān, was appointed to the government of the new province of the empire, and supplies, treasure, and reinforcements, under the nominal command of Sultān Shujā', were hastily pushed into Kandahār. An attempt by a force from Khurāsān and some discontented troops of the former garrison to recover the city was defeated. As the reward of his treachery 'Alī Mardān Khān received a hundred thousand rupees, the command of 5000 horse, and the title of Amīr-ul-Umarā, and was ordered to remain at Kābul for the time, and to be ready to march to the relief of Kandahār should any attempt be made to recover it.

Elsewhere the empire was not at peace. The governor of Bengal, through no fault of his own, became involved in war with the Āhom king of Assam, the imperial troops were driven from Kāmrūp, and the war lasted for two years, with great loss of life and treasure. In 1639, after Shāhjahān had left Āgra for Lahore, Champat Rai rose in rebellion in the ever-turbulent province of Bundelkhand. Various officers were sent against him, but it was not until 1642, when Shāhjahān sent Pahār Singh, a son of Bīr Singh, into Bundelkhand, and permitted him to take charge of the state of Orchha, that order was restored, and even then but imperfectly. Between Kābul and the Panjāb, the Khattaks of the Bangash had been constantly giving trouble, but Jagat Singh of Nūrpur succeeded in repressing them, and later, in 1650, the equally turbulent Yūsufzais were reduced to order, and from that time onward the constant movement of troops between the

Panjab, Kābul, and Kandahār compelled the tribes to keep the peace. After dealing with the Khattaks, Jagat Singh was permitted, in 1640, to return to Nūrpur, where his son, Rājrūp, was in rebellion, but after his return he himself rebelled, and the imperial officers sent against him were unable to reduce him to obedience. In the same year Murād Bakhsh, Shāhjahān's fourth son, was placed in charge of the operations against him, and in 1642 he submitted, was pardoned, and remained ever afterwards a loyal subject and servant of the emperor.

In 1641 Shāhjahān suffered a severe loss by the death of his minister and father-in-law, Āsaf Khān. Āsaf Khān's sister and Shāhjahān's old enemy, Nūr Jahān, survived until December, 1645, but lived in retirement, and never again caused him trouble.

In March, 1644, a lighted candle caught the dress of Shāhjahān's daughter, Jahānārā, and she was so severely burned that for some time her life was in grave danger. As she lay between life and death, her brothers were permitted to leave the seats of their provincial government and visit her. In view of later events the characters of these brothers, and their relations one with another, begin to be important. Dārā Shikūh, the eldest, was his father's favourite and lived almost constantly at court, being permitted to perform by deputy the duties of the high appointments which he held in the provinces. The favour of his father, who had nominated him as his heir, probably increased the natural violence and arrogance of his temper, and encouraged the airs of superiority which rendered him odious to his brothers. Shujā', the second son, was of a more pleasing and conciliatory disposition, but was devoted to sensual pleasure and lacked determination, promptitude of decision, and force of character. Aurangzīb, the third, unquestionably the ablest of the brothers, was astute, determined, and unscrupulous. Murād Bakhsh, the fourth, was a simple soldier and nothing more. All four were physically brave, but if there were any distinction he was perhaps the bravest. But he was a drunkard, headstrong, passionate, brutal, and brainless. Religious differences aggravated the animosity between the brothers. Dārā, like his father, professed the Sunni religion, and practised its rites; but he was known to be deeply interested in Ṣūfī-ism; like his great-grandfather, he delighted in religious discussion; and he was suspected of an inclination to Christianity, to which, according to Manucci, he desired to be converted before his death. Shujā' was strongly inclined towards the Shiah form of Islam, and Murād was suspected of an inclination towards that faith, but seems to have been little troubled by religion in any form. Aurangzīb was an orthodox and bigoted Sunni, who firmly believed and rigidly practised all the rites and ordinances of his faith. To Dārā he was "the prayer-monger", as Dārā was to him "the infidel", and the prayer-monger had little difficulty in persuading his other brothers that Dārā was no Muslim, while Dārā's attitude to all did nothing to conciliate them.

At this time Aurangzīb fell into disgrace, was deprived of his appointment in the Deccan, and retired into private life. The true cause of his father's displeasure has not been disclosed, but it is not true, as has sometimes been stated, that Aurangzīb's retirement was voluntary, and that in an access of religious zeal he resolved to cut himself off from worldly affairs and devote himself to religion. There can be little doubt but that his eldest brother was at the bottom of the trouble, and inflamed his father's wrath against Aurangzīb. Jahānārā, however, recovered from her burns, and on her recovery effected a reconciliation between her father and his third son, but Aurangzīb received the government of Gujarāt, a post far less important than the vice-royalty of the four provinces of the Deccan. He pocketed the slight and left for Gujarāt.

The house of Tīmūr regarded Transoxiana as its ancestral home, and, ever since Bābur's expulsion from Farghāna, had longed to recover the original domain of its great ancestor; but this longing had remained no more than a dream. Bābur had been fully occupied in establishing himself first in Kābul and then in Āgra. His son was driven from his kingdom, and, though he eventually recovered it, left to his son Akbar little more than the ground covered by his troops. Akbar was occupied throughout his long reign in extending and consolidating his Indian dominions. Rājasthān, the Deccan, and his son's rebellion gave the slothful Jahāngīr all the occupation which he needed. An elusive prospect of recovering Transoxiana was reserved for Shāhjahān. The quarrels of the Jānids, who had succeeded the Shaibānids on the throne of that land, tempted him to intervene: Nasr Muhammad, governor of Balkh, had expelled his blind brother from Samarkand, and had, in his turn, been expelled in

favour of his son, 'Abd-ul-'azīz. In 1645 Asālat Khān was sent
to Kābul, there to concert with 'Alī Mardān Khān measures for
the conquest of Badakhshān and Balkh, with a view to that of
Transoxiana. The two officers invaded Badakhshān, and in 1646
Nasr Muhammad unwittingly played into Shāhjahān's hands by
seeking his aid to recover Samarkand from 'Abd-ul-'azīz. Shāhjahān consented, and appointed his youngest son, Murād Bakhsh,
to the command of the army of the north. The youth was slothful,
but, urged on by his father, traversed Badakhshān. As he approached Balkh, Nasr Muhammad, suspecting his intentions,
fled from that city into Persia. The prince took the first step
towards the recovery of Transoxiana by occupying Balkh, and
then, to the disgust of his father, who intended to appoint him
to the viceroyalty of Transoxiana, demanded permission to return. Neither he nor his officers could maintain order in their
conquests. The tribal organisation of the bitterly hostile Uzbegs
was beyond their understanding and control. Nothing was to
be gained by keeping the prince in Balkh against his will, and
Shāhjahān was obliged to allow him to return. Aurangzīb was
then summoned from Gujarāt, and appointed to the government
of Balkh. His troops were attacked by those of 'Abd-ul-'azīz,
but, though he defeated the enemy in the field more than once,
his administration was no more successful than that of his brother,
and in October, 1642, he too retired from Balkh. Shāhjahān was
not yet an old man, but he had more than once been seriously
ill, and neither prince wished to be far from the capital in the
event of the throne becoming vacant. Nor was this the only
reason for their disgust with their surroundings. They were
degenerate descendants of the hardy warrior who had led his
troops from the north to the conquest first of Kābul and then of
India. The icy passes of the Hindu Kush and the bitter cold of
the mountain-homes of their fathers had little attraction for
"pale persons in muslin petticoats" whose idea of campaigning
was leisurely progress over a sunny plain with a city of canvas
palaces. The dream of recovering the land of their fathers faded,
to Shāhjahān's great disappointment, but he learned at length
that the current of the historical stream of conquest could not be
turned backwards in its course.

Although Delhi had never lost its official status as the imperial
capital, "Abode of the Caliphate", Āgra had been the residential

capital of the Timurid monarchs ever since the days of Bābur. It had been greatly enriched, and adorned by Akbar, who re-named it Akbarābād. His temporary capital, Fathpur Sīkrī, was a mere whim, and before the end of his reign he had ceased to visit it. Of all the princes of his line Shāhjahān was the greatest builder. Many monuments left by him at Āgra, and, above all, the Tāj Mahal, one of the most beautiful buildings in the world, "a great ideal conception which belongs more to sculpture than to architecture", testify to his taste, but failed to satisfy his ambition, for which he found scope in the restoration of imperial Delhi as the first city in his dominions. He had for some time devoted his attention to the revival of its glories, and had laid out, on the western bank of the Jumna, immediately to the north of the older cities of former dynasties, a new city, to which he gave the name of Shāhjahānābād, or the abode of Shāhjahān, and which he adorned with many magnificent buildings, the most conspicuous of which are the imperial palace, with its splendid halls of audience, and the great "gathering mosque", of red sandstone like the palace, with which it is in harmony, but with white marble minarets. In March, 1648, the new city was in-augurated as the capital, and here, seated on the splendid Peacock Throne, which he had had made for himself, the emperor sought consolation for the failure of his attempt to recover the home of his fathers, but was not long left in peace. Shāh 'Abbās II, who had in 1642 succeeded his father on the throne of Persia, was menacing Kandahār, and Shāhjahān would have set out for Kābul at once to send help to the city, had not his slothful nobles dissuaded him from leaving his new capital so soon. Daulat Khān, the governor of Kandahār, was unable to withstand the army of Persia, and was obliged to surrender the fortress. In November Shāhjahān left Delhi, and early in 1649 Aurangzīb, who, after his retreat from Balkh, had been appointed to the province of Multān, was provided with a great army and ordered to recover Kandahār. He claimed one victory over the Persian troops in the field, but on the defences of the city he could make no impression, and in July his father ordered him to retire. In April, 1652, the same prince, at the head of a larger and better-equipped army, was sent to make a second attempt to recover the fortress, but again his artillery was found to be unequal to the task, and in July he retired. These failures embittered the relations

between him and his eldest brother, for Dārā Shikūh taunted him
with his lack of success, and in April, 1653, was himself sent from
Kābul, with an army larger and better found than either of those
commanded by his brother, to make a third attempt. The foolish
prince, as a prelude to the siege, sent to the commander of the
garrison a vainglorious poem, warning him of his approaching
fate, and met with but ridicule in reply. He was no more successful
than Aurangzīb, and in September was recalled by his father.
It was then the younger brother's turn to taunt the elder, and
relations between them became so strained that Aurangzīb was
appointed for the second time to the viceroyalty of the Deccan,
in order that he might be at a distance from court.

The cause of the three failures of the imperial troops to recover
Kandahār was their inferiority to their opponents, who from
constant warfare with the Ottoman Turks and from their instruction and reorganisation by the Sherley brothers in the reign of
'Abbās the Great, had learned much of European methods of
warfare, and particularly of the casting of guns and the use of
artillery. The Indian troops had hardly advanced beyond the use
of irregular cavalry, and their cavalry was not fit to face even
the cavalry, much less the infantry, of the Persians. They had guns,
huge hollow cylinders, with balls of irregular shapes, but they
could seldom be fired, their fire was most inaccurate, owing to
windage, and the Indian troops relied rather on their moral than on
their material effect. Moreover, in each of the successive attempts
to recover Kandahār it became more evident that the Indian
troops were no match in discipline, physique, or courage for
the Persians, and that their artillery, as an engine of war, was
contemptible. Aurangzīb, on arriving in the Deccan for the
second time, took up his residence in Malik 'Ambar's former
capital, Khirkī, which he rebuilt and renamed Aurangābād. His
policy from now onwards was to encroach upon, and, if possible,
to conquer the kingdoms of Bījāpur and Golconda, and so to
enrich himself with their resources as to be in a position to contest
the succession to the throne whenever it should fall vacant. But
grave difficulties stood in his way, for the frontier between the
imperial dominions and the two kingdoms had been determined
by the treaties concluded with them by Shāhjahān in 1636, which
could not be violated without good cause, and Dārā Shikūh
exerted all his influence over his father to induce him to cur-

Aurangzīb's ambition. It was with difficulty, and only after much
delay, that Shāhjahān sanctioned his entering into direct correspondence with the vassal kingdoms, but Aurangzīb, assisted by
a most capable Persian financial adviser, introduced into the
Deccan those administrative reforms which Todar Mal had, in
Akbar's reign, established in northern India, and gradually so
restored prosperity to a country which, on his arrival, had been
incapable of supporting troops sufficient for the maintenance of
order within its boundaries, as to enable it to maintain a force
sufficiently strong and efficient to excite the suspicion and alarm
of Dārā Shikūh.

It was Golconda that Aurangzīb first attacked. The tribute from
that kingdom, which had fallen into arrears, was fixed in gold
hūns, but was payable in rupees. The exchange value of the *hūn*
had risen from four to five rupees, and Aurangzīb demanded
immediate payment of the arrears at the higher rate. This was a
crushing demand, but in addition to it he took 'Abdullāh to task
for having undertaken conquests without the emperor's sanction.
The great kingdom of Vijayanagar, after its overthrow in 1565,
had dissolved into a number of petty Hindu states, in the absorption of which Bījāpur and Golconda had been competing in the
Carnatic, to the south of the Krishnā and the Tungabhadrā. The
chief share had fallen to Bījāpur, but 'Abdullāh's minister,
Muhammad Sa'īd, entitled Mīr Jumla, a rich and capable Persian
adventurer, had conquered a considerable tract of very rich territory, which he ruled virtually as an independent sovereign, remitting no tribute to his master. He retained, however, his post
at court, in which his son, Muhammad Amīn, acted as his deputy,
and treated 'Abdullāh Kutb Shāh with scant courtesy. The feeble
monarch endured much, for he feared both father and son, until
Muhammad Amīn came to court drunk, and vomited over the
king's personal carpet. This was too much, even for 'Abdullāh,
and the offender and his family were thrown into prison, his
property being confiscated. 'Abdullāh had already contemplated
crushing Mīr Jumla, and Mīr Jumla had been in secret correspondence with Aurangzīb. On hearing of his son's imprisonment he offered his services to the emperor, and his letter was
forwarded to Shāhjahān, who, at the end of 1655, informed
Aurangzīb that both Mīr Jumla and his son had been admitted
to the imperial service. 'Abdullāh, unaware of this corre-

spondence, had already refused to release Muhammad Amīn, and Aurangzīb, concealing from his father 'Abdullāh's ignorance of the acceptance of the services of Mīr Jumla and his son, obtained permission to invade the kingdom of Golconda. In January, 1656, he sent his eldest son, Muhammad Sultān, across the frontier with a large force of cavalry, and followed him with the main body of his army. On his way Muhammad Sultān received in his camp Muhammad Amīn and his family, who had been released and sent to him by 'Abdullāh Kutb Shāh, but nevertheless pressed on. 'Abdullāh fled from his capital to the fortress of Golconda, and the prince's army plundered Hyderabad. Aurangzīb himself then appeared on the scene, and prepared to open the siege of Golconda, but meanwhile 'Abdullāh's agent at Delhi had incensed Dārā Shikūh and his sister, Jahānārā Begum, by acquainting them with Aurangzīb's duplicity, and they persuaded their father to issue peremptory orders to Aurangzīb to quit the kingdom of Golconda. He retired in March, but before leaving, had obliged 'Abdullāh to give his second daughter in marriage to his son, and, by a secret agreement, to acknowledge Muhammad Sultān as his heir. Thus the result of the campaign, though bitterly disappointing to Aurangzīb, was not wholly infructuous, for, besides gaining much booty, and the advantages already mentioned, he was joined before he left by Mīr Jumla, with a force of 15,000 cavalry, besides elephants and artillery. Mīr Jumla was sent to court, and after presenting to Shāhjahān most costly gifts, was appointed commander of 6000 horse and chief minister of the empire.

Aurangzīb's return from Golconda was followed by an acrimonious dispute with his father regarding the partition of the tribute, plunder, and indemnity gained from Hyderabad, and the question of Mīr Jumla's conquests in the Carnatic still remained open. 'Abdullāh Kutb Shāh contended that these formed part of his kingdom, but Shāhjahān insisted that they were the personal property of Mīr Jumla, and must be ceded to the empire. The officials of Golconda threw every obstacle in the way of the cession of this valuable territory, from which they reaped much benefit, and the imperial officers were unable to enforce it.

The turn of Bījāpur came next. During the reign of Muhammad, the seventh of the 'Ādil Shāhī dynasty, this kingdom reached its greatest extent and prosperity. It had received some of the southern districts of the former kingdom of Ahmadnagar, and had annexed the greater part of the Carnatic, from sea to sea, and was a prize well worth winning. Muhammad 'Ādil Shāh died in November, 1656, and his son, 'Alī 'Ādil Shāh II, a young man of eighteen, was enthroned in his stead. Aurangzīb, whose aggressive policy in the Deccan had gained a powerful supporter in the new minister, reported to his father, without a shred of evidence in support of his allegations, that 'Alī was not a son of Muhammad, but a supposititious child who had been enthroned by the intrigues of the late king's minister and his widow. The quarrels between various parties in the state and the great and powerful fief-holders in the Carnatic were sedulously fomented by Aurangzīb's agents, and disorder became so rife that the prince, at Mīr Jumla's instigation, received permission to invade the kingdom of Bījāpur and to settle its affairs as seemed to him best. He was joined by a reinforcement of 20,000 horse, and Mīr Jumla was sent to his aid, and, having crossed the frontier, he opened, in March, 1657, the siege of Bīdar. The fortress was valiantly defended, but Mīr Jumla's artillery, and the explosion of a powder-magazine, enabled the imperial troops to take it after a month's siege, and to acquire considerable booty. The country was then ravaged to the south and west of Bīdar, and, a fortnight after the fall of the fortress, a large force of the army of Bījāpur was defeated in the field. In April Aurangzīb arrived before Kalyāni, and opened the siege of that fortress. It was stoutly defended by Dilāvar Khān, the African, but two determined attempts to relieve it were defeated by the imperial troops, who on the second occasion put the army of Bījāpur to flight and plundered its camp. Dilāvar Khān was then obliged to surrender the keys to Aurangzīb, and 'Alī 'Ādil Shāh II sued for peace. His agents at Delhi enlisted the sympathy of Dārā Shikūh, and peace was concluded on the condition of the cession of the fortresses of Bīdar, Kalyāni, and Parenda, and the payment of an indemnity of ten millions of rupees. Thus, once more baulked by his eldest brother, Aurangzīb retreated from Kalyāni in October, and, owing to his embarrassment, was not able to enforce the cession of Parenda.

Shāhjahān was now over sixty years of age. Since the death of his much-loved wife he had lived a life of gross self-indulgence, though there is no foundation for the malicious slander repeated by Bernier that he was guilty of the crime of incest. His health was failing, and in September, 1657, he fell seriously ill. On obtaining some relief from his malady, he left Delhi for Āgra, where his beloved wife was buried. During his illness his eldest son, who carefully tended him, was obliged to exercise much of his authority, and one of his acts was to dismiss from his post as chief minister Aurangzīb's *protégé*, Mīr Jumla. Reports of the emperor's illness, and even premature rumours of his death, reached all parts of his dominions, and gained credence, and his younger sons professed to believe that letters which they received from him, announcing his recovery, were forgeries, executed by their eldest brother. His second son, Shujā', governor of Bengal, was so convinced of his father's death that he assumed the imperial title, and Shāhjahān sent against him an army commanded by Dārā's son, Sulaimān Shikūh. Aurangzīb, as we know, was in the Deccan, and Murād Bakhsh, the fourth son, was in Gujarāt, where, on a false accusation of secret correspondence with Dārā, he had murdered with his own hand 'Alī Nakī, a trustworthy financial adviser who had been sent to him by his father. Early in December he, too, assumed the imperial title. The wily Aurangzīb refrained from committing himself in this manner, but, from the time when he first heard of his father's illness, opened a secret correspondence with Murād Bakhsh, seeking an alliance, and promising to divide the empire with him. In January, 1658, Aurangzīb left Aurangābād on his march towards Āgra, and a month later Murād left Ahmadābād. In April the armies of the two princes met at Dīpālpur in Mālwā, and thence marched together towards Ujjain, but at Dharmat[1] Rāja Jaswant Singh of Jodhpur and Kāsim Khān, who had been sent by Shāhjahān to arrest their progress, barred the way. In the battle which ensued the Rājput troops under Jaswant Singh fought with great valour, but they were ill supported by their Muslim colleagues, were mown down by Aurangzīb's artillery, and were at length defeated with great slaughter. After the battle the two princes continued their march, and in May reached Gwalior, where they learned that Dārā Shikūh had advanced to Dholpur, with a view to holding them on the Chambal. Aurangzīb crossed the river by an unguarded ford forty miles to the east of Dārā's camp, and thus turned his flank, whereupon Dārā retreated to Samūgarh, about eight miles east of Āgra.

[1] Situated in 23° N. and 75° 39' E.

Then were seen the disastrous effects of Shāhjahān's mistaken treatment of his eldest son. The prince's personal faults have already been noticed, but apart from them he suffered from grave disadvantages. His father, in his love for him, had insisted on keeping him always at court, and had thus deprived him of the opportunities which his brothers, and especially Aurangzīb, had enjoyed, of gaining experience of civil and military business.

Aurangzīb and Murād Bakhsh reached Samūgarh on June 7, 1658, their forces weary and spent after a long and waterless march in the great heat. Dārā's troops were fresh, and had he attacked the rebels at once he could hardly have failed to defeat them; but, having watched their dispositions, he retired to his tents, and refrained from attacking them, thus allowing them leisure for refreshment and repose

The battle began at noon on the following day. It is not possible here to enter into all its details. Aurangzīb's artillery wrought havoc among Dārā's troops, but the Rājputs, as usual, fought with great valour, at times both Aurangzīb and Murād Bakhsh were in grave personal danger, and Murād Bakhsh was wounded, but both exhibited great courage and presence of mind. Dārā Shikūh made many errors which hampered the movements of his own men and the efficient service of his guns, and, finally, when the artillery and musketry fire of the rebels was concentrated on his own elephant, descended and mounted his horse. His elephant's empty howdah convinced his troops that he had fallen; they broke and fled; and nothing was left for him but to follow their example. The wretched prince reached Āgra after nightfall, too despairing even to wait upon his father, and, before dawn on the following morning, fled with his family towards Delhi.

After the battle Aurangzīb visited Murād Bakhsh, saw his wounds tended, congratulated him on the victory, which, he said, was due to his valour and exertions, and informed him that his reign would date from that day. The two princes then reached Āgra in two marches, and encamped before the city, Shāhjahān having striven to put the fort into a state of defence. He begged Aurangzīb to visit him, but the prince, having been warned of a plot for his assassination, declined to wait on his father, sent his son, Muhammad Sultān, to occupy the city, and, as his guns made little impression on the walls of the fort, seized the water-gate, thus denying those within access to the Jumna. The water-supply from the wells within the fort was insufficient and barely drinkable; most of Shāhjahān's adherents began to desert him for Aurangzīb; and the old emperor begged his son not to allow his father to die of thirst. To this appeal Aurangzīb turned a deaf ear, and on June 21, 1658, Shāhjahān, throwing open the gates of the fort, retired into his harem, which he never again left until he was carried forth to be laid beside his wife in the beautiful tomb which he had built many years before. From this date begins the reign of Aurangzīb, who, on ascending the throne, took the title of 'Ālamgīr. He is, however, more famous under his original name, to which we shall adhere.

Shāhjahān had reigned for thirty-one years, during which time the empire of his house reached the height of its glory and its wealth. He lived for nearly eight years after his incarceration by his son, and before his death pardoned him the wrong he had done. He died in January, 1666, in the seventy-fifth year of his age, and in accordance with his will was buried beside the wife whom he had loved so well.

CHAPTER XII

Aurangzīb, 1658-1680

Having secured his father in the harem of his palace at Āgra, Aurangzīb set out with Murād Bakhsh in pursuit of Dārā Shikūh, but, before coming up with him, was obliged to deal with Murād. That prince perceived that Aurangzīb, who had promised to share the empire with him, was gradually usurping all authority, and his followers warned him that his power was waning. He therefore seduced some of the imperial officers and troops from their allegiance to Aurangzīb, added to the numbers of his army, and began to treat his elder brother as an inferior. Matters came to a head at Mathura, on the way to Delhi. There Aurangzīb arranged a banquet to celebrate Murād's complete recovery from his wounds, and Murād was beguiled into attending the feast given in his honour. He was treated by Aurangzīb with the honours due to royalty, and that pious Muslim saw that he was well-plied with the forbidden drink. After the meal he retired, and when he had fallen into a drunken sleep he was disarmed, bound, and sent off at midnight as a prisoner, first to Salīmgarh, and then to Gwalior. There he remained for four years until, in an evil moment for himself, he attempted to escape. Aurangzīb then prompted a son of 'Alī Nakī, the man whom Murād Bakhsh had murdered in Gujarāt, to come forward and demand, under the Islamic law of retaliation, the death of his father's murderer. His demand was strictly legal, and Murād Bakhsh was executed.

On the disappearance of their leader, Murād's forces fell into confusion, but none knew what had become of him, and of personal loyalty there was little in his camp. His troops had no choice between entering Aurangzīb's service and losing their employment, and he had no difficulty in gaining their allegiance. Dārā Shikūh, by seizing the treasury at Delhi, was able to raise the number of his troops to 10,000, but as Aurangzīb approached he fled to Lahore. On July 31, 1658, Aurangzīb ascended the throne in Delhi, dispatched Bahādur Khān in pursuit of Dārā, appointed Khalīlullāh Khān to the government of the Panjāb, and sent him to support Bahādur Khān in the pursuit of Dārā.

When the troops of these two officers crossed the Sutlej, and Aurangzīb himself left Delhi, Dārā Shikūh again fled from Lahore to Multān. Aurangzīb having followed him to this city, he again fled, first to Sukkur and then to Sehwān. From Multān, Aurangzīb was obliged to turn back, in order to deal with Shujāʿ, but he left a force sufficient to pursue Dārā, who was deserted by all his troops but 3000. The pursuing force overtook him at Sehwān, but owing to its weakness in boats he was able to escape, and fled towards Gujarāt. His pursuers were then recalled to court. From the Rājput chiefs of Kachch and Kāthiāwār he received assistance which enabled him to raise the numbers of his force to 22,000, and, having received an invitation from Jaswant Singh of Jodhpur, marched on Ajmīr, in the hope of being able to reach Āgra before Aurangzīb had finished dealing with Shujāʿ.

Shujāʿ, as has been mentioned, had assumed the imperial title at Rājmahal, and had marched towards Āgra, but early in February, 1658, had been surprised and defeated near Benares by Sulaimān Shikūh and Rāja Jai Singh of Jaipur, who had captured his camp and treasure, while Shujāʿ made his escape by boat, and his army fled by land to Patna. He then made a stand near Monghyr, and Sulaimān, after having been held up there for some months, retired on receiving news of the battle of Dharmat, but was too late to help his father at Samūgarh, and attempted, by eluding Aurangzīb's army, to join him in the Panjab.

Aurangzīb, after ascending the throne, had attempted to placate Shujāʿ by recognising him as viceroy of Bihar as well as Bengal and Orissa, and was pursuing Dārā Shikūh in the Panjab, but Shujā, taking advantage of his absence from his capital, had recruited his forces, and in the autumn of 1658 left Patna with an army of 25,000, and by the end of the year had passed Allāhābād and reached Khajwa,[1] but was here confronted by Muhammad Sultān, Aurangzīb's eldest son. Aurangzīb had meanwhile returned rapidly to Delhi, and, before any action had been fought, had joined his son, with Mīr Jumla, at Kora, ten miles from the position taken up by Shujāʿ. At 8 a.m. on January 14, 1659, the battle began, Shujāʿ, whose troops were outnumbered by three to one, taking the offensive. The result was for a time doubtful, and Aurangzīb was in danger of losing both his throne and his life, but at last numbers and generalship prevailed. Shujāʿ was

---

[1] Situated in 26° 3′ N. and 80° 35′ E.

defeated and fled, leaving both his camp and his guns in Aurangzīb's hands. The pursuit was left to Muhammad Sultān and Mīr Jumla, for Dārā's advance on Ajmīr called Aurangzīb into Rājasthān.

Ill-fortune dogged the miserable Dārā wherever he turned. Aurangzīb, with the assistance of Jai Singh, had persuaded Jaswant Singh to transfer his allegiance from Dārā to himself, and then hastened towards Ajmīr to meet his brother. Dārā, wisely declining to meet his superior forces in the open plain, held the pass of Deorai, four miles to the south of Ajmīr, and commanding the approach to the city. A frontal attack on his lines of trenches was hopeless, and an attempt to drive him from them by artillery fire failed, while his artillery did much execution on the imperial troops. On March 23, another attack, supported by artillery fire, was made, but was merely a feint, for while Dārā was engaged with it the mountaineers of Rāja Kāmrūp of Jammū were scaling the heights behind his left flank, and when they reached the summit Dārā perceived that his rear was menaced. His troops still fought bravely for some time, but it soon became clear that the day was lost, and they broke and fled. Dārā and his younger son, Sipihr Shikūh, fled towards Gujarāt, hard pressed by a pursuing force under Jai Singh and Bahādur Khān, and, on learning that they would not be again received in Gujarāt, turned towards Lower Sind, but there too Aurangzīb had forestalled them, and Dārā then turned northwards, crossed the Indus, and took refuge with Malik Jivan, fief-holder of Dādār, near the entrance to the Bolān Pass, whose life he had saved some time before, when he had been sentenced to death by Shāhjahān. On the way to Dādār Dārā's wife died, and when he reached that place not one of his few followers consented to accompany him into Persia. Malik Jivan, forgetful of his obligation to the prince, basely surrendered him to Bahādur Khān, and he, his son Sipihr Shikūh, aged fourteen, and his two daughters were carried to Delhi, where father and son, in miserable guise, were paraded through the streets on a small elephant amid the lamentations of the people. The decision of Dārā's fate was hastened by a rising of the citizens against the traitor Jivan, whom Aurangzīb had promoted to the command of a thousand horse, and had entitled Bakhtiyār Khān. On the night of August 30, 1659, the executioners entered Dārā's prison, removed his son, and cut him down. His corpse was paraded through the streets and was then buried in Humāyūn's tomb

Sulaimān Shikūh had not succeeded in joining his father, for his troops, on learning of Aurangzīb's success, had deserted him in such numbers that he was left almost without followers, and was obliged to seek refuge with Prithivī Singh, raja of Srīnagar in Garhwāl. There he remained in peace until Aurangzīb had defeated his father at Deorai, and Prithivī Singh refused to surrender him to Aurangzīb's envoys. But the raja's son, Mednī Singh, was more complaisant, and to his father's anger and disgust delivered the prince to an agent of the emperor. In January, 1662, he was brought before his uncle, who assured him that he should be kindly treated. The prince begged that he might be put to death at once if it were intended to destroy him by means of *pūst*, a decoction of poppy-heads which acted as a slow poison. Aurangzīb solemnly assured him that he need fear no such treatment, and sent him to the state-prison at Gwalior, where, despite the promise made to him, he died a few months later from the effects of opium-poisoning.

The campaign against Shujā' in Bengal progressed but slowly. His troops were outnumbered, but were better provided with boats than were the imperial troops, whose movements were hampered by the rivers and water-logged country. Muhammad Sultān chafed under the tutelage of Mīr Jumla, and entered into treasonable correspondence with his uncle, who promised him his daughter in marriage, and his assistance in gaining the crown. The prince, who was in an advanced position, took the bait, deserted his troops, crossed the Ganges, and joined Shujā' near Tānda. His flight threw his force into confusion, but Mīr Jumla at once visited it, restored order, and retained the troops in the imperial service. In February, 1660, Mīr Jumla effected the passage of the Ganges near Mālda, between Rājmahal and Tānda, and Shujā', whose line of retreat was threatened, fled towards Dacca, which he reached in April. When Mīr Jumla crossed the Ganges Muhammad Sultān deserted his uncle and rejoined the imperial camp, but his father never forgave him, and he spent the rest of his life in prison.

Shujā' was unable to maintain himself in Dacca, for the local landholders were not prepared to support a fugitive prince against the imperial power, and in May he set sail for Arakan, of the king of which country he had already sought aid. He was met by a flotilla of the Arakanese fleet, and was granted an asylum in Arakan, but was shortly afterwards detected in a plot to slay his host and seize his kingdom, as a base from which to attempt the recovery of Bengal. On learning that the king intended to put him to death he fled into the forest with a few followers, but was pursued and slain by the Arakanese.

Aurangzīb was thus rid of all possible competitors for the throne, and his reign began indeed. His father yet lived in confinement in the harem of his palace at Āgra, and it was probably for this reason that Aurangzīb chose Delhi as his residential capital, and on June 15, 1659, enthroned himself, with greater solemnity than on the former occasion, and ordered that every regnal year should be reckoned from Ramadān I, afterwards altered to Shawwāl I, the festival at the close of the month of fasting, as the first day of the fast was not suitable for the celebration of a feast. Aurangzīb has already been described as a rigid Sunni. He was no hypocrite, for he observed the commands and prohibitions of the sacred law of Islam throughout his long reign. The religious history of his house is well known. Akbar had abjured Islam, and invented a religion of his own. His son Jahāngīr remained nominally a Muslim, but habitually transgressed the law of Islam, and inherited so much of his father's tastes as to encourage discussion, and to dabble at times in Christianity and Hinduism. Shāhjahān, more orthodox than either his father or his grandfather, persecuted Christians, encouraged, or at least countenanced the destruction of Hindu temples, and abolished Akbar's most offensive institution of *sijda*, or prostration before the emperor, on the ground that prostration was due to God alone. Aurangzīb was a better Muslim than any of his forbears, and therefore a worse ruler, in the eyes of the majority of his subjects. He refrained from stamping the symbol of Islam and the names of the orthodox caliphs on his coins, lest they should be dishonoured and polluted by passing through the hands of infidels; he discontinued the celebration of the pagan festival of the *Naurūz*, or New Year's Day; he appointed a censor of morals to enforce the law of Islam, and to prevent the manufacture, sale, and consumption of intoxicating liquors; he restored ruined mosques, and appointed officials to them; he forbade music at court; he removed the stone elephants set up by Jahāngīr at the gate of the Āgra fort; he discontinued the practice of appearing every morning at the *jharokha*, or oriel window, as savouring of the Hindu ceremony of *darshan*; he forbade the Hindu form of salute by raising the hand to the head; and, as he grew older, he introduced other rules directed towards the discouragement of Hindu practices and the enforcement of the commands and prohibitions of the law of Islam. He gradually discovered, as others have since discovered, that the legal prohibition of practices not morally reprehensible could not be enforced, and tended only to provoke opposition and to excite contempt for law. Zeal for orthodoxy led naturally to the persecution of the heterodox. Theologians, mystics, and pantheists, among whom were some whom Dārā Shikūh had honoured, were among his victims. One was fortunate enough to die on his way to court; another, Sarmad, a pantheist whose moral character was not above reproach, who was in the habit of going about stark naked, and whose doctrines resembled, in some respects, those of the Dukhobors of Russia, was executed for heresy; a Christian friar, who had embraced Islam and then reverted to his former faith, was put to death for apostasy; later, a Shiah official was put to death for cursing the first three successors of Muhammad; the leader of the Bohras of Ahmadābād, a community of Shiahs of the Ismā'īli sect, was put to death with 700 of his followers. The Shiah practice of cursing as usurpers the first three successors of Muhammad always aroused the ire of Aurangzīb, as an orthodox Sunni, and provided him with a pretext, if any were needed, for visiting it upon the Kutb Shāhī kings of Golconda, who, as zealous Shiahs, encouraged the practice. It also led to acrimonious correspondence with the court of Persia. Shāh 'Abbās II dispatched to the Indian court a splendid embassy, with rich gifts and a friendly letter, to congratulate him on his success in seizing the throne. To this attention Aurangzīb responded by sending an embassy almost equally splendid, but bearing a letter vaunting his achievements, and declaring that he needed no human aid, as it was evident from his success that God was his helper. He would have done well to beware of the mordant and caustic wit of Persia, for Shāh 'Abbās replied twitting him with his failure to subdue the infidel Sīvajī, and with his assumption of the title of 'Ālamgīr, or world-conqueror, when his only conquests had been the imprisonment of his father and the murder of his brother.

An embassy to Mecca was more successful. Whether Aurangzīb's conscience pricked him or not is uncertain, but he desired recognition by the sharīf of the holy city, and the rich gifts which he sent not only purchased recognition, but also whetted the appetite of the holy man, who thereafter sent envoys to India every year, until Aurangzīb was goaded into replying that the sharīf seemed to believe that the wealth of India was inexhaustible, and that the money which was sent to Mecca was meant for the poor, and not for him.

Aurangzīb's reign of fifty years falls into two equal parts. During the first twenty-five years he resided in the north, chiefly at Delhi, and personally occupied himself with the affairs of northern India, leaving those of the Deccan, which had been his chief interest before his ascent of the throne, in the hands of his viceroys. Late in 1681 he was obliged, by the rebellion of one of his sons, to return to the Deccan, and never again left it. He died, a disappointed and worn-out man, at Ahmadnagar in 1707. The earlier conquests of the reign were of little importance, and some were afterwards abandoned. The first was that of western Assam. The Āhoms, a tribe of the Shān race, whose original home lay between the Irawadi and the Salwīn rivers, had established in Assam, in the thirteenth century, a kingdom which included the greater part of the Brahmaputra valley. In 1612 Jahāngīr's governor of Bengal, in the course of aiding the raja of Kūch Bihar against a rebellious son, conquered that son's principality, and thus extended the imperial dominions to the frontier of the Āhom kingdom, with which the empire was almost immediately involved in a war which lasted for twenty-six years, and ended in the annexation of the principality of Kāmrūp, as far east as the Barnadī. In 1658, after Shujā' had for the first time left Bengal with his troops, in his attempt to reach Āgra, the raja of Kūch Bihar trespassed on imperial territory, and the Āhom viceroy of western Assam invaded Kāmrūp, and occupied its capital, Gauhati; but in 1660 Aurangzīb appointed Mīr Jumla viceroy of Bengal, and ordered him to punish the intruders. He made Dacca his headquarters, and after the rainy season in the following year left that city with a force of 12,000 horse and 30,000 foot, and a fleet of 323 boats. He first invaded Kūch Bihar and occupied its capital, which he renamed 'Ālamgīrnagar, destroyed the principal temple in the town, built a mosque in its place, and annexed the whole kingdom. After a brief rest he set out early in 1662 for Assam, and crossed the frontier. The imperial troops met with very little opposition from the Āhom army, which was too enfeebled by cholera to withstand them, but their progress was very slow, owing to the density of the forest and the difficult nature of the country, and the army suffered great hardships. The Āhom fleet was destroyed, and in March Mīr Jumla arrived at Gargāon[1] (now Nāzira), the capital of the Āhom raja, Jayadhwaj, having captured a great quantity of spoil in cash, supplies, arms, and elephants, and more than 1000 boats. In this neighbourhood he went into quarters for the rainy season, while the imperial troops held the city, though harassed and attacked throughout the rainy season by the Āhom army. Their sufferings were great. After the opening of the rains in May no supplies reached them, and their horses and cattle died for want of proper food. In August their numbers were greatly reduced by a terrible epidemic, and it was not until late in September that the floods went down and the roads became passable and the river navigable. The troops were then again able to take the field, and the Āhom army gradually melted away before them. One by one its principal officers deserted to Mīr Jumla, but the raja, though deserted in the hills of Kāmrūp, was safe, for the imperial troops refused to advance farther into his country.

Through the instrumentality of his own principal lieutenant, Dilīr Khān, Mīr Jumla then concluded a treaty with Jayadhwaj. Under its terms, which were most advantageous to the invaders, the raja ceded to the empire the western provinces of his kingdom, which were exceedingly rich in elephants, and bound himself to send his daughter to the imperial court, to pay a very heavy indemnity in specie and elephants, to surrender hostages as security for its payment, and to pay an annual tribute of elephants.

After the conclusion of this treaty Mīr Jumla led his army from Assam. He had personally undergone all the hardships suffered by the meanest of his troops, and had suffered from fever and pleurisy during the campaign. At first, in January, 1663, he marched with his troops, but was obliged, at length, to embark on a boat in order to reach Dacca with greater ease, but he died in April before arriving at the city.

Of all who served Aurangzīb Mīr Jumla was the ablest and

[1] Situated in 26° 56′ N. and 94° 45′ E.

the most noble. "His character shone with supreme excellence
in this enterprise. No other general of that age conducted war
with so much humanity and justice." Under the most adverse
conditions he not only maintained among his troops the strictest
discipline, but retained the affection of his officers and men. By
far the wealthiest noble of the empire, he spared himself no toil
and no suffering in his master's service, and it was no fault of his
that his army suffered as it did or that the fruits of his military
success proved to be worthless. In 1667, Chaknadhwaj, who had
succeeded Jayadhwaj in 1663, recovered all the territory conquered by Mīr Jumla, and, though Rām Singh of Jaipur attempted
to reconquer it for the empire, his attempt failed.

Mīr Jumla had been ordered to punish the ruler of Arakan,
as well as the Āhom raja. Arakan was a maritime kingdom
inhabited by a people called the Maghs, whose most northerly
port was Chatgām, or Chittagong. The Maghs were pirates,
whose descents on the coasts of Bengal and rain up the rivers of
the deltas of the Ganges and the Brahmaputra depopulated and
impoverished Lower Bengal. The Portuguese had established a
settlement at Chittagong more than a century before this time
and, following their usual policy, had allied themselves with the
enemies of the Muslims and had, with their descendants of mixed
blood, become partly the servants, partly the partners of the
Magh ruler. The Maghs alone had struck terror into the hearts
of the people of Lower Bengal, but with their Portuguese allies
they were irresistible, for the Muslims of India are not a maritime
community, and, with all their wealth, could neither build nor
man any navy capable of facing the Portuguese on the sea. The
country was ravaged, and both Hindus and Muslims were carried
off in large numbers, and either kept as slaves in Arakan or sold
to the settlements of English, Dutch, and French merchants.

The grievous loss which the empire had suffered by the death
of Mīr Jumla had delayed the opening of a campaign against the
pirates, but in 1664 Aurangzīb appointed his maternal uncle,
Shāyista Khān, to the government of Bengal with instructions
to complete the tasks assigned to Mīr Jumla. Shāyista Khān, who
was a most capable and energetic official, governed Bengal for
fourteen years (1664-77). He found that the imperial navy of
Bengal had been well-nigh destroyed by the pirates and that he
would be obliged to build a new fleet. The dockyards of Lower

Bengal were kept busily employed for over a year, at the end of which time a new fleet of 300 sail had been built, equipped and manned.

Just beyond the mouth of the main stream of the Brahmaputra lay the island of Sandwīp, which was held as an independent estate by Dilāvar Khān, an officer who had deserted from the imperial navy. In 1665 this island was captured, and Dilāvar Khān was taken prisoner and sent to Dacca. Sandwīp was an excellent base for an attack on Chittagong, but the Muslims could not have faced the Portuguese on the sea. Fortunately for Shāyista Khān these pirates had quarrelled violently with their masters or confederates, the Maghs, and Shāyista Khān was able to inveigle them by promises into the imperial service. In December, 1665, they fled from Chittagong and crossed the frontier into the imperial territory, and their leaders received high naval commands. At the beginning of 1666 the army of Bengal left Dacca under the command of Buzurg Ummīd Khān, son of Shāyista Khān, and marched along the coast, cutting a road through the jungle as it proceeded, while the fleet accompanied it, sailing close in-shore. At the beginning of February the army crossed the Fenny river, which was the frontier between the empire and Arakan, and a few days later the Bengal navy, led by the Portuguese ships, sailed out of a creek and defeated the light squadron of the Arakanese navy. On the following day it entered the Karnaphalī river, and, after a fiercely contested battle, overcame the fleet of Arakan, capturing 135 ships, and two days later compelled the governor of the citadel of Chittagong to capitulate. A day or two later the army arrived and made a triumphal entry into the city, renamed Islāmābād and made the headquarters of an imperial *faujdar*. The more formidable pirates had entered the imperial service, and the rest were extinguished.

Trouble next arose beyond the Indus, between Peshāwar and Kābul. No power has yet been able permanently to reduce to order the warlike tribes inhabiting the mountainous country on the present frontier between India and Afghanistan, from Dīr to Pishīn, or to induce them to live peaceably under a settled government. Even their own tribal system is often rendered futile by a lawless individualism, and, apart from cultivating such grain as they need for their support, their principal occupations have been robbery and blood-feuds, tribe against tribe, clan against clan, and family against family. Late in Akbar's reign the Yūsuf-zais of Swāt and Bajaur and the sect of the Raushanīs had given serious trouble, and Bīrbal and Zain Khān had been heavily defeated, the former being slain. Punitive measures had been taken, but the effect of these never lasted long, and the usual means of keeping the tribes quiet had been to bribe the chiefs to keep the peace and to wink at acts of aggression. In 1667 the Yūsufzais again rose under a chief and a local mulla, crossed the Indus well above Attock, possessed themselves of the district through which ran the main road into Kashmīr, and encroached on imperial territory further south. Three columns were sent against them. One, from Attock, defeated them on the Indus, slew three thousand of them, and drove numbers into the river, where they were drowned; another, from Kābul, invaded their country, destroyed their crops, and burned their villages in the lowlands. Further blows were dealt and their lands were devastated by a large force under Muhammad Amīn Khān, son of Mīr Jumla. These measures cowed the tribes for some years, but in 1672 Akmal Khān, chief of the Afrīdis, irritated by the behaviour of the governor of Jalālābād, rose in rebellion, assumed the royal title, and summoned all the tribes to join him in a war against the empire. Muhammad Amīn Khān, governor of Kābul, left Peshāwar for that city in the spring of 1672. The Afrīdis held the Khaibar Pass against him, but he pressed on and entrenched himself at 'Alī Masjid. The Afrīdis descended on him, cut him off from the source of his water-supply, so that many of his men and animals died of thirst, threw the whole army into confusion by rolling down on them great rocks from the heights, and then charged down on them and plundered their camp. Ten thousand of the imperial troops were slain, the survivors were captured and sold into slavery, and cash and property worth twenty million rupees fell into the hands of the victors. Muhammad Amīn contrived, with some of his principal officers, to escape to Peshāwar, but his family was taken by the Afrīdis, and he was obliged to pay a great sum for their ransom. The Khattaks then rose under their chief, Khushhāl Khān, a noted poet in his own language, and joined the Afrīdis. Never before had the empire suffered so heavily at the hands of the tribesmen, and Akmal Khān's victory encouraged nearly all the tribes, even those usually hostile to one another, to join him, and the rising was general "from Kandahār to Attock".

Muhammad Amīn Khān was degraded, and Mahābat Khān was transferred from the government of Gujarāt to that of Kābul, and was ordered to crush the rebellion. But he feared the fate of his predecessor, and provided for his safety by entering into secret agreements with the tribes, by means of which he contrived to reach Kābul by the Karāpa Pass. The news of his dealings with the tribes angered the emperor, and he placed Shujā'at Khān, a competent officer of humble origin, in command of a large independent force, supported by Jaswant Singh and his Rājputs, to subdue and punish the tribes, but the two generals could not work in harmony, and early in 1674 Shujā'at Khān was defeated and slain in the Karāpa Pass, and his army was saved from annihilation only by the exertions of a band of Jaswant Singh's Rāthors. In the summer of that year Aurangzīb himself moved from Delhi to Hasan Abdal to direct operations. He dismissed Mahābat Khān from the government of Kābul on the ground that he had connived at Shujā'at Khān's defeat, and summoned from the Deccan Aghar Khān, an able Turkish officer, who knew how to deal with the tribesmen, and inflicted a crushing defeat on the Mohmands and their confederates. He failed to open the Khaibar Pass, where he was wounded, and suffered heavy losses; but, after this failure, he was uniformly successful against the tribes. Other imperial officers, however, suffered reverses; Fidai Khān in the Jagdallak Pass, where he at first lost heavily, but beat off the enemy, and was relieved by Aghar Khān, who forced the pass; Muharram Khān also was defeated in Bajaur; Hizabr Khān was defeated and slain at Jagdallak, and the commandant of Bārīkāb and Surkhāb was driven from his post with heavy losses; but the balance of military success lay with the imperial troops. Military posts were established in the country of the rebellious tribes, and they were severely punished, but Aurangzīb's guile was more effective than his arms. Tribes which were prepared to submit escaped punishment by betraying their confederates, and a section of the Afrīdis under Daryā Khān promised to deliver the head of Akmal Khān to the emperor. Thus, by the end of 1675, the situation was in hand, and Aurangzīb was able to return to Delhi. Rather more than a year later Amīr Khān, son of Khalīlullāh Khān, was appointed to the government of Kābul, and for twenty years maintained order in the province by following Aurangzīb's policy of setting tribe against tribe, and by paying subsidies to chiefs to induce them to keep their tribes quiet. After the death of Akmal even the Afrīdīs came to terms, and Khushhāl Khān, chief of the Khattaks, was betrayed and imprisoned.

The religious policy of Aurangzīb was disastrous. His great-grandfather had striven to remove the religious and social barriers which divided the various classes of his subjects, and, though exception can be taken to his methods, none can be taken to the end which he had in view. His grandfather, the son of a Hindu mother, held liberal, even lax views on religion. His father was a better Muslim than either Akbar or Jahāngīr, but, except in the case of political offenders, bridled his zeal. But Aurangzīb was a bigot to whom the religion of the great majority of his subjects was anathema, misbelief, and idolatry, which it was his duty before heaven to persecute, and if possible to stamp out. His methods were iconoclasm, sacrilege, economic repression, bribery, forced conversion and restriction of worship. As governor of Gujarāt he had displayed his bigotry by defiling and destroying a Hindu temple and building a mosque on its site. After ascending the throne he commanded the demolition of "all schools and temples of the infidels" and the suppression of their teaching and practices. Under his orders the second temple of Somnāth in Gujarāt, the Vishvanāth temple in Benares, and the Keshava Rai temple in Mathura were destroyed, the name of Mathura was changed to Islāmābād, and on the site of the temple in Benares was raised the mosque which yet towers above all the temples of the Hindus in their most sacred city. Religious grants to the Hindus were resumed, and in 1680 the temples in Amber, the capital of a state which had ever been loyal to the empire, were destroyed. Hindus were, for the first time, debarred from holding the post of revenue-collector, and in those parts of India in which the office was hereditary the holder was not allowed to retain it unless he embraced Islam. Customs-duties or octroi were levied on all goods and merchandise brought for sale, at the rate of $2\frac{1}{2}$ per cent. *ad valorem* from Muslims and 5 per cent. from Hindus, but in 1667 Muslims were exempted from the payment of any duty, while from Hindus it was levied at the old rate. Hindus were persuaded by offers of public office, and even cruder means, to accept Islam; criminals were granted pardons on professing their readiness to embrace that faith; later in the reign no Hindus but Rājputs were permitted to use palanquins, to bear arms, or to ride on elephants or good horses; religious fairs were prohibited; and the celebration of the principal Hindu festivals was subjected to vexatious control. But Aurangzīb's supreme act of folly, exhibiting his ignorance of the principles of his own sacred law, was the imposition of the *jizya*, or poll-tax, on all classes of Hindus. This is a tax levied from all who are not Muslims and in a state governed in accordance with the principles of the law of Islam may be justified, for there none but Muslims are permitted to bear arms, and it is held that those who are exempted under the law from military service may justly be called upon to contribute in cash to the cost of the defence of the state. But the levy of the tax could not be justified in India, where the Rājputs not only bore arms, but were among the best soldiers of the state. The imposition of the tax upon them was therefore not only unjust, but was a gross insult, and as such it was resented.

These measures produced their natural result. The destruction of the temple in the holy city of Mathura caused a rising of the Jāt peasantry. These sturdy tillers of the soil will be remembered as the antagonists of Mahmūd of Ghaznī, first when he crossed the Indus after his destruction of the temple of Somnāth, and again, when he led his last expedition into India to punish them for molesting him on his retreat. A large community of this tribe was settled in the districts to the south of Delhi, and it was Aurangzīb's foolish policy that first brought them into political prominence. They rose under the leadership of Gokla, a landholder of Tilpat, about fifteen miles to the south of Delhi, and throughout 1669 the whole district of Mathura was in a turmoil, but in January, 1670, the rebels were defeated in the field and afterwards besieged in Tilpat, which was taken by storm after great slaughter. Gokla was publicly hewn in pieces and the rebellion was suppressed, but in 1686 the Jāts again rose.

The next rebellion had its origin in a purely secular dispute between a sect of unitarians, known as Satnāmis, whose headquarters was at Nārnaul, and an imperial soldier whom the Satnāmis beat nearly to death. The rebellion soon assumed a religious character, and the Satnāmis seized Nārnaul, defeated the local force of imperial troops, and destroyed the mosques in the town. The rebellion in this rich district caused a scarcity of supplies in Delhi, and an imperial force was sent against the rebels, some thousands strong. In March, 1672, they were defeated after a fiercely contested battle, "very few of them escaped and that tract of the country was cleared of the infidels".

The Sikh community, founded late in the fifteenth century by Bābā Nānak, near Lahore, remained a purely religious body until the death of its fifth *guru*, Arjūn, who suffered at the hands of Jahāngīr for his indiscretion in making a gift or a loan to his son Khusraw when he was in rebellion. Under Arjūn's son and successor, Har Govind, it acquired a definitely military and political character, and defeated near Amritsar, which had then become its headquarters, an army sent against it by Shāhjahān, to punish it for some acts of contumacy. Other armies were sent against the Sikhs and at length Har Govind's house and property were plundered, and he was driven into the Kashmīr hills, where he died. He was succeeded by his son Har Kishan, on whose death, in 1664, Har Govind's youngest son, Tegh Bahādur, was, after a disputed succession, accepted as *guru*. His hostility to Islam and to its champion was aroused by Aurangzīb's persecution of both Hindus and Sikhs. He openly defied the emperor, but was captured and carried to Delhi, where, after refusing to accept Islam, he was first tortured and then beheaded. His son, Govind Rai, was the tenth and last *guru* of the Sikhs. He perfected their organisation as a military brotherhood, the *Khālsa*, and spent his life in conflicts with the hill-chiefs, from Jammū to Garhwāl, and with the imperial troops which were sent to their aid. Ānandpur, his place of residence, was at length reduced; he lost his four sons, and eventually was hunted through the lower Himālāya by Aurangzīb's troops. On the death of Aurangzīb Govind Rai, with a force of cavalry and infantry, accompanied Bahādur Shāh I through Rājasthān into the Deccan, and took up his residence at Nānder, on the Godāvarī, where, in 1708, he fell at the hands of an Afghan assassin. He was the last *guru* and on his death the Sikhs were, for a time, disorganised, but eventually succeeded in establishing a military state in the Panjab.

The pollution and destruction of temples, the general policy of persecution, and above all the emperor's decision that the poll-tax should be levied from Hindus of all classes, seriously agitated the chiefs of Rājasthān, who had served the empire faithfully. But Aurangzīb, not yet content, betrayed an intention of robbing the chiefs of their ancestral domains, and annexing them to the empire. Late in 1678 Mahārāja Jaswant Singh of Mārwār died at Jamrūd, in the Khaibar Pass, leaving no son at the time of his death. His state was in confusion, for no ruler remained, and the best of its troops were serving in the Kābul province. Aurangzīb annexed Mārwār, and sent his officers into the state to administer it as a province of the empire, but, in consideration of a bribe of three and a half million rupees, installed Indra Singh of Nāgaur, a grand-nephew of Jaswant Singh, as titular chief of the state. In 1679, however, two of Jaswant Singh's widows gave birth to posthumous sons at Lahore. One child did not long survive his birth, but the other, Ajīt Singh, was destined for Aurangzīb's harem, there to be educated, presumably as a Muslim. The widows and the child were brought to Delhi, and, when a party of troops visited their mansion to conduct them and the child to the imperial palace, the spirit of the Rājputs was aroused, and one heroic band fell on the troops, while the gallant Durga Dās, the son of Jaswant, left by another gate with the widows and the child and rode for Mārwār. The imperial troops were so long delayed by the attack which the Rājputs made on them that the fugitives were not overtaken until they had travelled nine miles. Then another and again another band of Rājputs fell on them, and at length they gave up the chase and Ajīt Singh was carried off in safety into Mārwār. Aurangzīb made Ajmir his head-quarters and sent an army under his fourth son, Muhammad Akbar, into Mārwār, to complete the conquest of the country, and deposed Indra Singh. The Rāthors carried on a guerilla warfare, but their land was parcelled out among imperial officers, Jodhpur and other cities were occupied, their temples were destroyed, and mosques built on their sites. The state was regarded, though it was in great disorder, as an imperial province, and Aurangzīb turned his attention to Mewār, for he had grounds for displeasure with the rāna, Rāj Singh.

Some time before this Aurangzīb had demanded the hand of a princess of a cadet branch of the rāna's house; but the proud Rājput lady threatened to destroy herself if she were forced to become the mate of the "monkey-faced barbarian", and threw herself on the protection of the chief of her race, who responded by cutting up her escort of imperial guards and carrying her off to Udaipur as his wife. When it was decreed that the poll-tax should be levied from the Rājputs, Rāj Singh had sent a dignified letter of protest to the emperor, and, when Mārwār was overrun, he granted to his kinswoman, the widow of Jaswant Singh, her young son Ajīt Singh, and Durga Dās an asylum in the hills of Mewār. Aurangzīb therefore invaded his state, and the Rājputs withdrew into the hills, which the imperial troops feared to penetrate; but their advanced guard, in January, 1680, inflicted a defeat on the rāna; the lowlands of the state, from which his troops drew all their supplies of food, were overrun and devastated; the capital, Udaipur, was occupied; and nearly 250 temples were destroyed there and at Chitor. Aurangzīb then returned to Ajmir, leaving his fourth son, Akbar, at Chitor in command of the field operations in Mewār. The rāna, holding the Aravallī Range, which separated Mewār from Mārwār, was able to descend on either side of it on military posts isolated among a hostile force, to cut off their supplies, surprise them, harass them, and render outpost duty so arduous and perilous that neither officers nor men would undertake it. Akbar, complaining that his army was motionless through fear, remained inactive at Chitor until his father transferred him to Mārwār, and was relieved in Mewār by his brother A'zam, Aurangzīb's third son. A new scheme for the conquest of Rājasthān was then formed. Mu'azzam, Aurangzīb's second son, was summoned from the Deccan, and was placed in command of a force which was to enter the Aravallīs from the north, while A'zam entered them from the east, and Akbar from the west; but the scheme failed. A'zam was loth to enter the mountains, and Tahavvur Khān, commanding Akbar's advanced guard, refused to advance. Akbar, urged on by his father, made some slight advance, but was already meditating treason. Using Tahavvur Khān as his intermediary he was in communication both with the Sesodias of Mewār and the Rāthors of Mārwār, who had no difficulty in convincing Akbar that his father's policy of subduing the Rājputs was imperilling the empire. They urged him to depose his father, seize the throne, and revert to the wise policy of his ancestors. Aurangzīb was at Ajmir, unprotected but by his personal guards, the bulk of his army having been distributed among the field forces commanded by his three sons. The proposal fell on willing ears; the Rājputs promised their support; and the foolish young man was easily persuaded that he was a match for his father.

Negotiations were delayed by the death of the rāna, Rāj Singh, and by the month of mourning which followed his death; but his successor, Jai Singh, concluded the compact, and on January 12, 1681, Akbar set out on his march to Ajmir, accompanied by his allies. He had previously attempted to lull his father's suspicions by reporting that he was escorting the new rāna and Durga Dās, the Rāthor, to the imperial camp to make their submission; but two or three days later threw off all disguise by causing himself to be proclaimed emperor, and appointing Tahavvur Khān to the office of minister. Speed was then essential to the success of the enterprise, but the foolish prince loitered on his way to Ajmir and allowed his father time to double his forces by summoning to his aid his second son, Mu'azzam. On January 25 Akbar halted within three miles of his father's camp, which had been moved forward to the pass in which Dārā Shikūh had been defeated, and was prepared to meet his father's army on the following day; but Aurangzīb had obliged Tahavvur Khān's father-in-law to write to him promising him forgiveness if he should return to his duty and warning him that if he hesitated his wives would be publicly outraged and his sons sold into slavery. Tahavvur Khān secretly visited the imperial camp, but was there slain by Aurangzīb's attendants as he was attempting to force his way armed into the presence chamber. Aurangzīb had meanwhile written to Akbar, praising him for having so faithfully carried out his instructions to beguile the Rājput chiefs into accompanying him to Ajmir, and desiring him to place them in the van of his forces on the following day, that they might be hemmed in by his own forces attacking them in front and Akbar's attacking them in rear. By Aurangzīb's instructions the letter was allowed to fall first into the hands of Durga Dās, who at once called upon Akbar for an explanation, but found that he was asleep and had given orders that he was not to be disturbed. He next sought Tahavvur Khān, and, on learning that he had left for the imperial camp, was convinced that the Rājputs had been betrayed. They seized what they could lay hands on in Akbar's camp, and at once took the road to Mārwār. When morning broke Akbar's army had melted away. Only 350 horse remained to him, and with this small body he rapidly followed the Rājputs. Durga Dās, who had almost immediately discovered Aurangzīb's ruse, turned back and met the prince, who was concealed and protected by the Rājputs for four months, while a large force under his brother, Mu'azzam, hunted him through Mārwār. In May he crossed the Nerbudda, then the Taptī, and in June he joined Sīvajī's son, Sambhujī, in the Konkan. Sambhujī received him with royal honours and took him under his protection.

Neither party had then anything to gain by continuing the war in Rājputāna. The imperial troops, scattered over an inhospitable region amid a hostile population, were constantly exposed to the attacks of a valiant enemy whose fastnesses they dared not approach. The Rājputs, free and unconquered in their mountains, were yet starving. After a raid of the Sesodias into the fertile province of Gujarāt, negotiations were opened between the emperor and the rāna. Three districts were ceded by the rāna to the empire in lieu of the poll-tax, from which the rāna's subjects were exempted. The rest of Mewār was restored to Jai Singh, whose title as rāna was recognised and who received the rank of a commander of 5000 horse. Mārwār, however, was not evacuated, and was occupied by the imperial forces for the next thirty years; but the Rāthors gave the troops no rest, and attacked and harassed them until many of their officers purchased respite from constant scarcity, annoyance and danger by secretly paying blackmail, until in 1709 Ajīt Singh regained possession of Jodhpur, and his title and lordship were formally recognised by Aurangzīb's son and successor, Bahādur Shāh I.

CHAPTER XIII

Aurangzīb in the Deccan, 1680–1707

The reception of the rebel prince Akbar at the court of the
Marātha raja, Sambhujī, obliged Aurangzīb to return to the
Deccan, which he had twice ruled as viceroy in his father's reign,
but had not visited since his accession to the throne. We must,
therefore, revert to the history of the Deccan, in order to explain
the situation which the emperor found himself called upon to
face. He, it will be remembered, had patched up a peace with
'Alī II of Bījāpur, from whom he extorted a heavy indemnity
which materially aided him in his enterprise.

After Shāhjahān's treaty with the kingdoms of the Deccan on
the extinction of the kingdom of Ahmadnagar in 1633 Shāhjī
the Marātha had been permitted to enter the service of Bījāpur,
in the northern districts of which he held important fiefs in the
neighbourhood of Poona. He afterwards acquired extensive fiefs
in the districts of the Carnatic conquered by Bījāpur, and in these
fiefs he usually resided with his elder and favourite son, Sambhujī,
leaving his northern estates under the management of an agent,
to whom was also entrusted the education of his younger son,
Sīvajī. On the death of his father's agent Sīvajī assumed the
management of these estates as though they were his own, remitting revenue neither to his father nor to the state. He captured
a number of hill forts and annexed the districts which they
dominated, and the state, too weak to attack him, suspected that
he was acting under secret instructions from his father, who was
seized and imprisoned. Shāhjī appealed to the emperor Shāhjahān,
and 'Alī II, fearing lest Sīvajī should transfer his estates and his
services to the empire, released Shāhjī and permitted him to
return to the government of the Carnatic.

Sīvajī, one of the greatest soldiers whom India has produced,
was a statesman no less than a soldier. His ambition was to
establish in India a great Hindu power, and for the attainment
of this object he was most favourably situated. The kingdom of
Bījāpur was entering upon the last stages of decay. When Aurangzīb, as viceroy, had invaded the kingdom Sīvajī had stood aloof.
After Aurangzīb had left the Deccan for Āgra, 'Alī II attempted

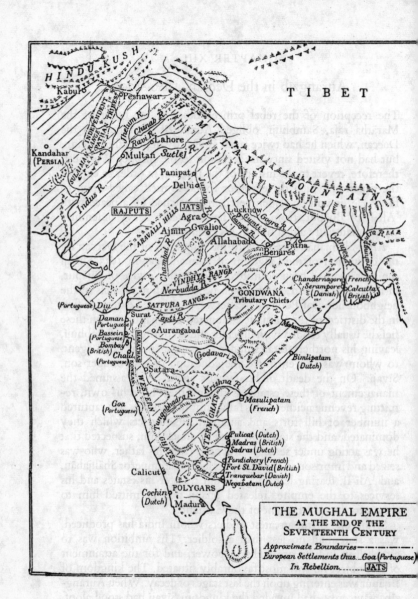

THE MUGHAL EMPIRE
AT THE END OF THE
SEVENTEENTH CENTURY

Approximate Boundaries ———
European Settlements thus ..Goa *(Portuguese)*
In Rebellion..........JATS

to punish the rebel, but Sīvajī slew, at a private interview, the commander of the forces sent against him, and dispersed his troops. Having eluded another force he encroached on the imperial province of the Deccan, and raided it almost to the gates of its capital, Aurangābād. Aurangzīb then appointed his maternal uncle, Shāyista Khān, to the viceroyalty, and in 1660 he entered into a treaty with 'Alī II for a combined attack on Sīvajī. Of the Marātha's estates some were devastated and of his forts many were captured, but he retained the southern Konkan. In June, 1661, Sīvajī descended from his fortress capital in disguise, entered Poona with a few followers, broke at night into the house occupied by the viceroy, slew his son and his guard, and wounded Shāyista Khān himself, who narrowly escaped with his life. Shāyista Khān was then recalled, and Aurangzīb sent as viceroy to the Deccan his second son, Mu'azzam, an unwarlike prince, with whom Sīvajī, whose funds were now ample, was able to conclude an armistice on very favourable terms. On his father's death in 1664 Sīvajī assumed the title of rāja, struck coin in his own name, and shortly afterwards sacked the imperial city of Surat. Aurangzīb could not ignore these acts of defiance and aggression, and sent against the rebel his ablest generals, Jai Singh of Amber and Dilīr Khān.

The campaign against the Marātha was pursued with great vigour, and Sīvajī was reduced to such straits that he sued for peace. Jai Singh received him with great courtesy, and at Pāndharpur concluded with him a convention under which Sīvajī agreed to attend the imperial court under a safe-conduct granted by the rāna. He left the Deccan in March, 1666, and in May, on Aurangzīb's fiftieth birthday, was presented at court with ten of his officers by Jai Singh's son, Rām Singh. There he was informed that he, his young son Sambhujī, and his master of the horse, Netajī, were appointed commanders of 5000 horse. Sīvajī regarded the association of his young son and his servant with him in the rank conferred on him, and the place assigned to him at court, as studied insults, and was so enraged that he fainted. After being carried out, he protested to Aurangzīb against the treatment which he had received, and was consequently placed under arrest. Rām Singh was ordered to accommodate him in the Amber house at Āgra, and was made responsible for his custody. The Rājput prince regarded these orders as a breach of the safe-conduct which his father had granted, and Sīvajī was not subjected to any galling restraint. His escort was permitted to return to the Deccan, and shortly afterwards he and his son escaped, hidden in baskets borne on the backs of coolies. Sīvajī made his way to Mathura, disguised as a pilgrim, and thence journeyed to the Deccan by devious routes, reaching his fortress capital, Raigarh, after an absence of nine months. He was joyously welcomed by his servants and his subjects, and lost no time in settling his account with the emperor. He recovered the Konkan and most of the other possessions which he had ceded under the convention of Pāndharpur. Jai Singh was besieging Bījāpur, but with little prospect of success, and, perceiving that his line of retreat was threatened by Sīvajī, retired to Aurangābād, but was recalled from the Deccan. On his way to court he died at Burhānpur, worn out by age and long service. Mu'azzam was again sent to the Deccan, and was again cajoled by Sīvajī not only into making peace, but even into obtaining Aurangzīb's sanction to Sīvajī's retention of the forts and lands which he had recovered, and to the revival in his favour of the title of raja, which had been conferred by the Ahmadnagar kingdom on his grandfather, Mālojī.

Sīvajī, at peace both with the empire and with Bījāpur, had leisure to perfect his system of administration. His government was organised in eight departments, each presided over by a responsible minister, the chief minister being dignified by the Persian title of Pēshwā. The machinery of the administration was simple, but efficient; the pernicious old Marātha institution of hereditary office was set aside, and Sīvajī, recognising the danger of a powerful feudal aristocracy, granted no fiefs, public servants, of all ranks, both civil and military, being paid directly from the treasury. All were subject to summary dismissal for misconduct or inefficiency. He was accessible to all his subjects, and commanded such devotion as no other contemporary ruler in India received. The districts permanently occupied by him enjoyed better government than any of the neighbouring provinces, either of the empire or of Bījāpur.

The unusual calm in the Deccan and the growth of Sīvajī's power aroused in Aurangzīb's mind the suspicion that Mu'azzam was conspiring with the Marātha to treat him as he had treated his father. The prince was accordingly ordered to arrest Sīvajī and send him to court, but private information that such orders were being prepared enabled Mu'azzam to anticipate their arrival by privately warning Sīvajī, who accordingly withdrew his representatives from Aurangābād, and the prince was able to report that it was impossible to execute the command. But the issue of these orders again disturbed the peace of the Deccan. Sīvajī captured several imperial forts, once more plundered Surat, and, invading the kingdom of Golconda, extorted from its ruler a large sum of money as the ransom of his capital.

On June 6, 1674, Sīvajī was crowned, and assumed the titles of mahārāja and *chhatrapati*, or "Lord of the Umbrella". This was an act of defiance, and Sīvajī anticipated that Aurangzīb, who had hitherto affected to regard him with contempt, might at length perceive that he was a danger to the empire, and put forth his whole strength against him. He therefore formed a plan for the extension of his powers. With this object he prepared to wrest from his half-brother, Vyankojī, the share which he claimed in the rich fiefs in the Carnatic of their father, Shāhjī. He bribed Bahādur Khān, viceroy of the Deccan, to refrain from attacking his northern dominions during his absence, and led an army of 70,000 men through the kingdom of Bījāpur into that of Golconda. There he visited the king, Abul Hasan, at Hyderabad, and gained his active sympathy by entering into an offensive and defensive alliance with him against the empire.

The Carnatic campaign was the greatest military exploit of Sīvajī's life, and marks him as the greatest soldier of his age in India. The Carnatic was part of the kingdom of Bījāpur, of which his brother, Vyankojī, was a vassal, and he overcame both the troops of Bījāpur and those of Vyankojī. As the modern historian of the Marāthas says, "In the course of eighteen months at a distance of 700 miles from his base, he had conquered a territory as large as his former kingdom. While a single reverse would have been fatal, he had not suffered even a single check. Victory had succeeded victory; town had fallen after town. As he went, he organised his conquests, and, when he returned to Raigarh, his new possessions were securely bound together from sea to sea by a line of fortified strongholds held by garrisons brave to the death and devoted to his cause". He allowed his brother to retain, as his vassal, Tanjore and some territory in its neighbourhood.

Bahādur Khān's treachery was discovered, and he was recalled from the Deccan. His successor, Dilīr Khān, had, in alliance with Bījāpur, attacked the kingdom of Golconda, Sīvajī's ally; but the Bījāpur troops had not been paid and had melted away, and Dilīr Khān was unable, without their help, to cope with the army of Golconda. Mu'azzam was sent again to the Deccan as viceroy, and Dilīr Khān was ordered to invade the feeble kingdom of Bījāpur, on the pretext that Pādshāh Begum, the sister of the young king, Sikandar 'Ādil Shāh, who had been betrothed to one of Aurangzīb's sons, had not been sent to court. The princess surrendered herself, but Dilīr Khān continued his advance, and the regent of Bījāpur appealed to Sīvajī for help. Sīvajī cut the communications of the invading force and sent his son, Sambhujī, to the relief of the city, but Sambhujī deserted to the imperial army, and was rewarded for his treachery with the command of 7000 horse, and the siege continued. Aurangzīb could not trust anybody for long, and ordered Dilīr Khān to seize Sambhujī, who merited the confidence of none, and to send him to court, but Dilīr Khān, more honourable than his master, allowed his guest to escape. Meanwhile Sīvajī had cut off supplies both from the besieging troops and from Aurangābād, their source of supply. In acknowledgement of his aid Sīvajī received a grant of all the territory which he had conquered in the Carnatic, and the Bījāpur state recognised Vyankojī as his vassal, not its own.

Sīvajī had then reached the zenith of his power. "He had freed the bulk of the Marāthī-speaking people. By his new alliance with Bījāpur and Golconda, and still more by the chain of fortresses which he had built from Bednor to Tanjore, he had secured his conquests." His last days were darkened by domestic trouble. His son Sambhujī had proved himself unfit to succeed him; his third wife, Soyara Bai, harassed him to designate her young son Rājarām as his heir; and his brother Vyankojī, neglecting all the public business of his great charge in the Carnatic, was posing as a religious recluse. Sīvajī sent him an affectionate but reproachful letter, the last which he ever wrote, and on April 5, 1680, died, in the fifty-third year of his age.

Aurangzīb had always affected to despise his great opponent, whom he styled "the mountain rat", but was at length compelled to recognise that he was a great captain, and added, "My armies have been employed against him for nineteen years, and nevertheless his state has always been increasing".

His younger son, Rājarām, was enthroned in Raigarh on his death, but Sambhujī, displaying unwonted energy, secured the allegiance of the greater part of the army, entered Raigarh, confined his young brother, and, summoning the boy's mother before him, grossly insulted her, accused her of having poisoned his father, and put her to a cruel and lingering death. He was enthroned as mahārāja in August, 1680, and it was in the following year that the young Akbar sought an asylum with him. Sambhujī, when receiving him, saluted him as emperor and held out some hope that he would help him to dethrone his father, but first occupied himself in an unsuccessful attempt to seize some of the ports of the Konkan. Thus affairs stood when Aurangzīb, at the end of 1681, appeared once more in the Deccan, where he was doomed to spend the remainder of his long reign in the vain attempt to crush the power of the Marāthas. 'Alī 'Ādil Shāh II of Bījāpur and 'Abdullāh Kutb Shāh of Golconda had died in 1672 and had been succeeded, the former by his son Sikandar, a child of four, and the latter by his son-in-law Abul Hasan, a weak and worthless ruler. Dilīr Khān had been obliged to raise the siege of Bījāpur before Sīvajī's death and had been disgraced and recalled at the time when Mu'azzam was recalled from the Deccan in 1680 to aid his father in Rājasthān. Bahādur Khān was then again appointed viceroy of the Deccan.

For three years after his arrival in the Deccan, Aurangzīb was occupied in the attempt to suppress Sambhujī, now a powerful monarch who raided the territories of the empire and Bījāpur indiscriminately. The course of politics in the Deccan was so tortuous that it is impossible to follow it in detail. Akbar, perceiving that Sambhujī had no intention of affording him such assistance as would enable him to overcome his father, quarrelled with him and left his court; and after a complicated series of intrigues with Marāthas and Portuguese, and a raid into his father's territory, in which he was defeated, sailed early in 1687 for Persia, and in 1688 reached the court of Sulaimān at Isfahān.

Aurangzīb vainly demanded that Bījāpur should join with him in suppressing the infidel, Sambhujī. Sambhujī was indeed a rebel against that state as well as against the empire, but the regent of Bījāpur was not blind to his value as a protection against imperial aggression. While they were fully occupied with him they had no leisure to attack Bījāpur, and should they attack Bījāpur it was expected that the Marāthas would come to its aid. Aurangzīb's demands were therefore ignored, until, in 1684, Sikandar definitely refused to co-operate with the imperial troops except on the most stringent conditions, and Aurangzīb decided that the time had come to annex the kingdom.

Aurangzīb had two sons with him in the Deccan, Mu'azzam, who had received the title of Shāh 'Ālam, and A'zam. The elder, Mu'azzam, was sent in 1683 to invade the Konkan, and at first had some success, but foolishly quarrelled with the Portuguese, who cut off his sea-borne supplies, so that his army was almost annihilated, first by famine, and then by a pestilence which followed close on its heels, and in the summer of 1684 he returned to Ahmadnagar with nought but a remnant of the army which eight months before he had led into the Konkan.

After Sikandar's refusal to co-operate with the emperor's troops against Sambhujī, diplomatic relations with the empire were broken off and Sikandar openly allied himself with the Marātha. In April, 1685, the siege of Bījāpur was opened and three months later A'zam, the younger prince, took command of the besieging force. The garrison and their allies in the field, Marāthas and others, fought desperately, and not always unsuccessfully, against the prince's army, harassed him, and cut off his supplies, in which they were aided, after the outbreak of the rainy season, by the forces of nature, which closed the road between their camp and Aurangzīb's headquarters. The troops were reduced to such straits that Aurangzīb ordered A'zam to raise the siege and retreat, but A'zam, eager to show his superiority to his brother, refused to retire, and his father sent him a large convoy of supplies which "turned scarcity to plenty" in his camp.

Meanwhile Mu'azzam had been sent to deal with Abul Hasan Kutb Shāh of Golconda against whom Aurangzīb had several causes of complaint. He had sent a field force to the relief of Bījāpur, he paid the Marātha raja an annual subsidy in consideration of his promise to protect the state against the emperor, and he had allowed the administration of his kingdom to fall entirely into the hands of two Brāhman brothers, Mādanna and Ākanna, who persecuted Muslims and insulted their religion. He was, moreover, a Shiah and permitted and even encouraged the practices of that sect most offensive to orthodox Sunnis. In October, 1685, Mu'azzam captured and occupied Hyderabad, the capital of the kingdom, while Abul Hasan withdrew into Golconda, his fortress capital.

By June, 1686, the siege of Bījāpur had lasted for fifteen months, partly owing to the personal jealousy and quarrels of the imperial officers. Aurangzīb in that month left Sholapur and personally assumed command of the siege. Mu'azzam had been recalled from Hyderabad and virtually the whole of the imperial army in the Deccan, except such troops as were required as convoys and road guards, was engaged in the operations. The siege was vigorously pressed, and, though the besieger suffered severely from scarcity, due to a famine in the Deccan, the garrison was in worse case, and in September lost heart. Sikandar, the last of the 'Ādil Shāhī dynasty, then a young man of eighteen, left his palace and was escorted to Aurangzīb's tent, where he made his obeisance and resigned his kingdom into his hands. He was at first sent to the state prison in Daulatābād, but was afterwards permitted to accompany the imperial camp in the Deccan. He died in 1700, in his thirty-second year, and was buried at Bījāpur.

Before Mu'azzam had left the Golconda state to rejoin his father, the Muslim mob had risen and put to death the two Brāhmans, whom they regarded as the authors of their woes, and their heads were sent as a peace offering to the emperor.

When he had finished with Bījāpur, Aurangzīb was free to deal with Golconda. He set forth, and in February, 1687, arrived before the fortress, and the siege was opened. Again operations were delayed or rendered futile by jealousy and treachery. Mu'azzam, partly from generous feelings towards a helpless foe, partly in hope of receiving a large bribe, and partly in order to forestall a success which might possibly be attributed to his brother and rival, A'zam, entered into treasonable correspondence with Abul Hasan, and, this having been detected, was placed under arrest with his family, and remained in disgrace for seven years. The records of the siege, which are very complete, are a disgrace to the imperial arms. The two heroes were a dog, who, by his barking, gave warning of an attempt at an escalade by night, which was repulsed, and 'Abdur Razzāk of Lār, a gallant Persian who fought almost to his last gasp when, after a siege of nearly eight months, traitors admitted the imperial troops, and afterwards long resisted Aurangzīb's importunate invitations to enter his service. The dog was ennobled by Abul Hasan, and 'Abdur Razzāk, who recovered from seventy wounds, at length entered the imperial service. Abul Hasan was sent to Daulatābād as a state prisoner, and there spent the remainder of his days.

While Aurangzīb had been engaged in the sieges of Bījāpur and Golconda Sambhujī had not been idle. Besides aiding the two beleaguered cities with field forces, which hovered in the rear of the besiegers and, without affecting the result of either siege, harassed them, cut off their supplies, and reduced them to great distress; his troops had systematically raided all imperial posts within their reach and the surrounding country. After the fall of Golconda the imperial troops were free to deal with the Marātha scourge. Sambhujī was sunk in debauchery and odious to all his leading officers owing to his neglect of public business and to the severity and cruelty with which he treated all suspected, whether with or without grounds, of trafficking with the imperial officers. Among his principal enemies were the Shirkes, the family of his murdered stepmother, who twice rebelled gainst him. His principal officers constantly conspired against him, and he entrusted the control of his administration to a Brāhman of Oudh, whom he entitled Kavikalāsh. In the autumn of 1688 Sambhujī was obliged to march to the relief of his favourite, whom the rebellious Shirkes were besieging in Khelna, and, having beaten off the rebels, halted, on his return towards his capital, at Sangameshwar, where he abandoned himself to drunkenness and debauchery, believing himself to be secure from attack. Mukarrab Khān, who, having deserted the service of Golconda for that of Aurangzīb, had been rewarded with an important command, made a forced march from Kolhapur to Sangameshwar and appeared before the place at the head of no more than 300 horse. Kavikalāsh, who attempted to defend the place, was wounded, and the imperial troops captured him, his master and twenty-five of his principal followers with their families. In February 1689, the mahārāja of the Marāthas was led into the imperial camp at Bahādurgarh with every circumstance of insult and ignominy. When invited to accept Islam he coarsely demanded one of the emperor's daughters for his bed and foully abused Muhammad and the religion founded by him. He was blinded, and after a fortnight's torture was hacked limb from limb, and his flesh was thrown to the dogs.

After his death his half-brother, Rājarām, was released from prison and enthroned by the Marātha chiefs, but led the life of a hunted fugitive until he was able, in November, 1689, to escape to the fortress of Jinji, in the Carnatic, where for a time he was safe. A few months after Sambhujī's death the fortress of Raigarh was captured, and with it Sambhujī's son Shāhjī, a boy of seven, and the widows and,wives of Sīvajī, Sambhujī, and Rājarām. The boy Shāhjī, who was nicknamed Sāhū, received the nominal command of 7000 horse, but was detained as a prisoner in Aurangzīb's camp.

· Little was gained by Sambhujī's death, for though, while he lived, he retained the loyalty of some and the semblance of control over others, the government of the Marātha nation was already decentralised owing to his neglect of public business, and on his death every Hindu leader became the chief of a force hostile to the empire, and the Marātha chiefs were gradually becoming a confederacy of princes. In September, 1690, Zul-fikār Khān, under the order of his father, Asad Khān, Aurangzīb's minister, sat down before Jinji, but was unable for lack of troops to invest it, and five months later Rājarām returned to the fortress. The siege, officially so described, was a mere farce, and in the winter of 1692 a force of over 30,000 Marātha horse overran the Carnatic. One division surrounded and captured 'Alī Mardān Khān, *faujdar* of Conjeeveram, with 1500 horses and six elephants, and another attacked the force before Jinji and captured one of its leaders, Ismā'il Khān, with 500 horses and. two elephants. The young prince Kām Bakhsh, the child of Aurangzīb's old age, resenting the control to which he was subjected by Asad Khān and his son Zul-fikār Khān, and trusting to a rumour that Aurangzīb was dead and that Mu'azzam Shāh 'Ālam had seized the throne, conceived the design· of enlisting the aid of the Marāthas for the purpose of ousting his brother, and entered into treasonable correspondence with Rājarām. The plot was discovered, and the prince was placed under surveillance, but later reopened his correspondence with the Marāthas. Zul-fikār Khān then with great difficulty raised the siege and retired, after suffering heavy losses from the Marāthas, to the camp of his father. The prince was arrested, and the army which had been so lately besieging Jinji was itself in a state of siege. Famine was rife in the camp, and Asad Khān, after bribing the Marāthas not to molest him, withdrew from the neighbourhood of Jinji to Wandiwash, where abundant supplies were conveyed to it, after a severe contest with the Marāthas. There the troops remained until May, 1693, but Kām Bakhsh was taken by Asad Khān before his father, who was encamped at Galgala.

From 1694 until 1697, a confused series of campaigns continued in the Carnatic, the belligerents being the Marāthas, the imperial troops, and the local Hindu chieftains, who had been imperfectly subdued by the kingdoms of Bījāpur and Golconda, and were not disposed to submit to the imperial arms. The imperial forces, under the chief command of Zul-fikār Khān, gained little. They were inferior both in numbers and in mobility to the Marāthas, who cut off their supplies, and Zul-fikār Khān was ill-supplied with money, but succeeded in holding Arcot, where he concentrated his forces. He was long unable to engage the Marāthas, who eluded him when he took the field, but eventually their two leaders quarrelled and one defeated the other, and expelled him from the Carnatic, so that after the close of the rainy season of 1697, Zul-fikār was able to reopen the siege of Jinji. He was at first in no hurry to reduce the place, but soon discovered that unless he captured it he would be disgraced. He then warned Rājarām that he was about to deliver an assault, and Rājarām and his principal officers hurriedly escaped to Vellore; the outer fort was taken, and the citadel surrendered on terms. After the fall of Jinji Rājarām made his way into the Konkan and returned to Satāra, which he made his capital. He fled from that city in the autumn of 1699, on learning that Aurangzīb intended to invest it, and removed his family to Khelna, whence he himself marched towards Surat, but was defeated on his way thither. Another Marātha force, however, crossed the Nerbudda for the first time and raided the southern districts of Mālwā.

In the spring of 1700 Rājarām died of fever at Singarh, and his death was followed by a dispute between his widows, the mothers of his two legitimate sons. Tārā Bai, the elder widow, gained the support of the troops, and her son was enthroned as Sīvajī III, but the younger, Rājas Bai, also set up her son, Sambhujī II, as a rival king. Tārā Bai, an able and astute woman, was herself the chief power in the Marātha state, and in 1703 Aurangzīb conceived the device of sowing discord in the nation by liberating the legitimate heir, Sāhū, the son of Sambhujī. He first invited him to accept Islam, but desisted when Sāhū refused to apostatise, and attempted, through his youngest son, Kām Bakhsh, to induce the Marāthas to accept Sāhū, a feudatory of the empire, as their king. The Marātha chiefs were too wary to fall into so transparent a snare. They had practically won the Deccan, where nearly all the imperial officers were on the defensive, and most were obliged to yield to the demand for *hauth*, a payment of blackmail amounting to a quarter of the revenue, or else helplessly to witness the distress of unfortunate peasants who were obliged to pay the land rent or tax to the Marāthas as well as to the imperial collectors. Despite the annexation of the kingdoms of Bījāpur and Golconda, the attempt to subdue the Deccan had ended in failure, and the successors of the "mountain-rat" disputed the possession of every acre beyond the land actually covered by the camps of the imperial troops.

Aurangzīb decided that the most effective means of reducing the Marāthas to obedience was the reduction of their strongholds and, having lost faith both in the fidelity and the efficiency of his officers, resolved himself to undertake the task. From the autumn of 1699 until the spring of 1705 the aged emperor was in the field, and the fortresses of Satāra, Pārli, Panhāla, Khelna, Singarh, Raigarh and Toma were successively reduced, but only the last was taken by assault. The others fell by the treachery of their commanders, who accepted the heavy bribes offered by the emperor. Early in 1705 the siege of Wākhinkhera, defended by the Berad tribe, was opened. The fortress held out until May, and the garrison inflicted heavy losses on the besieging force, but at length Pīdia, the chief of the Berads, discovering that the place was no longer tenable, evacuated it secretly by night, and fled with his allies, the Marāthas, leaving to Aurangzīb an empty fort, a small quantity of booty, and some powder magazines which exploded during the occupation of the place, causing considerable casualties among the imperial troops. In April Aurangzīb retired to Devapur, where he fell sick, but early in November he had recovered his health sufficiently to be able to continue his march to Ahmadnagar, which he reached in January, 1706, declaring it to be his journey's end. Throughout these later years the Marāthas harassed not only all parts of the Deccan, but also the imperial provinces of Berar and Gujarāt, which they invaded and plundered, and in the latter province they inflicted a severe defeat on the imperial troops in the field.

For nearly a quarter of a century Aurangzīb had devoted his tireless energy and most of his great resources to his vain attempt to subdue the Deccan. He had crushed two kingdoms, but had failed to crush or even to check the growth of the power founded by the "mountain-rat", a power which year by year contested with him, ever more .menacingly, the rule of southern India. Meanwhile the northern provinces of his great empire were neglected. The Deccan absorbed all his best troops, and incompetent officers, with insufficient forces and funds, were unable to maintain order in the great cities and fertile and populous provinces of the north. After the departure of Akbar Mīrzā for Persia in 1687, the faithful Durga Dās had returned to Mārwār, where warfare continued for thirty years, rendering the cultivation of the soil always difficult and sometimes impossible, and where famine and pestilence were often rife. After the return of Durga Dās the spirit of the Rāthors revived. In 1698 Ajīt Singh received a pardon from the emperor, and some districts of his state as a fief, and in 1705 Durga Dās made his submission, but in the following year both he and the rāja rose in rebellion, and in March 1707 Ajīt Singh expelled the imperial governor and entered Jodhpur in triumph. "Durga Dās's life's work was thus crowned with success."

The rebellion of the Jāts under Gokla had been suppressed at the beginning of 1670, but the tribe was not crushed, and in 1685 two new leaders, Rājarām and Rāmchehra, had risen. Their strongholds were forts in the dense jungle; they plundered all travellers on the roads almost to the gates of Āgra; and Safi Khān, the governor of the city and province, was powerless to deal with them. Soon they ventured to attack imperial officers on the march with their troops; they slew Aghar Khān, on his way from Kābul to Bījāpur, and attacked and robbed Mīr Ibrāhīm, on his way from the Deccan to assume the government of Kābul. Later in 1688 they plundered the splendid tomb of Akbar at Sikandra, burned the great emperor's bones, and scattered the ashes to the wind, but in that year Bīdār Bakht, the eldest son of Prince A'zam, was appointed to the government of Āgra, and was less supine than Safi Khān. Rājarām was shortly afterwards slain in a battle between two Rājput clans, and in 1689 an elaborate campaign against the Jāts was undertaken. Bīdār Bakht captured the stronghold of Sinsanī, slaying 1500 of the tribe, and in 1691 Bishan Singh of Jaipur captured Sogar, the other stronghold of the Jāts. Rājarām's nephew, Churāman, succeeded to the leadership, and, though he was forced to go into hiding, improved and strengthened its forces, and after Aurangzīb's death came into prominence. In 1685 Rājput rebels in Bundelkhand raided Mālwā as well as Bundelkhand, and, having later gained a victory of some importance over the imperial troops, in 1690 slew the *faujdar* of Gwalior. It was not until 1692 that these rebels submitted, and were admitted into the imperial army.

Gangarām, a Brāhman who administered the fiefs of Khānjahān Bahādur in Allāhābād and Bihar during that noble's absence in the Deccan, rose in rebellion, proclaimed as emperor a pretender who personated Prince Akbar, and besieged Patna, but was driven out of Bihar by imperial troops, and died on a plundering expedition into Mālwā.

The English East India Company had in 1633 opened factories in Orissa, and later in Bengal. In 1685 disputes regarding customs-duties led to an outbreak of hostilities between the merchants in Bengal, whose chief was Job Charnock, and the imperial troops. The details of these hostilities will be found elsewhere, but eventually Aurangzīb, having discovered that the English commanded the sea route from India to the Hijāz, came to terms with them, rescinded his orders for their imprisonment, and permitted them to trade.

Such was the condition of the empire when Aurangzīb reached his journey's end, and there are few more pathetic passages in history than the account of the last stages of that journey. On Friday, March 2, 1707, having recited the morning ritual prayer, he became unconscious, and, though his fingers continued to move over the beads of his rosary, at ten o'clock he passed away, in the eighty-ninth year of his age and the forty-ninth of his reign. During his long life he had faithfully and zealously served his god, according to his lights. He had crushed the heretics; he had tortured and slain infidels; to the end of his life he had striven in person against the misbelievers; and he had extended to the sea the great empire which he had received from his father, only to witness, with his own eyes, the unmistakable symptoms of its dissolution. It was only by bribing the misbelievers, and by sacrificing his subjects to their demands, that his officers were able to hold their posts in the Deccan, and at the end of his long life of toil and self-denial the old emperor had his doubts. His farewell letters to his sons are among the saddest historical documents extant. "My fever has left me", he writes to his second son, "leaving but the skin and the husks behind it. All the soldiers are helpless, bewildered, and perturbed, like me. I brought nothing with me into the world, and am taking from it but the fruits of my sins. I know not what punishment will befall me. Though I have a firm hope in God's grace, yet for my deeds anxiety ever remains with me." Such was the end of a long life of devotion to duty as he understood it. He had certainly earned salvation according to the tenets of his creed, and yet he feared what awaited him.

His body was carried from Ahmadnagar to the hills above Daulatābād, and was there buried in a simple grave near the tomb of the saint, Zain-ud-dīn.

CHAPTER XIV

The Successors of Aurangzīb, 1707–1719

Of Aurangzīb's five sons the eldest had died in prison and the fourth an exile in a foreign land; and there remained but three, Mu'azzam, entitled Shāh 'Ālam, A'zam, and Kām Bakhsh. Shāh 'Ālam, imprisoned during the siege of Golconda, was not pardoned until 1685, when he was released and appointed to the government of the Panjab and Kābul. A week or ten days before his death Aurangzīb had appointed A'zam to the government of Mālwā and Kām Bakhsh to that of Bījāpur, but A'zam, aware of the precarious state of his father's health, had marched very slowly towards Māndū, and was able to return to Ahmadnagar very shortly after his father's death and to arrange for his burial. Shāh 'Ālam was in Jamrūd when the news reached him, and immediately marched on Āgra, crowning himself on the way under the title of Bahādur Shāh. Kām Bakhsh also assumed the imperial title in Bījāpur, and A'zam strove to reach Āgra and seize the imperial treasure there before Bahādur Shāh could do so. But Bahādur's second son, who was governor of Bengal and Bihar, forestalled him and seized the city for his father; and on Bahādur's arrival the fort was surrendered to him A'zam, fearing the ambition of his own son, Bīdār Bakht, had not allowed him to advance on Āgra, and ordered him to await his arrival at Gwalior. Much precious time was thus lost, and, when A'zam and his son advanced on Āgra, they were met by Bahādur, on June 9, north of Jajau and near the field of Samūgarh. A'zam was defeated and slain, and his head was carried before Bahādur and treated with indignity. In October Bahādur led an expedition into Rājasthān against the rāna of Udaipur and Ajīt Singh of Mārwār, but was obliged by the behaviour of his youngest brother to turn to the Deccan. He had already written to Kām Bakhsh confirming him in the government of Bījāpur and adding to it that of Golconda, and all the dependencies of both provinces, on the sole condition that the *khūtba* was recited and coin minted in the emperor's name. Kām Bakhsh refused this generous offer and insisted on contesting the succession with his elder brother.

His folly and barbarous cruelty had alienated from him all his followers, and when, on January 13, 1709, a force of 25,000 troops met him near Hyderabad, he was at the head of no more than 350 horse. This small force was dispersed and he was mortally wounded.

Bahādur was then at leisure to return to Rājasthān, and reached Ajmīr in June, 1710. The rāna, Jai Singh, and Ajīt Singh, of Mārwār, were, in fact, in rebellion, but a serious revolt of the Sikhs in the Panjab obliged Bahādur to come to terms with the Rājputs—pardons were granted to the rāna and Ajīt Singh, who waited on Bahādur and were dismissed to their states with rich gifts.

Govind, the last *guru* of the Sikhs, had accompanied Bahādur to the Deccan, but had been assassinated at Nānder in November, 1708, leaving no son; but his followers produced a man who closely resembled him and secretly sent him to the Panjab, where he claimed to be Govind, miraculously restored to life for the purpose of leading the Sikhs in a war of independence against the Muslims. He raised a force of 40,000, captured some towns of the Panjab, and, having taken Sirhind, sacked the town for four days, defiled the mosques, slaughtered the Muslims, and outraged their women. The Sikhs enriched themselves by twenty millions of rupees in cash and kind. They plundered many towns and villages, and all the country surrounding them, and attacked Lahore. They failed to take the city, but plundered the suburbs and completely closed the road between Delhi and Lahore.

This was the rising which had compelled Bahādur to come to terms with the Rājputs. The impostor, known as Banda, but styling himself Sachā Pādshāh, the "True King", was holding his court at Sadhaura, in the Ambāla district, where he struck coins and used the royal title. Bahādur left Ajmīr at the end of June 1710, but did not reach Sadhaura until December. On his approach Banda withdrew to the fortress of Lohgarh, in the hills near Sadhaura. After some hard fighting the Sikhs were driven out of Lohgarh, but Banda escaped. In January 1711 the imperial troops reoccupied Sirhind, but Banda during the remainder of the reign of Bahādur frequently descended from the hills and ravaged the plain of the Panjab.

After the Lohgarh campaign Bahādur, then seventy years of age, retired to Lahore and encamped in the plain before the city.

There he lived for but six months, concerning himself little with affairs of state, but arousing much resentment by ordaining that the *khūtba*, or Friday bidding prayer, should be recited in the Shiah form. The opposition of the citizens of Lahore and the Afghan soldiery, who were all Sunnis, to this innovation obliged the old emperor, who was peaceably disposed and whose spirit had been broken by the imprisonment which he had suffered during his father's reign, to give way, and to permit the recitation of the *khūtba* in its usual form.

On February 24, 1712, Bahādur fell ill, and died three days later. He was a ruler of feeble character and during his short reign the power of the crown was upheld chiefly by the able officials who had served his father, and whom Bahādur retained in their posts, and trusted; but he was unable to suppress their jealousies and disputes, and it was in his reign that factions were formed resembling those which contended one with another in the reigns of the later Bahmanids and in the five independent kingdoms of the Deccan, and that personal rivalries began to agitate the imperial court at the time when union was most to be desired, if the dominant power were not to lose its dominance. There were three factions, the Turanian, consisting of nobles from Transoxiana, the Persian, and the Hindustani, or native. Of these the first and last generally favoured the tenets of the Sunnis, and the other those of the Shiahs, but there were exceptions which cut across the boundary lines of nationalistic differences. The Sayyids of Bārha, for instance, who had been prominent among the soldiers of the empire since the days of Akbar, and the Sayyids of Bīlgrām, as prominent in literature as were those of Bārha in arms, were Shiahs, yet both families were Hindustani.

Bahādur had four sons, all of whom were with him at the time of his death, Mu'izz-ud-dīn, 'Azīm-ush-shān, Rafī'-ush-shān, and Jahānshāh. The second son, 'Azīm-ush-shān, the ablest of the four seized Bahādur's camp on his death, but, instead of striking immediately, remained on the defensive, thus allowing his brothers time to recruit their forces, with the result that they besieged him in his camp with their artillery. He was deserted by most of his troops, and, when his camp was attacked on March 17, 1712, his elephant, struck by a gunshot, rushed into the river, and, with its rider, was swallowed up in a quicksand.

Zul-fikār Khān, now supreme in the state, favoured the cause of Mu'izz-ud-dīn, but on March 26 Jahānshāh, the youngest of the brothers, attacked the eldest and in the course of two days' fighting defeated him and put him to flight, but was shot dead while his troops had dispersed in search of plunder. Rafī'-ush-shān, who had refrained from taking the field in the hope of being able to gain an easy victory over the exhausted troops of the victor, then attacked Mu'izz-ud-dīn, but was deserted by most of his officers. His troops fled and he was slain, and the eldest brother was proclaimed emperor under the title of Jahāndār Shāh, and made Zul-fikār Khān his minister.

Jahāndār almost immediately marched from Lahore to Delhi, and, on arriving at that city on June 22, 1712, learned that Farrukhsiyar, the elder son of 'Azīm-ush-shān, who had been left as his father's deputy in Bengal, had assembled his forces and had already reached Patna, on his way to Delhi to assert a claim to the throne. He was supported by two brothers, Hasan 'Alī and Husain 'Alī, Sayyids of Bārha, who, after some vicissitudes, had attained the rank of commanders of 4000 horse, and had been appointed by 'Azīm-ush-shān governors of Allāhābād and Bihar.

Jahāndār was one of the most contemptible rulers who ever sat upon the throne of Delhi. On reaching Delhi he abandoned himself to the grossest debauchery, in company with his favourite concubine, Lāl Kumārī. This woman and her kinsmen plundered and misruled the capital and grossly insulted the principal nobles of the state, and, while the wretched Jahāndār was sunk in sloth and drunkenness, attempted to wield the power which, in Jahāngīr's reign, had been enjoyed by Nūr Jahān. The emperor was too slothful even to attempt to defend the throne to which Zul-fikār Khān had raised him, and sent against Farrukhsiyar his eldest son, A'azz-ud-dīn, an inexperienced and cowardly youth, with a force of 50,000 horse. Meanwhile Farrukhsiyar's forces had gradually swelled, many openly espoused his cause, and on November 24, 1712, he reached Khajwa, where Aurangzīb had defeated Shujā' in 1659, and where A'azz-ud-dīn was encamped. After a few days' bombardment Farrukhsiyar ordered that A'azz-ud-dīn's camp should be stormed on November 28; but it was discovered that during the night the miserable poltroon had fled to Āgra, leaving his camp and his treasure as a prize to Farrukhsiyar. Jahāndār, on learning of his son's flight, marched

from Delhi to Āgra, but the financial condition of the state was
such that he could not pay his troops. On December 29, he
reached Āgra and was there joined by his wretched son, and by
the Jāts under their leader, Churāman. Jahāndār marched out
to Samūgarh and on January 2, 1713, Farrukhsiyar approached
the opposite bank of the Jumna. His forces forded the river above
Samūgarh a few days later, and Jahāndār in alarm retired on the
city. On January 10, the two armies met beneath the walls of
Āgra. On Jahāndār's side, Zul-fikār Khān displayed none of his
wonted energy, the Turānī nobles had been bribed to hold themselves aloof from the strife, and the Jāts plundered the imperial
camp. A division of Farrukhsiyar's troops attacked the imperial
army in rear and the whole force was thrown into confusion.
Zul-fikār Khān withdrew his troops in good order into the city,
but Jahāndār fled, in the disguise of a peasant, to Delhi. Zul-fikār
Khān reached that city, and he and his father, Asad Khān, inveigled
the wretched Jahāndār into their hands and imprisoned him. On
February 11, he was put to death in his prison by the orders of
Farrukhsiyar. On January 11, after the battle, Farrukhsiyar enthroned himself in Āgra, and, on February 12, entered Delhi in
triumph, Hasan 'Alī, entitled 'Abdullāh Khān Kutb-ul-mulk,
having already taken possession of the city. Zul-fikār Khān and
his old father, Asad Khān, Aurangzīb's minister, were inveigled
into the presence of the new emperor, and Asad Khān was allowed
to depart in peace, but his son, who had caused Farrukhsiyar's
father and brother to be put to death, was strangled, and the
property of both father and son was confiscated.

Sayyid 'Abdullāh Khān, the elder of the Sayyid brothers, was
created minister by Farrukhsiyar, his brother receiving the title
of Amīr-ul-umarā and the post of muster-master general. Muhammad Amīn Khān Chīn, leader of the Turānīs, and his son received
high offices, but the new emperor's personal favourites acted as
"King's friends" and often thwarted the designs of his official
advisers. The Sayyid brothers received the provincial governments of Multān and Bihar, but were allowed to act by deputy,
and the viceroyalty of the six provinces of the Deccan was conferred upon Chīn Kilīj Khān, entitled Nizām-ul-mulk, a leader
of the Turānī faction, cousin of Amīn Khān, and the ablest man
in the empire. Many of the adherents of Jahāndār were put to
death and some of the imperial princes, including Farrukhsiyar's
own brother, were blinded.

Ajīt Singh of Mārwār had expelled the imperial officers from his state during the wars of succession, and had captured Ajmir. Husain 'Alī Khān was sent against him, but the emperor, at the instance of his favourites, who were hostile to the Sayyids, secretly encouraged Ajīt Singh to resist the imperial troops. His resistance was, however, of no avail. Husain 'Alī overran Jodhpur, and Ajīt Singh was obliged to submit, to send his son to court, and to offer a daughter in marriage to Farrukhsiyar. During Husain 'Alī's absence the enemies of the brothers, led by Mīr Jumla, had continued to poison the emperor's mind against them, and Farrukhsiyar even urged Sayyid 'Abdullāh to resign the ministry, which, indeed, he was not competent to fill, being a soldier and no administrator, and habitually leaving his official business to be managed by his Hindu steward, Ratan Chānd. Husain 'Alī then returned to court and found that two nobles, Khān Daurān and Mīr Jumla, had been appointed to posts equivalent to those held by himself and his brother, and that plots against their lives had been formed in the palace. He also gained possession of some of Farrukhsiyar's letters to Ajīt Singh, and the brothers therefore refused to wait on the emperor and stood on the defensive in their own houses. Neither Farrukhsiyar nor his favourites dared to attack them openly and Farrukhsiyar was at last obliged to submit to them, but, nevertheless, continued his intrigues. Under the new arrangement between the Sayyids and the emperor, Husain 'Alī agreed to leave the court for the viceroyalty of the Deccan; but Farrukhsiyar instigated Dāūd Khān, the governor of Burhānpur, to oppose him, with the result that Dāūd was defeated and slain.

In this reign Banda, the false *guru* of the Sikhs, suffered for his crimes. His followers were driven from Sadhaura and Lohgarh, and he was ultimately besieged in Gurdāspur. The Sikhs fought gallantly, but were so closely beleaguered that they were compelled, when nearly perishing of hunger, to surrender unconditionally. They were paraded through Delhi and put to death on refusing to accept Islam. The impostor Banda and his infant son were barbarously cut to pieces on June 19, 1715, and the Sikh rebellion was finally crushed.

Under Churāman the Jāts continued their depredations in the country to the west of Āgra, and Jai Singh of Jaipur unsuccessfully besieged him for nearly two years in his fortress of Thūn.

Churāman opened negotiations with the court, and the siege was raised on his undertaking to pay a tribute of five million rupees.

Farrukhsiyar was too feeble and timid to overcome the Sayyids, whom he regarded as his enemies. Those who allied themselves to him with this object in view soon abandoned the cause of a master whom they could not trust, and Farrukhsiyar's attempts to reform the corrupt administration of the empire only raised up enemies against him. At length at the end of 1718 Husain 'Alī was recalled from the Deccan by his elder brother, and arrived at Delhi in February, 1719, accompanied by Bālājī Vishvanāth, Pēshwā of the Marāthas, with 11,000 Marātha troops. Farrukhsiyar humbled himself before the Sayyid brothers and granted all their demands, but they would no longer trust him, and at the end of February Farrukhsiyar was dragged from the harem of his palace, where he had taken refuge, deposed, blinded, imprisoned, and two months later put to death. "It is not too much to say", says Irvine, "that Farrukhsiyar prepared for himself the fate which finally overtook him. Feeble, false, cowardly, contemptible, it is impossible either to admire or regret him."

The Sayyid brothers raised to the throne the puppet Rafī'-uddarajāt, the second son of Bahādur's son, Rafī'-ush-shān, an intelligent youth of twenty; but the garrison of Āgra fort proclaimed Prince Akbar's son, Nīkū-siyar, as emperor. Rafī'-uddarajāt was in an advanced stage of consumption when he was raised to the throne. On June 4, 1719, he was deposed, and died a week later. On June 6, his elder brother, Rafī'-ud-daula, was proclaimed as Shāhjahān II, and the Sayyid brothers foiled a dangerous plot which had been formed for their overthrow. Husain 'Alī then marched to Āgra, compelled the fortress to surrender after a siege of less than two months, and sent Nīkū-siyar to a more secure state-prison. His principal partisan, a Brāhman named Mitrasen, committed suicide. The Sayyid brothers were then obliged to take the field against Jai Singh of Jaipur, and met at Fathpur Sīkrī, where they divided the spoils of Āgra. The puppet emperor, Shāhjahān II, died of diarrhoea in their camp on September 17, but they concealed his death for nine days, and then raised to the throne, under the title of Muhammad Shāh, Raushan Akhtar, the second son of Jahānshāh, son of Bahādur.

CHAPTER XV

Muhammad Shāh

Muhammad Shāh proved to be less of a cipher than his cousins who had preceded him on the throne of Delhi, and the party opposed to the domination of the Sayyid brothers was gaining strength. Ja'far Khān was virtually independent in Bengal, Bihar and Orissa, and Nizām-ul-mulk, one of the two chiefs of the Turanian party, held Mālwā, bitterly resenting the loss of the great viceroyalty of the Deccan, of which he had been deprived by Husain 'Alī, on whose behalf it was held by his nephew 'Ālim 'Alī. Chabela Rām was in rebellion in the province of Allāhābād, and on his death at this time his nephew Girdhār succeeded him, but was induced to surrender the province in exchange for the government of the rich province of Oudh. Meanwhile the brothers had quarrelled over the division of the spoils of Mālwā. They quarrelled again over the best means of dealing with Nizām-ul-mulk, but finally recalled him from Mālwā. Nizām-ul-mulk, instead of obeying the summons, invaded the viceroyalty of the Deccan, and seized Asīr and Burhānpur. He defeated near Khāndwa a force sent against him by the Sayyids. In August he met 'Ālim 'Alī Khān, between Bālāpur and Shegām and defeated and slew him. The Sayyid brothers were overwhelmed with grief and consternation, and Husain 'Alī, taking with him the emperor, set out for the Deccan, leaving his brother 'Abdullāh Khān as regent in Delhi. But the nobles, both of the Turanian and the Persian factions, were weary of the domination of the king-makers, and formed a plot for their destruction. On October 9, 1720, in the imperial camp near Toda Bhīm, about eighty miles west of Āgra, Husain 'Alī was assassinated by a follower of Amīn Khān, chief of the Turanian party, his tent and treasure were plundered, and Ratan Chānd, his brother's steward, was arrested and imprisoned. 'Abdullāh Khān, who was returning from the camp towards Delhi, hastened on his way, and at the capital caused Ibrāhīm, brother of Muhammad's two predecessors on the throne, to be proclaimed emperor on October 18, and assembled what troops he could to withstand the army

with Muhammad Shāh, who was returning to Delhi with the
head of Husain 'Alī borne aloft on a bamboo in his cortège.
Abdullāh Khān's raw levies were defeated by the imperial troops,
and 'Abdullāh and his puppet emperor, Ibrāhīm, were captured.
On November 23, Muhammad re-entered his capital in triumph,
and there received the viceroys and governors who waited on him
to congratulate him on his victory over the Sayyids. Amīn Khān,
who had been appointed minister on the death of Husain 'Alī,
died within three months, and Ajīt Singh of Jodhpur, who held
the government of Ajmir and Gujarāt as well as that of his own
state, and had been a partisan of the Sayyids, refused to recognise
the new government and was dismissed from his appointments.
Shujā'at Khān, deputy of Haidar Kulī Khān, succeeded him without difficulty in Gujarāt, but it was not so easy to expel him from
Ajmir. Ajīt Singh, however, on learning that Nizām-ul-mulk
was on his way from the Deccan to court, submitted to the
authority of Muhammad Shāh, and was allowed to retain the
province of Ajmir. Nizām-ul-mulk reached Delhi on January 29,
1722, and within a month was appointed minister. He ordered
Haidar Kulī Khān to repair to Gujarāt, of which he held the
government; but Haidar Kulī so misgoverned the province that
he was dismissed and Nizām-ul-mulk marched to expel him and
to seize the government of Gujarāt for himself. Haidar Kulī fled
to Delhi, and Nizām-ul-mulk, too, returned to the capital,
leaving his uncle Hamīd Khān as his deputy in Gujarāt.

On October 12, 1722, 'Abdullāh Khān, who was still in confinement, was put to death by a dose of poison. The Jāts then
again gave trouble. The Persian, Sa'ādat Khān, entitled Burhān-
ul-mulk, who had been appointed to the government of Āgra
and Oudh, had left as his deputy in Āgra a Hindu named Nīlkanth.
Nīlkanth was shot by a Jāt, and Khān Daurān appointed Jai Singh
of Jaipur to the government of Āgra, and ordered him to crush
the predatory Jāts. Jai Singh attached to himself Badan Singh,
Churāman's nephew, with whose assistance he besieged Churāman in Thūn. Churāman poisoned himself, his son Mukham
Singh fled, and Jai Singh's troops occupied Thūn. Badan Singh,
on undertaking to pay tribute, was recognised as raja of Dīg,
where he laid the foundations of the Bhartpur state.

Haidar Kulī was then appointed governor of Ajmir and expelled Ajīt Singh's officers from the province. Nizām-ul-mulk

was not happy at Delhi. The emperor was surrounded by younger and more frivolous courtiers, and rejected the advice of his minister, who on December 18, 1723, left Delhi for a shooting tour in the doāb, and thence wrote to the emperor, informing him that his presence was required in the Deccan. He left for the south without the emperor's permission, and his enemies at court easily persuaded Muhammad that he was in rebellion, and induced him to send secret instructions to Mubāriz Khān, governor of Hyderabad, to attack him, promising him the vice-royalty of the Deccan in the event of his defeating the minister.

Mubāriz Khān met his old master at Shakarkhelda in Berar on October 14, 1724, and was there defeated and slain. Nizām-ul-mulk re-named the scene of his victory Fathkhelda, and in bitter irony sent the head of his opponent to court with a letter congratulating the emperor on the victory gained by his troops over the rebel. The wretched emperor was constrained to con-ciliate him by conferring on him the title of Āsaf Jāh, still borne by his descendant. From the day of the battle of Shakarkhelda dates the virtual independence of the Hyderabad state of the empire of Delhi.

Nizām-ul-mulk held the provinces of Mālwā and Gujarāt as well as the viceroyalty of the Deccan, and steps were taken to restrict his great power and influence. His nominee was removed from the command of the imperial artillery; Girdhār Bahādur was appointed to the government of Mālwā, and Sarbuland Khān to that of Gujarāt. Nizām-ul-mulk, to protect himself against these attacks, allied himself with the Marāthas, and his uncle Hamīd Khān, having purchased their assistance by acknow-ledging their right to levy *chauth* and *sardeshmukhi*, with their aid defeated and slew Sarbuland's deputy when he attempted to establish his authority in that province. Sarbuland Khān himself, with a large force, defeated Hamīd Khān and his allies, and drove him to take refuge with his nephew in the Deccan. He and the Marāthas were again defeated and expelled from Gujarāt, when they invaded the province in the following year (1726), but, when the Marāthas returned in 1727, Sarbuland Khān, deprived of the subsidy which had enabled him to maintain a numerous army, was obliged to admit their claim to *chauth* and *sardesh-mukhi*. This was a pretext for his dismissal from the government of Gujarāt, to which Abhay Singh, who had succeeded to the state of Jodhpur on murdering his father, Ajīt Singh, was appointed. Sarbuland Khān defeated and drove from the province two deputies sent by Abhay Singh to assume its government, and finally defeated Abhay Singh himself, but, finding himself unable to maintain his position, vacated his office, allowing Abhay Singh to assume it. On his way to Delhi, after his retirement, Sarbuland Khān was arrested and was imprisoned in Āgra.

The object of Nizām-ul-mulk's encouragement of the Marāthas to extend their depredations and their power north of the Nerbudda was to free his dominions, as far as possible, of their influence and institutions, but he was unable to maintain peace with both factions of the Marāthas, and in 1727 and 1728 the northern districts of the Deccan were ravaged by Bāji Rāo Pēshwā. The Pēshwā was inveigled into invading Gujarāt when Nizām-ul-mulk had secretly arranged that he should be withstood by other Marātha leaders, and, after a campaign there which was only partly successful, Nizām-ul-mulk pacified him, on his return to the Deccan, by disclosing to him his design for the extension of Marātha influence to the north. Bāji Rāo welcomed the proposal and sent his brother Chimnaji to the help of Malhar Rāo Holkar, who was already ravaging Mālwā. The imperial governor of that province was slain in battle and the state of the country was appalling. The land was out of cultivation, most of the inhabitants left were in league with marauding parties of Marāthas, and by the end of 1731 nearly 100,000 Marātha horse were in the country, and another body of 25,000 horse was ready to invade it. Muhammad Khān Bangash, a stout Afghan soldier of fortune, who had already been defeated in Bundelkhand by a confederacy of Baghela Rājputs and Marāthas, was appointed to Mālwā, but received no support from Khān Daurān, the minister who had appointed him, and, being powerless against the invaders, was recalled. Jai Singh of Jaipur, who was appointed in his place, was little more successful, but made a futile and undignified attempt to conciliate the Marāthas. Early in 1733 these marauders raided the neighbourhood of Āgra, but withdrew before the emperor could reach the city. In 1734 they captured and occupied Hindaun, only seventy miles from Āgra, but retired before a force sent against them. A military promenade through Mālwā was ineffectual; in 1735 they invaded Rājasthān and sacked Sāmbhar; they obliged the emperor tacitly to accept

Bāji Rāo as governor of Mālwā; and later in the year it was only with Marātha help that the imperial governor of Gujarāt was able to drive from the province a former imperial governor who declined to vacate his post.

Bāji Rāo Pēshwā was in serious financial difficulties owing to the cost of the enormous army which his ambitious schemes obliged him to maintain; and the weakness of the court, and its conciliatory attitude, so encouraged his impudence that his demands exceeded the bounds of reason. They included the cession to him as a fief of the province of Mālwā and the districts of Allāhābād, Benares, Gāya and Mathura, the recognition of his right as hereditary *sardeshmukh* and *sardeshpāndya* of the six provinces of the Deccan, and an annual subsidy of five millions of rupees. This demand threw the emperor into the arms of Nizām-ul-mulk, who was implored to forget the past and to save the empire from destruction, and in March, 1737, Khān Daurān and Kamar-ud-dīn Khān, Amīn Khān's son, each at the head of a great army, advanced by different routes against the Marāthas. Burhān-ul-mulk defeated Holkar, and turned northwards to attack the Pēshwā, but Khān Daurān, jealous of his rival's recent successes, implored him not to be so rash as to attack the Pēshwā single-handed, and promised to join him. He joined him at his leisure, and, while the two armies were carousing together, the Pēshwā evaded them, marched to Delhi, encamped a few miles from its walls, and defeated a force sent out from the city against him. "I was resolved", he said, "to tell the emperor truth, to prove that I was yet in Hindūstān, and to show him flames and Marāthas at the gates of his capital." Learning that the forces of Khān Daurān, Kamar-ud-dīn, and Burhān-ul-mulk were closing in on him, the Pēshwā retired unmolested, and Khān Daurān, fearing lest the credit of settling affairs with the Marāthas should fall to Nizām-ul-mulk, who was marching northwards, concluded a treaty which conferred on the Pēshwā the government of Mālwā and assigned to him an annual subsidy of nearly three and a half millions of rupees.

Ghāzī-ud-dīn, the eldest son of Nizām-ul-mulk, was then appointed to the government of Mālwā and Gujarāt, on condition of his expelling the Marāthas, and Nizām-ul-mulk, avoiding the Pēshwā who was on his way to the Konkan, moved to Bhopāl. There he entrenched himself, when the Pēshwā returned from the Konkan and invaded Mālwā with 34,000 horse. The Marātha troops beleaguered Nizām-ul-mulk and reduced his troops to such distress that he was obliged to retreat on Sironj, and on January 17, 1738, signed a convention undertaking to secure for Bāji Rāo the government of Mālwā, with sovereignty over the territory between the Nerbudda and the Chambal, and a subsidy of five millions of rupees. These terms, on which he was allowed to continue his march unmolested, were disgraceful, but he gave away nothing which was his own, and the cession of sovereignty in the tract between the two rivers created a buffer state between the empire and his own dominions.

In 1737 Nādir Shāh, who had ascended the throne of Persia in 1736, opened the siege of Kandahār, his object being to punish the Ghilzai tribe which had recently conquered and overrun Persia and which he had driven back to its home with fearful loss. Fearing lest many of the tribe should escape over the frontier into the Indian province of Kābul he had warned Muhammad Shāh, who had promised not to admit fugitives into his dominions. The promise was not kept and many of the tribesmen fled over the frontier into the Kābul province. An envoy who had been sent to complain of Muhammad's breach of faith was detained at Delhi, and after the fall of Kandahār, on March 24, 1738, Nādir crossed the frontier, occupied Ghaznī, and reached Kābul on June 21. The citadel surrendered to him about a week later and he marched on, defeated the governor, who had retired to the Khaibar Pass, and captured Peshāwar. After crossing the Indus at Attock, he brushed aside a force which met him at Wazirābād on the Chināb, defeated Zakariya Khān, the governor of Lahore, received from him the keys of the city, and marched from Lahore on February 6, 1739.

The news that he intended to invade India had been received at Delhi with ridicule, but, as he advanced, incredulity gave way to panic. Summonses were issued to the provincial governors to hasten to Delhi with their contingents, and to the chiefs of Rājasthān, but the latter paid no heed to the call, and the great-grandson of Aurangzīb could not command a single one of those Rājput horsemen who would have given their lives in thousands for Akbar. Muhammad Shāh marched from Delhi and in the latter half of February reached Karnāl, where a defensive position was chosen.

The Indian army was distracted with terror and fervent prayers went up for the speedy arrival of Burhān-ul-mulk, who was bringing his contingent of 30,000 horse from Oudh. Nādir Shāh encamped two leagues to the west of Karnāl and Burhān-ul-mulk joined Muhammad Shāh on February 24, but, on learning that his baggage had fallen into the hands of some of the Persian troops, began the battle by an attempt to recover it. The Indian army was not prepared for action. Burhān-ul-mulk was taken prisoner, and Khān Daurān, who went to his assistance, was mortally wounded. Meanwhile the rest of the army was drawn up in the plain before its fortified camp, and the Persian army fell upon it. Muhammad Shāh had 200,000 horse and foot and 5000 field-guns, outnumbering the Persians by at least two to one, but the Indian troops were no match for the Persians, and the *mêlée* was rather a massacre than a battle. Of the Indian army 30,000 according to one account, 17,000 according to another, were slain, and the survivors took refuge in their fortified camp, where provisions soon ran short. Burhān-ul-mulk persuaded Nādir to allow Muhammad to retain his throne, but, being dissatisfied with the reward which it was suggested that he should receive, urged the conqueror to come to no final settlement until he reached Delhi. Muhammad twice waited on Nādir, who rated him for his cowardice and his mismanagement of the affairs of his empire, and informed him that he possessed but three faithful servants and that all his officers except those three had been in treasonable correspondence with him. Nādir entered Delhi just before March 21, on which day the Persian festival of the New Year and the Muslim feast of the sacrifice coincided. Muhammad had been sent before to prepare his reception, and on that day the *khūtba* was recited in the conqueror's name in the mosques of Delhi. The next day a few Persians were killed in the course of a dispute, a rumour spread that Nādir himself had been slain, and a tumult arose. The elephant-stables had been seized by a force which was intended to overawe the foreign troops, and on the next morning Nādir rode through the city in order to ascertain what losses his army had suffered. A few hundreds had been slain, and, as he returned to the mosque of Raushan-ud-daula, some stones were thrown at him and an officer by his side was killed by a musket-shot. Retiring into the mosque, he ordered a general massacre, and 470 men who had

seized the elephant-stables were brought before him and put to
the sword. The work of blood among the populace lasted from
morning until evening, and the tale of the slain had reached
30,000 when Nizām-ul-mulk and Kamar-ud-dīn waited on the
conqueror and besought him, in their master's name, to stay the
hands of the slayers. The order went forth, and at once the
slaughter ceased and the flames were extinguished, but not before
a great part of the city was in ruins.

The imperial treasury was at Nādir's disposal, but there remained the task of levying contributions from the great nobles.
The treasure collected is described as being beyond computation
and included the Peacock Throne, the jewels set in which were
valued at twenty million rupees. Nādir's own historian says that
his master carried off nearly nineteen millions sterling in coined
money. A Scottish writer says that he carried off nearly a hundred
and nineteen millions in cash and kind. He compelled Muhammad to cede to him all the imperial territory to the west of the
Indus, and the province of Sind, and to give a daughter in
marriage to his younger son, and he quitted Delhi on May 16,
leaving Muhammad and his nobles stupefied with the blow which
had fallen on them. A plot formed by Muhammad with the
object of breaking the power of Nizām-ul-mulk and the Turanian
faction failed. Safdar Jang was confirmed in the government of
Oudh, to which he had succeeded on the death of his father,
Burhān-ul-mulk, from a malignant tumour; and Zakariya in
that of the Panjab, where he had hitherto acted as the deputy of
his father, Khān Daurān. Ja'far Khān, originally the deputy of
the king-makers, and afterwards of Khān Daurān, in Bengal,
Bihar, and Orissa, had died in 1726 and had been succeeded by
his son-in-law, Shujā'-ud-daula, who died in 1739, while Nādir
was at Delhi. The viceroyalty was wrested from his incompetent
son, 'Alā-ud-daula, by Alahwirdi Khān Mahābat Jang, deputy
governor of Bihar, who defeated and slew his rival, and, on
May 12, 1740, entered Murshidābād as viceroy of Bengal, Bihar,
and Orissa.

Bāji Rāo, the Pēshwā, died on April 28, 1740, and on his death
the Turanian party appointed one of their own number as
governor of Mālwā. The Marātha commonwealth had become
a confederacy of hereditary princes. Sīvajī's descendant, the
mahārāja, was a cipher, the Pēshwā being president of the con-

federacy. Damajī Gaikwar had succeeded his father, Pilajī, in Gujarāt; Rānojī Sindhia was collector of the Marāthas' share of the revenue in Mālwā; Malhar Rāo Holkar administered territory corresponding nearly to the state now ruled by his descendant; and Rāghūji Bhonsla, who governed Berar as the Pēshwā's deputy, shortly after this time established himself at Nāgpur. He was at the moment engaged in the Carnatic, where his troops had defeated and slain Dost 'Alī, the nephew and successor of Dāūd Khān Panī, governor of that province. Bāji Rāo was succeeded as Pēshwā by his son, Bālājī Rāo. Nāsir Jang, second son of Nizām-ul-mulk, was acting as his father's deputy in the vice-royalty of the Deccan, but in August, 1740, Nizām-ul-mulk was obliged to leave Delhi to call Nāsir Jang to account for his auto-cratic measures in a state in which he was merely his father's agent. The son took up arms against his father, and, in August, 1741, attacked him near Aurangābād, but was taken prisoner and confined in the fortress of Kandhār.

The new Pēshwā, Bālājī Rāo, regarded the appointment of a Muslim noble to Mālwā as an invasion of his rights, and, as 'Azīmullāh's agent failed to expel the Marāthas from the province, or even to check their depredations, the emperor, glad of the opportunity of humbling a Turānī noble, dismissed 'Azīmullāh from the government of Mālwā and from another lucrative post at court.

Alahwirdi Khān had already established his authority over Bengal and Bihar, and was engaged in driving his opponents from Orissa when a Marātha army under Bhāskar Pant, Bhonsla's agent, so harassed and menaced him that he sought aid both of the emperor and of the Pēshwā, but succeeded in driving Bhāskar Pant's troops from the province without their help. In 1743 Rāghūji Bhonsla himself, having returned from the Carnatic, invaded Bengal to establish his claim to the *chauth* and *sardesh-mukhi* of the province, but was driven out by Bālājī Pēshwā, who received as a reward the government of Mālwā and an assignment of the arrears of *chauth* from Bihar.

The empire of the Timurids was now in a condition of dis-ruption. Mālwā was in the hands of the Pēshwā; no Muslim noble could be induced to attempt to wrest Gujarāt from those of Damajī Gaikwar; Rāghūji Bhonsla held Berar and the country to the east of that province as far as the frontier of Bengal; and

a great part of the Deccan and of the Carnatic was under the
sway of the Marāthas. In 1743 most of the viceroys and provincial
governors had excused themselves, or been excused on various
grounds, from obeying a summons to court, and for some time
a new power had been growing to the east of the Ganges in
the province once known as Katehr, but afterwards as Rohilkhand.
There 'Alī Muhammad Khān, a Hindu who had been brought
up by Afghans, had established himself with an army of Afghans,
and had assumed independence. In 1745 Muhammad left Delhi
to reduce him to obedience. He surrendered and was thenceforward kept under surveillance.

On the death of Zakariya Khān, governor of the Panjab and
Multān, the government of those provinces had been seized by
his younger son, Shāh Nawāz Khān, who in defiance of orders
from court had ousted his elder brother, Yahyā. Shāh Nawāz
Khān entered into treasonable correspondence with Ahmad Shāh
Abdāli, founder of the kingdom of Afghanistan. On the death of
Nādir Shāh the great Persian empire, restored by him, had dissolved, its northern provinces falling into the hands of the Kūjār
tribe, its southern provinces into those of Karīm Khān, a chieftain
of the Zand tribe, and the provinces of Herat and Kandahār
into those of Ahmad Khān Abdāli, the principal Afghan officer in
Nādir's army. Ahmad afterwards seized Kābul and founded the
modern kingdom of Afghanistan. Shāh Nawāz Khān first concluded an 1lliance with Ahmad, but was afterwards persuaded by
his uncle, Kamar-ud-dīn Khān, Muhammad's minister, who
tempted him with the promise of the government of the provinces
of Kābul, Kashmīr, Sind, and Multān, to repudiate this alliance, so
that when Ahmad demanded a free passage for his troops through
the Panjab, in accordance with the terms of his secret treaty with
Shāh Nawāz, he met with a flat refusal. Infuriated by this breach
of faith, Ahmad crossed the Indus and invaded the Panjab with
30,000 horse. He defeated Shāh Nawāz Khān at Lahore, and his
men sacked the city, while the imperial troops fled to Delhi.
There preparations had already been made to repel the invader,
and a large army under the nominal command of the emperor's
son, Prince Ahmad, but including the contingents of all the
leading nobles and of some of the chiefs of Rājasthān, left Delhi
on January 19, 1748, and marched to Māchhīwāra on the Sutlej.
Ahmad Shāh, eluding this army, marched to Sirhind and sacked

it. Prince Ahmad retraced his steps and marched against Ahmad
Shāh at Sirhind, where he entrenched himself. The minister,
Kamar-ud-dīn Khān, was killed in his tent by a gunshot, and the
Rājput chiefs deserted, but some of the imperial officers, after
enduring a fortnight's siege, plucked up spirit and not only
resisted the attack of the invaders, but threw their army into confusion. Ahmad Shāh Abdāli withdrew during the night from
Sirhind, and began his retreat to Afghanistan, and the news of the
victory was received with great joy in Delhi. A Turkish officer,
Muʻīn-ul-mulk, was rewarded for his services with the government of the Panjab, and set out for Lahore, while the rest of the
army returned towards Delhi.

Muhammad Shāh, having fallen sick of dropsy, grew rapidly
worse, and sent messages to his son begging him to hasten his
return, that he might see him before he died; but on reaching
Pānīpat Ahmad received the news that his father had died on
April 26, 1748. On April 29, the prince was enthroned in the
Shālīmār garden as Ahmad Shāh.

CHAPTER XVI

Ahmad Shāh and the Last Days of the Mughals

The new emperor was a young man of twenty-one, vicious, dissipated, perfidious, pusillanimous, and utterly worthless. His nobles were employed in dividing among themselves the miserable remnant of the great dominions of the House of Tīmūr, and in redistributing, without reference to him, the great offices of state. The vacant post of minister fell to Safdar Jang, viceroy of Oudh, who governed that province by deputy. Nizām-ul-mulk, viceroy of the Deccan, on his death on June 1, 1748, was succeeded, as a matter of course, by his second son, Nāsir Jang, his eldest son remaining at Delhi. Ahmad Shāh's own party, "the King's friends", was a cabal of eunuchs and women. 'Alī Muhammad Khān, governor of Katehr, had been imprisoned in Sirhind, but escaped when that town was captured by Ahmad Shāh Abdālī, and returned to Morādābād, where, on his death, he was succeeded by his son Sa'dullāh, whose father-in-law, Hāfiz Rahmat Khān, governed the province as regent. Kutb-ud-dīn, a rash soldier, was appointed governor by Safdar Jang, but was defeated and slain by Hāfiz Rahmat Khān. Kāim Jang, who had succeeded his father, Muhammad Khān Bangash, as governor of the south-eastern districts of the doāb, with his capital at Farrukh-ābād, was next appointed governor of Katehr, but fared no better than Kutb-ud-dīn, and was defeated and slain by Sa'dullāh. On the death of Kāim Jang, Safdar Jang annexed most of his territory and placed in charge of it Rāja Naval Rai, his deputy in Oudh; but Ahmad Khān, Kāim Jang's brother, surprised Naval Rai, and slew him, and afterwards, to the joy of Ahmad Shāh and the court party, defeated Safdar Jang himself, and then plundered and burned the city of Allāhābād, while his son, Mahmūd Khān, invaded Oudh and occupied Lucknow, but the citizens rose against his Afghan troops, drove them out of the city, and captured their artillery. The Afghans were driven from Oudh, but were still besieging the fort of Allāhābād when Safdar Jang, heedless of the danger of allowing the Marāthas to concern themselves in disputes in the neighbourhood of the capital, sum-

moned to his aid Malhar Rāo Holkar from Mālwā, Jai Appa
Sindhia from Narnaul, and the son of Badan Singh the Jāt,
Suraj Mal, who in 1733 had established himself in Bhartpur.
Safdar Jang and his allies met at Āgra, captured Koïl from Ahmad
Khān's governor, and marched on Farrukhābād, to which town
Ahmad Khān, having raised the siege of Allāhābād, had retired.
As the minister and his allies approached Farrukhābād, Ahmad
Khān withdrew to Husainpur (now Fathgarh), and appealed to
Sa'dullāh Khān of Moradābād for aid. Sa'dullāh marched to his
assistance, but, by the time that he arrived, a bridge of boats had
been thrown over the Ganges and the Marāthas, having crossed
the river, defeated the allied Afghan forces. The Afghans lost
twelve thousand in killed, wounded and prisoners, and fled to
the forest at the foot of the Kumāon hills. The Marāthas occupied
Rohilkhand through the rainy season of 1751 and were rewarded
for their services with the *parganas* of Koïl, Jalwar, Mau, Farrukhābād and Kora, but after the rainy season, when the Afghans
submitted, they received the *pargana* of Farrukhābād and fiefs
with an annual rental of Rs. 1,600,000. The power of the Bangash
nawabs of Farrukhābād was, however, broken.

At the beginning of Ahmad Shāh's reign the provinces of
Allāhābād and Āgra had been held by Zul-fikār Khān, Amīr-ul-
umarā, but the minister, Safdar Jang, annexed Allāhābād to his
province of Oudh, and conferred on the Amīr-ul-umara the
province of Ajmir, as compensation. The change suited the
Amīr-ul-umarā, for Bakht Singh of Mārwār was in rebellion
against his nephew, Rām Singh, who had succeeded his father,
Abhay Singh, in that state, and was in rebellion against the
emperor. The Amīr-ul-umarā expected to profit by helping
Bakht Singh on his way to Ajmir. However, he foolishly
embroiled himself with the Jāts and was severely defeated by
Suraj Mal, who, after the battle, allied himself with his beaten
foe, and volunteered to help him in Rājasthān. They marched
together to Nāgaur, but Bakht Singh refused to allow a Jāt to
intervene in the affairs of Rājasthān, and Suraj Mal was obliged
to return to Bhartpur while Amīr-ul-umarā proceeded to Ajmir,
and, after being joined by Bakht Singh, marched against Rām
Singh, who was supported by Khande Rāo, son of Malhar Rāo
Holkar. In a battle fought at Pipār the Amīr-ul-umarā foolishly
exposed his troops, in close order, to the fire of the Jodhpur

army, and, to Bakht Singh's disgust, withdrew from the field
and opened negotiations with Rām Singh. He obtained for himself a large sum of money and supplies for his troops, and hastened
back to Delhi, hoping to supplant the minister, Safdar Jang, after
his defeat by Ahmad Khān Bangash. He found, however, that
Safdar Jang's position was unassailable; he himself was unable to
pay his troops; his property was confiscated; and he was deprived
of his title, which was conferred upon Ghāzī-ud-dīn Khān Fīrūz
Jang, the eldest son of the late Nizām-ul-mulk.

Ahmad Shāh then summoned Nāsir Jang from the Deccan,
believing that with his help he would be able to free himself
from the control of Safdar Jang; but Safdar Jang seems to have
suspected the design, and Nāsir Jang, on reaching the Nerbudda,
received an order cancelling the summons. On his departure
from Aurangābād, his sister's son, Muzaffar Jang, had risen in
rebellion against him. The course of this rebellion will be described
in a later chapter. Nāsir Jang was shot by one of his own officers.
Muzaffar Jang was proclaimed by the French as viceroy of the
Deccan, but lost his life in a mutiny of his Afghan troops before
he could reach Hyderabad. The French then proclaimed Salābat
Jang, third son of Nizām-ul-mulk, as viceroy of the Deccan.

Ahmad Shāh Abdāli had invaded the Panjab for the second
time in 1749, but had been induced by the governor, Muʻīn-ul-
mulk, to retire on receiving a heavy indemnity. In 1752 he
invaded the Panjab for the third time and defeated the governor.
Ahmad Shāh of Delhi and his courtiers were overcome with
terror, anticipating a repetition of the invasion of 1739. Safdar
Jang, who was in Oudh, was summoned to Delhi, but, before
he could reach the capital, the poltroon, Ahmad Shāh, had purchased peace by the cession of the Panjab and Multān to the
Afghan. Safdar Jang was furious, for he had purchased the support of Holkar by the promise of large subsidies, which he was
no longer in a position to pay. Fīrūz Jang offered a solution of the
difficulty. He offered to relieve Safdar Jang of his obligations
to Holkar in return for a commission conferring on him his
father's viceroyalty, the Deccan, to establish himself in which he
required Holkar's help. The commission was issued, and, on
May 18, 1752, Fīrūz Jang with Holkar left Delhi for the Deccan,
having already received a promise of support from Bālājī Rāo,
the Pēshwā.

Salābat Jang, with the assistance of the French, marched against the Pēshwā and defeated him, but could not keep the field, as his troops were mutinous for want of pay, and was thus obliged to return to Hyderabad.

Fīrūz Jang and Malhar Rāo Holkar reached Aurangābād at the end of September, 1752, having been joined at Burhānpur by the Pēshwā. Their combined forces amounted to 150,000 men and Salābat Jang's position, in spite of his alliance with the French, was difficult, until it was relieved by the death of Fīrūz Jang, who was poisoned by the mother either of Salābat Jang or of Nizām 'Alī, the younger half-brother of both claimants. After his death his titles were conferred on his son, Shihāb-ud-dīn, who allied himself with the emperor against Safdar Jang. He encouraged Ahmad Shāh to deprive the minister of his command of the imperial artillery, and thus drove him into rebellion. Safdar Jang proclaimed as emperor a man of unknown origin whom he represented to be a prince of the imperial house, and on May 4, 1753, a civil war, which took the form of incessant combats in the streets and neighbourhood of the capital, broke out and lasted for six months. Safdar Jang being a Shiah, the religious element was imported into the quarrel and greatly embittered it, but neither party obtained any decided advantage, and both at length grew weary of the strife and came to terms. Safdar Jang was permitted to depart to Oudh and Intīzām-ud-daula, the young Fīrūz Jang's maternal uncle, remained minister. Fīrūz Jang employed Malhar Rāo Holkar and Jai Appa Sindhia, whom he had summoned to his aid, to punish Suraj Mal, the Jāt; but the fortresses of the Jāts could not be taken without guns, and Ahmad Shāh, on the advice of Intīzām-ud-daula, refused to place the imperial artillery at the disposal of the turbulent youth, and the emperor and his minister marched with their troops to Sikandra, to watch Fīrūz Jang's movements. Fīrūz Jang resented this, and Holkar, whose son Khande Rāo had been killed in action against the Jāts, marched with his troops towards the emperor's camp, to compel him to place his artillery at the disposal of the army, which was besieging Dīg. On learning of his approach, Ahmad Shāh and his minister, whose cowardice was notorious, fled to Delhi, leaving the army to its fate. Holkar disarmed the troops, took their horses, and captured the ladies of the imperial harem, whom he treated with respect. The siege of Dīg was then raised, and Fīrūz Jang and 'Holkar marched to Delhi, and compelled Ahmad Shāh to dismiss Intīzām-ud-daula and appoint Fīrūz Jang minister. On June 2, 1754, they deposed Ahmad Shāh and enthroned 'Azīz-ud-dīn, the eldest surviving son of Jahāndār Shāh, under the title of 'Ālamgīr II. A week later Ahmad Shāh and his mother were blinded.

Fīrūz Jang, carrying with him the puppet emperor, next left Delhi for the Panjab, which he hoped to recover. Mu'īn-ul-mulk, who had been retained as its governor by the Afghan king, was dead, and under the government of his widow the province was in a state of anarchy, but at Pānīpat the finest corps in the minister's service mutinied, and handled him severely. After escaping from their hands, he caused the corps to be massacred by the troops of Najīb Khān, a ferocious Afghan, and led the army and the emperor back to Delhi. When his troops were again ready to take the field he marched to Ludhiāna, and desired Mu'īn-ul-mulk's widow to send to him her daughter, to whom he was betrothed. She sent her daughter, and Fīrūz Jang, having married the girl, sent to Lahore a force which arrested her mother. He then bestowed the government of the Panjab on Adīna Khān, a traitor who had for many years been the evil genius of every governor.

Ahmad Shāh Abdāli, incensed by this act of aggression, marched on Lahore, put Adīna Khān to flight, and then continued his march to Delhi. Fīrūz Jang, in great alarm, appeared before him as a suppliant, and was pardoned and allowed to retain his post as minister. Delhi was plundered by the Afghans, and the daughter of the emperor's deceased brother was married to Tīmūr, Ahmad Abdāli's eldest son. Ahmad Abdāli then sent some of his troops with Fīrūz Jang to punish Suraj Mal, the Jāt, and himself followed the army, which passed on from the Jāt forts into the doāb to collect the indemnity demanded by Ahmad. From the doāb the army passed into Oudh, where Safdar Jang, who had died in October, 1754, had been succeeded by his son, Shujā'-ud-daula, who met the invaders at Bīlgrām, where he was supported by Sa'dullāh Khān of Rohilkhand. After one or two unimportant actions the viceroy bought off the aggressors with an indemnity of half a million rupees, and they retired. Ahmad Shāh Abdāli had meanwhile been dealing with the Jāts after his own fashion. Having taken the fort of Ballabgarh, he put its garrison to the sword, and sent to Mathura a force which massacred there a large number of unarmed Hindu pilgrims. He then retired to Delhi whence, owing to the fierce heat of the Indian summer and a pestilence which broke out in his army, he retired to Kābul, after appointing Najīb Khān, the Afghan, with the titles of Najīb-ud-daula, and Amīr-ul-umarā, guardian of the unfortunate emperor, 'Ālamgīr II, who was apprehensive of violence from Fīrūz Jang.

On the invader's departure Fīrūz Jang appointed Ahmad Khān Bangash Amīr-ul-umarā, and, with the assistance of Rāghunāth Rāo, the Pēshwā's brother, and Holkar, besieged the emperor and Najīb Khān in Delhi. After a siege of forty-five days Najīb Khān left the fort and retired to his estates at Sahāranpur, and Fīrūz Jang and Ahmad Khān entered the fort and assumed charge of the person of the emperor and of the administration of the empire. 'Alī Gauhar, the emperor's son, who had been sent out to collect troops to aid his father, was recalled to Delhi, where he was attacked by Fīrūz Jang's troops, but escaped and made his way to the camp of Vithal Rāo, a Marāthā who had remained in the doāb with his troops after the departure of the Pēshwā's brother and Holkar. From that camp he made his way to Lucknow, where he was entertained by Shujā'-ud-daula, and thence went to Allāhābād.

In 1751 the province of Orissa had virtually been ceded to Mīr Habīb, agent of Rāghūji Bhonsla, in settlement of the Marāthā claims to the *chauth* and *sardeshmukhi* of the provinces of Bengal, Bihar, and Orissa. On April 9, 1756, Alahwirdi Khān had died and had been succeeded by his grandson Sirāj-ud-daula. The history of this monster will be treated in a later chapter, but the victory of Plassey, won by Clive on June 23, 1757, had established the supremacy of the English in Bengal, and 'Alī Gauhar left Allāhābād in the hope of recovering Bengal, Bihar, and Orissa for the empire. He has been described as a rebel but this description is not accurate. He was in rebellion against Fīrūz Jang, who, as minister, issued commands which purported to be those of the emperor, but there is no reason to believe that the prince was acting against his father's wishes. The prince and Muhammad Kulī, Shujā'-ud-daula's governor of Allāhābād, invaded Bihar and besieged Patna, but Clive despatched from Murshidābād a force of 450 Europeans and 2500 Sepoys which dispersed their army without striking a blow, and caused them to return to Allāhābād.

Meanwhile, on October 10, 1759, Fīrūz Jang, angered by the emperor's giving what support he could to Najīb Khān when the Afghan was attacked by a force of Marāthas, caused him to be assassinated, and proclaimed, under the title of Shāhjahān III, a grandson of Kām Bakhsh, the youngest son of Aurangzīb, but 'Alī Gauhar, at Allāhābād, assumed the imperial title as Shāh 'Ālam.

The Marāthas had overrun the greater part of Hindustan and Mālwā and considerable tracts in Rājasthān, and were suspected of the design of overthrowing the pageant of Mughal sovereignty at Delhi. Their pretensions were odious not only to the Muslim nobles of Delhi, but to many of the chiefs of Rājasthān, and Ahmad Shāh Abdāli received letters from many imploring him to free the country of the burden of Marātha oppression. Rāghunāth Rāo, the Pēshwā's brother, had offended the Afghan king by invading the Panjab, then a province of Kābul under the government of Tīmur, the son of Ahmad Shāh Abdāli, and in September 1758 Jānkojī Sindhia insolently appointed Sābājī Bhonsla to the government of the Panjab.

In August, 1759, therefore, Ahmad Shāh Abdāli crossed the Indus, driving the Marātha outposts before him, and Sābājī retreated rapidly towards Delhi. Ahmad, having levied tribute from Ranjit Deo, raja of Jammū, continued his march towards Delhi. Fīrūz Jang fled and took refuge with Suraj Mal the Jāt, and Dattājī Sindhia crossed the Jumna and advanced with 40,000 horse towards Sirhind to oppose the Afghan's advance. Ahmad Shāh was joined by the Rohilla chiefs, Sa'dullāh Khān, Hāfiz Rahmat Khān, and Dūndi Khān, and by Najīb Khān and Ahmad Khān Bangash. In January, 1760, he defeated and slew Dattājī Sindhia at Bādlī, near Delhi, but Jānkojī, Sindhia's nephew, contrived to escape, though pursued, and hastened to the Deccan to raise the Marātha forces. Holkar, encamped in the doāb, failed to persuade Suraj Mal to take the field against the invader, and was himself surprised and routed by a column sent from Ahmad Shāh's army. The Pēshwā, whose cousin, Sadāsiva Bhāu, had recently defeated Salābat Jang and compelled him to cede a large tract of territory, was encamped on the Mānjira river in Salābat Jang's dominions, and nominated his son, Visvās Rāo, whom he destined for the throne of Delhi, to the command of the Marātha host which was sent against Ahmad Shāh, with his cousin Sadāsiva Bhāu in actual command.

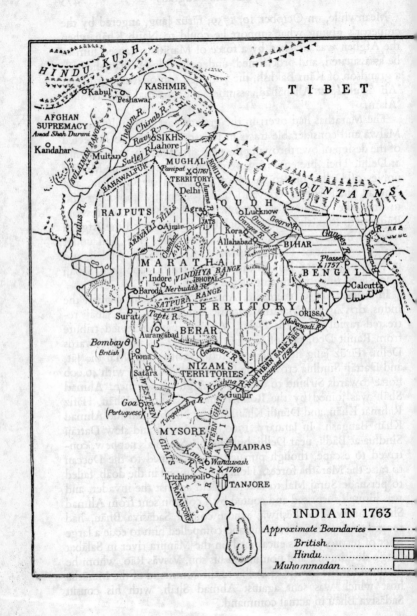

HINDU KUSH

Kabul○ ○Peshawar

KASHMIR

TIBET

AFGHAN
SUPREMACY
Amad Shah Durani

Kandahar○

○Multan

SULAIMAN RANGE

Jhelum R.

Chinab R.

Ravi R.

SIKHS

○Lahore

Sutlej R.

HIMALAYA MOUNTAINS

BAHAWALPUR

MUGHAL
TERRITORY
Panipat ×○1761

○Delhi

ROHILLAS

OUDH

Jumna R.

○Lucknow

Gumti R.

Gogra R.

Indus R.

RAJPUTS

ARAVALI HILLS

○Ajmir

JATS

○Agra

Chambal R.

○Kora

○Allahabad

Ganges R.

BIHAR

Ganges R.

Plassey
×1757

Brahmaputra R.

R.

MARATHA

○Indore

VINDHYA RANGE

BHOPAL

Nerbudda R.

○Baroda

SATPURA RANGE

TERRITORY

BENGAL

Calcutta○

○Surat

Tapti R.

BERAR

○Aurangabad

ORISSA

Mahanadi R.

Bombay ⊖
(British)

○Poona

Godavari R.

NIZAM'S
TERRITORIES

NORTHERN SARKARS
occupied 1758-9

○Satara

WESTERN GHATS

Krishna R.

○Guntur

Goa
(Portuguese)

Tungabhadra R.

MYSORE

EASTERN GHATS

CARNATIC

Kaveri R.

○Wandiwash
×1760

MADRAS

○Trichinopoli

TANJORE

TRAVANCORE

INDIA IN 1763

Approximate Boundaries -----

British ....
Hindu ....
Muhammadan ....

The Marāthas had long ceased to be merely the predatory and exceedingly mobile light cavalry which could harass and starve a less mobile army in the field. They had acquired some of the unmilitary vices of the imperial troops. Their officers were clad in cloth of gold and lodged in splendid pavilions, and the army of 30,000 which left the Deccan under the command of Visvās Rāo and Sadāsiva Bhāu was accompanied by a corps of 10,000 infantry and artillery under Ibrāhīm Khān Gārdī, a Muslim officer who had been trained by Bussy.

Ahmad Shāh Abdāli encamped, at the outbreak of the rainy season, at Sikandarābād in the doāb, and was there joined by Shujā'-ud-daula with 10,000 horse. The Marātha army seized the capital and on October 10, 1760, dethroned and imprisoned Shāhjahān III, and enthroned Jawān Bakht, the son of 'Alī Gauhar. Sadāsiva Bhāu then marched to Karnāl, with a view to cutting Ahmad Shāh's line of retreat. Ahmad Shāh then crossed the Jumna and marched in pursuit of him, on learning of which movement Sadāsiva Bhāu turned back and halted at Pānīpat, where, contrary to Marātha custom, he strongly entrenched himself. Many of the Marātha officers wished to adopt the usual Marātha tactics, but Ibrāhīm Gārdī insisted on entrenchment, for the safety of his guns. The Marātha army, estimated at 55,000 horse and 15,000 foot, with 200 guns and Pindāris and followers numbering 200,000, was cooped up in the town of Pānīpat and its immediate neighbourhood, and experienced the sufferings which the Marāthas had so often, in their palmy days, inflicted on their foes. Their supplies were cut off, and to the misery of famine was added the pestilential stench arising from the accumulation of filth within the narrow limits of their camp. Ahmad Shāh would listen to no terms and the misery of the Marāthas was extreme. "The cup is now full to the brim and cannot hold another drop", wrote the Bhāu despondently, and on the evening of January 12 the troops were ordered to prepare for battle and received all the grain left, that they might have at least one full meal before the fight. Before dawn on January 13, they marched out to attack. Their impetuosity at first threw Ahmad Shāh's army into confusion all along the line, but the Afghans recovered themselves and bore back the Marāthas by repeated charges. Early in the afternoon Visvās Rāo and Sadāsiva Bhāu fell mortally wounded, and Malhar Rāo Holkar and Damajī Gaikwar rode off while their troops fled towards Pānīpat. Thousands were cut down in the pursuit and perished by suffocation in the ditch of the entrenched camp. The town was surrounded for the night and in the morning the dense mass of the defeated army was led forth, and the captives were divided among the victors. Twenty-two thousand boys and women were retained as slaves, but the men were put to the sword, and it is estimated that nearly 200,000 perished.

This, the most desperate of the three battles fought on the field of Pānīpat, destroyed the great Marātha confederacy, and, for a time, the power of the Marātha chiefs. On the eve of the battle India, from the Indus and the Himālaya almost to the extreme limits of the peninsula, had been forced either to own their sway or to purchase their forbearance. Before twenty-four hours had passed their dominion had slipped from them. Mahādaji Sindhia in Gwalior, Rāghūji Bhonsla in Nāgpur, Malhar Rāo Holkar in Mālwā, and Damajī Gaikwar in Gujarāt recovered portions of their territories, but the Pēshwā's authority was broken, cohesion was lost, and all hopes of a Marātha empire were destroyed at Pānīpat. The calamity plunged the Marātha nation into grief and mourning, and Bālājī Rāo Pēshwā, who never recovered from the shock, died five months later.

Ahmad Shāh Abdāli, before leaving India, nominated 'Alī Gauhar as emperor of Delhi under the title of Shāh 'Ālam. Shujā'-ud-daula was appointed minister, from which circumstance he and his successors in Oudh were known to the British as nawab wazir, or "Nabob-Vizier", until permitted, in 1819, to assume the royal title, and Najīb Khān was confirmed in the rank and appointment of Amīr-ul-umarā.

The third battle of Pānīpat closes the history of the Mughal Empire. The destruction of the Marātha power did nothing to weld together the various states into which it had been broken, or to restore the power and authority of the emperor. Shāh 'Ālam was brutally blinded in 1788 by an Afghan ruffian, Ghulām Kādir, and in 1803 was formally taken under the protection of the power which the victory of Plassey had designated as the successor of the Great Mughals. His son Akbar II (1806–37) ived and died a pensioner of the same power, whose outraged athority sent his grandson, Bahādur II, to end his days as an exile in Rangoon.

Part III

BRITISH INDIA

CHAPTER I

The Coming of European Influence

The epochs of Indian history have been determined by the appearance from time to time of foreign influences. At the dawn of recorded events is the coming of the Āryan, whose intermingling with the peoples of India begot the elaborate social system and the philosophy of life which we know as Hinduism. For a thousand years it followed the normal human cycles of development and decay, and then the Muslims burst upon India, first merely touching an outlying province, but later establishing themselves firmly over the north, founding great states, building mosques to the might of Islam out of the stones of desecrated temples, and cleaving the population into two most sharply defined sections, differing profoundly in outlook, in faith, in philosophy, in politics. Lastly, eight centuries afterwards came European influences, unlike the others for they arrived, not by the Afghan passes, but by the ocean, bringing powers yet more subversive than Āryan metaphysic or the Muslim sword.

The coming of the Portuguese marks the first impact of modern western science upon the Indian world. Earlier relations between East and West had produced little but the exchange of goods. Greek and Roman, Genoese and Venetian had bought in Indian markets, pepper and cloves, gaily-dyed calicoes and rich silks; but their intercourse had been politically sterile. Different as were the ideas of European and Indian, the dominion of both the one and the other over the realm of nature was subject to the same narrow limitations. But with the European renascence Western man became the master of ocean travel. Of all the agents of political and social change none have been so powerful as the inventions which have increased human powers of movement; and politically the great achievement of the fourteenth and fifteenth centuries was neither the revolution in political or religious thought, nor the transformation of the European state-system, but the development of the art of guiding ships to unseen points across the ocean and the building of vessels stout enough to brave the storms of the open sea.

In this great work the Portuguese had led the way. A number of causes co-operated. Fronting on the Atlantic Ocean, the country had bred a race of mariners accustomed to the constant risk of life. The history of the kingdom had been in its earlier stages a long crusade against the Moors, and once these had been expelled it was most natural to pursue the attack on the African shore. In 1415 Ceuta was captured. In this exploit a young prince of barely twenty-one took part. He proved to be a man equally great in character and in intelligence. Prince Henry, whom historians have commonly called "the Navigator", grasped to the full the importance of maritime exploration and of nautical skill. The shape of the world was still a matter of speculation. The configuration of Asia and Africa was still uncertain. The existence of the New World was not even guessed. The African coast down as far as Cape Bojador was vaguely known, but the paths beyond were barred not only by shoals and currents, but by yet more terrifying beliefs borrowed from Arab legend, that all who passed beyond would turn black like the inhabitants, that they would be devoured by dragons, that they would be lost for ever in the Green Sea of Night.

It is not easy to understand what stout hearts and strong leadership were needed by adventurers into these regions of unknown peril. Prince Henry set himself to replace fancy by observed fact. At Sagres, close to Cape St Vincent, he built a naval arsenal and an observatory, and devoted his life to improving the rough instruments by which men directed their course at sea, to sending forth missions of exploration, to studying their reports, and plotting out on maps the information thus secured. By the time of his death in 1463 the African coast had been explored as far as Cape Mesurado, trading factories had been set up, the trade in gums and gold and slaves had been established, and the papal bull *Romanus Pontifex* had bestowed on the king of Portugal exclusive rights on the African coast from Cape Non to Guinea.

The voyages by which these results had been accomplished had been mere coasting voyages. But the Portuguese shipwrights were gradually mastering the art of naval construction. Their problems were not simple. Great ships (as men in those days reckoned greatness) were needed, in part the more easily to ride the great waves that came in from the Atlantic, in part to accommodate large numbers of men and the provisions that they required for voyages of most uncertain length. Under this pressure the art of shipbuilding rapidly improved. By the middle of the fifteenth century, by the time that the Turks had captured Constantinople, the Portuguese had made great strides towards the objects which Prince Henry had set before his countrymen.

His motive had been principally religious. The stars of his horoscope destined him to spread the faith. Azurara, the Portuguese chronicler, describes him as eager to bring Christianity to "the vast tribes lying under the wrath of God", to find out the real strength of the Moorish enemy, and to join hands with Prester John, the fabled Christian prince of the East, so that Islam might be completely and finally overthrown. Closely interwoven with these religious motives were the hopes of national wealth and power, and no doubt in lesser minds mere personal objects were predominant. But for the moment the capture of Constantinople disposed men to set the crusading motive foremost. In easy, tolerant Italy men might jest at the possible replacement of the pope by the sultan, but in Spain and Portugal, where men had fought for the faith, the idea of revived Muslim dominion was an abomination.

King João II, who ruled Portugal from 1481 to 1495, with extraordinary energy and hope, carried on the work that Prince Henry had begun. By his time the African trade had begun to have an importance of its own. In the year of his accession he sent an expedition to found a permanent settlement on the Guinea coast. He built the fortress of St George of the Mine—*São Jorge da Mina*. It soon received the title and privileges of a city, and in its church a daily mass was said for the great prince whose farsighted efforts had made its building possible. King João at the same time pushed his enquiries by sending expeditions overland. One directed southwards reached Timbuctoo, and another eastwards reached the Malabar coast. In the words of Barros, the king "roared round Africa like a famished lion", in the hope that his vessels would find the southern extremity of the continent, lay open the sea-route to India, and release the Eastern trade from the shackles which Turkish dominion in the Levant had set upon all that passed by the familiar overland ways. The reward of his persistance was that in 1486 Bartholomew Dias was driven by storms far to the southward and discovered what he called the Cape of Storms on his return, the king renaming the discovery the Cape of Good Hope, in allusion to his unfulfilled desire of reaching India.

In 1495 he was succeeded by Manoel, in whom religious zeal burned with extraordinary vigour. The new king even expelled the Jews from his kingdom for the sake of marrying a daughter of Ferdinand and Isabella. But he pursued the same eastern goal as his predecessor. In 1497 he despatched a new expedition, consisting of four ships under Vasco da Gama. Though Vasco's earlier exploits are unknown, he was a born leader of men. His own energy and endurance were extraordinary; his anger terrible, cruel, unforgetting; his courage indomitable. He sailed in the *São Gabriel*, whose figurehead is said still to be preserved in a monastery at Belem; and with him went three smaller vessels. Putting to sea on July 8, he reached the Natal coast at Christmas. He then sailed northwards up the African coast to Melinda, whence information, gathered from traders following the overland route, had assured the Portuguese that they could strike across direct to India. On May 17, 1498, da Gama made his landfall eight miles north of Calicut. The sea-route to the Indies had been made clear by nearly a century of unabating effort.

In four respects the Portuguese were singularly fortunate. Arriving on the Malabar Coast, they found themselves in touch with a multitude of small princes divided by mutual jealousy, so that hostility in one was certain to be accompanied by friendship in another. Furthermore, the country round Cochin and Calicut did not at that time produce enough rice for the needs of the inhabitants, who were supplied by Muslim vessels with grain from the Coromandel Coast; the region was therefore peculiarly sensitive to a blockade by sea. Again, reaching India at the close of the fifteenth century, the Portuguese found no state which could make either great or sustained efforts to prevent their establishment. And lastly the difficulties which they had had to meet and overcome implied that for purposes of war their vessels would be stouter and more formidable than any ships they would meet in Indian waters. This last was of all the most important, for the position which the Portuguese would occupy in the East certainly depended upon naval power. Their nation was too small, in view of the conditions of land warfare, for them to dream of establishing a military empire. They were vowed to the destruction (if they could possibly contrive it) of

Muslim states, and therefore could not contemplate taking up the position of unarmed and helpless traders. Supremacy at sea was the essential condition of success. And the physical circumstances which had fostered the early development of eastern seafaring had not promoted sustained progress. The regular and periodic winds which blow in the Indian seas had permitted men to sail easily and regularly at certain seasons of the year from Aden and Basra to Gujarāt, from Bengal to Malacca, from Malacca to Malabar; but their very strength and regularity had forbidden all attempts to sail against them, while cyclone and typhoon were too awful in their might for primitive sailors to dream of meeting and outliving them. Eastern mariners and vessels were therefore trained and built for voyaging with reliable and favourable winds. Their vessels were frail compared with the ships built to resist Atlantic storms. The consequence was firstly that Portuguese shipping could hold the seas in weather which would send all possible enemies fleeing for the first windward port and secondly that the Portuguese could mount cannon, the recoil of which would have shaken Indian vessels to pieces at the first discharge.

The results were not long in appearing. Da Gama reached Lisbon in August, 1499, with cargoes of spice, which he had obtained at Calicut in spite of the opposition of the Moplah traders. In the following year a new expedition was despatched. This consisted of thirteen vessels, heavily armed and carrying 1200 men, able to meet and destroy any Muslim enemies whom they might find in the Indian seas. Stretching well to the westward, in order to avoid the calms which had prolonged da Gama's voyage, the new expedition made a much more rapid passage, reaching Calicut in only a few days over six months, having touched the Brazilian coast on its way. The leader, Cabral, after long discussions with the Zamorin of Calicut, probably over the admission of Muslim vessels to trade, broke irrevocably with the Zamorin and, with only two of his ships laded, sailed to the neighbouring but independent port of Cochin. There he was welcomed, and found cargoes much easier to procure. Only five of the ships found their way back to Portugal, but their lading sufficed to cover the whole cost of the expedition, and from this time Cochin was regarded as the trading headquarters. Its harbour was excellent, its communications with the pepper country good, and its jealousy of Calicut permanent.

Cabral's expedition led to a great development of Portuguese policy. This was marked by the king's assuming the title of "Lord of the Navigation, Conquest, and Trade of Ethiopia, Arabia, Persia and India", and by the despatch of a great expedition—da Gama's second voyage—to assert the claim. The fleet consisted of twenty vessels, five of which were to remain in Indian waters when the rest returned to Europe. A regular trade was to be accompanied by a permanent force. Da Gama sailed in 1502. His conduct was marked by a consistent and even ferocious hostility towards Muslim ships and traders and the ports which protected them. Falling in with a vessel from Jeddah bound for Calicut, he plundered and destroyed it with all on board. At Calicut, being denied the expulsion which he demanded of every Muslim, he seized a great number of small craft, bombarded the town, hanged his prisoners at the yard-arm, and sent their heads and hands ashore.

In the next year, 1503, more ships were sent from Portugal, with orders to build a fort at Cochin to protect it from the attacks which the Zamorin would certainly make upon it. Though the proposal was unwelcome to some at least of the raja's advisers, "yet", as Albuquerque wrote, "to furnish his estate the more safely, and to preserve the friendship of the king of Portugal, and also to keep the great profit which accrued to him from this commerce, he...was pleased to grant a site for the building of the fortress". Temporary defences of wood and earth were at once thrown up; and though the Zamorin, in 1503 and 1504, repeatedly attacked Cochin with all the forces he could assemble, his attacks were beaten off with the aid of a small body of Portuguese under the famous Duarte Pacheco, who clearly established the military value of the Portuguese as allies. Portuguese power at sea became even clearer in 1506, when the Zamorin and the Moplahs, seeking safety in numbers, prepared a flotilla of between two and three hundred craft for the Red Sea. The flotilla was engaged by four Portuguese vessels, which destroyed the greater part of it without a single Portuguese being killed.

Meanwhile the Portuguese court had taken a further step with its eastern policy. In 1504 Albuquerque, who had held high command in the squadron despatched to India in 1503, returned to Portugal and at once urged the importance of preventing the

Moplah traders from renewing their trade or disturbing the friendly rajas of Cochin and Cannanore during the long interval between the departure of one expedition and the arrival of the next. The question was discussed in the council, which at last resolved upon a definite plan of action. It resolved to avoid all occupation of territory, to build forts only where needed to protect trade, but to maintain on the Malabar Coast as large a squadron as possible and to send a permanent governor to remain for three years in India. Francisco de Almeida was therefore appointed with the title of viceroy. He was sent out with a large fleet and 1500 soldiers. On his arrival he built a second fort at Cannanore and rebuilt the earlier one at Cochin in stone. He made Cochin his headquarters, and aimed at the control of the Malabar Coast, considering that the extension of Portuguese influence into either the Red Sea or the Straits of Malacca could lead only to a weakening of the Portuguese position.

In any case the interests of Muslim traders would have led them to resist the establishment of a new route and a new group of merchants threatening their monopoly of Indian trade westwards. But the bitterly hostile attitude which from the first had been displayed by the Portuguese made a desperate struggle certain. Other interests also were involved. The appearance of the Portuguese and the activity of their squadrons dislocated the trade up the Red Sea to Suez and Alexandria. At the close of the fifteenth century the Venetians were, and had long been, the chief distributors of eastern produce in Europe. In 1498 they had not cared to buy all the pepper that had reached Alexandria that season; in 1502 they had not been able fully to lade their galleys. They had at once urged upon Kansauh al-Ghaurī (the last Mameluke sultan of Egypt) the importance of checking without delay this danger to their own trade and to the Egyptian customs. But the sultan's power was threatened by internal dangers, and he had at first contented himself with idle threats to destroy the Christian Holy Places and drive every Christian out of his dominions. At the end of 1505 he resolved on war. Twelve vessels were built at Suez. Early in 1507 they were at last ready. Fifteen hundred fighting men were put aboard them and they sailed for India, reaching Diū in September. Though they displayed no eagerness to seek out and destroy the Portuguese, they met a squadron under the command of Almeida's son off Chaul in March, 1508, and destroyed the commander's vessel. The viceroy at once set to work to equip a fleet able to destroy the new enemy. After nine months' delay, and having emptied Cochin and Cannanore of every man that could be spared, he sailed northwards with eighteen vessels and 1200 men. On February 2, 1509, he appeared off Diū where the Egyptian squadron lay. The next day the Muslim vessels were destroyed at anchor, and the Portuguese recovered their threatened supremacy. They were indeed fortunate in having to meet the danger only when they had already accumulated considerable resources in India.

Shortly after this event the great Albuquerque arrived on the Malabar Coast. He had been despatched from Portugal in 1506, with instructions to operate against the Muslims in the Red Sea and to succeed Almeida in the chief command on the expiry of his term of office in 1507. Reaching eastern waters in 1507, he had seized Socotra and built a fort there, in order to block up the Red Sea, and had then attacked Ormuz in order to do the like by the Persian Gulf. After sinking every vessel that he found at Ormuz, he had attacked the place itself, and compelled the rais to become tributory to the king of Portugal and to suffer the Portuguese to build a fort on the island. These exploits signified an inclination greatly to expand the sphere of Portuguese operations. When Albuquerque reached Cannanore, Almeida refused to deliver up the government, and imprisoned his successor, on the score of the dangers involved in this policy of expansion. With the arrival of the new shipping in the autumn of 1509, however, the despatches from Portugal made it impossible for Almeida to continue his opposition. On November 4 he resigned and next day sailed for Europe.

His successor gave to the Portuguese position in India its specific form. Almeida had sought to dominate the Malabar Coast. Albuquerque considered that so limited a power could not easily be maintained. Its revenues would be small, its forces slender, its basis insecure. If, however, the Portuguese boldly seized the strategic points from which the whole traffic of the Indian seas could be controlled, and if, moreover, they set up their headquarters in a city of their own, rich, populous, and strong, their revenue would be great enough to maintain an irresistible power, while continuing to feed the wealth of their

mother-country with eastern exports. His policy was therefore
an extension of the principles which Almeida had laid down
rather than a departure from them.

In 1507 and 1508 his operations at Socotra and Ormuz had
partially secured the control of the Red Sea and the Persian Gulf.
The next step was the establishment of a Portuguese capital in
India. At Cochin authority continued with the raja, who could
at any time hinder provisions from coming into the Portuguese
fort. But higher up the coast lay an island-town, with an excellent harbour, recently conquered by the Muslim kingdom of
Bījāpur from the Hindus. This was Goa. It had lately afforded
refuge to a number of Turks who had escaped from the Egyptian
fleet when Almeida destroyed it, and these men were reported
to be building ships and galleys after the Portuguese style. It was
a place of great trade; caravans of merchants came there from the
Muslim and Hindu capitals; and the trade in horses from the
Persian Gulf was centred there. Early in 1510 Albuquerque
assembled twenty-three ships and a force of 1200 Portuguese. His
ostensible reason was to attack the Muslim forces in the Red Sea.
But off Goa he was joined by a body of Hindu vessels and seamen,
and proceeded to attack the place. A fort commanding the
entrance to the harbour was stormed, and the town was then
abandoned by the Muslims and occupied by Albuquerque. This
was quickly resented by the sultan of Bījāpur, and the Portuguese
were soon obliged to forsake their new conquest. But before
the end of the year Albuquerque attacked it again, stormed it,
and exterminated its Muslim inhabitants, in part as vengeance
for their having aided the Bījāpur forces, in part "because it was
necessary that there should be none but Hindus within it".

Up to this time the Portuguese had troubled little about the
eastern division of the Indian trade. But under the influence of
the new policy of expansion, of which King Manoel had become
as strong a supporter as Albuquerque himself, an expedition was
despatched from the Tagus in 1508 to Malacca, the great entrepot
of far-eastern commerce with India. The sultan of Malacca regarded the new arrivals with well-grounded distrust, and, after
some futile hostilities, the expedition departed. In May, 1511,
however, Albuquerque sailed in person with nineteen ships,
800 Europeans, and 600 Indians in the Portuguese service. On
the sultan's refusal to give up the Portuguese prisoners whom he

had seized in 1509, the place was attacked and captured after over a week of furious street-fighting. A fortress was at once constructed on the quay-side, at first of timber, then of stone taken from the mosques and the tombs of by-gone rulers. Portuguese power was thus extended into the Malay archipelago.

For the moment this marked the limit of Portuguese expansion. In 1513 Albuquerque failed in an endeavour to secure control of the Red Sea by capturing Aden; and in 1515 he went a second time to Ormuz, where he crushed opposition that had arisen to Portuguese control. He died within sight of Goa on the return voyage, and was buried in the church which he had built there. In many ways he anticipated the qualities which were to mark out the great Englishman, Clive. Both were great military leaders, whose courage and insight rose with danger. Both were men of unshakable constancy, ready to meet any foe however numerous; of a high spirit, which imposed itself on their followers; of a good fortune, which daunted their enemies. Both were capable of acts of treachery; but both resorted to treachery so rarely that they never lost the confidence of other men. Both had the skill to discern essential conditions of success and to ignore all else. Albuquerque seems to have stood alone in his generation in perceiving that "a dominion founded on a navy alone cannot last".[1] He insisted against all opposition from Portugal on the importance of maintaining Goa as the centre of Portuguese power in the east, as a great dockyard in which vessels could always be refitted, remanned, and revictualled, and as a great city whence reserves of troops could always be drawn. In this he was certainly justified. When a century afterwards the Portuguese found themselves involved in a war of life and death, they could not possibly have maintained the struggle for over fifty years but for the resources which had been accumulated at Goa.

On the foundations thus laid by Albuquerque the Portuguese gradually built up a position of extraordinary predominance in eastern waters. The conquest of Malacca led naturally to the conquest of the Moluccas—small islands producing the most precious spices, cloves and nutmeg—to participation in the important trade in silk goods with China, and the establishment of a settlement off the Chinese southern coast at Macao; and to

[1] Albuquerque, *Commentaries*, iii, 260.

trading and missionary activities in Japan. This entrance into the far-eastern trade was important financially rather than politically, for it provided the Portuguese with goods readily exchangeable for Indian commodities, and so relieved them of the need of sending from Europe great quantities of the precious metals. Then again they established a control over Ceylon. The island was too large, and its central areas too difficult, ever to be conquered by the Portuguese with the small forces that could be spared. But they built a fort at Colombo in 1518, and then spread round the coast, occupying the points which enabled them to master the trade of the island and to dominate the cinnamon-growing regions, while the frequent wars between rival Singhalese rajas prevented any persistent endeavour to expel them from the country.

In the course of time a small number of settlements grew up on the Coromandel Coast at Negapatam and St Thomé, in Arakan and Bengal at Chittagong and Hugli, in Pegu at Syriam; but these factories in eastern India never became of great importance. The Portuguese position in Ceylon and the Straits carried with it the mastery of the Bay of Bengal and its trade, and so rendered large establishments unnecessary. Consequently the settlements north of Negapatam were mainly formed and occupied by adventurers under hardly any official control and with little official encouragement. It was indeed more important for the Portuguese to strengthen themselves in western rather than in eastern India; in the latter area no attacks were to be feared, but in the former the Muslim states, with whom the Portuguese were generally on ill terms, might at any time receive help from the arch-enemy of Christendom, the Turks.

When in 1517 the Turks had overthrown the Mameluke rule in Egypt, they inherited the feud which had arisen between the Mamelukes and the Portuguese in consequence of the interference of the latter with the Red Sea trade. Commercial interests thus reinforced religious animosity. The Portuguese leaders were keenly conscious of this situation and eager to prepare against its probable results. Co-operation between the Turks and the Deccani sultanates was unlikely, for the southern Muslim states were under Shiah rulers whom the Turks, as Sunnis, regarded with great distaste. So long too as the Hindu kingdom of Vijayanagar continued to hold its own, Hindu-Muslim hostility was a

strong safeguard against attack. But to the northward lay the
sultanate of Gujarāt. Not only was the ruling family Sunni, but
also the Gujarāti ports—Surat, Bassein, Diū—had always driven
an active trade with the Red Sea, which the Portuguese were
eager to control and limit, in order to complete their growing
dominance of the European markets in eastern produce. The
Gujarātis were therefore certain to seek Turkish help and certain
of receiving Turkish sympathy. The Egyptian fleet which Almeida
had destroyed had found a welcome in Gujarāti harbours.
A strong position on the Gujarāti coast was therefore the great
object of Portuguese policy in the period following the death
of Albuquerque. In 1519 and again in 1521 attempts were made
to secure Diū, as the point from which communications with the
Red Sea could most easily be commanded. Both failed. Ten
years later another attempt was made by Nuno da Cunha, but
was checked by the arrival of Turkish reinforcements. However,
the pressure of Portuguese sea-power compelled the sultan,
Bahādur, to abandon Bassein which the Portuguese had seized,
and to agree that all the Gujarāti ships should touch at Bassein
to take Portuguese permits and pay customs-dues, and that no
Turks should in future be allowed to enter his kingdom.

The rise of the Mughal power in India at last gave the Portuguese their real opportunity. In 1535 Bahādur was attacked and
defeated by Humāyūn. In great alarm the sultan applied for help
to both the Turks and the Portuguese. The Turks for the moment
did nothing. Nuno da Cunha, however, went in person to Diū,
where in return for promises of help against the Mughals he
obtained the grant of a site on which the Portuguese might build
a fortress at Diū. The fortress was begun at once and completed
in the next year. But to Bahādur the bargain proved most im-
provident. The military science of Europe, unlike its naval
science, was still very far from being able to confer marked
superiority in open warfare. The few men—50 horse and 100
matchlock-men—whom the Portuguese could spare for their
new ally were of no material help. Events in northern India
compelled Humāyūn to withdraw the bulk of his forces, while
Bahādur was able by himself to defeat the detachments which
remained. He thus found that he had given away the control
of his principal port, and the mastery of his merchants' external
trade, virtually for nothing. He began to repent his hasty agree-

ment, and, being much given to liquor, was probably unable always to disguise his feelings. The same weakness in an envoy whom he sent to Goa is reported to have revealed to the Portuguese a design to expel them from Diū.   any case the latter resolved to seize Bahādur on the first chance that offered. One such occurred at the close of 1536, when the sultan with a few followers visited the fort; and the captain of the fort who suffered him to depart, was severely rebuked by Nuno da Cunha for his weakness of heart. Early in 1537 da Cunha himself visited Diū; and a visit which Bahādur paid to the governor of India on board ship concluded with a *mêlée* in which the sultan was wounded and drowned.

For this unhappy conclusion the Portuguese were certainly to blame. But it is certain also that the sultan himself was not guiltless. He had appealed to the Turks for help, and had probably been seeking merely to gain time until they should arrive, while the Portuguese had been bent on provoking a crisis before that should happen. When in the following year, 1538, a Turkish fleet reached Diū, it found the Portuguese in a position of considerable strength.

The Turkish expedition, which had been leisurely got together at Suez, consisted of 72 vessels, with 6500 men. It had paused on its way to seize and sack Aden. Its commander, the eunuch Sulaimān, had been ordered to engage and destroy the Portuguese fleet. He preferred, however, to join the Gujarātis who were besieging the Portuguese fort. The Turkish artillery soon effected a breach; but the Turks quarrelled with the Gujarātis, who withdrew from the siege; the Portuguese resistance was most obstinate; and after two months' persistent attack the besiegers retired just when one more desperate effort might have carried the place. On September 4, when the siege began, the defenders had numbered 1400 men; on November 4, after the repulse of the final attack, only 40 remained fit for duty. The stubborn conduct of the garrison stands out the more strongly beca se the considerable force collected at Goa to relieve Diū hesitated to set sail until the Turks had withdrawn, and only arrived in January, 1539.

This attack on the Portuguese position by the Turks was alarming enough to produce efforts both in Europe and in India to end the danger. In Europe proposals (which, however, came to nothing) were made in 1541 for the delivery of fixed quantities of pepper at Basra to be paid for in wheat, on condition that none of the pepper should be re-exported to Europe and that Portuguese ships should have free entrance into Turkish ports on the Red Sea. In the same year in India a strong expedition under Estevão da Gama was sent into the Red Sea. But although da Gama succeeded in plundering and burning Suakim, Suez proved too difficult, and the Turkish vessels there too numerous, to be attacked. A body of 400 men was landed at Massowah to help the Abyssinians who were being attacked by the Turks, and with their aid the king succeeded in recovering his territories. But apart from this the expedition produced no results.

However, from this time the Turkish menace died away, for Turkish ambitions lay rather in the direction of dominating the Mediterranean and extending their power in eastern Europe than in assailing the Portuguese position in the Indian Ocean. Consequently, till the appearance of a European enemy, the Portuguese sea-power remained unassailed, and the only enemies they had to meet were the land forces of the Indian states. In 1546 Diū underwent a prolonged siege, extending over seven months, by the Gujarāti forces under Rūmi Khān. The siege was concluded by a notable victory which Dom João de Castro, the last great governor of Portuguese India, obtained over the besiegers. Another crisis arose in 1570–71, when Goa was unsuccessfully attacked by the combined forces of Bījāpur and Ahmadnagar, and the northern ports, Damān and Bassein, were besieged by the Mughal forces which had under Akbar just conquered the sultanate of Gujarāt. But these attacks lacked the danger involved in the Turkish struggle. The sea remained open; the Portuguese fleets could carry forces and provisions wherever they were needed; and the position established by Albuquerque remained intact.

That position was essentially a maritime dominion covering a commercial monopoly. It rested on the occupation of points by which sea-borne trade must pass, and the maintenance of a naval power sufficient to meet and overthrow any marine enemy. Territorial dominion was never sought. From this point of view Goa was excellently chosen. It lay on the dividing line of Hindu and Muslim influence and was therefore relatively secure from attack, since each party would view the progress of the other with great jealousy. It was situated on an island, and was there-fore easy of defence. It had a good harbour, and so was well-fitted to be the base of a naval power. It was hedged in to the eastwards by the great wall of the Western Ghauts, and so its possession was not calculated to tempt the Portuguese into schemes of inland conquest. Its position was moreover central. Malacca and Ceylon on the east, Mozambique on the west, Ormuz on the north, could communicate with it more readily than they could have done with any other headquarters established in a different region.

From these fixed points the Portuguese fleets could operate, certain of meeting with any trading ships which the state of the monsoons allowed to put to sea. Of all these vessels they took toll. Any ship found in eastern waters without a pass from the recognised Portuguese authorities was liable to seizure. These passes—*cartas*, they were called—were specific in their terms. They named the port to which the vessel was bound; they enumerated the arms and men that might be carried; they specified the com-modities, such as pepper, which the Portuguese reserved for their own trade. Any infraction of the terms of a *carta* might involve the forfeiture of the vessel and all that she carried. By these means the royal monopolies of pepper, cloves, nutmeg, mace, silk and lac, both in the trade from India to Europe and in the port-to-port trade of India itself, were secured from external interference, to the impoverishment of Turk and Venetian, and to the enrich-ment of Portugal.

Save for a brief period after 1571, when three separate govern-ments of Mozambique, Goa and Malacca were constituted, the general control of the Portuguese establishments and trade was vested in the official who bore the title of viceroy or governor of India, according as he came out direct from Portugal with his patent of appointment, or succeeded to the office by the death or unexpected departure of its holder. His position was one of great dignity. He received the honours of royalty. None spoke to him with covered head. None save the archbishop of Goa ate with him at table. He exercised supreme civil and military authority, though in matters of importance he was supposed to consult his council. He held office for three years. The saying ran that in his first year he learnt his duties, in his second he filled his purse, in his third he visited the subordinate governments to receive presents from the occupants. The term was certainly too brief for efficiency; but it had two advantages which the home authorities thought outweighed its defects. It made the Goa government more closely dependent upon the government of Lisbon than would otherwise have been the case, and it increased the number of nobles who in a given period of time could be enriched and rewarded by holding the office. The official at Goa next in importance was the *vedor da fazenda*. He was in charge of the arsenal, docks and mint. His was a most profitable office, for he had the disposal of all the goods sent out to India on the king's account, and provided the stores needed in the dockyards, making, it was said, cent per cent on what he supplied. The chief judge was the *ouvidor general* till 1544, when he was replaced by a court of several judges. Criminal sentences needed the viceroy's or governor's approval, and civil decisions of sufficient importance might be reopened before the supreme court at Lisbon. But though the judges were technically independent of the executive, they were generally young, poor and desirous of wealth; and justice is described as having been venal, slow, and ruinously expensive. Within the city itself administration was vested in a corporation entitled to the same privileges and powers as the corporation of Lisbon. The aldermen and other officials were in theory elective; but in practice they soon came to be nominated either by the king or by the viceroy. The chief value of the corporation probably lay in its right to address petitions directly to the king, so that it afforded a channel by which the people might complain against the misconduct of the government.

Under the government of Goa were a number of subordinate governments, usually administered by an official with the title of *capitan*. Like the viceroy, he was the head of both the civil and the military establishments; and in practice he was liable to very little interference from above. The chief subordinate governments were those of Mozambique, Ormuz, Colombo and Malacca. The payment of viceroy and *capitan*, and indeed of all officials, was divided into two parts. One was the *mantimento*—maintenance allowance, to cover expenses such as diet and lodging usually drawn regularly; the other was the *ordenado*—the salary attached to the office, payable only by special warrant and normally in arrears. But besides these there quickly sprang up an endless number of perquisites—*percalços*—vastly exceeding the acknowledged payments. The salary of the *capitan* of Malacca was about £300 a year; his perquisites were reckoned to be £20,000. He was, however, in a singularly favoured position, owing to the large number of vessels which were obliged by the Portuguese regulations to touch there, and which would certainly be seriously delayed in their voyage if the *capitan* were not satisfied.

The organisation of the Portuguese government at Lisbon was ill-designed to exercise an effective control over its remoter possessions. Till 1591 there was neither a council nor a minister whose special duty it was to watch over colonial affairs, to prepare royal orders, or to secure their due observance. It is true that Indian finance was placed under the management of the *vedores da fazenda* at Lisbon. But their duties were limited to enlisting soldiers for service overseas, and to the purchase and sale of outward and inward cargoes. They had no authority over the Indian government. When Portugal passed into the possession of the Spanish crown, a special section of the finance department was devoted to colonial business, and in 1604 the Council of the Indies was set up. But by that time the Portuguese power in India had already begun to wane and the control of affairs had fallen into the confused corruption natural to a distant and unregulated administration.

Portuguese government can hardly be described as other than weak and inefficient. But the Portuguese, in the east as in Brazil, succeeded in a notable degree in passing on their culture to the peoples under their rule. They effected this by a zealous propagation of Christianity, by promoting mixed marriages, and by encouraging with the prospect of distinguished honours Indians who embraced their faith. The extension of the Christian faith had been the prime condition under which the Church of Rome had recognised the exclusive title which the Portuguese had claimed as the right of the discoverer. But the degree in which this duty was accepted had been a matter of growth. At first ecclesiastics had been few, and the conduct of the Portuguese leaders determined largely by secular considerations. But as their settlements grew, the ecclesiastical element increased swiftly. Goa was made the seat of a bishopric in 1534; in 1560 the organisation was developed by the creation of subordinate sees and the elevation of Goa into an archbishopric. In the same period the religious

D I

orders—especially the Franciscans, Dominicans and Jesuits—
became more active in Portuguese India. The Jesuits became
specially prominent in the work of education as well as conversion. In 1540 had been founded the Confraternity of the Holy
Faith. Its house at Goa had been completed on the Feast of the
Conversion of St Paul, in whose name it was dedicated in 1543;
and after the death of the founders, the House of St Paul had
been taken over by the Jesuits; thence they derived the name of
Paulists by which they became commonly known in India. By
1552 complaints were already being made that the religious were
absorbing an undue share of the royal revenues, but the cost of
religious establishments more than trebled in the following fifty
years, while in 1623 it was reckoned that at Goa and elsewhere
there were twice as many priests as Portuguese laymen. Under
this ecclesiastical pressure the religious policy developed rapidly.
In 1567 it was ordered, on the recommendation of the first
provincial council held at Goa, that no Christians should keep
infidel servants; that the public worship of both Hindus and
Muslims should cease; that all heathen residents should attend
every alternate Sunday to hear a sermon on the benefits of
Christianity; and that children left orphans should be brought
up in the Christian faith. In 1575, in consequence of orders from
Lisbon, the system was amplified. Where a heathen died without
sons, his property could be claimed by the nearest Christian
relative; converted members of Hindu families could claim immediate partition of the joint property; female converts could
claim the same share as they would have been entitled to had
they been males; and converts could claim all the legal privileges
of Portuguese nationality. Under the pressure of these rules and
the unwearying persuasions of the religious, Goa became a city
of Christians.

Though this religious policy certainly impaired the trade of
Goa, through the reluctance of great Hindu and Muslim merchants to submit themselves to such regulations, it did not
provoke any great resentment. The chief complaint which the
Muslim chroniclers make is against the cruelty of educating
orphans as Christians. In Bījāpur the sultans endowed several
Portuguese missions some of which survived into the nineteenth
century. Perhaps this attitude is to be explained by the degree
in which the Portuguese settlers became indianised in all but

religion. From the time of Albuquerque mixed marriages had been encouraged. Portuguese emigrants were almost all male. In 1524 three Portuguese women were publicly whipped at Goa for having come out clandestinely. In the second half of the century a few orphans, dowered by the king, were sent out to Goa; but in nearly every household the wife was either Indian or of mixed blood.

The position of Indian converts was decidedly favourable. They could claim the rights of Portuguese blood. They were eligible for honours and distinctions. One Malabar convert, for example, was entrusted with important commands, was made a Knight of the Order of Christ, and when, in 1571, he was killed in action, his body was brought to Goa and buried there with great ceremony.

But by the close of the sixteenth century the Portuguese dominion was fast falling into decay. The officials were corrupt; the fortresses unrepaired and unarmed; trade was declining. Even more significant was the dissolution of Portuguese union and solidarity. When the raja of Cochin had resolved to accept the Portuguese alliance, he had been moved by admiration for their discipline, which was such that, had a cabin-boy arrived with the king's orders to command them, he would have been obeyed. But when Francisco da Gama was viceroy at Goa from 1597 to 1600, he was subjected to the grossest insults. The statue of his great ancestor Vasco was thrown down and broken; and on the day when he embarked for his homeward voyage, forty men went aboard and hung him in effigy from his own yard-arm. Some of the causes of this decline are evident. Portugal was but a small country; she had undertaken two great enterprises—the occupation of Brazil and the conquest of Indian waters. Both took a heavy toll of her manhood. The mortality on board ship and in tropical climates was extraordinary. Few of the gallant, adventurous men who built up the Portuguese position in the east ever returned to their native country. The breed, robbed of its finest elements, decayed; and their successors were not the equals of the early adventurers. Even by 1538 difficulties were found in securing the necessary number of men. Outlaws were tempted by a general pardon to all, heretics and traitors excepted, who would volunteer for Indian service. Criminals sentenced to death were respited and sent out into perpetual banishment; and lesser criminals were offered pardon in return for three or more years' service. The Portuguese settlements were being reinforced by men bringing little of civic virtue, who would probably mate and breed with the lowest classes of the Indian population.

At the same time the Portuguese were falling into a condition of mental stagnancy. The astonishing progress which they had made in the allied arts of shipbuilding and navigation ceased. They remained supreme in Indian waters, but were doomed to succumb should they be called on to meet men who should have learnt to build or sail or fight their ships better than the Portuguese had learnt to do by the time of Vasco da Gama and the great Albuquerque. Goa was in fact destined to become the burial-place of reputations.

The circumstances which were to lead to this emerged in the last quarter of the sixteenth century. In 1566 the Netherlands had broken into revolt against the Spanish dominion; in 1580 Portugal passed under the Spanish crown; in the course of the two previous generations the Dutch had replaced the Venetians as the chief distributors in northern and western Europe of the eastern produce which they purchased at Lisbon. The establishment of Spanish authority in Portugal gradually brought this most profitable trade to an end. Dutch ships were seized in Portuguese harbours, and from about 1590 the situation had become so difficult as to demand the exploration of new avenues of trade. Attempts were made by Dutch seamen to open a route to India through the Arctic seas. But the obvious dangers of the way, even before its impossibility was recognised, induced Dutch merchants to invade the route which till then had been a Portuguese monopoly. Companies were formed at Enkhuisen and Amsterdam in 1594 to trade to Guinea and the Far East.

The latter, the *Compagnie van Verre*, based its plans on information furnished to it by Linschoten, who had served the Portuguese and even resided for some time at Goa. The command of the fleet was given to Cornelis van Houtmann, who had studied the spice-trade at Lisbon and had himself made the voyage to India. Houtmann sailed from the Texel in April 1595. He was destined for Bantam. Two reasons determined the choice of his destination. The object of the voyage was the purchase of spices, and therefore he aimed at reaching the Malay archipelago rather than India itself; further the main strength of the Portuguese lay along the western coast of India, and therefore the archipelago was a region where attack in force was less likely. He returned with three out of his four ships in 1597, and immediately a number of new companies were formed to share in the new trade. In the five years 1598–1602 no less than thirteen fleets were sent out to the archipelago. But all this competition proved disadvantageous. It lowered the rate of profit; and it hindered co-operation against Portuguese attacks. Therefore under the guidance of the Dutch statesman, Oldenbarnevelt, the eight existing companies were amalgamated in 1602 into the United East India Company, to which was confided the monopoly of the Indian trade for a term of twenty-one years.

The constitution of the united company was strongly marked by the circumstances of its origin. Great jealousy existed not only among the various provinces forming the United Netherlands, but also among the merchants of the principal cities. In order therefore to conciliate this local patriotism and to secure the advantages of a centralised control, the company was to be composed of six chambers—one situated at each city where one or more of the amalgamated companies had been established. General control was placed in the hands of seventeen directors representing the various chambers. But the seventeen merely laid down general policy, decreeing the number of ships and men, the amounts of the cargoes, and the persons in whom the superior command should be vested; while the individual chambers conducted the detail of fitting out the ships, purchasing the outward cargoes, and disposing of the goods returned, in proportion to their share in the capital of the company. The body thus established speedily became a very powerful corporation. Although the stock was subscribed by a large number of private persons, the stock-holders had little or no share in the management. Almost from the first the directors of the chambers were the nominees of the magistracy of the city where the chamber sat. The governing body of the chamber was thus identified with the governing body of the city, and popular control over the conduct of the chambers was completely wanting. In like manner the seventeen was virtually free from political interference. The states-general, which formed the supreme authority within the United Provinces, was with the possible exception of the Polish

Diet the weakest sovereign body in Europe. It had no judicial power. Unanimity was required for all important decisions. Its financial resources consisted of the subsidies doled out to it by the individual states. The Dutch East India Company therefore speedily became not merely a commercial association but also a political body charged with an almost independent direction of colonial interests in the east. Its policy was necessarily national, for it was directed by the same groups which determined the political conduct of the states. As in Portuguese India the king was supreme, so also in Dutch India was the commercial oligarchy. In neither was there any external body which could enforce reform if and when reform was needed. At any time the Latin tag might apply—*Quis custodiat ipsos custodes?*

These new rivals soon displayed that superiority at sea which was to be decisive in the struggle for the trade of the east. The Dutch vessels were as strong and more manageable than the high-built Portuguese shipping; and their navigators were more skilful. The Dutch had begun where the Portuguese had left off in the matter of naval technique; and the monopoly which European science had enabled the Portuguese to set up was to be broken down not by any eastern hostility but by further developments of that science in which the Portuguese had not participated. The Dutch aimed at the entire control of the Moluccas, Amboyna and Banda, a region where the Portuguese were relatively weak, where they had no fortresses of note, and where they could be overcome by the destruction or dispersal of their squadrons. The local chiefs were ready to enter into alliance with anyone who offered to free them from Portuguese control; and Portuguese commanders soon learnt to dread the fighting capacity of the newcomers, preferring whenever possible to secure safety by flight, even when superior in numbers. Amboyna was occupied by the Dutch in 1605, and they easily established a control over the Banda islands. But in this period all their attacks on the Portuguese strongholds failed, and an attempt in 1603 to enter into an alliance with the Singhalese king Wimala Dharma ended in the murder of the Dutch leader and his companions.

The twenty-one-year truce which was negotiated between Spain and the United Netherlands in 1609 conceded to the Dutch the privilege of trading in the Spanish (and Portuguese) dependencies subject to the king's permission. This agreement, which should have come into force in the east in 1610, recognised the gains which the Dutch had actually secured, but would have greatly limited their further expansion. However, the Spanish officials in the east refused to acknowledge it. The result was thus entirely to the advantage of the Dutch company, which was freed from the dangers of war in European waters and from the restrictions of peace in the spice islands. During this period the Dutch busied themselves almost entirely with Java and the archipelago. However, they established themselves on the Coromandel Coast (where the Portuguese were weakest), founding a fortified factory at Pulicat in 1609, for the provision of cotton goods for which a ready market was to be found in the archipelago.

The Dutch still lacked an administrative centre from which their operations, military, naval, and commercial could be controlled. In 1618 this was at last supplied by the genius and vigour of Coen, who determined the future character of the Dutch position much as Albuquerque had that of the Portuguese. Coen held the view that the company should in the first place secure territory large and populous enough to maintain a considerable trade. He sought centres of production. This constitutes the essential difference between his and Albuquerque's policy. The latter aimed at the naval control of commerce by the occupation of strategic posts; the former aimed at the possession of the productive areas themselves. With this end in view, Coen decided to establish his headquarters at Batavia, a site possessing an admirable harbour near the extreme north-west corner of the great island of Java. There he built a small fortified factory, to be garrisoned by about a hundred men. It was excellently fitted for his purpose. It had all the facilities for becoming a great port. It gave the Dutch a foothold in Java and therefore great scope for territorial expansion. It commanded the western entrance into the archipelago and yet occupied a central position from which the archipelago could be dominated. The Dutch were thus seeking to employ sea-power in a manner essentially different from that of the Portuguese. They were preparing, not to monopolise the whole trade of eastern waters, but to concentrate upon securing the exclusive control of a great series of islands where sea-power would enable them to assume not merely commercial, but also a political and perhaps even a territorial predominance. Into the detail of their progress it is not necessary to enter. But in course of the next eighty years they achieved the supremacy in the archipelago which they had sought. Batavia grew rapidly into a great city, thronged with traders, strongly fortified, centre of a great military and naval power, mistress of great revenues, and the headquarters of a government far stronger in resources of men, shipping and wealth than that of Goa even in its richest days.

The early stages of this expansion had much engrossed the attention of the Dutch authorities, who paid little attention to India itself save in so far as it would enable them to complete their cycle of trade. With this object they established trading factories, the chief of which were at Chinsura in Bengal, at Surat in Gujarāt, and at Bandar 'Abbās in Persia. In 1636 they renewed their attacks upon the Portuguese settlements, seeking to weaken and destroy them by blockading Goa throughout that part of the year when the monsoons permitted ships to ride off the western coast of India. Their immediate object was to secure the monopoly of pepper in Malabar and of cinnamon in Ceylon. But their blockades of Goa were less effective than they had hoped. Encouraged by the offers of alliance made to the chief of Pulicat by the Singhalese king Rāja Singha, they sent expeditions to Ceylon. In 1638 they took Battikaloa; but the king's friendship cooled when he recognised that Dutch success would merely mean the exchange of one master for another. In 1641 the Dutch captured Malacca after a year's siege.

The recovery of Portuguese independence in 1640 brought a change into the political situation, for the wars with the Dutch had been the wars of Spain, not those of Portugal. Negotiations for peace were at once opened, but the Dutch were unwilling to concede more than a ten years' truce. This was concluded in June, 1641, and was to come into force in the east twelve months later. But the Dutch were making great efforts to extend their power in Ceylon. Intentional delays prevented the necessary authorisations from reaching the Dutch leaders in the island till March, 1643, and even then they refused to cease hostilities, alleging that the Portuguese would not surrender lands which the Dutch claimed to have been mortgaged to them by Rāja Singha. By the time that the Dutch commander, Maetsuycker, and the viceroy of Goa had come to terms, in November, 1644, the Dutch had added Galle and Negombo to their conquests. The truce expired in 1653, and active operations were renewed in 1655. Colombo was taken in the following year. In 1658 the surrender of Jaffnapatam marked the expulsion of the Portuguese from Ceylon. In the same year Portuguese power vanished from the Coromandel Coast with the fall of Negapatam, which some years later the Dutch made their headquarters in southern India. In 1661 the Portuguese forts on the Malabar Coast were attacked. In Europe the Portuguese succeeded at last in making peace with the Dutch on August 6, 1661. But various pretexts were found to evade its promulgation in India until Cochin and Cranganore had fallen into Dutch hands. Thus by force and guile the Dutch wrested from their Portuguese rivals all the posts which commanded the trade they sought. Goa and the more northerly ports, Bassein, Chaul, Damān, Diū, were valueless from the Dutch point of view.

At this moment the Dutch were incomparably more powerful than any other people in the eastern seas. But there was a great difference between the situation in 1663 and that which had existed at the height of the Portuguese dominion. This was exemplified by the regions which the two had selected as the respective centres of their operations. The Portuguese had established themselves on the western coast of India, ready to meet and destroy any rivals. They claimed the monopoly of the entire eastern waters, and European ships other than their own ran the risk of seizure, while any Protestant adventurers might find themselves handed over to the Inquisition at Goa. The Dutch, however, cast their claims less widely. The spice monopoly they were resolved to hold. So their centre lay not in India but in the eastern archipelago. There they might perpetrate extraordinary acts, as the English knew to their cost, but they laid no claim to a complete monopoly of the Indian trade. The Dutch overthrow of the Portuguese signified the opening of the Indian trade to all the nations of the west.

The system of administration which grew up in the Dutch settlements is interesting, for it exemplified the difficulties which a trading corporation had to encounter and the typical manner in which they were met. The greatest of all, that of exercising due control over the management of remote dependencies, was and remained without solution among the Dutch as among the Portuguese. The Dutch directors gave comparatively little attention to the administration of their settlements, while the absence of any court of justice in the United Netherlands competent to try men accused of misconduct abroad relieved the Dutch company's servants of any fear of criminal prosecution on their return. While then, as we have already seen, there was no effective political control over the company at home, so also in the east the company's government was a law unto itself.

At first the admiral of the fleet had constituted the chief authority over the Dutch; but in 1609 it was decided to set up a permanent organisation. This consisted of a council of seven members (later increased to nine) presided over by an official designated the governor-general. This body was empowered to deal with all matters of trade, administration, war, and justice, in every Dutch settlement and factory established within the scope of the company's kclusive privileges. By the instructions which were issued, the governor-general enjoyed no special powers except that of giving a casting vote when the council was equally divided. Nevertheless, he soon became the virtual master of the Dutch Indies. The chief reason for this unintended development seems to have lain in the fact that he was the special representative of the directors, who until 1680 appointed him personally, while the vacancies in the council were filled by co-option. In case of disputes with the council his views were usually upheld; and he often held office for a considerable term of years. Maetsuycker remained governor-general from 1653 to 1678. A further reason lay in the power bestowed upon the governor-general in 1617 of sending (with the council's assent) members on special missions, so that the councillors came to be influenced by the fear of being sent on profitless, and the hope of being sent on advantageous, services. His ascendancy over the council became so complete that one governor-general, Camphuis, at the close of the seventeenth century, overruled a hostile majority on the ground that he was specially responsible to the directors, and even refused to be present at meetings of the council. Only one governor-general was ever punished for misconduct, and only one was ever recalled from his office.

Under this "High Government" at Batavia there came into existence a number of subordinate governments, framed on the

same model, under a chief official—styled governor, director, or
commander—assisted by a council. Ceylon was placed under a
governor and council; so were the Coromandel factories. The
Malabar factories were under a commander and council; those
in Bengal under a director and council. These councils not only
controlled trade and administration, but also constituted the chief
local court of justice, though an appeal lay from their decision
to the "High Government" at Batavia, and below them were
land-raden—country courts—which included representatives of
the inhabitants of the territory in question. Their distance from
Batavia and the difficulty of communications often made uniform
control impossible. At one time a plan had been devised for the
regular inspection of the subordinate governments by officials from
Batavia. But this scheme was never put into operation and the
"High Government" in practice did no more than depute one of its
members to look into matters when serious trouble broke out.

Administrative and commercial business was carried on by a
body of servants, nominated by the directors of the various
chambers. They were organised in grades, rising from writer to
assistant, and then to under- and upper-merchants, on salaries
ranging from about one to twenty pounds a month. Besides
this they were entitled to money allowances for food and fixed
quantities of liquor, oil, wood, rice, etc. But their chief advantages lay, not in their salaries and allowances, but in the private
trade which they conducted. This was from the first prohibited
by the company. Great penalties were imposed; a special official
was appointed—the fiscal—to see that the regulations were
observed; the servants were kept short of money by being allowed to draw only half their salary until they returned home;
and they were required to carry all their savings back to Europe
in bills drawn on the company's treasury. But all these precautions proved entirely useless. In Bengal, for instance, a private
company was formed by the Dutch officials to conduct the large
and profitable trade in opium to Batavia. A special inspector—
Van Rheede tot Drakestein—was sent out from Europe to reform
these abuses in 1684. He died in 1691 before he had visited all
the Indian factories and without having been able to suggest
any remedy. The prohibition of private trade was continued;
but the directors resigned themselves to the existence of abuses
which they could not prevent.

This policy was short-sighted and disastrous, for it bred in the company's servants a contempt not only for the company's orders regarding private trade, but also for all orders affecting their private interests. As the territorial possessions increased, administrative corruption added to illicit trading profits. Presents on various occasions, bribes paid for the adjudication of tax-farms, fraudulent weighments of produce received as part of the company's revenues, all came into frequent use. Usurious loans were made to the principal natives. The mode of appointing the company's servants offered no guarantee against such abuses, and even afforded convincing reason against attacking the guilty so long as their malversations provoked no public outbreak.

The Dutch military forces were ill-recruited, ill-paid, and ill-organised. Their European troops were got together by crimps who gathered the riff-raff of the cities and made up their complements with boys of thirteen or fourteen. Only half their pay was issued to them in the east, for fear they too should trade, and even that was delivered partly in clothing on which the company took 75 per cent. profit, partly in the over-valued currency of the Dutch Indies, on which it gained 33 per cent. The company always distrusted its military servants, did not admit them to its councils till 1786, and for a long time would not admit its officers to any rank higher than that of major, so that the slowness of promotion afforded small incentive to activity.

At the height of its power the company maintained some 8000 or 9000 European troops in the east. These were supplemented by the enlistment of native troops. Of these some were in regular service, but, while they received a certain amount of drill, they were never efficiently organised or trained. A striking illustration is afforded by the Malay troops who accompanied the expedition to Bengal in 1759. They were armed with the old type of screw-bayonet which fitted into the muzzle of the musket and prevented firing as soon as bayonets had been fixed. These weapons had been disused among all European troops for over fifty years.

The Dutch company's administration was probably never strong or efficient. Its seeming power was due to the military weakness of its enemies; and its establishment was brought about, not by military, but by naval strength. Its concentration to the eastward of India left the great sub-continent open to other European powers. The attention of the "High Government", directed closely to the affairs of the archipelago, missed that critical moment in the affairs of India when it might perhaps have intervened there with prospects of success. Such was the price which the Dutch company was called upon to pay for its initial success in monopolising the spice trade of the east.

CHAPTER II

The East India Company, 1600–1740

The East India Company was incorporated by Elizabeth on December 31, 1600. The great discoveries made by adventurers under the Spanish and Portuguese crowns had excited great interest in England as in other maritime states. But the exclusive rights claimed by the peninsular kingdoms had long deterred English merchants from seeking their share in the new trade-routes which had been opened and the new territories which had been discovered. English and Dutch alike had at first sought other routes to the east, the fancied north-eastern and north-western passages, which might be navigated without invading the Portuguese and Spanish zones. But .these attempts were foredoomed to failure by the arctic icefields. Under repeated losses the northern mariners began to turn their attention to the southern seas. The union of Spain and Portugal in 1580 and the state of half-war which existed between Spain and England assisted the process. Drake's great voyage round the world was completed in 1580. Open war with Spain, the defeat of the Armada, the spoils of Portuguese carracks, enlisted the rising national spirit and brought to London samples of the riches of the Indies. In 1591 Lancaster sailed for the east and reached Penang. In 1596 a fleet of vessels under Benjamin Wood sailed eastwards. In these years, too, the Dutch became increasingly active, sending out no less than twenty vessels in 1598. When, therefore, negotiations for a Spanish peace broke down, Elizabeth assented to the proposals of the London merchants, many of whom were already interested in the eastern trade by way of the Levant. The new company received a monopoly of the commerce in the great region stretching from the Cape of Good Hope to the Straits of Magellan, and its privileges were to continue for fifteen years.

At the close of the sixteenth century the idea of the joint-stock company was still in its infancy. The great privileged companies of the past had been "regulated" companies. Under these no one who was not a member could share in the branch of trade reserved for the company, and the company enjoyed the power of laying down regulations to determine the way in which the trade should be conducted, and of appointing officials to enforce its regulations and collect the dues which it imposed. But within the limits of these regulations individual members were free to trade to as great an extent as they chose. A merchant might become a member of such a company, or, in technical phrase, acquire the freedom of the company in a number of ways—by fine (or payment of a fixed entry-fee), by service, or by inheritance. The early organisation of the East India Company closely resembled that of the regulated companies. But in its financial arrangements it differed wholly from them. Its trade was conducted not by individual members employing their own capital, but by servants of the company employing capital which the members had subscribed. In short, while the company's formal organisation was that of the regulated company, its financial arrangements were those of the joint-stock company. Till then the joint-stock company had been mainly employed as the most convenient method of financing short and hazardous ventures, such as privateering voyages, at the conclusion of which the concern would be wound up, and the capital with any profits be distributed among the share-holders. Similar ideas governed the early financial operations of the East India Company. The members were invited to subscribe capital, at first for a single voyage, and later for more prolonged but definitely terminable operations. Hence the bewildering series of joint-stocks which appear in the early history of the East India Company, and the elaborate arrangements, not merely for the division of profits but also for the return of the capital. Not until the Restoration did the company adopt the modern method of securing a permanent capital and of paying to the stock-holders only such profits as the court of directors resolved to divide. In this respect the English company followed, more slowly and reluctantly, the course followed by the United Dutch Company. When the latter was formed in 1602, the capital was declared to be returnable after ten years; but this provision was in fact ignored, and the capital subscribed speedily became a permanent stock. The comparative slowness of the English development was perhaps brought about by the absence of those political responsibilities which the Dutch company was forced to assume in the first half of the seventeenth century and which

rendered uncertainty regarding capital resources highly embarrassing.

The English company's early voyages were directed to Sumatra, Java and the Moluccas, in order to secure a share in the
spice trade which formed the predominant element in eastern
commerce. In 1608, however, the first attempt was made to
establish factories in India itself. For this there were two reasons.
Peace had been made with Spain in 1604 without obtaining the
desired permission to trade in Spanish and Portuguese possessions,
so that political difficulties would follow on further invasions of
the Portuguese sphere of control. But probably more powerful
than this was the fact that the easiest way of obtaining the spices
grown in the archipelago was to lade thither not European goods,
which were in small demand, but cotton cloths and opium from
India. The company therefore sent out William Hawkins, who
was familiar with the Levant trade and could speak Turkish.
He reached the Mughal court in 1609. Though at first well
received, he soon met difficulties created by the Portuguese, who
used every effort to prevent the English from being allowed
to settle at Surat. The Surat merchants were warned that the
admission of the English would mean war with the Portuguese,
and their representations led Jahāngīr to refuse Hawkins's petition. He left Āgra in 1611, and at Surat he met three English
ships under the command of Sir Henry Middleton. The latter,
on being ordered to depart by the Surat authorities, resolved on
a measure of retribution. He sailed to the Straits of Bāb-ul-
mandab, and compelled the ships of Diū and Surat, not only to
exchange their Indian for his British commodities, but also to
pay a heavy ransom. This closure of the Red Sea trade greatly
alarmed the merchants of Surat. When, in 1612, two English
vessels under Thomas Best arrived off the port, they were readily
admitted to trade. The Portuguese sent a force against them, but
this was smartly repulsed by Best, and early in 1613 Jahāngīr
sent down orders permitting the establishment of a permanent
English factory. This concession provoked the Portuguese to
renewed action. They seized a Surat ship in her return from the
Red Sea, although she was provided with the regular Portuguese
pass. The Mughal authorities retaliated by laying siege to Damān,
and, when four English vessels reached Surat in October, 1614,
under Nicholas Downton, demanded English co-operation

against the common enemy. Downton was much perplexed.
The company's interests demanded, while national policy forbade, an attack on the Portuguese. But the viceroy of Goa
delivered him from his perplexity. The viceroy sailed in person
with a powerful fleet to destroy the English, but, after an action
off Swally Hole, was driven off. This second success strengthened
the position of the English at Surat, and in the latter part of 1615
the Portuguese made peace with Jahāngīr.

Shortly before this happened a new English fleet reached Surat
with an ambassador paid by the company but duly accredited
by the king to the court of Āgra. In this the English were following the established practice of the Levant Company, and
hoped to secure similar results. The Levant Company maintained at Constantinople an English ambassador nominated by
the English crown on the principle that an eastern court would
pay more attention to the words of a personal representative of
the king of England than to the requests of a body of merchants;
and within the Turkish dominions trade was conducted under
the "capitulations", a series of treaties granting special privileges
in matters of taxation and the administration of justice. By
sending an ambassador to Āgra the East India Company hoped
to obtain a treaty with Jahāngīr similar to the Turkish capitulations. The person chosen for this task was Sir Thomas Roe, a
man of high character, ability and insight, who had acquired
some knowledge of oriental courts at Constantinople. From the
end of 1615 till late in 1618 Roe resided constantly at Jahāngīr's
court and formed relations with the chief people there. His
character and breeding did much to raise the Mughal opinion
of the English nation; and, although he found that the court
would not hear of any treaty on commercial matters, he succeeded in obtaining grants from the viceroy of Gujarāt, Prince
Khurram (Shāhjahān), which secured the position of the English
at Surat, and he further brought to punishment local officials
who had oppressed English merchants or their agents. In 1618
the organisation of the company's factories was beginning to
take shape. The headquarters were settled at Surat, where the
company had its president and council, who controlled the up-
country factories at Ahmadābād, Broach and Āgra.

About the same time the English were seeking entry into the
Persian trade. The Persian kingdom had been much strengthened

and extended by the Safavid rulers, who had carried their conquests down to the shore of the Persian Gulf only to find that the external trade of southern Persia was closely controlled by the Portuguese at Ormuz. This was the more annoying to Shāh 'Abbās, the ruling monarch, because the silk exports of his northern provinces had to pass through the territory and pay the customs-dues of the Turks, his constant enemies. He was therefore predisposed to welcome the English proposals to open a trade with his ports on the Persian Gulf. The Portuguese resented this intrusion as bitterly but as ineffectually as they had resented the establishment of an English factory at Surat. They attempted to keep the English out by force. The first result was a sea-fight off Jask at the end of 1620, in which the Portuguese were worsted. They then attempted to coerce the Persians by attacking their ports. On this Shāh 'Abbās caused an army to be assembled against Ormuz. This was useless without support at sea. So, when in December, 1621, an English fleet arrived in the gulf, the Persian leaders demanded its co-operation against Ormuz under threats of exclusion from the Persian trade if this was refused. The English complied; Ormuz was captured in April, 1622; and the Portuguese thus lost their principal post on the trade-routes to the Mediterranean. In these early years the East India Company had thus been driven into a policy in western India and Persia which corresponded with that which the Dutch were pursuing to the eastward in the archipelago. But this seeming community of purpose in two different areas did not signify any real identity of policy. At first sight one might suppose that the two Protestant nations might have united to overthrow the position of the Roman Catholic and generally hostile power; and in Europe indeed considerable efforts were made to secure this. But the political and European interests of the Dutch were clearly overborne by their economic and Asiatic interests. The great prize of eastern commerce was the spice trade. The Dutch, as has been seen, early established themselves in the spice islands, entering into exclusive agreements with the local princes, and undertaking considerable expenditure on forts, garrisons and fleets, to keep a secure hold on the region from which they had driven their enemies. The English thus found increasing difficulty in procuring spices in the eastern islands, and resented their exclusion. The Dutch on their side claimed that they had borne all the cost and risk of expelling the Portuguese, and were entitled to the whole advantage of their successes. English attempts to trade among the islands led to fierce disputes, and, on occasion, to actual fighting; and, as the Dutch were strong in the archipelago, while the English were weak, the former got the better of their rivals. In 1619, in consequence of political pressure from both governments, the two companies entered into an agreement which was to regulate their conduct in the east. This provided for the maintenance of a joint fleet, consisting of ten Dutch and ten English ships, to keep the Portuguese in check; for the admission of English factors into the Dutch settlements; and for the division of the trade in fixed shares between the two nations. But this agreement was quite contrary to the policy which, under the inspiration of Coen, the Dutch company's agents were pursuing. Coen judged rightly that the complete control of the spice islands was within the reach of the Dutch, and he was resolved on making that project a reality. The English, too, soon proved unable to maintain their agreed squadron to take part in the active operations which the Dutch launched against the Portuguese. Quarrels then arose about the allotment of the military and naval charges, and English factors disliked their subjection to the Dutch law and Dutch tribunals at Batavia. Finally, just after the English president and council at Surat had resolved to withdraw all the English servants from the Dutch factories, the English agents at Amboyna were seized by the Dutch on a charge of conspiring to capture the fort; and these unfortunate men were put to the torture and then executed. This "massacre of Amboyna" was long and bitterly resented, and in fact ended the alliance. Although further negotiations took place in London, and English factors for a while returned to Batavia, they were withdrawn in 1628 and a separate English factory was established at Bantam under a ruler hostile to the Dutch. The English company, however, was too weak effectually to compete with its great rival in the latter's chosen stronghold. The steady and persistent expansion of Dutch power and influence, always seeking the complete exclusion of foreign interests, barred the possibility of developing an active trade in the archipelago. The English maintained a precarious position at Bantam until 1682, when the factory was withdrawn; but thereafter they possessed in this area only a few ill-controlled and often mismanaged factories on the island of Sumatra which were exchanged in 1824 for the remaining Dutch interests in India itself. This failure of the English to secure a position for themselves beside the Dutch in the archipelago was accompanied by a similar failure to establish themselves on the adjacent mainland of Indo-China and the Malay peninsula, and also led to the abandonment of the early attempts to open up commerce with Japan. For the moment therefore the Dutch were left to dominate the seas of Further Asia, while the English turned to develop the trade between India itself and Europe, and so compensated themselves for their virtual exclusion from the commerce of the archipelago which they had originally sought. In fact, faced with the alternatives of Portuguese hostility in India and of Dutch hostility to the eastward, they elected to meet the first rather than the second. The prize to be gained might be less attractive; but the policy of concentrating upon the Indian trade meant encountering a weaker enemy, and probably gaining the support of far more powerful princes than were to be found among the eastern islands.

The course of events soon proved the wisdom of this choice. The Portuguese, hard pressed by the Dutch, inclined to abate their hostility to the English. Although the Treaty of Madrid, which in 1630 closed the Spanish war, left the position in India unaltered, five years later the viceroy of Goa and William Methwold, president at Surat, signed an agreement establishing friendly relations between the two nations in India. This was confirmed by the Anglo-Portuguese treaty of 1642; and by Cromwell's treaty with the Portuguese of 1654 the admission of the English into all Portuguese harbours except Macao was formally recognised.

The results of the Anglo-Dutch wars in the time of Cromwell and Charles II confirmed this direction of the English company's policy. Cromwell's victories compelled the Dutch not only to promise indemnities for past injuries, but also to cede the island of Pulo Run in the Banda Islands. This island had been placed by its inhabitants under English protection in 1616, and had been recognised by the Dutch as an English possession in 1623. But the company had been too weak to occupy it, and it had passed under Dutch control. Its cession was most unwelcome to the Dutch, for it would have admitted the English to a probable share in the clove trade. They therefore used every pretext for delay, and only handed the island over in 1665. In the next year, on the renewal of the Dutch war, the island was at once retaken by the Dutch, and the peace of 1667 transferred the island to them. The trend of European politics thus facilitated expansion of trade in India and enforced withdrawal from the archipelago.

In western India the development under the head-factory of Surat has already been mentioned. It consisted in the establishment of factories in Broach and Baroda, in order to buy at first hand the piece-goods woven in those neighbourhoods, and at Āgra, for the sale of broad-cloth, to the followers of the imperial court, for the sake of maintaining relations with the court itself, and for the purchase of indigo, the best qualities of which were manufactured at Bayāna. Elsewhere a factory had been established at Masulipatam as early as 1611. This place was at the time the chief port on the Coromandel Coast. It supplied piece-goods, plain and chintz, which could be sold to advantage both at the company's factory at Bantam and in the ports of the Persian Gulf. In 1634 the sultan of Golconda granted the company freedom from customs-dues. But this did not exempt the factory from the frequent demands of local officials. The factors soon learnt that the blue and check cloths which found a ready sale in the archipelago could be bought much cheaper to the south-ward, in areas to which Muslim rule had not yet extended. Already in 1626 an experiment had been made by opening a factory at Armagon, a few miles north of the Dutch settlement of Pulicat. But the roadstead proved shallow and dangerous. In 1639, therefore, when the Convention of Goa had rendered the Portuguese less dangerous neighbours, the company obtained from the nāyak of Chandragiri a grant of the town of Madras-patam, close to the decayed Portuguese settlement of San Thomé. The company was permitted to build a fortified factory, and to exercise administrative authority over the town in return for the payment of a small annual quit-rent. At this time the Carnatic was in a state of great disorder. The small Hindu chiefs, who had exercised authority after the fall of Vijayanagar in the previous century, had been fighting among themselves whenever they were not resisting the raids of their northern neighbours, the Muslim sultans of Bījāpur and Golconda. In 1647 the region round Madras fell into the hands of Mīr Jumla, who at this time was serving the sultan of Golconda. Fortunately Mīr Jumla was himself a great merchant as well as a soldier and administrator. He was already on friendly terms with the English, and agreed to confirm their privileges at Madras on condition that they would pay to the Golconda authorities half the customs-dues received from strangers. This arrangement proved very unsatisfactory to the company, for it opened the way to demands that it should receive Golconda officials into the settlement. In 1658 it was agreed to commute the sultan's share for an annual payment of 380 pagodas. After prolonged disputes this sum was raised in 1672 to 1200 pagodas a year.

The next stage was English expansion into Bengal. An approach had been made by setting up factories first at Hariharpur and then at Balasore. In 1650-1 a factory was established at Hugli, and soon after others were opened at Patna and Kāsimbāzār. These seem at first to have been established in the interests of the factors' private trade rather than on the company's account; and some time elapsed before the company's trade in Bengal became unquestionably advantageous.

While the East India Company was thus being compelled by political conditions to develop the trade with India and so to establish factories in the principal trading areas, its privileges were meeting with much criticism in England. It was not possible for it to finance its purchases of Indian goods by its sales of broad-cloths and other European commodities; and it was therefore obliged regularly to export considerable amounts of the precious metals. At a time when men believed that the accumulation of gold and silver was the chief method of increasing national wealth, the company's trade was constantly liable to the attacks of pamphleteers, although Mun's famous pamphlet, *England's Treasure by Foreign Trade*, did something to spread sounder economic ideas. More dangerous to the company's position, however, than the attacks of theorists was the uncertain attitude of the first two Stuarts. James I was at one time induced to contemplate the establishment of a Scottish East India Company, and Charles I was persuaded to authorise a specific infraction of the company's privileges. In 1637 he granted to a group of merchants headed by Sir William Courteen letters patent permitting it to trade to places within the company's limits where the company had no factory, and the new traders failed to observe even these limitations.

The company's position, already embarrassed by this rivalry, was worsened by the civil war which soon followed. With the fall of the king, it was no longer able to claim the exclusive rights bestowed upon it by royal charter, and the new government long delayed to restore it to its old position. It also suffered heavy losses in the course of the First Dutch War, and in 1655 was unable to raise new capital.

This, however, proved to be the last of its misfortunes. In 1657 Cromwell granted it a new charter; and, though the Protectorate was then on the point of ending, the Restoration brought with it a vigorous and consistent policy of extending English foreign trade by the agency of chartered companies. The charters of Charles II and James II confirmed the old privileges and enlarged the company's powers. At the same time the establishment of a permanent joint-stock relieved the company of the recurrent difficulties which in the past it had had to encounter. The thirty years following on 1660 were years of expanding trade and great prosperity.

Among the provisions of the charters of this period were grants of authority to build and maintain fortresses, to enlist and discipline armed men, to maintain vessels of war, to coin money, and to administer justice both civil and criminal. At the same time the company became the formally recognised agent of the crown in the first of English territorial acquisitions in India. It was indeed characteristic of the new policy that Charles II should have been willing to accept as part of his Portuguese bride's dowry the remote island of Bombay. After many difficulties had been raised by the Portuguese officials in India, the place was made over to the English in 1665. In 1668, in consequence of the inconvenience and cost of administering a small, isolated settlement, it was transferred to the company, to be held of and administered for the crown at an annual quit-rent of £10 per annum. Thus the company came to exercise sovereign powers in two of its Indian settlements, at Bombay as representative of the king of England, at Madras under grants from Indian rulers, and questions of administration emerged prominently alongside of matters of trade.

The dominant personality in the company's directorate in the time of the later Stuarts was that of Sir Josia Child, under whose influence broad views of policy began to appear. Though far from neglecting the commercial interests of the company, and acutely conscious that the company needed the support of English public opinion as well as legal privilege and royal favour, he urged the importance of just government in India and the need of choosing wise governors for the English settlements. In one striking despatch, clearly inspired by his views, the company described the character which its servants should possess to qualify them for offices of political trust. It was not enough, it declared, to have dwelt many years in India, or to be familiar with all the intricacies of· trade, or even to be versed in the country languages; these things indeed were needful, but beyond them the servant fitted for the company's highest offices must be a man of parts and education, a statesman as well as a merchant. In this attitude the English company offered a sharp contrast to the contemporary Dutch directors, who fixed all their attention upon matters of trade and left administration to take care of itself. In fiscal matters, however, Child urged·that the example of the Dutch should be laid closely to heart. He thought rightly that the company's settlements should establish a regular revenue system, and that the inhabitants should be encouraged not by exemption from taxation but by a fair system equitably administered.

Indeed the latter part of the seventeenth century was a time of considerable growth, both at Madras and at Bombay. Internal wars were beginning again to afflict the country, and the fundamental hostility between Islam and Hinduism was encouraged by the unwise policy of Aurangzīb. In western India the Marātha war was throwing the country-side into confusion. The twofold sack of Surat was teaching Indian merchants that even the greatest of Mughal ports was but an insecure place of habitation, while the conduct of Mughal governors led Hindu traders to think of seeking refuge under the foreign rulers of Bombay, especially under the.wise and moderate government of Gerald Aungier. At Madras men lived in security while the country round was ravaged by Sīvajī's raiders, and while the Golconda government was being overthrown by Mughal armies. These conditions emphasised the wisdom and foresight of Child's demands for increased attention to administrative questions. The purpose of the company (as he viewed it) was "to establish such a politie of civill and military power, and to create and secure such a large revenue to secure both, . . . as may be the foundation of a large, well-grounded, sure English dominion in India for all time to come".

In fact, however, he judged the future more accurately than the present, and underestimated the effective force of the Mughal empire, misled, perhaps, by the disorganisation of western India and the ease with which Sīvajī had swooped down from his mountains upon Mughal garrisons and cities. The English factories in Bengal had always been harassed by demands for land-customs on goods in transit and for presents for leading officials. In this matter the position of the Bengal trade was peculiar. Elsewhere the goods which formed the staple articles of trade were purchased at no great distance from the coast. Indeed the trend of the company's trade in the second half of the seventeenth century displays a growing inclination to avoid transactions at remote inland factories such as Āgra. But in Bengal the great markets lay far up the water-ways of the province. Silk could only be procured to the best advantage at Kāsimbāzār, salt-petre at Patna, muslins at Dacca. The Bengal trade thus lay at the mercy of a multitude of customs-posts, and could be brought to a complete stand-still at any moment by official orders. In 1656 the governor of the province had exempted the English trade from internal dues on condition of a fixed annual payment. But his successors had refused to recognise his grant. In 1678 a new grant from the governor was at last procured; and in 1680 a *farmān* was obtained from the emperor Aurangzīb. But neither the governor's nor the emperor's grant ended the demands which were made. The English factors came therefore to the conclusion that they needed a fortified settlement near the mouth of the Hugli, whither they might withdraw in time of trouble, and from which they might blockade the sea-borne trade of the province in case of need. In 1686 the company attempted to put this plan into operation. It sent out a number of ships with a small force of men to Bengal, and the Mughal ports of western India were also to be blockaded. In the war which followed, though the Mughal attack on the factory at Hugli was repelled, the English soon abandoned it and dropped down the river, first to the village where Calcutta was afterwards to arise, and then to a fever-stricken island at the mouth, whence the cool and experienced English agent, Job Charnock, opened negotiations

which permitted the English in the autumn of 1687 to return
to Sūtanūtī. In the next year, however, a fresh naval force
arrived from London with orders to attack and occupy Chittagong. Its commander, William Heath, refused to listen to
Charnock's arguments for leaving well alone. He insisted on
abandoning Sūtanūtī, sailed to Chittagong which he found too
strong to be attacked, and then retired to Madras. These irresolute
and foolish proceedings were brought to a close by the peace
which was made with the Mughals by the president and council
of Bombay, which in May, 1687, had replaced Surat as the
headquarters of the company in India. The Bombay factors had
hesitated for some time to break their peaceful relations with
Aurangzīb. In the latter part of 1688, however, they had seized
a number of Indian vessels, in revenge for which the factors at
Surat had been imprisoned, and Bombay itself had been blockaded.
In 1690 it was agreed to pay a large sum in compensation for
the seizure of the Indian ships, and to remove the president himself, Sir John Child, from his office. In fact, he died shortly
before the discussions were completed.

It was as well that the company was thus speedily relieved from
a struggle for which it possessed neither sufficient forces nor
adequate organisation. The restoration of peace was soon followed by the return of the English to Bengal. The Mughal
governor, moved probably by the complaints of Indian merchants
whose trade was suffering, invited Charnock back. The latter
refused to stir until an agreement had been reached on the
question of customs-dues. In February, 1691, a *farmān* was
granted exempting English trade from these payments in return
for Rs. 3000 a year. But before this, trusting in the governor's
promises, Charnock had already returned, in August, 1690, to
Sūtanūtī. Guarded by marshes on the east and by the river itself
on the west, the place was well suited for defence. Great ships
could ascend the river and anchor close inshore. No great
Mughal official dwelt in its neighbourhood. It was therefore
much better suited for an English settlement than the city of
Hugli higher up the river, while the market which would be
created by its establishment would soon attract a considerable
population. In 1696, when the local zamindars broke into rebellion, leave was obtained to fortify the factory. In 1698 the
company was granted the zamindari of three villages—Sūtanūtī,

Kālighāt, and Govindpur. In 1700 the Bengal factories were placed under the separate control of a president and council, established in this new headquarters called Fort William in Bengal. In one respect at least the settlement thus formed was peculiar. At Bombay the company ruled on behalf of the English crown and no Indian prince could claim jurisdiction there. At Madras it held a position which was more dubious. In fact its agents ruled the city, but some element of Indian supremacy existed, as was shown by the annual quit-rent paid to Golconda and, after the overthrow of that kingdom, to the representative of the Mughal empire in the Carnatic. From time to time claims were put forward by this local authority to jurisdiction over the Indian inhabitants, and, although these claims were in every instance successfully resisted, the independence of the company was incomplete. Its powers at Madras rested upon the acquiescence of Indian rulers, as well as upon its position under its English charters; and the predominance of English authority was in part at least due to the remoteness of its situation and the comparative weakness of Mughal rulers in southern India. In Bengal this dual source of the company's position was much more evident. Over all English subjects its authority was derived from English law and English charters; but over the Indian inhabitants it ruled as zamindar, as the local agent of the *faujdar* of Hugli. To a considerable degree, therefore, the position created later on by the grant of the *dīwāni* of Bengal merely extended over the whole province an anomaly which had existed at Calcutta for two generations.

The commercial prosperity which the company enjoyed under Charles II and James II provoked great jealousy of its exclusive trading privileges. The average return which its stock-holders received in the thirty years from 1662 to 1691 was 22 per cent. Private traders began to infringe its monopoly, and, when their vessels were seized in accordance with the rights conferred by the company's charters, tested the matter at law. The courts upheld the validity of the charters, and the company remained strong in the king's favour. But the position was abruptly changed by the revolution of 1688. The interlopers, as the private traders were called, having met with nothing but opposition from the king and his Tory supporters, had turned for assistance to the Whigs, who secured power by the overthrow of James II.

The Whigs themselves were hostile to a corporation which had been closely allied with the fallen government. So private interests and political prejudice combined in an attack ostensibly directed against the company's monopoly. After a series of discussions in parliament, the House of Commons voted in 1694 that all English subjects had an equal right to trade to India unless prohibited by statute. The unreality of this decision was displayed in the following year, when the same House of Commons threatened to impeach the Englishmen who had promised financial help to the Scottish project for a great overseas trading company. Two cross-currents were in fact at work. One was formed by the efforts of those politicians who aimed at reducing the powers of the crown in relation to trade; the other by the merchants who desired not to abolish but to share the monopoly of the eastern trade.

The subsequent course of events illustrates these divergent efforts. In 1698 a bill was passed into law creating a new company in return for a loan of £2,000,000 to the state. This body was framed on the lines of a regulated company, in order to avoid the narrower monopoly incidental to a joint-stock company, while provision was also made for its superintendence by the Privy Council. The old company at once became a member of the "General Society", as this new body was called, in order to preserve the right of trading to India. Shortly afterwards the great majority of the other subscribers were incorporated into a second joint-stock company under the name of the "English Company of Merchants". But this body, though it set out with a great show of activity, sending an ambassador, Sir Henry Norris, to the emperor Aurangzīb, and obtaining the title of consul for its principal agents, was from the first embarrassed by a lack of trading capital, for its funds had been lent to the state and its available resources consisted only in the interest which it received. Its rival had large funds in hand as well as long-established settlements and privileges conferred by Indian rulers. But as against this the appearance in the east of agents representing the new company raised many difficulties and disputes. The two joint-stock companies, under some pressure from the ministry, resolved therefore on amalgamation, which was agreed upon in 1702 and completed under the arbitration of Godolphin in 1709. Thus the struggle resulted, not in any relaxation of the monopoly, but in an extension of the circle which enjoyed its advantages. In 1730 proposals for the establishment of a regulated company were feebly revived but in fact the united company's legal monopoly remained untouched till 1793.

The further development of the company's position in India during the first forty years of the eighteenth century was quiet, gradual, and lacking in dramatic events. Yet it was none the less important. While confusion spread through India, while the imperial power decayed within the Mughal provinces, while the Marāthās widened their financial claims without undertaking the corresponding responsibilities of public order and administration, the company's settlements remained relatively undisturbed. Trade became more hazardous, but the hazards were compensated by a high rate of profit. Bombay, Madras, and Calcutta all grew rapidly, alike in wealth and population. Sir Josia Child's idea of a regular and certain revenue to support the costs of government was realised. The revenue system corresponded closely to the established rules of Indian finance, save that the scanty territory under the company's rule did not permit land revenue to be the chief source of income. The customs-dues, as was natural in city-states, provided the bulk of the revenue. Octroi-dues were collected on the imports by land, sea-customs and port-dues on the much more important trade by sea. Besides these, quit-rents were levied on the houses of the settlements, and monopoly revenues, on such articles of common consumption as betel and tobacco, were farmed out to Indian contractors. But despite these imposts, the inhabitants of the English settlements were probably the most lightly taxed subjects in India.

It was of course true that they lived under an authority which united the disparate functions of trade and government. At a later time, when conditions had been completely transformed, Adam Smith had small difficulty in demonstrating the incompatibility of commerce and administration. However, it has to be remembered that not the company only, but also its servants, the governors and councillors of the various settlements, were deeply interested in trade. That privilege had been most reluctantly conceded by the East India Company. In the early seventeenth century, great endeavours had been made to prevent the company's servants from trading at all. In this respect, the English were but following the example of the Dutch, who obstinately refused to allow men to exercise on their own behalf the talents which they were intended to exercise on behalf of their employers. In the case of the Dutch, the result had been that the regulations prohibiting private trade had been wholly ignored. But the English proved more amenable to experience. From 1679 the company's servants were allowed to trade from port to port in India, provided they did not touch those branches of commerce which the company reserved for itself. Private trade thus ceased to be underhand or illicit, and became the open and recognised method by which the company's servants attained to wealth.

It was at this early period difficult for them to use their administrative authority in oppressive support of their trading privilege. Oppression would have speedily driven away Indian merchants to other European settlements. Authority was indeed too narrowly limited in area, and trade too dependent on the support and co-operation of Indian merchants to render such a course profitable. Probably few vessels save those belonging to the East India Company itself sailed from Bombay, Madras, or Calcutta without large Indian interests aboard. Cargo and vessel would be insured by groups of Indian merchants; capital would be provided by loans locally known as *respondentia* loans, or by the direct subscription of shares. The rapid growth of wealth and population of the three chief towns shows plainly that Indians found the rule of foreign traders milder, juster, safer, or more profitable than the government of neighbouring Indian princes, and, as conditions throughout the country became more disturbed, they sent their wealth and their families into the English settlements for safety, or came themselves to live and trade there.

In the early part of the eighteenth century the English began to run swiftly ahead of their former great rivals, the Dutch. About 1700 Negapatam, the principal Dutch settlement on the Coromandel Coast, was probably as large and wealthy as Madras; on the Hugli, Chinsura vied with Calcutta. But in the course of the next forty years Dutch trade at best remained stationary, while the English trade rapidly expanded.

The chief political event of this period was the great embassy, despatched after long correspondence and preparation, to the Mughal court in 1714. Its object was to secure a general grant of privileges throughout Mughal India together with a number of villages around Calcutta. It was conducted by John Surman, a Bengal servant of the company, assisted by an Armenian merchant who acted as interpreter. After three years *farmāns* were obtained, directing the rulers of the provinces concerned to comply with most of the company's requests. But by this time the imperial authority was rapidly failing. The emperor Farrukhsiyar was himself little more than the puppet of a court clique, and the governor of Bengal flatly refused to make over to the English the additional villages which had been granted to them. The embassy therefore effected little beyond giving the company claims against the empire which the local governors would not satisfy.

At Bombay the most significant development was the foundation of the naval force long known as the Bombay Marine. From early days English trade had been threatened by the attacks of Arab pirates in the Persian Gulf and of small maritime chiefs on the Malabar Coast. In the early part of the eighteenth century the latter were overshadowed by the rise of Kānhoji Angria, who became first the commander of the Marātha fleet and then an independent chieftain. He dominated the coast from Goa to Bombay from two strongholds, Gheria (or Vijayadrug) and Suvarndrug, and plundered vessels of every nationality. Under the government of Charles Boone (1715-22) the armed ships of the company were materially increased in order to deal with this menace. Various attacks were made upon the Marātha pirates from 1717 onwards, but little permanent success was obtained till almost forty years later. Then in conjunction with the Pēshwā a concerted attack was launched against the Angrias. In 1755 Commodore James captured Suvarndrug; and in 1757 Clive and Watson, sent to Bombay to attack the French at Hyderabad with Marātha help, were diverted from their original purpose to attack and capture Gheria.

Meanwhile the company's organisation had changed much from its early form in the seventeenth century. Like the Portuguese and Dutch, the English had begun by attempting to control trade and administration from a single centre. The president and council at Surat had at first been entrusted with the universal management; and this body had later been replaced by the general, or captain-general and council, of Bombay. This centralised control over widely scattered factories carried with it obvious inconveniences, and from time to time attempts were made to remedy them by investing certain subordinate settlements with powers of local control. For instance, at one time Madras was placed in charge not only of the local factories on the Coromandel Coast, but also of those in Bengal. However, as local jealousies were always obstructing such arrangements, it was decided at the close of the century to vest the government in three equal and co-ordinate bodies, established at Bombay, Madras and Calcutta.

These bodies consisted of a president, who also bore the title of governor, and council. The title of governor goes back to the first charter of Charles II, which empowered the company to administer justice in those settlements where it maintained a governor and council. At Madras, therefore, where the chief official had generally borne the title of agent, he now received the designation of agent and governor. A similar office was created at Bombay when that island passed into the company's hands. The title of governor, however, was not merely connected with the administration of justice. It signified also powers of military command within a fortified town. It marked out the holder as head of the garrison, while the title of president marked him out as head of the civil administration. The president and governor, however, was not in theory more than the senior member and chairman of the council to which alone authority was entrusted. His only recognised privilege was that of giving a casting vote where the council was equally divided. But in practice he exerted a wide though undefined influence over the proceedings of the government. The other members of the council were the heads of the various mercantile offices. One was accountant, another paymaster, a third had charge of the goods sent out on the company's account from Europe. Therefore as soon as the council had dispersed, the powers of individual councillors were limited to making entries in a ledger or issuing a bale of goods or performing some other politically insignificant duty. The president was thus the sole political executive. He translated the decisions of the council into action, and he alone corresponded with the neighbouring princes. That position of itself made him something more than the senior member of council. Then, also, his appointment was usually the direct act of the company at home, and he was thus designated as the man specially trusted by the supreme authority in England. He also enjoyed certain customary privileges of nomination, while his commercial interests made him both useful as a friend and dangerous as an enemy. A similar development appeared among the Dutch. At Batavia the governor-general occupied precisely the same theoretical position as the English president and governor; but he speedily came completely to dominate his council, and sometimes even refused to attend its meetings. But the English president was subject to a curb from which the Dutch governor-general was free. The English company was ever keenly interested in the administrative as well as the commercial conduct of its servants, and sharply watched to see that no infraction of its established system of council-government was allowed. It repeatedly intervened when it thought its presidents were exceeding their due functions, and thus the presidents never succeeded in establishing a predominance such as long prevailed among the Dutch.

The chief administrative difficulties which emerged in the early English settlements arose from judicial questions. From the first some judicial authority had been indispensably necessary to maintain order among the crews of the company's ships. This had been provided by the grant of power to hold courts martial. and to exercise martial law. The charters of Charles II, as has been mentioned, empowered the company to administer justice where it maintained a governor and council, and, under this authority, a court of law for the trial of European offenders came into being at Madras, consisting of the governor and council. When Bombay was transferred to the company, the island was divided into two precincts, with a bench of justices in each, and the governor and council sat as a court of appeal from their decisions. The charter of 1683 authorised the establishment of a court of judicature designed to hear mercantile and maritime suits; and professional judges, trained in the civil law by which such cases were principally decided, were sent out to Bombay in 1684 and to Madras in 1686. But this practice was not kept up, and the settlements speedily lost the advantage of trained lawyers. In 1687 the company set up, under the sanction of a special charter of 1686, a corporation and mayor's court at Madras. The court was to consist of the mayor and twelve aldermen, who included one Frenchman, two Portuguese, three

Jews, and three Indians, as well as three of the company's servants, to represent the principal trading interests of the place. It was to possess both civil and criminal jurisdiction, with an appeal to the governor and council where the amount at issue exceeded three pagodas (about 24s.) or where an offender was sentenced to lose life or limb. The last important change to be made in the seventeenth century was the issue of letters patent constituting courts of vice-admiralty in the East Indies in accordance with a statute, passed in 1698, for the punishment of offences committed on the high seas.

Such were the arrangements made by the English authorities for administering justice at Bombay and Madras. They proved to be quite insufficient, especially in regard to the trial of criminals. English criminal process was elaborate; any flaw in the proceedings might invalidate the whole process, and so expose the persons acting as judges to heavy penalties in the English courts. The company's servants naturally shrank from exposing themselves to dangers which, in view of their ignorance of legal technicalities, were far from unreal. Moreover, as the attack on the company's privileges began to develop, men questioned the validity of the courts as well as the legality of the trading monopoly; and finally, when the old company surrendered its charters and merged itself in the new, the position became still more uncertain, for the language of the new charter was far less specific than had been the grants of the old ones. The consequence was that the vice-admiralty courts remained the sole criminal tribunals the jurisdiction of which was unquestionable in English law; so that while crime at sea could certainly be punished, crime ashore, when committed by a British-born subject, could only be dealt with by arrest and deportation to England. This most unsatisfactory position was not amended till the issue of a new charter in 1726.

On the Indian side, however, at Madras and Calcutta the company's jurisdiction was on a firmer basis. At both these places it represented autocratic Indian powers as well as the constitutional authority of the English crown. At Madras its servants had maintained the customary court held by the chief executive official, the *adigar*. As other tribunals were established, they inherited the higher jurisdiction of the *adigar*, leaving petty cases to the decision of what was called locally the choultry court.

At Calcutta the company as zamindar set up the zamindar's court, which heard and determined according to local custom all causes, criminal and civil, touching the Indian inhabitants, probably reporting capital sentences to the *faujdar* of Hugli for confirmation.

In 1726 the confusion of the early courts was brought to an end by the issue of new grants in England. These directed the establishment at Bombay, Madras and Calcutta, of a mayor's court with full civil jurisdiction, and of a court of quarter sessions to punish all crimes except high treason. Appeals were to lie from the mayor's court to the governor and council, and thence, when the amount at stake exceeded 1000 pagodas, to the Privy Council. The justices of quarter sessions comprised the majority of the council.

The effect of this change was to establish at Bombay and Madras uniform jurisdiction over Indian and European alike; and, while the new courts were directed generally to conform to English procedure and the principles of English law, they were not bound down to observe the technicalities of the first or to ignore the customary law prevalent in India. When an Indian was indicted for a capital offence, his case was heard before a petty jury consisting of six Indians and six Europeans. The jurisdiction of the mayor's court provoked some complaint among the Indian inhabitants, especially in connection with the oaths required of witnesses; and when these courts were modified in 1753 Indians were exempted from the jurisdiction of the mayor's courts save in disputes under a contract which expressly declared that differences should be referred to these courts for decision.

At Calcutta, however, the establishment of the new courts was complicated by the existence of the Mughal jurisdiction. Although, therefore, the courts were set up in accordance with the letters patent, the zamindar's court continued in existence, and in practice dealt with civil suits and criminal charges in which Indians were involved; and this position continued until 1757, when Mughal authority vanished from Calcutta and the English courts began to operate in the same way as at Bombay and Madras.

CHAPTER III

Dupleix and Clive

The French had not taken part in the earlier phases of the European movement to secure a position in the eastern trade. The country was ill-placed to pursue overseas adventures with success. Her long land-frontiers, the continental views and interests of her rulers, and the religious disputes which had convulsed the nation, had made efforts such as those of the Portuguese or the Dutch unattractive and inopportune. Economic causes made in the same direction. The French mercantile classes, in proportion to the wealth and population of the state, were far smaller, poorer and less influential than the corresponding classes of Amsterdam or London, nor was there at Paris or any other French city the like accumulation of liquid funds which might be employed in financing distant and speculative commerce. In the sixteenth and early seventeenth centuries, therefore, the spirit of adventure carried a few French ships into eastern seas, but no concerted effort, such as the Dutch and English merchants made, could appear among the merchants of France.

Nevertheless leading Frenchmen were alive to the importance of developing an eastern trade; Henry IV attempted to set up an East India Company, and Richelieu, despite his continental preoccupations, believed that the trade should not be neglected. A little later Colbert proceeded to develop a great scheme, by which France was to become a naval and colonising power. He perceived that naval power could only be built up on maritime trade, and that maritime trade demanded overseas settlements. In 1664 therefore he launched a project for establishing a French East India Company to colonise Madagascar, already visited by French ships, and to open up a regular trade with India and Persia. A royal edict was issued creating a company modelled in its constitution on the Dutch company. But from the first, despite the similarity of organisation, there was one profound difference. The Dutch company had been created and financed by merchants. The French company was created and in great part financed by the state. In spite of active official propaganda, it was impossible to procure the subscription of the fifteen million *livres* announced as the capital of the new company; and it began its operations with only five and a half millions, of which three had been provided by the king. This state interest was soon manifested in another way. In 1670 a strong squadron of royal vessels was dispatched to the east under the command of de la Haye. He was to establish fortified posts, from which the company's trade might be conducted, besides the factories at Surat and Masulipatam which had already been opened. French adventure in the East was evidently going to follow the lines of the Portuguese rather than those of the Dutch and English policy, however much it might appear to be a mercantile concern.

The naval expedition of 1670 was ill-conducted. It attempted in vain to secure possession of Trincomalee. It then seized San Thomé, close to Madras; but the French were speedily besieged there by Golconda troops ashore and a Dutch fleet at sea, and, though de la Haye held out for two years, he was forced at last to capitulate. The one tangible consequence of his expedition was the establishment of the French at Pondichery, a little to the southward of the Golconda frontier. There the French obtained a grant in 1673, and in the next year Francois Martin took charge of the settlement. A little later he built a small fort for its protection, naming it Fort Louis. Though it could not resist a Dutch attack in 1693, it was restored to the French by the Treaty of Ryswick, and became the headquarters of the French in India.

In this early period the great difficulty which had to be met by Martin and his successors was the feebleness of the company itself. It had needed reconstruction in 1686. Early in the eighteenth century it was reduced to selling permits to merchants of St Malo. It was reorganised by Law and formed a part of his great and over-ambitious scheme in 1719. But with his collapse it fell once more, and emerged in 1721 without liquid funds and under the complete control of the ministry. In the course of the next twenty years it traded on borrowed money, and thanks to the able management of Lenoir and Dumas, who governed Pondichery from 1720 to 1742, its profits rose and its financial position eased. It had, moreover, established factories in Bengal at Chandernagore, and on the Malabar coast at Mahé; while it had also occupied two derelict islands, Bourbon and Mauritius, occupying an important strategic position about half-way between the Cape of Good Hope and Cape Comorin. In 1742 La Bourdonnais, the governor, was busily seeking to develop the resources of these islands, and especially Port Louis, with its remarkable harbour, on Mauritius, while in that year Dupleix, who had long occupied the position of chief at Chandernagore, was appointed governor of Pondichery.

Meanwhile events in India had been demonstrating how precarious was the political situation. In 1739 northern India had been terrified by the irresistible invasion of Nādir Shāh, by the sack and slaughter which had marked his entrance into Delhi, by the restoration of Persian authority on its ancient boundary of the Indus, and by the impotence of the Mughal empire to defend either its provinces, or its capital, or the remnants of its wealth. In the next year the Carnatic was similarly afflicted, though not by the armies of a foreign sovereign. The Marāthas thought the time ripe to levy plunder in lieu of *chauth*. Fateh Singh and Rāghūji Bhonsla were sent southwards with a host of cavalry. At the entrance to the Carnatic, in the Dāmalcheri Pass, they found the nawab Dost 'Alī, seeking to prevent their entrance. Him they overpowered and slew, and then proceeded thoroughly to ravage the province. Many refugees and much treasure passed for safety into the European settlements on the coast, and Dost 'Alī's son, Safdar 'Alī, was obliged to promise the Marāthas a great sum to withdraw. They then moved southwards against Trichinopoly, where Dost 'Alī's son-in-law, Chanda Sāhib, had recently established himself at the expense of a Hindu ruling family. In 1741 they compelled Chanda Sāhib to surrender and carried him off a prisoner to Satāra.

These events shattered public order in the Carnatic. In 1742 Safdar 'Alī was murdered by a cousin; and in 1743 Nizām-ul-mulk, the subahdar of the Deccan, marched in order to re-establish peace. He recovered Trichinopoly from the Marātha garrison, and named an old servant of his own, Anwar-ud-dīn, as nawab of Arcot. But for thirty years the Carnatic had been governed by a single family. Its members had received the command of all the chief fortresses and enjoyed large *jāgīrs*. They viewed the new nawab with jealousy, and he was never strong enough to expel them from their position, while the country was pervaded with rumours that Anwar-ud-dīn would speedily be removed and some member of the old family appointed in his place.

At this time, in 1744, France and Great Britain became involved in the War of the Austrian Succession. That did not necessarily imply war between the two companies in India. During the last war Madras and Pondichery had remained on friendly terms, and the French had received assistance against the blockade which the Dutch had sought to establish, even though vessels of the French navy had captured English vessels in the Bay of Bengal. The troubles which had broken out between the Malabar factories at Tellicherry and Mahé in 1725 had been composed by an arrangement which had stipulated that neither factory should attack the other even if the two nations went to war in Europe. On the Coromandel Coast in 1744 both Madras and Pondichery had small garrisons, but neither had any vessels of war and hostilities therefore appeared unlikely and disadvantageous. Dupleix at once proposed to the English council at Madras to make a neutrality agreement similar to that which had been made in Malabar. But the position had changed considerably. The French company's trade had expanded and become an object of jealousy to the English company. More important than this was the likelihood of French naval action in the east. In the previous war they had sent out a squadron. In 1740, when it seemed likely that France would join in the war which had broken out between Spain and England in 1739, La Bourdonnais had induced the ministry at Paris to dispatch men-of-war. The scare had blown over, the men-of-war had been recalled, but the threat remained. On the instant that war was declared, the English directors approached the ministry with a request for a naval squadron to protect the English and cruise upon French shipping in the east. The request was granted and early in the year Commodore Barnett announced his arrival by capturing the French company's China fleet and a number of richly laden French vessels engaged in private trade.

On this Dupleix appealed to La Bourdonnais at Mauritius to equip a squadron to redress the situation. The latter with rare vigour set to work, and in 1746 appeared off the coast with eight vessels against the English four. The new-comers were not the equals of the English in either speed or weight of guns; but these disadvantages were more than compensated by a superiority of command. Barnett had died, and been succeeded by the senior captain, Peyton, who proved an incompetent leader. An indecisive action was fought on June 25, after which Peyton gave the French ships leisure to refit and increase their armament of guns at Pondichery. He then refused a further action and sailed off to Calcutta, while La Bourdonnais landed the troops he had brought with him before Madras, which capitulated on September 21 after the feeblest of defences. The place surrendered under an informal promise of ransom. But after La Bourdonnais had signed an agreement, and had received a handsome present in acknowledgement of his conduct, but before the convention could receive its full effect, a cyclone struck the coast, shattering the French vessels lying before Madras. This event obliged La Bourdonnais to withdraw, leaving behind him many men whom he could no longer accommodate on his reduced squadron, and charging Dupleix to give effect to the arrangement which the latter had bitterly opposed. As soon as he had secured control, Dupleix denounced the convention, and officers from Pondichery proceeded to pillage Madras from top to bottom, while La Bourdonnais, on his return to France, was imprisoned for some years on the charges which Dupleix hastened to send home against him.

In these events the Mughal nawab at Arcot had vainly sought to intervene. On the outbreak of hostilities Dupleix had endeavoured to screen French trade behind the nawab's flag; but Barnett had refused to be deceived by such a transparent subterfuge. He had seized French-owned vessels regardless of whether they chose to fly the French colours or the white flag edged with green which purported to stand for the authority of Arcot. The French had complained to the nawab; the nawab had demanded an explanation from the governor and council of Madras; and the latter had made answer that they had no authority over the commodore. With this Anwar-ud-dīn had remained content, and, when the French had proceeded to wage hostilities ashore, he had at the English instance demanded French withdrawal. Undeceived by the evasive answer returned to him, he sent a force, too late to relieve Madras but charged to expel the French. His troops attempted to blockade the place, but were so roughly handled in two actions that they withdrew and after a while the nawab made peace with Pondichery. The importance of these events lay in their revealing two things—one the incapacity of the local ruler, the other the military superiority conferred on European arms by recent developments in military technique.

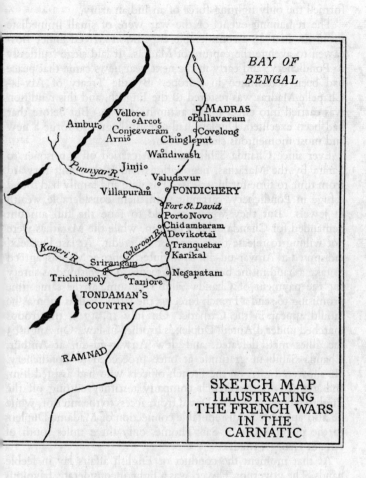

BAY OF
BENGAL

Vellore
Ambur Arcot
       Conjeeveram
Arni
        Chingleput
     Wandiwash
Jinji
     Valudavur
Villapuram   PONDICHERY
         Fort St.David
         Porto Novo
         Chidambaram
         Devikottai
         Tranquebar
         Karikal
Srirangam
         Negapatam
Trichinopoly Tanjore
TONDAMAN'S
COUNTRY

RAMNAD

MADRAS
Pallavaram
Covelong

Punnyar R.

Kaveri R. Coleroon R.

SKETCH MAP
ILLUSTRATING
THE FRENCH WARS
IN THE
CARNATIC

Small units of European foot and artillery could now confront and defy the ill-disciplined and ill-conducted cavalry which still formed the only fighting force of an Indian army.

The remaining events of the war were of small immediate moment. In 1748 a considerable expedition arrived under Boscawen to avenge the capture of Madras. It laid siege fruitlessly to Pondichery; and early in the next year news came that peace had been determined in Europe. By the Treaty of Aix-la-Chapelle Madras was restored to the English, and this rendition was carried into effect in the autumn of 1749. But before that had been executed, Dupleix had already begun to forge a new and most momentous chain of events.

Ever since Chanda Sāhib had been carried off a prisoner to Satāra by the Marāthas, negotiations had been going forward from time to time for his release. His wife and family had found refuge in Pondichery, carrying with them considerable wealth in jewels. But they were not able to raise the full amount demanded for Chanda Sāhib's ransom, while the Marāthas were not willing to release their prisoner on credit. At last Dupleix, indisposed to Anwar-ud-dīn by his interference at Madras, agreed to take a hand in the business. He seems to have stood as surety for the payment of Chanda Sāhib's ransom, at the same time promising to send a French force to the latter's aid as soon as he should appear in the Carnatic. On July 16, 1749, the troops marched under d'Auteil, Dupleix's brother-in-law. On August 3 the allies met, defeated, and slew Anwar-ud-dīn at Ambūr. Chanda Sāhib in gratitude at once proceeded to Pondichery. He showered gifts on the French officers who had assisted him, and granted to the French company territory cutting off the English factory at Fort St David from access to the interior, while he also appointed a disreputable connection of Madame Dupleix to the government of San Thomé, only three miles south of Fort St George, Madras.

At that moment the conduct of English affairs lay in feeble hands. The governor, Floyer, was a light, inconsiderate, frivolous man. On the news of Chanda Sāhib's victory he had hastened to write letters of congratulation. But even he could not but perceive the menace to English trade implied in these new grants to the French. A son of Anwar-ud-dīn, Muhammad 'Alī by name, had found refuge in Trichinopoly, and claimed to be entitled to his father's succession. From him Floyer obtained grants of Bahur and San Thomé, and at once put them in execution, turning out the French agents and replacing them by English forces. He also sought another ally. The great Nizām-ul-mulk had died in 1748. His second son, Nāsir Jang, had succeeded to the rule of his territories. But Chanda Sāhib had been accompanied by a grandson of Nizām-ul-mulk, Muzaffar Jang, who claimed to have been named as heir by his grandfather. Floyer therefore sent agents to Nāsir Jang, urging him in his own interests to march south and extinguish this rebellion before it extended to the region under his direct government.

At the close of 1749 Floyer was replaced as governor by Thomas Saunders. Saunders was in his way a remarkable man. He possessed none of the dazzling talent, the versatility, the inexhaustible resource of Dupleix. He cherished no great designs and contemplated no revolution in policy. But he had a cool, clear brain, strong good sense, a shrewd judgment of men, an inflexible resolution. He harboured no thoughts of empire, but he was fiercely, inalterably resolved that the position of the company he served and of the nation he represented should not suffer through the intrigues of any foreign governor. His firm grasp of realities and his invincible obstinacy of purpose made of him a dangerous enemy, none the less dangerous because his lack of showy gifts might lead to an underestimate of his real quality. He was not a great man. But many great men have been far less effective. He it was, after all, who in defiance of all principles of military etiquette chose Clive for independent command, and chose the very point where a tiny force might exert an influence out of all proportion to its numbers.

At the end of 1749 Chanda Sāhib had moved south, accompanied by his French allies, with the object of besieging Trichinopoly and capturing his rival, Muhammad 'Alī. But he paused on his way to lay siege to Tanjore in the hope of extracting from the raja money with which to refill his treasury, exhausted by his gifts to the French. But before his hopes could be realised, the approach of Nāsir Jang with a numerous army induced Chanda Sāhib to march back hastily to Pondichery. Nāsir Jang was joined by an English detachment; the rival forces met near Valudavūr, west of the French settlement; and a battle seemed imminent when the officers with the French troops, either struck with panic or dissatisfied with the lack of a new donation at this crisis, abandoned their troops and retired into Pondichery. This not only disorganised the French force but also threw Chanda Sāhib's own followers into the utmost confusion. They sought refuge under the guns of the French fortifications; Chanda Sāhib took refuge with Dupleix; Muzaffar Jang gave himself up to his uncle, Nāsir Jang. The latter, reckoning the person of his rival the main object to be secured, then fell back on Arcot, where he spent the hot weather of 1750. This permitted Dupleix to re-organise his troops and open one of those political intrigues at which he excelled. The chiefs who had accompanied Nāsir Jang were discontented with their prolonged absence from the Deccan. One group in particular, the Pathān nawabs of Cuddapah, Kurnool and Savanūr, was known to be wavering. With them Dupleix opened a correspondence, which led to an agreement to join the French against their master. In September a body of French troops under Bussy stormed Jinji, reputed to be im-pregnable. Later in the year Nāsir Jang again moved south. On the night of December 16 his camp was surprised by the French under the command of La Touche. Nāsir Jang, in the confusion of the onset, was slain by one of the Pathān nawabs. His army at once broke. Muzaffar Jang was freed and conducted to Pondi-chery. The great treasure which Nāsir Jang had carried with him fell into the hands of the French. This brilliant success, alike in the disparity of numbers, the treachery of Indian leaders to their chief, and the magnitude of the reward, anticipated in important features the victory of Plassey.

Dupleix now believed that success lay in his hand. He at once prepared to send Muzaffar Jang to the Deccan with a French detachment under the command of Bussy in order that the prince might establish himself as the due and regular successor of his dead uncle. By this means Dupleix hoped to be able to control not only the nawab of Arcot, Chanda Sāhib, but also the subahdar of the Deccan, and thus to secure such a legitimacy for his claims as neither the English nor Muhammad 'Alī would dare to dispute. In this he was guilty of a gross miscalculation. The subahdar might no doubt obtain a formal confirmation of his position at Delhi, and might ratify whatever grants Dupleix desired in southern India. But would the English admit the validity of such grants? All men knew that the power of the empire had vanished.

Could its rights be recognised when they were diverted by French policy into the creation of a French empire, supported by French bayonets? To expect English recognition involved an assumption of such folly in an enemy as could not reasonably be anticipated. The expedition to the Deccan was based therefore on a mistaken estimate of English conduct; and it carried with it a great disadvantage. It involved sending far away to the northward a considerable body of troops under the command of the ablest French officer. Whatever might be the political effects of setting up a French nominee at Hyderabad, they were liable to be wholly overset by the military consequences of dividing a weak French force and entrusting the command against the English to incompetent leaders.

Muzaffar Jang marched northward under Bussy's escort on January 15, 1751. A little later in the year an English force marched southwards to prevent the French from overwhelming Muhammad 'Alī at Trichinopoly. There followed a campaign as futile and uninteresting as a children's game of chess. Both leaders were unintelligent and lethargic. Clive, who burned for action, could not be entrusted with the general command over the heads of officers far senior to him. But Saunders sent him off on an independent command to attack Arcot, which had been left poorly defended. He seized the place. Chanda Sāhib hastily detached a force from before Trichinopoly to recover his capital. But Clive held it triumphantly. This was the first real military success that the English had secured in the struggle. It was followed in the next year by a triumph which had far-reaching consequences. Lawrence, who had already served the company in south India, returned from England as the commander of the company's forces. He was no man of genius, but a sound soldier whom his men followed with confidence, and whose military rank and experience—he had served in the king's army— dominated the senior officers' jealousy of Clive. Early in 1752 he marched with reinforcements to Trichinopoly, taking Clive with him. They found the French troops commanded by Jacques Law, a gallant man in himself but a most timid leader. Muhammad 'Alī's cause was at this moment supported by contingents from two Hindu kingdoms, Tanjore and Mysore, both of which feared the success of Chanda Sāhib. Under Lawrence's control, the allies speedily drove Chanda Sāhib and the French into the island of Srirangam, formed by the Kāveri opposite Trichinopoly. While Lawrence watched them from the south bank of the river, Clive was sent with a detachment to cut them off on the north. Against an enterprising commander such a division of the English forces might have been fatal. Even as it was, Clive was surprised and almost overwhelmed. But events proved that the English had accurately measured the talent of the French leader, who permitted himself to be shut up in the island. In May, Chanda Sāhib, despairing of his position, surrendered. With singular ill-judgment he placed himself in the hands of the Tanjoreans. He had in his day of power repeatedly ravaged their country. By order of the raja and with the assent of Muhammad 'Alī he was now beheaded. Law had already surrendered to the English, and a considerable body of the French forces thus passed into Muhammad 'Alī's prisons at Trichinopoly.

Nothing so well proves Dupleix's fertility of mind as the fact that even this crushing blow did not bring the war to an end. Bereft for the moment of force, he resorted to intrigue, as he had done in the case of Nāsir Jang. The Mysoreans were easily detached from their alliance with Muhammad 'Alī because he had promised them possession of Trichinopoly, and, when the French had been defeated, refused to make good his promise. Morāri Rāo, the commander of a Marātha force of mercenaries, was also induced by large promises to join the French. So that Trichinopoly was soon blockaded again, though now by forces which had formerly been defending it. Dupleix received reinforcements from Europe and sent them down under a variety of leaders to attack the place. But he could not lay his hand upon a man of outstanding military talent. Though Trichinopoly remained beleaguered all through 1753 and a great part of 1754, and though the French made several desperate efforts to destroy the English covering force under Lawrence and to escalade the town, their attempts all failed, and in August, 1754, news arrived that the French authorities had decided to recall Dupleix. This was in a large degree the consequence of the slow development of his plans. His alliance with Chanda Sāhib in 1749 had been inspired by no ideas of dominion. He had hired out a body of French troops in order to secure large personal rewards for himself and a privileged position for the French East India Company in the Carnatic. The destruction of Nāsir Jang had widened his theatre of action but hardly changed his aims. Not until he perceived the success of Bussy in the Deccan does he seem to have begun to consider the possibility of a disguised or avowed sovereignty. Then in the course of 1752 and 1753 he began to expound to the authorities at Paris wider schemes, the acquisition of a great revenue, and the financing of the company's trade from Indian resources. Moreover he had consistently represented the opposition of the English and Muhammad 'Alī as a trifling obstacle which would be immediately overcome without cost to the company. At first the French directors and ministers had welcomed a policy which they supposed to be beneficial without serious risk. They sent out to India considerable reinforcements, larger in fact than the reinforcements sent out by the English; but they did not enlarge their supplies of finance, since Dupleix had constantly assured them that his operations were paying for themselves. But on this point Dupleix had deceived both himself and his superiors in Europe. He had expected the English opposition to collapse, leaving him free to collect the Carnatic revenues to pay for his military operations. But the English opposition had proved stubborn. The Carnatic revenues had fallen away while the military expenditure had risen. In these circumstances it had not been possible to maintain the Carnatic investment at its usual figure, and the company found its shipments falling away. This was the first hint that the schemes of Dupleix were not as sound as they appeared on paper. Then, at the close of 1752, came disquieting news from London. The English claimed to have secured a notable success. At first Paris discounted these statements as mere English brag. But when it learnt belatedly from Dupleix that Chanda Sāhib had perished, that a large French force had surrendered, but that he was as optimistic as ever, that he was finding new allies, and that the English resistance would be crushed within a year, Paris began to doubt whether the reports received from Pondichery were in any degree reliable. About the same time Paris received from London copies of letters which Dupleix had addressed to the English governor, Thomas Saunders, putting forth claims in which the English declared they never would acquiesce, while the English ambassador was instructed to inform the foreign minister of France that the policy of Dupleix was manifestly injurious to English interests. At the moment France did not desire war with Great Britain, nor did

the trading interests of her East India Company seem to demand
a bellicose policy. There was room in the markets of India for
the trade of both companies. In these circumstances the French
company and ministry agreed upon recalling Dupleix, whose
continuance in office was indeed a strong obstacle to the conclusion of a working compromise with the English in India.
Negotiations were begun between the companies in London,
and a new agent, Godeheu, was dispatched to Pondichery to
replace Dupleix and arrange a temporary suspension of hostilities
on the spot. In order the more easily to induce the English to
desist from war, Godeheu was accompanied by a large body of
troops. He reached Pondichery in August, 1754. Dazzled by the
brilliance of Dupleix's projects, historians have usually condemned
the action of the French authorities. But the problem was not so
simple as has usually been represented. France was not prepared
to lavish men and money, or to run the risk of instant war with
England, in support of schemes which had never been adequately
explained. Godeheu was therefore charged to make the best of
the position as he found it, and this he proceeded to do. The
influence of the troops he carried with him was neutralised by
the arrival on the coast of English reinforcements—a small naval
squadron under Admiral Watson, and a royal regiment. But
the attitude of the English was not aggressive. They were far
more anxious to secure their trading position than to continue
an expensive war. A truce was made, and then a provisional
treaty was signed at the end of 1754. This latter stipulated for a
position of equality between the two nations, alike in the Carnatic
and in the Deccan. But the treaty was not to come into force
until it had been confirmed in Europe. The immediate effect of
the arrangement was therefore very beneficial to the French.
They were relieved of the burden of war by the truce, while they
still retained the territory and revenues actually in their possession
in August, 1754, unless and until the authorities at Paris assented
to their relinquishment. Godeheu, so far from sacrificing national
interests, secured for the moment all the material advantages
which had been won, free at last from the mortgage of a war
which Dupleix had not been strong enough to win and which
he had not been pliant enough to end by a compromise.

His attitude had doubtless been much stiffened by the successes
which Bussy had secured in the Deccan. Bussy had marched

northwards in January, 1751, with Muzaffar Jang. But very soon
the Pathān nawabs who had conspired against Nāsir Jang conspired against his successor; and although their troops were
routed, Muzaffar Jang was killed in action on February 14.
Bussy at once halted and awaited confirmation of his recognising
Nizām 'Alī, a younger brother of the dead Nāsir Jang. Dupleix,
however, annulled this, and directed his lieutenant to install an
elder brother, Salābat Jang. This was done. The army moved
onwards. Hyderabad was occupied, and Salābat Jang emptied
the treasury to reward the successes of the French officers on his
behalf. They then moved to Aurangābād, the traditional capital
of the province. This success had inspired Dupleix to dream of
yet more extensive operations. He proposed to Bussy that the
latter should march with Salābat Jang against Alahwirdi Khān,
nawab of Bengal, and establish the new French *protégé* as ruler
of that province too. The project, however, was characteristically
founded on hopes rather than possibilities. First came an attack
from Bālājī Rāo, the Pēshwā, who thought he saw in recent events
chances for an expansion of Marātha power. When he made
peace on January 17, 1752, Bussy began to find his position
threatened by intrigues at the durbar against French influence.
The Hindu *dīwān*, Rāmdās Pandit, who had been chosen by
Dupleix, was murdered on May 4. Then Salābat Jang's eldest
brother, Ghāzī-ud-dīn, came south from Delhi to claim his
father's succession. When he had been removed by poison,
Salābat Jang's army, deep in arrears of pay, refused to march
against Mysore; and Bussy, weary and in bad health, retired to
recuperate at Masulipatam. As soon as he had gone, Sayyid
Lashkar Khān, the new *dīwān*, put in action a scheme to expel the
French altogether from the Deccan. A small body remained as
bodyguard of the subahdar, but the rest were broken up into
parties and sent to collect arrears of revenue. On this news
Bussy hurried back from the coast, assembled the scattered troops,
and in November, 1753, moved to Aurangābād. There he demanded that the position of the French should be assured by
the grant to him as a personal *jāgīr* of the coastal area known as
the Northern Circars, stretching from Masulipatam to the
Chilka Lake. It was reckoned that the revenues of these districts
would provide for the pay of Bussy's troops and so obviate direct
demands on Salābat Jang's treasury. During most of 1754 Bussy

was occupied with administrative affairs in the new *jāgīr*. When he returned to Hyderabad in January, 1755, he found his position more delicate than ever. Shāh Nawāz Khān, the *dīwān* who had succeeded Sayyid Lashkar Khān, was obstinately hostile, and took advantage of the easy terms which Bussy allowed to Morārī Rão, the chief of Gooty, to declare that Salābat Jang's interests were being sacrificed. Morārī Rão had in fact considerable claims on the French; and this was doubtless the reason why Bussy's aid had been demanded for his reduction. On this score Bussy was dismissed, and letters were hurriedly sent to Madras requesting the assistance of an English force to replace the French. Bussy retired to Hyderabad and occupied a defensive position till he could receive reinforcements. The despatch of the English expedition was prevented by news of Sirāj-ud-daula's capture of Calcutta. Shāh Nawāz Khān's blockade of Bussy collapsed, and Bussy resumed his place in the councils of Salābat Jang, and retained it until he was summoned by Lally in 1758 to take part in the attack upon Madras. This brought the French adventure in the Deccan to an end, and the capture of Masulipatam by Colonel Forde with a force from Bengal in April, 1759, marked the end of French dominion in the Northern Circars. The importance of this episode has generally been misunderstood. So far as the French were concerned, it led nowhere. The English refused to be deceived by the shadow of legitimacy which it allowed Dupleix to cast over his projects. Its advantages were private, not public. Bussy and his chief officers, including some of Dupleix's own relations, made large fortunes; but the company received no financial benefit. The Northern Circars did not in fact produce the expected revenues, and Bussy was never able to help the campaigns of Dupleix with either troops or money, while the division of the French forces produced by this northern excursion and the absence from the Carnatic of the one French officer of unquestionably superior talents must be regarded as having materially aided the defeat of the French at Trichinopoly in 1752—the defeat which led directly to the recall of Dupleix himself. An expedition which secured no public advantage and which contributed to the French defeat elsewhere can only be considered a grievous mistake. But Bussy's brilliant though fruitless management of a Muslim durbar provided the English with a notable example of what might be done, and pointed the way on more than one occasion for Clive in his management of Mīr Ja'far in Bengal. Therein lies the real importance of Bussy's short-lived predominance in the Deccan.

The policy of Dupleix indeed lacked the elements of permanent success, and could never have survived a European war. Had he never been recalled, Coote or some other English leader would none the less have besieged, captured, and ruined Pondichery. The indispensable condition of political expansion in the east lay in the eighteenth century, as it had lain in the sixteenth and seventeenth, in predominance at sea. But this condition, as events were to prove, was not possessed by France. Dupleix's success was only obtained under temporary conditions of a most favourable nature. He launched his campaign after the war of the Austrian Succession. The most powerful weapon of the English, their naval power, was for the moment out of action. They could not pursue, intercept, or destroy the vessels which carried out to Pondichery recruits and munitions. Without this advantage it is unlikely that Dupleix would have obtained as high a degree of success as he in fact secured.

As it was, however, the schemes of the great French leader contributed largely to that expansion of English influence which shortly followed. In order to check the plans of the French, the English had been compelled to assemble on the Coromandel Coast a greater military and naval force than they had ever before gathered together in India. There were Admiral Watson and his squadron, a royal regiment, and the company's European troops strengthened not only by the recruits destined for Madras but also by those intended for Bengal. Besides these there was a considerable body of sepoys. The credit of being the first to drill and organise these troops in the European manner has been falsely ascribed by many to Dupleix. But recent research has shown that his English enemies led the way in attaching to them European drill-sergeants and officers, under whose training they became the best body of native infantry in India. In the middle of 1756 a combined force had been destined to march to Hyderabad at Salābat Jang's request, to deliver him from French control. But its march had been prevented by alarming news from Calcutta.

Alahwirdi Khān, who had ruled Bengal in virtual independence after a prolonged struggle with the Marāthas, died in

April, 1756. He was succeeded by his great-nephew, Sirāj-ud-daula, a young man at once inconsiderate and irresolute. His predecessor had favoured the Hindus, and had employed a number of them in high office. Sirāj-ud-daula had reversed this policy, and speedily alarmed and disgusted the principal Hindus of the provinces. Attempts have been made in recent times to rehabilitate his character. But contemporary Muslim writers lend no support to this change of view, and the young nawab seems to have deserved no more sympathy or respect than his own generation bestowed upon him. He had been alarmed by the events which had been taking place in southern India, and had been closely watching the Europeans settled on the Hugli, lest they should attempt to repeat in Bengal operations which had involved the overthrow or death of four Muslim rulers in the Carnatic and the Deccan. The English, the French, and the Dutch alike possessed factories which had once been fortified. Of these, the Dutch and the French were much stronger than the English factory, which was a fort only in name, and had been declared by every military officer who had seen it to be untenable against any sustained attack. But rumours of a new war in Europe with the French had led the president and council at Calcutta to build new batteries on the river-side, lest a French squadron should sail up the river to attack their virtually unprotected settlement. Sirāj-ud-daula at once demanded an explanation, and required the removal of the new defences. The president, Roger Drake, replied that they were necessary in view of a possible French attack. The nawab, who was marching against a rival, Shaukat Jang, in Purnea, at once returned to his capital, Murshidābād. He seized the English factory hard-by at Kāsimbāzār. He then marched against Calcutta. On June 16 he appeared before it; on the 18th the English were driven from their outposts; on the 19th the president and the commandant of the garrison sought refuge aboard ship; and on the 20th Fort William surrendered. The prisoners were shut up for the night in the military prison, the Black Hole, in which a number of them were suffocated. This event does not deserve the title of "massacre" by which it has long been known, for there is nothing to show that the fate of the prisoners was in any way designed. But neither does there appear ground for discrediting the evidence of more than one survivor or for supposing that no such incident occurred.

Despite Sirāj-ud-daula's triumph in capturing Calcutta, he had
chosen his time most unfortunately. If he had but waited until
the French and English were again at war, he would have been
certain of French co-operation had he required it, and would
have been secure from the reprisals of the other English settlements in India, at all events for a time. As it was, the presidency
of Madras had the means, and, under the inspiration of Orme,
the historian, the will, immediately to take up the challenge.
The troops intended to join Salābat Jang had not marched when
the news arrived from Bengal. Ships were collected. A new
expedition was prepared. Its command was entrusted to Clive
and Watson, who arrived in the Hugli a few days before
Christmas. On January 2, 1757, they reoccupied Calcutta without resistance. The nawab at once returned. But a night-attack
directed by Clive, though inflicting no great loss, shook Sirāj-ud-
daula's nerve, and he at once made peace, agreeing to confirm
all English privileges, to make good all the loss caused by the
capture of Calcutta, to permit its fortification, and to allow the
coinage of rupees there.

Then emerged the question of the French. At the end of 1756
it was known that war had broken out in Europe. The French
at Chandernagore at once made proposals for a neutrality. The
subject was repeatedly discussed, but came to nothing, because
the chief of Chandernagore could bind only himself and his
council and could not limit the action either of Pondichery or
of any officers who might come from Europe. Chandernagore
was thus exposed to attack as soon as the nawab permitted such
a step. The two nations were represented at Murshidābād by
William Watts and Jean Law, who used their utmost efforts to
induce the nawab to give, or to withhold, his assent. On the
whole the durbar favoured the English. Then, too, came an alarm
that Ahmad Shāh Durāni meant to advance against Bengal, and
Sirāj-ud-daula offered the English a lakh a month for aid against
the Afghans. At the same moment came a strong complaint
from Calcutta that the treaty had not been carried into effect;
and on March 10, the nawab's secretary wrote a letter, which
received the nawab's seal, permitting the English to attack
Chandernagore. Almost at once Sirāj-ud-daula changed his
mind. He ordered a force to march to protect the place; then,
on hearing from Nandakumār, his *faujdar* at Hugli, that the

French were certain to be beaten, he cancelled this order; but he also wrote imploring Bussy to march into Bengal and deliver him from the English. Meanwhile Clive and Watson, on receiving the nawab's letter, had moved at once, and the French surrendered after one day's fighting.

The result was that the nawab was deprived of his natural allies against the English, at the very time when he had betrayed his hostility to the latter by summoning Bussy to his aid. His simultaneous abandonment of Chandernagore and invitation to Bussy was the conduct of one who could neither perceive the sound course of action nor persevere in any. It is likely too that the nawab was the victim of treacherous advice received from his own durbar. The Seths hated him. Rāi Durlabh, who had held a great position, had been placed under the orders of a favourite named Mohan Lāl. Mīr Ja'far, the *bakhshī*, had been dismissed with insult. Already at the end of 1756 Omichand, one of the chief merchants of Calcutta, had sounded the English about a plan to replace Sirāj-ud-daula by a new and better nawab. In April, 1757, they were again approached by discontented Hindus and Muslims. The Frenchman, Law, believed, probably with justice, that these projects would have come to nothing without the backing of the Seths. But it was also clear that nothing would be done unless the English acted as the spear-head of the movement. In these circumstances an agreement was framed between the English and Mīr Ja'far. On June 11 the document was delivered at Calcutta, and immediately afterwards Clive set out on the march destined to lead to English dominion in Bengal. His force consisted of 800 Europeans and 2200 sepoys. He had with him no cavalry, and a zamindar who had been invited to join him with a body of horse preferred to wait until he saw how matters went. So did Mīr Ja'far himself. He was to have joined the English on the march. In fact he only gave them promises of help. When Clive reached the point at which he would have to cross the river in order to make contact with the enemy, he hesitated and sought the counsel of his officers. They advised a halt. But reflection quickly restored Clive's confidence, and on the eve of June 23 he encamped at Plassey Grove, close to Sirāj-ud-daula's camp. Many knew or had made a shrewd guess at what was going forward. Omichand, the Calcutta merchant who had taken a share in the early projects, had demanded a great reward—a quarter of the jewels and a twentieth of the treasure—as the price of his acquiescence. He had been half-silenced by the trick of a forged treaty in which his claims were allowed but which was not to receive effect. Nevertheless, the nawab had had ample notice of the English intentions, and had assembled his forces. But he was as ever hampered by his own indecision and the sinister advice which he received from his officials. He himself was no soldier. He ordered an attack on the English camp. It was feebly led and easily repulsed. Mīr Ja'far, who commanded a division of the nawab's army, drew aside and took no part. Then Clive advanced. Sirāj-ud-daula fled. His troops disbanded. Mīr Ja'far entered the English camp. On the 28th he was formally installed as nawab at Murshidābād, and on July 2 Sirāj-ud-daula, betrayed by a fakir whose ears he had cut off, was brought in a prisoner by Mīr Ja'far's son and at once put to death. These events precisely paralleled the events in the south. Once more an incoherent Indian army had been scattered, and the ruler of a province overthrown, by little more than the resolute advance of a small but well-organised force and its firm front on the battlefield. The people acquiesced in this decree of fate. The new nawab was accepted in Bengal with the same indifference with which Chanda Sāhib had been accepted in the Çarnatic and Salābat Jang in the Deccan. Muslim rule was being destroyed as easily as in the day of its power it had established its ascendency. The people at large remained utterly unmoved.

The new nawab was more humane but hardly more competent than the man he had displaced. He was indeed strong in the strength of his English allies, but he was burdened with the rewards which (like Dupleix's puppets) he had promised in return for assistance. All who had taken part in the revolution had stipulated for ample consideration. Like Salābat Jang, therefore, Mīr Ja'far succeeded to a treasury which was heavily mortgaged. Instead of reorganising and improving his administration, he projected despoiling the Hindu officials who had survived Sirāj-ud-daula's government. The chief of these were Rāi Durlabh, who had been and still was the *dīwān*, and Rāmnarāyan the deputy of Bihar. The latter had had no part in the late revolution; the former had done his utmost to favour it though he had cautiously abstained from any but verbal engagements.

Within six months Mīr Ja'far was accusing him of plotting to set up another nawab. Watts made strong representations on his behalf and for the moment the matter was smoothed over. But a little later the nawab's son, Mīrān, made a strong attack on him, and he was compelled to take refuge in Calcutta. Rāmnarāyan's case was different. He had at first been suspected of favouring Sirāj-ud-daula, and immediately after Plassey Eyre Coote, then a captain of the king's troops, had been sent up to Patna to effect his removal. Coote had been dissuaded from this by Mīr Kāsim, Mīr Ja'far's son-in-law, who seems to have sought a freer opportunity of despoiling the deputy. Later in the year Clive himself, having received assurances of Rāmnarāyan's fidelity to the new nawab, changed his attitude and accompanied Mīr Ja'far up to Patna to take part in the Bihar settlement. Rāmnarāyan refused to place himself in the nawab's power without a guarantee from the English. This was given, and under Clive's influence the nawab reluctantly agreed to confirm the deputy in his post for 9 lakhs of rupees; and Rāmnarāyan was promised by Clive that so long as he did not intrigue with foreign powers and paid the revenues regularly he should not be disturbed. Clive was already therefore checking the nawab in his policy towards his chief Hindu servants.

The recovery of Calcutta had been followed by the resumption of authority by the old governor, Roger Drake, and council. But Clive remained the dominating influence among his countrymen. When in July, 1758, a despatch was received from the company ordering the establishment of four governors to rule each for a month at a time, the council decided that so foolish a plan could not be put into operation, and invited Clive to act as governor till the company should send out orders on the news of the revolution of 1757. Later in the year a despatch arrived formally appointing Clive to the position which he was occupying.

In 1759 Prince 'Alī Gauhar—afterwards Shāh 'Ālam II—appeared on the borders of Bihar. He had fled to Oudh from the confusion reigning at Delhi, and hoped to establish himself in the eastern provinces. But Rāmnarāyan refused to give up Patna, and, when English reinforcements arrived, the prince retired to Oudh. His advance had much alarmed Mīr Ja'far, who feared that he would either succeed in his invasion or be joined by the

English. On his withdrawal the nawab bestowed on Clive the quit-rent which he had reserved when he had granted the 24-Parganas to the company in 1757. But he was already weary of the control under which he lay, and had begun to intrigue with the Dutch. The latter had viewed the establishment of English influence in Bengal with the same apprehension as the English had felt regarding the projects of Dupleix. They had lost the saltpetre monopoly which they had formerly enjoyed, and were eager for change. They therefore approached Mirān with offers to set him up in his father's place. A little later they opened communications with Mīr Ja'far himself, proposing to bring a force from Batavia to reduce the English. An understanding was reached. In 1759 the Dutch governor-general sent to India 300 Europeans and 600 Malay troops to carry out the plan. These were directed to proceed first to Negapatam, where they waited a month doing nothing. Moreover, a captain of the Dutch squadron, in hopes of commercial gain, had sailed direct to the Hugli. Clive was thus forewarned. He coolly made his preparations, and, when in October the Dutch troops reached the Hugli, Mīr Ja'far was at Calcutta under Clive's eye. He agreed to forbid his new allies to enter the river. They hesitated for a month. At last they resolved to force their way up. They began by seizing some small English vessels, thus providing Clive with an unanswerable case for hostilities. Their land-forces were scattered and broken by an action at Biderra. Their ships were defeated and captured the same day. Mirān suddenly appeared with a body of horse with which he had hoped to chase the broken English, but which he now set to blockade Chinsura. The Dutch made peace hurriedly. They admitted they had begun the fighting; they agreed to limit their forces; they promised to pay ten lakhs indemnity. Thus once more Clive had made certain that Bengal should not be the scene of a prolonged European war as had happened in the Carnatic.

Immediately after this success, in January, 1760, he resigned and sailed for England. His three years in Bengal had given to the English the position which Dupleix had established for a moment in the south. He had shown a tenacity and political skill equal to that of the great Frenchman; he had shown a vigour and promptitude of action which has seldom if ever been exceeded; he had shown a power of personal influence, a domination over other men, a gift of leadership, of extraordinary quality. He lacked the foresight of Dupleix; the charm of Hastings; but in the circumstances of the time his gifts had the fullest scope, and neither Dupleix nor Hastings could have accomplished all that he accomplished between 1756 and 1759.

The period of these great changes in Bengal had been marked in the south by the collapse of the French effort inaugurated by Dupleix. The outbreak of the Seven Years' War in 1756 had at first made small difference to either Madras or Pondichery. The former had sent all spare troops with Clive to Bengal, the latter to Bussy at Hyderabad. The uneasy truce arranged in 1754 was thus succeeded by a year of eventless war. In the autumn of 1757, however, a French royal regiment arrived, and in April, 1758, this was followed by an expedition comprising a squadron of nine ships under d'Aché, another royal regiment, and Lally as commandant-general of the French settlements in India. The English squadron, now commanded by Admiral Pocock and consisting of seven ships, had already appeared on the coast, but the position in Bengal was judged too uncertain for Clive to return the military forces sent up in 1756. The two squadrons engaged on April 28. The action was indecisive, but the French lost almost four times as many men as the English.

Ashore, however, the English could do little to oppose Lally's operations. They had concentrated their troops, and held only Madras, Fort St David, Chingleput and Trichinopoly. As soon as Lally had landed he hurried on to attack Fort St David, which fell on June 2. Lally then proposed to attack Madras by both land and sea. But in this d'Aché refused to co-operate, and Lally therefore deferred his project till later in the year when the northeast monsoon should have driven Pocock off the coast. Meanwhile he marched against Tanjore, in the hope of compelling the raja to pay the seventy lakhs he had promised to Chanda Sāhib in 1749. His preparations were hasty and incomplete. His men lacked supplies and ammunition. He opened the siege of Tanjore, but had not been able seriously to press the place when on August 8 he learnt that d'Aché had been defeated by Pocock off Kārikāl. He then retired to the coast with great loss of reputation.

The naval action of which he had heard had been fought on August 3. D'Aché in an hour's fighting lost 500 men. He returned to the Pondichery roadstead under the shelter of the batteries ashore; but was resolved to remain no longer. Councils of the chief military and naval officers were held. The former declared loudly and bitterly that d'Aché would ruin the prospects of the campaign if he left the coast. The latter with one accord declared that they could not again encounter the English. On September 3 d'Aché therefore sailed for Mauritius, and did not reappear till a year later, and Lally was thus left without the assistance of a squadron. He resolved nevertheless to attack Madras. On December 14 he appeared before it and formed the siege. Great preparations had been made for the defence. Provisions and ammunition had been collected in plenty. The works had been skilfully reconstructed. The governor, George Pigot, the commandant, Stringer Lawrence, the engineer, John Call, were resolute and talented; and although the garrison lacked protection from the shells that Lally constantly threw into the place, it never lost heart. The besiegers, too, were harassed by a force drawn from Trichinopoly and Chingleput. In the middle of February, when the defences had been severely battered, a squadron of ships hove in sight. It proved to be English. Lally did not venture to attempt a storm, but abandoned his trenches and retired.

This was the turning-point of the war on land. In the following April Colonel Forde, who had been dispatched by Clive from Bengal to attack the French in the Northern Circars, captured Masulipatam. Later in the year Lieutenant-Colonel Eyre Coote arrived from England with reinforcements which enabled the English to meet the French in the field. On January 22, 1760, Coote defeated Lally severely at Wandiwash. In a third action at sea Pocock had already defeated d'Aché, inflicting on him a crushing loss of men who could not be replaced. D'Aché had thus again been driven off the coast, this time never to return. These naval and military successes enabled the English to blockade Pondichery by sea and land. On January 16, 1761, it was compelled to surrender. The French effort to hold the gains of Dupleix had been completely broken.

The main cause of the English success lay in the supremacy which the English squadron established at sea, permitting them to receive men, money and provisions from Bengal and England, enabling them to transport, and cover the operations of, their forces, and depriving the French of their supplies. This placed

Lally at a grievous disadvantage, and the elusive authority which Dupleix had seized vanished at the first touch of that naval power which had not been applicable when he was projecting his schemes. Then, too, while Bussy's exploits had not contributed a man or a rupee to French aid, the English in Bengal were able at a critical time to send down both troops and money. Lastly Lally himself was hampered by personal defects and confronted by an impossible task. As a leader he was hasty, inconsiderate, violent. He expected others to attend to the detail of supplies, and never reflected on the hindrances which might be caused by the councillors whom he abused. Moreover, no man could at once conduct a war against the English and reform the Pondichery methods of administration. The knowledge that he was charged with the latter duty made every servant of the company desire to see him return to Europe discredited by defeat.

The fall of Pondichery left the English without serious European rivals in India for the moment, and thus enabled them to consolidate their position in Bengal. When Clive had sailed for England in January, 1760, he was succeeded by Holwell. This change increased the immediate difficulties of the situation. The new governor was merely a stop-gap, who had succeeded to the chair by accident and would speedily be replaced by a man with more influential interest. The nawab, whom even Clive had not persuaded to reduce his expenditure, was unwilling to listen to the advice of a new and transient authority. Affairs were further complicated by the reappearance of the prince whom Clive had driven away in 1759. On this occasion he slipped round the forces sent against him and raided Bengal itself, exciting great disturbance and alarm. It was moreover believed that he had been encouraged by the nawab himself. Though he was speedily expelled by the exertions of Colonel Caillaud, relations between Calcutta and Murshidābād were severely strained, and a crisis was precipitated by the death of the nawab's son, Mirān, which raised the question of the succession to Mīr Ja'far.

Holwell, after long discussions, came to the conclusion that the only sound course of action was for the company to assume the direct government of the province. He saw clearly that this was in the long run inevitable, and rightly believed that no good would come of either tolerating Mīr Ja'far's mismanagement or replacing him by another. At the same time, in view of his approaching retirement he could take no immediate action. Matters were left over, therefore, until the new governor, Henry Vansittart, should arrive.

Vansittart assumed the government in August, 1760. He was a Madras servant of some standing, who had secured the friendship of Clive and who enjoyed a good reputation for character and ability. But he lacked personality, and was much better fitted to carry out the orders of others than to frame and pursue a policy of his own. His appointment was most unwelcome in Bengal. All the members of council regarded it as an unfair supersession and were not likely willingly to co-operate with him in any policy which they disliked. The first question to be decided was that of the nawab's succession. In the interval between Mirān's death and Vansittart's arrival the claims of the nawab's son-in-law, Mīr Kāsim, had been skilfully put forward. The aspirant offered a strong contrast to Mīr Ja'far. He was careful where the other was extravagant, and resolute where the other was timid. He was moreover skilled in playing on the interests of others. This man was bent on securing the support of the Calcutta council. He won over Holwell, promising him a large present if he were named successor to Mīr Ja'far. Holwell, forgetting the policy which he had advocated earlier in the year, espoused his cause, and a number of conferences were held at Calcutta between him and Mīr Kāsim. The latter was willing to promise whatever was demanded of him. On condition of his nomination as heir to Mīr Ja'far, he agreed to cede new territory to the company, to provide immediate payment of the arrears due from the nawab to the company, and to reduce the military forces of the nawab to a specified number. These offers won over the council and it was resolved that Vansittart should proceed to Murshidābād at once to announce the decision to the nawab and obtain his assent. In fact, however, Mīr Kāsim had lured the council into an impossible position. He had returned at once to Murshidābād, and, when Vansittart arrived there, he found the nawab unalterably opposed to the new plan. His life, he declared, would not be worth a day's purchase once Mīr Kāsim had been recognised, and he would rather retire to Calcutta than continue to occupy the carpet of state—the masnad—on such terms. Vansittart, faced with this refusal, decided to install Mīr Kāsim at once as nawab, on condition that he would pay to his predecessor such an allowance as would permit him to live in comfort at Calcutta. This was done, and Mīr Ja'far was escorted down the river to the English settlement.

This revolution was a great triumph for the new nawab. He must have expected, if he had not inspired, Mīr Ja'far's opposition to his nomination. The issue was a tribute to his own insight and to the blindness of the new governor who had been unable to see through the outer semblance of the proposals laid before him. He signalised his gratitude by promising large gifts to the governor and council, and by carrying into immediate effect the agreement into which he had entered at Calcutta. He made over to the English the three districts of Bardwān, Midnapur, and Chittagong—outlying and disturbed districts of which he was not sorry to be relieved; and he made the payments of arrears which in fact permitted the siege of Pondichery to be carried to its successful conclusion. But the change carried with it the certainty of a new struggle. The old nawab had been replaced by a far better one. The government of the province would be improved. The payments to the company would be made with regularity. But the abler the nawab, the more certain he would be to seek to recover his independence, and the more strongly he would resent the position of superiority which the English occupied. Vansittart's policy was in fact inconsistent with itself. He sought to give Bengal a good ruler; but he was not willing to set his nation back in the position which it had occupied before the battle of Plassey.

From the first therefore subjects of dispute arose. The prince 'Alī Gauhar was threatening Patna once more. Rāmnarāyan defended the place with resolution until an English force arrived, and on January 15, 1761, Major Carnac defeated the prince on the river Sōn. The latter, being now refused refuge in Oudh, came into the English camp and for a while abode in Patna. He was anxious to procure English help to establish himself as emperor at Delhi, and at this time assumed the title of Shāh 'Ālam II. Vansittart was inclined to comply with his desires, but Mīr Kāsim viewed the discussions with jealousy and fear. He thought the English might be over-persuaded to accept from this needy monarch territorial rights over Bengal and Bihar. Though these suspicions were entirely baseless, his opposition brought the discussions to an end. He had succeeded in imposing his views on the governor and council of Calcutta.

His success in this matter was followed later in the year by one far more remarkable. Mīr Kāsim desired to get rid of Rāmnarāyan, the deputy governor of Bihar. He had for this two powerful reasons. One was that the deputy was believed to have accumulated great sums of money during the course of his rule and Mīr Kāsim hoped by plundering him to make good the sums he had disbursed to the English. The second was that Rāmnarāyan had been preserved in his office by English protection in accordance with Clive's policy of watching over the interests of the leading Hindus of the province. His destruction would therefore be a sign to the province at large that English favour was no longer any guard against the nawab's power. For a while Vansittart refused to abandon the policy of Clive, but he gradually weakened before Mīr Kāsim's persistence, and in September, 1761, gave a reluctant assent to the removal of the deputy. Rāmnarāyan was at once removed from office, imprisoned, plundered, and subsequently put to death.

At the same time the nawab was busy reorganising his power. He removed his capital from Murshidābād, dangerously near to Calcutta, to Monghyr, on the borders of Bengal and Bihar. He reorganised his troops, and placed them under the command of two Armenian leaders. He set up factories for the manufacture of arms. He ignored the complaints of Vansittart that he was not complying with his promises to reduce his military forces. At last when all was ready, at the end of 1761, he began to stop the trade of the company's servants in salt and betel. If they submitted, they would be reduced to the position which they had occupied before the victories of Clive and the nawab might regard his independence as achieved.

Participation in the internal trade of the province had long been a vexed question. The imperial *farmāns*, under which the trade alike of the company and of its servants had been conducted, had made no difference between goods of internal consumption and goods for export. But the nawabs had always limited the English trade to the latter class, and this had always been resented by the company's servants as a tyrannous exercise of power, exerted not on behalf of the interests of the province, but in the interest of the favourites to whom the nawab gave the monopolies of salt and betel, the chief articles concerned. In 1757 Clive had been instructed by the council to get the matter put right.

In consequence Mīr Ja'far had issued *parwanas* to his servants phrased in universal terms. "Whatever goods the company's *gumastas* [agents] may bring or carry to or from their factories... you shall neither ask for nor receive any sum however trifling." These orders covered all kinds of goods, and applied equally to the trade of the company and of its servants. Moreover, the nawab deprived himself of jurisdiction over any disputes that might arise out of this trade. "Whoever acts contrary to these orders," the *parwanas* continued, "the English have power to punish them." These orders had been duly acted upon. The company's servants had traded in salt and betel duty-free; and, when the internal customs-men had attempted to interfere, they had been punished by the authorities of the nearest English factory.

Though Mīr Ja'far had repented of the extraordinary concession which he had thus made, and had even applied to Holwell for its abolition, the system was certainly in full force in 1760 when Mīr Kāsim accepted the government from Vansittart, nor had he objected to it before his elevation to power. Indeed, it is clear that if he had done so, neither Holwell nor any one else would have dreamt of supporting his candidature. A year later, however, he began to describe the practice as a new and grievous innovation. In principle he was unquestionably right. The privilege which had been extorted from the weakness of Mīr Ja'far was not one which should ever have been demanded. But Mīr Kāsim had unquestionably condoned it. His demands that it should now cease were resented by the council as an attack upon the English. At the same time the latent jealousy of Vansittart was stirred up by the nawab's allowing his private trade to pass untouched, while he stopped the trade of everyone else. After long discussions, Vansittart visited the nawab at the end of 1762 and arranged a compromise with him. This provided for the payment of a small duty on salt and the abandonment of the privilege of punishing the nawab's officials. The change was at once rejected by the council, which sent up two of its members to the nawab to arrange less unfavourable terms. Anger ran high. The hot-tempered chief of the Patna factory, Ellis, alarmed by the increase of the Patna garrison and by the walling-up of the gate close to the English factory, made an unsuccessful attempt to seize the town. At the same time the two councillors who had been deputed to the nawab were murdered by the nawab's troops on their return down the river. War at once followed.

The campaign was short and completely successful. Major Adams, who commanded the troops which were sent from Calcutta, stormed position after position which the nawab had entrenched in the hope of checking an advance which he had long foreseen. When his capital, Monghyr, fell into English hands, Mīr Kāsim came to fancy that he had been betrayed. He put to death his Armenian commanders. He put to death the Seths. He ordered his unfortunate European prisoners, fifty-six in number, to be slain. Then he fled into Oudh with all the treasure which he had been able to carry away with him. The nawab wazir of Oudh resolved to assist him. In the next year, 1764, a long campaign followed around Patna, chequered by mutinies of the English troops, first of the Europeans and then of the sepoys, due in part to the great numbers of foreign deserters and in part to promises of reward which had been rashly made to the men. But when these difficulties had been dealt with by Major Hector Munro, who succeeded to Major Adams, the battle of Buxar on October 23 brought the matter to a decisive conclusion. The Oudh forces were broken. The conquest of Oudh itself followed. The nawab wazir fled into the Rohilla country. The control of affairs had passed more fully than ever into the hands of the government of Calcutta.

On the outbreak of the war Mīr Ja'far had been sent back once more to Murshidābād as nawab, on terms which had been dictated to him. English-owned salt was to pay no more than $2\frac{1}{2}$ per cent. The nawab's forces were to be limited. He was to receive a permanent resident. He was to make good all the losses which might be involved in the war with Mīr Kāsim. But he was still left free to choose his ministers. He selected the Brāhman, Nandakumār. The new government gave little satisfaction to the English authorities. It failed to supply the troops with provisions during the war with Mīr Kāsim and Oudh. It was believed to have entered into relations with the nawab wazir. On February 5, 1765, the old nawab died. He left a son, Najm-ud-daula. A deputation of the council proceeded from Calcutta to the capital. It was empowered to offer to recognise Najm-ud-daula's succession on condition that the English were to be allowed to select the principal ministers of the nawab. Inspired by Nandakumār, the prince made every effort to avoid this demand. But in vain. He was obliged to assent, and Muhammad Riza Khān was appointed deputy to act on behalf of the nawab in all matters. The nawab was installed on March 3, but in fact the council of Calcutta had assumed the supreme authority in the provinces. The nawab was a mere figure-head, able to act only through a minister nominated by and responsible to others.

Meanwhile, on news of the revolution of 1763, which was strongly disapproved at London, Clive had been appointed once more governor of Fort William in Bengal. He arrived in May, 1765, to find a situation open to any political settlement which he might think fit to impose. Fearful of extending too widely the dominions of the company, he resolved to hand back to the nawab wazir the country of Oudh, on condition of his paying an indemnity of thirty lakhs. Shāh 'Ālam was denied the military assistance which he had persistently demanded; nor was he even given the territory of Oudh which it had been in contemplation to bestow upon him. Instead he received the districts of Kora and Allāhābād, with an agreement to pay him twenty-six lakhs a year out of the revenues of Bengal, in return for which he issued a grant to the East India Company of the *dīwāni* of Bengal, Bihar and Orissa. The decision to restore the nawab wazir to his former dominions was unquestionably wise. It set up a friendly prince on the western borders of Bihar and thus covered the English interests from direct attack. The settlement with Shāh 'Ālam was less satisfactory. It introduced a new element of make-believe into the position of the company in Bengal. The Calcutta government was already exercising supreme control over the nawab, and the grant of the *dīwāni* weakened rather than confirmed its position besides laying it under the obligation of paying a large annual sum for nothing save the dubious advantage of having the nominal and powerless emperor reside under the company's protection. In this matter Clive's action seems to have been inspired by considerations of English rather than Indian conditions. Although in 1757 he had desired to see the English ministry take over the political duties of the company, he had changed his view after he had become the dominant influence in the company itself, and his great aim in 1765 was to make ministerial interference as difficult as possible. That object was well secured by the grant of the *dīwāni*. The ministry might have insisted on assuming the government of territories which the company had acquired or the protection of princes ruling under the company's control. But it could not assume on behalf of the king of Great Britain the privilege of collecting the revenues of Bengal under the authority of the emperor of Delhi. In fact the consequences of Clive's action at this time are clearly to be seen in the difficulties with which the ministry was confronted when in 1773 it attempted to legislate for the government of Bengal. From both points of view the results of his action were unfortunate, and it would have been better had he been content to leave untouched the supremacy over the nawab of Bengal which he found existing on his arrival.

The remainder of Clive's second period of government was occupied with administrative reforms. The sudden transformation of the East India Company from a commercial into a political body had resulted in a multitude of abuses. The company's servants were infected with the idea of using political methods of acquiring swift riches. In this Clive himself had led the way. He had taken great presents after Plassey and a *jāgīr* after the expulsion of Prince 'Alī Gauhar. In 1760 revolution had again been followed by great gifts to the chief movers. In 1763 Mīr Ja'far had been expected to pay for the privilege of being restored to his former government. In 1765 his son had been required to pay for succeeding to his father's position, and his chief minister had been made to pay for his selection. All this was entirely in accordance with the custom of the country: but the custom was noxious, and was producing the belief that the policy of the council was inspired solely by greed of gain. The presents of 1765 were peculiarly evil because the company had already sent out to India orders forbidding such conduct. These orders had been ignored because it was already known that Clive had been nominated to the government and the council thought it impossible that he would enforce orders of such a nature in view of his own past conduct. But in this it was entirely mistaken. Clive rightly believed that the presents which he had accepted were of a nature quite different from those which had been extorted in 1765. In spite of the strong discontent which the measure excited, he insisted that all the company's servants should sign bonds obliging themselves under penalty to accept no presents whatever. Declaring that none of the Bengal servants were senior enough or of character good enough to deserve promotion into the council, he filled vacancies with servants from Madras, and by stern discipline did his utmost to restore obedience. He recognised, however, that most of the evils had arisen from the practice of paying the company's servants small salaries and expecting them to make money by other means. He therefore devoted the salt monopoly to provide a fund for the increase of the salaries of the senior servants, both civil and military. This he did under the guise of forming a salt company to be managed by a committee of the company's servants: and, since this appeared to conflict with the company's orders prohibiting privileges in trade, his measure was reversed by the home authorities, although additional allowances of less amount were granted from the territorial revenues.

The question of army pay also offered him great difficulties. In 1763 the company had ordered a reduction of the field allowances paid to the officers under the denomination of *batta*. These were almost twice as high as the corresponding allowances at Madras, but the Calcutta council had shrunk from attempting to enforce the reduction. Clive proceeded to cut down the amounts, permitting the old rates only to be paid when officers were on service outside Bengal and Bihar. Stimulated by the discontent of the civil servants, the officers resolved to lay down their commissions simultaneously, so as to compel the governor to revoke his proposals. But the resignations were accepted; non-commissioned officers were promoted; officers were hurriedly brought up from Madras; the ringleaders were sent down to Calcutta; a few were tried by court martial for mutiny. The net result was that a number of officers were sent to England, and that the remainder submitted and entered into new agreements which for the first time placed the company's officers under military law.

Early in 1767 Clive sailed back to Europe, worn out by the efforts of his second government. He had shown himself to be as direct, as resolute and forceful as ever. He had met and triumphed over each situation as it arose. But the circumstances of the time had offered less scope to his special talents than had been the case ten years earlier. He was at his greatest in times demanding instant and decisive action. But he was a man of insight rather than one of foresight. His administrative settlement bequeathed a crop of difficulties to his successors and soon had to be remodelled.

CHAPTER IV

Warren Hastings and the Regulating Act

The return of Clive to England in 1767 was followed by extraordinary activity at the India House. The news of his acquisition of the *dīwāni* was hailed with ignorant enthusiasm. Everyone believed that he had made the fortune of the company, that it would pay huge dividends, that its stock would rise to prodigious heights. Such famous men as Henry Fox and Edmund Burke gambled in the stock, while others like Henry Vansittart and Laurence Sulivan sought to repair their crippled fortunes by buying for control in the hopes of procuring for themselves and their friends lucrative appointments. These activities drew political attention to the affairs of the company. In 1766 Chatham had already informed the directors that Indian affairs must be laid before parliament. But Chatham's health did not allow him personally to deal with the matter, and at last Charles Townshend, as chancellor of the exchequer, compounded with the company for an annual payment of £400,000. In 1769, when the intrigues of Vansittart and Sulivan had borne fruit, the court of directors resolved to send out a commission of reform, to be headed by Vansittart. The ministry, in which Lord Weymouth was then predominant, decided to intervene. It had already been requested to send a naval squadron to the east. When the company refused to join the commander of the squadron in its commission of reform, Weymouth resolved to give the commodore a secret mission. He was to enquire into the treatment of the princes of India by the company's servants. This attempt to secure control over the Indian administration failed before the obstinate opposition which the company's government offered to the commodore's interposition in matters which did not touch naval affairs. Then in 1772 parliament appointed select and secret committees to enquire into the company's political and financial conduct. Though Clive defended himself with success, the select committee elicited much discreditable evidence regarding the actions of many of the company's servants, and finally in 1773 the Regulating Act was passed. In many points it was inspired by the advice of Clive himself. For the government of Bengal it set up a new council which was named in the act. The council chosen consisted of three members sent out from London, and two company's servants. One of the latter, Warren Hastings, who had been governor of Fort William since 1772, was named governor-general, mainly, it would seem, in order to conduct affairs till the senior councillor should have learnt enough to assume the control himself. To the new council was entrusted the charge of superintending the political conduct of the other presidencies. A special court was to be established by royal authority at Calcutta and empowered to try cases in which the natives of Bengal suffered under the oppression of the government. In future only one sixth of the directors were to be elected each year, instead of the whole body being chosen annually. It would be difficult to exaggerate either the benevolent intentions with which the act was passed or the maleficent consequences by which it was followed.

Meanwhile, in Bengal Clive had been succeeded first by two nonentities and then by a man of genius. Under Verelst and Cartier, who were governors from 1767 till 1772, one at least of Clive's political arrangements had begun to crumble. The emperor at Allāhābād soon wearied of English protection. General Richard Smith, who commanded the troops there, and who was afterwards to take part in the attack on Hastings, was an unaccommodating man who would not allow his morning's rest to be disturbed by the beating of the imperial kettle-drums. The Marāthas, who were beginning to recover from their disastrous overthrow at Pānīpat, and were seeking once more the lordship of northern India, re-occupied Delhi, threatened Oudh, and sent flattering messages to Shāh 'Ālam offering to establish him in the palace of his ancestors. The English tried to dissuade him from accepting. But he, refusing to listen, marched off and joined his new friends. About the same time, the Marāthas, in order more easily to attack Oudh, made overtures to the Rohilla chiefs, and then attempted to coerce them into compliance. The Rohillas in alarm made an agreement with the nawab wazir.

At the outset of his government in 1772 Hastings was thus confronted by two main political problems. The emperor, now under Marātha protection, was loudly demanding the payment of his twenty-six lakhs a year. The famine which had afflicted the provinces in 1769 had necessitated its suspension; and Hastings resolved to make that an excuse for ceasing altogether to pay out a large sum of money which would have fallen into the hands of the Marāthas and assisted them in their designs on northern India. He took the view that the cession of the *dīwāni* had been merely a solemn farce, that the company had in fact conquered Bengal, and that the emperor could not give what it was not in his power to bestow. Hastings had on his accession to office been required to undertake the direct administration of the provincial finances. He had soon perceived that it was not practicable to limit the scope of the company's government to half the administration only. He had therefore deliberately sought to make Calcutta the capital, transferring thither the treasury and centralising there the administration of justice. He aimed at establishing English sovereignty; and his refusal to continue Clive's arrangement with the emperor was in fact but another step in the same direction.

The second problem was that offered by Oudh. Its maintenance as a buffer-state was clearly most desirable; but if it was duly to fulfil its function of sheltering the company's territories, it had to be strong enough to protect itself. Hastings made over to the nawab wazir the two districts which the emperor had abandoned. They lay at a distance from the company's territories, and their retention would have been inconvenient. This was arranged at conferences which Hastings held with the nawab wazir in 1773. At the same time the latter complained that the Rohillas were not keeping the agreement into which they had entered with him, and proposed that the company's forces should assist him in reducing them and adding their country to his own. Strategically the project was desirable, for the Rohilkhand afforded the best route for an invasion of Oudh from the west, and its possession would materially strengthen the nawab. But at the moment no decision was taken. Later in the year the nawab repeated his demands, and the matter was laid before the council at Calcutta. It was persuaded by the arguments of the governor to agree. A force was marched westwards to co-operate in the conquest of the Rohilkhand, which speedily followed. Hastings found it necessary in more than one instance to protect the nawab from the demands which the commander, Colonel Champion, made upon him.

While the English force was still in the Rohilkhand, the new councillors and the new judges reached Calcutta. The first included General Clavering, selected by the personal favour of the king, whose aide-de-camp he had been; Colonel Monson, who had served in south India, and proved himself to be an honest but irascible man of limited judgment; and Philip Francis, who, wearied of his subordinate position in the office of the secretary at war, had been seeking employment outside England. His father was a client of the Grenvilles; he himself was known to them; and probably through that channel he had made the acquaintance of Clive. Whether Clive recommended him to Lord North does not appear; but immediately after his nomination, he visited Clive, and was speedily indoctrinated with Clive's ideas on Indian administration. The fact is important. It meant that the one man of intelligence sent out from England in 1774 carried with him conceptions the exact opposite of those which Warren Hastings had been seeking to put into practice and that the dead hand of Clive would be laid upon the government with all the weight of the majority of the council.

The councillors reached Calcutta on October 19, and within a week had declared war on the governor-general. Their motives have been hotly debated. But there is no doubt that they reached India in a hostile temper, that they complained bitterly of such a trifle as a lack of punctiliousness in their reception, and that before they stepped ashore they had been in communication with men whose interests had been hurt by Warren Hastings's reforms. The responsibility for their action probably lay with Francis. The voyage had afforded him time to judge the capacity of his fellow-councillors and to establish over them the ascendancy of his talents. It rested with him to determine whether they should for a while rest inactive spectators of what was going forward or enter at once upon the fray. His own interests as a mere junior member of council demanded the latter course. In Clive's principles he possessed a whole armoury of weapons for attack. He resolved therefore to drive Warren Hastings from office at the first possible moment, in order to bring nearer the realisation of a dream in which he was already beginning to indulge, that of himself succeeding to the office of governor-general.

The Rohilla War afforded the pretext for their action. Francis denounced it as "the conquest of all the little states about us, who were our friends, who were our barriers". Champion, whose perquisites had been cut down by Hastings, was ready to denounce the policy which had led to so bootless a campaign. A legend of atrocities was developed, leading men to fancy that peaceful cultivators with their wives and children had been massacred wholesale, whereas Champion himself admitted that not a person had been slain except on the battlefield. The Rohilla chief, Hāfiz Rahmat, had perished in battle, his family for a while had suffered privations, but by the end of the year two of his sons had accepted Shujā'-ud-daula's service, and the narrative afterwards compiled by a member of his family makes no mention of atrocities. The current Indian view is expressed by the author of the *Siyyar-ul-Mutakherin*. Doubtless it was high time, he says, that the Rohillas should undergo the treatment which they had long been meting out to others. But despite all that could be said about a policy which was of course calculated in the interests of the East India Company rather than in compliance with humanitarian ideas, the majority, led by Francis, prepared despatches warning the company that their interests and prospects in India had been jeopardised by the conduct of the governor-general.

Their next step was aimed more directly at the personal conduct of Hastings. Joseph Fowke, a *protégé* of Clavering and a company's servant of dubious character, together with Nandakumār, who was presented to Clavering by Fowke, brought forward accusations of bribery. Nandakumār had a strong grudge against the governor-general. He had hoped that when the company's Indian deputy, Muhammad Riza Khān, was removed from office, he would be chosen as his successor. Instead, under the orders of the company, Hastings had assumed the direct administration of affairs. Nandakumār now accused the latter of having accepted a large bribe from Munni Begum, one of the late Mīr Ja'far's wives, and, without delay, the majority resolved that "there is no species of peculation from which the Honourable the Governor-General has thought it right to abstain". Hastings promptly brought forward a charge of conspiracy against Nandakumār and Fowke, but, while this charge was still pending, a further charge of forgery was brought against Nandakumār. It has generally been surmised that the charge was brought at the suggestion of Hastings himself. This seems unlikely. The charge of forgery was a revival of a suit which had lapsed owing to the institution of the new court of justice at Calcutta under the Regulating Act, and the accuser is known to have been seeking legal help for his suit before Nandakumār had opened his mouth against Hastings. Nandakumār was committed to prison on May 6. He was tried in the second week of June under an act which made forgery a capital offence, he was found guilty by the petty jury, and he was executed by warrant of the Supreme Court on August 5.

The commentary on these events supplied by Burke and afterwards by Macaulay is well known. Briefly it accuses Hastings of having sought deliberately to put Nandakumār out of the way, and the chief justice, Elijah Impey, of having been misled by his school-time friendship with Hastings into straining justice against the prisoner and wrongfully putting him to death. This explanation seems false, for it ignores a great number of facts. The court by which the accused was tried consisted of all four judges, of whom, if Impey was a friend of the governor-general, another, Chambers, was a close friend of Francis. This friend of Francis declared that he considered the verdict of guilty justified by the evidence. The jury, which returned the verdict, had been empannelled by the brother-in-law of Francis. The applicability of the act under which Nandakumār was tried seemed established by the fact that in 1765 an Indian had been tried under it and sentenced to death by the Court of Quarter Sessions. No reason appears for supposing that the trial was unfair or that any of the judges, including Chambers, doubted the correctness of the sentence. But at that point the court ought to have stopped. It was clearly undesirable to execute the principal witness against the governor-general while the latter's cause was still undecided. The court should therefore have exercised its powers of respite, and kept the accused alive at least until his evidence was no longer required. This step was proposed by Chambers, but rejected by the other three judges. One reason given was that no grounds appeared upon the face of the trial for the exercise of mercy. But their chief motive was afforded by the conduct of the majority of the council. The latter had strongly taken the side of the accused. They had visited him in prison. Reports had spread through the city that if he were condemned they would use force to release him. Worst of all, on the morning on which the trial opened, the majority had addressed a threatening letter to two of the judges, warning them that they had better be careful what they did. To men brought up in the traditions of the English bar this letter was bound to recall Stuart rule and the vanished supremacy of the executive over the judicature. They knew well that the Supreme Court had been deliberately constituted so as to be completely independent of the government of Fort William. This attempt to intimidate them was certain to incline them to administer the strictest justice to the accused lest they should be themselves accused of truckling to the wishes of the councillors. The majority, having thus indisposed the court against the prisoner, waited patiently for the trial to take its course. On the eve of the day fixed for the execution, Clavering received a letter from Nandakumār. It could have had but one object—to pray the majority to request the court for a respite of sentence. Clavering did not open the letter till after the execution, and did not lay it before the council till the 14th, when on the motion of Francis the majority resolved to burn the letter as a libel on the court and to expunge it from the records of the council. In other words the majority deliberately abstained from asking the court to defer the execution of the chief witness against the governor-general—a request which the court could hardly have refused. It has been asserted that Hastings should have foreseen the consequences of the execution and urged his friend Impey to keep Nandakumār alive. But that duty lay no less clearly upon the majority, whose conduct before, during, and after the trial can scarcely be explained unless they desired to see him safely hanged. After all, the evidence of Nandakumār against Hastings, like the evidence which he had formerly given against his enemy Muhammad Riza Khān, had little corroboration. The case was not likely to be proved. But Nandakumār's death would restore all the venom to his charges against the governor-general.

While these events had been taking place, the majority had given a singular expression to their views of foreign policy. Early in 1775 the nawab wazir, Shujā'-ud-daula, had died, lamented by his subjects. He was succeeded by his son, Āsaf-ud-daula. The majority at once declared that treaties were binding only during the lifetime of the parties, and denounced Hastings's agreements with the late nawab. Āsaf-ud-daula needed the company's assistance and was obliged to accept hard terms. His payments for military assistance were increased and he was obliged to cede Benares to the company. Thus his charges were raised while his resources were reduced, and the agent whom the majority had employed was voted a reward of a lakh of rupees. This new treaty, signed on May 21, 1775, marks the beginning of the ruin of Oudh. Āsaf-ud-daula was a weak prince, who at once set up in office his own favourites in place of his father's experienced ministers. His treasury was exhausted; his troops unpaid and mutinous. But the late nawab's wives had possessed themselves of the large resources in specie which the nawab had left behind. With the aid of the agent, Bristow, fifty-six lakhs were extracted from these ladies in the five months following on the treaty, under promises that no more should be demanded of them. But disputes between the nawab and the begums, and between the nawab and his ministers, continued unabated. The result of the majority's policy was disastrous. The state which Hastings had tried to strengthen was weakened by the excessive demands which were made upon it, by the promise of protection which Bristow was at last allowed to give to the begums, by the failure to restore discipline in the military forces of the state, and by the consequent spirit of disorder which developed among the great landholders, who refused to pay the revenue till coerced by actual force. This also was the period in which the administration of the Rohilla country fell into confusion, so that what Macaulay represents as due to the conduct of Hastings was rather due to the policy of the majority who wrested power from his hands and reversed his measures.

Whatever may have been the purpose of the conduct pursued by Francis and his associates, Hastings was driven to contemplate the resignation of his office. At first he had resolved to wait and see what the directors and ministry thought of the behaviour of the majority. Early in 1775 he sent to England as his agent an officer named Macleane, to represent his difficulties and try to secure support for him. In a moment of temporary and most unusual hesitation, he even empowered Macleane to tender his resignation if support could not be had. But a few weeks later he retracted this decision and wrote informing Macleane of his change of mind. In London Lord North was fully disposed to back his nominees; the ministerial agent, John Robinson, won over a majority of the directors by promises of patronage and rewards, so that the ministry and the company seemed to be united in opposition to Hastings. In May, 1776, the directors agreed to move the crown to dismiss Hastings from office. But Hastings's friends hurriedly called a special meeting of the proprietors, who resolved that this proposal should not receive effect. Thus the ministry was itself defeated owing to the provisions of its own act, which, while limiting the number of directors to be elected year by year, had done nothing to meet the case of differences arising between the directors and proprietors. On this check, the ministry decided to modify the act so as to disable Hastings's friends among the proprietors from hindering his removal. Macleane, daunted by the hostility which he found in London, then proposed an accommodation. Hastings was to resign on condition of being well received on his return. Since this would have made way for Clavering's advance to the chair, the sole point in which North was really interested, the suggestion was accepted. The Order of the Bath was conferred upon Clavering as a mark of ministerial favour, and it seemed as though North had reached the object which he had been seeking by his usual devious means.

Events in India, however, moved quite contrary to his expectations. Monson had died in 1776, thus transferring the actual control of government into the hands of the governor-general, who had been consistently supported by Barwell (the other company's servant on the council) and whose casting vote now gave him a majority whenever he desired. He had not used his recovered power to introduce any great changes, conscious that his tenure of office was most uncertain; but he had recalled the majority agent, Bristow, from Oudh. In June, 1777, news reached Calcutta of the results of Macleane's negotiations. Clavering, who thought the game in his own hands, at once began to act as though he were governor-general. He summoned the council to meet, and prepared orders announcing the change of government to the garrison of Fort William. Hastings hesitated. On the one hand his friends had written informing him that they considered the bestowal of the Bath on Clavering with no corresponding honour for himself to be a breach of Macleane's agreement with the ministry and advising him not to resign. Having retracted his authority to Macleane, he certainly lay under no obligation to retire. He was most unwilling to deliver over the charge of the company's affairs to a man who (he felt sure) would ruin them. But on the other hand he had to recognise the implacable hostility which appeared to have possessed the minds of the authorities in England. In these circumstances the precipitation of Clavering's conduct seems to have determined him to retain his office. He had not resigned; he had not been dismissed; yet the general was assuming the powers of his office. Hastings therefore defied him, and claimed that in acting as governor-general Clavering had tacitly vacated his office of commander-in-chief. On Hastings's suggestion the matter was referred to the judges for their opinion. They held that Hastings was still governor-general and Clavering still commander-in-chief. The latter reluctantly gave way, but could not overcome the chagrin which the turn of events had caused him. Elderly, high-living men almost always found the Indian climate fatal. For some months Clavering had fallen into poor health. He was covered with boils which exasperated a temper naturally violent. In August he was attacked with dysentery, and died on the 30th.

The news of these events reached London in the course of 1778. Since two of the three ministerial nominees had died, the third, Francis, hoped that his chance had come at last. He wrote to all his friends demanding their utmost activity in his favour, and he seems even to have received some sort of promise from North that he should be considered as a possible successor to Hastings's place as soon as the latter should have been removed. But Clavering's death had taken away North's main object in trying to get rid of Hastings. Moreover, public affairs were becoming difficult. To the American rebellion had just been added a war with France. North was unwilling to endanger the British position in India by removing a man of admitted capacity to make way for one who had never held high office and who was supported by no great parliamentary interests. Consequently the enmity against Hastings evaporated, and in 1779 the ministry even entered into an alliance with the friends of the governor-general on condition of receiving their aid in parliament. This arrangement led to the disappearance of Francis from Calcutta. He soon wearied of his fruitless opposition on ground where Hastings had clearly triumphed. He had secured the main purpose with which he had sailed to India, for he had made a large fortune at the whist table, mainly at the expense of Barwell.

But he was not to depart without one more dramatic incident. In 1780 Hastings had come to an ill-defined agreement with Francis in order to permit of Barwell's return to England. In the latter part of 1780, in consequence of differences over the conduct of the war which had broken out, Hastings recorded a minute in which he charged his enemy with an habitual breach of faith, public and private alike. Francis was obliged to respond to this by a challenge. In the duel which followed, Francis fired first, and missed. Hastings, with characteristic deliberation, waited till his aim had steadied, and Francis fell with a wound in the side. As soon as he recovered, he took a passage for England, to continue the struggle on ground with which he was more familiar and where his peculiar talents for intrigue would find freer scope. But for the moment the enemies sent out against the governor-general in 1773 had "sickened, died, and fled".

Nevertheless, it must be remembered that for seven years the chief efforts of Warren Hastings had been diverted by the consequences of the Regulating Act to defending his own position against a hostile element within his own council and against the hostility of the ministry in England, with small leisure to develop and continue the policy of reform which had marked the two years of his uncontested power. Nor was this the only handicap which the act laid upon him. In the field of foreign policy also he found his government invested with responsibility without power. The act was intended to give to the governor-general and council authority over the conduct of relations with the other rulers of India. But their legal rights were limited to the sanction of declarations of war and the conclusion of peace. The subordinate presidencies of Bombay and Madras could legally defy the intervention of the presidency of Bengal in all intermediate relations. They could so conduct their external affairs as to render war inevitable, and so mismanage a war as to render peace on any terms beneficial, while the evil tradition of the political functions of the commanding officer of the naval squadron still permitted the intervention of his authority however unexpected and inexpedient that might be. These difficulties first emerged in connection with the relations of Bombay with the Marāthās. In 1761 the great Pēshwā Bāji Rāo had died heart-broken at the defeat of Pānīpat. He had been succeeded by his son, Madhu Rāo, aged only seventeen, and naturally under guardianship. The regent was his uncle, Rāghunāth Rāo, a man of unquestioned personal bravery but of a weak, vacillating character. In the next year, however, the young Pēshwā insisted on assuming the authority of his office. Wars followed with the Nizām and with Hyder 'Alī of Mysore, leading to projects of alliance on the part of the English with one or other of the contending parties. Internal difficulties also arose, and Rāghunāth, who had intrigued with other Marātha chiefs, was attacked and made prisoner. But Madhu Rāo's health soon began to fail. He was attacked by consumption, and died on November 18, 1772. He was succeeded by his brother Narāyan Rāo, and Rāghunāth Rāo enjoyed once more the regency of affairs. At the capital, Poona, however, he was opposed by the ablest of all the Marātha officials, Bālājī Janardhan, better known as Nāna Phadnavis, who had been brought forward by the late Madhu Rāo. At the same time affairs were complicated by the hostility which raged between Gopika Bai, the Pēshwā's mother, and Ānanda Bai, Rāghunāth Rāo's wife. As a result of their quarrels Rāghunāth Rāo was imprisoned in the palace. Further intrigues followed. The army was discontented. Rāghunāth sought to take advantage of this to secure his own release, while his wife sought vengeance against the Pēshwā and his mother. On August 30, 1773, a mutiny broke out. A party of infantry forced its way into the palace, and, although Rāghunāth Rāo interceded for his nephew, Narāyan Rāo was murdered, and Rāghunāth Rāo recognised as Pēshwā.

His success was short-lived. At Poona a strong party, headed by Nāna Phadnavis, counteracted his measures, and, when in the following year the late Pēshwā's wife was delivered of a son, the infant was formally recognised and a council of regency formed to conduct the administration. Rāghunāth Rāo, who had been campaigning against Hyder 'Ali, had hastened back to Poona on receiving the news of the probable birth of the child and had defeated a force sent to oppose him. But he had failed to follow up his victory, and so missed his opportunity of turning out the council of regency. Finding that Nāna Phadnavis was too strong for him, he then appealed for English help. Here, as in the Carnatic and elsewhere in India, European intervention was produced not by the aggressive ambitions of the European, but by the decay of the Indian states themselves and the desire of Indian princes for European support.

Bombay at this time was the weakest of the three presidencies. It comprised only a tiny island, facing the mainland where the strongest power in India held control. Under Bālājī Rāo the Marāthas had conquered from the Portuguese the fort of Bassein and the island of Salsette, thus rendering their control of the surrounding territory complete. Good relations with Poona were thus essential to Bombay, and in 1772 the company had wisely ordered the council to maintain a regular envoy with the Pēshwā, in the hope of securing privileges for the company's trade and if possible the cession of Bassein and Salsette, which would make the position of Bombay much more secure. Rāghunāth's overtures seemed to provide the opportunity of obtaining those places. But he, hoping to enlist Sindhia and Holkar in his cause, refused the English terms. Learning that the Portuguese at Goa had lately received large reinforcements and that they were about to use them in recovering Salsette and Bassein, the Bombay council resolved on instant action. One reason was that if the places passed again into the hands of the ancient ally of Great Britain their acquisition would become virtually impossible; the other that the Portuguese possession of Salsette would place all English trade with the interior under their control. Thāna, the chief post in Salsette, was attacked and captured on December 31, 1774. A little later, Rāghunāth, having failed to procure Marātha help from northern India, reopened discussions with the English, and, on March 7, 1775, the Treaty of Surat was signed. By this the English agreed to support Rāghunāth with a force of 2500 men, provided he bore the cost; in return he agreed to refrain from alliance with any enemy of the company, to make over Bassein and Salsette, and to deposit six lakhs as a security. A force under Colonel Keating had already reached Surat on February 27. On May 18 the allies met the Poona troops at Adas and completely defeated them after a prolonged contest. At the same time Commodore John Moore destroyed the Marātha fleet, and, encouraged by these victories, Fateh Singh Gaikwar, a claimant to Gujarāt, allied himself with the Bombay government. At Poona the supporters of Nāna Phadnavis began to desert him, and a resolute advance would probably have established Rāghunāth Rāo as Pēshwā, at all events for the time being.

This war had been begun and the Treaty of Surat had been signed without reference to the governor-general and council.

For this the Bombay council was not without excuse. Events had come to a crisis just before the new government at Calcutta had announced its assumption of office, and therefore before the Regulating Act need be considered in force. The signature of the treaty and the commencement of Keating's campaign were defended on the score of the company's positive orders and the pressing need of immediate action. On the receipt of the news the Bengal government unanimously condemned the conduct of its supposed subordinate. But it was more difficult to decide what course ought to be pursued. Hastings considered that any sudden reversal of policy was likely to cause more evil than good. The abandonment of Rāghunāth would make every Indian prince dubious of English faith. It was undeniable that the company had laid great stress on the acquisition of Salsette and Bassein. He therefore desired to limit and control the future action of Bombay rather than abruptly to denounce the treaty into which it had entered. The majority, however, was resolved to enforce its own views. On May 31 a despatch was addressed to the Bombay council requiring it at once to recall the company's forces "unless their safety may be endangered by an instant retreat". Later in the year it sent Colonel Upton to negotiate a peace with the Poona regency in its own name. Upton was ill-fitted for the duty. Neither he nor his secretary knew a word of Marāthi, and were in fact dependent on the interpreters supplied to them by the Marāthas themselves. Moreover, the Calcutta authorities had shown themselves manifestly eager for peace, and were so misguided as to fancy that they might get Salsette and Bassein in return for their pacific sentiments. Nāna Phadnavis of course sought to take advantage of this attitude. He refused to consider the possibility of any cessions of territory and demanded the surrender of Rāghunāth Rāo. This was more than Upton's instructions permitted, and, when he reported the deadlock, in February, 1776, the council suddenly became bellicose and threatened to resume hostilities. On March 1 the wisdom of this change of front was exhibited by the signature of the Treaty of Purandhar. It annulled the Treaty of Surat; it admitted the retention of Salsette and the cession of the Broach revenues; it agreed to the payment of twelve lakhs of rupees by Poona to cover the costs of the English campaign. Rāghunāth Rāo was to live in retirement in Gujarāt on a pension of three lakhs a year.

But the treaty never took effect. Rāghunāth Rāo, having received some encouragement from Sindhia, refused to accept the terms offered to him. The Bombay government, despite the protests of Upton, gave him shelter at Surat. The Poona regency never made any payments, and in the next year received a French adventurer with distinguished honours and agreed to grant the French a port in western India. Further complications arose from the conduct of the East India Company. Towards the close of 1776 a despatch from England approved the Treaty of Surat, on which the Bombay authorities at once invited Rāghunāth Rāo to take up his residence at Bombay. In the following year a further despatch arrived, regretting the Treaty of Purandhar and authorising the government of Bombay to make a new alliance with Rāghunāth if the Poona government attempted to evade its stipulations. The governor and council at once did so.

By this time the majority had fallen from power at Calcutta, leaving Hastings to meet the difficulties caused both by their own conduct and by the provisions of the act which had placed them in power. In 1778 Hastings learnt from Bombay that dissensions had at last broken out at Poona. The regency had long been divided between Sakharām Bāpu, a wavering and unreliable man, and Nāna Phadnavis, able but unscrupulous. Holkar promised Sakharām his help, and Maroba Phadnavis, a cousin of Nāna, joined him. This new group opened negotiations with Rāghunāth at Bombay, and the government of the presidency promised its support. This corresponded too closely with the orders of the company to be opposed by Hastings. He therefore decided to send a force from Bengal to march overland and join the Bombay troops. But almost at once the party with which the English hoped to co-operate began to dissolve. Nāna, who had for the moment been forced to flee from Poona, bought over Holkar with nine lakhs of rupees, induced his cousin to rejoin him and then shut him up in prison, and thus recovered the headship of affairs. Governor Hornby from Bombay at once called upon him to declare whether he was willing to give full effect to the Treaty of Purandhar and dismiss the French adventurer with whom he was still negotiating. When he refused to give an explicit answer, the council resolved to plunge at once into war. It proposed to establish Rāghunāth Rāo as regent on behalf of the young Pēshwā Madhu Rāo Narāyan. In November, 1778, the·

Bombay forces took the field. They consisted of 600 Europeans and 3300 sepoys. The military command was placed in the hands of Colonel Egerton, an officer of indifferent health and no Indian experience, but the control really lay with a committee of three, consisting of the commander and two members of the council. It does not seem to have occurred to the Bombay government that if it could not trust its commander it had better not go to war. Rāghunāth accompanied the expedition. It carried with it an enormous baggage-train of 19,000 bullocks, and could march barely two miles an hour. In January, 1779, Egerton resigned his command and was succeeded by Colonel Cockburn. On the 9th at Talegāon at the top of the Ghauts a large Marātha army was encountered. Cockburn considered that he could force his way to Poona twenty miles off if he abandoned his baggage. But the committee, despite Rāghunāth's entreaties, resolved to retire. The stores were burnt; the guns thrown into a tank; and on the 12th the army marched three miles to Wadgāon, harassed by perpetual attacks. Further retreat being deemed impossible, the committee entered into negotiations, Rāghunāth took refuge with Sindhia, and the Convention of Wadgāon was signed. It promised the surrender of all territory acquired since 1773, the withdrawal of the force advancing from Bengal, the transfer of the Broach revenues to Sindhia, and the giving of hostages as a security for the due performance of the terms. Although Hornby and his council had not authorised and promptly disavowed these disgraceful terms, they cannot be acquitted of having brought about the failure of their enterprise, both by the unwise arrangements made for the control of the expedition, and by the haste with which they had embarked on their action without awaiting the promised support from Bengal.

On January 30 the Bengal detachment marched into Burhānpur, and on February 26 reached Surat. Hastings had rightly calculated that neither Sindhia nor Holkar would care to oppose its movements, since by so doing they would endanger the safety of their own territories. Colonel Leslie, the officer under whose command the detachment had at first been placed, had proved to be slack and unenterprising. But he had died in October, 1778, and the command had then been given to Colonel Goddard, who had thus carried to a successful end the project from which Francis had anticipated nothing but failure. Goddard remained under

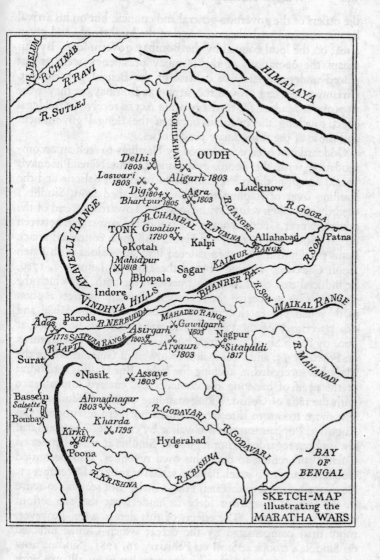

R.JHELUM
R.CHINAB
R.RAVI
R.SUTLEJ
HIMALAYA
ROHILKHAND
OUDH
Delhi
1803
Laswari
1803
Aligarh 1803
Dig 1804
Bhartpur 1805
Agra
1803
Lucknow
R.GANGES
R.GOGRA
ARAVELLI RANGE
TONK
R.CHAMBAL
Gwalior
1780
Kotah
Kalpi
R.JUMNA
Allahabad
Patna
KAIMUR RANGE
R.SON
Mahidpur
1818
Sagar
Bhopal
Indore
VINDHYA HILLS
BHANBER RA.
R.SON
MAIKAL RANGE
Adas
Baroda
R.NERBUDDA
MAHADEO RANGE
Gawilgarh
1803
Asirgarh
1803
Argaun
1803
Nagpur
Sitabaldi
1817
R.MAHANADI
1775 SATPURA RANGE
R.TAPTI
Surat
Nasik
Assaye
1803
Bassein
Salsette
Is.
Bombay
Ahmadnagar
1803
Kharda
1795
Kirki
1817
Poona
Hyderabad
R.GODAVARI
R.GODAVARI
R.KRISHNA
R.KRISHNA
BAY
OF
BENGAL

SKETCH-MAP
illustrating the
MARATHA WARS

the orders of the governor-general and council, but on his arrival he was invested with the command of the local troops and given a seat on the local council by the Bombay government. By this means the operations of the Bombay presidency were at last placed under the effective control of the Bengal government. Circumstances had proved too strong at Bombay, as they were to prove at Madras, for the Regulating Act to receive its full legal effect touching the relations between the Bengal government and those of the subordinate presidencies.

Goddard had been empowered by Hastings to seek an accommodation with the Poona government. But Nāna Phadnavis would accept nothing less than the surrender of Salsette and the handing over of Rāghunāth, who had escaped from Sindhia's custody and taken refuge with Goddard. Towards the end of the rains, however, Goddard heard of a rumoured agreement between the Marāthas, the Nizām, and Hyder 'Alī for a concerted attack upon the English. He then entered into discussions with Fateh Singh Gaekwar. Having crossed the Taptī on January 1, 1780, he induced that chief to sign a treaty on the 26th, by which the English were to receive the revenues of certain districts as soon as they had put Fateh Singh in possession of Ahmadābād and other territory of the Pēshwā, and meanwhile to be joined at once by Fateh Singh with 3000 horse. Ahmadābād was captured on February 15, and a campaign followed in Gujarāt, where the Marāthas succeeded in keeping the field. But Hastings, mindful of the need of breaking the confederacy, entered into alliance with the rāna of Gohad, a long-standing enemy of Sindhia, and sent more troops to threaten Sindhia's northern territories. On August 3, Popham captured Gwalior by escalade. The place had always been regarded as impregnable. Sindhia at once abandoned Gujarāt and retired to cover his own revenues. This permitted Goddard to move to attack Bassein, which he took on December 11. He then attempted to threaten Poona itself. But seeking to retire in the face of a superior force he underwent the one serious reverse of his career. The effects of this defeat were, however, more than compensated by the defeat which Camac inflicted on Sindhia's troops at Siprī on February 16, 1781. Sindhia now came to the conclusion that his interests lay in an alliance with the English. He had long been aiming at the control of the Marātha Confederacy. His own defeats and the success which

Holkar had just secured meant a set-back in his plans. He therefore opened negotiations, and on October 13 agreed to a cessation
of hostilities and undertook to effect a treaty between the English
and the Poona government. This led to the Treaty of Sālbāi,
signed on May 17, 1782, though not ratified by Nāna Phadnavis
till February 26, 1783. At first sight the clauses of the treaty do
not seem specially important. All English conquests made since
the Treaty of Purandhar were to be restored. Rāghunāth was
to receive no more help from the English. Hyder 'Alī, who was
not a party to the treaty, was to give up the territories which he
had seized from the nawab of Arcot. It thus stipulated for the
mere *status quo ante bellum*. But it nevertheless marks a turning-
point in the history both of the Marāthas and of the English
company. Mahādaji Sindhia, through whose agency the treaty
was made, was the greatest Indian prince of his day. He was
looking forward to the establishment of a powerful state in
northern India, centring round Delhi, fortified with the prestige
of the imperial name, and gathering round itself as satellites the
other Marātha states, so as to renew the old confederacy under
fresh leadership and on fresh terms. His alliance with the English
meant that so long as he did not attack their interests he would
be free to pursue his plans. On the English side it marked a great
triumph for Hastings's skill and tenacity. The year 1780 had
formed a tremendous crisis. No man could tell if some powerful
French expedition might not arrive in Indian waters, just at the
moment when the company was menaced by the two chief
leaders of India. The revenues of Bengal were visibly weakening
under the strain of maintaining war in several theatres at once.
Most of Hastings's advisers and colleagues were clamouring for
peace with Poona on any terms. But he, with the same constancy
with which he had faced the pistol of Francis, drove on his course
until he had wrested from circumstance a favourable conclusion.
"If you would employ effectual means for obtaining peace", he
had written, "you must seek them in the terrors of a continued
war. . . . If you expect to obtain it by concession and entreaty, . . .
you will be disappointed." The Treaty of Sālbāi was the vindication of his words.

But if the conduct of the Bombay council had involved
Hastings in a policy which he himself had never chosen and which
reduced him to the need of making the best of a bad business,

the conduct of Madras affairs involved him in worse difficulties still, for it brought on new disasters at a most critical moment. The fall of Pondichery in 1761 had established in the south a position not unlike that in Bengal following on the battle of Plassey. The nawab, Muhammad 'Alī, was wholly dependent on the English for the maintenance of his position. On his western borders had arisen a new state. A Muslim adventurer of great capacity both in war and in administration, Hyder 'Alī, had over-thrown the old Hindu dynasty and set up his own rule. He had on the whole been disposed to cultivate friendship with the English, who were his neighbours on both sides of India. But that design had proved impossible. Hyder, like all newly established and ambitious princes, coveted the lands on his borders. He was always at war with the Marāthas; he was always threatening the Carnatic. But whereas his hostility to the Marāthas might easily have made him an acceptable ally of Bombay, his hostility to Muhammad 'Alī made him an in-evitable enemy of Madras. In 1767, by a course of policy the causes of which remain obscure, war had broken out between him and the nawab. The Carnatic had been severely ravaged; and, though Hyder had been defeated in pitched battles at Changama and Trinomalai, he had much the best of the war, which was ended in 1769 by a treaty concluded at Madras. Muhammad 'Alī's finances, which remained under his own in-competent management, had been thrown into complete con-fusion. The French war had left him with a large debt to the company. In the next few years he had seemed to be paying off this debt, but in fact he was only doing so by borrowing from the company's servants and other persons at Madras at a much higher rate of interest than was due to the company. As soon as the directors learned of this, they prohibited their servants from participating in such loans in future and ordered the rate of interest to be reduced. But the private debt remained the dominant political interest at Madras. Paul Benfield, an engineer in the company's service, who in modern times would have made a great name as a financier, became a most active agent in the matter. At one time he was said to have in his hands the fortunes of everyone in Madras, allowing them 2 per cent. a month, while he was prin al manager of the nawab's finances as well. The importance of increasing the nawab's revenues came thus to outweigh every other consideration. It furnished the motive for two expeditions against the raja of Tanjore in 1771 and 1773, the second of which ended in the annexation of the state by the nawab. On learning of this, the directors at once ordered the restoration of the raja to his territories, and appointed governor of Madras Lord Pigot, who had formerly held the same office during the crisis of the Seven Years' War. Vigorous rather than tactful, Pigot encountered the bitterest opposition. This was headed by the commander-in-chief, Sir Robert Fletcher. He had already distinguished himself by playing a more than dubious part in the opposition to Clive in Bengal in 1766. He and Benfield's friends succeeded in securing a majority on the council against the governor, and, though they did not dare to refuse compliance with the company's orders, they placed the governor under arrest in 1776, and kept him in confinement till he died a year later. In 1778 this state of internal confusion was ended by the appointment of Sir Thomas Rumbold as governor.

But Rumbold proved neither more honest nor more capable than his predecessors. Madras was poverty-stricken; the nawab's loans had fallen to a great discount; but policy still hinged upon the debt and the possibility of wringing gifts from the nawab. As an example it may be mentioned that Rumbold invited the nawab to act as godfather to a son who was born to him at Madras and who was therefore baptized after his godfather by the name of Anwaer. This and other acts of complaisance are said to have cost the nawab over fifteen lakhs of rupees. These gifts, however, meant that the nawab was not to be pressed more than could be avoided for the payments on which the main-tenance of the company's military forces depended. The ex-pedient which occurred to Rumbold to relieve the financial situation was to get rid of the tribute annually payable to the Nizām for the Northern Circars. Those districts had been granted by Shāh 'Ālam to the company at the same time as the *dīwāni* of Bengal. But when the Madras government had attempted to act upon this grant, it had found that the *farmān* was valueless without the assent of Nizām 'Alī who actually possessed the Circars. By a treaty with the latter, three out of the four were transferred to the company on condition of an annual payment of five lakhs of rupees. This was already two years in arrears when Rumbold proposed to the Nizām that it should cease altogether. Another subject of difference had also occurred. It had been agreed that the Circar of Guntoor should be held by Basālat Jang, the Nizām's brother, for life and should afterwards revert to the company. Basālat Jang had agitated the Madras government by taking a body of French troops into his pay. At first attempts had been made to secure their removal. Then in January, 1779, when Basālat Jang was being threatened by Hyder 'Alī, a treaty was made with him by which he ceded the circar to the company. The circar was at once leased out to Muhammad 'Alī and an English force was sent to protect the district from Hyder. These measures completely indisposed the Nizām and Hyder 'Alī against the company. The Nizām contented himself with stirring up discontent. But Hyder, with his usual decision of character, resolved upon war, for which the contest between the English and the Marāthas provided him with a most favourable opportunity. At the same time he hoped to receive the co-operation of the French, who had lately declared war on Great Britain. He steadily prepared himself but for the moment withheld his attack. In the spring of 1780 Rumbold decided to return to England, confident that, since the presidency had lately received a royal regiment from England, Hyder would not dare to risk a war. In July Hyder suddenly invaded the Carnatic, which was wholly unprepared to resist. Hector Munro, the former victor of Buxar, was commander-in-chief. He marched out in full confidence of driving the invaders out of the Carnatic. But a party of English troops moving to join him was severely defeated at Pollilūr. He retired hastily on Madras. The council, at its wits' end, informed Bengal that all was lost unless assistance in men and money could be instantly sent.

In the development of these events the governor-general and council had hardly been consulted. Rumbold indeed held the view that the Regulating Act was to be understood literally and that so long as he neither went to war nor signed a treaty Bengal had no control over his actions. Nor had Bengal interfered until it seemed likely that the Nizām would be driven into the arms of the Marāthas, when it assumed the conduct of political relations with him, and succeeded in smoothing down his ruffled sensibilities. Nevertheless, Hastings found himself in 1780 committed to a new war with which he had had nothing to do. He must either send help from Bengal or allow Hyder to besiege

Madras. In these circumstances he resolved to send Sir Eyre Coote, the commander-in-chief, with as large a body of men as could be spared and a considerable sum of money. But these resources were not to be wasted by the incompetent council. Coote was to procure the resignation of Whitehill, who had succeeded to the chair on Rumbold's departure, assume the whole conduct of the war, and keep the funds under his own management. He was intended to do at Madras what Goddard had succeeded in doing at Bombay—establish the control of the governor-general and council.

These measures secured a partial success. Coote, who enjoyed a deservedly high reputation as a soldier, soon restored the confidence of the Madras army, defeated Hyder at Porto Novo, Pollilūr and Sholingarh, but, like the commander in the former Mysore war, failed altogether to expel Hyder from the Carnatic. The chief cause of this lay in the superior mobility of Hyder's troops. He was strong, Coote was excessively weak, in cavalry. Coote was moreover burdened with an immense transport train. He had to carry with him a disproportionate amount of artillery in order to keep Hyder's horse at a respectful distance; the number of his camp-followers was enormous, and he was not willing to incur unpopularity by insisting on their reduction. The consequence was that his demands on the Madras council for cattle and grain were greater than could be supplied from an area already wasted by war. For this he fiercely blamed the civil authorities, and his vituperations have usually been repeated. The fault, however, lay elsewhere. The plan of the campaign was wrong. The easiest way by which Hyder could have been compelled to withdraw from the Carnatic was not to march after him at the rate of two miles an hour but, as Hastings had done in the case of Sindhia, to carry the war into his territories. He had conquered the districts lying along the Malabar Coast from a number of small Hindu chiefs, and they resented the Muslim domination. Coote should have been content to protect Madras itself and despatch the strongest force he could spare to attack Hyder on the west coast, where the enemy would have been compelled either to lay waste his own territories and destroy his own revenues or meet the invaders in the field. But Coote was probably too eager to multiply his laurels by defeating Hyder in the Carnatic to adopt a plan which would either have removed himself from the Carnatic or have diminished the forces under his immediate command. He therefore remained in the Carnatic till the autumn of 1782, failing to achieve the purpose of his campaign and seeking to throw all the blame on the civil authorities.

It was not to be expected that this should be borne meekly. In the middle of 1781 a new governor, Lord Macartney, had arrived from England. He was a man of character, with both administrative and diplomatic experience, and had been chosen in order to free the Madras government from its subservience to the corrupt influences of the nawab's debt. The war with Hyder had not been heard of when he had left England, and the position which he found on his arrival was a grievous disappointment to him. The first step which he decided to take was to induce the nawab to make over to the English for the period of the war the administration of the Carnatic revenues. This he succeeded in doing. But the nawab then refused to appoint the agents whom Macartney recommended. The effect of this would have been to nullify the transfer of the management; Macartney therefore insisted on appointing them himself. This action revived the combination which had overthrown Pigot in 1776. The nawab, Paul Benfield, and others did their utmost to cancel the assignment of the revenues. They appealed to Warren Hastings. They sought to lure Coote into the business by offering him an illusory assignment of the revenues in his own name. This quarrel was complicated by disputes which had arisen between Madras and Bengal regarding the conduct of the war. Just before Macartney's arrival Hastings had urged the Madras council to leave the whole management of the war to Coote. The council, overawed, had complied, and Macartney had acquiesced in the situation which he found in being. When Coote reiterated his complaints, Hastings urged Macartney to humour the commander-in-chief. Macartney agreed provided that the responsibility also was to rest on Coote's shoulders. But that was a burden which Coote was not willing to bear. Coote kept his plans entirely to himself, limited his communications to demands for money, cattle, and supplies, and at the same time threatened Macartney with accusations of ruining the campaign. Hastings's position was one of great embarrassment. He did not wish to disoblige Coote, lest he should in a huff return to Calcutta and vote against the measures of the governor-general. He did not wish to disoblige Benfield, whose friends had greatly assisted in the accommodation between himself and Lord North. He thus found himself obliged to support the nawab's cause and Coote's cause against the governor of Madras. This led to an open breach between the two governments. Bengal ordered Madras to resign the assignment of the Carnatic revenues; Madras refused.

Early in 1783 Coote, who had passed the cold weather at Calcutta, was about to return to the south. He demanded powers to overrule the local council and if necessary to displace Macartney. Hastings favoured compliance with his demands; but in this he was not supported by the other members of his council, and Coote finally sailed without the authority he had desired. On his way down his vessel was chased by a French frigate. The agitation caused by fear of capture brought on a stroke of apoplexy. The old general was carried ashore at Madras speechless, and died almost at once. It was perhaps fortunate. Macartney had determined to resist by every means in his power what he believed to be unwarranted demands which would ruin the British cause in the south. The command of the Madras troops passed into the hands of Major-General James Stuart, as quarrelsome as Coote, but a far less formidable opponent of the civil government. Early in the year a great expedition had at last arrived from France under the command of Bussy, now old and worn out. Bussy had landed and occupied Cuddalore. Stuart was ordered to march southwards and attack him. Resenting orders of any sort, Stuart languidly pursued his march, spending six weeks over the hundred miles separating Madras from Cuddalore. He then attacked the French position, and two stubborn actions followed in which both sides lost heavily. But events at sea had placed the English in a desperate position.

Throughout the war an English squadron had been maintained on the coast, at first under the command of Vernon and afterwards under that of Sir Edward Hughes. In 1782 a French squadron had arrived under the greatest admiral whom the French ever produced. This was the Bailli de Suffren. He was filled with an indomitable energy; and his one thought was not the safety of his ships but the destruction of the enemy. He was moreover a fighter of great intelligence, and was ever thinking out plans for modifying the stereotyped methods of naval manœuvre. A series of engagements followed his arrival.

Hughes at first succeeded in holding his own, though with difficulty. More than once Suffren succeeded in concentrating a superior force of ships against a part of Hughes's line of battle. But the decisive victory which Suffren was seeking evaded his grasp. His subordinate officers were of inferior quality and failed to understand the instructions which they received; and in every circumstance he was encountered by a most obstinate resistance. Nevertheless, he was wearing down the enemy. Finally in June, 1783, he attacked the English off Cuddalore, where they were covering the operations of Stuart, and inflicted on them so much damage that they were obliged to retire to Madras to refit. That event left Stuart helpless. He could receive no further supplies of food, and must have been reduced either to ignominious surrender or to disastrous retreat but for the first piece of good fortune which had befallen the English in the course of the war. This was the arrival of the news of the conclusion of peace in Europe. A suspension of arms followed, and the fruit of Suffren's vigour and skill was lost.

Macartney had been most dissatisfied with Stuart's military conduct. The general was therefore recalled, as soon as news of peace was received. The order was reluctantly obeyed, and, as soon as Stuart reached Madras, he began a series of intrigues, which looked the more threatening since he had been the officer selected in 1776 to arrest Lord Pigot. The real point at issue was whether the military forces should or should not be under the command of the governor and council. Macartney was resolved that his authority should be obeyed, and decided to arrest Stuart and send him off to England. This was accordingly done. But even then his difficulties were not at an end. The officer next in seniority was Sir John Burgoyne, a king's officer. He was offered the command provided he was willing to execute whatever orders he should receive from the civil government. On his refusal, a company's officer was named commander-in-chief. This was a dangerous measure which almost led to a conflict between the king's and company's troops. Burgoyne, however, though unwise, had nothing of Stuart's malignity of character, and the matter was smoothed over, although a mutiny actually broke out among the king's regiments as the result of the unsettlement which these events had produced.

Meanwhile the war had been pursued against Mysore with

better success than had at first attended the British plans. Hyder 'Alī had died at the end of 1782, and had been succeeded by his son Tipu Sultān. Hastings had long been urging on both Madras and Bombay the need of an expedition to attack the Malabar possessions of Mysore. At last in 1783 a force was sent from Bombay under a company's officer named Matthews, who landed at Mangalore and occupied the capital of the province of Bednor. This at once compelled Tipu to recall his forces from the Carnatic, and he himself hastily marched to expel the intruders. Matthews had imprudently scattered his force, and was besides much embarrassed by the jealousy exhibited by the king's officers who had been placed under his orders. He was besieged in Bednor and compelled to surrender. Tipu then marched to recover Mangalore, which was held by a king's officer, Colonel Campbell. The latter defended the place gallantly, but at last agreed to an armistice on very unfavourable terms, under which he was precluded from receiving supplies by sea, the only way by which they could possibly be sent. The consequence was that when supplies arrived by sea and the English insisted on their being admitted into the place, Tipu considered himself free again to carry on his siege-works.

As soon as he had removed Stuart from the command of the army, Macartney had sent a force to attack Tipu's southern possessions. Dindigul had been taken early in 1783. In June Dharapuram was taken, and the English were preparing to advance when they were ordered to halt and await the issue of proposals which had been made to Tipu for peace. One of the terms of the agreement made by Sindhia's means at Sālbāi had been that Tipu should be compelled to make peace with the English. But the Marāthas had been so long without making any move in that direction that Macartney had come to disbelieve in their sincerity. Since the preliminaries of peace declared that the allies of both combatants should be invited to accede, he thought it best to make direct proposals to Mysore, and sent commissioners to confer with Tipu, who was still before Mangalore. In December, on reports that hostilities had again broken out there, Macleod on the Malabar Coast seized Cannanore, while the English in the south captured Palghaut and Coimbatore, before their movements could be countermanded by the commissioners. On January 29 Mangalore was surrendered by Campbell, owing to the sickness which prevailed in the garrison. Shortly afterwards the commissioners reached Tipu's camp. They then negotiated the Treaty of Mangalore, by which each side restored all conquests and agreed to release all prisoners. Military officers, indignant at peace at the moment when success seemed possible, spread numerous stories about the conclusion of this treaty. But there is no reason to suppose that the commissioners were treated with worse than the contemptuous pride which was to have been expected. Tipu believed himself to have won the war and behaved accordingly. A large number of English prisoners were then released. But those who had been coerced into adopting Islam during their captivity were retained. The treatment of the prisoners had been severe, but no ground exists for believing the stories which were told of many having been deliberately put to death. The treaty was strongly disapproved by Hastings, mainly on the ground that it made no reference to the Treaty of Sālbāi. He actually moved that Macartney should be suspended from his office of governor on the ground of his having disobeyed the orders of the Bengal government. But this proposal was not accepted by his councillors, probably for no better reason than that Macartney had influential friends in England.

Amid this confusion of authorities, of quarrels between the civil and military powers at Madras, between the king's and company's officers, between the councils of Madras and Bengal, it had been completely impossible for Hastings to direct the conduct of affairs. They had passed out of his control, but, as in Bombay, he was left to pay the bill. The Marātha and Mysore wars had burdened the Bengal finances to such a point that the company's investment had to be provided by private subscription. Hastings was driven by this state of things to extraordinary expedients which were afterwards made the subject of accusation against him, without sufficient consideration of the difficulties under which he had lain, and without memory of the anarchical conditions created by the Regulating Act. The two famous incidents which occurred in this connection were the affair of Chait Singh and the affair of the Begums of Oudh. Chait Singh was the zamindar of Benares. As soon as the French war broke out, Hastings proposed that he should be called upon for an extra contribution to help meet the costs of the war. In this he was

justified by the well-established practice of India, where the
ruler's demands were limited only by his will and sense of the
expedient. Later on new demands were made and in 1780
Hastings resolved to visit Benares personally in order to overcome Chait Singh's delays. Chait Singh does not seem to have
intended opposition. He met Hastings at Buxar, and submitted
to the arrest in which Hastings placed him. On reaching Benares,
a tumult broke out, a company of sepoys was destroyed, and
Hastings had to flee for his life to Chunār. There he gathered
together forces, reoccupied Benares, declared the fugitive Chait
Singh dispossessed of the zamindari, regranted it to a nephew
of the dispossessed chief, and increased the tribute from two and
a quarter to four lakhs of rupees a year. Hastings's enemies
attempted to prove that Chait Singh was not a mere zamindar,
and that the company had no right to claim more from him than
the fixed tribute. The first point seems untenable. Benares was
handed over to the company by the ruler of Oudh, whose
authority was henceforth exercised by the government of Calcutta; Chait Singh certainly never possessed sovereignty. The
custom of India again strongly favoured the contention of
Hastings that the tribute payable was unlimited. Hastings acted
therefore within the rights which any other ruler of India would
not have hesitated to use. At the same time it is clear that Chait
Singh was treated with severity, and that Hastings's conduct at
Benares in 1780 was precipitate. The fact doubtless was that
Hastings was feeling the results of a long period of strife and
disappointment, that his judgment was less clear and calm than
usual, and that he was urged on by the spur of need. It is likely
also that Hastings had never forgiven Chait Singh for having sent
a messenger to Clavering in the crisis of 1777, and was not sorry
to exhibit to the Indian world the consequences of incurring his
displeasure.

Perhaps, however, the chief criticism which should be passed
on his conduct towards Chait Singh is that it failed of its immediate object. He was in need of money at once; and the outbreak at Benares disappointed him of the sum which he had
hoped to obtain, although his settlement augmented the future
resources of the company. He thus found himself obliged to
seek out some new source of finance. Āsaf-ud-daula, the nawab
of Oudh, owed the company at this time some fifteen lakhs

of rupees. In 1781 in consequence of Hastings's urgent demands, he proposed to resume the *jāgīrs* and seize the treasure of which his late father's wives had improperly possessed themselves. This matter had long been a subject of dispute between the two parties, and at an earlier time the begums had been compelled to disgorge part of their spoils under a promise made by Bristow, the resident appointed by the majority, that no more should be demanded of them. Āsaf-ud-daula, who was a man of feeble character, possibly hoped that the former promise might serve as an obstacle to the acceptance of his proposal, while his offer might relieve him from immediate pressure for money. But since Hastings's need of money was great and growing, the nawab was urged to carry his suggestion into effect. The begums were therefore placed under restraint, and their chief agents were imprisoned for almost a year. In December, 1782, they agreed to pay over a large sum of money and were duly released. The defence put forward for withdrawing the promise of protection from the begums was that they had promoted rebellion in the Benares country. But for this little evidence appears. Like Chait Singh, the begums were treated with severity, although the degree of their ill-treatment was greatly exaggerated by Hastings's enemies, and in their case the matter was darkened by something like a breach of faith.

In February, 1785, Hastings sailed for England, being convinced by the terms of Pitt's India Act that he was not likely to remain undisturbed in the office which he had held for so long. Indeed, for years Francis had been busily employing his matchless talents for slander against the governor-general. He sedulously inflamed the enthusiasm of Edmund Burke against what he declared to be a system of torture and corruption. When Shelburne went out of office and the Coalition Ministry of Fox and North was formed, official hostility reappeared, stronger than ever it had been before. All the Whigs were united against Hastings, while the Tories were languid in his defence. The fall of the coalition and the accession of Pitt to power did nothing to change this state of things. Early in 1786, shortly after Hastings's return to England, Burke brought forward charges on which the impeachment of Hastings was subsequently founded. Then arose the situation which Burke himself had foreseen in an earlier day. "God defend me", he had once exclaimed in the House of

Commons, "from the justice of this house when supported by neither the faction of one side nor the venality of the other." An informed survey of the career of Hastings revealed errors, revealed occasional acts which cannot well be defended, but revealed also a high and noble constancy of purpose, a mind of extraordinary qualities, as hard, as flexible, and as resistant as the finest-tempered steel. Justice would have demanded condemnation of his errors, but recognition of his great and unequalled services. Probably not another man of his generation could have carried the company's government through the period during which the Regulating Act remained in force without incurring great, perhaps irretrievable, disaster. In every other part of the outer realms of George III rebellion, defeat, humiliation had been the national portion. In India alone national interests remained unharmed. And the reward prepared by Francis and Burke was a series of accusations, vague and general, such as no court of law would ever have entertained, accusations supported by an unending stream of eloquence, designed to make the worse appear the better reason.

After long debates the impeachment was resolved on twenty-two articles in May, 1787. The charges involved the violation of treaties with Oudh, the unrighteous sale of Kora and Allāhābād, the oppression of Chait Singh and the Begums of Oudh, the arbitrary settlement of the land revenues of Bengal, and fraud and corruption in general administration. On April 23, 1795, Hastings was acquitted on all the charges which were pressed to a conclusion. The redeeming feature of the trial was the care with which the lords reviewed the evidence submitted to them, and the view which evidently inspired them at the conclusion that Hastings had suffered far more than any mistakes and misconduct of which he had been guilty could possibly demand. It was but just that Burke never recovered from this decisive condemnation of his conduct in the matter. Throughout the trial he had been the leading spirit, and after it he was a broken man. Hastings on the other hand showed his true spirit. He bore his seven years' ordeal as he had withstood the majority in the council-room of Fort William. He believed with reason that he had saved English interests in India, that he had governed the territories committed to his charge with justice, that the inhabitants of Bengal had heard of his departure with sorrow, and that the princes of India would have welcomed his return to direct the affairs of the East India Company. Indeed, it is hardly less than tragic to think that the one supremely great man whom England sent to rule India was checked in every action either by opposition in his own council, or by hostility of the home government, or by the provisions of the worst piece of legislation which ever passed the British parliament regarding India. If Burke had wished to impeach any one, he would have done well to choose his old enemy Lord North, the author of the Regulating Act, rather than Warren Hastings, its unhappy victim.

CHAPTER V

The Establishment of the East India Company as the Supreme Power in India, 1784–1818

The resignation of Warren Hastings marks the end of one and the beginning of a new period in the history of the East India Company. The disastrous experiment of the Regulating Act was brought to a close by Pitt's India Act. As will be shown in the following chapter, an effective system of government was at last established. The political conduct of the East India Company was placed in due subordination to the policy of the national government; and the governor-general and council of Bengal received power sufficient to permit their control of British policy in India. In the previous generation Clive and Hastings had led the way in a great experiment. With imperfect powers and insignificant resources they had established the company as a vital force in Indian politics. Clive had seized a lucky opportunity; and Hastings had maintained the company's position in defiance of difficulties created principally by the folly and ignorance of London. His successors were now to enjoy advantages which he had never known—consistent support, freedom from interference, untrammelled authority.

Hastings had been ignorantly supposed to pursue a policy of aggression. Such conduct was specially disliked at London. The directors feared that it might endanger the advantages which had been obtained; the ministry feared that the resources of the nation might be involved in some great struggle. Therefore the India Act sought to prevent the future representatives of the company from following Hastings's supposed example. It specifically declared that wars of aggression were contrary to the wishes, the interests, and the policy of the nation. But this attempt to regulate the conduct of external policy by moral maxims was foredoomed to fail. Wars of aggression are probably the most exceptional events in history. One state attacks another because its rights have been injured, because its interests are threatened, because it fears that unless it attacks it will itself be attacked at a disadvantage. Almost all wars, in the eyes of both parties, are wars of defence. The period ushered in by this pacific declaration was therefore as militant as that which had preceded it.

Some have put forward the view that this was due to the brutal and ferocious policy of the governors-general. But this facile explanation takes no account of the state of India. The country remained in the state of flux to which it had been reduced by the collapse of the Mughal empire. A number of new states had emerged, but none of them recognised any natural boundaries, and every prince was eager to extend his territories. But their position varied greatly. The Rājput states, the Carnatic, Oudh, Hyderabad, feared their neighbours, and were prepared to take any measures and to welcome any allies promising even a temporary relief from their immediate dangers. Two of these, Oudh and the Carnatic, had already accepted the alliance of the East India Company, and in fact depended for their continued existence on the military support of their ally. Hyderabad was at constant war with its Marātha neighbours at Poona, and was usually worsted. The Rājput princes feared the advance of the Marātha chiefs who had established themselves in northern India and who threatened to reduce them to tributary subordinates. On the other side there were two states which clearly aspired to greater power than at the moment they possessed. One of these was Mysore under the rule of Hyder 'Alī's son, Tipu Sultān. Tipu lacked his father's capacity for government, but inherited all his ambition. He had declared himself king in his own right, thus expressly disclaiming any dependence on the Mughal empire, still recognised by every other prince and ruler of India with the exception of the Marātha Holkar. He was extremely orthodox, and afflicted his Hindu subjects, especially on the Malabar Coast, where they were newly conquered and unsubmissive, with forced conversion and the destruction of temples, like another Aurangzīb. Like the Nizām of Hyderabad, he was constantly at war with the Marāthas on his northern frontier: but, unlike the Nizām, he was able to meet them on equal terms. He also yearned to redeem the Carnatic from its subservience to the infidel authority of the English, whom his father had reduced to such straits in 1780. Beside him was the group of states known as the Marātha Confederacy. This formed by far the most powerful political unit in India. The confederacy was composed of that part of the Deccan under the direct rule of the Pēshwā from Poona, of Baroda under the Gaekwar, of Nāgpur under the Bhonslas, of two groups of territory round Ahmadābād and round Gwalior under Mahādaji Sindhia, and of Indore under Holkar. Of all these the Pēshwā was the nominal head. But his effective authority had already begun to break. Princes who had willingly obeyed Bālājī Rāo or Bāji Rāo at an earlier time, when the Pēshwā's power was great and their own small, had adopted more independent views when the power of the Pēshwā had been reduced by the struggles centring round Rāghunāth Rāo and when their own power and dominions had increased. Now Mahādaji Sindhia aspired to succeed to the headship of the Marāthas. He had widely extended his dominions in northern India; he had occupied Delhi and taken the emperor under his protection. From his protégé he had required the appointment of the Pēshwā as the chief lieutenant of the empire, with himself as the Pēshwā's deputy. As has been seen in the previous chapter, he had intervened in the war between the Pēshwā and the English, and had agreed with the latter to bring it to a conclusion. But his ambitions were viewed with great jealousy. Holkar was always ready to support the ministers at Poona if Sindhia attacked them. Great as the confederacy still was, it was seamed with divisions, no longer capable of common action, and ready to break asunder under the pressure of conflicting interests.

After a short interval during which John Macpherson acted as governor-general, Cornwallis arrived as his successor. He reached Calcutta on September 12, 1786, bent on giving the fullest effect to the acts of parliament and on abstaining from all interference in the politics of India. So far as northern India was concerned he succeeded. The only event of note in which he was involved in that area occurred when Sindhia, having become the emperor's deputy chief-lieutenant, thought of claiming the annual twenty-six lakhs of rupees which Clive had agreed to pay for the *dīwāni* of Bengal. Cornwallis promptly and firmly warned Sindhia that any attempt to promote that claim would be treated as an unfriendly act. The warning was sufficient. Sindhia, who was only testing the attitude of the new governor-general, dropped the matter immediately. But affairs in the south were less easy to manage. Tipu's attitude was definitely hostile. The Treaty of Mangalore had named the raja of Travancore as one of the allies of the company whom Tipu agreed not to threaten or attack. The raja had lately purchased from the Dutch certain factories and forts which, in the decaying state of their trade, they no longer wished to retain. Tipu claimed that these places were dependencies of chiefs who had recognised his own supremacy, and demanded that they should be handed over to him. On learning of this, Cornwallis at once ordered John Hollond, the governor of Madras, to inform Tipu that any attack on Travancore would be deemed an attack on the East India Company. The governor, however, was not willing to carry out the order. He belonged to the old, bad generation which had been deeply interested in the nawab's debts. He feared that a war with Tipu would mean the ravaging of the Carnatic as in the time of Hyder 'Alī, and that the nawab would be unable to pay his private creditors. Tipu therefore was not warned as early or as firmly as Cornwallis had intended. He attacked Travancore, commanding in person the troops who were employed; and this action led at once to the Third Mysore War. But the circumstances of the moment were very different from those in which Hyder had attacked the English in 1780. Tipu had cherished hopes of overthrowing first the Nizām, then the Marāthas, and finally the English. He had sent embassies to Paris, and, although the French government was not prepared actively to assist his plans, it was not at all unwilling to see its old European enemy opposed and thwarted in the east. Tipu received encouragement which he was unlucky and unwise enough to take at its face-value. In 1785–87 he was engaged in war with Poona and Hyderabad, leading to an inconclusive peace. Cornwallis, judging from Tipu's embassy to Paris, concluded that war with France would mean immediate war with Tipu, and that the company's safety demanded an alliance with Tipu's late enemies. The India Act precluded him from entering into treaties with them at once, for it forbade any alliance in preparation for war. But he took care to cultivate a good understanding with Nāna Phadnavis, who still controlled affairs at Poona, and, when he arranged with the Nizām a settlement of the Guntoor question, he gave him an informal promise of support provided he refrained from attacking any ally of the English. A list of the English allies given to the Nizām did not include the name of Tipu Sultān. This was certainly a violation of the spirit of the India Act. That so honest and moderate a man as

Cornwallis should have deemed such a course necessary displays the impossibility of conducting foreign policy in accordance with general maxims. But when war broke out, Cornwallis had already provided himself with allies who threatened the long line of Tipu's northern frontier. The war began in May, 1790, and treaties for common action by the English, the Nizām, and the Marāthas, were signed in June and July following. The position of 1780 was exactly reversed. The Carnatic lay untouched, while the English and their allies invaded the Mysore territories.

Their initial operations were not marked by success. In 1791, therefore, Cornwallis came south to take the command in person. He succeeded in taking Bangalore, but although he advanced towards Tipu's capital of Seringapatam he was prevented by a shortage of supplies from laying siege to it. In the next year, however, he advanced again, besieged the place, and compelled Tipu to accept severe terms. Tipu was to cede to the allies most of the conquests which his father and himself had made, and he was to pay a great indemnity. As security for the due execution of these terms, he gave two of his sons into English keeping. By this settlement Cornwallis hoped that he had established peace on a firm basis in the south. He considered that he had cut down the power of Tipu to the point at which he would not dare again to attack the English, and that the cessions made to the English allies would enable them to meet any attack which Tipu might launch against them. In short he attempted to apply the principle of the balance of power, strengthening the weak and reducing the strong.

Such calculations, however, took no account of the ever-shifting character of Indian alliances. Cornwallis's departure in 1793 was soon followed by a war between his late allies, the Nizām and the Marāthas. Shore, the new governor-general, refused to take part in the struggle, which ended in the defeat of the Nizām, in the battle of Kharda. The Nizām, who already had a considerable force in his service under the command of the famous Frenchman, Raymond, then proceeded to increase this branch of his troops. French influence thus threatened to become predominant not only at Seringapatam but at Hyderabad as well. In 1793 war had broken out again between Great Britain and the revolutionary French government. The possibility of French interference in Indian affairs had thus again become a question of importance. When in

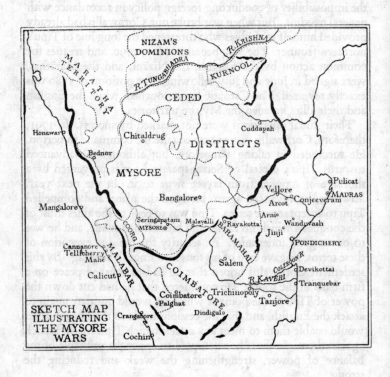

April, 1798, Richard Wellesley, Lord Mornington, arrived as governor-general, he found the balance which Cornwallis had tried to set up already overturned. In the middle of October, when he learnt of the French invasion of Egypt, he resolved that Tipu must either renounce the French alliance or be destroyed.

Tipu had in fact welcomed the Anglo-French war as promising him his revenge for the defeat of 1792. He had opened negotiations for help from France both with the governor of the French island of Mauritius and with the Paris authorities. Shortly after Mornington's arrival, the latter had heard of a bombastic proclamation in which Malartič, at Mauritius, had called for volunteers to aid Tipu to destroy the English power, and of the arrival at Mangalore of a small party of Frenchmen who had in consequence joined Tipu's service. The conduct of the sultan in thus seeking the aid of the French was singularly unwise, and betrayed a deplorable lack of information. It was not in Malartic's power to give Mysore any material help. Tipu's mission to Mauritius and the landing of the small body of men whom he obtained warned Mornington of his intentions without strengthening himself. Tipu did his utmost to counteract the effects of his own conduct. But the governor-general interpreted his smooth letters as designed to allay English fears until arrangements for effective French support should have been completed.

In Mornington's eyes the first step to be taken was to root out French influence from Hyderabad. In this he soon succeeded. The Nizām accepted his offers to maintain a force of company's troops at Hyderabad on condition of the Nizām's providing for their pay and of conducting his foreign policy in accordance with English wishes. The French force which Raymond had formed was thus broken up. The officers were carried off to Calcutta as prisoners of war and sent back to Europe, while the sepoys for the most part took service with the English. This danger removed, the affair with Tipu was brought to an issue. Mornington calculated that no French force could arrive from the Red Sea until the middle of 1799. At the close of 1798 therefore he moved south to Madras, and required from Tipu categorical answers to the demands which he had made. Tipu played for time. But Mornington would not wait till circumstances should favour the sultan. On February 22 he ordered the invasion of Tipu's territories by the army which had been assembled. The campaign was marked by unbroken success. Tipu was defeated in the field at Sedasere and Mallavelly. In April, Seringapatam was again besieged. On May 4 it was stormed and Tipu perished in the defence. The generation of conflict between the Muslim rulers of Mysore and the company had come to a close. Mornington's services were recognised by the bestowal of an Irish marquisate, and he was thenceforth known as the Marquis Wellesley.

His settlement was characteristic. On this occasion the Marā-thas had refused to co-operate with the company in the war, and even massed troops as though preparing to assist Tipu. Wellesley therefore needed to consider no other interests than those of the company and of the Nizām. He decided to reduce Mysore to its old boundaries, within which a representative of the Hindu ruling house was to be set up. Most of the territories thus cut off were to be divided between the Nizām and the company, and shortly afterwards the Nizām handed over his share to the company in return for the abolition of his annual payments for the maintenance of the subsidiary force. Certain districts were set aside to be offered to the Pēshwā, Bāji Rāo II (son of the old English ally Rāghunāth Rāo), whom Nāna Phadnavis, after a period of bitter conflict with Sindhia, had established at Poona. These districts were to be the price of the acceptance by the Marāthas of an English alliance similar to that which had been made with the Nizām. With the new Hindu prince a treaty, till then without parallel, was signed. Wellesley was resolved that, if it could be avoided, the company's alliance should not be disgraced by the evil consequences which had followed in the Carnatic and in Oudh. The prince was given his principality, not only on condition of military and political subordination to the government of Calcutta, but also on condition of following such advice on administrative and financial matters as the governor-general might offer him. A neglect of these conditions might be followed by the English resumption of the raja's territories.

The effect of these arrangements was to establish the company as the unquestioned arbiter of affairs in the south. Wellesley himself cherished the hope of securing a similar position for the company in the north as well. This depended upon inducing the Marāthas to accept a subsidiary alliance. Nāna Phadnavis had rejected Wellesley's offer of part of the conquests made from Tipu. But he had died in 1800, and there followed a struggle for supremacy at Poona, between Holkar and Daulat Rāo, who had succeeded Mahādaji Rāo Sindhia. The Pēshwā found himself helpless between the two rivals. He was himself a man possessed of neither wisdom nor good faith. He made an alliance with Sindhia in order to wreak vengeance on the friends of the late Nāna who had held him in tutelage. Jaswant Rāo Holkar marched south, defeated Sindhia's army, captured Poona, and plundered it from top to bottom. Bāji Rāo fled to Bassein. He begged for English help. Wellesley agreed to give it provided he would accept English mediation in his disputes with other Indian princes, and provided he would accept a subsidiary force such as the Nizām had received. Bāji Rāo consented to these terms, and on December 31, 1802, signed the Treaty of Bassein.

The effect of this treaty was to establish English influence at the very heart of the Marātha Confederacy. This was not likely to be accepted by the Marātha chiefs with calm. In London this seemed a reason for disliking the policy which had brought it about, because it would involve the company in "the endless and complicated distractions of the turbulent Mahrattah empire". To Wellesley, however, the continuance of the wars in which the Marātha princes had been constantly engaged appeared a far greater danger. It would accelerate the growing poverty of the country; it might lead to the formation of a single Marātha state under an ambitious leader with whom the company would have to fight for its existence; above all, the existence of strong states unconnected with the company meant the existence of openings into which French influence might intrude. Like the Nizām, Sindhia had employed French officers to organise and train his army. First de Boigne and then Perron had commanded large bodies of his troops, and had received *jāgīrs* from the revenues of which the sepoys were paid, so that the commander was, or at any time might become, independent of his employer and free to promote his national rather than his employer's interests. From all these points of view Wellesley judged the establishment of English influence among the Marātha states a matter of the first importance. He did not believe that the Marātha princes could unite against any enemy. English control at Poona would deprive them of their common rallying point. The treaty, he supposed, might perhaps lead to war with individual chiefs, but not to war with the Marāthas as a whole. The event was to prove the accuracy of his judgement.

It soon became evident that small reliance could be placed on the fidelity of the new English ally. Bāji Rāo desired only to be freed from the domination of Holkar, and at once sought to free himself from the new bonds which he had so lightly accepted. He tried to form a combination of all the chiefs. But Holkar was too disgusted with Bāji Rāo to co-operate. Complaining that the Marātha power had been sold to the English, he withdrew sullenly to his possessions in Mālwā. The Gaekwar, too, refused to participate in any scheme against his ally the company, whom he feared much less than he feared the Pēshwā. Daulat Rāo Sindhia and the raja of Nāgpur alone assembled their troops and crossed the Nerbudda. Wellesley desired them to separate and withdraw their forces. On their refusal, war was declared in August, 1803. Arthur Wellesley was placed by his brother in political and military control of the operations in the Deccan; Lord Lake received the like authority in Upper India. Arthur Wellesley defeated the combined armies of Sindhia and the Bhonsla at Assaye; Sindhia then agreed to a truce, during which the Nāgpur forces were beaten at Argāon. Nāgpur then made peace at Deogāon, agreeing to cede to the company the district of Cuttack, thus completing the company's command of the eastern sea-board of India, besides making other cessions to the Nizām. Meanwhile, Lake had captured Aligarh, on which Perron had resigned Sindhia's service and taken refuge in British territory, being no longer able to command the obedience of his French subordinates. Delhi had then been taken, the emperor had passed from Marātha to British custody, and in November Sindhia's remaining forces had been scattered at Laswari. Sindhia then made peace, surrendering much territory and transferring his political rights in Upper India to the company. The war thus appeared to have ended as triumphantly as the war with Tipu. But Holkar, who had looked on contemptuously while his rival Sindhia was being beaten, resolved to teach the English what a Marātha war was like. He rejected the proposals which Lake made to him at the end of 1803, and invaded the territory of the raja of Jaipur, an ally of the company. A new war therefore broke out in April 1804. The English hoped to hem him in in western India, but their plans miscarried, and one of their detachments was overwhelmed and beat a disorderly retreat to Āgra. Holkar, however, could not repeat this success. He was repulsed in an attack on

Delhi. Later in the year his troops were defeated at Dīg and again at Farrukhābād, and Holkar himself was chased by Lake across the Sutlej into the dominions of the rising Sikh chief, Ranjit Singh. While these events had been in progress, Sindhia had shown signs of wishing to renew the struggle, but had thought better of it. So in 1805 the company retained the position of supremacy which had been claimed by the Treaty of Bassein and asserted by the campaigns against Sindhia and the Bhonsla raja.

But at the moment when Wellesley seemed about to reap the harvest of his policy, he learnt that he had been recalled and Cornwallis reappointed governor-general. The directors at London were on principle opposed to a policy of expansion. When Henry Dundas had left the Board of Control in 1801, he had been succeeded first by Lord Lewisham and then by Castlereagh; and his departure had been marked by a diminution of the support which the governor-general had till then received from the cabinet. Castlereagh thought with the directors that Wellesley's policy had been unduly adventurous. Like them he had been alarmed by the outbreak of war with Holkar into thinking that the struggle with the Marāthas would never be brought to a successful conclusion. Cornwallis, though sixty-seven and infirm, was therefore induced to return to India to make peace with the Marāthas. He arrived on July 30, and died at Ghāzīpur on October 5 following, before he had carried his instructions into effect. The senior member of council, Sir George Barlow, took his place. This man had earned a great reputation as a covenanted servant. Under Cornwallis he had been employed to draft that ill-omened code by which it had been hoped to bestow justice on Bengal. To Wellesley, just before the latter sailed for India, Cornwallis had recommended Barlow as a man to whom to turn for advice in a difficulty. Barlow had supported Wellesley's policy consistently. But now, seeing into what trouble with London it had brought the late governor-general, he hastily made peace with Holkar and concessions to Sindhia, convincing the Pēshwā, Sindhia and Holkar alike, that war with the English carried with it small hazard, since such irresolute enemies were sure to resign the fruits of victory. Holkar recovered his territories. Sindhia received back Gohad and Gwalior. Barlow further declared that the company had no interests in the region west of the Chambal. This policy was not only foolish but also

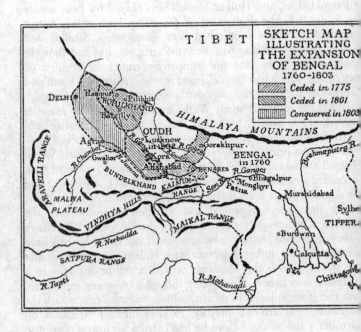

SKETCH MAP ILLUSTRATING THE EXPANSION OF BENGAL 1760–1803

Ceded in 1775
Ceded in 1801
Conquered in 1803

TIBET

HIMALAYA MOUNTAINS

DELHI · Rampur · Pilibhit
ROHILKHAND
Bareilly

OUDH
Agra · Lucknow in 1802 · Gorakhpur
R. Chambal · R. Ganges · R. Gogra
Gwalior · R. Jumna · Kalpa · R. Kausi
BUNDELKHAND · Allahabad · BENARES
R. Ganges
KAIMUR · Bhagalpur
RANGE · Sona · Monghyr
Patna · Murshidabad

ARAVELLI RANGE

MALWA PLATEAU

VINDHYA HILLS

MAIKAL RANGE

SATPURA RANGE

R. Nerbudda

R. Tapti

R. Mahanadi

BENGAL in 1760

Brahmaputra R.

Sylhe
TIPPERA

Burdwan
Calcutta

Chittagong

unjust. It abandoned the Rājput states which had entered into alliance with Wellesley and the Sikh princes east of the Sutlej to whom Wellesley had given the company's protection. It renounced the responsibility for the well-being and public peace of India which Wellesley had been first among the governors-general deliberately to undertake.

Indeed, Wellesley was the first English ruler to foresee and accept the full consequences of the unstable conduct of Indian princes and of the military superiority of the company. Just as in the administration of Bengal he insisted on the company's servants being trained and educated not as merchants but as statesmen, creating the College of Fort William not merely to teach them the languages of the country but also to provide them with the liberal education which many of them lacked; just as in his external policy he sought to bring the principal Indian states into alliance with the company in order to check the constant flux of power and end a whole century of ceaseless war; so also in his relations with the allies of the company he was most averse from the system of blind, irresponsible support to which he found himself committed both in the Carnatic and in Oudh. In both cases the ruler was a client of the company; in both cases the company declined responsibility for its client's conduct. In the Carnatic several attempts had been made to bring order into the nawab's administration. The enquiries which had been made in Macartney's time had revealed an extraordinary wastage of the public revenues. At Trichinopoly, for instance, the disbursements amounted to a lakh of rupees more than the revenues of the district, owing chiefly to a multitude of pensions charged upon them. Then, too, the practice of assigning whole districts to the management of creditors meant that the revenues would be managed in the worst possible way by men who had no interests beyond the early realisation of their advances. In 1787 the nawab had agreed to pay nine lakhs of pagodas to the company and twelve to his creditors. But this arrangement fell at once into arrears. In 1792 Cornwallis attempted a new settlement. It was based on the optimistic view that if the nawab's obligations were reduced, he would be able to restore order in his administration. Under the scheme the nawab was to pay nine lakhs as before to the company but only six to his creditors. If his payments fell into arrears, certain specified districts, over which he promised no longer to grant assignments, were to be taken over by the company. If he were involved in war, the whole administration of the Carnatic was at once to be assumed by the company for the duration of the war. But even this treaty was not kept. Assignments were in fact granted on the districts specified. In 1795 the governor of Madras, Lord Hobart, desired to take advantage of the old nawab's death, which occurred in that year, to impose new terms on his son and successor, 'Umdat-ul-'umara. Hobart proposed to bring the treaty into action by taking over the direct administration of the "mortgaged" districts. But the governorgeneral, Shore, disclaimed in the most emphatic terms the least responsibility for the state of the nawab's territories. Hobart then resigned, and was succeeded by Lord Clive, son of the victor of Plassey. The new governor was a man of less energy of character than Hobart, but at almost the same time Shore was displaced by Wellesley. The British authorities then attempted once more to induce the nawab to modify the method of his government. But 'Umdat obstinately refused all concessions. The war with Tipu strengthened his opposition, for either the company would be beaten and he would be relieved for the moment from further pressure, or Tipu would be overthrown and the danger of war, and the risk of the Carnatic administration being assumed, would disappear. Unluckily for the nawab, the victors found at Seringapatam papers which rendered the traditional fidelity of Muhammad 'Alī to the company at least suspect. These papers proved that the nawab and both his sons had been in correspondence with Hyder 'Alī and Tipu, that arrangements had been made for a secret cypher, and that the nawab had expressed himself bitterly on the subject of his English allies. Probably this exchange of letters and passing of messengers signified no more than the customary instability of Indian rulers at this time. But it was fatal to the old nawab's character as the company's unalterable friend. The company had repeatedly refused to allow pressure to be put upon him on the score that his loyalty was unimpeachable. That defence could no longer be made, and all reason for continuing past policy disappeared. Wellesley referred the question to England. He received authority to settle the Carnatic. About the same time 'Umdat-ul-'umara died. Wellesley offered to recognise the succession of his son if in return for one-sixth of the net revenues of the Carnatic he would make over the entire government of the province to the English. The son refused. The same offer was then made to a nephew of the late nawab. The nephew accepted. So in 1801 the company "assumed" the administration of the Carnatic, and the disastrous plan of separating military control and civil administration was brought to an end. Here, as in Mysore, Wellesley carried into effect his deliberate policy of undertaking the responsibility for the government in regions which had been placed by political developments under the company's power. In Mysore he set up a prince who was to rule in accordance with English advice. In the Carnatic he would have been content with an arrangement of the like nature. But being defeated in this by the refusal of the nawab, annexation remained the only method by which responsibility could be assumed.

In Oudh events followed a course not at all dissimilar to that just described. English policy followed the same development; but the nawab in Oudh proved more flexible than the southern ruler had been. The result therefore lay midway between the settlement in Mysore and the settlement in the Carnatic. In Oudh there emerged under the feeble conduct of Āsaf-ud-daula the same financial disorder, the same public debt to the company and private debt to individuals, the same disorder in the government, the same refusal to pay the revenues except under compulsion. The nawab of Oudh, like the nawab of Arcot, could not have maintained his position for a year without the armed help of the company. He was threatened by the insubordination of his unpaid troops, by the disobedience of his turbulent land-holders, and by the ambition of his Marātha neighbours. The English defended him against these enemies, but did nothing to re-establish order in his dominions. On Cornwallis's arrival, an attempt was made to apply the same fallacious remedy as was applied in the Carnatic. He reduced the company's demands on the nawab by fifty per cent. But affairs continued in their old course. At last in 1797 Āsaf-ud-daula died. He was at first succeeded by his reputed son Wazir 'Alī. But after a short period of hesitation Shore, departing from his usual policy of non-intervention, declared the new nawab spurious, declared all Āsaf-ud-daula's other reputed sons spurious likewise, and installed Sa'ādat 'Alī, the late nawab's brother, in Wazir 'Alī's stead. In return for this Sa'ādat 'Alī agreed to increase the annual payments to a trifle more than the amount payable before Cornwallis's reduction, to reduce the number of his own undisciplined troops, and to receive a larger garrison of the company's forces as a measure of protection against the anticipated invasion of northern India by Zamān Shāh, the ruler of Afghanistan. Such was the position on Wellesley's arrival as governor-general. The nawab, however, demanded an increase of the English forces as a protection against his own people. Wellesley increased it to 20,000 men and for this required an increased subsidy of fifty lakhs of rupees. Sa'ādat 'Alī, too, proved to be the most inconsistent of rulers. He would not reduce his troops though he needed protection against them. Under pressure, he demanded to be allowed to resign. When Wellesley agreed, he withdrew his offer. Wellesley sent to Lucknow first Colonel Scott, and then his own brother, Henry Wellesley, destined to make a reputation in Europe as a diplomatist. A treaty was to be made which would settle the Oudh question definitively. Wellesley desired in the first place no longer to be dependent on the nawab for the payments due to the company, since his financial management was entirely unreliable. In the second place, since the defence of Oudh depended on the company, he desired the cession of a tract of country which would prevent any enemy from attacking Oudh without coming into direct conflict with its protector. In the third place he felt that the company was disgraced by maintaining so disreputable a government, and that the nawab should be made to listen to the advice of the governor-general. In November, 1801, a treaty embodying these points was forced upon Sa'ādat 'Alī. The first two objects were secured by the cession of lands forming "a barrier between the dominions of the wazir and any foreign enemy". Thus Oudh ceased to be the buffer state, which it had formed in the days of Clive and Warren Hastings. The change marks clearly and emphatically the alteration which had occurred in the political situation of India. Under the guidance of its representatives at Calcutta, and very much against the wishes of the directors at London, the company was standing forth as the leader of the Indian political world. The third point was covered by the nawab's promise to set up in his country such a government as should conduce to the happiness and prosperity of his people. This clause did not in fact secure the purpose with which it was drafted. But that was not the fault of the treaty or of the policy which had inspired it. It was brought about by the fact that Wellesley's successors cherished a more confined conception of the company's duties in the regions under its influence but outside the sphere of its immediate authority. Here, quite as much as in the exact foresight displayed in his military and political arrangements, Wellesley showed himself possessed of great qualities. He approached the problems of the company's position in India in the same spirit as that displayed by Lord Grenville in his speech in 1813 in the House of Lords. Wellesley, like Grenville, was convinced that the interests of India and Great Britain were interlocked, and that by establishing peace in India and by promoting good administration, not only in the British provinces but also in the provinces ruled by the company's allies, he was securing the welfare of a multitude of men. The courage with which he faced the responsibilities of the task marks him out as a great leader. If Clive created the British-Indian empire, and Hastings maintained it through a period of extraordinary difficulties, Wellesley may claim to have been the first to recognise its moral and political significance.

Unfortunately other men were unwilling to shoulder so great a load as responsibility for the entire sub-continent. Wellesley's supersession in 1805 has already been mentioned, together with the reversal of the policy which he had followed. The set-back, however, was not long-continued. In 1807 the first Lord Minto succeeded Barlow. As Sir Gilbert Elliot he had taken a prominent part in the impeachment of Hastings and the attempted impeachment of Impey. In 1805 he had been appointed president of the Board of Control, though without a seat in the cabinet, and then was chosen to replace Barlow, whose administration had provoked great discontent in India, culminating in the mutiny of a large number of military officers at Madras. Minto devoted himself in the first place to the task of excluding French influence from the east. On the outbreak of the Revolutionary War, Pondichery and Chandernagore had at once been occupied, and Wellesley had evaded their restoration to the French during the short truce opened by the Peace of Amiens. But the French still held the islands of Mauritius and Bourbon. The first of these formed a centre from which numerous privateers preyed upon English shipping, inflicting very serious losses upon private merchants and the company itself. Moreover, the establishment of

French influence in Holland threatened to extend French power into the Dutch colonies, especially the Cape, Java, and Ceylon. During Shore's government Ceylon had been captured by a force from India, and the Cape by an expedition sent from Europe. About the same time certain islands in the archipelago, Amboyna and the chief spice islands, had also been seized by the English. But the government of Java passed under French control, so that British enemies were entrenched in positions east and west of India. This position meant the possibility of French intrigue with discontented Indian chiefs and of the sudden appearance of a French force on the coasts of India. In 1807, too, the French threatened to approach India by way of Persia. In that year Russia was at war with both Persia and France. In order to alarm Russia, Napoleon entered into a treaty with the shah, and sent a French general to Teherān with instructions to collect all possible information about the routes through Persia to India. Minto did not credit the stories of a French advance in force. But the appearance of even a small body on the Indian borders would certainly excite much alarm and trouble in the country. He therefore sent embassies to Persia, to Afghanistan, and to Lahore. They were to obtain promises of co-operation against the French if any advance overland should be attempted. For the moment the mission to Persia, conducted by Malcolm, failed. But the Persians soon found that Napoleon had been concerned solely with his own political interests. The French embassy was dismissed, and after long delay, due largely to squabbles between representatives of the government of Bengal and of the ministry at home, a treaty was signed between Great Britain and the shah. At Peshāwar, whither Elphinstone, the future historian, was sent, the ruling prince was Shāh Shujaʻ, who had displaced Zamān Shāh, who a few years earlier had been a serious danger to the peace of northern India. But Asiatic kingships decay with extraordinary rapidity. The Afghan kingship was falling into the ruin of family feuds, and, though Shujāʻ was willing to make a treaty, he was too distracted by rebellions to make an effective ally. At Lahore, however, Minto's envoy, Metcalfe, found a ruler of a different stamp. Ranjit Singh, head of one of the chief *misls*, or groups, into which the Sikhs were divided, had gradually extended his authority over the Panjab, and had organised a strong military state. In 1807 he was busily seeking to establish his power over the Sikh chiefs on the east bank of the Sutlej. In the days of Mahādaji Sindhia they had been reduced to recognising his suzerainty. Wellesley's treaty of 1803 had transferred Sindhia's political rights in that region to the company, and Minto was determined not to allow Ranjit to substitute himself for the company as the overlord of the Cis-Sutlej states. Metcalfe's mission thus was difficult. He was required to obtain Ranjit's promise of co-operation against the French if they made any attempts against India, and at the same time to induce Ranjit to desist from a project on which he had set his heart. His negotiations were prolonged and delicate. At one moment he even had to inform the prince that any movement of his troops across the Sutlej would be resisted by the company's forces, and Ranjit hesitated between peace and war with the English. At last he decided to ally himself with the strongest power in India. He signed a treaty of friendship, agreeing to recognise the Cis-Sutlej states as under the protection of the company and to regard the friends and enemies of the company as his own friends and his own enemies. Minto was thus relieved from fears for the security of the English position on the north-west.

His next step was to attack the French islands in order to end the activity of their privateers and to deprive them of a possible naval base from which an attack on India might be launched. The islands were first blockaded. Then in 1810 an expedition from India captured Bourbon and Mauritius, so that a French squadron reaching eastern waters would find itself deprived of any place where it could revictual or refit after its long voyage. Finally in 1811 an attack was made upon Java, where a French regiment had been landed. For two centuries Dutch influence had been supreme in the archipelago. The Dutch company had made a great number of treaties with the local chiefs, binding the latter not to admit foreign vessels to their harbours. On the strength of these agreements the Dutch had claimed the right to exclude foreign, and especially English vessels, from the free navigation of the neighbouring waters. They had reluctantly abandoned these exclusive claims by the treaty ending the war of the American Revolution, but nevertheless they had continued to punish the chiefs who dared to admit the English to trade. The commerce of the archipelago, however, was far too valuable an adjunct to the trade of India, affording a profitable outlet for the sale of opium and cotton goods, for the English company easily to acquiesce in this position. It retained a few small factories in Sumatra, formed mainly for the supply of pepper. In the time of Cornwallis English interests had been extended by the acquisition of the island of Penang in the Straits of Malacca. It had been hoped that the island would form a naval base as well as give the English access to the trade of the archipelago. But these hopes had hardly been realised. The eastern settlements remained unimportant. They were peculiarly unhealthy, and were avoided as much as possible by the company's servants. By accident a man of great ability, Stamford Raffles, was included in the Sumatra establishment. He was known for his familiarity with the languages and peoples of the archipelago, and, when Minto proposed to turn the French out of Java, he was summoned to Calcutta to advise the governor-general. The expedition, which sailed in 1811, met with speedy success. The French were ill-led and unpopular even with the Dutch. Their defeat was followed at once by the surrender of the island, which was entrusted to the management of Raffles as lieutenant-governor. For the moment English naval influence was supreme from the Cape of Good Hope eastwards as far as Canton.

The settlement which followed the end of the Napoleonic wars in 1814 and 1815 somewhat reduced this position of monopoly. The French were readmitted to their old settlements on the Indian mainland. They recovered the island of Bourbon, which from its lack of a harbour could not be made into a naval base. The Dutch recovered their eastern possessions. But Great Britain retained the Cape of Good Hope. Her sovereignty over the possessions of the East India Company was for the first time recognised by both the Dutch and the French. Though Java was restored to Holland, Raffles's activity and foresight speedily secured for the English, by his occupation of Singapore in 1819, a stronghold in the very centre of the archipelago, thus effectively breaking the monopoly of control which till 1811 the Dutch had enjoyed. Moreover, although the French were readmitted to India, they returned under the obligation of limiting their military forces to the needs of their settlements for internal police, so that they were no more to form a political danger. Finally, in 1824, the Dutch exchanged their remaining Indian factories for the factories which the English company still held on the island of

umatra, while in 1845 the Danes sold to the English the settlements of Tranquebar and Serampore. These subsequent changes
thus emphasised the predominance of English interests over those
f all other European nations established by the treaties of 1814 and
815. Politically neither the French at Pondichery nor the
Portuguese at Goa could attempt to rival the position of the East
ndia Company or to undermine its authority. This consequence
esulted, not from the successes which Cornwallis, Wellesley, and
Minto had obtained in the east, but on the overwhelming
upremacy which the British navy had established on the oceans
f the world. The triumphs culminating in the victory of
Trafalgar and the blockade which the English fleets had thereafter
pplied to the coasts of France, alone had prevented the appearance
1 the east of French forces which would have set all India
blaze. As supremacy at sea had transferred the dominion of
ndian waters from the Portuguese to the Dutch, and produced
he downfall of the Portuguese power and the establishment of the
Dutch empire in the archipelago, so now supremacy at sea had
etermined the prolonged struggle between the French and the
English for predominance on the Indian mainland. The validity
f victories in India depended on the issue of the naval war. Had
Nelson failed, neither the fall of Seringapatam, nor the victories
f Assaye and Laswari, could have produced more than the most
ransient results. But his success permitted the company to con-
olidate its power.

As has been seen, Wellesley had sought to establish a position
f supremacy in anticipation of these events, but had been
rustrated by the narrow views and reluctance to accept responsi-
ility displayed by the home authorities. His work was now to be
ompleted. In 1813, the year in which the British parliament first
sserted the sovereignty of the crown over the company's terri-
ories, Lord Moira was appointed governor-general in succession
o Minto. Moira was by profession a soldier and received like
Cornwallis the combined offices of governor-general and
ommander-in-chief. He speedily found himself involved in
roubles with the Gurkhas. In the course of the eighteenth
entury these hardy hillmen had conquered a wide stretch of the
Himālāyan tract. In 1768 they had conquered the Nepāl valley
nd gradually expanded until they ruled from the Sutlej as far
astwards as Sikkim. They touched English territories for over

700 miles, and the border districts constantly suffered from thei
incursions. Barlow offered concessions. Minto remonstrated
Moira decided to garrison the disputed districts. The Gurkha
slew the garrisons. In November, 1814, Moira declared war upo
them. The British officers in India had at that time small ex
perience of hill-fighting or of the organisation of hill-transport
Against the fine fighting qualities of the Gurkhas they met at firs
with numerous reverses. Moira, who had personally planned th
campaign, was much disconcerted by the tactical failures whic
occurred. But his military talent soon discerned that his sub
ordinates were not making proper use of their advantages. H
insisted that mortars, which till then had been little used excep
in siege-operations, were as effective against an enemy wh
sheltered himself from direct fire behind a hill as against one wh
sheltered himself behind walls. The instructions which he issued
coupled with the appearance of a new and most competen
commander, Colonel Ochterlony, led to a rapid reversal of th
position. The Gurkhas were defeated in the field. Kumāon wa
captured in April, 1815; their stronghold of Malāon was take
in the next month. In consequence the Gurkhas sued for peace
By the Treaty of Sagauli, concluded in 1816, after unsuccessfu
negotiations and a brief renewal of the war, the Gurkhas cede
Garhwāl and Kumāon together with a large part of the Tarai
they withdrew from Sikkim; and they agreed to receive
permanent British resident at their capital of Kāthmāndu. Th
settlement proved definitive, and the alliance between them an
the English has never since been broken.

The Gurkha War, however, was but in the nature of an inter
lude. The far more serious question of the Marāthas had still to b
determined. Barlow's conduct after the death of Cornwallis ha
convinced them that the British were as stupid in negotiation a
they were formidable in the field. But they lacked leaders. N
Marātha prince appeared capable of giving them guidance. Th
Pēshwā, Bāji Rāo II, was one whom no man could wisely trus
He endeavoured to crush his own feudal nobility, the *jāgīrdār*
in order to increase his own revenues: with the result that he wa
hated throughout the territories under his immediate control. A
Indore the peaceful rule of Ahalya Bai, who had governed fro
her husband's death in 1766 till her own death in 1795, had bee
followed by confusion and chaos. Jaswant Rāo, the rival

Daulat Rāo Sindhia, had died mad in 1811. He had been succeeded by Malhar Rāo, under whom the state had been torn to pieces between two factions, the Marātha under his mother Tulsi Bai, and the Pathan under Amīr Khān, a leader of mercenaries. Revenue was gathered at the point of the sword, and appropriated by the gatherer. Sindhia's dominions were hardly better off. Daulat Rāo had been greatly weakened by his war with the English. His lands had been overrun by Holkar's troops in search of plunder. His own army was unpaid. Independent bodies of troops, well known under the name of Pindāris, established themselves under him with his half-willing consent, on the understanding that they would serve him in case of need in return for finding with him a place of shelter. The Gaekwar was distracted by differences with the Pēshwā over claims which the latter had upon him. Nāgpur was barely able to maintain a settled administration.

From the point of view of Calcutta the most pressing problem was offered by the activities of the Pindāris. These freebooters, composed of both Muslim and Hindu bands under rival commanders, formed a growing menace to the whole of India. They would gather at the festival of the *Dasara* in the autumn when the rains were over, and march whithersoever they chose, plundering as they went. Central India and the domains of the Nizām were repeatedly pillaged, and in 1812 they began to attack the company's possessions. In that year they harried Mīrzāpur and the southern districts of Bihar. In 1816 they invaded the Northern Circars. In one village which they approached, the inhabitants preferred to burn themselves with their wives and children rather than fall into the hands of these savage enemies. Those who shrank from so extreme a measure had small cause to congratulate themselves on their wisdom. These outrages in the latter part of 1816 at last compelled the company to permit its government in India to take measures to bring them to an end. Out of this sprang the Pindāri War, which extended to all the Marātha states except Baroda and concluded with their complete overthrow and the final consolidation of the East India Company's power in India.

For some time the position at Poona had been most uncertain. Political relations had been conducted by two very able servants of the company, first by Barry Close, and then by Mountstuart

Elphinstone. Neither had been able to induce Bāji Rāo to forsake his perpetual intrigue. The Pēshwā hoped once more to head a confederacy against the English and was constantly seeking to incite the chief Marātha princes to attack them, but he was unwilling to commit any overt act of hostility till he should be assured of a general support. His intrigues were betrayed, and he was therefore closely watched; but matters did not come to a head till 1814. In the hope of settling the disputes between the Pēshwā and the Gaekwar, the latter was induced to send his principal minister, Gaṅgadhar Sāstri, to Poona under the Pēshwā's safe-conduct. The Sāstri was a strong adherent of the English alliance. He even borrowed English ways, walking fast, speaking broken English, given to calling the Pēshwā and his people "dam fools". He was consequently much disliked in Marātha circles. He accompanied the Pēshwā to Nasik, to take part in a religious festival. He was murdered there, apparently by agents of the Pēshwā's favourite, Trimbakji Danglia, and probably with the Pēshwā's connivance. In punishment for this breach of faith, the Pēshwā was compelled by Elphinstone to surrender Trimbakji after prolonged delay. But in 1816 he escaped, it was believed with the assistance of the Pēshwā. Matters were then looking most threatening. Bāji Rāo was certainly seeking to stir up the other Marātha chiefs, and the Pindāri inroads proved that the chiefs were making no attempts to restrain the actions of their dependents.

The governor-general, now relieved of the Gurkha war, prepared to meet this combination of dangers. His first measure related to Nāgpur. The late ruler, Rāghūji Rāo, had been succeeded by an imbecile, Parsaji. Parsaji had a capable but unscrupulous cousin, Appa Sāhib, who aspired to the government and desired as a preparatory measure to be invested with the regency. In 1816 he was recognised by the company in return for the signature of a subsidiary alliance. This meant the establishment of a strong force of company's troops at Nāgpur. Moira's immediate object was to check any possible movements of the Pindāris or other Marātha troops to the south-eastwards, and to detach Nāgpur from any possible league of the Marātha states. The next measure related to the Pēshwā. In 1817 Bāji Rāo was compelled reluctantly to sign a new treaty by which he renounced the headship of the Marātha confederacy, acknowledged th independence of the Gaekwar, and ceded to the English the Konkan and other districts. Later in the same year, having assembled an overwhelming force on Sindhia's frontiers, Moira compelled him to sign the Treaty of Gwalior. This bound him to co-operate in measures against the Pindāris and released the company from the obligation, into which Barlow had so lightly entered, of abstaining from political activity beyond the Chambal. This permitted the conclusion of a number of treaties with the Rājput states, which had been threatened with extinction by the attacks of their Marātha neighbours. Having blocked Pindāri movements into the Nāgpur territories and westwards into Rājputāna, Moira then began to attack the Pindāris themselves. For this purpose he had assembled a force of over 100,000 men and 300 guns. Had the Marātha chiefs been content to watch the destruction of the Pindāris, and sink without another effort into dependence upon the company's government, no general war need have followed. Had they been wise enough to combine their forces and act together, they might have fallen gallantly. But once more, as after the Treaty of Bassein, they were to fight one by one. Perhaps nothing illustrates more forcibly the political imbecility into which India had fallen than that the one Hindu power which had arisen after the fall of the Mughal empire should have proved to be utterly incapable of uniting in the face of a foreign power. In fact the eighteenth century, marked by the establishment of European predominance, merely repeats the history of those earlier centuries in which the pre-Āryan states fell before the Āryans, and in which the Hindu princes submitted to the Muslims. While Holkar's durbar was still undecided and while Sindhia was signing the Treaty of Gwalior, the Pēshwā and Appa Sāhib resolved to attack the company.

The Pēshwā attacked and burnt the residency at Poona, and then with 27,000 men attacked 2800 under Colonel Burr at Khirkī. Even his enormous preponderance of men did not save him from a heavy defeat. Two more battles followed, at Koregāon and Ashti. In the second the Pēshwā's general, Bāpu Gokhala, was killed, and in both the Marāthas were defeated. In the middle of 1818 Bāji Rāo, tired of being hunted all over his territories, surrendered to Sir John Malcolm, under promise of personal safety and of a pension of eight lakhs of rupees a year. His dominions were annexed and placed under the administration of the presidency of Bombay. Meanwhile in Nāgpur Appa Sāhib had attacked the resident, had been defeated like Bāji Rāo, and had fled to the Panjab. A boy belonging to the ruling family was established as raja of Nāgpur, and the districts north of the Nerbudda were annexed to the company's territories. Holkar's durbar had refused all offers of peace, but, unable to give help to, or to receive any from, the other Marātha rulers, it had been completely defeated at the battle of Mahidpur by Hislop, who commanded the southern portion of the company's army, and compelled in January, 1818, to sign the Treaty of Mandasor, by which it surrendered all districts south of the Nerbudda, abandoned all claims on the Rājput chiefs, recognised one of its mercenary commanders as nawab of Tānk, and accepted a permanent resident at Indore. Sindhia, who had proved unable to assist the English against the Pindāris, agreed to a fresh treaty ceding Ajmir to the company and making a certain readjustment of boundaries. The Marāthas had vanished as a political power.

The settlement of 1818 marks the beginning of the paramountcy of the East India Company. No state remained which could challenge its supremacy. No state remained which could reject its alliance. The project of Wellesley had been realised. All the principal states of India had been brought into agreement with the company, and had placed in its hands the conduct of political relations. Many had accepted a subsidiary force, which implied a position of dependency. The peace of India had been assured. The wars which for a century and a half had desolated India had been brought to an end. But if the political project of Wellesley had been completed, one aspect at least had been neglected. The treaties into which Moira had entered had not been treaties such as Wellesley would have ratified, for they all omitted those stipulations on which he would have set a high importance. Moira's treaties all included some clause intended to avoid all possibility of interference on the part of the company's government in matters of internal administration. Unlike Wellesley, Moira limited his views to the regions under the direct control of the East India Company, while Wellesley had envisaged the good of India as a whole. Consequently the company found itself committed to a number of alliances by which it was bound to support the reigning prince without much regard for the quality of his administration. The relations which

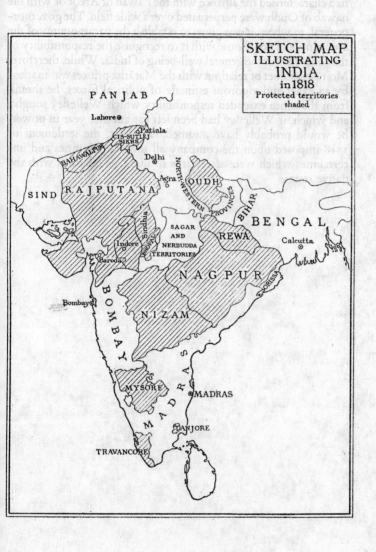

SKETCH MAP
ILLUSTRATING
INDIA
in 1818
Protected territories
shaded

had characterised the alliance with the nawab of Arcot or with the nawab of Oudh were perpetuated over a wide field. The governor-general, to whom it was given to establish the paramountcy of the company, did not choose with it to recognise the responsibility of the company for the general well-being of India. While, therefore, Moira's conduct of relations with the Marātha princes was marked by an exact and vigorous estimate of political forces, he shrank from the more extended responsibility which Wellesley sought, and which, if Wellesley had been left for another year in power, he would probably have assumed. In short, the settlement of 1818 imposed upon the company all those ambiguities and uncertainties which were afterwards to mark its relations with the native states.

CHAPTER VI

The Growth of the Company's System of Government

In a previous chapter some reference has already been made to the results of the Regulating Act on the position of Warren Hastings. The matter must now be considered from a more general point of view, and some attempt made to sketch the growth of the company's government, alike in its higher organisation and in the subordinate branches which brought it into direct contact with the peasantry of the country. It will be most convenient to deal first with the home government, then with the governments of Bengal and of the subordinate presidencies, and lastly with the district administrations which grew up in Bengal and Madras, Bombay being reserved for later consideration, since that presidency in its territorial form was scarcely constituted till 1818.

Down to 1773 the home government had consisted solely of the directors and proprietors of the East India Company. The former had been annually elected by the latter, and the two had constituted the only body authorised to issue orders to the governments in India. No prolonged conflict between the two parts of this body had been possible, because the policy desired by the proprietors was necessarily reflected every year in the choice of the directors. The Regulating Act laid down that of the twenty-four directors only six should be chosen in each year. The power of the proprietors to overrule decisions of the directors was left unchanged. Thus it might come to pass that the proprietors desired one thing and the majority of the directors another, for an indefinite period, and in that case the directors could be prevented from carrying out the policy of their choice by resolution of the lower body. The act thus gave an opening, in the home as in the Indian governments, for prolonged and bitter strife, as actually came to pass. The directors, under the corrupt influence of the ministry, desired to remove Hastings from office, while the proprietors resolved that he should not be removed. Nor did the act give to the ministry power of interfering in the company's transactions. Despatches relating to the political and administrative affairs of India were to be sent to one of the secretaries of state; but no power of control was taken. North evidently looked to managing the directors as he managed the House of Commons.

Ten years later in 1783 Fox introduced his famous bills which proposed the complete supersession of the company. Seven commissioners were named in the bill to administer Indian affairs, holding office for a fixed term of seven years. This proposal was strongly attacked on constitutional grounds. The commissioners would have exercised all patronage; they were nominees of Fox; and Pitt described the bill as bestowing the patronage of India on Charles Fox whether in or out of office. This criticism has usually been ignored as dictated solely by party purposes. But a great jealousy of the executive was felt at that time. It was expressed by Dunning's famous motion, "That the power of the crown has increased, is increasing, and ought to be diminished". If to the ordinary patronage of the crown were added the patronage of India, would not the Coalition fix its power in parliament for at least a generation? And was it desirable to increase the ministerial powers of corrupting members of parliament? These doubts were widely and deeply felt, and materially contributed to the decisive overthrow of the Coalition at the general election of 1784. That election placed Pitt firmly in office, and in the same year he introduced and carried his famous India Act, which settled the main lines of the home and Indian governments for over seventy years.

This act set up a Board of Control, which was at first meant to be a cabinet committee. This was to receive copies of all despatches received from India and drafts of all orders proposed to be sent out. No orders could be sent without its approval, and, in matters of secrecy or urgency, the board could draft orders which had to be forwarded at once to India by a committee of the directors known as the Committee of Secrecy. The new body differed from Fox's commissioners in two important respects. It represented the government of the nation and was variable by ordinary constitutional methods. Save in a limited class of matters, which in practice was confined to questions of external policy, it had no powers of initiation. It had no powers of patronage. Pitt himself described his object as "to give to the crown the power of guiding the politics of India, with as little means of corrupt influence as possible". In this he had clearly succeeded. At the same time the possibility of the company's action being hindered by internal conflict was avoided by a clause which declared that the proprietors could not veto a proposal made by the directors and approved by the Board of Control, while the creation of the board itself prevented the recurrence of the position which had developed under Lord North, when the ministry had been unable to carry into effect its policy on Indian subjects.

At the same time the company retained far more than nominal power. Its right of initiating despatches on ordinary subjects meant that while it might be restrained from acting, it could hardly be compelled to act against its will. It would be entirely wrong to suppose that the government of the company's territories was transferred by Pitt's India Act to the ministry. A system of control was established, by which for the first time the East India Company was brought into organic connection with the sovereign power of Great Britain. The board, however, evolved in a manner somewhat different from that which had been anticipated. Pitt had expected that the Indian business would not be more than ministers could consider in the leisure which their other offices afforded them. But it soon proved to be far too voluminous and far too complicated for a secretary of state or a chancellor of the exchequer to be able to master in the spare time at his disposal. Consequently Dundas, who had devoted more study to Indian affairs than any other member of the cabinet, first took the lead, then became president of the board, and at last monopolised its business.

The structure of the government of Bengal was reformed by Pitt and Dundas with equal thoroughness. But here the changes introduced by the India Act were more tentative. All that was done at first was to reduce the size of the council from five to four inclusive of the governor-general. By the exercise of his casting vote the latter could always secure the adoption of his policy provided he could obtain the support of a single member. But the governor-general remained merely the head of the council with no special powers. Hastings had repeatedly urged the importance of investing his office with superior authority. Macartney, to whom the office had been offered on Hastings's resignation, refused it unless he should receive specific powers of over-ruling his council. Cornwallis, to whom the government was then offered, made the same demand, and added to it the requirement that he should be appointed commander-in-chief as well. The cabinet desired his acceptance too much to refuse his terms. The directors appointed him governor-general, and the cabinet brought in an amending bill to permit the union of offices and the bestowal of the powers demanded. The choice of Cornwallis and the changes connected with his appointment constituted a reform of the utmost importance. In the first place the governor-general would no longer find himself in the position of impotence to which Warren Hastings had been reduced. In the second place the conflict between the civil and military authorities was ended when the head of the state became the head of the army too. It is true that after Cornwallis's government some recrudescence of military insubordination did occur; but by then the civil government had been reorganised and strengthened, so that the position was far less dangerous than before. In the third place the selection of the head of the government from London, while the remainder of the council was formed from the company's civil servants, showed that Pitt and Dundas had learnt at least one of the lessons provided by the Regulating Act. To nominate a majority, designed to supervise and if necessary check the action of the governor-general was to establish faction in the heart of government. If Hastings deserved the office to which North had named him, he should have been trusted not to abuse his powers. Pitt's method was wholly different. He united power and responsibility in the same hands, while giving Cornwallis the advisers who could make good his ignorance of the technicalities of Indian administration. Moreover, once the custom of naming English noblemen to the office of governor-general had been established, another great source of weakness vanished. The company's servant who had spent all his life in India could never rely on finding support on either side of the House of Commons. That was the reason why Hastings's position from first to last had been so extraordinarily precarious. But the new practice meant that, so long as the governor-general behaved like a gentleman, he was sure of the support of his party in London. He was able therefore to approach his work with that confidence in the future which Hastings had never possessed.

In another point also the India Act introduced a much-needed change. In the recent past the power of superintendence vested in the Bengal government had done as much harm as good. No effective central power had been created, and the subordinate presidencies had been able to defy all attempts to co-ordinate British policy. But the India Act gave to the Bengal government power of control "over all transactions with the country powers" and over the entire conduct of any war that might break out. Nor could the subordinate presidencies excuse themselves from obedience on the plea that the orders of Bengal exceeded their legal powers. That point was to be determined by the Bengal government itself and by the home authorities. The sole case in which obedience might be delayed was when contrary orders which had reached Madras or Bombay from England were still unknown in Bengal.

Before Cornwallis had left India, a final change was made in the governor-general's position. This was designed to meet difficulties caused by the great distance and slow communications of India. Cornwallis had thought fit to assume the command of the war which broke out with Tipu Sultān. His council passed a resolution enabling him to act separately from it with as much authority as if he were acting in council. This was held in England to exceed the powers legally granted, and a special act was passed in 1791 to validate whatever he had done under those defective powers. In 1793, when the privileges of the company were extended for twenty years, provision was made to enable the governor-general to visit any part of the company's dominions, to act with the local council with as much authority as he possessed when acting with the council of Bengal, and to issue orders to any of the company's servants without consulting the local council at all.

By these various measures an effective central government was at last built up in British India. The changes made in the subordinate governments were less important, but were still considerable. In them also the councils were reduced by the India Act to four members, inclusive of the governor. In 1793 the governors received powers of over-ruling their councils. From the appointment of Macartney as governor of Madras in 1780 the custom of selecting provincial governors from the political world of London instead of from among the company's servants came into force, although it was never so rigid as in the case of the governor-general, and occasional exceptions were made for the benefit of specially eminent members of the administrative services, such as Malcolm, Munro, and Elphinstone. The chief defect in this organisation certainly lay in the provision made for the administration of the province of Bengal, and the dual task imposed upon the government of managing local detail and controlling general policy. The consequence was likely to be that whatever system of administration was adopted for Bengal would tend to be thrust upon the other provinces, because the central government would be slow to admit the existence of fundamental differences between the province with which it was familiar and the provinces with which it was not.

From the beginning the administration of Bengal offered peculiar difficulties. The system of government had fallen into great confusion. A powerful class, known locally as *zamindars*, had sprung up between the government and the cultivators. These zamindars were derived from two distinct sources. Some of them, such as the zamindars of Bardwān or Rājshāhi, represented old Hindu families which had formerly borne sway in the country and had submitted to the Muslim conquerors on condition of retaining a position of dignity and paying annual tribute. Others were descended from farmers of the land revenue and other officials who had acquired hereditary status. These persons claimed to represent the government within the areas committed to their charge. They collected the land revenue and other dues, as well as a number of unauthorised cesses; they administered justice; they represented the only police and magisterial authority. Under the Mughal government nobody had troubled to define their rights over the soil. As was usual in India, such matters had been left to the determination of custom. But the amount of revenue which they should hand over to the treasury had been a cause of unceasing dispute. In order to keep a check over their payments, officials called *kanungos*, or declarers of custom, had been instituted. These were supposed to keep exact registers of each zamindari, showing the amounts of revenue which ought to be collected. But the kanungos had gradually slipped from the control of the government and had become the servants of the zamindars themselves. The official organisation had thus broken down before the company was in any way interested in the administration. Then too the province had fallen as a whole into English hands. In 1765 the company suddenly became master of the revenues, with great responsibilities for the maintenance of the government and the payment of forces large enough to protect Bengal from external invasion and internal rebellion. Its servants had indeed attempted to administer certain limited districts, which had already been granted to the English; but they had hardly learnt more than that the task was complex and difficult. The prime need, before which all else fell into insignificance, was to secure the regular payment of sums sufficient to maintain the military forces. Clive had therefore made no attempt to modify the mode of administration, but had handed over the company's duties to the charge of Muhammad Riza Khān, who, he hoped, would be able to keep matters on at least their old footing.

This plan, like the similar attempt of Dupleix to collect the Carnatic revenues through Pāpayya Pillai, proved a failure. Muhammad Riza Khān received a huge salary, but his administration was lax, while the decisions in the courts of justice were asserted by Verelst, a well-informed and honest if not vigorous man, to be corrupt bargains with the highest bidders. Since the resident at Murshidābād could not exercise sufficient supervision over the conduct of the company's deputy, supervisors were appointed in 1769, with orders to investigate the revenue position and above all to ascertain the amounts which the zamindars collected from the cultivators. But such attempts were frustrated by the passive opposition of the zamindars and their servants the kanungos. In 1772 Hastings was ordered by the company to remove the deputy and undertake the direct administration of the company's duties as *dīwān*. With these orders the English administration of Bengal begins.

It was determined to reappoint the supervisors, under the new title of collectors, to each district, to give them the assistance of Indian officials called *dīwāns*, to farm out the revenues for a term of five years, and to create a Committee of Circuit to tour the province and suggest a suitable organisation for adoption by the council. On the proposal of the committee it was resolved to set up two courts of justice in each district. The civil court consisted of the collector with a number of Indian officials, and was called the *mofassal dīwāni 'adālat*. The criminal court, the *faujdari* 'adālat, consisted of Muslim law officers, whose decisions were to be revised by the collectors, and submitted for the approval of an Indian official stationed at Calcutta and appointed by the nawab on the nomination of the governor. This official was known as the superintendent of the court—*daroga-i 'adālat*.

The five-year settlement of 1772 proved to be much higher than could be realised. Speculators desirous of the dignity of association with the land, and zamindars fearful of being dispossessed of their old position, bid up the farms recklessly. The collectors reported their opinion that the settlement could not be maintained. But the governor and council resolved that every effort should be made to prevent arrears. One reason was that they fancied that the farmers were deceiving the collectors; the second, that if the terms were rigorously enforced, it would be possible at the end of the settlement to make a good guess at the revenues which could normally be obtained. In 1773, on the private advice of Hastings, the company decided to withdraw the collectors from the districts, and a new system was introduced, by which the collectors were grouped into a number of provincial councils, charged with administering civil justice and with supervising the *dīwāns*, who were left in executive control of the various districts. But a new influence was destined to throw the system into confusion. In the next year the councillors and judges appointed under the Regulating Act reached Calcutta. Francis brought with him the administrative ideas of Clive, and the judges the legal ideas of England. Francis was convinced that every attempt to manage directly the administration of Bengal was doomed to failure, and was eager to see Muhammad Riza Khān restored to his old position or one as like it as possible. He also soon developed the theory, borrowed from some of the company's servants who had been employed in district administration, that the land revenue ought to be settled permanently and never varied. These ideas led to great controversy whenever the council proceeded to the discussion of revenue business; but Francis had not developed his theories in time to make use of the majority opposing Hastings before its disappearance with the death of Monson in 1776, and consequently the discussions led to no practical results. The interference of the Supreme Court, however, was a different matter. The judges held the view that every person concerned with the collection of the revenues must be deemed to be in the service of the company, and, therefore, under the Regulating Act, subject to the jurisdiction of the court; that it had been constituted in Bengal in order to check oppression; that persons wrongfully imprisoned were entitled to appeal to the court for interference by seeking a writ of *habeas corpus*; and that such writs should be granted on the filing of an affidavit such as would authorise the issue of the writ in question in England. The result was that many renters, imprisoned by order of the provincial councils for non-payment of revenues, and ryots imprisoned at the suit of renters for the same reason, applied to the court for redress; the court issued writs accordingly; and the imprisoned persons were in fact released. This interference threatened to bring the revenue collections to a standstill. Similar action on the part of the Supreme Court dealt an equally severe blow to the operations of the provincial courts of justice which Hastings had set up. In what was called the Patna Case, for instance, the Muslim law officers of the Patna Provincial Council were cast in heavy damages in consequence of a sentence given by the council. In 1780, in order to bring the deadlock thus created to an end, Hastings invited the chief justice, Sir Elijah Impey, to accept the presidency of the appeal court at Calcutta, the *sadr dīwāni 'adālat*. This arrangement permitted the Supreme Court, now feeling sure that improper sentences delivered by the district courts would receive due correction by a trained and expert judge, to abstain from further interference. The arrangement was, however, disallowed by the company, and Hastings's enemies made of it a charge against Impey. They represented the affair as a bribe to the chief justice for ceasing to inconvenience the administration, and as a violation of the Regulating Act, which forbade the acceptance of salaried office by persons appointed under the act. They attempted to impeach Impey on this and other grounds. But their efforts broke down completely before the defence which Impey made before the House of Commons. Indeed, the partisan nature of the accusation was clear from the fact that they sought to impeach Impey, Hastings's friend, for accepting a paid office, while they said nothing of Mr Justice Chambers, the friend of Francis, who had likewise accepted the paid office of judge at Chinsura.

In 1776, when the five-year settlement was drawing to an end, Hastings proposed the formation of a new commission intended to tour through Bengal and collect information on which a new settlement could be based. This was appointed accordingly, in spite of the strong opposition of Clavering and Francis. It became known as the *Amini* Commission, and its report is justly described as the most important document relating to the revenues of Bengal at this period. It bears striking evidence of the alienation of lands and of the oppression of the ryots under the influence of the settlement of 1772. In 1781 it was followed by a reorganisation of the revenue machinery. The collectors were to be re-established in the districts, acting under a central Committee of Revenue set up at Calcutta: but they were not invested with effective power. This involved a greater concentration of authority than the plan adopted in 1773. The settlements were made by the Committee of Revenue, not by the collectors, who were not allowed to interfere with such matters. The farmers were thus left without any local control, and did not hesitate to flog ryots presumptuous enough to complain of oppression or extortion.

Shortly after Hastings's departure from Bengal, a new scheme was introduced by his successor, John Macpherson. The provinces were to be divided into thirty-five districts (reduced in the next year to twenty-three). The collector in each district now became the authority by whom the settlement was to be made, and his conduct was supervised by the central committee, now called the Board of Revenue. On Cornwallis's arrival, the collectors once more received the office of head of the *dīwāni* 'adālats, with an Indian assistant to hear the smaller cases. Thus, the system of 1772 was for a while restored. But great changes were made in the mode of paying the collectors. In 1772 they had possessed the privilege of private trade, which had provided the chief reason for Hastings's dislike of their employment in the districts. They were now to receive 1500 rupees a month, besides a commission on the revenue which they collected, and this was expected to afford them an addition of about as much as their fixed pay. They were also given two covenanted servants as assistants. Criminal justice remained under the management of Muhammad Riza Khān, who had been restored by the majority in Hastings's government to his former office of *naib nāzīm*, deputy for the nawab in that branch of government not covered by the *dīwāni*.

Cornwallis's first measures were only temporary expedients, which had been chiefly dictated by the company's desire for economy in the administration. An entirely new system was introduced between 1790 and 1793. The basis of this was a new settlement of the land revenue. When Cornwallis arrived, he found two schools of opinion on revenue matters. One was headed by James Grant, who had explored a quantity of ancient revenue accounts. These led him to the view that the zamindars had long succeeded in secreting a vast proportion of the revenues of the country, and that the actual collections fell far below the amount that ought to be realised. The second was headed by John Shore, who was probably the most experienced revenue servant in the presidency, and who believed that Grant's researches bore no relation to the actual facts of the time. Matters were further complicated by the ascendancy which the ideas of Francis had obtained in England for the time being, and that Cornwallis's instructions required him to effect a permanent settlement as soon as possible. In 1787 the Board of Revenue was ordered to prepare to settle the revenue for a long term of years. Two years later, when the necessary reports had been received from the collectors, Cornwallis came to the conclusion that nothing would be gained by a longer delay, and that, if the home authorities approved, the long-term settlement ought to be made permanent. In 1790 the long-term settlement came into force; and in 1793, with the approval of the company, it was declared unalterable. Even Shore, Cornwallis's most trusted adviser, was opposed to this measure. But the governor-general was convinced of its necessity, not from the revenue point of view but from that of general administration. So long as settlements were made annually, so long the zamindars would have the strongest possible incentive to corrupt the revenue officials. The stake was large, and the bribes offered would be great. But if the revenue demand were settled once and for all, this source of corruption would vanish. The permanent zamindari settlement thus came into being.

This change made way for the transformation of the system of district administration. On principle Cornwallis had disliked the concentration of revenue and judicial powers in the hands of the collectors. He considered that it gave too much authority to individuals, whose character would form the sole security for the due exercise of their functions. Moreover, the traditional Indian system of government, in which the executive official played so large a part, was wholly unfamiliar to him. He was accustomed to a mode of government under which the law was administered by a series of courts, and the duties of executive officials were reduced to a minimum. This was in his eyes the best method, and the one which he resolved to set up. Since it was in every point utterly different from that which he found in use, he thought that the conduct of the new system must be confined entirely to the English servants of the company. Hence that exclusion of Indians from responsible employment which marked the Cornwallis method of administration.

Henceforward the collectors were to be only fiscal agents, required to collect the fixed revenues from the zamindars. They would need for their duties only a small number of subordinates, who would be employed in the collectors' offices at the district headquarters; and they would have no possible reason for travelling about the area entrusted to their fiscal charge. It would not matter whether they knew much or little about the condition of the people, about the extent of cultivation, or the economic resources of the country. It was not their business to redress any wrongs. It was not their function to rule. In future the head of the district and the real representative of government was to be the district judge. To him, or to those acting under him, complaints for redress were to be preferred. Should a ryot be wronged by a zamindar, the ryot was to sue the zamindar in one of the courts of justice which were to be set up, in accordance with a new code of laws which was to be enacted. The judge was moreover to be head of the police and magistrate, responsible not only for the administration of civil justice, but also for the maintenance of public peace and the prevention or punishment of crime.

For the administration of justice a complete chain of courts was established. The district, or *zillah* judge, as he was called, was entrusted with the determination of all civil suits of importance and revenue suits, with the help of a registrar who was empowered to try cases referred to him by the judge. Suits for small amounts might be heard by Indian judges, *munsiffs* and *sadr amīns,* who were to be paid by fees in order that they should seek to attract suitors to their courts by the impartiality of their decisions. In his magisterial capacity, the zillah judge could commit persons accused of crime for trial by one of the four courts of circuit which were established for the punishment of crime. These courts of circuit were also to serve as courts of appeal from the civil decisions of the zillah judge, and consisted of three English judges. In civil cases a further appeal lay to the governor-general in council, who formed the *sadr dīwāni 'adālat*.

As regards the police, the districts were to be divided into several areas, each in charge of an Indian official called the *daroga*, who had under his command a body of salaried police, and who could also require the assistance of the village-watchmen. The darogas were responsible to the zillah judge in his capacity as magistrate.

In order to complete the system a series of regulations was passed in 1793, drafted mainly by the chief secretary, Barlow. These enacted a measure declaring the land revenue settlement permanent and unchangeable, laid down a form of procedure for the courts of justice, defined the qualifications of the law officers, Hindu and Muslim, who were attached to the courts, and dealt with a considerable variety of other matters.

This system was evidently inspired by a spirit of true philanthropy. It set up a great ideal, the supremacy of the law and the authority of the courts of justice. But in a large number of respects it was most unsuited to the needs of the province, and, like the revenue settlement which formed an integral part of the system, was full of unexpected evils. In its benevolent intentions and its unfortunate results it bears a marked affinity to the Regulating Act, and for the same reason. Both were founded upon ignorance. Ignorance was indeed the chief feature of the revenue settlement. No collector knew the resources, the rights, or even the limits of the zamindaris which he was required to settle for ever. The grants which were issued to the zamindars showed the names of the villages included in their estates, but the boundaries were undefined and unknown. Great areas of uncultivated waste were thus signed away without the government's possessing any idea of the magnitude of the gift it was making. That affected merely the rights of government. But the rights of the villagers were affected also. No attempt was made to define the rights of the customary tenants, who were entitled to cultivate their holdings at fixed rents. It was expected that such matters would be cleared up by the gradual operation of the courts. This proved to be an entire miscalculation, and the general effect was to bestow on the zamindars the fee simple of large areas in which a multitude of peasants had enjoyed extensive rights. And, based as it was on ignorance, the system made no provision for the future acquisition of knowledge. The collector, tied to his office at headquarters, had neither authority nor opportunity to learn the condition of the people. The judge, in like manner, could learn nothing but the affairs of the suitors who appeared before him. Yet the administration was, and was intended to be, a foreign administration. Cornwallis would have no Indians in high office. But if there is one thing above all which a foreign administration needs it is knowledge of the economic and social condition of the people over whom it rules. That was removed from all possibility by the revenue and administrative methods established in Bengal.

Nor were the endeavours made to provide the people with justice marked by success. New laws were made, but no means existed by which they could be brought to the knowledge of the people at large. They were framed in English, of which only a few Indians living in Calcutta itself could read a word. They were translated into Bengali and posted at the district headquarters; but how many peasants would tramp thither to read them? How many could read them if they tramped thither? Above all, how many could understand their elaborate verbiage when they had done so? The consequence was that the legislation benefited the few persons who could become aware of its contents, a group of sharp-witted Calcutta *banyans* and *sarkārs*—agents and head-servants—who studied them closely and made great advantage of their knowledge. Nor was real justice to be expected from the courts themselves. Their procedure was imitated from the complex and interminable procedure of the English courts. Witnesses were examined on oath. But the taking of oaths was a thing which the respectable Hindu had never been able to stomach. The consequence was that even a good case had to be supported by false witness. Men had to be hired to declare they had seen what they had not seen. The fact, says John Shore's son after long judicial experience, that a Hindu gave evidence in a British court was presumptive evidence against the respectability of his character. Then, too, law was costly. Pleaders had to be employed, because the procedure was elaborate. The great liberty of appeal permitted the man with funds to wear out the man without. The advantage lay altogether with the rich against the poor. Nor were the courts numerous enough to cope with the cases which were brought. Arrears increased to enormous proportions. It came to be a saying that with luck a decision might be reached in the life-time of the grandson of an original suitor. In fact Cornwallis had confounded law and law-courts with justice.

Nor must the police be omitted from this tale of woes. The darogas, under the supervision of a sedentary judge who could be trusted never to pay them a sudden visit and who in any case was, much too busy to attend to them, enjoyed a most enviable position. They were empowered to arrest on suspicion. All they had to do therefore was to inform a well-to-do person that they proposed to lay him under the social stigma of arrest, unless he dissuaded them with gifts, to obtain whatever they liked to ask in reason. The office of daroga of police became the most sought-after of all the places open to Indians under British authority.

Cornwallis's successors sought to remedy some of the evils which began to emerge from this unsuitable mode of conducting the business of government. The permanent settlement was heavy, and at first the zamindars had great difficulty in meeting their obligations. Shore therefore increased their power of coercing the ryots, and Wellesley increased those powers and permitted the zamindars to seize the lands of defaulting ryots. These measures, designed to facilitate the collection of the revenues, emphasised the position of dependence in which Cornwallis had in effect placed the cultivator. To meet the evil of delay, the number of judges was increased, the duties of the governor-general and council as the supreme appeal court were transferred to three judges who in future formed the *sadr dīwāni 'adālat*, freedom of appeal was limited, and the payment of fees was required before a suitor could file a suit. But all these changes only palliated the evils of a system fundamentally unsuited to the circumstances of the time.

Until 1808 the home authorities had approved without any hesitation the system established by Cornwallis. But in that year Thomas Munro went to England on leave. He had acquired a great knowledge of district administration, not indeed in Bengal but in Madras, and was a strong critic of the Bengal methods, above all of the ignorance of the Bengal collectors and of the complete supremacy of the zillah judges. He was called upon to give evidence before a select committee of the House of Commons, and made a deep impression upon all who heard him. His energy,

knowledge and character carried conviction. The directors began
to wonder why the system which Munro had employed in
Madras had never been adopted in Bengal, and how it was that
their collectors there knew so little of the condition and occupations of the people placed under their charge. They noticed too
that when a collector was called upon to manage a zamindari
during the minority of the zamindar or on its resumption by
government for the non-payment of rent, he found insuperable
difficulties in executing duties which Munro and others discharged
with ease in the south. They therefore ceased to desire the extension of the Bengal system to the other provinces under their
rule. This was fortunate. The Bengal government was still
convinced that its methods were the only sound methods of
managing the land revenues and was bent upon establishing them
in every region under its authority. But for the conversion of the
directors, the influence of the Cornwallis system would have been
much more extensive and injurious than was actually the case.

In Madras early revenue management had followed much the
same methods as in Bengal. The company's servants knew little
of the languages of the people or of their customs. Farming the
revenues had appeared the easiest and best course to follow. In
the Northern Circars, for instance, where the company had
exercised control since 1767, the councils at Masulipatam and
Vizagapatam had let out the farms, sometimes to local chiefs,
sometimes to prominent Indian merchants, as ignorantly as had
been done in Bengal. A committee of circuit had been appointed,
as under Warren Hastings, to gather information; but, though it
succeeded in its task far better than its Bengal counterpart, its
reports had led to no change of management. Nor had any steps
been taken to set up an adequate system of justice. That function
had been confided to the renters and zamindars of the region.
Even in the area surrounding Madras itself, which had been
bestowed on the company as a *jāgīr* by the nawab Muhammad
'Alī, the revenues had been rented out either to the nawab himself
or to one of his nominees.

In southern India as a whole conditions varied greatly. In some
regions, such as the hilly portions of the Northern Circars, the
southern hills of Tinnevelly and Madura, or the hilly region lying
due west of Madras, hereditary chiefs existed who had been wont
to pay such tribute as the nawab's power permitted him to exact

from them. Elsewhere no hereditary middlemen intervened between the government and the cultivators. The nawab appointed *faujdars*, or commandants, and *tahsildars* or collectors, to manage the affairs of the state. The first were military officers intended to support the authority of the tahsildars and compel a reluctant people to pay what was demanded of them. The lands were classified as wet and dry, according as they had or had not a perennial supply of water from one of the numerous tanks which constituted the main source of irrigation. The wet lands, which grew rice, were assessed at a proportion of the crop; and the officials insisted on selling the state-share in the markets before the ryots were allowed to dispose of any of their own grain. The dry lands, and garden lands where betel or tobacco was grown, were assessed at a money-rate, which was based on the amount which could be extracted from the ryot in a good year. Here, as in other parts of India, the authority of the state had fallen so low as no longer to command the voluntary payment of the taxes. The realisation of the revenues was always a matter of violence. The ryots of a group of villages would be gathered together; they would declare their complete inability to pay what was demanded of them: they would then be beaten, or stood in the burning sun with a heavy stone weighing down their heads, until they reluctantly produced the coins which they had brought with them. It was a point of honour never to pay on demand, and he was reckoned a leader among them who endured longer than his fellows. In most of the villages there was a headman, nominated by the government from among the members of a particular family, who was held responsible for the maintenance of cultivation and public order in his village. In some districts, however, especially in Tanjore and the Arcot country, there was a superior class known by the Persian term *mirāsdars*, claiming exclusive rights over the waste-lands of the village and often entitled to a share of the produce of the lands occupied by others than themselves. In most parts of the country, however, individual families owned specific plots of land, over which no other possessed rights apart from the demands of the state and the customary shares of the crops due to the village temple and the village craftsmen.

Towards the close of the century the financial distress of the nawab introduced great confusion into a country already disorganised. Numberless pensions were granted to individuals as the reward of their services; these pensions took the form of an assignment of the land revenues of a certain area. Creditors were given assignments of the revenues over large districts as security for their debts; and where this was done, the whole administration of the district passed into their hands. Village officials and persons in favour with the higher officers of government saw to it that their own lands were lightly assessed, and that the deficit was made up by imposing heavier burdens on the lands of less fortunate men. Under the name of *moturfa* a great variety of impositions was established, of ever varying amount, levied on artisans and other persons believed able to pay even the smallest sums. In these ways the task confronting the company's servants was more difficult than in Bengal, because the old system had fallen into a state of greater confusion. But as against this must be set the fact that no established class of middle-men had come into being, except in certain limited areas, and that, as soon as the company's servants began to assume the responsibilities corresponding with their power, they would find no concerted opposition to their enquiries and no great difficulty in reaching direct contact with the cultivators themselves. This difference, fundamentally a difference between the landed tenures of south India and those of Bengal, implied different methods and a different attitude of administration.

In 1786, under instructions which the company issued after Pitt had passed his India Act, a board of revenue was established at Madras. It consisted of three company's servants under the presidency of a member of the council. Much needed reforms were introduced by this new authority. In 1794 the old chiefs and councils in the Northern Circars and elsewhere were abolished and their administrative duties were given to collectors. But at this time the centre of interest lies outside the old possessions of the company. In 1793 Tipu Sultān had been compelled to cede to the English the districts known as the Bārāmahal, which now form the districts of Salem and Coimbatore. Cornwallis had taken a close personal interest in forming the administration of the new acquisitions. He had himself chosen the men to whom the charge was to be confided. Deeming that familiarity with the languages of the people formed an indispensable qualification, he had ruled out all the covenanted servants of sufficient standing not otherwise employed: and at last he had selected Alexander Read, a lieutenant-colonel of the Madras army, to serve as the head of the administration. Read was a man of great talent. He was entirely honest. He had no skill in expressing his ideas upon paper, but his ideas themselves were clear, vigorous, and sound. He was convinced that knowledge formed the foundation of all good administration, and set to work, with his assistants, to acquire it. Among the latter was another officer of the Madras army, Thomas Munro, equally honest and hard-working, but possessed of an imagination and the gift of clear and forcible expression which Read lacked. These two men laid the foundations of the Madras revenue system in accordance with the custom of the country. They resolved to get rid of the traditional English method of employing renters of the revenue and to manage it directly. That meant the formation of a multitude of assessments on small patches of land, and therefore a revenue survey was the first condition. This step, the lack of which had vitiated all the revenue work in Bengal, was undertaken and carried out. It was found that much cultivation had been concealed by fraudulent exclusion from the revenue accounts. Adopting the rate of assessment current under Tipu's government, half the gross produce, they succeeded in drawing from the districts about the same amount as had been drawn in Tipu's time to cover both the demand of the state and the defalcations of individuals. This demand was, however, heavier than could be paid in any but a good season. Like other early settlements, Read's in the Bārāmahal was heavier than the country could bear. But Read's method of careful and persistent enquiry carried with it the seeds of improvement. Munro in particular came to form a theory of the system which would be appropriate to the country in general. He thought that the revenue should be permanently fixed on each holding, that the ryot should be left free to cultivate his customary fields as he chose, and even to take more if any fell vacant, and that the traditional practices of compelling the ryot to cultivate a certain area and of making additional assessments to cover failure on the part of any cultivators should be abandoned. Later experience in Canara and the Deccan confirmed him in his opinions.

The governor-general and council, however, had long been pressing Madras to introduce the system which had already been introduced into Bengal. In 1798 formal orders were sent down to do this without further delay. A permanent zamindari settlement was therefore begun. This was easy in those parts of the country where a zamindari class existed. The zamindars of the Northern Circars and the poligars, as they were called in the other districts, were invested with the same rights as had been bestowed in Bengal. In many cases the settlement was based, not on any calculation of what the estates could reasonably pay, but on a commutation of the zamindars' obligation of maintaining military forces to keep the public peace. But where no zamindars existed, they had to be created. Villages were grouped together, and the right of collecting the revenues was put up for sale. At the same time attempts were made to introduce the Bengal system of justice. Zillah judges were appointed, invested with the control of the police, and the collectors were for the moment reduced to the same position as they occupied in Bengal. Since in 1802 the territories of the nawab of the Carnatic were annexed, the area over which these revolutionary changes were enforced was very extensive.

Save where zamindars existed already, the Madras permanent settlement did not last long. The *muttahdars*, as the new zamindars were called, soon found their position untenable and the revenue demands higher than could be met. They abandoned their rights, and a new plan had to be devised. In 1808–9 an experiment was made of leasing out villages either to the *mirāsdars* or to the village headmen. These at first were to be made for a term of three years and, when that had expired, a further term of ten years was ordered. These village leases, however, also failed. The revenue demand was too high, the village officials abused their position, the collectors and their staffs lost touch with village conditions. In 1812 the Madras government was required by the company, under Munro's influence, to abandon the Bengal system, to re-introduce the ryotwari settlement, as the assessment of small individual holdings was called, and to reduce the authority of the zillah judges. Munro himself was sent back to Madras as a special commissioner to carry these orders into effect.

In 1816 a series of regulations was passed into law establishing these changes. The collector became a magistrate and recovered the control of the district police. A considerable number of subordinate Indian judges, under the title of district *munsiffs*, was appointed: and the village headmen were empowered to try petty suits, and, at the request of the parties, to constitute boards of arbitrators, known as *panchayats*, to determine causes of whatever amount. This attempt to revive the traditional mode of settling differences failed completely, mainly, it would seem, because of the popularity enjoyed by the district *munsiffs*. In 1818 the Board of Revenue ordered the re-introduction of the ryotwari system.

Thus the attempt to extend the Cornwallis system to Madras failed completely. In fact what was destined to become the characteristic mode of district administration developed, not in Bengal, but in Madras. There the collector emerges for the first time invested with a detailed control of the land revenue, possessed of an extensive revenue staff, spending much of his time touring through the villages of his district investigating conditions and hearing complaints, responsible for the public peace, but leaving to the district judge the determination of civil disputes and the punishment of serious crime. He was neither the unquestioned autocrat nor the unimportant tax-gatherer who had alternately appeared in Bengal. But he was the local representative of the government; it was his business to know all that could be known about his district; on his annual settlement of the land revenue depended the well-being of every villager; on his activity depended the execution of the wishes of government. Many of the men who filled this position in such a manner that their names are still remembered in their districts, would have cut but a poor figure in a competitive examination. They knew the vernacular in no scholarly way. But they could converse familiarly with the ryot about the matters which most nearly touched his interests and did not live in the isolation of a Bengal cutchery. The courts did not rank so high as in Bengal. It was characteristic that the designation of the Madras collector was "collector and magistrate" whereas, even when Bentinck had to some extent brought the Bengal system into line with the practice of the subordinate presidency, the Bengal collector was a "magistrate and collector". In short, under the influence of Munro the English at Madras wisely abandoned the attempt to subordinate the position of the executive official to that of the judge. The Madras system was in fact a middle way between the old Indian plan of making the executive official the sole agent of government, and the English plan of subordinating all to law and law-court.

CHAPTER VII

The North-Western Approaches to India

From the beginning of the sixteenth to the end of the eighteenth century, the nations of Europe had sought to approach India from the south-west, by way of the Cape of Good Hope. The conclusion of the Napoleonic wars had left Great Britain in firm occupation of that route. Rivals began therefore to seek out some alternative way of reaching the great dependency which had been built up under the protection of the British navy. Indications of the coming change had already been given. Napoleon's invasion of Egypt, and still more the plans which had been formed both by him and by Russia for military expeditions after the manner of Alexander the Great, showed how European policy was moving. Accordingly the nineteenth century was marked by the development of new approaches by the north-west; and the intermediate regions, Persia, 'Irak, Egypt, and the tangle of mountains on the frontier of India itself, acquired a new and dominant influence on the foreign policy of the Anglo-Indian government. These regions included three possibly vital areas. The farthest away was Egypt, commanding the neck of land which parted the Mediterranean from the Red Sea; then came 'Irak, through which, if the upper reaches of the Euphrates could be attained, an enemy could drop down the river to the head of the Persian Gulf; and nearest of all was Afghanistan, the age-long key to India, from which an enemy, neglecting Suez and Basra, could attack the Panjab and thence spread over the valley of the Ganges. These possibilities complicated the problem of Indian defence, and destroyed the all-sufficiency of maritime power, although through the Red Sea and the Persian Gulf the water-ways bit so deeply into the land.

With those water-ways the vessels of the Presidency of Bombay had been long familiar. It had been obliged, for the protection of its local trade from Marātha pirates, to build a fleet organised for police and war under the name of the Bombay Marine. Its shipping was mostly built at Bombay itself, and when, in 1759, Surat was taken by the forces of the company, the latter became admiral of the Mughal empire and undertook the duty of con-

voying Indian vessels plying to the ports of the Red Sea and
Persian Gulf. For the next seventy years the officer appointed to
act as deputy for the company flew the company's colours at the
peak but the Mughal flag at the main. The duties of convoy
brought this force into conflict with the pirate tribes of the Persian
Gulf and Red Sea, and a number of officers were employed in
surveying and charting the coasts. The alarm created by the French
occupation of Egypt suggested the expediency of blocking up the
Red Sea. An attempt had been made to occupy Perim, and, when
that was defeated by lack of water, the English had been welcomed
at Aden by the sultan, with whom the naval commander made a
treaty in 1802. In the early years of the nineteenth century various
expeditions were directed into the Persian Gulf. Alliances were
made with some of the chiefs, notably the *imām* of Maskat, and in
1819, after the pirate stronghold of Rās-ul-khāima had been
captured, the principal maritime tribes had been compelled to
enter into a league with the company, renouncing both piracy and
the slave-trade. For the second time in history, fleets directed
from India were controlling Arabian waters.

In both cases the motives were the same. The Portuguese and
the English alike were interested in maintaining peace and order
on the great trade-routes; both were concerned to guard their
position against possible attack by Mediterranean powers. The
developments of the nineteenth century were to render these
regions more critical than ever. Two causes in particular contributed to this result. One was the rising power of Muhammad
'Alī in Egypt, the expansion of his authority, first into Arabia and
then into Syria, and the likelihood of his establishing his rule over
all the coasts of the Red Sea and the Persian Gulf. The other was
the invention of the marine steam-engine, which made the
navigation of the Red Sea possible at all seasons of the year instead of being narrowly limited by periodic winds as in the past.
The ocean-sailing ship had brought India into effective contact
with Europe; the development of the fire-arm had subjected India
to European domination; the development of steam-power,
abolishing the slow travel of the past, and destined ultimately to
unify India, at the moment was to transfer the control of India
from Calcutta to London and interlock the external policy of
India and England.

The first effect of these changes was to revive projects for

opening a trade-route to Europe by way of Suez. Earlier attempts
had been frustrated by the confusion which had reigned in Egypt
in the eighteenth century. But now that it was clear that letters,
if not goods, could be conveyed much more safely and rapidly by
Suez than by the Cape of Good Hope, merchants set actively to
work. Committees were formed at the presidency towns and in
London. Bombay took the lead in a matter in which it was
vitally interested, and the government of Bombay, under Elphinstone and Malcolm, proved by experiment that the route from
Bombay to Suez could be used at all seasons of the year, even by
the feeble steam-ships of the period. Muhammad 'Alī was eager
to co-operate in a movement which promised him wealth and
influence. Under the pressure of public opinion, the English
government and the East India Company organised a system of
monthly steamers between England and Alexandria on the western
section of the route, and between Suez and Bombay on the
eastern section. In 1837 the sultan of Aden was unwise enough to
seize and plunder the cargo of a Madras-owned vessel which was
wrecked off that port. The steam-ships of those days could not
carry coal enough for prolonged voyages, and Aden was by
nature marked out as the ideal coaling-station on the eastern run,
apart from its strategic value as commanding the entrance to the
Red Sea. The company's government demanded reparation; the
sultan promised and then retracted; in January, 1839, therefore,
Aden was captured by the Bombay marine and military forces.
The treaties with the tribes of the Persian Gulf together with the
occupation of Aden gave the company's government control of
the two avenues of approach towards India from the north-west
by way of the sea.

Similar, if less successful, activity had been displayed along the
continental approach to India. The alliance of Persia had been
sought and obtained. But it was still important to learn the
geographical conditions, the routes, their passibility for wheeled
traffic, the supplies of water and provisions, the things which
would hinder or facilitate military movements through this north-
west zone. In 1809 and 1810 three officers, Grant, Pottinger, and
Christie, explored the ways through the Makrān and Balūchistan
into Persia, and Christie was the first Englishman to visit Herat
and call attention to its military importance. Only a little later
Moorcroft crossed the Himālāyas and visited Ladākh. Thence he

penetrated to Bukhāra, and was seeking to return by Herat when he died of disease. In 1830 Arthur Conolly, setting out from Tabriz, attempted to reach the khanate of Khiva in the hopes of learning its military strength. He was captured and held to ransom. He then passed back into India by way of Kandahār, where for a while he had to lie in hiding, amusing himself by hunting hyenas with the boys of the village where he found refuge. In 1832 Alexander Burnes, with the approval of the governor-general and the financial support of the government, set out in the reverse direction, from India to Kābul and Bukhāra. His purpose was two-fold, to survey the possible routes of an advance towards India and to test possible friendships which the British might form in that region. He concluded that Herat, being covered on the north by extensive deserts, was not likely to be attacked save from the side of Persia, but that any movement on India would be likely to follow more than one road, and to the eastwards he indicated the possibility of an advance by way of Chitral and Kashmīr. He hoped that the states on the Oxus might be brought into political and commercial relations with British India and that an alliance might be formed with Dost Muhammad, the ruler of Kābul. In 1836 he was sent back to Kābul as commercial agent.

To some extent adventure had been the motive of these explorations. But adventure had been reinforced by political aims. The projects of Napoleon and Paul had directed attention to Central Asia, and the development of Russian policy in Persia had invested the matter with a more pressing interest. The decay of Turkish power in the eighteenth century had laid Persia open to Russian aggression; and, as soon as Russian power was well established in the Caucasus, Russian forces began to press southwards. The Persians had attempted to persuade the French to come to their help. In 1807 Napoleon by the Treaty of Finkenstein had guaranteed the integrity of Persia and had sent a military mission to Teherān. But immediately afterwards he had made peace with Russia and refused even to act as a mediator on behalf of the shah. The Persians had then hoped to get help from England. After long negotiations the Treaty of Teherān was signed, by which protection was promised in case Persia were attacked by any external power. In accordance with this arrangement a body of officers of the company's armies was lent to re-organise the military forces of Persia. This treaty had been negotiated by a representative not of the company but of the crown, so that it was clear that the policy of Wellesley and Minto of covering the routes to India by an alliance with Persia was supported by London as well as by Calcutta. It seems, however, that the policy had been adopted without counting the cost. The only power likely to attack Persia was Russia. Was England prepared to go to war with Russia for the protection of the shah? Was she prepared to send into Persia such a force as would enable Persia to meet her invaders on equal terms? These questions either had never been considered or must have been answered in the negative. It is true that the Treaty of Teherān gave a loop-hole by which actual war might be avoided. In the first place the obligation did not arise except in the case of foreign aggression. It would not be difficult to jockey the shah into military movements constituting Persian aggression. And even if the aggression came unquestionably from the other side, England still had the choice of giving military or mere financial assistance. For some years nothing happened. But in 1826 the Russians and Persians went to war again. The shah, Fath 'Alī, began the attack on the sound principle that aggression is the best form of defence. But Canning, who was at the time secretary of state for foreign affairs, and much engrossed with questions arising out of the Greek war, was not prepared to sacrifice the success of his policy in Europe by supporting the shah in circumstances in which no formal treaty obligation had arisen. He therefore compounded with the shah by giving him a moderate subsidy. The Persians were defeated. In 1828 they were reduced to making more territorial cessions by the Treaty of Turkomanchai, and concluded that their interests would best be served by cultivating the friendship of the Russian emperor.

The establishment of Russian influence at Teherān was followed by disquieting events. The Russians encouraged the Persians to seek expansion eastwards. The advice jumped with the shah's inclinations, while it promised to Russia the extension of her own influence through that of her client. In 1831 an expedition against Khiva was planned. In 1832 Khurāsān was overrun. Next year an expedition against Herat was only interrupted by the death of the shah's heir. In 1834 the shah himself died and was succeeded by his grandson, Muhammad, who leant heavily on his Russian advisers. He projected not only the renewal of the expedition against Herat but also the capture of Kandahār. In 1837, in spite of strong representations made by the British envoy at Teherān, the shah laid siege to Herat. Persia under Russian control was seeking to recover the provinces which had formed the empire of Nādir Shāh and from which he had sallied out to conquer Delhi.

While Persia was pushing out towards long-lost frontiers, not in her own strength, which was small, but in reliance on Russian power, which was great, the position in Afghanistan was most uncertain. After the murder of Nādir Shāh in 1747, Ahmad Shāh Durāni had built up a strong power stretching northwards to the Oxus, westwards to Persia, eastwards to the Sutlej and the Indus. Under his son Tīmūr Shāh, who reigned from 1773 to 1793, the state began to decay. Ten years later it fell into the hands of Shāh Shujāʿ, a thoroughly incapable prince, who was driven out in 1809, and, after some years' wandering, found refuge under British authority at Ludhiāna. In Afghanistan itself prolonged civil wars followed, first between princes of the reigning Sadozai family, then between them and a new family, the Barakzais, and then among the Barakzais themselves. The upshot of these conflicts was that the Sadozais, represented in 1830 by a prince named Kāmrān, retained Herat; while the triumphant Barakzai, Dost Muhammad, established himself as amir of Kābul. The Indian provinces had been completely lost. Sind, never very closely attached to the Durāni empire, had become virtually independent under the amirs of the Tālpura family. In the Panjab had arisen the power of Ranjit Singh and his Sikhs, who had taken advantage of the civil wars in Afghanistan not only to establish their own independence but also to conquer from the Afghans Kashmīr and Peshāwar. In these circumstances Dost Muhammad was uncertain which way to turn. In 1834 Shāh Shujāʿ, with the countenance of both Ranjit Singh and of the English, had made an unsuccessful attempt to recover his vanished kingdom. In the hope of obtaining aid from one quarter or another, Dost Muhammad made overtures to the Persians, to Russia, and to the English.

In 1835 Lord Auckland had been appointed governor-general in succession to Lord William Bentinck, and assumed his office on March 4, 1836. The views of the British cabinet, in which Palmerston had charge of foreign affairs, were inspired by the desire of checking the progress which Russia had made in the regions bordering on India. In 1836 Palmerston appointed McNeill, a prominent Russophobe, minister to the shah; in the same year instructions were addressed to Auckland, pointing out the need of securing the north-west frontier and of counteracting "the progress of Russian influence in a quarter, which, from its proximity to our Indian possessions, could not fail, if it were once established, to act injuriously on the system of our Indian alliances, and possibly to interfere even with the tranquillity of our own territory". He was given entire discretion to select his mode of action, as soon as he should be convinced "that the time has arrived at which it would be right for you to interfere decidedly in the affairs of Afghanistan".

Auckland's position was most embarrassing. He was separated from the area in which he was to act by the interposition of independent though allied states; and the treaties did not contemplate the use of the territories of Sind or of the Panjab either as a base for war or even for the passage of armies. Worse than this was the irreconcilable hostility of Sikh and Afghan. They were divided by religion, by a long course of merciless war, by an obstinate determination on the one side to retain, and on the other to recover, the spoils of conquest, especially Peshāwar and its dependencies. Burnes, at Kābul as commercial agent, soon found himself involved in political discussions. Dost Muhammad leant towards a British alliance. He had written to St Petersburg, and, in December, 1837, Vitkevitch, a Russian agent, was sent in answer. But the amir still would have chosen the British side could he but have obtained from them the terms on which he had set his heart. One was not a matter over which Auckland would have hesitated for a moment. It was a promise of protection from any attacks by Persia. But the other was the transfer of Peshāwar to Afghanistan. This would have involved the abandonment of the long-standing alliance with Ranjit Singh. That prince was already stricken in years and could not be expected much longer to rule at Lahore. It was not unlikely that on his death much confusion would arise, for it was clear that he had no son, genuine or supposed, able to carry on his work. War with the Sikhs in that contingency was not improbable, and then the alliance of Dost Muhammad would be most valuable. But, as things stood, nothing could more contribute to such a war than a formal alliance with the ruler of Kābul; and, were the surrender of

Peshāwar to be one of the terms of the alliance, nothing could be more certain to bring that war about. Auckland had therefore to choose between alienating the Sikhs or the Afghans, between abandoning an old, sensible, and honest ally of the company, and throwing Dost Muhammad into the arms of Russia. The first would mean war on the Sutlej; the second would mean either the tolerance of Russian influence at Kābul or the removal by force of arms of a ruler with whom the English had no quarrel save that he would not ally himself with them on their own terms.

Auckland judged that the arrival of the Russian envoy at Kābul had created the situation in which interference in Afghanistan had become necessary; and that a vigorous attempt to remove Dost Muhammad from his throne was a lesser evil than to antagonise Ranjit Singh. He still acted with great deliberation. In May, 1838, he sent his foreign secretary, Macnaghten, to frame an arrangement with Ranjit Singh. The outcome of this was the Tripartite Treaty which was signed on June 26. This treaty seems to have gone farther than Auckland had intended. He had meant to revive the projects of 1834 for the re-establishment of Shāh Shujā' at Kābul without doing more than making a military demonstration, or alternatively to promote hostilities between Ranjit Singh and Dost Muhammad. Ranjit, however, was not willing to attack Afghanistan without much more than the passive support of the English. Finally a joint attack was decided on in the name of the old shah. Then, when detailed arrangements for the actual operations began to be made, it became clear that if anything effectual was to be done the English would have to take the lead. Orders were issued for the assemblage of a great army to invade Afghanistan by way of the Bolān Pass and to establish Shāh Shujā' as ruler of Kābul and Kandahār. Thus Auckland had gradually drifted into a far more extensive action than he had contemplated. His excuse was that the establishment of a friendly prince at Kābul, the assurance of peace with the Panjab, and the creation of a controlling influence in Sind were worth the risks which he knew he was running.

In October, 1838, it became known that the Persians had given up the siege of Herat. By some Auckland has been criticised for not having then abandoned his projected attack on Dost Muhammad. But that criticism seems to overlook the fact that Auckland and Dost Muhammad had been unable to agree on terms of alliance and that the Afghan ruler was thought to have committed himself to friendship with Russia. Auckland therefore made no change in his plans beyond reducing the force with which he proposed to invade Afghanistan. The Army of the Indus, as it was called, was to march through Sind, the Bombay and Bengal detachments assembling at Bukkar, where the river was to be crossed. The amirs of Sind had in the first instance to be coerced into permitting the passage of the company's troops through their territory. When that had been done, the army moved onward, and, after a march of great hardship, it entered Kandahār in April, 1839. Shāh Shujā' was at once proclaimed. A move was then made against Kābul. On the way Ghaznī was stormed by a brilliant feat of arms. On August 2 Dost Muhammad, who had marched out to defend his capital, finding his army unwilling to fight, was compelled to flee. He took refuge first in Bāmiān and later in Bukhāra, where the amir shut him up in prison. Shāh Shujā' made a triumphant entry into Kābul, and was installed once more in the Bālā Hissār, the "high fortress", overlooking the city. At this moment it looked as if Auckland's policy had completely succeeded. In reward he was made an earl, the commander, Sir John Keane, was made a baron, and Macnaghten, who was in political control, was made a baronet and a little later named governor of Bombay, an office which he did not live to hold.

The success, however, was entirely superficial. Shāh Shujā' was as incompetent as ever. His own troops were worthless. His ministers were untrustworthy. It was soon clear that he would only remain at Kābul as long as the English kept him there. On Macnaghten devolved the task of settling the administration of the country. He was a good Persian scholar, and a man of quick wit, but he was incurably optimistic, of uncertain judgment and small administrative knowledge. The first need was to provide the shah with a regular revenue. This provoked the liveliest opposition. The tribes did not greatly care who called himself amir of Kābul so long as he did not attempt to levy taxes on them. Sporadic troubles occurred all over the country, and a number of chiefs were only kept quiet by receiving monthly allowances which for the time being had to be paid by the Government of India. Before long Auckland found the establishment of Shāh Shujā' was going to cost much more than he had reckoned.

Moreover external troubles multiplied. News came that the Russians had sent out a great expedition to attack Khiva. The expedition failed, but the alarm which the news caused spread far and wide. Worse than this, Ranjit Singh died, and no reliance could be placed on Nau Nihāl Singh, who had succeeded him. Then Dost Muhammad escaped from his prison at Bukhāra, and appeared in Afghan territory at the head of numerous followers, including troops who had been raised in the name of Shāh Shujā'. The ex-amir was indeed defeated in September, 1840, and in the following November surrendered himself to Macnaghten. But this success was followed within a year by overwhelming disaster.

In 1841 the company, shocked at the cost of occupying Afghanistan, ordered economies to be introduced. The military force was therefore lessened, and the stipends which had been paid to some of the chiefs were cut off. Local discontent spread as acquiescence became less profitable and the means of punishing disturbances weakened. In the latter part of the year few districts remained quiet. At Kābul itself was a brigade consisting of one queen's regiment of foot, three of sepoys, with a proportion of cavalry and artillery, in all 4500 combatants and 12,000 camp-followers. It was commanded by a queen's officer, Elphinstone, of undoubted personal bravery, but old, inactive, and sick. The brigade was quartered in cantonments outside the city, while the stores were in the city itself and the cantonments were untenable against any serious attack. On November 2 a riot broke out in the city. Alexander Burnes, who had been nominated to succeed Macnaghten as soon as the latter should go down to take up his government at Bombay, was murdered, with his brother Charles and another English officer, in the house which they occupied. The shah's treasury, which was in the city instead of in the Bālā Hissār, was plundered. Shāh Shujā' sent one of his regiments to suppress the tumult, but it did nothing, and Macnaghten and Elphinstone did nothing either. At first they seem to have thought the matter a mere riot of no importance. The next day a feeble attempt was made to suppress the movement, but failed. The city at once passed altogether out of control, and the tribesmen rapidly gathered. Dost Muhammad's son, Muhammad Akbar Khān, soon arrived to take the lead.

Elphinstone's position had been difficult. He had had to choose between suppressing the riot with severity, in which case partisan historians would doubtless have held him up to execration, and leaving the shah to deal with his tumultuous subjects. In view of the disturbed state of the country, and the indefensible nature of the cantonments, he ought certainly to have chosen the method of severity. But the responsibility does not rest with him alone. Throughout the expedition control had sedulously been kept in the hands of the civil authorities and exercised through the political officers with Macnaghten at their head. This arrangement recalled the unfortunate campaign against Hyder 'Alī in 1767, or that still worse campaign against the Marāthas in 1779, when the councils of Madras and Bombay had so distrusted the conduct of their military officers that they had saddled them with a committee. In Afghanistan the political department had enjoyed exclusive control. Its local representatives had decided when, and where, and how many troops should be employed. Generals had been placed under the orders of lieutenants invested with superiority by employment in the foreign department. This measure had been taken under colour of maintaining the supremacy of the civil government. But Auckland and Macnaghten had forgotten that their supremacy should not be pressed too far in matters of war, that the position in Afghanistan remained fundamentally a military position, and that the first need was to maintain the military control of the occupied country. Difficulties had perpetually arisen in consequence of the interference of the political officers in the disposition and conduct of troops. The military officer commanding at Kābul would have been, not merely a strong man, but an insubordinate one, had he insisted that the military measures necessary for the safety of his troops should be taken in defiance of the opinion of Macnaghten.

A fortnight elapsed, while Macnaghten gave money to some and promised it to others, in the vain hope of buying back the security which had been established only by force of arms. The cantonments were surrounded and attacked, and the measures taken in their defence were feeble and never more than partly successful. A proposal was made that the brigade should retire into the Bālā Hissār, which could at least have been defended against any Afghan attack; but Macnaghten, supported by the second-in-command, rejected the proposal. When the troops, disheartened by the evident incompetence of their leaders, showed themselves reluctant to go into action, it was resolved to negotiate. Akbar Khān, who had assumed the leadership on behalf of his father, a prisoner in India, was not unwilling to come to terms, and on December 11 he and Macnaghten agreed that the English were to evacuate the country, that Shāh Shujā' might go with them or remain as he chose, and that, as soon as the English reached Peshāwar, Dost Muhammad was to be permitted to return. At this time the roads were still clear, and, if the English were going to march, they should have done so at once before the snow began to fall. But Macnaghten still delayed. He seems to have hoped by bribery to divide the chiefs and re-establish the English position. Renewed conferences were held. On the 23rd he with one of his companions was murdered by Akbar Khān and the remainder of the party became prisoners.

On this event the demands of the Afghans redoubled. The treasure, the guns, the ammunition, of the brigade were to be handed over. Elphinstone was ready to agree to almost anything. On January 1, 1842, a fresh capitulation was made. The troops were to march down to Peshāwar under the escort of a body of Afghans. On the 6th, finding that the escort did not appear, the soldiers, completely demoralised by the incapacity of their leaders, insisted on setting out. The cold was intense. The Afghans hung upon their flanks, and followed up their rear. After a while the enemy began to fire down upon them from the hills. Frozen, starved, and hopeless, the brigade soon lost every vestige of military order. In the first two days' march it covered only ten miles. The attacks became closer and more persistent. In the long Khurd-Kābul Pass, running for five miles between high hills, 3000 men are said to have been killed with scarce an effort at resistance. The wives of the officers were given up to Akbar Khān as the sole means of saving their lives. Elphinstone concluded his active service by surrendering himself. At Jagdallak a barrier lay across the road. Of the few who passed it some reached Gandammak. Six arrived living at Fathābād. One man alone, the surgeon Dr Brydon, escaped to Jalālābād. This needless massacre of brave men with weapons in their hands was the greatest catastrophe that ever befell the forces of the East India Company. A whole European regiment was destroyed. But what was far worse, the sepoys and the camp-followers whose lives were thrown away bequeathed to their brothers-in-arms a distrust of the leadership which till then had been marked by conspicuous and almost unbroken success. The Sikh soldiers at Lahore began to say that if the Afghans could slaughter English armies like a flock of sheep, the time was coming when the army of the Khalsa might march down to Delhi and sack it as Nādir Shāh had done. Elphinstone's military incapacity, Macnaghten's political blindness, Auckland's foolish deference to London opinion and inability to choose able men to execute his policy, had contributed much to bring nearer the Sikh wars and the incomparable disaster of the Indian Mutiny.

The destruction of the Kābul brigade had not exterminated the British forces in Afghanistan. At the time of the Kābul outbreak Sale had been engaged in withdrawing from Afghanistan a brigade which Auckland had supposed to be no longer needed there. Sale, thinking himself unable with any prospects of success to attempt to march back to Kābul, had thrown himself into Jalālābād, and had prepared to hold that place until reinforcements should arrive from India. In January a message was received from Kābul ordering Sale to evacuate it. Sale refused. On the 13th the solitary survivor of the massacre arrived. For some eight weeks the town was besieged by Afghan tribesmen. For a moment, in February, its abandonment was considered. But this idea was put aside mainly owing to the determination of Havelock. On the 19th the walls were severely shaken by earthquake: but they were repaired, and on March 11 a sortie drove the Afghans away. Besides Sale's force, a small garrison had held Ghaznī, while Nott with a brigade was at Kandahār. The Ghaznī detachment surrendered and was massacred. Nott was strong enough and resolute enough to hold his ground. But the future evidently depended on the policy of the governor-general.

Auckland belonged to that large class of men who are easily elated by success and pass swiftly from confidence to despair with the first change of fortune. The terrible news from Kābul inspired him with a frantic desire to get out of Afghanistan at the earliest possible moment. He issued a spirited proclamation; but neither courage nor decision lay behind his brave words. Half-hearted attempts, inspired principally by Clerk, the political agent at Peshāwar, and other local officials, were made to rescue the beleaguered garrisons. One force attempted to move by way of the Khaibar, but for lack of transport had to fall back on Jamrūd;

another attempted to reach Kandahār by the Bolān Pass, but fell back with much loss of reputation on Quetta. On February 28 Auckland was at last relieved of a task far exceeding his capacity by the arrival of a new governor-general.

Towards the close of 1841 a change of government had taken place. The Whigs' long tenure of office came to an end and Sir Robert Peel became prime minister. Lord Ellenborough, who had already served at the Board of Control, at first was re-appointed to that office; but shortly afterwards he had been offered the government of India. His virtues and failings were almost the exact opposite of Auckland's. Auckland was always ready to carry out his party's policy; Ellenborough insisted on determining his own. Auckland was a man of sober mind, never rising above mediocrity; Ellenborough was capable of deep insight and puerile extravagance. Auckland was slow, timid, irresolute; Ellenborough was hasty, rash, and obstinate. Auckland's charming manners made official business with him pleasant; Ellenborough was overbearing and lacked the art of managing men. Only two of Auckland's predecessors would ever have brought the national interests in the east to such a pass; Ellenborough was the very man for a situation demanding instant decision and resolute action. The change produced by his determined control of affairs soon became apparent. Preparations for the relief of the British garrisons in Afghanistan were pushed on with vigour. Pollock, with adequate transport and artillery, forced the Khaibar and marched on Jalālābād; and a concerted movement of the forces at Kandahār and at Quetta enabled the latter to march through the Khojak Pass. These successes induced Ellenborough to modify the views which at first he had entertained. On his arrival he had decided that the first necessity was to withdraw the troops from Afghanistan. In this he was overruling the advice of the foreign department, which was pressing for the re-occupation of the country. But he had from the first seen that a considerable latitude must be left to the local commanders in the execution of his orders. He was very much afraid that he might suddenly find himself on the verge of war with the Sikhs, and therefore was resolved against any prolonged operations in Afghanistan. But he also felt that anything which would make the Sikhs think twice before attacking the company would be of great political advantage. If such a defeat could be inflicted on the

Afghans as would make the withdrawal from their country appear a voluntary action, the Sikhs would probably feel less bellicose. Ellenborough therefore issued to Nott and Pollock discretional instructions, permitting them, if they thought it expedient, to join hands at Kābul and return together by way of the Khaibar.

This decision has been grossly misrepresented. Kaye, the leading historian of the First Afghan War, describes the instructions to Nott as calculated to throw the responsibility for any misfortunes that might occur on him instead of on the governor-general. But Ellenborough was never guilty of shirking responsibility; and Wellington, than whom no man alive was more competent to judge, considered the orders wise, appropriate, and proper. Another point of Ellenborough's instructions was for political reasons made the butt of unending ridicule. He authorised Nott, if he should march by Ghaznī, to carry away with him the club hanging over the tomb of the great Mahmūd and the gates which were traditionally believed to have been stolen from the Temple of Somnāth. In this Ellenborough desired to strike the imagination of the people of India. House of Commons speakers made great fun of this idea. But though Ellenborough's language was pompous and on the whole ridiculous, the idea was not nearly so incongruous as Whig speakers pretended. The plan did not originate in the hot brain of the governor-general. It had first appeared in discussions of the terms on which Ranjit Singh had been willing to help Shāh Shujā' to recover Afghanistan. Ranjit is said to have demanded that the shah should pledge himself to deliver those very gates, and the shah is said to have refused on the ground that the Afghans would never forgive him for doing so. Ranjit was no sentimentalist; Shāh Shujā' was not likely to quarrel with a possible ally over a trifle. What Ranjit thought worth asking, and what Shāh Shujā' thought he could not grant, would form an undeniable trophy of success. For other reasons the project came to nothing. The club had been looted by some former conqueror; and the gates proved to be the work of mere local craftsmen, made to replace Mahmūd's mouldering spoils.

Apart from this, however, the Afghan War was concluded in accordance with Ellenborough's plans. Pollock and Nott advanced on Kābul from Jalālābād and Kandahār respectively.

Pollock met with considerable opposition; but at Tezin, near the Khurd-Kābul Pass, he drove Akbar Khān before him in headlong flight and on September 15 he entered Kābul. Two days later Nott arrived, having destroyed the fortifications of Ghaznī on the way. A relief party was sent out to rescue the prisoners who had fallen into Akbar's hands during Elphinstone's fatal march. The news of the reappearance of the English had filled the Afghan chiefs with dismay. The prisoners had already recovered their liberty, and met the rescue party on the day on which Nott appeared before Kābul. Troops sent out under McCaskill to disperse a hostile concentration in Kohistān found the enemy at Istalif and inflicted on them a severe defeat. In revenge for the rising at Kābul and the massacre which had followed, the Grand Bazaar was blown up, and on October 12 the English forces marched away, no one daring to hinder their going. They left as purely nominal ruler of Afghanistan one of Shāh Shujā''s sons. Shāh Shujā' himself had been murdered after the collapse of the English authority at Kābul.

The armies then withdrew through the Khaibar, destroying the fortifications of Jalālābād and 'Alī Masjid as they passed. In December they were met and welcomed at Fīrūzpūr, in British territory, by the governor-general and the army of reserve which he had prudently collected in case the Sikhs should attempt to take advantage of British embarrassments. The Afghan prisoners in India, including Dost Muhammad, were released, and Ellenborough declared himself ready to recognise any government accepted by the Afghans themselves and ready to live at peace with its neighbours. The result was the restoration of Dost Muhammad, probably the only man capable at the time of imposing himself on the Afghan tribes. In all his operations Ellenborough's chief object had been to re-establish the prestige of the company's arms, and to concentrate its forces once more before any Indian enemy could be tempted into an attack. Nothing more could wisely have been attempted, and Ellenborough certainly secured these purposes as far as was possible. But this foolish adventure into Afghanistan had weakened the company's position and lowered its reputation, both with other states and with its own sepoys. It was perhaps fortunate that the development of affairs in Europe and some experience of the difficulties of operations in Central Asia indisposed the Russians to continue the provocative policy

which had lured Palmerston and Auckland into their Afghan
adventure. In 1844, in the course of a visit which the emperor
Nicholas paid to Queen Victoria, an informal agreement was
reached relieving the English from anxiety regarding the immediate future of Central Asia. Afghanistan on the south bank of the
Oxus, and the khanates on the north of the river, became in effect
a neutral zone in which neither the English nor the Russians were
to undertake political operations. This understanding was maintained until the Near East once more provided the two empires
with a subject of quarrel, and the Crimean War brought the
informal agreement to an end. Then once more the Russians
sought to influence British policy in Europe by threatening the
security of British interests in Asia.

CHAPTER VIII

The Company's Last Conquests

From the death of Ranjit Singh in 1839 Indian politics had been dominated by the problem of the Sikhs. Until the early years of the nineteenth century the Sikhs had possessed no leader whom they were prepared to follow as a body since the time of Banda. They were ranged in groups called *misls*, under the hereditary leadership of certain families. From time to time these leaders had met together to concert a common policy, but their efforts at united action had seldom met with great success. They had submitted reluctantly to the supremacy of the Durāni empire, and the Panjab continued to be at least in name a province of the Afghan government. The Sikhs themselves were a formidable military body, but they disdained every kind of service except the cavalry. In 1791 Ranjit Singh had succeeded to the headship of the Sukarchakia *misl*, and in 1797 he had accepted the governor-ship of Lahore from Zamān Shāh. He had employed this position to extend his authority over the whole of the Panjab, and in 1806 he was seeking to bring the Cis-Sutlej Sikhs under his authority also. This project brought him, as has already been noted, into conflict with English policy, and the outcome was the Treaty of Friendship of 1809, by which he agreed to limit the troops main-tained by him on the east bank of the river to the number required for the maintenance of internal peace, and not to encroach upon the territories of the Sikh chiefs established there. He then turned his restless arms in other directions. In 1809–11 he was at war with the Gurkhas, taking from them the district of Kāngra. He then engaged in a constant war with his Afghan neighbours. At first he did not meet with great success. He failed to take Multān; he failed to occupy Kashmīr. But the domestic troubles of the Sadozais at last gave him his opportunity. In 1818 he captured Multān. In 1819 he conquered Kashmīr. In 1823 he annexed Peshāwar, which he had taken in 1818, though then he had not thought it wise to retain it in his own hands. These military successes were the fruit of the vigorous military policy which he pursued. The Sikh customs had been devised in order to make the

Sikhs good soldiers and to avoid the disadvantages imposed on Hindu troops by caste and other religious observances. Ranjit possessed therefore admirable material. But until his time Sikh fighters had been notably impatient of discipline and disdainful of all but their customary mode of fighting. They had despised the infantry and artillery, and had always refused to serve in them. But under the pressure which their ruler now placed upon them, and their trust in his ability, they came to enlist freely in all three arms. Ranjit Singh's army thus was homogeneous in a degree peculiar in Indian armies. Not that it was exclusively composed of Sikhs, for it included many Muslims and Hindus, but that in all three arms the Sikhs were predominant and gave the tone. Other Indian armies were far less united. In Sindhia's, for instance, the cavalry was Marātha; the infantry was mixed; the artillery was mainly Goanese. Nor was it only in composition that the Sikh army differed from the others. Ranjit Singh, like other Indian princes, was convinced of the superiority of European military methods. Like other Indian princes he employed Europeans to train his men. But unlike his fellows, he kept his European officers in strict subordination to his own authority. Under him no officers were to be found in the semi-independent position enjoyed by Raymond under the Nizām or by Perron under Sindhia. The Sikh army thus remained unbroken by sectional interests or by divided command. It was a national army in the sense in which the Marātha army under the early Pēshwās had been; and while the Marātha army had been positively weakened by the introduction of European instructors and methods of war, the Sikh army was strengthened.

Ranjit Singh had thus forged a weapon of great strength. But it was the only institution which he endowed with vigour enough to survive him. His government was a purely personal rule. His political advisers were his personal servants, whose wealth and position depended on his good will. No member of his durbar had any rights as against the mahārāja. The administration was conducted by his personal agents, in accordance with his personal instructions; and though they enjoyed much discretional authority, and were allowed a large measure of perquisites, they were inspired at best by personal devotion to their master, and at worst by personal ambition for themselves. The maintenance of such personal rule depends on the chance that one great man will be followed by another. Ranjit was succeeded by his son, Kharak Singh, an imbecile, with a reputed brother, Shīr Singh, who hoped to displace him; and a son, Nau Nihāl Singh, bold and vicious, who wished to succeed him. At the durbar the wazir, Dhiān Singh, and his brother, Gulāb Singh, known as the Jammū rajas, hated Kharak Singh because he preferred his favourite, Chet Singh, to them, and hated Nau Nihāl Singh because he was seeking to displace them. The two heads of the Sindhianwala family, Atar and Ajīt Singh, were the chief rivals of the Jammū brothers. None of these men seems to have been inspired by any higher motive than that of getting as much wealth and power for himself as he could. The inevitable consequence was a series of personal intrigues carried to murderous lengths. Chet Singh was killed a few months after Ranjit's death. In the next year Kharak Singh died. His son, returning from the funeral rites, was killed by the fall of a gateway through which he had to pass. No one knows whether this was accidental; but few Sikhs believed that it was. The Jammū brothers had too much to gain by his removal. For the moment Kharak Singh's widow became regent, with Shīr Singh as her deputy and Dhiān Singh as wazir. But in January, 1841, Shīr Singh seized Lahore, and was proclaimed mahārāja. This left the Jammū brothers still in power, and the Sindhianwalas took to flight. In 1843, however, the Jammū brothers and their enemies came to an agreement, with the result that in September Ajīt Singh murdered Shīr Singh and his son, and then, turning on his new allies, murdered also Dhiān Singh. Dhiān's son, Hīra Singh, then came forward, overthrew the Sindhianwalas, slew two of them, and proclaimed Dalīp Singh mahārāja. Dalīp was a supposed son of Ranjit by Rāni Jindan.

Amid this confusion of change and murder, while every aspirant looked to the army for assistance, the soldiery found itself the real repository of power. The discipline of the army vanished. *Panchayats* were formed in every unit, and nothing could be done without their assent. Repeated demands were made by the troops that their numbers should be raised and their pay increased. Their demands could not be resisted, although the resources of the state were rapidly declining. The army fell into heavy arrears of pay. It became ever more insubordinate. Sooner or later some desperate politician as his last gamble with fate, or some group of more sober men perceiving that order could not be restored till the army had been destroyed, would throw it upon the English.

In 1842, while these events were still developing but when their probable outcome was already clear, Ellenborough was deeply concerned at the political position which he had inherited. He had succeeded in withdrawing the troops from Afghanistan without a breach with the Panjab. But it was necessary to bear in mind the probability of a future war with the Sikhs, and the need of placing the company in the strongest possible position to meet such a contingency. From that point of view, it would be advantageous if the company were enabled to attack the Sikhs, not merely along the line of the Sutlej but also on another front. The occupation of Sind became therefore a desirable object. Moreover, various difficulties had arisen with the amirs of that country. When the development of commercial relations with Central Asia had been in the forefront, Lord William Bentinck had made a treaty with the amirs designed to liberate the Indus as a channel of trade from the numerous tolls which were imposed on boats passing up and down the river. The amirs had agreed to set up a fixed tariff on condition that no military stores should be allowed to pass. In 1836, when Ranjit Singh had been preparing to attack Sind, Auckland had intervened to prevent this expansion of Sikh power and at the same time had made a new treaty with the amirs by which the latter agreed to accept a permanent British resident. When, in connection with the invasion of Afghanistan, Auckland decided to make use of the Sind route, he had demanded that the amirs should show themselves friends of the British by co-operating with them in the war. They were required to allow the Bombay troops to pass up the river, and to make over the island of Bukkar as a depot on the British line of communications. The amirs were most reluctant to concede these points. But they were forced to consent, and in 1839 Karāchī was occupied. When the Afghan disasters became known, they thought that the time had come for their revenge. They began to intrigue with the Afghans and with Persia. Their intrigue did not amount to much more than declarations of hostility against the infidel and of desire to see his power destroyed. They would have done better to keep these natural but imprudent views to themselves. They had not adhered to the fixed tariff which had been set up on the Indus; and their administration was such as to shock any European observer. Ellenborough came to the conclusion that the position in Sind must be cleared up, and that the British forces there should not be withdrawn until the amirs had accepted the company's suzerainty in the clearest terms.

He appointed Sir Charles Napier to command the forces in Sind, and at the same time empowered him to conduct the political negotiations with the amirs. At this time the amirs formed two groups, governing Upper Sind from Khairpur and Lower Sind from Hyderabad. Both groups agreed verbally to accept a treaty which Napier proposed to them; but both proceeded to collect troops, with the intention of resisting. At the end of 1842 a number of the Khairpur amirs fled to Imāmgarh, a desert fortress about halfway between Khairpur and Hyderabad. It was difficult of access and enjoyed the local reputation of being impregnable. Taking this as a defiance, Napier marched against the place in January, 1843, and on his appearance it surrendered and was promptly blown up. More discussions followed. Outram, the resident, believed that he could settle everything if Napier would allow him to go down to Hyderabad. There he got the signatures to the treaty of all but one of the amirs. But when he seemed to be on the verge of a peaceful settlement, he was beset in the streets and then attacked in the residency. Napier, with 2800 men, was moving down towards Hyderabad. The amirs had assembled a force of over 20,000 at Miani. They certainly thought they could overwhelm the English. Napier attacked. A fierce battle followed in which the Balūchis were completely defeated. Six of the amirs at once surrendered, and Hyderabad was occupied. A second battle followed a month afterwards at Dabo, six miles from that city. The Balūchis were again beaten, and Napier hastened to occupy the chief places in the province. These events led to the annexation of Sind.

In this Ellenborough's policy has almost universally been condemned. The directors of the company made it a pretext for an embittered attack on a man who had offended them in other ways: and the Whigs naturally were glad to attack the man who had not hesitated to expose Auckland's misconduct. Napier's phrase, "a good, honest, useful piece of rascality", represents the common judgment. But the notion that the amirs were attacked and their country annexed simply because they were weak is scarcely tenable. The main culpability lies with Auckland. Ellenborough's responsibility is limited to his treatment of the situation which he inherited. He found the rulers of this frontier state engaged in intrigues which were hostile though certainly not in themselves dangerous. He was clearly entitled to decide whether or not to exact the penalty. That was a question not of political morals but of political expediency. The size of the state, the immediate danger of its intrigues, are not relevant matters. Viewed broadly, the annexation of Sind seems comparable with the assumption of the Carnatic. In both cases advantage was taken of foolish and hostile conduct to secure a considerable political advantage. Ellenborough, like Wellesley, was more concerned to consolidate and strengthen the position of the East India Company than to make benevolent gestures in the idle hope that others would follow so futile an example.

The annexation of Sind was followed by the establishment of a simple and direct administration closely modelled on that which it displaced. Napier remained in civil charge of the province which he had conquered; and for some years the management of Sind was conducted, not by the Government of India and the dual government in England, but by the governor-general in correspondence with the secret committee of the court of directors, that is, with the president of the Board of Control. Sind therefore escaped the elaborate administration, with its long chain of courts of justice and careful division of functions, which had grown up in the older provinces. In each district Napier appointed an officer, more often chosen from the army than from the company's civil service, to exercise revenue, police and judicial authority. This system was naturally and strongly disapproved by those who had been brought up in the system of Bengal. But Henry Lawrence, who had at first condemned Napier's administration, on learning more of it confessed that he had been mistaken. The simple system worked well and effectively. When the Indian Mutiny broke out, Bartle Frere, who was in charge of the province, was able to denude it of troops in order to assist the Panjab on the one hand and Bombay on the other, without in any way endangering the peace and security of the country. The people apparently did not desire the restoration of their fallen rulers.

As has already been pointed out, relations with the Sikhs at this time were most uncertain. They could only be viewed, as Ellenborough wrote, "in the light of an armed truce". Nau Nihāl Singh had been violently anti-British. Dhiān Singh had hated the resident, Wade, almost as much as he had hated his

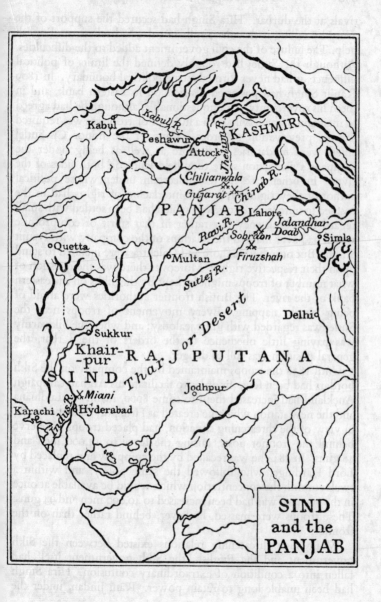

Kabul

Kabul R.

Peshawur

KASHMIR

Attock

Jhelum R.

Chilianwala

Gujarat

Chinab R.

PANJAB

Lahore

Ravi R.

Jalandhar
Doab

Sobraon

Simla

Quetta

Multan

Firuzshah

Sutlej R.

Delhi

Sukkur

Khair-
-pur

RAJPUTANA

SIND

Thar or Desert

Jodhpur

Karachi

Miani

Hyderabad

Indus R.

**SIND
and the
PANJAB**

rivals at the durbar. Hīra Singh had secured the support of the army by telling it that the Sindhianwalas had relied on English help. The failure of the civil government added to the difficulties. Although the Sutlej had roughly defined the limits of political influence, it had never formed a true political boundary. In 1809 Ranjit Singh had possessed districts on its eastern bank, and in them his sovereignty was unquestionable, although he had agreed to maintain in them only such a number of troops as was required for the preservation of order. Some of the minor Cis-Sutlej chiefs were feudatories of Lahore as well as being under the company's protection since they held lands on both sides of the river. In other cases it was uncertain under whose political authority they rightly fell. This interlacing of rights had in the past led to numerous discussions which had been settled with small regard for consistency but rather in that spirit of compromise which had ever marked the relations of the company with Ranjit Singh. But now both Lahore and Calcutta were inclined to stand upon their respective rights. Moreover there was the question of what number of troops might be kept by the Sikhs on the eastern bank of the river. The British frontier authorities were afraid of being caught napping. Every movement of troops near the Sutlej was regarded with great jealousy; and when the Sikh army was paying little obedience to the orders of the durbar, the general position was full of danger.

Until 1838 the troops maintained by the company on the Sikh borders had been few. In order to facilitate his Afghan campaign Auckland had increased them to some 8000, mainly at Ludhiāna and the new station which he created at Firūzpūr. Ellenborough, in view of the threatening situation, had placed troops in reserve behind the frontier posts, raising the force to 14,000 men and 48 guns. In 1844 he was recalled by the company and replaced by Lord Hardinge, who followed the same policy, and within a twelvemonth the concentration which would be available at once in the event of war had been increased to 40,000 men and 94 guns. These troops were massed, however, behind rather than on the frontier.

While such threatening relations existed between the Sikh government and the English, the Sikh government itself had fallen into a condition of extraordinary confusion. Hīra Singh had been unable long to retain power. Rāni Jindan, under the

influence of her brother, Jawāhir Singh, and her lover, Lāl Singh,
won over the army. Hīra Singh, finding his position undermined,
fled from Lahore, but was pursued and slain at the end of 1844.
The rāni then attempted to attack Hīra Singh's uncle, Gulāb
Singh, in Jammū. Gulāb, finding himself too weak to resist by
open force, bribed the troops sent against him, and submitted so
far as to proceed to Lahore and promise to pay a fine of nearly
seven lakhs, besides surrendering certain districts. Jawāhir Singh
was then, in May, 1845, formally installed as wazir. For the
moment the rāni's party seemed supreme. But it was divided.
Lāl Singh, the favoured lover, aspired to the post of wazir himself.
The army, too, had never trusted Jawāhir Singh. Before he had
succeeded to the semblance of power, he had only been restrained
by force from fleeing to the English with the young mahārāja.
As soon as he had become wazir, he had punished the commander
who had made him a prisoner by cutting off his ears and nose. In
the middle of 1845 Peshāwara Singh, a son of Ranjit living in his
jāgīr of Sialkot, and encouraged by Gulāb Singh and other
enemies of the wazir, surprised Attock and proclaimed himself
mahārāja. The rebellion was immediately crushed. Peshāwara
Singh submitted and was at once put to death. This finally
disgusted the army, which still nourished a strong respect for the
blood of their late master. The *panchayats* of the regiments
gathered together and resolved that the wazir should be put to
death. This decision was carried out on September 21. For several
weeks no new wazir was appointed. Then in November Lāl
Singh was installed, and Tej Singh named commander-in-chief.
But their real authority was small. Many leading Sikhs had long
felt that the reduction of the army was the first need of the state.
But that could not be accomplished by any internal means. It
might be secured by directing it against the English. The Sikhs had
watched the increase of military forces beyond the Sutlej with
suspicion, and feared that it preluded an invasion of the Panjab.
The army and the durbar came therefore to the same conclusion,
and the army took the offensive by crossing the Sutlej on
December 11, 1845.

The English forces were commanded by Sir Hugh Gough. The
first encounter took place at Mūdki, where the Sikhs were defeated with the loss of seventeen guns. This was followed by the
great battle of Fīrūzshāh on December 21–22. After a fierce and

most obstinate fight the Sikh camp was taken, seventy-three guns were captured, and several thousand Sikhs slain. But Gough had lost one man out of every seven, and the spirit of his army, and especially the spirit of his sepoy troops, was shaken. After this came a pause while the English gathered reinforcements. Then, on January 28, one Sikh force was driven across the Sutlej at Aliwāl, and on February 10 their main body after another fierce and bloody battle at Sobrāon was driven, not across but into the Sutlej with enormous loss. Gough and Hardinge hastened to cross the river and march on Lahore before the Sikhs had recovered from the effects of this crushing blow. On February 20 the capital was occupied.

Hardinge had neither sought nor desired the conquest of the Panjab. He did desire a well ordered and friendly state upon his north-western frontier. This evidently excluded all idea of annexation. In Hardinge's view it also excluded the traditional policy of a subsidiary alliance, which would have made the company in fact if not in name responsible for the good government of the territory. By the treaty which was signed on March 9, 1846, Dalīp Singh was formally recognised as mahārāja; the Sikhs were to surrender all lands and claims to the southward of the Sutlej; they were to pay an indemnity of a crore and a half of rupees, but of this only the half crore was to be paid in cash, the balance being liquidated by the cession of the Jalandhar doāb and the province of Kashmīr; the army was to be reduced and re-organised, and the arrears due to the soldiers who should be discharged were to be paid in full. By supplementary articles signed two days later Hardinge agreed to leave at Lahore till the end of 1846 troops sufficient to protect the person of the mahārāja and to maintain public order, but the governor-general was at liberty to withdraw the troops if the durbar did not proceed at once to the reorganisation of the army. By a separate treaty with Gulāb Singh Kashmīr was assigned to him for a payment of seventy-five lakhs of rupees. Both Gulāb and the durbar agreed to refer to the governor-general any disputes which might arise between them.

Hardinge's purpose in making these arrangements was to give the Sikh government a breathing space in which it might set its affairs in order, and Henry Lawrence was appointed British agent at Lahore. But effective reform was virtually impossible. The durbar itself, under Lāl Singh as wazir, was composed of men who cared for nothing but their personal interests. The army could not be paid off and reorganised because there was no money. There was no money because great tracts of country had been assigned as *jāgīr* to various chiefs, who would not submit to any reduction of their privileges. Great difficulties arose in connection with this fundamental matter, and in fact Lawrence was allowed to advance money from the company's treasury for the payment of arrears to permit the disbandment of a number of men. Nor was the transfer of Kashmīr to Gulāb Singh carried out without much trouble. Although the durbar had agreed to recognise his independence, this went sorely against the grain with men who had always been his rivals and enemies. Long delays occurred. Then an insurrection broke out. It had to be suppressed by force of arms, and, when it appeared that Lāl Singh had been at the bottom of the movement, the resident demanded and the durbar agreed to his removal from the office of wazir. By this time the year was drawing to its close, and little had been done in the way of reformation. The durbar, certain that it could not maintain its position when the English had withdrawn, demanded that the English forces should be left at Lahore for a further term.

At a durbar which Hardinge had held on the day on which the Treaty of Lahore had been signed, he had declared to the assembled chiefs that success or failure was in their own hands; that he would co-operate with them; but that, if they lost their present opportunity, no aid from external friends could save the state. He had soon perceived that the Sikh government was not in the least likely to profit by the respite which he had given it, and had begun to consider what course of action he should pursue when the expected crisis should arise. By September he had begun to entertain the idea of undertaking the administration in Dalīp Singh's name during his minority. Some eight years would elapse before the mahārāja could exercise power in person, and meanwhile the government might be carried on by a British minister assisted by a Sikh council. "By British interposition", he wrote, "justice and moderation are secured by an administration through native executive agency in accordance with the customs, feelings, and prejudices of the people." At the request of the durbar for the continuance of the British garrison, Hardinge revisited Lahore. He was ready, he said, to withdraw the garrison in accordance with the treaty; but if it was to be continued, conditions must be accepted. The durbar was in no position to bargain. Hardinge's terms were accepted, and a new treaty was signed on December 16. This was signed by thirteen chiefs "acting with the unanimous consent and concurrence of the chiefs and sardars of the state assembled at Lahore". It provided that "a British officer with an efficient establishment of assistants shall be appointed by the governor-general to remain at Lahore, which officer shall have full authority to direct and control all matters in every department of the state". The administration was to be conducted by local officials appointed and superintended by a council of regency of eight members named in the treaty and not subject to change without the consent of the resident and the orders of the governor-general. This council was to act "in consultation with the British resident, who shall have full authority to direct and control the duties of every department". The arrangement was to continue till Dalip Singh came of age on September 4, 1854, and the durbar was to pay twenty-two lakhs a year for the maintenance of the army of occupation, while the governor-general was to be free to garrison any fortresses he chose within Sikh territory.

This second treaty in effect recognised that the first had failed of its purpose. Left to itself with a minimum of interference and even a certain measure of financial help, the durbar had reformed nothing, and the wazir had even sought to counteract the treaty under which he had been continued in office. Hardinge's new plan was to place the Sikh government under British superintendence. This, he hoped, would provide a driving power towards reform which had been lacking under the former régime. If this too failed, annexation was still held in reserve as a last resort. Hardinge desired above all that his policy should be free from all taint of haste or aggressiveness.

Lāl Singh had been deprived of his office as wazir and removed into British territory as a preliminary condition of the treaty of December 16. His removal was intended to exclude Rāni Jindan from farther participation in the management of affairs. Vexed by the exile of her lover, and humiliated by the reduction of her importance, she strove to avoid her political extinction. The result was that she was removed from Lahore to Benares. Henry Lawrence, who was continued as resident, was nevertheless faced with a task of extraordinary difficulty. He enjoyed the assistance of the ablest men Hardinge could find for him, and it is noteworthy that the leaders of that remarkable group which Dalhousie afterwards employed to govern the Panjab had already been employed in the province by Hardinge and Lawrence. They included Henry's brother, George Lawrence, Herbert Edwardes, John Nicholson, Lumsden of the Guides—men of great energy and talent. A deliberate part of the new plan had been to maintain the native character of the administration, to act only through the customary channels, and to veil as completely as possible the reality of the resident's predominance. The task was therefore not that merely of reforming the government, but the much more delicate one of reforming as well the practices of men bred in the traditional methods of squeeze and graft. Lawrence was called on to effect the political education of the governing class, and through them to introduce into the country that regularity, honesty, and justice which formed the ideal of the company's administration. His strong sympathy with the Sikh aristocracy, his knowledge of the people, the union of gentleness and force which marked his character, gave him unrivalled qualifications for such a business. Yet he failed completely. As soon as one of the resident's assistants was sent into a district to investigate complaints and advise reforms, he was besieged by men demanding his direct interposition in their affairs. In the frontier districts especially, distracted by the century-long feuds between Muslim and Sikh, something very like direct British authority was established. It was impossible to conceal British control. The durbar's agents were ignored, the resident's assistants were sought after and obeyed. This experience under Lawrence in the Panjab is perhaps the best answer to the critics who enquire why reformer after reformer in British India refused to employ Indian agency in the superior offices of government.

This position enjoyed by the resident and his officers did not pass unresented. The chiefs who were not members of the council of regency and whose influence and profits were curtailed by reforms which Lawrence tried to introduce, were urged to opposition by both pride and interest. The Sikh soldiery, too, were full of desire to try conclusions once more with the men whom they had almost overthrown at Fīrūzshāh. Some event or other was sure to set fire to the people of the *Khālsa*, as the Sikhs called themselves. The spark actually came from Multān. The governor, Mūlrāj, had succeeded his father, who had been murdered in 1844, and regarded himself as something more than a mere agent of the durbar. The new régime was more exact than the old in the matter of accounts, and demands were made on the governor for large arrears. Mūlrāj offered to resign his office. A new governor was appointed, and two of the resident's assistants were sent to install him. On their entry into the city they were beset by an excited crowd and murdered. Mūlrāj promptly prepared for a siege, gathering troops and strengthening the fortifications of Multān.

This murder occurred on April 20, 1848. Early in the year Lawrence had gone to England on leave with Hardinge, who had been succeeded by Lord Dalhousie as governor-general. Sir Frederic Currie, who had become resident at Lahore, reported the untoward development to the Government of India, requesting immediate help to suppress the rebellion of Mūlrāj. Dalhousie and Gough, who was still commander-in-chief, agreed that the hasty despatch of small bodies of troops would be a mistake. The hot weather was just approaching, and would make military movements difficult and costly of life. That, however, was not the principal consideration. It had long been apparent that the Sikhs were discontented with the control which was being exercised over their administration. If, as Dalhousie believed, the rebellion of Mūlrāj was only the prelude to a general revolt, a small force sent against Multān might be destroyed, while the despatch of a large force might prevent the Sikhs from breaking out without in any way improving the general situation. It was therefore decided to take no immediate steps, but to prepare a strong force which should be ready to operate against any enemy who should appear when the hot weather was over, when the rains had fallen, and when military operations would be feasible. This decision was certainly wise. If the Sikhs wanted a renewal of the war, it had better be such a war as they would not wish to repeat, a war which would convince him of the military strength of the company.

The situation developed in accordance with Dalhousie's expectations. Herbert Edwardes under Currie's orders got together a small force which marched on Multān and attempted vainly to besiege it. Meantime excitement among the Sikhs rose high.

Troubles broke out on the Afghan frontier. A Sikh chief obtained a promise of help from Dost Muhammad in return for the agreement to give back to him the city of Peshāwar. Sikh troops gathered. The siege of Multān had to be abandoned. By the middle of October Dalhousie informed the resident at Lahore that he considered the Sikh government to be virtually at war with the company. On November 9 Gough, with the army which had been assembled, crossed the Sutlej into Sikh territory, on the 13th he reached Lahore, and on the 22nd forced the Sikh army, under the command of Shīr Singh, across the Jhelum. In December the siege of Multān was reformed, and on January 22 the place was captured. But before this, on January 13, Gough had fought another of those bloody and expensive battles for which he is remembered. After a four hours' march, he had come upon the Sikh army at Chilianwāla, had attacked it, had driven it from its ground with heavy loss, but had himself lost many men, four guns, and the colours of three regiments. Like Hardinge after the battle of Fīrūzshāh, Dalhousie concluded that Gough was too wasteful of his men to be left in charge of the campaign. He applied to London for his recall, and Gough was accordingly superseded by Sir Charles Napier. But before Napier could arrive, Gough as in the former war redeemed his reputation as a general by the complete triumph of Gujrāt. The Sikhs were scattered and could never form again. Within three weeks of this victory they had surrendered, the Afghans had withdrawn hurriedly from the Panjab, and Peshāwar had been occupied by British forces. The Second Sikh War was over.

Dalhousie now put into force the policy towards which Hardinge had reluctantly drifted. He annexed the province. Dalīp Singh was deposed, given a pension, and required to reside outside the Panjab. Attempts were made to represent him as illused. He had had nothing to do with the second war. But neither could he hold out the faintest probability of his being able to control the Sikhs and transform them into the friendly neighbours of whom Hardinge had dreamed. The policy of friendship had been tried; the policy of guidance had been tried; and at last remained only the policy of annexation. Thus the company took control of one more of the provinces of the Mughal empire. Military superiority was once more consolidating the fragments into which the country had broken up in the eighteenth century.

The whole country from Peshāwar to Cape Comorin now lay under the control, in one form or another, of the East India Company. Either the direct government of the company had been set up or the rule was in the hands of princes who were bound both by treaty and self-interest to comply with the demands which the company might make upon them.

Kābul was the one province which had not been recovered. But in other directions the company had exceeded the boundaries of the Mughals. Owing to its combinati n of predominance ashore and afloat, it had found no difficulty in bestriding the barrier which the Vindhya and Sātpura hills cast across the peninsula. The Mughal empire had broken down under the strain of holding both northern and southern India; the Marāthas had lost their union of purpose in the effort to expand northwards; but the company, with its alternative routes, its power of landing troops at any point of the Indian sea-board, its communications unthreatened by an enemy save at two brief moments, had found no difficulty in establishing its authority over India as a whole. This same union of military and naval power facilitated its expansion into a region into which the Mughals had never penetrated. From the first appearance of the Europeans in the east they had attempted without much success to trade with the kingdoms established on the east coast of the Bay of Bengal. Portuguese, Dutch, and French had each in turn opened factories and abandoned them when they found that foreign trade was looked on as a royal monopoly and foreign settlers as an increase in the king's people. The English from Masulipatam and Madras on the other side of the Bay had been more persistent but hardly more successful than their rivals. Addison, the essayist, had hoped to inherit a great fortune from the trade to Syriam of his brother, a company's servant at Madras, but had been grievously disappointed. In 1753 a factory was opened on Negrais Island, but six years later the inhabitants were massacred by the Burmese. What trade there was consisted only of private ventures, and the company took no interest in a commerce which promised neither profit nor advantage commensurate with its risks. A few vagrant Englishmen were to be found at Rangoon, but they were men of neither wealth nor influence. Under a vigorous king, Alaungpaya, the Burmese in the middle of the eighteenth century overcame the Talaings in the Irawadi delta and Tenasserim. Under his successor,

Bodawpaya, they expanded northwards, conquering Arakan in 1785, Manipur in 1813, and Assam in 1816. In 1818, remembering that some centuries earlier Arakan had received tribute from the Ganges delta, they demanded that the British should surrender to them Chittagong, Dacca, and Murshidābād. For years, owing to the Burmese operations, the regions lying on the borderlands had been most unsettled. Fugitives from the conquered lands had taken refuge in British territory. Fifty thousand Arakanese had fled to Chittagong, and some under a spirited leader, Nga Chin Pyan, had made raids upon the Burmese. The British had seized a number of his chief followers, but had refused to hand them over to the Burmese to be tortured to death. The Burmese conquest of Assam had been followed by great massacres, while 30,000 had been driven in slave-gangs down to the conqueror's capital at Ava. The more fortunate found shelter in Bengal, and attempted reprisals. Every endeavour was made to prevent hostile excursions from leaving British territory, but the British were not willing to give the Burmese the only satisfaction with which they would have been content, the unconditional surrender of men whose only crime was that of seeking to recover their country.

Several attempts had been made to establish regular political relations with the Burmese court at Ava. Symes was sent in 1795, Cox in 1797, Symes again in 1802, and Canning thrice between 1803 and 1811. They were received with contempt, after the Chinese manner. They were made to live on an island in the river reserved for scavengers. They were told that they represented no one more important than a servant and that no envoy could be received unless he came direct from the king of England. In 1823-4 the Burmese, confident in their power, invaded the company's territories in force. Their orders were to capture Calcutta. Amherst, who was then governor-general, contented himself with checking their advance on the land frontier, but at the same time he sent an expedition, drawn mainly from Madras, under the command of Sir Archibald Campbell and Captain Marryat, the novelist. They occupied Rangoon on May 11, 1824. It had been expected that the Talaings would rise in their favour: but the Talaings had been deported, and the country round was left deserted. A long and ill-conducted campaign followed. The English had poor information, bad medical arrangements, ineffective supply. Whenever the Burmese attacked, they were routed. But the fighting was for the most part jungle fighting, in which regular troops lost much of their technical advantage. However, after making prodigious efforts to destroy the invaders, the Burmese were compelled to make peace in February, 1826. The king agreed to give up Tenasserim in the south, and Arakan, Assam, Cachar, Jaintia, and Manipur, in the north. He was also to pay an indemnity of ten lakhs of rupees, and receive a British resident at Ava as well as maintaining one at Calcutta.

This agreement, known as the Treaty of Yandabo, brought peace but no permanent settlement. The Burmese king, Bagyidaw, would not maintain a resident at Calcutta; and on his death in 1837, the new king, Tharrawaddy, refused to admit that the treaty was binding on him at all. "The English beat my brother, not me", he declared. In 1840 consequently the residency was withdrawn. From this time onwards the position of the few English inhabitants of Rangoon was extremely precarious. But the company's government generally refused to consider their complaints, on the ground that anyone choosing to live under Burmese government did so at his own risk. But in 1850 matters came to a head. In that year was appointed a governor of Rangoon who when drunk used to threaten to torture and behead the whole population of the town. A British barque ran aground near Rangoon. The pilot jumped overboard and swam ashore. The governor accused the captain of throwing the pilot overboard, detained him and his crew for eight days, and fined him 1005 rupees. In another case a lascar died on board a British vessel on the day she anchored off Rangoon. The governor accused the captain of murder, threatened to behead him, detained him for three weeks, and at last fined him 700 rupees. Dalhousie sent a King's ship, the *Fox*, frigate, under Commodore Lambert, to request the removal of this unjust governor and compensation for the two English captains who had suffered from his exactions. King Pagān, who was then ruling, was willing to accommodate matters, appointing a new governor with authority to settle the dispute. But the officers sent by Lambert to welcome the new governor were not admitted to his presence; the new governor had come down accompanied by a large force of men; and Lambert, mistaking these portents, declared a blockade of Rangoon and seized one of the king's ships. On this the land batteries opened fire on the *Fox*. This event led to the Second Burmese War.

This new war was in every way except its termination a complete contrast to the first. Under Dalhousie's superintendence careful arrangements were made to supply the men with food and the hospitals with medicines. The Talaings in the delta rose in favour of the English. The Shāns refused to send levies to help the Burmese king. Rangoon and Mārtabān were occupied at once; then Bassein was taken, followed by Prome and the Pegu country. The campaign ended by Dalhousie's refusing to allow his commanders to advance farther and annexing Pegu by proclamation on December 20, 1852. He left it to the king to accept a treaty or not as he chose, but warned him that, if again he provoked hostilities, they would end in the complete subjection of the Burmese power.

The Second Burmese War thus ended in giving the company the complete control of the shores of the Bay of Bengal, together with the port of Rangoon, while the Burmese monarchy was driven back into the interior whence it had emerged in the middle of the eighteenth century.

SKETCH MAP
ILLUSTRATING
THE ABSORPTION OF
BURMA

CHAPTER IX

The Growth of British Sovereignty and the Company's Relations with the Indian States

When the company set out on its career of expansion in the years following on the battle of Plassey, various circumstances combined to conceal the political significance of its action. The company itself, fearing lest the national government should seize its acquisitions on behalf of the crown, disliked the idea of territorial gains, which could only be made in the name of King George III. The result was the establishment of the system of dual government, by which everything was to be done in the name of some powerless and dependent prince by the servants and for the benefit of the East India Company. Despite the efforts of Warren Hastings to get rid of this legacy imposed upon him by Clive, the position in Bengal long remained most anomalous. In theory the company was only the *dīwān*; in practice it exercised full authority. But that authority was asserted only by the refusal to continue the payment to the emperor Shāh 'Ālam of the annual tribute promised by Clive and by the transfer of the districts of Kora and Allāhābād from the emperor to the nawab wazir of Oudh. In other formal respects the company's government continued to recognise the authority of the emperor. The seal of the governor-general purported to be that of a servant of the Mughal. The coinage was still struck in Shāh 'Ālam's name. In international discussions the English did not claim sovereignty except in Calcutta and the surrounding region, posing elsewhere as the influential adviser of the nawab who reigned, but did not rule, at Murshidābād. The French and the Dutch could thus avoid all public recognition of the supreme position which the company occupied throughout the province.

It has been thought that this obscure position was designed to conciliate Indian sentiment and to conceal foreign dominion. But for that view small justification exists. The leading men of the province knew well who exercised authority; the people neither knew nor cared who governed so long as they were not taxed beyond customary limits. Wars and revolutions were affairs in which they took no interest, in which they had no concern. No one had raised a finger to aid Sirāj-ud-daula after his defeat; no one had sought to bring back Mīr Kāsim after his expulsion; no conspiracies were formed against the English company. Had popular feeling been the sole factor to be taken into consideration, the vicious system adopted by Clive need never have been set up and would never have been perpetuated. It was directed not to deceive the Indian inhabitants of the province, but to prevent probable encroachments of the ministry at London and probable complaint from the capitals of Europe.

This extraordinary position continued for a long period of time. Neither the Regulating Act of 1773, nor the India Act of 1784, nor the act extending the company's privileges in 1793, made the least attempt to assert English sovereignty over the company's possessions. They legislated for them, altering the form of the company's administration, setting up a Supreme Court of Judicature, defining the powers which the company's government might exercise, but nowhere asserting that the inhabitants of Bengal, Bihar, and Orissa were the subjects of King George. In fact the position in India was to be wholly transformed before the great revolution was recognised in English law. Cornwallis was the first governor-general to object to the empty formulas in which the company's government was accustomed to protest obedience in its letters to the emperor. Wellesley, who indeed projected the establishment of British predominance in India, carried matters much further. By Lord Lake's victory at Delhi, the person of the emperor passed into the custody of the East India Company. By the arrangements which Wellesley then made, the administration of Delhi was to be conducted in the imperial name, but the only spot in which the imperial orders were really effective was the palace and its precincts. Following on this, the act of 1813, while renewing the company's privileges for another twenty years, declared that its authority was "without prejudice to the undoubted sovereignty of the crown of the United Kingdom...". The conclusion of the Napoleonic wars in 1815 led to the recognition of the new position by the states chiefly interested in the Indian situation. The treaties of 1814 and 1815 expressly recognised British sovereignty within the Indian possessions of the East India Company. These legislative and diplomatic facts gave an added impulse to the movement in India. Lord Moira, who arrived as governor-general in 1813, brought out with him a fixed determination to make an end of "the fiction of the Mogul government". The phrase denoting the imperial supremacy was removed from his seal. No more ceremonial gifts were offered to the emperor in the governor-general's name. He refused to meet the emperor, Akbar II, Shāh 'Ālam's son, unless he waived all authority over the company's possessions. This suggestion was refused. But in 1827 the emperor consented to meet Moira's successor, Amherst, on equal terms. The meeting took place in the *Dīwān-i khās* at Delhi. The two entered from opposite sides at the same instant. They sat down, the emperor on his throne, the governor-general on a chair placed on the right, simultaneously. No gift was offered by the latter. From this time onwards, though all letters from the governor-general to the emperor were addressed as to a superior, they avoided all those terms which would have implied vassalage on the part of the company's government. In 1835 the coinage of Bengal ceased to be struck in the name of the dead emperor, Shāh 'Ālam, whose titles had continued to appear on the company's rupees till that year. Then it was resolved to induce the imperial family to remove from the old palace at Delhi to a new residence which was to be built for it near the Kutb Minār, and at last Canning decided no longer to recognise the imperial title after the demise of the existing emperor, Bahādur Shāh. Immediately after this the Mutiny broke out. After the fall of Delhi, the emperor was placed on his trial for complicity in the murders which had taken place at Delhi and, more doubtfully, for rebellion against the East India Company. He was declared deposed; he passed the rest of his days as a state-prisoner at Rangoon, and the British government became both in form and in substance supreme as well as sovereign in India.

This development had a considerable reaction upon the relations of the East India Company with its Indian allies. From the time of Clive onwards, those relations had been very different from those of equals. The nawab wazir of Oudh and the nawab of the Carnatic had speedily become dependent on the military support of the company and had therefore tended to fall into the class of political clients. For their protection, alike from foreign enemies and from their own subjects, detachments of the company's troops were stationed in their territories; but, although these subsidiary forces were paid for by the prince in question, they remained under the orders of the company's government. From the company's point of view such subsidiary alliances had great advantages. They rendered the princes who accepted them allies who could never afford to break their alliance; and they provided the means for an increase of military force without casting any burden on the resources of the company's territories. Wellesley, who first formulated the idea of uniting all India in a league under the general direction of the company, naturally developed into a formal policy what had begun as a casual expedient. He made subsidiary alliances with three of the major states of India—with Hyderabad, with Poona, and with Mysore. In the first two cases the princes who accepted a subsidiary alliance did so as a defence against external dangers in no way caused by the company: the Nizām accepted a subsidiary force as a protection against his over-powerful Marātha neighbours, and the Pēshwā accepted one as a protection against the attacks of his nominal subordinate, Holkar. At Mysore the treaty was part of Wellesley's scheme for the reorganisation of the state after the overthrow of Tipu Sultān. In two respects these treaties contained new features. They all bound the princes to settle foreign disputes in consultation with the governor-general; and they all bound them not to admit to their service any foreign Europeans without the governor-general's consent. But from Wellesley's stand-point this did not go far enough, for it offered no guarantee for a good administration within the territories of the company's allies. The condition of Oudh and of the Carnatic afforded striking examples of the evils which might arise out of the protection of the company. Wellesley was therefore eager to engraft on the subsidiary policy further provisions which would obviate this evil. He desired that the company should become guide as well as protector, and that the allied princes should be bound to accept such advice as might be offered to them by the governor-general. Naturally, though unwisely, the princes shrank from admitting this right of interference in their internal affairs. In two cases only was Wellesley able to give effect to his desires. In Mysore he was able to dictate the terms on which he was willing to restore the Hindu royal family to the throne from which it had been expelled by Hyder 'Alī. In Mysore therefore the governor-general's right to give advice to the prince, and, in case of need, to re-enter on the Mysore territory, was fully admitted. In Oudh too the position of the nawab wazir was so precarious, and the need of casting the protecting arm of the company around his dominions so undeniable, that Wellesley was able to insist on a promise that an improved system of administration should be adopted and attention paid to British advice. Elsewhere this policy was not practicable; and the most that the governor-general could do towards freeing the company from responsibility for corrupt and inefficient administration was to procure grants of territory to be placed under the company's administration instead of the periodical payments due for the support of the subsidiary forces.

Unhappily neither Wellesley's successors nor the directors of the East India Company were disposed to accept the responsibility which he alone among the company's governors-general was prepared to recognise as incumbent upon the predominance towards which the company was evidently moving. In this respect the treaties which Lord Moira concluded at the end of the Marātha War in 1818 offer a remarkable contrast to those which Wellesley arranged. In 1818 Moira had a great opportunity. His victory was complete, and no prince was prepared to question the power of the company's government. The predominance which Wellesley had foreseen had come to pass. In such circumstances Wellesley would almost certainly have made the privilege of the company's alliance depend upon the princes' willingness to accept political guidance, not only in matters of external policy, but also in those of internal administration. But Moira, like the directors, shrank from assuming so great a responsibility, and his treaties followed the usual lines of the subsidiary system, with the formal addition that neither the company nor its officials should interfere in the internal government of its allies. Thus a principle was laid down that the company was in no wise responsible for the administration of the Indian states, so long as their mismanagement did not lead to disorders within the company's own possessions, and that all interference in the internal affairs of the states was as far as possible to be avoided.

This position was, however, extraordinarily difficult to maintain. The company's government controlled by far the largest group of territories in India, and it was in military power the equal of all the other states combined. These facts alone made it something different from the equal ally of the treaties. Its wishes carried all the influence of power and the prestige of victory. The very constitution of its government, confined as that was to a single class of men from a distant country, was, in the ideas of the time, likely to invest it with the respect due to a caste specially given to war and statecraft. This strange, efficiently organised and closely united power was unique in India, and offered the greatest possible contrast to the position of the other Indian states. They were not merely disunited among themselves, but their governments were cleft by a thousand internal differences. No prince could rely upon the whole-hearted support of all his subjects, on the unhesitating allegiance of all his troops, or on the confidence of the bankers of his state. Moreover the establishment of the company as the common ally of them all, with the consequent disappearance of war, created an artificial situation, in which political vices ceased to exercise their normal effects. Each prince was secure on his throne, notwithstanding the discontent of his people or the jealous eyes with which he was regarded by his abler neighbours. He lacked that most powerful motive, self-interest, which in other circumstances would have compelled him to keep his government sound under pain of destruction if he failed. While, then, the company's government, under pressure of English opinion, was all the time seeking to improve its administrative system, the Indian princes were sinking into a swift decay, and the same causes which had secured the political predominance of the company rapidly gathered weight and momentum.

The material superiority of the company thus grew swiftly in the forty years which followed on the victories of Lord Moira, and constantly tended to pass into political control. In regions such as Kāthiāwār and Central India, divided among a great number of petty chiefs, close control proved to be a political necessity. It was needed to prevent ceaseless squabbles among neighbours or the encroachments of the overlord. In Kāthiāwār, under the management of Colonel Walker, famous for his campaign against female infanticide, an active supervision was established over the conduct of the lesser chiefs. In Central India, which was placed under the management of Sir John Malcolm, the British government not only guaranteed the settlement of the tributes due to Sindhia but also recognised a carefully graduated scale of powers which might be exercised by the tributories. Nor was the tendency confined to the smaller states. At Baroda, for instance, where difficulties arose over the debts due from the Gaekwar to the bankers of his state, it was found necessary to guarantee a settlement of their claims, leading in fact to much supervision of the internal management of the prince. In Hyderabad revenue maladministration produced interference. The vicious practice of farming out the revenues was carried there to extraordinary lengths. It was currently said that a newly appointed revenue-farmer, setting out from the capital to take up his charge, always rode facing his horse's tail in order to watch whether he was followed by some rival who had displaced him either by superior favour or by larger bribes. Metcalfe, when resident with the Nizām, made a strong attempt to introduce reforms into this branch of the Nizām's administration, although this policy was not persisted in. In the same state difficulties arose over the Arab mercenaries who formed a considerable part of the forces of the state. These men always insisted, as part of the terms of their enlistment, that they should not be subject to the law of the state but only to their own tribal law, enforced by their own tribal courts. They followed the frugal custom of saving a great part of their pay and entrusting it to their officers who used it to buy revenue farms in the districts in which they were quartered. The consequence was that in certain areas of the state the authority of the Nizām counted for nothing, and that the Arab troops lived in virtual independence. The assistance of British troops was required to reduce the Arabs to obedience. Here too the finance of the contingent which the British government required the Nizām to maintain, was a constant source of trouble, and led to the accumulation of heavy claims for arrears which were at last only liquidated by the lease of the Berars to the British government in 1853. In Mysore the financial mismanagement of the raja provoked a rebellion in the state in 1830. Here the treaty of Wellesley had provided the company with ample authority to interfere in case of need. But the prevalent views of policy had led to a neglect of the duties imposed by the treaty. The raja had been suffered to persist in his system of government long after he should have been called to an exact account. The rebellion brought matters to a head; and Lord William Bentinck, who was then governor-general, decided to relieve the raja altogether of his powers and appointed Mark Cubbon to administer the state. At

Gwalior during a minority the parties at the durbar quarrelled bitterly among themselves and the army of the state, some 40,000 strong, passed out of control. Ellenborough decided to intervene, and moved with a strong body of troops across the Chambal. The state army resisted and was defeated at the battle of Mahārājpur in 1843, when new terms were imposed on the state, including the limitation of the military forces maintained by it. Thus in a large number of cases the declared policy of non-intervention broke down and was replaced by active interference. As Elphinstone observed in 1832: "This has arisen from the weakness and bad reputation of the native governments. They have often been obliged to request our support against insubordinate chiefs or other subjects...and they have also been obliged to solicit our guarantee to pecuniary arrangements and other settlements where the other contracting party could not depend on their faith".

It had at first been hoped that the practice of having a large voice in the selection of the chief ministers of the major states would obviate the need of further interference. From 1810, for example, the governor-general had insisted that the chief minister at Hyderabad should be a person enjoying his confidence as well as that of his master, the Nizām. Chandu Lāl, who held office for over thirty years, owed his prolonged tenure of office entirely to the support of the resident. From a narrowly political point of view the plan was successful. The minister who rested upon British support was not likely to countenance intrigue hostile to the British government, and his overthrow would be a clear signal of political danger ahead. Ellenborough's campaign in Gwalior was brought about by the violent overthrow of the minister in office. Nevertheless, the system had many disadvantages. The most that can be said for it is that it was imposed on the British government in consequence of its declared policy of non-intervention. Metcalfe, recalling the sound doctrine of the school of Wellesley in which he himself had been brought up, wrote with profound truth, "If possible, I would leave all native states to their own government without interference. But we are always dragged in somehow, and then it is difficult to say what should be done. The worst plan of all, I think, is to keep in a minister against the will of the prince, and to support the man without regard to his measures. Yet this is the mode we have generally slidden into; and as it has been adopted by wiser heads than mine, it is probably right or inavoidable. I would prefer leaving the minister to the choice of the prince, and interfering only as to measures".

In any case, the general effect of the policy of avoiding interference was contrary to the interests of the princes themselves. If the authority which Wellesley had taken in Mysore and Oudh had been exercised with ordinary wisdom the administration of the first need not have been assumed for forty years, and the territories of the second need not have been annexed at all. But from about 1832 a new spirit seems to have entered into the policy of the East India Company. Till then every accession of territory had been regarded as a matter of the most dubious advantage. Indeed, until a workable system of administration had been devised, the transfer of an area from Indian to British control was no very obvious advantage to its inhabitants. But with the formation of a regular system of government, with the improvements which the needs and circumstances of the other British provinces introduced into the system devised by Cornwallis for Bengal, with the growing knowledge of the customs and life of the people which the company's servants were acquiring everywhere outside that unfortunate province, with the increasing activity of missionary effort, and with the formation of an educational policy, large and influential classes in England, which till then had rejected with horror every suggestion of an increase in the company's power, began to hold that India would benefit by every extension of British authority. Therefore, the dislike with which all annexations had been regarded did not indeed vanish but unquestionably began to abate. The future continuance of the Indian states thus became uncertain. Men began to argue, with Elphinstone, that the Indian governments, like every despotism, were essentially ephemeral, and that any stable government founded in their midst must sooner or later swallow them all up.

This change of view was exemplified in two ways. In the first place the company formally declared that in future no just and honourable opportunity of acquiring territory was to be rejected. In the second place, and in consequence of this declaration, it began to take an active interest in the question of successions. At first this matter had been considered to lie outside the scope of the company's interests. So late as 1829 it had taken Metcalfe severely to task for having ventured in a minute to assert a claim to determine the succession in Bhartpur. That attitude was now abandoned. All successions were examined, and the new position was adopted that no succession was valid until it had been recognised by the company's government. The claim was not unreasonable, though unsupported by the letter of the treaties. In the event of a demise, the successor inherited the treaty obligations of the late ruler, so that it was a subject of the company's concern that the power of the state should not pass to one unlikely to observe them. Moreover the Indian rules of succession were extraordinarily lax in European eyes. Among Muslim ruling families the will of the late ruler was usually the only criterion by which one son was preferred to another. Among Hindu chiefs, the rule was that where there was no son, the throne passed to an adopted son, who might be adopted either by the chief himself or after his death by his widow. In both classes therefore the lack of clear and definite rules was likely to produce much intrigue leading possibly to open war. The decision of some external authority was on general grounds most expedient. Nor was the exercise of such authority in any way alien to Indian custom.

The chief difficulty emerged in the matter of adoptions. The company developed the view that its approval was necessary for an adoption to carry with it the political consequence of succession to government. The Indian practice in regard to subordinate chiefs, as for instance in Central India under the Marātha states, was to demand that permission should be sought before the adoption took place, and that otherwise it was invalid. The company was thus assuming that it occupied towards the Indian states the same position that Sindhia held as regards a Rājput feudatory. However, it did not precisely follow Indian precedent. Indian rulers seldom refused permission to adopt, but they almost invariably imposed terms, such as a reduction of territory or a special payment known as *nazarāna*. The company never demanded such concessions, but on some occasions it refused permission altogether, and where it refused permission it annexed the state.

An analysis of the cases which occurred before the time of Dalhousie does not disclose any principles on which permission was given or refused. But Dalhousie endeavoured to introduce consistency into this practice of escheat. In a series of minutes he discussed the position of the various classes of states. These he considered were three in number. In the first class were those which were in every respect independent when they entered into alliance with the company. Such were the old Rājput states of Jodhpur or Jaipur. In the second were those which were dependent on some other prince before they fell within the company's orbit. Such were the Cis-Sutlej chiefs who had been dependent on Sindhia, or the Bundelkhand chiefs who had been dependent on the Pēshwā. In the third were those which had been created by the company's government. Such were Mysore, Satāra, or Nāgpur. He considered that the chiefs of the first class should receive permission to adopt in every case in which they applied for it; that the chiefs of the second class should receive permission if on any ground it appeared expedient to give it; but that chiefs of the third class normally should not receive such permission. This was what became known as "the doctrine of lapse". It will be noticed that comparatively few states, and very few major states, were threatened with extinction by the principles thus defined. They affected no Muslim ruling family and no major state except Mysore and Nāgpur. On these grounds he recommended the annexation of a small group of states. They included Satāra, Nāgpur, and Jhānsi.

More generally dangerous to the preservation of the states was the doctrine that a persistent course of maladministration might lead to their annexation. This doctrine was the correlative of the principle of non-intervention. That policy had a pleasing air of leaving the Indian princes free to do as they liked; but it carried with it the disagreeable risk of leaving them to run into such confusion as would threaten the peace of their great neighbour or at least demand a choice between interference and the disorder which would follow the withdrawal of the company's protection. When Dalhousie went out to India, the condition of two of the great states was regarded with considerable apprehension. In both Hyderabad and Oudh the government was extremely bad, the land revenue systems in disorder, the taxes collected only by military force, and the amounts due from the states to the company running into great sums. In both cases Dalhousie was authorised to annex the state if he thought that the proper course to take. His conduct shows how far he was from pursuing such a policy of general annexation as is usually ascribed to him. Instead of annexing Hyderabad he came to an agreement with the Nizām's government by which, as has already been indicated, the difficulties were smoothed over by the assignment of Berar to the company on lease. In Oudh previous governors-general, instead of acting on the treaty which Wellesley had made, had contented themselves with warning the king, as he had styled himself since the time of Moira, that if he did not reform his government they would have to interfere. In 1837 Auckland had made a new treaty empowering the company if necessary to assume the administration; but this treaty had not been confirmed by the company. It was not therefore valid. But that did not affect the position that the king was obliged by the earlier treaty to reform his administration. In 1847 Hardinge warned him that he must introduce reforms, a demand amply justified by the later reports of Colonel Sleeman, who was charged by Dalhousie with the task of investigating the condition of the country. After careful consideration Dalhousie concluded that it would be improper to require the king to abdicate, partly because he and his predecessors had been consistent supporters of the company's government, partly because a share in the responsibility for the condition of the kingdom must be laid at the company's door for its earlier failure to enforce reform. But since reform was now imperative, the administration should be taken over by the British government with the king's assent. The council desired to see stronger measures taken than Dalhousie had proposed, and the court of directors took the same view, ordering the province to be annexed to the British possessions. The execution of these orders was among the last duties of Dalhousie, who can in no degree be held responsible for the course adopted. Indeed, although he added extensive territories to the company's dominions, to annexation for its own sake he was strongly opposed. It has already been pointed out how carefully he defined and limited the claims of the company to acquire territory by escheat. At Hyderabad he had refrained from taking advantage of the discretion with which he had been invested. In Oudh he was opposed to annexation. It is clear that he sought accessions of territory only where they were to be desired for specific reasons, where, as in Nāgpur, acquisition would consolidate the company's possessions and facilitate communications between the various provinces, or as in the Panjab, where the establishment of British rule would strengthen the strategic position.

Meanwhile every accession of territory had increased the

general influence which the company's government exercised over the governments of the Indian princes. The equal alliances which the treaties appeared to establish were obviously purely fictitious. The claim which the company had set up to regulate the matter of successions formed a long step towards the assumption of superior powers and a superiority of status. The fact that in important states such as Hyderabad no minister had for fifty years held office without the approval of the resident weighed down the scales on the same side, for what so large a state as Hyderabad had submitted to could hardly be refused with prudence by any lesser state. Thus had come into being a series of powers exercised by the company for the preservation of the general peace, and reluctantly acquiesced in by the princes. These powers constituted the paramountcy of the East India Company in India. They rested on no documentary basis. They could be justified only on consideration of the general well-being of the country. Who was sovereign in India? Or was sovereignty split up among a great number of rulers? The powers which the company claimed were clearly infringements of the sovereign powers of the princes. But since conquest and treaties had not only established the company as the direct ruler of two-thirds of the country but had also made it the arbiter of foreign relations throughout the whole land, it may be argued that the political unit which it had brought into being extended beyond its own borders, that it constituted the supreme power in India, and that the question of the authority which it should exercise was a constitutional, not a diplomatic question. From that point of view the development which has here been sketched is to be compared not to the assumption of authority by one equal state over another, but to the struggle between the English king and the English parliament for ultimate control of the administration. The weakness of the company's position lay not so much in the defect of treaty power as in the reluctance of the company, and of almost all its governors-general, to undertake that general responsibility for the well-being of India which would have placed its claims over the Indian states on a constitutional basis.

CHAPTER X

The Company's Administrative System and Policy, 1818–1858

The early period of the East India Company's dominion in India was above all a time of experiment. The parliament and the court of directors in England, Clive, Warren Hastings and Cornwallis in India, had been feeling their way amid great uncertainty towards a system of administration which would work. British sovereignty had been asserted; the last great external enemy had been overthrown; a district administration had been outlined; land revenue enquiries had begun in earnest. But none could pretend that the political structure was in any way complete, and the following period was one of great development. It will be most convenient to deal first with the changes in the home government and in the superior governments in India, then with the growth of the district administration, and lastly with the changes in general policy, both social and administrative.

I

The outstanding anomaly in the character of the company in 1818 was its continued union of commercial and administrative duties. The statute of 1813 had abolished its monopoly of the trade between India and Great Britain. But it still continued to monopolise the trade with China and to maintain large commercial establishments in India. The situation was already becoming complicated by the progress of the industrial revolution. The application of steam power to the spinning and weaving of cotton, and improvements in the process of stamping them with designs, was making the import of Indian piece-goods a profitless business. In 1818 the directors were already seeking some more beneficial employment for their commercial funds. In the next year they had lying unsold in their warehouses Coromandel piece-goods which had cost them over a million pounds sterling. In 1822 the commercial establishment was cut down. In 1828 the directors were hesitating whether to carry on the trade at a great and increasing loss or to abandon it altogether. On the other hand the growing consumption of tea was rendering the Chinese monopoly a valuable commercial asset. But this latter fact rendered the monopoly the more distasteful to dealers in eastern produce, for they desired a direct share in the profits of the trade. The combination of commercial opposition with the political dislike of the company's united functions produced in 1833 the complete abolition of its commercial privileges. It was required as soon as possible after April 12, 1834, to close down its commercial business and to pension or otherwise provide for its commercial servants. In consequence of this act the company became a purely administrative body.

The act of 1833 continued with small change the existing dual organisation of the home government. A number of critics like Lord Ellenborough were eager to place India at once under the immediate government of the crown. But the Whigs who were at this time in office were still inspired with their old jealousy of the executive. Authority, Macaulay declared in the House of Commons, ought not to be vested in the crown alone, for in such matters parliament could not provide the necessary criticism and control. "What we want", he said, "is a body independent of the government and no more than independent—not a tool of the treasury, not a tool of the opposition….The company is such a body." Its administrative functions were therefore continued for another twenty years.

To some extent it lost ground in this period to the Board of Control representing the ministry of the day. As Sir Charles Wood stated in the debates of 1853, the responsibility for foreign policy lay exclusively with the president of the board, and through him with the cabinet. But in fact this was the branch of policy in which home control was least effective. Macaulay's phrase— "India is and must be governed in India"—was particularly true of foreign affairs. So that the province of government in which the authority of the board was supreme was also that in which home authority could be least exercised. And even here the company could exert considerable influence in extreme cases by its unrestrained power of recalling the governor-general. In 1825 the ministry had had much ado to persuade the directors not to recall Lord Amherst; in 1844 the cabinet had been unable to prevent the recall of Lord Ellenborough. With such a weapon in their armoury the directors could always exercise considerable influence even where they had no direct power. In the sphere of general administration their position was stronger, for here they possessed the power of initiating proposals, and it was difficult for the board to carry through a measure from which the directors were really averse.

However, although in 1853 the company's powers were continued, this time without the customary limitation of twenty years, the statute passed in that year marked a growing disposition to strengthen the position of the ministry as against the directors. The new act provided for a reduction of the directors from twenty-four to eighteen, and for the immediate appointment of three (rising gradually to six) by the crown. Since at the same time the quorum for business was lowered from thirteen to ten, it would be possible, when the scheme was in full operation, for the crown nominees to constitute a majority. The intention (as was stated in the debates) was to prepare for the time when the directors might be reduced to a mere consultative council advising a minister of the crown.

The changes made in the Indian governments were more considerable. The original bill introduced in 1833 proposed to vest "the whole civil and military government...in a governor-general and counsellors". This would in effect have annihilated the presidency governments. It was argued that the central government would be overwhelmed with unnecessary detail, and the clause was therefore modified so as to substitute "the superintendence, direction and control" for "the whole...government". However, this alteration probably made small difference, for the government had ample authority to enforce its will upon refractory subordinates. More important was the abandonment of another proposal. It had been intended to add another covenanted servant to the governor-general's council, and to divide the Bengal presidency into two. This (it seems) was meant to permit the appointment of a covenanted servant from each of the four contemplated presidencies. It seems a pity that this proposal was dropped. It would have given the governor-general councillors personally acquainted with the whole of British India; whereas the continuance of the former practice of selecting the governor-general's councillors entirely from Bengal meant that his advisers would continue to know nothing about any other province, and, it must be added, not too much about their own. The only practical result was the formation of the Āgra (or North-Western) Provinces as a separate government under a covenanted servant as lieutenant-governor, instead of the creation of a new presidency with a governor and council. Although, too, the central government received the new designation of "the governor-general and council of India", the governor-general still remained directly responsible for the administration of Bengal. This most serious defect in the governmental machine persisted till the act of 1853, which authorised the appointment of a lieutenant-governor of Bengal.

But in the matter of legislation the act of 1833 introduced sweeping changes. Till then the governor-general and council had legislated for the Bengal presidency, and the provincial governments for the others. Thus three series of regulations (as their enactments were called) had come into existence. These were frequently ill-drawn, having been drafted by inexperienced men; frequently conflicting, in some cases as the result of varying conditions, in others merely by accident; and in all cases enforcible only by the company's courts of law and outside the limits of the presidency towns. Besides these regulations existed uncertain and ill-defined bodies of Hindu and Muslim law and custom. Lastly the English statute and common law and equity were within certain limitations applied by the Supreme Courts in the presidency towns themselves. These diverse systems of law were enforcible by two different and often hostile judicatures—the king's or Supreme Courts and the company's courts—with ill-defined jurisdictions. The legal position was thus not only full of defects in a theoretical sense but also about to become a matter of great practical importance. The abolition of the company's trade was to be accompanied by the withdrawal of the right to license British-born subjects proceeding to India and summarily to remove them if they had no licence or if the provincial government pleased to cancel it. Large numbers of merchants and traders were expected to settle in India. It would be most inexpedient to permit such of these as chose to reside outside the presidency towns to be perpetually appealing to the Supreme Courts from the jurisdiction or the decisions of the company's tribunals. For these reasons it was resolved to extend and to concentrate the legislative authority in India. Law was in future to be made solely by the governor-general and council; and the need of special laws to suit local peculiarities was met by empowering the presidency governments to submit draft laws for enactment by the central authority. The powers of legislation granted to the Government of India were much wider than any till then entrusted to an Indian legislature. It could repeal or alter any laws or regulations then in force; it could make laws for all persons, British, foreign or Indian; it could regulate the jurisdiction of all courts, whether set up by the crown or otherwise; it could not modify the new act, the Mutiny Act, any future act of parliament relating to India, or the sovereignty of the crown; but apart from this its acts should possess "the same force and effect" as an act of parliament and be enforced by all courts of justice, king's or company's. Till then the king's courts had lain under no obligation to enforce the enactments of Indian legislatures; and still less had the latter possessed power in any way to touch the jurisdiction of the king's courts.

In connection with these changes in the legislature two further innovations deserve mention. One was the inclusion of an additional member in the Council of India. The definition of his qualifications was purely negative. He was not to be a member of the company's civil or military service. It was also laid down that he was entitled to speak and vote only at meetings held for the consideration of legislative business. The office thus obscurely defined speedily became known as that of law member. He was intended to devote himself particularly to the consideration of legislative proposals and to the drafting of acts, and to provide the council with that qualified technical criticism, lack of which had marred many of the earlier regulations. Macaulay was the first to hold this new office; and though he was far from being an eminent jurist, his appointment was undoubtedly a great success. The creation of the law member is further noteworthy since it represents the first step taken to differentiate the council in its executive from the council in its legislative capacity. The governor-general in council was further directed to appoint "Indian law commissioners" to consider and report on the changes desirable in the jurisdictions of the various courts and above all the codification of the disparate bodies of law recognised by the various Indian tribunals. The body, largely under the inspiration of Macaulay, did much preliminary work facilitating the preparation of the codes which became law soon after the assumption of direct government by the crown.

The act of 1853 revised and considerably improved the legislative organ created by the act of 1833. For one thing the governor-general, who had enjoyed merely a casting vote in legislative business under the earlier act, was given a specific power of veto, which till then had been lodged in the home government alone. For another the law member became an ordinary member of council, entitled to speak and vote at all its meetings. For a third the differentiation of the legislative body was carried a long step onwards. Certain additional persons were to be added under the statutory title of "legislative councillors". These were to consist of a covenanted servant nominated by each governor or lieutenant-governor, together with the chief justice of the Supreme Court of Calcutta, one of the puisne judges of the court, and two other covenanted servants. These changes increased the legal element and introduced a new and much needed provincial element. But they also produced a very unexpected consequence —the relaxation of executive control over the legislature. The judges were obviously independent members; and the provincial members, though covenanted servants, were always men of considerable seniority who regarded their legislative councillorships as the last office they would hold in India and who did not look to the Government of India for promotion of any sort. The result was that the enlarged council of 1853 proved to be an independent and very troublesome body, far from what the president of the board, Sir Charles Wood, had intended to establish.

At the same time the structure of the Government of India was materially altered—not for the better. Until 1853 membership of the Council of India had been the highest office within the reach of covenanted servants. But by the new act the salaries of councillors were reduced to 80,000 rupees a year while those of lieutenant-governors were raised to 100,000. In effect the latter office was elevated above the former. The governor-general was thus deprived, or relieved, of that independent, disinterested advice which might be expected so long as his council did not look to him for further promotion and dignity. But now the councillors were provided with a motive for acquiescing whenever possible in the governor-general's views, and the supreme council lost the supreme position commensurate with its dignity and duties.

The acts of 1833 and 1853 introduced one other most important administrative change. The covenanted servants, who by the act of 1793 could alone be named to any civil office in the regulation provinces carrying a salary of over £800 a year, had always been nominated by the court of directors; and consequently had always been chosen from among their relations and friends. In 1813 Lord Grenville had suggested that it would be better if the service were recruited according to the results of a competitive examination. In 1833 an attempt was made to introduce a modification of this idea. The act of that year directed that the directors should annually nominate three times as many candidates as there were places to be filled, and that one-third of their nominees should be selected by competition. This plan if enforced might have combined the merits of nomination with those of competition. The candidates, as before, would have sprung from families connected with India, would have carried out with them family traditions, and would have been welcomed in India by family friends, Indian and European. At the same time competition would have weeded out the bad bargains. But the directors were too tenacious of their patronage easily to give way. In the next year they induced the easy-going president of the board to introduce an amending bill permitting the introduction of the new measure to be deferred. It was in consequence never brought into operation. But in 1853 Macaulay, who had been the prime mover in the earlier proposal, delivered a most eloquent defence of competition as a means of selecting public servants. The plan was adopted, and the directors' patronage thus vanished altogether. Here as elsewhere it is difficult not to regret Macaulay's success, however much the motives underlying his policy merit sympathy. The system certainly secured for India the services of a greater number of brilliant men than could have been obtained in any other way. But it may be doubted whether it provided her with as many devoted and understanding servants. And it carried with it another disadvantage. The act of 1833 had declared that high employment in India should not be a matter of race or creed or colour. But the establishment of competition involved in practice the exclusion of Indians from high office for many years. Lord Stanley was in the right when he opposed the proposal in 1853.

It was, he declared, a step back, not a step forward, for "while the old system could not have been permanent, the present plan would not be felt as an abuse in this country, whatever it might be in India, and it would therefore be allowed to continue without improvement". Lord Stanley's forecast was fulfilled to the letter. But here, as in other points relating to the structure of the Indian government, the main outlines were fixed in the period 1818–58 in the form in which they were to continue for another half-century.

II

In the sphere of district administration the forty years following 1818 were strongly formative. The earlier years had been experimental. But with experience certain methods of district organisation developed as most suitable and effective, and mark a considerable change of conception from that underlying the district system originally established in Bengal. That had been founded on the permanent zamindari settlement of the land revenue. It had been hoped that, as the settlement would reduce the labour of collecting the land revenue to a minimum, it would therefore enable the foreign administrators to devote themselves to the more important aspects of government, to the suppression of crime and to the hearing of civil suits. But it was found to involve one most grievous disadvantage. The collector had no need to know more of his district than that certain zamindars were annually liable for certain sums of money. The judge could merely hear such suits as were brought before him. Neither had any need, and neither was in fact permitted, to tour his district except in very special circumstances. Neither learned to know the people entrusted to his control. No general survey was attempted, although Lord Hastings in 1822 had dwelt upon the importance of surveying Bengal and Bihar and placing on record the various rights of individuals to the soil. Thus the permanent settlement was not only the fruit of ignorance, but the perpetuator of ignorance.

By good fortune the land tenures and therefore the land revenue settlements in the other provinces were of a wholly different nature. In most of Madras, in Bombay, in Āgra, in the Panjab, the land-holders were generally peasant-proprietors, either owning their fields individually, or forming communities of collective owners. In either case a revenue settlement could not be accomplished without going into great detail. So from the first the company's servants were forced into learning all they could about the economic condition, the social organisation, the customs and languages, of the people. Again the amount of detail involved in the revenue collections made a large revenue staff necessary. Whereas in Bengal a collector for long had no assistants beyond the clerks at his headquarters, elsewhere in each *taluk* or *tahsil* (as the sub-divisions of a district were variously called) the collector had a tahsildar (in Madras or Āgra) or a māmlatdar (in Bombay), and under them a host of village headmen, all of whom could be required to furnish him with information. The consequent difference was remarkable. In 1824 the court of directors was already calling pointed attention to the fact that in Madras a competent collector could manage the revenue detail of a whole district, but if in Bengal a small tract or two had to be managed directly instead of through a zamindar, it was "almost always managed ill".

It should not, however, be supposed that the provincial settlements outside Bengal were from the first satisfactory. They were not. But constantly accumulating information permitted and even promoted their improvement, while the only change for the better in Bengal lay in a growing, uneasy sense of the ignorance amid which the administrator worked. In Madras, for instance, the period begins with the restoration of a ryotwari system instead of the village leases by which the former had been for a while displaced. But the assessments under this "middle ryotwari", as it is technically called, remained heavy and unequal. They were heavy, because they were largely based on old assessments framed in Mughal days when the ideal was a maximum rate—the "perfect assessment"—which could indeed seldom be realised but towards which the *amlah* were expected to strive. They were unequal, because the village accounts had generally been manipulated to favour some at the expense of others, and because no complete and professional survey had been attempted. Neither was there as yet any standard method by which assessments were made. A field might be measured; or its crop roughly estimated; or a lump sum might be imposed on a village and then roughly divided among the cultivators. But even so a number of reforms were gradually made. The ancient custom of compelling the other inhabitants of a village to make good the arrears of one of their number was abandoned. So was another ancient practice—that of compelling ryots to cultivate a larger area than they wished. So also was the long-established use of levying increased rates on the more valuable crops which were grown if the owner sank a well to irrigate his land. Finally in 1855 a professional field-to-field survey was determined on; and in the same year began a prolonged discussion of the principles on which the revenue ought to be assessed, leading at last in 1864 to the adoption of the principles which characterise "new ryotwari"—that not more than half the net produce should be taken and that the assessment should remain unchanged for thirty years.

The history of ryotwari in Bombay is not dissimilar. There the company's government inherited from the Marāthas a *kāmil* or perfect assessment which could hardly ever be realised. After some years of a desultory farming of the land revenue, and a projected introduction of village settlements suggested by the existence of joint villages in Gujarāt and traces of a joint village system in the Deccan, a ryotwari survey and settlement were attempted, but proved worse even than the previous mode of collection. The survey was rough and inaccurate. The classification of the soils was over-elaborate. The assessment was impossibly onerous, and could never be realised. But this proved to be no worse than a bad beginning. In 1835 a revision was begun, and by 1847 the well-known *Joint Report* laid down the principles of modern assessment for the presidency. Whatever may be said of its initial stages, the ryotwari system proved to be singularly capable of improvement and reform.

In Āgra the land tenures demanded a different treatment. Wellesley had wished to apply the Bengal system there, just as he had attempted to do in the Madras presidency. But the unsuitability of that system was so evident that the commission appointed to introduce a permanent settlement reported that it was impracticable. A similar view was taken by the Court of Directors, who had been considerably impressed by the evidence of Munro on the subject of land revenue management. Āgra therefore escaped a permanent settlement, although the earlier assessments were often nothing better than the acceptance of the bids of revenue farmers. In 1822, however, the foundation of a better system was laid. Holt Mackenzie, a distinguished covenanted servant on the Bengal establishment, secured the adoption of a law known as Regulation VII of 1822. This laid down certain fundamental principles for the revenue settlement in Āgra. These included the execution of an exact field-to-field survey, and the preparation of registers showing all existing rights over the soil. Areas were only to be assessed after a local enquiry had been held, and tenant-right was to be recognised and protected. The standard rate at which the revenue was to be assessed was fixed at five-sixths of the rental. A good deal of difficulty was found in determining rental values. Money rents were most unusual, and rental values generally depended on estimates of crop-values. The system was therefore modified. Under Bird and Thomason rules were at last prepared by which the demand was reduced from five-sixths to two-thirds of the rental value, and the process was simplified by framing the aggregate demand on a tract of country and then distributing it in detail. The cadastral survey, as it proceeded, threw much light on the organisation of the village communities of the province. These were bodies much more closely knit than the villages of South India and the Deccan, where the village lands were commonly divided out into separate and individual holdings. The Āgra villages were mostly "joint" villages—owned in common by a family or group of families holding a superior position, but tilled by an inferior group. The latter, however, often claimed occupancy rights over the land they actually cultivated, and the extent to which such rights should be recognised was very difficult to determine. In a practical sense this matter was settled by adopting a rule originally proposed by Lord William Bentinck in 1832, recognising persons who could prove a continuous occupation for twelve years as possessed of heritable rights to cultivate the land in question at a rent which in case of dispute was to be determined by a court of law.

The prevalence of the "joint" village in the Panjab led naturally, when that province passed into the company's possession, to the application of the revenue system which had grown up in Āgra. Tenant-right was recognised in the Panjab from the first. The twelve-year rule was commonly applied. The settlements were made on special local enquiries, and moderation in assessment was urged from the first.

The mode of land settlement thus corresponded with the characteristic land tenures. In Bengal the existence of great zamindars led to a zamindari settlement marred by a practical neglect of tenant-right; in Madras and Bombay the prevalence of small individual holdings produced a ryotwari system; while in Āgra and the Panjab the existence of a strong village system led to a method of village settlements. In Bengal the zamindari system made a detailed survey appear needless; in the other provinces a minute survey was found to be the indispensable basis of a settlement.

It followed that the executive officials at the head of the districts played a far larger part in the administration of the other provinces than was the case in Bengal. Not only was the collector elsewhere responsible for all the detail involved in village or ryotwari assessments, but he was in charge also of other administrative work that closely touched the ryot. He decided boundary disputes, disputes about the sharing of water, disputes about rents or customary payments. He directed the repair of water-channels and the clearing of irrigation tanks. Such matters necessitated constant relations, wholly unknown in Bengal, between the peasant on the one side and the collector and his revenue subordinates on the other.

In all the older provinces the administration of justice and the management of the police were more nearly assimilated to the system established in Bengal than was the case with the revenue administration; but even here remarkable differences long continued to exist, and here it was the Bengal system which came ultimately to be modified. In Bengal in 1818 civil justice was administered by district judges, with a considerable number of subordinate Indian judges under them. Reforms introduced by Bentinck improved the status of the latter by the creation of a new and superior grade entitled "principal sadr amīns", who could try cases involving values up to 5000 rupees. On the criminal side the district judges were also magistrates, who might deal with cases summarily or commit the accused for trial by courts of circuit presided over by members of the four provincial courts which heard appeals in civil causes from the decision of the district judges. For police purposes the districts were divided into fifteen or twenty circles called *thānas*, each under the control of a *daroga* who directed the activities of a number of paid police and who might call upon the services of the village-watchmen—*chaukidars*. The police-force was under the general control of four superintendents, stationed at Calcutta, Dacca, Patna and Murshidābād; but in each district responsibility lay with the civil judge in his capacity as magistrate. The underlying principle of these arrangements was the complete separation of revenue functions from those of justice and police.

Precisely the same organisation had at first been established in Madras, but there, as in Bengal, produced a host of evils. The district judges, oppressed with heavy judicial duties, could not even attempt to supervise the police. Judicial processes were elaborate and expensive. The regulations which they administered were unknown to the peasant, and in fact could not be made known to him in the existing state of communications and illiteracy. The great opponent of this system was Thomas Munro. "It has left the ryots in a worse state", he wrote, "than under any native government".[1] In consequence of his criticisms the control of the police was transferred from the civil judge to the collector, who became the collector and magistrate, with the tahsildar in charge of the police-force within the *taluk*. Similar arrangements were adopted in the Bombay presidency and later in the Āgra province. The change was an undoubted improvement. The union of revenue and police control in the hands of a collector who was accustomed to tour his district, see things for himself, and discuss local affairs with the villagers, meant that his means of information would be greatly increased, along with his powers of action, while he would also be better able to estimate the accuracy or falsehood of the reports which came to him from either department. The control of the police still remained very inadequate. The first steps to amend it were taken in Bombay in 1852, when the system of semi-military police established by Sir Charles Napier in Sind was extended to the rest of the province. In Madras a prolonged and exhaustive enquiry into the misconduct of the police—the Torture Commission of 1855—led to the reorganisation of the department under an inspector-general, with a special superintendent in every district. In the North-Western Provinces—as Āgra came to be called—no change was made till 1861.

But in spite of these defects the administrative superiority of the system operating outside Bengal was sufficiently marked to induce efforts to reform conditions in Bengal itself. In 1829 Bentinck

[1] Gleig, *Life of Munro*, 1, 460.

attempted for a while to restore the vigour of the administration by creating commissioners, with general authority over both revenue and judicial functionaries in groups of districts. These commissioners replaced the provincial courts of appeal. They were to hold assizes for the punishment of serious crime, and to supervise the conduct of both the collectors and the judge-magistrates. In 1831, since these duties were found to be beyond the powers of a single person, the duty of holding assizes was transferred to the district judges. Soon afterwards experiments were made in the direction of creating separate magistrates in each district, so that for a while the normal district control was vested in a judge exercising both civil and criminal jurisdiction, a magistrate controlling the police, and a collector. But at last on the urgent recommendations of Halliday, the first lieutenant-governor of Bengal, of Dalhousie, and of Canning, it was decided in 1859 to invest the collector with the control of the police-establishment. This meant the adoption in Bengal of the district-organisation which had grown up, a generation earlier, in Madras, Bombay, and Āgra, though the Bengal collector remained shackled by the zamindari settlement and bereft of the revenue subordinates who were the eyes and ears of the collectors in other provinces.

The history of district-administration from 1818 to 1858 thus displays the escape of the other provinces from the thraldom of the Cornwallis system, and the way in which the permanent zamindari settlement obstructed the attempts made in Bengal in the same direction. The stagnancy of the administration in Bengal as compared with the progress made in the other provinces illustrates the same truth. In 1810 Minto when governor-general had lamented the prevalence of dacoity, and complained that the dacoit leaders were known popularly as *hakim* or governor, and that the district authorities could not secure the least aid for their apprehension. In 1852, despite the passing of two special acts in 1843 and 1851, the magistrate at Hugli reported the existence of 35 gangs of dacoits operating round Calcutta. In 1856 the lieutenant-governor could still assert that the conduct of criminal justice was popularly regarded as a lottery, and that while the people thought a dacoity bad they regarded the subsequent police-enquiry as worse. Education only touched the inhabitants of Calcutta itself. The province was left virtually without roads.

Cultivation had undoubtedly expanded, but this had weakened the position of the tenant by depriving him of the power of migration which in the past had always limited the zamindar's power of extortion.

In contrast with this, the other provinces exhibit considerable efforts to improve the condition of the people. In Madras, for instance, ever-increasing attention was given to the maintenance of the irrigation-tanks. In 1819 a special department (the *maramat* or repair department) was organised under the collectors. In 1825 it was placed under the superintendence of the Board of Revenue, under which civil engineers were placed in charge of groups of districts. In 1852 a committee of enquiry sat, in consequence of which the modern Public Works Department was set up in 1858. Much was also done to extend irrigation. Under the conduct of Arthur Cotton the repair and extension of the Kāveri works was begun in 1836; the same engineer began the Godāvarī dam in 1846; in 1850 the Krishnā delta system was begun. In Bombay the Bombay Education Society and the Bombay Native Education Society opened and maintained primary schools in various districts. In 1840 a Board of Education was formed, consisting of four European members nominated by government and three Indian members nominated by the Native Education Society; when in 1852 government increased its subsidy from one-and-a-half to two-and-a-half lakhs of rupees, the board undertook to open a school in any village where the inhabitants would provide a building and the necessary books, and agree to find half the schoolmaster's salary. In Āgra, where the population was specially exposed to famine, irrigation received much attention. Between 1815 and 1827 military officers restored the canal dug by Fīrūz Shāh, now known as the West Jumna Canal. Then a smaller canal—the East Jumna Canal—was restored. In 1836 a new project—the Upper Ganges Canal—was proposed, and completed by Cautley in 1854.

All these provinces were what were technically known as "Regulation" provinces. These were marked by being ruled under definite bodies of enactments—the regulations passed by the company's presidency governments up to 1833, and the legislation passed by the Government of India after that date. For the enforcement of these laws there was an elaborate chain of courts with strict and elaborate rules of procedure. The judges were

entirely separate from the revenue and executive officials; and by
English statute both judges and revenue officials could be ap-
pointed only from the ranks of the company's covenanted service.
At first this method formed the standard pattern of administration.
Originating in Bengal, it was extended as a matter of course to
Benares, to the Madras Presidency, to the Bombay Presidency,
and to the territories which were to form the North-Western
Provinces. But even in Bengal it soon became apparent that this
was too elaborate and mechanical a system to be universally
applicable. In Bengal for instance the districts fringing the north-
east frontier—Rangpur, Assam, Arakan—were inhabited by or in
close contact with primitive tribes for whom complicated forms
and procedure were strange and incomprehensible. The same was
the case with parts of Orissa. A striking illustration of the futility
of hoping to provide justice by making law and setting up courts
was afforded by the Santhāl rebellion in 1835. The Santhāls, a
numerous group of primitive tribes, being oppressed by Bengali
and Bihari landlords, never thought of appealing to the courts of
law but broke into rebellion, torturing and exterminating all the
Bengalis they could find. Regular troops had to be sent against
them, and, when the rebellion had been reduced, the Santhāl
country was made into a separate district in which, as in Rangpur
and Assam, the Regulation system was declared not to apply.
A similar course was found necessary in the Madras Presidency in
the hill tracts of the Northern Circars, and in Bombay in the Bhīl
country, where a special agency was established in 1825 and
furnished occupation to the young Outram.

The special features of these "non-regulation" areas were that
ordinary law did not apply unless specially extended. The governor-
general, or the governor, in his executive capacity would issue as
orders such rules as he desired to be observed. He could, moreover, select to conduct the administration persons whom he
judged to be particularly suitable, irrespective of their belonging
to the covenanted service. The mode of government was personal
and paternal, all authority, executive, revenue and judicial, being
usually concentrated in the same official; and the general purpose
was to disturb tribal or local custom as little as possible, and to
make changes only with the greatest caution and on some evident
necessity.

The earliest acquisition thus to be dealt with was the Delhi territory. But the reason for this was political rather than administrative, for the government, though conducted by the authority of the governor-general, was carried on in the name of the Mughal emperor. Sind afforded the earliest illustration of the non-regulation system applied on a considerable scale. There the reasons were partly personal. The conqueror of Sind, Sir Charles Napier, had conceived a strong distaste for the civil government of the Bombay Presidency. The hot-headed Ellenborough distrusted his members of council, his foreign secretary, and many others of the covenanted servants with whom he came in contact. Both therefore preferred to staff the province with military officers, and consequently the form of government was inevitably non-regulation. Napier divided the province into three collectorates with a head-collector in each, and a number of deputies. All were magistrates as well as collectors, with limited powers of punishment. Ordinary civil disputes were referred to a *panchayat* constituted by the collector-magistrate, the members receiving a small payment to compensate their loss of time. The *kārdars*—or village headmen—were maintained in their former functions; and a body of police under military discipline was organised, directly commanded by their own officers but at the disposition of the collector-magistrates. This system at first provoked much criticism; but its successful working came gradually if reluctantly to be recognised, and when Dalhousie conquered and annexed the Panjab, he followed the precedent set by Napier and Ellenborough. The country was organised in eight divisions, each under a commissioner, and twenty-four districts, each under a deputy-commissioner, and placed under the management of a peculiarly able group of men. They included the two Lawrences, John Nicholson, Robert Montgomery, Herbert Edwardes, Robert Napier, and Donald Macleod, and thus represented both the covenanted and the military services. There were no separate courts. The commissioners and deputy-commissioners exercised full criminal jurisdiction, and in civil causes made much use of panchayats. The law administered was at first customary law and a rough equity. But rules were gradually laid down by executive order. In 1855 a civil code was issued embodying a great amount of the customary law of the province. A Public Works Department was immediately organised, and set to work to make roads and improve the irrigation-canals, not only cleaning and extending the "inundation" canals which filled only in the flood season, but also constructing the first perennial canal—the Upper Bāri doāb Canal—between 1851 and 1859.

III.

While the mechanism of district management was thus being elaborated, the spirit of the government was also being transformed, so that the new efficiency was being applied to new purposes. From 1818 until the close of the century British rule in India remained virtually unassailed except by the catastrophe of the Indian Mutiny; and that event being mainly military in its detail if not in its causes, one is apt to look back upon the period as one in which the government rested upon unassailable foundations. But that was not the view of contemporaries. So early as 1794 Shore doubted whether the English government in Bengal would last another fifty years. Wellesley within a month of overthrowing Tipu Sultān was demanding increased military forces lest his countrymen should "suffer the fate of those whose minds are unequal to the magnitude of their fortunes and who are afraid of their own strength".[1] Elphinstone was alarmed by "the great strides we are making towards universal dominion", and likened the empire to steel "which cuts through everything if you keep its edge even, but is very apt to snap short if it falls into unskilful hands".[2] Metcalfe was "ever anxiously alive to the instability of our Indian empire". The British provinces, he believed, held many internal enemies, "ready for change if not ripe for insurrection". John Shore's son declared that the constant presence of troops alone prevented disturbances.

The strength of the British dominion resided in positive and negative groups of factors. The positive group included such obvious things as British naval supremacy, uncontested since the battle of Trafalgar; British military skill and obstinacy, proved on battle-field after battle-field, and ultimately victorious in the hills of Nepāl, as in the jungles of Burma; and British solidarity, attested equally in parliamentary debate and in the obedience shown in India to the commands of the governor-general in council. The negative group consisted in the complete lack of union among Indians, Muslim and Hindu, Brāhman and out-caste,

[1] Wellesley, *Despatches*, II, 42.
[2] Colebrooke, *Life of Elphinstone*, II, 167.

Rājput and Bābu, being wholly unable to find any common cause against the foreigner; in the weariness of everlasting war, pillage, and unsettlement, which had been the general lot outside the British provinces for half a century and more; and above all in the political apathy which for ages had characterised the bulk of the population. "They take no interest", wrote Thomas Munro with complete truth, "in political revolutions; they consider defeat and victory as no concern of their own, but merely as the good or bad fortune of their masters; and they only prefer one to another in proportion as he respects their religious prejudices or spares taxation".[1] But it could not be supposed that these negatives offered a permanent foundation. Political apathy might wear away; the terror of marauding armies would gradually be forgotten; religion might offer a cause which could unite, if not the general body of the people, at least great sections of them.

The company's government was at first deeply conscious of all this, and most reluctant to do or suffer to be done anything which could appear like an attack on social customs or religion. But gradually its attitude changed. Under the impulsion of liberal ideas in politics and evangelical ideas in religion, under the guidance of Whig governors-general like Bentinck, Auckland, and Dalhousie, missionary activities developed, an educational policy was adopted, humanitarian ideals were pursued, in a manner which would have shocked and alarmed an earlier generation. The *laissez-faire* of the Cornwallis régime gave way to the paternalism of the 'non-regulation' system in the moral as well as in the administrative sphere.

The change was demonstrated by the admission of new missionary bodies to India, and by a growing support of them by members of the company's services. Early in the eighteenth century the Danish missionaries, established at the Danish settlement of Tranquebar on the Coromandel Coast, had received considerable financial help from the English Society for Promoting Christian Knowledge, and from time to time members of the mission had been employed as interpreters and chaplains by the Madras Government. But this was at a time when the company was not a great territorial power in southern India. In Bengal for many years after its acquisition missionary activity was strongly discouraged. A Bengal regulation passed in 1793 declared that

[1] Gleig, *op. cit.* I, 203.

Hindu and Muslim law should be upheld, that all religious rites and customs were to be allowed, and all religious·endowments maintained. In the same year the company successfully resisted the efforts of Wilberforce and the Clapham Sect to impose upon it missionary responsibilities. In the same year again William Carey, the famous Baptist missionary, was·compelled to sail to Bengal by a foreign ship and to establish himself under the Danish flag at Serampore, where he and his companions, Marshman and Ward, taught, preached, and laid the foundations of Bengali prose by their translations from the Bible. Though the Serampore missionaries were countenanced and encouraged by Wellesley, difficulties arose with his successors, and on various occasions missionaries were deported from British India or not allowed to land. In 1813 the act continuing the company's privileges not only authorised the appointment of a bishop and archdeacons in India but also gave the Board of Control the power of reversing any refusal by the company to allow individual missionaries to proceed to India. After 1833 no licence at all was required. As a result of these changes and the growth of the Evangelical Movement in England, a considerable number of missionaries, both Scotch and English, went to India, where they preached Christianity with great zeal and did much to promote the cause of western education.

In other respects too their presence in India produced important changes. The company's government had inherited from the past customs such as that of turning out troops and firing salutes on certain Hindu festivals, taxes such as the pilgrim tax levied for the maintenance of certain temples, duties such as the administration of endowments bestowed upon temples, mosques, and tombs. All these were capable of being represented as unworthy support accorded by a Christian government to heathen worship. The missionaries did so represent them, and received sufficient support in England to secure the writing of a despatch in 1833 requiring their abandonment. For some years nothing was done. But (again in consequence of missionary representations) another despatch was sent in 1838 demanding immediate compliance with the previous orders. These were at last put into effect, save that in some places no suitable trustees could be found to manage the endowments, which therefore continued under the control of the revenue authorities till 1863. The government was, and on the whole remained, decidedly averse from any encouragement of

proselytism. But it was scarcely possible to resist the rising tide
of sentiment. Two of the most eminent of the Panjab school—
John Lawrence and Herbert Edwardes—leaned strongly to the
view that Providence had placed India in British hands in order
that the people might be Christianised; more than one colonel of
the Bengal Army preached the gospel zealously between parades;
and even Lord Palmerston, at a banquet given to Canning on his
appointment as governor-general, observed that "perhaps it might
be our lot to confer on the countless millions of India a higher and
nobler gift than any mere human knowledge".

Parallel with this movement went the development of an
educational policy. Here, as elsewhere, Bengal followed a special,
and, as might be expected, a faulty policy of its own. The men of
the eighteenth century, such as Warren Hastings and Jonathan
Duncan, and those who had inherited their tradition, had sought
to revive and strengthen the classical cultures of the Hindu and
the Muslim. Hastings had founded a school for the study of
Persian and Arabic; Duncan one for the study of Sanskrit. With
Hastings's support, Sir William Jones had founded the Bengal
Asiatic Society. When in 1813 the British Parliament authorised
expenditure on the promotion of useful learning in India, the
money was mainly used in printing in Sanskrit, Persian and Arabic
original works and some translations of English text-books, and in
providing scholarships for promising students of Indian classical
literatures. But already a strong contrary current of opinion had
arisen. David Hare, the free-thinking watchmaker of Calcutta,
planned a school where young Indians could be taught western
literature and science. In this scheme he succeeded in interesting
Europeans like Sir Hyde East, the chief justice, and Indians like
Rām Mohun Roy, with the result that an institution called "The
Abode of Learning"—Vidyalaya—was set up, known subsequently as the Hindu College and then the Presidency College.
The Serampore missionaries established a college under the
patronage of the king of Denmark and the governor-general to
teach western knowledge. In 1820 missionary bodies founded the
"Bishop's College" at Calcutta; in 1823 a college was founded
and endowed at Āgra by Pandit Gangadhar. These new institutions were designed to spread western knowledge and languages,
not to promote oriental studies. Rām Mohun Roy and his friends
indeed presented a petition to Lord Amherst, criticising the

orientalist policy of teaching "what was known two thousand years ago with the addition of vain and empty subtilties since produced by speculative men". Much anxiety was displayed by a wide circle of Indians to learn English, and Bishop Heber noticed a strong tendency to imitate English ways. It became increasingly evident that English studies were popular and that oriental studies were not. The Committee of Public Instruction, to which the administration of public funds had been entrusted, was rent in sunder between the two policies. Charles Trevelyan, a brilliant but erratic young covenanted servant, pointed out that while a private society had sold over 31,000 volumes of English text-books in two years, the committee had not sold enough of its Sanskrit and Arabic volumes in half as long again to meet its warehouse charges for two months; he added that the young men at the Sanskrit College had petitioned, representing that the knowledge they had acquired would not enable them to earn a living. The cause of western education was also strenuously advocated by a Scotch missionary, Alexander Duff, who had opened a secondary school at Calcutta with the assistance of Rām Mohun Roy. He argued that all save the literate castes were prohibited from learning Sanskrit. Even were modern works translated into that language (he added), every term in it was so saturated with Hindu philosophic ideas that the translation must fail altogether to convey the thought of the original.

In the autumn of 1834 Macaulay reached Calcutta as the first law member of the governor-general's council. He was at once appointed president of the education committee, and within a few months of his arrival was urging upon the governor-general, Bentinck, with all the force of his specious rhetoric, the wholesale adoption of the English policy. He recommended that the printing of Sanskrit and Arabic texts should cease, that the Muslim and Sanskrit colleges should be closed, that the scholarships to students of Islam and Hinduism should be discontinued, and that all the available state funds should be devoted to promoting the study of English and English literature. This, he supposed, would produce a class of persons "Indian in blood and colour, but English in tastes, in opinions, in morals, in intellect". Not many months later he had convinced himself that within a generation all the respectable classes of Bengal would have ceased to be Hindus.

These ideas were adopted and recommended by Bentinck, but

were strenuously opposed by H. T. Prinsep, who pointed out that the Muslims had as yet exhibited no inclination to study English, and that, even among the Hindus, only those who had had connections with the English through public or private service really regarded the study of their foreign tongue and alien literature as indispensable. But his opposition was unheeded. The proposal to abolish the government teaching of Sanskrit and Arabic was indeed dropped; but it was resolved to make English literature the main subject of instruction. The possibility of instruction in such subjects as science and agriculture was virtually ignored. The decision to make English the basis of Indian education was inevitable. It complied with a strong local demand; it was backed by missionary opinion; it fell in with the views of the government, both in Calcutta and in London, which desired to extend the range of appointments open to Indians; above all it was a necessary measure if British rule was to do more for India than establish internal peace and secure her from external invasion. But as a policy it was too limited. It left out of account the Muslims who believed no education of the least value unless based on Arabic, and women, who in the existing state of society never dreamed of attending schools and colleges. Essentially literary, it provided no corrective for the prevalent faults of classes whose education had always been of a literary nature. And the fact that it would be applied to boys and not to girls meant that it would be ineffective; the future mothers of the classes that embraced it would remain wedded to the old ideas; and what a boy learnt at school would therefore conflict with the atmosphere of the home.

Soon afterwards, in 1842, the Committee of Public Instruction vanished. In Calcutta it was replaced by a Council of Education, on which a number of Indians sat. Outside Calcutta the government undertook the direct responsibility. Hardinge announced in 1844 that candidates with a knowledge of English would be preferred for public appointments. This step was doubly unfortunate. Young men who had sat successfully for examinations held by the Council of Education were registered as eligible; but eligibility and appointment were different things; and great heart-burning was caused. What was even worse, it invested western education with adventitious attractions, leading men to seek it, not because they set any special value on western knowledge, but purely as a passport to government service. Little was done to promote the efficiency of indigenous schools, and about 1853 while government was assisting thirty schools and colleges in Bengal, where English was the chief medium of instruction, it was maintaining only thirty-three where the vernacular was in use. The Bengal educational policy was thus wedded to what was known as the "filtration" policy—of leaving elementary education to care for itself and concentrating on English and especially higher education in the hope that western culture would gradually permeate the whole population.

Authorities in the Agra province had followed a wholly different course. James Thomason, the lieutenant-governor from 1843 to 1853, was above all anxious to promote rural education. A plan was at length formed to group villages in circles of five and set up a school wherever the land-owners were willing to pay an additional cess of one per cent. on the land-revenue. In 1852–3 the scheme was brought into force in eight districts, and was afterwards extended. Another development of great importance was the establishment of the Thomason College of Engineering at Rūrkī. In Bombay too the "filtration" theory of education had been set aside. Elphinstone, the first governor of the presidency in its modern form, had done much to promote classical and vernacular studies. He had continued the custom followed by the Pēshwā, of granting allowances to distinguished Sanskrit scholars; and after a time this had led to the foundation of a Sanskrit college at Poona. He had also attempted to encourage and increase the vernacular schools of the presidency. But he had as well set up in Bombay a school for English, an engineering school, and a medical school. Malcolm, his successor, reckoned a knowledge of English as a very trivial qualification for service under government. While missionary enterprise, as in Bengal, had been active in providing English education, the government had rather applied its funds to vernacular schools, of which in 1853 it was maintaining 233 against the thirty-three so maintained in Bengal. In Madras, Munro, like Elphinstone, had been anxious to improve vernacular teaching, and had framed a plan for setting up two high schools in each district, together with a normal school for the training of teachers. But these proposals had been abandoned at his death in 1827. A government high-school was founded at Madras, but a very large number of missionary institutions grew up—more indeed than were to be found in all the rest of India.

Educational policy had thus exhibited great diversities of aim and method. To Dalhousie and Wood belong the credit of framing a general policy, which after long correspondence between the two was embodied in the educational despatch of July 19, 1854. It declared the need of "a properly articulated scheme of education from the primary school to the university". The vernacular schools were no longer to be neglected, and the method devised in the Āgra province was proposed for adoption elsewhere. Secondary schools were to be encouraged, and in general the system of making grants-in-aid was to be employed to encourage institutions maintained by missionary and other voluntary bodies, irrespective of their religion. Universities were to be established at Calcutta and Bombay, and perhaps at Madras as well, not indeed to teach, but to conduct examinations and award degrees; and the whole system of primary schools, secondary schools, and colleges was to be linked up by a series of scholarships, to enable persons of special talent to pursue studies from which they would otherwise be debarred by poverty. These orders were carried into execution. The various governments organised departments of public instruction to give effect to a scheme (as Dalhousie described it) "far wider and more comprehensive than the supreme or any local government could have ventured to suggest". But in practice the new policy proved to have inherited more of the emphasis on English studies and on higher education than the despatch itself would suggest. It stood, alongside of missionary effort, as the outstanding challenge of British influence to that old world into which the British had intruded.

The educational ideals thus adopted were purely secular and were in no wise designed as a direct attack upon Hinduism or Islam. They were indeed, as experience has shown, ill-calculated to promote the spread of Christianity. But there were certain social customs much interwoven with Hinduism which a western government could not easily or even honestly tolerate. After a great struggle the British had resolved in 1807 to abolish the slave-trade and in 1833 to emancipate all slaves in British territory. In 1833 when the company's privileges came again before Parliament for renewal, the Indian government was required to take measures for the suppression of slavery in India. To some extent this direction had already been anticipated. In 1789 Cornwallis had forbidden the purchase of slaves for transport to other parts of India or elsewhere. In 1811 the importation of slaves into India had been prohibited. But the institution of slavery was a more difficult thing to abolish. It was an ancient custom for men to sell themselves and their families into slavery in time of famine in order to escape from starvation; and in many parts of India there were whole classes of labourers bound to the soil and in many ways resembling the serfs of medieval Europe. In 1832 the sale of a slave brought from one district to another had become an offence. In 1843 an act was passed directing the courts no longer to recognise the status of slavery. Under the Penal Code of 1860 all keeping of or trafficking in slaves became punishable at law. In practice the status of slavery long survived; and it was not really brought to an end until the spread of education and the improved position of the labourer at the close of the century gave reality to the pious enactment of 1843. The fact illustrates the extreme difficulty with which a closely organised and most conservative society can be modified by law unsupported by economic or moral pressure.

Slavery in India had generally been so different a thing from the slavery of the West Indies that the British government had not felt any great need of rapidly sweeping it away. Other prevalent customs met with less tolerance. There was a practice of casting children into the sea at Sāgar Island in accomplishment of a vow. This was prohibited by Wellesley in 1802. An allied custom was female infanticide as practised by the Rājputs. Jonathan Duncan, when resident at Benares, had discovered its existence among the Rājkumārs and had induced them to forswear it. Custom, however, proved stronger than promises. Although the practice had been declared to be murder, the Rājkumārs were killing their infant daughters as freely in 1816 as they had been in 1795. Walker, political agent in Kāthiāwār, discovered the practice among the Rājputs of western India, and obtained from some of them a covenant such as the Rājkumārs had given to Duncan, but with little more success. The method followed—of refusing to suckle the child—was most difficult of proof. Constant pressure was put on the Rājput tribes both within and without British India by district officials and political agents. But no coercive measures were taken until 1870, when an act was passed permitting rules for the registration of births and verification of the survival of girls to be applied to such districts as seemed to require it.

The practice of burning the widow on her husband's pyre was one which had shocked all foreigners in India. It had been forbidden by the Muslims and by the Portuguese, though the prohibition by Muslim rulers had not been very rigorous or effective, and that by the Portuguese had been too limited in territorial scope to have any effect. While always barbarous in essence—perhaps the last relic of the massacres with which the obsequies of the kings of Ur were celebrated—individual cases varied greatly. If on the one side we have the widow who importuned Colonel Sleeman till at last she wrung from him a most reluctant assent, on the other we must set Rām Mohun Roy's sister-in-law—"an hysterical and unhappy sacrifice"—and the latter case appears to have been the more frequent of the two. Though stated to have been enjoined by a passage in the *Rig-Veda*, it had never been an integral part of Hinduism; and the earliest text cited in support of it has been proved to be a perversion of the original. But it was so closely associated with Hindu practices and so loudly applauded by popular opinion that British administrators long hesitated to interfere with it. Cornwallis in Bengal, Elphinstone in Bombay, would not assent to positive official suppression. It was, indeed, hoped that with the spread of British influence the custom would disappear. Various company's servants and the Serampore missionaries drew the attention of the Bengal government to its prevalence. Wellesley directed the chief criminal court, the *nizāmat 'adālat*, to report on the religious basis of the custom and the possibility of prohibiting it. The judges reported that it was permitted but not enjoined by the *shāstras*, and that it might be abolished in the districts where it was unusual and checked or prevented elsewhere. This report, dated in 1805, long lay unanswered. At last in 1812 the government ordered that all compulsion, intoxication or drugging of the victim should be prevented, and that sati should be allowed only where the case fell within the rules laid down by the *shāstras*. Further rules, intended to prevent the rite except when clearly within the accepted religious limits and requiring relatives to give notice of intended sati to the police, were issued in 1815 and 1817. In the circumstances it would perhaps have been better to do nothing than to issue rules which were interpreted as conveying at least a partial approval. The number of reported *satit* rose considerably, especially in the neighbourhood of Calcutta, where English opinion might have been expected to exercise most influence, and it was believed by the chief judge of the *nizāmat 'adālat* that many women were burned without the knowledge of the police. In view of the unsatisfactory state of police organisation, it seems more likely that police subordinates were often bribed not to report cases that took place. Much criticism was directed against the government both by missionary bodies and by its own officials, who urged that the rules were authorising widows to be sacrificed by their husbands' families. It was a singular fact that more than half the reported cases occurred in five districts of Bengal. At last, in 1823, the court of directors was moved by the pressure of public opinion in England to suggest to Lord Amherst the desirability of further action. But nothing was done. Amherst himself was an irresolute man, and his councillors were averse from action which might raise the cry of "Religion in danger" and which in any case seemed inconsistent with Cornwallis's regulation declaring that Hindu and Muslim law should be upheld. But when Bentinck arrived as governor-general, he resolved to enquire into the question of total prohibition. He found official opinion sharply divided. Even Rām Mohun Roy, who had organised a counter-petition against one which had been presented complaining of the increased stringency of the rules, advised him to wait a while. But relying mainly on the unanimous opinion of the *nizāmat 'adālat*, Bentinck decided on immediate action, and in 1829 passed a regulation declaring the act to be illegal, abetment to be punishable as culpable homicide, and compulsion a capital offence. This was the most daring interference with religious and social customs undertaken by the company's government. A considerable group of Hindus appealed to the Privy Council in the hope of getting he regulation declared invalid. They claimed that it interfered with their most ancient and sacred rites, violated the conscientious beliefs of a whole nation, and infringed the promise to maintain the Hindu religion, laws and customs. But the appeal was emphatically rejected. In the Rājput states the practice continued for a while but vanished before the insistence of Dalhousie and the gradual spread of knowledge among Rājput ladies that it was no longer permitted in British India. In the Panjab it lasted till Dalhousie conquered and annexed the province.

Of much the same nature was the suppression of human sacrifices among the Khonds of the Ganjam and Orissa hills, since that also was a barbaric custom conducted under religious sanction. But in this case the religion was primitive, the custom followed by only a small group of tribes, and its suppression did not carry with it the possibilities of political danger which had made the government hesitate so long in the case of sati. In the course of suppressing a rebellion that had broken out among the disorderly hill zamindars of that area, British officers discovered that the primitive Khond tribes performed an annual sacrifice designed to ensure the fertility of their fields. They kept a class of victims termed *meriahs*, consisting either of unfortunate persons kidnapped from the plains and sold to the Khonds, or of the children of victims so acquired. A number of *meriahs* were chosen yearly and hacked to pieces, every cultivator seeking to obtain a shred of flesh to bury in his field. In 1841 a single tribe sacrificed 240 victims in this manner. The area concerned lay partly in the presidency of Bengal, partly in that of Madras. For some time difficulty was found in co-ordinating the efforts of the two governments; but in 1845 a special agency was constituted under the governor-general. A military officer, Colonel Campbell, who had already served in that part of the country, was appointed agent with special instructions to wean the Khonds from their unpleasant ways; and in the long run he induced the people to substitute buffaloes for human beings, and released a large number of *meriahs*.

In this same period the crime of thagi was suppressed. This offered perhaps the most remarkable example of organised crime on record. Every autumn at the *Dasara* festival, the auspicious time at which to commence a campaign, the thags would assemble in bands ranging from a dozen men to a large company, conduct their operations over a great tract of country, and return about the beginning of the next hot weather to their homes, where they usually followed some ostensible occupation. The gangs were elaborately organised. Some were chosen as spies to go ahead of the rest and find out travellers with property or goods of value. Others again were appointed to prepare graves for the selected victims near the place designed for their murder. The most expert were the men who strangled the victims with a handkerchief—only on the rarest occasions was any other instrument employed. The thags plied their trade under the special protection of the Hindu goddess known variously as Bhowānni or Devi. At the commencement of each campaign propitiatory ceremonies were conducted and recruits initiated; and whenever a likely victim came under consideration the omens were carefully observed. If these were favourable, the traveller was regarded as delivered over by the goddess to death, and the thags believed that if he were not killed the goddess never again would be propitious. The customary process was for the band to fall in as it were by accident with parties of travellers selected by the spies; the place of murder would be chosen and grave-diggers sent on in advance; when nearing it the thags would distribute themselves so that a strangler would be posted beside each victim, and on the appointed signal all would be put to death. Within a few minutes the corpses would be buried. No witnesses would survive to tell the tale; no traces would remain on the road to betray to after-comers the tragedy that had occurred.

Such bands had existed in India for many centuries. As far as is known, no particular effort had ever been made to root them out, and they seem to have been regarded with resigned fatalism, like famine or cholera, to be feared, to be avoided, but not to be resisted. Their existence was well known to the company's governments years before any decided action was taken. The great difficulty was the question of evidence. Eye-witnesses were seldom to be found; and bankers who had lost money, and the relatives of victims, alike were reluctant to appear before distant courts which could restore to them neither their money nor their friends, but merely punish those popularly viewed as the instruments of God. Bentinck resolved to create a special agency for the suppression of thagi, to be placed under the management of Sleeman and other specially competent company's servants. Special courts were formed. Indian rulers like the Nizām and the king of Oudh were induced to waive their jurisdiction over men accused of thagi. Under promise of life a number of thags turned approvers. Their evidence was collated. Places where they said victims had been buried were examined. Thus a mass of evidence was collected, corroborated by statements taken locally from persons who had lost money or friends; and the bands were gradually broken up. Those against whom specific murders could be proved were hanged; the greater number, however, were

transported under a special act of 1836 which had made membership of a thag band a criminal offence.

The concluding part of the period exhibits no measures so
striking as Bentinck's war upon sati and thagi, or his adoption of
English as the basis of Indian education. But Dalhousie passed one
act and introduced another which in principle went much further
than the suppression of sati. Sati was not, and never had been
more than a permissive rite. Strongly encouraged as it had been
by vicious social influences, in itself it had ever been a work of
supererogation. But the re-marriage of a widow was utterly
prohibited by Hindu law. A bill declaring such re-marriages legal
was introduced under Dalhousie in 1855 and passed into law by
Canning in 1856. Hindu sentiment seems however to have been
more deeply affected by an earlier piece of legislation. In 1832
a regulation had been passed by the Bengal legislature relieving
persons who should change their religion from any consequent loss
of property. This had been enacted under missionary influence.
Missions had undoubtedly found their success impeded by the
existence of the Hindu joint family system, under which ancestral
property was owned in common by the family as a whole; and
conversion to Christianity had entailed not only the social consequences of exclusion from the family circle but also the economic
results of a forfeiture of all right to share in the family estate. In
1845 the Bishop of Bombay had complained that the Bengal
regulation did not extend to Bombay; and in 1850 Dalhousie
passed an act, valid for the whole of British India, directing the
courts of law to cease to give effect to any laws or usages inflicting
forfeiture of property or affecting rights of inheritance in the case
of persons changing their religious faith or being deprived of their
caste-rights. This act, like the regulation suppressing sati, produced
considerable alarm among orthodox Hindus. Petitions were
presented against it signed by 60,000 persons from Calcutta and
its neighbourhood. Sixteen years earlier a retired covenanted
servant, who had more than once occupied the chair of the Court
of Directors, had lamented the rising enthusiasm for conversion
which had "already done much to alienate the attachment of the
people, to shake their confidence, and to produce uneasiness and
alarm". Circumstances were to lend great support to his views.
It is clear that the forty years following the overthrow of the
Marāthas introduced many most disturbing influences. The

activity of missions, the evangelical spirit exhibited by many of the company's civil and military servants, educational activity, and the social reforms enforced with unexampled vigour, method and success upon an apathetic and reluctant people, of necessity carried with them a challenge to Hinduism none the less agitating because it was less direct than that which Aurangzīb had given to the Hindu world. It was evident that the foreign government was no longer content, as it once had been, to leave affairs to follow their traditional course, that it was being driven forward by ideals and purposes unquestionable by the modern world but strange, dubious, and alarming in the eyes of a people belonging to the world of the past. Two things should be evident to us who can look back with the knowledge of what was to come. One is that the British government was by its nature, its ideas, its western outlook, bound to give a series of shocks to the world of Hinduism; the other, that the Hindu world was bound to react sharply and convulsively to these external impulses.

CHAPTER XI

The Company's Armies and the Indian Mutiny

In one sense the mutiny of the company's Bengal Army was an inevitable consequence of previous developments; in another it was a mere unlucky accident. It was inevitable because the old Indian world was certain to react against the influence of a more efficient, more interfering, and more systematic government than the country had ever known before, inspired alike by views of social and legal obligation and by conceptions of economic and political progress utterly different from those current among Indians. Until 1818 India had felt little but the political effects of European dominion. She had changed masters with no more concerted opposition than she had offered to the establishment of Muslim domination. The ryot or the Brāhman cared little whether he tilled his fields or performed his rites under the rule of Mīr Kāsim or of Clive; the merchant and the banker definitely preferred the stronger, more efficient rule of the East India Company, though unprepared to risk anything to effect a change. The soldier was more ready to serve the English than any other employer, for their pay was regular and certain, they respected his caste and religious prejudices, and, though they would never suffer him to rise to high rank, their military superiority had been attested on a score of battle-fields and their ascendancy was accepted as a thing of course. So long as the company's government continued to be merely an Indian power, and even when Cornwallis introduced his administrative reforms, this situation persisted. Foreign dominion was nothing to peoples with no consciousness of nationality. But from 1818 the position began to change. This new and strong government proved to be associated with active missionaries who challenged the very foundations of Hinduism and Islam. It interfered to prevent sati, to permit the re-marriage of widows, to save converts from losing their interest in family property. It ceased to take that active and paternal interest that it once had shown in the celebration of festivals and the management of temple funds. It promoted a new type of education which made light of ancient learning. It began to build railways, in the carriages of which the Brāhman might find himself polluted by the touch of Pariahs. It constructed telegraph-lines which carried messages by magic. In what manner could a respectable Hindu consider this impingement of a new world upon his own which had remained unchanged so long? The answer is provided by a great variety of sources. The idea spread abroad that the whole country would soon be westernised and Christianised. At Bombay Parsis and Hindus were made to study Butler's *Analogy of Religion*. At Madras over-zealous missionaries taught Hindu boys to answer questions relating to the Christian faith in language which might have become a Christian but which sounded even to good Christians revolting when put into the mouths of orthodox Hindus. In Bihar the educational inspector's office was popularly known as the "Devil's Office"—the *Shaitani Daftar*. When it was resolved that prisoners might no longer carry their own water-vessels with them to gaol, this was taken to be the opening act of a general scheme to break all caste and convert the whole population to Christianity. Canning believed that "heads of families, and men of wealth and good position, are generally persuaded that their grandsons, if not their sons, will renounce their religion for Christianity". The belief spread from the populace to the sepoy. Before the outbreak of the Mutiny, Henry Lawrence had a long conversation with a Brāhman jamadar of excellent character belonging to the Oudh Artillery, and was quite unable to dissuade the man from believing that the government had been seeking for the previous ten years to break down the system of caste. These ideas were manifestly false; but the importance of a belief has no relation whatever to its truth. Such notions, false as they were, spread alarm, anxiety and distrust through large masses of the population.

Political affairs added to the general disquietude. The Afghan war had doubtless ended with a triumphant vindication of British arms. But the success of Nott and Pollock was far from having obliterated memories of the disaster at Kābul, the massacre of sepoy and Briton alike, and the bondage into which the sepoys' wives and families had fallen. The great strength of the Indian government had lain in opinion—the opinion of its invincibility. That had been rudely shaken. The conduct of more than one sepoy regiment in the Sikh wars suggests that it had not been restored. Then came the wars with Russia in 1854 and with Persia in 1856. The latter was unwelcome to the Muslims in India—even to the Sunnis, for the progressive decline of Islam was already inclining the Muslims to close their ranks and forget even the bitterest sectarian differences. The Russian war produced serious evidence of unrest. The general Indian belief, Dalhousie declared, was that Great Britain would be beaten. He found an uneasy feeling abroad, partly alarm, partly indefinite expectation. A rumour suddenly spread through Calcutta that a Russian fleet had reached the Sandheads; the bazaars closed; and men began to bury their money and jewels for safety.

All this was eagerly canvassed and exaggerated by certain sections of Muhammadans. The Wahhabis, who had their centre at Patna, had ever been an element of disquiet, in communication with fanatical groups on the North-West Frontier, at Swāt and Sitāna. Besides that they had sent preachers into many parts of India, especially the south, where they had provoked sedition at Hyderabad, inveigled the Nawab of Kurnool into the enterprise which cost him first his country and then his life, and preached rebellion at Vellore, the scene of a former bloody, though localised, mutiny in 1809. Even apart from them, the more zealous Muslims had marvelled how Shāh Shujā' could accept infidel help for the recovery of his kingdom of Afghanistan, and about 1852 a ballad had been secretly printed at Calcutta exhorting the faithful to rise and overthrow the infidel government. In 1855 the celebration of Muharram at Hyderabad had been marked by a disquieting incident, in which the resident had been attacked and wounded—it was thought, with the purpose of embroiling the Nizām with the British government. And while the Muslim population included these explosive elements, there were Muslim centres which might at any time serve as detonators. Of these Delhi was the principal. Its imperial traditions, though dimmed, were still unbroken, owing to the facility with which the company's government had suffered the forms of imperial authority to continue; while the recent decision of Canning's government to discontinue the recognition of the imperial family made Delhi abnormally sensitive. As Napier had written in 1850, "The Delhi king within the palace is a mere effigy; yet he forms a moral rallying point, round which gather the dreams of discontented princes, feeding upon prophecies. Such prophecies and traditions as those about Delhi oftentimes work out their own fulfilment".

Besides the descendant of Tīmūr surviving in mock majesty within the Fort at Delhi, there was yet another discontented inheritor of fallen imperial traditions. The Chitpāvan Brāhmans who had borne the title of Pēshwā had in the middle of the eighteenth century almost laid their hands upon the empire of India. They had failed, partly by reason of the strength and vigour of Afghan invaders, partly because they could not retain the loyal obedience of their own lieutenants like Sindhia and Holkar, partly because they had sunk before the waxing power of the East India Company. When the last Pēshwā, Bāji Rāo II, had died a pensioner of the company, Dalhousie resolved that his pension should die with him. In this there was no great injustice. Bāji Rāo had died son-less. His adopted son, Nāna Sāhib, was suffered to inherit Bāji Rāo's savings and estates. He was wealthy, and gave no hint of his discontent, living in friendly intercourse with the British officials. But he was an active, ambitious man, who dreamed if occasion ever served of reviving Brāhman rule. We may suppose him keenly alive to the alarm produced among orthodox Brāhmans by the company's new social and educational policy, and he may well have played a part in propagating and spreading that alarm.

Lastly there was the newly annexed province of Oudh. Probably few cared much for the fate of the deposed king. He and his family had done little for fifty years and more to earn the respect or affection of either his countrymen or his co-religionists. Orthodox sympathy had been alienated by the imitation of foreign ways which had long prevailed in the palace of Lucknow, and his royal title was derided as a sham, made evident by the forms of respect still shown to the company's resident. But the annexation had been grievously mismanaged. Oudh had become a country of great talukdars who corresponded in theoretical position with the great zamindars of Bengal, but who were practically much stronger, for they could command the services of a warlike and turbulent peasantry. Under the king they had lived in a state of perennial rebellion. They had their mud forts and armed retainers, and had been accustomed to defy the government. Dalhousie had resolved that, like the Panjab, the province should be disarmed and the forts rendered untenable. But Canning not only disregarded this decision but also gave the talukdars the most serious reasons for discontent. The first land-revenue settlement was made with the definite intention of restoring the old village communities, strong there as in the neighbouring province of Āgra, to a position of independence wherever there was reasonable ground for considering them entitled to it. The result was that many talukdari estates were materially cut down. The natural leaders of the people were thus provided with a good excuse for resentment and left in possession of the means to make their resentment felt.

Incidentally the annexation of Oudh affected the sepoys of the Bengal Army, largely recruited from that region. This was not because the sepoys felt special sympathy with the king or griev-ances against the revenue settlement. But annexation deprived them of the privileged position which till then they had enjoyed. In the past whenever the family of a sepoy had had a complaint to make against the king's government, the complaint had been laid by the sepoy before his commanding officer, who communi-cated it to the government of Calcutta, who instructed the resident at Lucknow to make enquiries, with the result that sepoys' families had found justice more easily than any other subjects of the king. But annexation reduced the sepoys and their families to the same level as other persons, and was therefore resented by them.

Thus in 1857 India was afflicted by a considerable number of causes all making for unrest and uncertainty: schools and mission-houses, the maintenance or disgrace of undesired widows, family bitterness over conversions followed by an enforced partition of the family property, Muslim discontent, the Oudh talukdars' bitterness—none of these by itself of great moment, none likely to produce more than a sporadic movement, but collectively making up a situation full of alarming possibilities. Yet any rebellion among the civil population was most unlikely, despite Muslim sermons, or the talk of Hindu agents, for there was no organisation, and no possibility of organisation in a land so seamed by age-old divisions of race and creed and caste. But the organised body lacking in civil life existed in the military sphere. In what circumstances was this body likely to catch the infection of popular feeling and turn against the government which had created it? Thomas Munro a generation earlier had, with rare insight, pondered on this problem and had reached a conclusion which circumstances were to prove unhappily correct. "The spirit of independence", he wrote, "will spring up in this army long before it is ever thought of among the people." And again: "All that is necessary is that they [the sepoys] shall have lost their present high respect for their officers and the European character; and whenever this happens they will rise against us, not for the sake of asserting the liberty of their country, but of obtaining power and plunder".

The history of the company's sepoy forces was long and honourable. The earliest English forts had been garrisoned by small bodies of European troops. But the struggle which Dupleix had precipitated produced a swiftly growing need of men. European battalions were supplemented therefore by bodies of Indian troops. The credit of this has falsely been ascribed to Dupleix. But both Portuguese and Dutch had freely entertained large numbers of sepoys. Dupleix did no more than they had done. He enlisted companies of men under their own leaders. The English at Madras did the same. But they soon introduced a change which no one else had thought of making. They began to provide these auxiliaries with European drill-sergeants; they then went on to organise them into battalions on the European model; and completed their work by providing the battalions with English officers. Under this new discipline the sepoys in the English service acquired a facility and steadiness of manœuvre which Indian troops had never before displayed. Under this new leadership they developed a new cohesion and confidence. French observers noted with dismay that the English sepoys would face French regiments while the French sepoys would not even face English sepoys. The latter thus became by far the most efficient body of Indian troops in the country, and, as war after war proved, in conjunction with the European troops were far more than a match for Mysorean, Marātha, or Sikh.

The company's forces were organised in three presidency armies, each under its separate commander-in-chief. In 1824, when they underwent re-organisation, the Bengal army included sixty-eight sepoy infantry regiments, the Madras army fifty-two, and the Bombay army twenty-four. Besides these, there were thirteen native cavalry regiments in Bengal, eight at Madras, and six at Bombay, with considerable bodies of native artillery as well. In normal times these forces were balanced by European troops in the usual proportion of one to three. The latter consisted partly of company's troops, partly of queen's regiments. But the exigencies of the Crimean War had led to the reduction of the latter. Dalhousie was most indignant. Ministers justified the recall of troops from India by quoting his assertion that India was tranquil. "So it will be," he commented, "if we are left strong. But if we are weakened, India cannot be warranted to continue either tranquil or secure." Despite his protests three regiments were recalled in 1854, and in 1857 still had never been replaced, and the proportion of European troops had thus fallen to less than one in six. Owing to the concentration of over a quarter of these troops in and about the Panjab, the strength of the European element elsewhere was much less even than one in six. If therefore the sepoy forces were disposed to mutiny, the years 1854–7 presented to them an opportunity of exceptional advantage.

Moreover, sepoy discipline had been decaying for at least a generation, especially in the Bengal army. Several causes had been operating to produce this effect. The growing centralisation of control had deprived commanding officers of much power. They were no longer competent to redress grievances or reward merit; and their influence with their men therefore declined. But what was much worse than this was the decay in the average quality of the officers, European and sepoy alike. Promotion by seniority produced commanding officers of long experience but little talent, exhausted by a long term of service. "Commanding officers are inefficient", wrote Dalhousie in 1851; "brigadiers are no better; divisional officers are worse than either because older and more done; and at the top of all they send commanders-in-chief seventy years old." Lord Roberts's father was appointed to command a division on the frontier; the authorities prided themselves on the youth and activity of their choice; General Roberts was at that time a mere sixty-nine years of age. But this was not all. Long-standing regulations permitted an officer to spend long periods of time in staff-employment and then to rejoin his regiment with a rank determined by his total service, not by his regimental experience. A man might serve twenty years in the Pay or Stud Department, and then, when he was a lieutenant-colonel, be appointed to command a regiment. The demands of the civil administration too had been severe and exhausting. In every government that Dalhousie organised, Nāgpur, Burma, the Panjab, he was bent on securing the finest personnel within his reach. Men were sought out who possessed special knowledge of Indian languages and customs, who cherished special sympathy with Indian peoples. Many such were found serving in the company's armies. Outram, Havelock, Henry Lawrence, John Nicholson, to name but a few, were withdrawn from military to political or administrative service. The result was that of a nominal establishment of twenty-five officers to a sepoy regiment, few units had more than a dozen actually serving. Nor were the consequences limited to a mere question of numbers. The system unhappily weeded out many of those best fitted to command the respect and affection of their men. This evil fell especially upon the Bengal Army, for its officers were in a special manner under the governor-general's eye and specially liable to selection.

The quality of sepoy officers in the Bengal Army was affected by the severity of the Bengal promotion rules. At Bombay and Madras selection by seniority was tempered by selection on merit. In Bengal the strict rule was regularly applied. The sepoy officers were automatically chosen, not from the gallantest, the most enterprising, the most intelligent, but from the longest-lived. In Bengal therefore the sepoy officers were not the natural leaders of the men; gallantry in action could hardly win for a private non-commissioned rank; the subadars of companies were usually aged, toothless, and incapable of keeping up with the troops on the march. As Outram declared before the outbreak of the Mutiny, they possessed no control over their men and owed gratitude for their promotion neither to their officers, nor to the government, but only to their own longevity.

Another influence making for laxity of discipline in the Bengal Army in particular lay in its comparatively high-caste character. In Bombay and Madras recruits were drawn from a great diversity of castes and peoples. In Bengal the predominant element consisted of Brāhmans and Rājputs from Oudh. The regiments were honey-combed with family groups; and classes which in the eighteenth century had been willing to ignore caste-scruples had come to be pertinacious in putting forward caste as a reason for avoiding unpopular duty.

While the bonds of discipline had thus loosened, causes of

discontent, both just and unjust, were operating. The recent expansion of the empire had widened the sphere of garrison-duty increased the distances to which the sepoy could be sent from home, and diminished the possible enemies against whom he might be sent to fight. While his service was becoming more irksome, his importance was diminishing. Small matters like the new post-office rules affected him. In the old days his letters had passed under the frank of his commanding officer; this privilege disappeared with the reorganisation of the post-office. More important still in the sepoy's eyes was the general enlistment oath Until Canning's time sepoys on recruitment had been sworn to service anywhere within the presidency of their enlistment. This led to various difficulties and Canning decided that in future recruits should be sworn to serve wherever needed. This change was most distasteful. It not only kept many out of the service and so created dissatisfaction among families accustomed to rely on the company's armies for the employment of their sons, but it also alarmed the whole body of sepoys already serving, for they feared that the new conditions would apply to themselves as well as to the men who had taken the new oath.

Thus it happened that while anxiety pervaded many most influential classes of the people, the Bengal Army had for years stood on the brink of mutiny. Neville Chamberlain, one of the ablest of the company's officers, declared that the sepoys were becoming worse than useless. Between 1844 and 1856 no less than four times had large bodies of Bengal sepoys refused to obey orders. These outbreaks were smoothed over rather than suppressed. The evil continued. The time had come which Munro had foretold, and Dalhousie had feared, when the professional Indian soldier was no longer dominated by the European element. Any spark might produce an explosion.

Chance produced the necessary combination of circumstances. Excited minds dwelt upon the old prophecy that the company's rule would end in bloodshed and tumult a hundred years after the battle of Plassey. A Hindu almanack for the *Samwat* year, of strangely ill-omened number, 1914, reproduced and emphasised it. Throughout northern India the prevalent agitation was indicated by the mysterious passing from village to village of flat, unleavened cakes known as *chupattis*. The village watchman would receive one from a neighbouring village with a message directing him to prepare five more and send them on with like messages. No explanation of this has ever been discovered; but it both occasioned and displayed great alarm in the native mind. At the same time the sepoys were convulsed over the cartridge question.

The company's troops were being re-armed with the Enfield rifle in place of the old smooth-bore musket. The new weapon required a much closer fit of cartridge and ball to the barrel than the old one had done; and consequently the new cartridges needed to be heavily greased to permit their being rammed down the barrel; and sepoys were being sent in parties to camps of exercise where they were taught the new drill. The cartridges issued to the Bengal Army were prepared at the arsenal at Dum-Dum. One day in January, 1857, a low-caste lascar employed there demanded the use of his water-vessel from a high-caste sepoy. The latter refused with disgust. The lascar then taunted him with being already defiled by cartridges, which, he declared, were greased with the fat of the sacred cow. The incident has all the appearance of having been deliberately planned. The story ran through the army like wild-fire. A new version, that the grease contained pig's fat, was used to excite the Muslim sepoys; men began to refuse to touch the cartridges; and the wild belief spread abroad that government had laid a deep plot to destroy Islam and Hinduism at once. Disorder followed. Huts were fired. The adjutant of the 34th Native Infantry was cut down while the quarter-guard looked on. The mutinous sepoys and the officer commanding the quarter-guard were tried and hanged. At Meerut eighty-five men of the 3rd Native Infantry were condemned to a long term of imprisonment for refusing to accept the cartridges. A punishment parade was held on May 9. One by one the delinquents were stripped of their uniforms, fettered, and marched off to prison, where they lay under a sepoy guard. The next evening a regiment of native cavalry broke into open mutiny. It dashed off to the jail, released the prisoners, and was joined by two battalions of native infantry. European officers were cut down, houses fired, bazaars looted, and the sepoys in confusion and alarm marched off along the Delhi road. In the knowledge of what was to follow, critics have usually demanded why the general officer commanding at Meerut did not instantly gather together the European troops—a regiment of dragoons, the 60th Rifles, and a strong body of horse and foot artillery—and pursue the mutineers. The general was undoubtedly unfit. He had in 1855 been transferred from Peshā-war as being too inactive. But no one knew whither the mutineers had gone or what might next happen. There were many scattered European women to be protected. The general therefore chose what seemed the safest course—he stood on the defensive and did nothing. It is but fair to add that Lord Roberts believed that pursuit could have secured no good effect.

The story of the cartridges that precipitated the general unrest into open mutiny is probably a fable with the slenderest possible foundation in fact. Animal fat had doubtless been used at Woolwich, where the earliest Enfield cartridges were made up. But those issued to the sepoy troops had all been prepared at Dum-dum, where Brāhman workmen had handled the fat with-out question. As soon as difficulties emerged, strict orders were given that nothing but mutton-fat and wax were to be used. At some stations in the hope of smoothing matters over the men were ordered to grease the cartridges themselves, so that they should have no possible pretext for suspecting the materials used. But in the excitement of the time these measures had small effect, and as often as not were interpreted as showing that the original story had been true. The more active minds behind the whole movement no doubt perceived that the new cartridges provided a good rallying cry on which to raise the whole sepoy army; and had not the Enfield rifle been introduced, some other incident would have been employed to give the necessary stimulus. As Dinkar Rāo observed later, the cartridges provided merely the occasion of the mutiny. The real cause lay in popular discontent, reflected in the army.

Munro had not been alone in anticipating that one day the sepoy forces would break into revolt. Some ten years earlier, in an article on the tragedy of Kābul, Henry Lawrence had asked whether any of the more important military stations in India was better prepared than Kābul had been against a sudden up-rising. The position at Delhi, he thought, was closely similar to that at the Afghan capital. Suppose, he wrote, three hundred men seized the Delhi magazine and treasury; that the troops in the cantonments merely strengthened the guard in the palace; that the palace commandant (like Colonel Skelton at Kābul) merely opened fire from the walls; and that this befell on June 2. In a day the rebels would swell into thousands, plough-shares would be beaten into swords; and the leader of any force that could be sent against the enemy would have to strike for very existence, at the most inclement season of the year. But suppose too, he continued, that the commandants of the neighbouring stations hesitated to spare troops and that movements were hindered by a lack of transport, "should we not have to strike anew for our Indian empire?" But while men like Lawrence and Dalhousie were certainly alive to the general possibilities of danger, no one seems to have perceived the ferocity and extent of the coming storm, until it was close at hand. Even in March, 1856, Lawrence himself does not seem to have thought that within fifteen months his guesses were to be fulfilled to the letter. Both the government and the high command believed that they had time in which gradually to carry out the reform of distribution, the development of railways, the removal of abuses, with nothing worse to fear than such local troubles as had already been met and reduced.

Consequently government was ill-prepared to suppress the mutiny on its first outbreak. The withdrawal of European troops for the Crimean War had never been made good, for the home authorities had first ignored and then forgotten Dalhousie's remonstrances. Of the European troops attached to the Bengal Army, most were concentrated on the frontier or in the Panjab. The valley of the Ganges was almost bare of them. None were at Allāhābād, a magazine and strategic centre of great importance, for it commanded the route from Calcutta up the Ganges valley. None were at Delhi, another great magazine, which had been the base of the troops operating in the Sikh wars. The arsenal stood within the city walls, and had long been regarded as unsatisfactory. Lord Gough in particular had urged the importance of its removal. Dalhousie had hoped to be able to deal with this question. His agreement with the emperor's heir for the transfer of the royal family from the fortress-palace to a new building near the Kutb, would have placed the fort in British hands and permitted the transfer of the arsenal from the city to the fort. Military opinion was agreed on the soundness of this plan. But the death of the Mughal's heir endangered the proposal. As a temporary measure Dalhousie reduced the arsenal from a first-class to a second-class magazine; but it still contained some 300 pieces of ordnance and a vast amount of percussion-caps, while the chief powder-magazine, though lying in the cantonments outside the city walls, remained under the guard of sepoy troops alone. At Allāhābād likewise the arsenal in the fort was protected only by a few European invalids. Outram, just before the Persian war, had urged on Canning the need of a British garrison; but nothing had been done. In fact the one precautionary measure of any value which had been taken was the recent treaty with Dost Muhammad of Kābul. So far as this was observed, no danger was to be feared on the north-west frontier. But, in the event of serious trouble arising in India itself, the troops in the Panjab could not be transferred elsewhere, until it was clear that the amir intended to abide by his agreement.

The difficulties of the position were for the moment enhanced by the character of the governor-general. Canning possessed many noble qualities. He was just, clear-minded, and resolute once he had adopted a course of action. But he was not the man to face a crisis, because he could not swiftly decide on any course of action. He saw all the sides of a complicated question, and could not without long delay determine what was, and what was not, essential. Dalhousie would have acted strongly and decisively the moment he judged a serious movement impending. Canning feared to precipitate a mutiny by preparing to crush it. He hoped to coax the sepoys back to discipline, at a time when coaxing was too late.

The morning after the outbreak at Meerut, the fugitive cavalry reached Delhi, and were admitted into the palace. Late the night before a messenger had arrived from Meerut with news of what had happened. The letter had been safely delivered to the commissioner, Simon Fraser. But, heavy with sleep, he had taken it from the servant's hand, mechanically put it into his pocket, and fallen asleep again. The mutinous cavalry were therefore their own heralds. They were soon followed by the infantry regiments. The sepoys in the cantonments joined the mutineers. The jail was thrown open. The arsenal in the city was attacked; and though the small magazine which it contained was blown up by its defenders the great magazine outside was plundered, part of its contents being carried off by marauders, the remainder being brought into the city. The troops declared allegiance to the emperor. His sons endeavoured to assume command of a movement which they hoped would lead to the restoration of Mughal

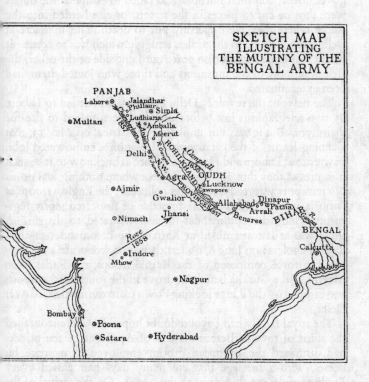

SKETCH MAP
ILLUSTRATING
THE MUTINY OF THE
BENGAL ARMY

PANJAB

Lahore
Jalandhar
Phillaur
Simla
Ludhiana
Ambala
Meerut
Multan
Delhi
ROHILKHAND
Campbell 1858
N.W. Agra
OUDH
PROVINCES 1857
Lucknow
Cawnpore
Ajmir
Gwalior
Allahabad
Dinapur
Patna
Benares
Arrah
BIHAR
Nimach
Jhansi
BENGAL
Rose 1858
Calcutta
Indore
Mhow
Nagpur
Bombay
Poona
Satara
Hyderabad

government; and such Europeans as failed to escape at the outset were shot or cut to pieces in the streets, or else herded into the palace where they were speedily put to death. This massacre at Delhi gave the tone to the pitiless struggle which was to come. It meant that there could be no peace until one side or the other, the British in India or the mutineers and those who joined them, had been exterminated.

The news of the revolt at Delhi had been forwarded to Lahore by two telegraphists just before they had been forced to flee for their lives. But it was not until two days later, on May 13, that Canning learnt of the catastrophe. He at once empowered John Lawrence at Lahore and Henry Lawrence at Lucknow to take such measures as they thought best. But elsewhere nothing was done. No transport was ready, no stores collected; the English troops at Ambāla were detained by the presence of suspected sepoy regiments which the commander-in-chief hesitated to disarm. A force was at last assembled at Karnāl; the commander-in-chief died of cholera; on June 8, no less than four weeks after the outbreak, a force composed of the Karnāl troops, the Rifles from Meerut, and a Gurkha battalion, drove in the mutineers' outposts and camped on the Ridge looking down from the northward over Delhi.

The royal family had beyond doubt hoped for and encouraged the spirit of revolt. Before the end of April one of the princes had dismissed the European groom employed to exercise his horses, with a message that ere many days had passed every English infidel should be put to the sword. On the arrival of the mutineers various princes assumed command of the several regiments. But they spoke only the corrupt Persian used in their phantom court, and could not communicate with their men except through an interpreter. Their command, like the authority of the aged king, Bahādur Shāh, proved a mere thing of words. The day after the arrival of the Meerut mutineers, a high-sounding proclamation was issued in the king's name, directing his ever-victorious armies to advance and destroy his enemies. Bahādur was carried in triumphal procession through the city. But the same day witnessed a scene betraying the emptiness of all these solemn pretensions. The sepoys crowded on the king in his durbar, shouting at him, seizing his hand or touching his beard to attract his attention. At last he was permitted to withdraw shocked, alarmed, and lamenting the evil days which had come upon him. A week later the mutineers declared the king to be too old and infirm, and chose one of his sons in his stead. Presently they tired of the prince and recognised his father once more. But what authority existed lay with a *junto* of sepoy officers constantly split by jealousy and mistrust. Nor was the imperial city much happier than the imperial court under its new masters. The men were demanding pay. On May 21 the palace was crowded by a howling mob, whose attitude was so threatening that the bankers raised a lakh of rupees to satisfy them. Long before the siege was over, the wealthier citizens had gone into hiding to escape the contributions constantly demanded under threats of plunder. The Muslims hoisted the standard of the *jihād* on the Jama Masjid; the Hindus complained and insisted on its being pulled down. Communal feeling became so strained that, when Bakr'Id approached, the death-penalty was proclaimed against any man who should sacrifice a cow.

The appearance of the English force before Delhi produced wild confusion in the city. Fugitives came pouring in through the Kashmīr, Lahore, and Kābul gates, and, could the English troops have advanced at once, they would have found the gates open, and the mutineers in panic. But the men were exhausted and the risk appeared too great. The walls were no longer the thin, ruinous, mud-patched defences which the English had found in 1803, but had been repaired with stone by English engineers. On the following day an attack was proposed; but the plan was rejected as desperate, probably with good reason. The assailants therefore fortified themselves upon the Ridge and there remained for some three months. The mutineers then recovered their courage. The English were constantly harassed by attacks, a prey to cholera and sunstroke, incapable of doing more than hold their ground.

The delay in recovering Delhi was in all respects disastrous. Every day that passed increased the strain upon the sepoy troops that had not yet joined the mutiny. Messengers from the revolted regiments were constantly beseeching them to join their brethren or taunting them with cowardice for their delay. Knowledge of the distrust with which they were regarded by the British authorities set a keener edge on their uneasiness, while the position at Delhi suggested to wavering minds that the prophecy of the company's fall was about to be fulfilled. So regiment after regiment broke, until the sepoy portion of the Bengal Army had almost wholly vanished. During the fatal four weeks that dragged so slowly out between the mutiny at Meerut and the occupation of the Delhi Ridge other mutinies occurred at Fīrūzpūr, at Aligarh, at Nasīrābād, at Āgra, at Lucknow, at Bareilly, at Allāhābād and Benares, at Nīmach, at Jhānsi, at Cawnpore. As June and July passed with Delhi still unsubdued, sepoys had to be disarmed at Multān and Barrackpore; Sindhia's and Holkar's contingents mutinied at Gwalior and Indore; and the troops at Fatehgarh, at Mhow, at Sāgar, at Sialkot, at Dinapur, broke from their allegiance. Preparations for a strong mobile force at the end of April, when the position was known to be full of danger, and swift action on the first outbreak, would have prevented many, if not all of these disasters. For there was no common and agreed plan throughout the army. Schemers had no doubt done all they could to produce a universal revolt; but the regiments broke piece-meal, and many might have been saved. Even as it was, some units were held fast by the resolute wisdom of their commanders, some by the unwavering spirit of the men themselves. The 47th Native Infantry, for instance, posted at Mīrzāpur, was kept with its colours by Lieutenant-Colonel Pott, who warded off attempt after attempt and at last persuaded his men to volunteer in a body for service in China; while a large body of the 13th at Lucknow joined with a devotion far beyond all praise in the defence of the Residency, and, when their commander Major Bruere was killed, carried his body to the grave regardless of pollution. But such fidelity could be secured only by men of strong, commanding character. A striking contrast is afforded by other regiments whose steadiness was regarded by their officers with the fullest confidence. In some cases the men mutinied and killed their officers; in others they were only prevented by being disarmed, and in at least one instance the colonel shot himself for grief and shame. Such blind trust is the poorest possible substitute for discernment.

The only bright feature of the situation consisted in the fact that the mutinies were almost wholly limited to the Bengal Army and concentrated in northern and central India. The Madras population, less emotional than their northern brethren, remained quiet; and the discipline of the Madras Army held good. Muslim agitators brought about a riot at Hyderabad, but the attack which the rioters made on the Residency was easily beaten off, and, under the influence of the rising statesman, Sālar Jang, the power of the Nizām's government was used vigorously to prevent any repetition of the event. The Madras Army was thus able to spare a considerable proportion of its European troops, who reached the valley of the Ganges under the command of Neill early in June. In Bombay the situation was more unsettled. Many land-owners in the Marātha country had been aggrieved by investigations into the validity of their exemption from the payment of land-revenue. Marātha sentiment was strong, and sympathised naturally with the efforts of Nāna Sāhib to revive Marātha power. His emissaries brought about a local rising; and a mutiny occurred at Kolhapur. But these movements were speedily suppressed. The Bombay sepoys, though restive, were kept under control. Sind, under the government which Napier had set up and at this time in the able hands of Bartle Frere, remained notably quiet, and spared troops for service elsewhere. After a while the Bombay government was able to organise the column which under Sir Hugh Rose restored British supremacy in Central India.

In Bengal and Bihar the situation suffered from the ill-grounded optimism or unwise hesitation of Canning. He refused the offers of volunteers, made immediately on the outbreak at Meerut, because he fancied that the evil had been checked. He refused at first to disarm the sepoys at Barrackpore, although he distrusted them with good reason and kept to watch them two European regiments whose services were most urgently required elsewhere. At last on June 14 the Barrackpore sepoys were disarmed. But the spirit of unjustified confidence still prevailed. Though Patna was the headquarters of the Wahhabī sect, well known to have been active in intrigue in many parts of India, Halliday, the lieutenant-governor, objected to the precautions which Tayler, the commissioner, wished to take and ridiculed the possibility of a mutiny at the neighbouring station of Dinapur. Tayler on his own responsibility arrested three leading Wahhabī moulvis, and suppressed a riot which broke out on July 3. On the 25th half-hearted measures at Dinapur produced the expected mutiny, and the sepoys marched off to join a Rājput zamindar, Kunwar Singh, who had risen in rebellion. They attacked Arrah, the headquarters of the most troubled district in the Patna division; but were kept at bay until Major Vincent Eyre scattered them on his way to Allāhābād, with the help of a small body of troops of which he assumed the command. Apart from this episode, the discredit of which must lie mainly on the lieutenant-governor, the province remained undisturbed.

At Āgra too the conduct of affairs was marked by unfortunate indecision. The lieutenant-governor, John Colvin, a sound administrator in untroubled times, was swayed alternately by hope and fear. First he proposed to take refuge in the fort. Then he persuaded himself that no real danger threatened, and would not disarm the sepoys at Āgra till May 31. The result of this inaction was the mutiny of every sepoy regiment in the Rohilkhand, where a Muslim pensioner, Khān Bahādur, proclaimed himself viceroy of the king of Delhi.

The situation in the Panjab was at once more dangerous and better managed. The recent conquest of the country, the possibility that the Sikhs would use the crisis to recover their independence, the neighbourhood of Afghanistan and the uncertain attitude of the frontier tribes, demanded the utmost vigilance. Luckily the telegraph line was broken, for the provincial government was composed of Dalhousie's picked men. John Lawrence was at its head. Under him were Robert Montgomery as judicial commissioner, and Herbert Edwardes, commissioner at Peshāwar. At the moment when the news of the revolt at Delhi reached Lahore, Lawrence was absent on leave. But Montgomery instantly took action. On May 13 the four sepoy regiments at Miān-mīr were disarmed. At Fīrūzpūr the brigadier imitated the hesitation of the commander at Dinapur, with the result that a regiment mutinied the day before it was to have been disarmed. But even there the magazine was secured. At Peshāwar Herbert Edwardes, on John Nicholson's advice, had instantly ordered the formation of a movable column, to be ready to march wherever danger might appear. The sepoy troops outnumbered the British by almost three to one. The closest watch was kept. Intercepted letters proved communications with the Hindustani fanatics of Sitāna, and on the night of May 21/22 news came that the 55th Native Infantry at Nowshera had mutinied. Next morning four regiments at Peshāwar were paraded and disarmed. On the 23rd Nicholson led a party to disarm the remaining companies of the 55th at Mardān. They fled at his approach, were pursued into the hills, wandered miserably and precariously there for a while, and at last those who had not surrendered themselves as slaves to the tribesmen surrendered to the British. Such vigorous action was reinforced by the enlistment of local levies. At first the Peshāwar chiefs had refused their aid, telling Edwardes bluntly that he must show them that he was the stronger. But after the events just noted, no further reluctance was shown. In the following month at Multān two sepoy regiments were disarmed by some Panjabi cavalry and infantry backed by a troop of Native Horse Artillery. It was clear that Panjabis, whether Sikh or Muslim, felt not the least sympathy with the *Purbiyyas*, the Easterners, as they called the sepoys of the eastern provinces.

Thus in northern India, while the central government was unprepared and irresolute, and the provincial governments of Bengal and Āgra were hampered by the consequences of their own indecision, the Panjab alone could strengthen the scanty and inadequate force which was all the governor-general and commander-in-chief had been able to assemble for the recovery of Delhi. In this task Lawrence was greatly aided by the attitude of the Cis-Sutlej chiefs. From the very first, under the leadership of Patiāla, they never hesitated but offered all their resources for the suppression of the mutiny. This did much to clear the road. The Guides who marched from Mardān under Daly as soon as the revolt at Delhi was announced, covered twenty-seven miles a day for three weeks, arrived on the Ridge only a day after the Karnāl troops, and engaged the mutineers within three hours of their arrival. As soon as the crisis in the Panjab began to ease, Lawrence prepared to follow them up with large bodies of additional troops—British and Panjabi. Thirteen battalions of infantry, four regiments of horse, 8000 auxiliaries supplied by local chiefs, stores of all kinds, and the siege-train that at last broke down the defences of the city, all came from the Panjab. At one moment Lawrence had judged the position so desperate that he had proposed to facilitate the despatch of reinforcements by abandoning Peshāwar to the Afghans. But this proposal, which Edwardes judged to be a disastrous confession of weakness, was rejected by Canning on Edwardes's vigorous remonstrance, and Lawrence was thus saved from the one serious error into which he had been in danger of falling.

Meanwhile at Delhi the British troops had maintained and

even strengthened their position on the Ridge, despite the constant attacks of the mutineers. The city formed a natural focus, and band after band of sepoys marched thither as the mutiny spread from unit to unit and from station to station. Their practice was to move out to engage the British immediately after their arrival. Within six weeks more than twenty assaults were delivered against the Ridge. These were steadily repulsed, but by the end of July the recovery of the city appeared as remote as ever, and even the Panjab was beginning to waver in its belief in the ultimate victory of the English. Early in September, however, the siege-train under the escort of Nicholson with the Panjab movable column arrived. The mutineers still outnumbered their assailants by about two to one, but an assault was planned. Breaching batteries were opened on the bastions and curtain of the northern wall. On September 14 the storming columns were assembled, a party of most gallant men blew in the Kashmīr Gate, and that day a lodgement was made in the city with the loss of about a quarter of the assailants. After some five days of bloody street-fighting, the mutineers were completely driven out, the fort captured, the emperor and four of his sons made prisoner at the Tomb of Humāyūn, and the latter shot by their captor, Major Hodson. The greatest British loss was the death of John Nicholson, who had commanded one of the columns of assault. Before the mutiny he had proved himself a most vigilant, fearless and successful frontier administrator. On its outbreak he had played a leading part among John Lawrence's lieutenants in maintaining order in the Panjab. As resolute and swift in action as Clive, he had, what Clive had not, the stern Hebraic piety of a seventeenth-century Puritan, and knew that to him the victory would be given. Men followed and obeyed him without question. He was beyond doubt the most heroic of a group of men all distinguished by their endurance, courage and resource.

The recovery of Delhi in September, 1857, was the turning-point of the mutiny. When the news reached Peshāwar, the townsmen thronged Edwardes's house with congratulations. The merchants apologised for their late reluctance to raise a loan of five lakhs, and government bonds which had been selling at 25 per cent. discount rose rapidly. But the four months' delay in its recovery had been dearly paid for by the course of events at Lucknow, Benares and Cawnpore. At Lucknow Henry Law rence had done all in his power to conciliate the chief people of the province; but, since he could not undo the revenue settlement, the talukdars still had a material grievance to nurse. He had already decided to defend the Residency, should affairs compel him to stand on the defensive. On May 25 he warned the women and children to take refuge there. On the 30th mutiny broke out in the cantonments, followed by riots in the city. But over 500 sepoys refused to follow their comrades, and played a great part in the subsequent struggle. Besides these, Lawrence had one queen's regiment—the 32nd Foot. The mutiny at Lucknow was followed during the next few days by mutinies at every other station in the province, and the complete collapse of all civil administration in the districts, though most of the talukdars contented themselves with resuming their lands, and some even sent promises of help to the Residency. Within Lucknow itself Lawrence succeeded for a while in maintaining his authority, although the mutineers were assembling in the neighbourhood. All available hands were kept hard at work preparing the Residency for a defence which every day made more inevitable. On June 30 an attempt was made, against Lawrence's own inclinations, to disperse the sepoys who had gathered at Chinhat, four miles away. The troops, exhausted by continuous labour on the fortifications and by the heat of the season, were compelled hurriedly to retreat with a loss of one third of their number. The mutineers at once entered and plundered the city and the siege of the Residency began. On July 2 Lawrence was mortally wounded by a bursting shell. Two days later he died, leaving about a thousand English soldiers and civilians and seven hundred loyal sepoys to defend the Residency against about 10,000 mutineers.

At Cawnpore were stationed four sepoy regiments, with about four hundred British gunners and invalids. On the news from Meerut, the commander, Sir Hugh Wheeler, resolved, like Lawrence at Lucknow, to secure a defensible position. The magazine offered by far the best. But Wheeler hesitated to withdraw the sepoy guard posted there lest he should precipitate a rising, and contented himself with throwing up a breastwork near the north-east corner of the town. On June 4 the native cavalry and one infantry regiment mutinied. On the 5th a second infantry regiment went over, and the third broke when Wheeler hastily fired into them with his artillery. Eighty still clung to their colours, but all the rest joined their revolted comrades. The mutineers gathered round Nāna Sāhib at his palace near Cawnpore. After some hesitation, he resolved to besiege Wheeler's feeble entrenchment. For three weeks the defenders held their ground, lacking food, lacking water, lacking shelter from the enemy's fire and from the heat of the day. On June 26 Wheeler surrendered, under promise of safe-conduct to Allāhābād. The survivors went aboard the boats provided for them early next morning. But as soon as they had got on board, the thatch-shelters of the boats were set on fire, while a hail of grape-shot and bullets was poured upon them by the sepoys who crowded round. Only one boat got away, and of those upon her only four men escaped with their lives. While this was going forward, orders came from Nāna Sāhib forbidding further massacre. The survivors were then imprisoned in a large building within the town. But the men were speedily taken out and killed. Later on the women and children were removed to a small house called the Bībīgarh, and after some days of the utmost misery, on news of an English advance up the river, were cut to pieces by the Nāna's orders on July 15. This slaughter displayed in its extreme form the ferocity with which the struggle was being fought out. The murder of English women at Meerut and their wholesale massacre in the Dīwān-i'am of the Delhi palace, had in the first place sharpened the determination of the English to punish the mutineers with a deterrent severity. Death was the accepted punishment for mutiny. A large number of mutineers had been hanged. This was the severest form in which death could be inflicted on high-caste men, for they were sent into the next world indelibly polluted by the touch of a low-caste or caste-less hangman. In some cases the authorities in the Panjab and elsewhere had adopted a mode of execution which had long been practised by Indian rulers, which had probably been introduced into India by the Mughals and which had certainly been employed by the Marāthas. It consisted in blowing the condemned men from guns. This more spectacular punishment has usually been regarded as indicating a peculiar ferocity on the part of the British. But unlike hanging it was instantaneous, unlike hanging it involved no inevitable pollution. The caste-sepoy would almost certainly have chosen it in preference to the rope. In any case every sepoy knew that he would be liable to death in one form or another if he broke into mutiny. Wholesale execution is the appropriate punishment of wholesale mutiny; and we must regret that the sepoy risked his stake rather than that he lost it, for his success could only have restored in India that welter of unending war in which the country had lain miserably in the eighteenth century. The blot on British conduct does not lie in the military punishments which were exacted, but in the conduct of a number of officers who took a bloody revenge upon guilty and innocent alike. Indiscriminate executions had accompanied the suppression of the mutinies at Benares and Allāhābād. They help to explain the pitiless slaughter of Cawnpore, and both miserably prove how cruel men are made by fear.

Weeks passed before any serious attempt could be made to recover Cawnpore and relieve the defenders of the Lucknow Residency. But Neill with the Madras Fusiliers reached Bengal from Madras; and the disarming of the sepoys at Barrackpore in the middle of June set other troops free. On June 3 Neill reached Benares on his way up the river with a detachment of his regiment. There an ill-managed disarming of sepoys led to mutiny which was immediately and severely repressed. Neill at once pushed on to Allāhābād, where he arrived on the 7th. Possession of that place was crucial, for, unless it was securely held, no attempt could be made from Bengal to maintain British authority at Cawnpore and Lucknow, known to be trembling in the balance. Mutiny had broken out at Allāhābād the day before Neill's arrival. But the fort was saved by Captain Brasyer and a company of the Ludhiāna Sikhs, though other companies of that regiment had mutinied at Benares. Neill had first to restore order among the volunteers who had seized the liquor in the fort, and he then swept the surrounding country of all elements of opposition. Many villages were burnt for harbouring sepoys who had mutinied, and many villagers were cut down at sight by the Sikh and volunteer parties which were sent out. Preparations were then made to relieve Wheeler at Cawnpore. Major Renaud, to whom the command was to be entrusted, received instructions for the extermination of every mutinous sepoy he could find.

When he was on the point of marching, Havelock reached Allāhābād to take over the command of the forces which had gradually assembled there. Havelock was another man of the type which emerged so prominently in this crisis. He was not only a soldier of long experience and deep study, but also, like Edwardes and Nicholson, he was a devout evangelical, constant in prayer, convinced that his cause was the cause of God as well as of his country. In fact the qualities of the rulers which had done much to bring about the mutiny aided strongly and resolutely in its suppression.

Renaud had moved off on June 30. On July 3 the surrender and destruction of Wheeler's force was known at Allāhābād. On the 7th Havelock advanced with about 1000 British troops, 130 Sikhs, twenty volunteer troopers and six guns. On the 12th he overtook Renaud. In the four following days he fought four actions, in the last defeating 5000 sepoys under the command of Nāna Sāhib in person. On the 17th he entered Cawnpore, two days after the slaughter of the women and children in the Bībīgarh. The sight of its blood-stained walls and its floor littered with shreds of muslin and long tresses of hair produced a terrible reaction. The fury of vengeance flared up into an intense burst of passion. Neill, to whom the command of the city was entrusted, resolved to punish such sepoys as he deemed particularly guilty not only with the physical pains of death but also with the highest degree of spiritual torture which he could inflict. Each of these was to be forced, if necessary with the lash, to lick the bloodstains from an appointed space: "After properly cleaning up his portion", the order concluded, "the culprit is to be immediately hanged".

After receiving reinforcements, Havelock advanced again with some 1500 men, leaving but three hundred to hold Cawnpore. He twice met and defeated the enemy; but his force was so wasted by cholera and by loss in action that he was obliged to fall back again, convinced that he could not yet accomplish the relief of the Lucknow Residency. Having been reinforced by a company of British infantry and half a battery of guns, he made another attempt, but once more, after meeting and driving back the sepoys at a point about half-way between Cawnpore and Lucknow, he was obliged to retire. Though he dispersed a body of 4000 sepoys who were threatening Neill in Cawnpore, the Oudh talukdars, encouraged by his inability to advance, began to comply with the demands of the mutineers for help.

Meanwhile the government had resolved to re-appoint Outram as chief commissioner of Oudh in the place of Henry Lawrence. The choice was questionable, for Outram seems to have owed his reputation to timely measures of self-advertisement. With still more doubtful wisdom, he was given the command of the relieving force, though as a soldier he lacked the experience, knowledge, and resolute skill which marked out Havelock. With characteristic caution, however, which was meant to be and in fact was hailed as noble self-sacrifice, Outram refused to exercise the military command, preferring to serve as a somewhat indocile subordinate to the older and better soldier. With him came substantial reinforcements. On September 21, a few days after the recovery of Delhi had been completed, Havelock marched for the third time towards Lucknow, with something over 3000 men. At 'Ālambāgh, two miles from Lucknow, he learnt of the recovery of Delhi. On the 25th the attack was made on a scheme dictated by Outram. The resistance proved stubborn. Outram hesitated and would have halted. But in this he was overborne by Havelock, and, after severe losses, the relievers forced their way through into the Residency. But though the besieged garrison was thus saved, the available forces were still unable to evacuate the women and children, or recover control of the city, still less of the province, for the mutineers had been strengthened by numerous bands which had fled from Delhi. The completion of the task had therefore to await a new commander and the forces which were at last beginning to arrive from Singapore, whence troops destined for the China war had been diverted to Calcutta, and from England, whence reinforcements were tediously travelling by way of the Cape although the Khedive had offered facilities for the much more expeditious route by Alexandria and Suez.

Sir Colin Campbell had been appointed commander-in-chief by the home authorities. He had risen from the ranks, had fought when scarcely more than a boy in the Peninsular War, and had commanded a division in the Crimea. He was beyond the custom of the time careful of the lives and comfort of his men, and, though no great general, was a sound and practical soldier. After completing his preparations for transport and communications, he moved up the river and reached Cawnpore on November 3. The place was threatened by Sindhia's revolted contingent, which had joined Tantia Topi, the ablest of Nāna Sāhib's commanders. Sir Colin therefore left a detachment to hold Cawnpore, and himself pushed on towards Lucknow. On November 16 and 17 he fought his way through the city and joined hands with the garrison. The Residency was evacuated; the women, children and wounded removed; and Outram was left with 4500 men to contain the mutineers in the city until Sir Colin could return to crush them. On November 27 the latter counter-marched towards Cawnpore, where Tantia Topi had scored two successes against the detachment defending it. He arrived in time to prevent any considerable mishap, and on December 6 engaged Tantia's forces. But, though he defeated them, his victory was far from decisive, for an opportunity of cutting off two-thirds of the mutineers was missed by his chief of staff.

However, from this point onward the ultimate issue was never in the smallest doubt; operations were no longer limited to the relief of small groups struggling against greatly superior numbers, but could be directed towards the re-establishment of British power over wide areas. The first object was the complete control of the Ganges-Jumna doāb. Converging columns were therefore directed on Fatehgarh, situated on the Ganges due east of Āgra. These drove large numbers of sepoys across the river into the Rohilkhand, and on their expulsion the villagers hastened to support the re-established civil administration. A force was then concentrated on the right bank of the Ganges to prevent the sepoys from re-entering the doāb, while Sir Colin himself proceeded to the re-conquest of Oudh.

At the end of February, 1858, he was able at last to march again on Lucknow, where 120,000 men had been attacking Outram at the 'Ālambāgh, which the British had occupied on the evacuation of the Residency. His attack succeeded after some days of severe fighting. But, as at Cawnpore, large bodies of the enemy numbering at least 30,000, were suffered to escape; so that the recovery of Lucknow, on March 21, left the province still in the hands of the rebels, and their resistance was stiffened by the proclamation in which Canning announced the policy which he intended to follow. It declared all lands confiscate, save those of a few individuals who had aided the government. At Outram's pressing request, a clause was added to the effect that those who immediately submitted might expect a large measure of indulgence. But the vague terms of this promise, coupled with the nature of the original British land-revenue settlement, did not conciliate the talukdārs. Accordingly a long struggle ensued, in which the rebel parties were invariably scattered when encountered, only to re-assemble at some other place. In October, 1858, however, Sir Colin was induced to employ mounted infantry. Their mobility enabled them to take much more effective action, and before the end of the year the surviving rebels were driven into the Raipur hills, while the talukdars were reassured by Montgomery, who succeeded Outram as chief commissioner, regarding the government's intentions.

In the region to the south and west of the doāb and Oudh operations had been conducted by forces organised from Bombay. Sindhia's contingent at Gwalior had mutinied in the middle of June, 1857. The widow of the late raja of Jhānsi had already raised a revolt in the hope of recovering the state which had been annexed in the time of Dalhousie. On July 1 mutinies broke out among the company's sepoys at Mhow and Sāgar, and in Holkar's contingent at Indore. As soon as the local troubles had been suppressed, Sir Hugh Rose with a Bombay column took the field. He marched from Mhow on January 6, 1858, and moved on Jhānsi, reducing rebel forts on his way and driving before him parties of mutineers. On March 22 he laid siege to Jhānsi. Tantia Topi with the Gwalior contingent attempted to raise the siege but was defeated, and on April 3 the place was carried by assault after a desperate resistance. The rani escaped and joined Tantia Topi. After a pause to rest his men and gather supplies, Rose moved against Tantia and defeated him at Kunch and Golauli. The latter success gave Rose possession of Kālpī, and he hoped that his campaign was virtually completed. But Tantia and the rani suddenly marched on Gwalior. Sindhia's wavering army joined them. On June 1 they occupied the fortress and proclaimed Nāna Sāhib Pēshwā. Rose immediately took the field again. On th 17th and 18th he defeated Tantia outside Gwalior, and restored Sindhia's authority, while Tantia fled with some 4000 men into Rājputāna. For eight months he succeeded in evading his pursuers. But at last his followers wearied and dispersed, while he himself was captured early in 1859, tried by court martial on a charge of rebellion, and hanged at Siprī, in Sindhia's territories, on April 18.

Thus northern India was re-conquered. In this operation the great mass of the population, save in Oudh, looked on with the same apathy with which it had witnessed the gradual extension of the company's authority. When civil government vanished, the villagers had plundered and sometimes murdered local money-lenders and grain-dealers, paying off old scores, and falling cheerfully into anarchy. But when the mutineers were beaten and the district officials reappeared, they were met with the old respect and obedience. The sole organised body of Indians had been the army. The army alone therefore responded to the atmosphere of alarm and anxiety which had prevailed early in 1857. The minor chiefs, too, had naturally provided a more turbulent factor. Especially in Central India and Oudh, they had been disposed to assist the mutineers rather than the government, which was lowering their dignity, their importance, and their wealth. But the princes had on the whole stood by the company, whatever grounds of complaint individuals among them might have had. Some had written messages of good-will to the old emperor in the first flush of the outbreak; but their words had not been followed up by action.

The Bengal sepoys had thus stood alone; and their mutiny of itself dissolved the organisation which had made them capable of common action. They did not trust their new leaders. In the early stages of the desperate struggle the Europeans, ever outnumbered, speedily recovered the prestige which for the moment they had lost. Soon the sepoys went into action expecting to be beaten. The individuals of a battalion might fight to the death, but the battalion had lost its military virtue. It speedily broke, and the sepoys perished in groups or fighting man by man. The mutiny was in fact foredoomed to failure, however overwhelming it appeared when station after station was bursting into revolt. Victory in the sepoy war, as in those which had preceded it, was determined by the greater vigour, the union, and the resolution of the victors. Caught in the early stages at a great disadvantage, they had done much to retrieve their position before reinforcements had even begun to arrive, and owed their success to a superiority of moral against a vast preponderance of material force. With the gradual recovery of power the vindictive indiscriminateness of punishment which had been shown in some (not in all) of the areas of conflict gave place to more measured action. Men remembered once more that co-operation had been and still must be the keynote of Indian government, and heeded Canning's wise resolve not to rule in anger. The net results of those two years of dreadful turmoil were the reassertion of British power, and the complete defeat of a convulsive effort to throw off the growing influences of the west. Two events notably typified the issue. The last shadow of the Mughal court vanished. Bahādur Shāh was tried for rebellion, condemned, and removed a prisoner to Rangoon. And with the court of Delhi the East India Company vanished also. By an act of 1858 its powers were cancelled, and direct government over the territories which it had acquired was henceforward vested in the queen.

CHAPTER XII

Crown Government and the Government of India after the Mutiny

The constitutional result of the Indian Mutiny was the abolition of the Mughal Court at Delhi, the disappearance of the last vestiges of sovereignty other than British within British India, and the termination of the powers and privileges of the East India Company. For a century the company had exercised political authority, despite the arguments of theorists like Adam Smith and the efforts of intemperate politicians like Charles James Fox in the eighteenth and Lord Ellenborough in the nineteenth century. But when in 1853 Macaulay had succeeded in substituting competition for the patronage of the directors as the method of recruiting the company's covenanted service, the company's real safeguard had vanished. Direct crown government would no longer invest the executive in England with new and extensive sources of patronage. Whig support, which had kept the company alive for over a generation, vanished. The Mutiny produced a widespread but unjust opinion that the company was specifically to blame for that great misfortune. In 1858 therefore both political parties were agreed that the company should be abolished and that thenceforward the government of British India should be exercised in the name of the queen.

But though parliament therefore paid small attention to the company's petition that no change should be made in the mode of government "without a full previous enquiry into the operation of the present system", the arguments of the petition itself exerted considerable influence on the new form of government which was actually adopted. The company had urged that any crown minister charged with the government of India would himself be unacquainted with India, and incapable of judging the solicitation of men either equally ignorant with himself or knowing enough to impose on others less informed, and in any case liable to seek party objects rather than the good government of the country. Such a minister would therefore need a council composed of men experienced in Indian affairs, and personally independent of the minister, in order that they might be able effectively to oppose proposals founded in ignorance or self-interest. Such a council could not be made up entirely of crown nominees, but must include a large proportion of men who owed their seats to no ministerial influence. Nor should any proposals seek to establish the executive government of India in London. The executive government must remain situated in India itself. The business of the home government was not to conduct the details of administration, but to revise past conduct, to lay down principles, to issue general instructions. Such functions demanded a deliberative rather than an executive body, and resembled those of parliament rather than those of the cabinet or of any administrative board.

The various schemes put forward, as well as that ultimately adopted, show how generally these conclusions were accepted. The bill introduced by Disraeli and inspired by Ellenborough, proposed to attach to the Indian minister a council partly nominated by the crown, partly elected by persons who had served in India, who had financial interests in that country, or who were parliamentary electors resident in the leading commercial cities or Great Britain and Ireland. This was speedily laughed down. But the bill which was substituted and which was passed into law in 1858 made careful provision for a council able to supervise the conduct of the minister. The new body was to be called the Council of India—a title till then borne by the executive council of the governor-general. It was to consist of fifteen members, a majority of whom must have served or at least resided in India for ten years at least. Eight members were to be nominated by the crown and the other seven were to be elected in the first instance by the members of the Court of Directors. Vacancies in the latter group were to be filled by co-option. All members were to hold office, like judges of the English bench, during good behaviour, and were removable only on an address of both houses of parliament. These provisions ensured that the new council would include a considerable element entirely independent of the minister, while the exceptional tenure of office enjoyed by every member permitted an expression of the frankest opinion on every question laid before him. The powers bestowed on the council illustrated similar views of the functions which it was designed to discharge. It could not indeed take any business into consideration except under a reference from the minister, its decisions might be overruled by him, and he might despatch to India without its concurrence orders which he ruled to be either urgent or secret. But all other proposed orders had to be laid before it for its opinion; where the minister refused to accept the council's opinion, he had to record reasons for his refusal; and in a wide variety of matters, especially all financial questions, the concurrence of a majority of the council was indispensable. In all matters excepting those of high policy it was thus deliberately intended that the minister's proposals should be submitted to a critical and effectual review.

Such limitations on the Indian minister's powers were undoubtedly sound and proper, for a House of Commons elected primarily to control the conduct of British affairs could not be expected to develop either the active interest or the informed criticism which influenced the management of the other great departments of government. The degree in which parliament was expected to participate in the business of Indian government was indicated in the act itself. Every year the minister was to submit the accounts of India for parliamentary approval with a statement showing "the moral and material progress" of the country. Besides this, aspects of policy likely to escape the criticism of the Council of India by being dealt with as urgent or secret were also to be discussed in parliament. Any declaration of war was to be laid before parliament within a prescribed period, and any military operations beyond the Indian frontiers, save for the purpose of repelling invasion, could not be paid for out of the Indian revenues without the approval of parliament.

For the actual conduct of affairs a new secretary of state was created to take the place of the former president of the Board of Control. This involved no fresh expense, for the salary attached to the latter office had already been raised in 1853 from £3000 a year to £5000, in view of its growing importance. But the change carried with it a rise in status. Future ministers for India would be men of greater political weight than the long succession of mediocrities who had sat at the Board of Control.

The net effect of these clauses in the Government of India Act of 1858 was an extension of the changes already introduced in 1853. In 1853 the crown had received the right to nominate six members out of the eighteen who formed the Court of Directors; it was now to nominate nine out of the sixteen members composing the new council. This new body was also much less powerful than the old one had been. The council could not initiate correspondence; it lacked the company's power of obstructing indefinitely administrative measures of which it disapproved; it could not recall a governor-general, and so lost a powerful lever for influencing the cabinet's policy. And while the successors of the directors were weaker, the successor of the Board of Control was stronger, holding higher rank in the cabinet and enjoying greater influence in the House of Commons. In fact the old system, under which the government of India had been managed by an independent body under the general control of a minister of the crown, had at last been replaced by a new system, under which a minister of the crown was to administer Indian affairs under the partial control of a semi-independent body.

On the formation of the new office the queen looked forward to participating as actively in its transactions as she was accustomed to do in those of the other departments of her government. She directed that its procedure should be based on that of the Foreign Office, that all important despatches should be submitted to her on their receipt, and that no important orders should be sent off without her previous approval. But this proved too much for even the tenacious industry of Queen Victoria. The volume of Indian business far exceeded her expectations, while its technical difficulties made much of it difficult to follow. Coupled with the fast-growing correspondence of the other public offices, these facts speedily led to a revision of her earlier intentions; and by the 'seventies the India Office was being required to communicate to her only outstanding information regarding Central Asia and the Indian states. She was, however, kept informed of the general situation by the regular correspondence which she maintained with the governor-general. This was a new feature, at all events in its regularity. Lord Ellenborough, when governor-general, had excited sharp jealousy in the minds of the directors by corresponding with the queen. Such objections now had disappeared. But constitutional considerations still demanded circumspection in the exercise of the privilege. On at least one occasion Lord Curzon greatly irritated the cabinet by appealing to King Edward VII in a dispute which had emerged between himself and the secretary of state. The assumption by the queen in 1877 of the title of Empress of India was, so far as the home government went, a matter of form, without constitutional significance.

The main question which the act of 1858 left uncertain as regards the home government was that of the relations between the secretary of state and his council. For this there existed no precedent. None of the principal secretaries had ever been limited in the discharge of his duties by the existence of such a body, while the council itself was disposed to magnify its importance. In the very early days of its existence it had laid claim to the directors' old privilege of initiating correspondence, and had submitted to the first secretary of state, Lord Stanley, a draft despatch. This had been immediately checked. Stanley had torn up the draft, and substituted another of his own. But section 41 of the act, requiring the council's assent to financial proposals, offered more lasting difficulties. The council was at times disposed to use its power of vetoing expenditure in order to secure control of policy. This was a natural consequence of the wide powers which the act of 1858 had conferred. In 1858 parliament had certainly considered that the council should be invested with real and effective powers, in order, as Sir Charles Wood afterwards stated, "to give the secretary of state the support requisite for resisting party-pressure, a pressure not always applied in a manner beneficial to India". But the limit of these powers was not defined, and the different sections of the act were liable to conflicting interpretations. In 1869 it was decided to modify the council's position. A bill was introduced which struck at the root of its independence by modifying the tenure from that of good behaviour to a fixed term of ten years, with a possible extension for special reasons for another five years. Lord Salisbury, who as Lord Cranborne had had much difficulty with the council, proposed an amendment, which was accepted, abolishing co-option and giving to the crown—which would act on the advice of the secretary of state— the right of nominating to all vacancies that should arise. Another amendment took away from the council its voice in appointing persons to the executive councils in India. By these changes the independent position of the council was visibly weakened. It was becoming not so much a controlling as an advisory body.

The question of its financial powers still remained. This was not determined by any alteration of the law. But in 1869 and 1880

the position was discussed in parliamentary debates which had the
practical effect of regulating usage if not of defining the constitutional position. The opinion which prevailed was that while
parliament had certainly intended to impose checks on the financial powers of the secretary of state, it had never intended to
enable the council by its financial control to hamper the execution
of policy involving imperial interests. The secretary of state was
a member of and represented the cabinet. As such he was supreme
over the council, not the council over him. The fact was that
difficulties of drafting or negligence in expression had seemed to
invest the council with far greater power than a small body of
Indian specialists could conceivably exercise. Maine justly observed that "any such power given to the council and exercised
by it would produce before long a combination of both the great
English parties to sweep away the council itself". When this had
been recognised, causes of friction between the secretary of state
and the council tended to disappear.

The subsequent developments of the home government down
to 1918 were almost negligible, and at no point touched important
constitutional principles. In 1878 the secretary of state was
permitted to appoint a limited number of special experts on the
old tenure of good behaviour; in 1889 he was allowed to leave
vacancies unfilled till the council should be reduced to ten members; in 1907 he began the practice of nominating members of
Indian birth, and about the same time the size of the council was
increased to fourteen members while their tenure of office was cut
down to seven years and their pay from £1200 to £1000. In 1913
and 1914 Lord Crewe, on the inspiration of Mr Edwin Montagu,
attempted to remodel the council; but in this he met with such
opposition in parliament that the proposal was abandoned.

The transference of government to the crown made no considerable alterations in the form of the Government of India. The
governor-general in council retained "the superintendence,
direction and control" of administration. The Government of
India was still regarded as unquestionably the executive government of the country. It was indeed required to pay due obedience
to all orders which it might receive from the secretary of state, but
this was no more than had formerly been due to the orders of the
Court of Directors. But although no changes were made in the
form of government by the act of 1858, important changes

speedily followed in the substance. The governor-general, Canning, who continued to hold office, preferred the new title of viceroy, as the personal representative of the queen in India, although "governor-general" continued to be his sole statutory designation. He seems to have considered that he was needlessly hampered by his executive council, and at once made proposals for its abolition. Since he was personally responsible, he wrote, he should be relieved of the necessity of discussing matters with a council. He therefore urged that the council should be abolished, that the government should vest solely in the governor-general, and that the appointment of secretaries in the various departments would provide him with all the assistance he required. These proposals were discussed at the India Office in 1859 and 1860, and it was agreed that they should be carried into effect, in spite of the criticisms levelled at them by H. T. Prinsep. Once again, therefore, the abolition of the executive councils was sanctioned by the home authorities. But when the reports adopted by two committees of the Council of India reached Calcutta, Bartle Frere, the first Bombay covenanted servant ever appointed to sit on the governor-general's council, succeeded in persuading Canning of the unsoundness of his views. He put forward particularly cogent arguments. The governor-general would have much more to do, and have less assistance in doing it. Moreover, since a council had been established in London, the abolition of the council at Calcutta would make the governor-general more dependent than ever before on the home government, for unless the Council of India agreed with his proposals the secretary of state would hesitate to assent; he would therefore still have to reckon with a council, and that no longer one with which he could discuss matters in person and which he could in the last resort overrule, but one on the other side of the globe, not only remote from but also independent of his authority. India too was changing with extraordinary rapidity. It would be most unwise to enhance the influence of the Council of India, which knew only the India of the past, in order to get rid of a council which knew India as it actually was. The remedy, Frere urged, was not the reduction of councillors to secretaries, but the introduction of the portfolio system, which would make the individual councillors more responsible and hasten the despatch of public business. These remarks appealed the more to Canning since he had already begun to experience the inclination of the new home government to interfere more actively in Indian administration than the old one had done, and had already experimented with introducing the portfolio system from the arrival of James Wilson, a financial expert nominated from London to reform Indian finance. Early in 1861 he withdrew the proposals which he had formerly sent home, and demanded instead that he should receive legal authority to establish rules for the conduct of business by his council. In consequence the bill prepared for the abolition of the executive council was abandoned; and clauses were introduced into another bill, primarily dealing with the legislative council, to define the composition of the executive body and to give the governor-general the powers he sought. By these clauses the executive council was fixed as before at five ordinary members, but now two instead of only one need not have been in the service of the crown or of the company in India for at least ten years. The service members consisted of a soldier of high rank as military member, and two covenanted civil servants. The other two ordinary members usually consisted of a financial expert and the law member. Besides them the commander-in-chief might be (and in practice always was) appointed an extraordinary member.

Under the clause which empowered the governor-general to make "rules and orders for the more convenient transaction of business in his council other than the business at legislative meetings", Canning proceeded to make permanent the distribution of business which he had already introduced. Until the Mutiny the council had dealt as a whole with all affairs laid before it. As administrative business grew, its meetings had lengthened out, its discussion of detail had become more unreal, its waste of time greater. Every paper that came in was circulated to all the members, who found each other's minutes provocative of further comments. But now a department or a group of departments was assigned to each. Papers in the first instance would be considered by one member only. Unimportant matters would be determined by him without reference to anyone else. Important matters would be discussed at the weekly meetings which each member held with the governor-general. In order to guard against the improper disposal of important questions without reference to the head of government, similar meetings were to be held weekly with the secretaries of the various departments. Questions of sufficient moment and those on which the governor-general and the member in question could not agree, were considered and discussed at meetings of the whole board.

The effect of these changes was two-fold. In the first place business was greatly expedited. A great mass of comparatively trivial detail was withdrawn from the consideration of the council as a whole and dealt with by men enjoying a special familiarity with the business of the department in which it arose. Much useless and often irritating writing of minutes was avoided. In the second place the responsibility and importance of the governor-general was enhanced. He himself in practice always took the portfolio of the Foreign Department. This was a continuance of the custom which had always closely identified him with foreign policy and had placed in his hands exclusively the duty of corresponding with the princes of India and of its borders. But in the past the methods of business had compelled him to pick out of a great and growing mass of correspondence the matters to which he would give special attention. Now all major affairs were automatically picked out, and discussed with him by individuals, each a master in his own sphere. The great majority of decisions was thus taken after discussion between a specialist in Indian administration and a man of wide and general political experience. The governor-general was, moreover, guarded from being misled by technical detail, for, if he were dissatisfied with the explanations of the member, he could discuss the matter further with the secretary. In this way he became the centre of all administration in a degree which had been altogether impossible for more than a generation. The power of making rules of business thus provided Canning with the advantages which he had expected from the abolition of the council while avoiding the evils which would have followed on his original proposals.

Few alterations were made in this system of government down to 1918. In 1874 an additional service member was appointed, who represented the Public Works Department till 1904 and thereafter the new department of commerce and industry. A more important change was made in 1905. Army affairs had been represented on the council by the military member as he lead of the Military Department of the civil government and by the commander-in-chief as executive head of the army itself. The latter was responsible for the organisation of the army, discipline and promotion, and preparation for war. In this capacity he required a considerable establishment, called Army Headquarters. The former was in special charge of military finance, preparing the military budget, entering into contracts for military supplies, such as victuals, clothing and medical stores, and maintaining transport, ordnance, and military works. Proposals for expenditure or reform were usually prepared in the commander-in-chief's office, and were presented to the governor-general by the military member with his comments. Thus in army matters the principle of providing the governor-general with two technical advisers was even more definitely established than was the case in the other departments of government, a position justified alike by the civilian's difficulty in forming a sound judgment on military questions and by the extreme importance of Indian defence. When Lord Kitchener became commander-in-chief during Curzon's term of office, the former attacked this dual organisation on two main grounds. He argued that the existence of the Military Department side by side with Army Headquarters involved a useless duplication of staffs and repetition of work, and should be abolished for the sake of economy. He further claimed that the commander-in-chief ought to be the governor-general's sole adviser in all military matters, declaring that the commander-in-chief's proposals could not properly be communicated and criticised by an officer junior to and less experienced than himself. Curzon and his council rejoined that this proposal was dangerous and unwise. It would leave the civil government with only a single military adviser, would invest the commander-in-chief with an undue preponderance, and would lay upon him a multiplicity of duties which he would be unable to discharge in time of war. But these weighty arguments were disregarded in England, where Kitchener's reputation stood high, and where Curzon's vigorous assertion of his rights as the head of the Indian executive had excited much opposition. Kitchener appears also to have made use of irregular and improper channels in order to procure the approval of his plans. The outcome was that Curzon was thrown over. The military member was replaced by a military supply member of inferior status and powers; and in 1909 the latter was abolished to make way for a new civil member for education and sanitation. No one can criticise the provision of a representative of those important departments, but the mode in which the provision was made was unfortunate. The mismanagement of military affairs in 1914 and 1915 in Mesopotamia showed that Curzon's anticipations had been justified.

The council as reconstituted by Canning worked more constantly and regularly with the governor-general than had sometimes been the case in the immediate past. A weak governor-general, Auckland, had made a practice of betaking himself to the heights of Simla, then recently discovered, for long periods of the year, leaving his councillors to stew in the moist heat of Calcutta while he himself arranged his foreign policy to his liking without the trouble of discussing it with them. The relief of escaping from the plains in the hot weather had been too great for his successors not to follow his example. Fortunately they had been better able to manage the affairs of India than he had been; but the regular period of separation had been much resented by the council, which found itself excluded alike from the discussion of important public questions and from the amenities of the hills. Canning's re-arrangement of council work made such a divorce between the head of the government and his legitimate advisers inconvenient as well as undesirable. The governor-general need now bring nothing under the general discussion of the council which he did not choose to refer to it; while the portfolio system rendered the presence of all the individual members necessary for the prompt despatch of business. Consequently in the time of John Lawrence's government the existing practice was changed. Henceforth the councillors accompanied the governor-general to Simla when the hot weather drew near.

While Canning's rules of business, coupled with the mistaken policy of 1853 in reducing the status of councillors below that of lieutenant-governors, rendered the governor-general able the more easily to maintain his predominance in the Government of India, and to play a greater part than ever before in the general administration of the country, the governor-general came to perceive more clearly the advantages of the council form of government. Canning's projects of abolition vanished not to be revived; and complaints of opposition in the council almost wholly disappeared. John Lawrence indeed fancied that there was some secret, underhand resistance to his measures; but he set out as governor-general under the disadvantage of lacking the prestige conferred by the wide experience and high rank which nearly all his predecessors and successors enjoyed. Lord Minto complained that the members chosen by Lord Morley were worse than useless; but this criticism was levelled at individuals rather than at the system. In general we find a chorus of approbation. Northbrook seeks to defend the statutory rights of his councillors; Ripon observes that they are easily manageable when allowed "to blow off steam"; Curzon declares their value to a governor-general of action. Indeed, it appears likely that their fault has lain rather in over-pliancy to the wishes of their political head than in any inclination to resist his policy. So far as is publicly known, on two occasions only since 1858 have they compelled the governor-general to bring into action his powers of overruling the decisions of a majority of his council. Lytton was forced to overrule his council in order to remove the import dues on cotton piece goods; and Elgin had to do the same in 1894 in order to establish a counter-vailing excise duty on cotton goods manufactured in India. The latter case was marked by a notable ruling by the secretary of state, Sir Henry Fowler, as a member of Gladstone's last cabinet. He declared that once policy had been decided, the members of the governor-general's executive council must either assist in carrying that policy into operation or resign their seats, and that in the legislative council they must vote for all government measures.

At the same time as Canning was empowered to make rules of business for his executive council, alterations were made in the machinery of Indian legislation. As has been shown above, the changes of 1853 had provoked much dispute. Two judges had been added to the legislative council in order to strengthen the legal element in the council and improve the technical character of the laws passed by it. Other foreign elements also had been introduced in the form of representatives of the subordinate governments. These new members had proved unexpectedly intractable. The judges were members of the Calcutta Supreme Court—a bench hostile by training and tradition to the autocratic Government of India, which was exempt from customary English limitations and paid small heed to the elaborate technicalities of unreformed English law. The provincial representatives were mostly covenanted servants of high standing, who were either not able enough or not accommodating enough to be promoted to the local executive councils. They were thus at the end of their service, with no further promotion in prospect, with their full pensions assured, and consequently without inclination to discuss matters except on their merits, irrespective of the desires of the Government of India or of the home authorities. Under Dalhousie's guidance the council had adopted a procedure and rules of discussion largely borrowed from those of the House of Lords. Its sittings were public. Its discussions were, if not lively, at all events extempore, for it had from the first prohibited the reading of those elaborately prepared essays in eloquence which made the proceedings of later councils so dreary and unprofitable. Nor was the governor-general invested with the power of overruling its decisions as in the executive council. He could refuse his assent to a bill, but he could not amend a bill or declare a rejected bill to be law. Disputes speedily arose, not with the Government of India but with the home authorities. Sir Charles Wood, who, as president of the Board, had formed the act of 1853, was surprised and shocked to find he had created a body with legislative independence, when he had meant to create merely a legislative adjunct to the executive government. Dalhousie, on the contrary, pointed out that the statute had undoubtedly conferred sole legislative authority in India on this body of men, and that no one could legally dictate what laws it was to pass. When it attempted to interfere with executive matters by calling for papers, he checked it sharply enough, but otherwise he would make no effort to coerce it. The climax was reached when the company disallowed part of an act fixing the allowances payable to the administrator-general from the estates of deceased persons. It was, however, argued that the company could only accept or disallow an act of the Indian legislature, that it could not amend an act, and that it could not dictate the terms of legislation. Under Canning the difficulties were accentuated. The governor-general who had proposed abolishing his executive advisers was not likely to sympathise with a legislature that claimed independence. It was therefore decided in 1861 to remodel the legislative council, and restore to the executive government the full power of controlling legislation, inadvertently abandoned in 1853.

It was, however, felt that it would not do to return to the old system by which executive and legislative power had been absolutely united in the same body. Frere strongly expressed this point of view, much as he disliked the composition and independence of the existing body. It was of no use, he declared, to discuss whether external elements were useful or injurious. "The days are gone", he wrote to Sir Charles Wood, "when you could govern India without caring what the Europeans and the Europeanised community say or think of your measures, and unless you have some barometer or safety-valve in the shape of a deliberative council, I believe you will always be liable to very unlooked-for and dangerous explosions." These views were generally accepted. But it was decided that the new legislature should be a barometer and nothing else. Wood harked back to the old position of 1833. Then the legislature consisted in the executive council with an extraordinary member; now the additional element was to be more numerous, so as to provide for a wider expression of opinion; but the legislative power was in fact to be exercised by the executive body. The governor-general was to have but one council. When he wished to make laws he was to summon at least six but not more than twelve additional members, who would hold office for two years. But though half of these at least were not to be the servants of government, the latter would constitute a majority ranging up to two to one should all twelve additional members be appointed. There was thus to be no separate legislative council. "You have no *legislative* council", Wood wrote at a later time to the governor-general, meaning that the legislature had ceased to have any existence apart from the executive. Further precautions were also taken. The chief justice of Bengal had raised an awkward doubt regarding the validity of the rules and regulations in force in the newer provinces, since they had been established by order of the governor-general in council instead of being passed by the competent legislative authority. A clause declared the validity of such rules. Moreover, the governor-general in person was authorised in case of emergency to frame and issue ordinances which would remain in force for six months. When the enlarged council met, it could consider nothing but legislative business. It could not move or adopt resolutions. It could not ask questions. It could not touch finance. It was a body through which the public might make its voice heard on legislative proposals. But, as the liberal Duke of Argyll declared in 1870, it did not enjoy independent power; it could not refuse to pass a legislative project laid before it. Supreme control lay with the secretary of state, and his directions must be obeyed no matter whether they related to legislative or executive action.

While in this respect the statute of 1861 constituted a reaction from the position established in 1853, in two other respects it marked an appreciable advance. The secretary of state refused to introduce a clause making the nomination of Indian members obligatory, on the ground that statutory distinctions should not be made between different classes of Her Majesty's subjects; but it was well understood that Indians would be included among the additional members. The advisability of this had long been urged. Dalhousie had recommended it to Wood when the bill of 1853 was under discussion. After the Mutiny Frere advised it as necessary to prevent serious legislative mistakes. Sayyid Ahmad, a Muslim of good birth who had long served the government and had distinguished himself in the Mutiny, produced a pamphlet in which he argued that many unpopular measures might have been avoided had Indians sat in the legislative council. The change was at last adopted. The nominees of 1862 included the Mahārāja of Patiāla, the Rāja of Benares and Sir Dinkar Rāo. These were succeeded by three great zamindars. After a while representatives of this class were mingled with retired officials like Sayyid Ahmad, and later still with members of the English-educated professional classes gradually rising into prominence.

The other advance made in 1861 consisted in a beneficial reversion to conditions abolished in 1833. The legislative centralisation was relaxed, and provincial legislatures were set up in Bengal, Madras, and Bombay, and afterwards extended to other provinces. No attempt was made to draw the line between the functions of the central and the subordinate bodies; the central legislature retained its competence to pass acts relating to the whole of India, and in a number of important subjects, such as religious and social customs, no bill could be introduced into a provincial council without the previous consent of the governor-general, while all bills were subject to a triple veto—that of the head of the province, of the governor-general, and of the home authorities. The powers of the new provincial legislatures were thus confined within very narrow limits. They recovered nothing of the general competence which they had enjoyed before 1833, when a central legislature did not exist in India. But the change facilitated the adaptation of existing law to local needs while preventing local acts from developing into antagonistic systems of law. Indian members were nominated on the new provincial bodies as on the central legislature.

One other important topic remains. While the changes described above were being introduced into the structure of the home and Indian governments, the law regarding the relations of these two bodies remained unchanged. The act of 1858, as has been already noted, merely substituted the secretary of state for the Court of Directors and enjoined the same general duty of obedience to the former as had been the legal right of the latter. The new minister of the crown possessed the same legal powers over the Government of India as had formerly been possessed by the East India Company. His commands carried no higher degree of legal authority than those of his predecessors. Both were entitled to implicit obedience. But new and changing circumstances were to produce great alterations in the degree in which the law actually operated. Some writers seem to have believed that no material change took place. Sir John Strachey, for instance, writing in 1888, rejected the view that the home government had come to engross a larger share of Indian administration. But the weight of evidence against this view is overwhelming.

The changes in the form of the home government itself made for a great and growing degree of interference. The directors might have been entitled to implicit obedience, but they had to reckon with the Board of Control, which might intervene to support its nominee, the governor-general, in the event of serious disputes, while the company's power of recall, though a formidable weapon, was ill-adapted for constant and regular use. In general administration the home authorities were indeed able to lay down and maintain general principles; but the Indian governments were left to settle the detail by which they should be carried into operation, while foreign policy was determined more by the governor-general than by anyone else. Down to 1858 the Government of India was undoubtedly the real executive government of the country. The statute of that year certainly contemplated the maintenance of this position. But the secretary of state enjoyed a freedom of action which the company had not possessed. Parliament left him alone. His council could be cajoled or overruled. His rank and weight in the political world ensured a preponderance of political support for the measures which he decided to adopt. A member of the executive government of his own country, he was not unlikely to forget that in constitutional theory he was not the head of the executive government of India. He was almost invariably a more prominent man than the governor-general of the day, whereas in the past the governor-general had with rare exceptions been a man of much greater political consequence than any of the directors or even the president of the Board. While the home authorities before 1858 had been inclined to defer to the judgment and experience of the governor-general, after 1858 the governor-general was disposed to defer to the secretary of state, backed as he was by the authority of the cabinet.

The establishment of the Council of India made in the same direction. The councillors all enjoyed experience of Indian administration. They were tempted by the fallacy of age to look upon their successors in India as men of less experience and weaker judgment than themselves. They had nothing to do but to attend to their duties, and were not distracted, as many of the East India directors had been, by the need of conducting large private mercantile affairs. They could not sit in parliament, as numerous directors had done, and so were not absorbed in party strife. They formed, therefore, a more active, better informed, and more opinionated body of supervisors than the directors of the company. The private correspondence of the early years of the new régime, notably that of Bartle Frere, abounds in complaints of their undue activity, of their insistence on initiating measures, of the way in which they hampered the wonted liberty of the Government of India.

Political interests also were enabled to act with greater force on Indian policy. The president of the Board had always been able to shelter himself behind the Court of Directors against the pressure of political groups. The secretary of state was in a weaker position, for his possible shelter was less effectual, while he himself was more directly and personally concerned with questions of parliamentary tactics and political exigencies.

Within a few years these tendencies were most powerfully reinforced and stimulated by one of those changes in general circumstances which constitute the most formative agents of political change. Though several proposals for the opening of telegraphic communications between India and London had been

put forward before the Mutiny, none had been adopted when
that cataclysm befell. However, it so sharply pointed the disastrous consequences of medieval communications that much
further delay became impossible. India was first linked up with
the European telegraph system by an overland line through Persia
connecting with both the Russian and the Turkish lines. Though
a great improvement, this route was in many ways unsatisfactory.
Sections of the line were often broken by the unsettled tribes of
southern Persia who found copper wire useful for a thousand
domestic purposes. Again the changes of jurisdiction and administration, from Persian to Turkish or to Russian, were found
to occasion manifold delays, while the expediency of depending
upon foreign states for the security of communications with India
was more than doubtful. A project was therefore brought
forward to lay a submarine cable by way of Bombay, Aden and
Suez; this would be entirely under British control and afford a
swifter and more regular service than the overland telegraph.
Initial difficulties were met with. The sharp rocks of the Red Sea
bottom frayed and broke the early cables that were laid. But at
last the work was successfully completed. From 1870 the Government of India was in effective telegraphic contact with the India
Office.

This achievement at once modified the actual position of the
Government of India. A wide discretion had always been exercised by the governor-general, especially in matters of foreign
policy. But the appearance of the telegraph at once reduced his
discretionary freedom. He could, and therefore he was obliged
to, take the secretary of state's orders even in matters where
formerly he would have acted on his own opinion. With this
change in practice went a change in constitutional theory. In
1858 the received view had been that the executive government
resided in India. Frere could tell Sir Charles Wood bluntly that
his business as secretary of state was to represent the governor-
general in the cabinet and in parliament. But later secretaries of
state like Lord Salisbury held that the governor-general occupied
a position similar to that of an ambassador under the Foreign
Office. When the governor-general, Lord Northbrook, contested
this view and opposed the foreign policy which Salisbury wished
him to carry into operation, the latter drove him from office and
secured the appointment of a successor more in harmony with his

ideas. When Lord Ripon became governor-general, he was astonished at the change which had occurred since the time a few years earlier when he had been under-secretary of state for India. He did not enjoy nearly that degree of freedom which he had expected, and doubted whether he would have accepted the governor-generalship had he known the actual state of affairs.

Thus the telegraph brought an ever-growing control of the Government of India by the secretary of state. This was often accentuated by the personal equation. Lord Elgin in the late 'nineties seems to have been reluctant to do anything without seeking the permission of Whitehall, and the only governor-general who succeeded in making even a temporary stand against these encroachments was Lord Curzon. His strong personality, his range of knowledge, his vigour of opinion, for a while succeeded in checking, if not reversing, the tendency, and, could he have ruled India before the days of the telegraph he would have left a reputation which might have been set beside those of Wellesley or Dalhousie. He claimed as the expert on the spot the right of taking decisions; where he could not secure the secretary of state's approval, he claimed a right of appeal to the cabinet; and where he could not persuade the cabinet, he might even invoke the influence of the crown. Mr Balfour's cabinet humoured him for a long time and to a remarkable degree. The secretary of state, Mr St John Brodrick, asserted in words which oddly recall Bartle Frere's exhortation to Sir Charles Wood, that he was acting as Curzon's ambassador in England. But this triumph was too contrary to the broad trend of events to be durable. The forces making for increased control from London were too strong permanently to be diverted from their normal action. Personal friendships, which had made Curzon's domination possible, were strained and weakened. In the end, as has been seen, the cabinet threw over Curzon in a controversy where he seems to have been entirely in the right, and he soon resigned his office. The next governor-general found himself confronted by a minister as domineering as Brodrick had been complaisant. With Morley the India Office resumed its earlier attitude, and the governor-general was regarded as the secretary of state's agent. Though Morley did not himself use the term in public, and even half-apologised when it dropped from the lips of his under-secretary, his language showed that he approved the sentiment even when he disowned the expression.

This tendency was natural and inevitable so long as the Government of India remained a bureaucracy. But it is clear that every step taken to invest the latter with a constitutional character brought into action forces which would weaken and ultimately arrest the prevailing current. Every expansion of the governor-general's council, every measure to associate non-official Indians more closely with the administration, made the governor-general the mouthpiece of opinions with which the home authorities could not be in touch but to which they were more and more disposed to defer. Such were the influences which were to reverse the tendencies introduced by the change of government in 1858 and the laying of the Red Sea cable.

CHAPTER XIII

Provincial and District Administration
after the Mutiny

The general scheme of provincial government was even less affected by the act of 1858 than the Government of India itself. The executive councils of the two presidencies were modified in 1861 in the same way as the executive council of the governor-general; and in that year, as has been already shown, some degree of legislative power was restored to the chief provinces. Apart from these changes the structure of the provincial governments remained unaltered. However, a good deal of re-distribution of territory took place. The over-grown province of Bengal, for example, was reduced in 1874 by the creation of Assam as a separate province under a chief commissioner. Thirty-one years later two provinces—one Western Bengal, Bihar and Orissa, and the other Eastern Bengal and Assam—were formed, each under a lieutenant-governor. In 1911 this arrangement was abandoned, Assam reverted to the separate charge of a chief commissioner, Bihar and Orissa were placed under a lieutenant-governor. Bengal was re-united and entrusted to a governor and council, thus recovering its former status as a presidency. In 1877 the North Western or Āgra Provinces were united with Oudh, and in 1902 received their modern name of the United Provinces. In 1861 the Central Provinces were formed by the union of the Nāgpur with the Sāgar and Nerbudda territories, and to these Berar was added in 1902 when it was leased in perpetuity to the Government of India by the Nizām. In 1902 the North-West Frontier Province was formed out of the Panjab territories beyond the Indus, and in 1912 the city of Delhi, on becoming the capital of British India, was formed into an "administrative enclave" under a separate chief commissioner.

The legal relations between these provincial administrations and the central government remained unchanged. The two presidencies in some respects enjoyed special privileges, derived from their original independence of the presidency of Fort William in

Bengal. They could correspond direct with the home government on matters not involving finance; they could appeal to it against the orders of the Government of India; they enjoyed the right of appointment to important provincial posts. But from 1833 complete financial control over all the provincial administrations had been vested in the Government of India. No attempt had ever been made to define the powers which should be exercised by the provincial governments, which had in law become the local agents of the central power.

This excessive centralisation had been tempered by two influences. The great extent of the country, the diverse social and economic conditions prevailing in the various provinces, linguistic differences which produced distinct technical vocabularies in the different provinces, first in the important matter of trade, then in the yet more important matter of land revenue, made it as difficult to rule India from Calcutta as it would be to rule Europe from Constantinople. The governor-general in his short term of office could not be expected to master such an array of disconcerting detail. His council, drawn exclusively from the Bengal services down to 1858, knew nothing of the southern and western provinces, into which their duties never led them, and little even of their own province where they were hampered by the consequences of the permanent settlement. Ignorance, therefore, went some way towards limiting the legal control of the governor-general in council. The other influence was the limitation of time. When all business was laid indiscriminately before the council as a whole, many points of detail had of necessity to be passed over with small consideration.

In these respects the system introduced by Canning brought about a considerable change. It not merely strengthened the control of the governor-general over the general conduct of the Government of India, but also strengthened the control of the Government of India over the provincial governments. The portfolio system multiplied the capacity of the central government for transacting business, and thus sharpened the scrutiny which could be given to provincial proposals. Then too the financial reorganisation begun by James Wilson, the first finance member, produced a closer and more systematic inspection of provincial finance. Stringent rules were adopted, requiring a preliminary sanction for all expenditure, involving a multitude of references on details much too minute for the consideration of the Government of India, and producing great friction with the subordinate governments, which felt themselves aggrieved at the limitation of their powers.

Some relaxation thus became necessary, in the interest of smooth working as well as efficiency, and from 1872 onwards a process of financial decentralisation was begun, the object of which was to free the provinces from needless control and to classify the revenues of the country into central and provincial. In the earlier days no distinction had been recognised. All taxation was collected on behalf of the Government of India, which annually assigned specific sums for the requirements, real or supposed, of the several provinces. No attempt had even been made to limit provincial expenditure to a certain proportion of the revenues raised within each province. The result had been an unfair allocation of funds as between the several provinces. The most clamant governments received more than their fair share; those which sought to practise economy suffered by this exercise of virtue. Funds were allotted in proportion rather to demands than to needs. The different systems of land revenue increased the inequality. The permanent settlement of the Bengal land revenue precluded the rising costs of administration from being met by increasing collections from this, the most prolific source of taxation within the province itself. The other provinces were therefore required to pay more in order that the land-owners of Bengal might continue to enjoy the benefits of a fixed assessment.

Lord Mayo began by assigning to the provincial authorities certain services, such as education and roads, for which they were to be responsible, providing additional money that might be needed beyond the fixed budget grants by savings or by local taxation. Under Lytton and Ripon, the work was carried on. Provincial governments were allowed to transfer savings in one section of their budget for expenditure under another. Certain small sources of income were transferred to their management, and they were to keep part of any net increase they could obtain from them. The vicious system of annual settlements with each province was abolished. Under this method of control all unexpended grants lapsed to the Government of India at the close of the financial year, so that in the last quarter of the year much needless expenditure was often incurred merely in order that grants might not lapse and that the Government of India might have no excuse for cutting down the ensuing annual budget on the ground that the scale of the former grants had been evidently excessive. In place of this was established a quinquennial settlement, under which balances could be carried forward and provincial governments could plan their expenditure over a period of years, instead of confining their outlook to twelve months only. Finally under Lord Curzon a great advance was made by the establishment of what were called "quasi-permanent settlements". These were based on a real attempt to classify revenues as central and provincial. It was imperfect, in that it was still found necessary for the provinces to assign a proportion of their land revenue and excise collections to the central treasury; but it was declared that the distribution of revenues between central and provincial needs would not be altered save in the event of some great calamity such as war or famine, which would imperatively require a temporary readjustment. These changes were accompanied by a progressive relaxation of control over financial detail. The limits of expenditure which might be sanctioned by provincial governments were raised, and appointments might be made and posts created by them which at an earlier time would have required the formal approval of the Government of India. The thirty years which closed in 1904 thus materially increased the authority of the provincial governments in matters of detail. Their formal power unquestionably rose.

But at the same time their degree of influence over the general course of policy tended to weaken. The growth of communications, which subjected the Government of India to the secretary of state, subjected the provincial governments to the Government of India. The centralisation of the period before 1858 had been a matter of law rather than one of practice. Provincial governors, lieutenant-governors, and high commissioners had all enjoyed large though varying powers of discretion. Varying systems of district administration and land-revenue collection had developed in the various provinces, usually justified by special local conditions. But now the influence of the telegraph, the spread of education, the growth of the press, the development of political interests, all tended to produce a growing uniformity of policy. Local differences were not indeed obliterated but they were reduced. The new period was one of constant reports, statistics, office work. Supervision was incomparably closer. Organisation came to be moulded rather on the theoretical perfection begotten of files in the pigeon-holes of Calcutta than on what the individual administrator thought to be indispensable. So that while the Government of India was surrendering its right to say whether a collector in Bombay or Madras should add a new clerk to his office establishment, it was laying down principles for universal application and earnestly pressing the provincial governments to put them into practice. This pressure, like that of the secretary of state, increased as the century waned. It reached its climax with the appointment of inspectors-general by the Government of India, designed to visit the provinces, to "advise" provincial officials, and to inform the Government of India of the extent to which its views were being carried into effect. Matters went so far that Bombay could not set up a university course of studies in agriculture because other provinces were not sufficiently advanced for such a step, and Burma had to stand perpetually on guard lest one of the revenue systems of northern India should be thrust upon the province. Curzon might complain that he knew less of what was going on in Madras than what was going on in Egypt. But the complaints of a tired man must not be taken too seriously; and if his language corresponded with the fact, that was because he lacked time or inclination to read the inexhaustible stream of papers which the central government exacted from every province.

A like tendency was illustrated by the reform of the law courts and the development of Indian law. A reform in this direction was long overdue, and had constituted one of the main purposes which were to have been secured by the reforms of 1833, although unexpected difficulties had prevented action for another generation. In 1858 the old evils still persisted. At the three presidency towns sat the three Supreme Courts, mainly administering English law and having no relation with the company's courts which operated everywhere else in British India. These latter administered strange and diverse mixtures of English, Muslim and Hindu law, more or less amplified and modified by the regulations and acts passed by the company's governments. The result was that the presidency towns had different systems of law from those of the countries of which they were the capitals. The first essential step to get rid of these anomalies was the amalgamation of the two sets of courts. This was much facilitated by the establishment of direct crown government, for it was manifestly absurd to replace two groups depending one upon the crown and the other upon the company, by two groups each depending upon the crown. In 1861 therefore the Indian High Courts Act was passed to fuse the two groups into one. The Supreme Courts were united with the company's courts of appeal—the *sadr 'adālats*—at each presidency town, the new courts receiving the new title of High Courts. These inherited the original jurisdiction of the Supreme Courts within the presidency towns and the appellate authority of the sadr courts over the territory dependent on each. Thus proposals for which Hastings and Impey had been violently assailed were at last, eighty years later, effected with the approval of all. The judges of the new courts, like those of the Supreme Courts, were to be appointed by the crown and hold office during pleasure. A third of each bench was to consist of members of the English, Irish, or Scotch bars, one third of covenanted servants, and the remainder of persons who had held judicial office or practised in the High Courts. An opening was thus made by which eminent Indian lawyers without European qualifications could be promoted to the bench. The constitution of these High Courts has remained unchanged; but a fourth was set up at Allāhābād in 1866, and a fifth at Patna in 1912.

The jurisdiction of the new High Courts was limited to the older or "regulation" provinces in which alone Supreme Courts had been created, and where no change could be made but by the legislature. In the other, more recently acquired provinces, a similar organisation was gradually established by the authority of the governor-general in council. Chief Courts, as these new bodies were called, were introduced in the Panjab in 1866, and later on in the Central Provinces, Sind, and Burma. Judges of the Chief Courts were appointed by the governor-general and held office during his pleasure.

The main cause which had delayed this judicial reorganisation had been the need of simplifying the law and determining the mode of procedure which was to be adopted, it being agreed by all except practising lawyers that some way out of the existing confusion must be found. It had been declared by a judge of the Calcutta Supreme Court in 1829 that "no one could then pronounce an opinion or form a judgment, however sound, upon any disputed right, regarding which doubt and confusion might not be raised by those who might choose to call it in question". In 1835 a law commission had been constituted with Macaulay as its president, to attempt a codification of the existing law. It had prepared the first draft of the Penal Code. In 1853 another law commission had been formed. This had sat in London instead of Calcutta, and had first produced the Code of Civil Procedure, passed into law in 1859. In 1860 the Penal Code as revised by later lawyers was passed. In 1861 a Criminal Procedure Code, prepared by the second law commission, was adopted. The way had thus been opened for the reform of the law courts by providing common procedures to be followed in civil and criminal causes throughout British India, although several revisions of each were afterwards found to be necessary, and other branches of law were codified at a later date. No doubt can be felt that the new laws were a great improvement on the incoherent mass of rules which they displaced. At the same time codification has not been found entirely free from disadvantage. The augmented certainty of the law has not diminished the frequency of appeal; and it has been acutely remarked that under the codes cases have come to be argued on over-subtle interpretation of the wording of the statutes or on points of perhaps minute procedure rather than on broad principle and the merits of the individual case.

Under British administration Muslim criminal law has ceased to operate. In the time of Warren Hastings the reform of Muslim criminal law began. It involved many points which were repugnant to western legal ideas. The rule that a murdered man's next-of-kin might choose the death of the murderer or a sum of money, the rule that the murderer could only be put to death by the murdered man's next-of-kin, the rule that an accused could be convicted only on the evidence of two eye-witnesses, or the rule that infidels could not be admitted as witnesses against Muslims, were easily evaded by orders to the courts. In 1793 the punishment of an eye for an eye was prohibited. In 1825 women were exempted from flogging. From 1849 the perjurer was no longer branded. At last in 1860 the Penal Code wholly replaced the criminal law which had been introduced into India by the Turks of Ghūr.

Family law, however, whether Muslim or Hindu, was scarcely touched. The Muslim law of divorce and successions remained substantially unaltered, while there was no sharp conflict between

Muslim and English conceptions of landed rights such as distinguished Hindu law from English. English knowledge of Hindu law had grown up slowly. Warren Hastings had led the way by causing a group of pundits to compile a digest of the recognised texts, which was translated into Persian and thence into English under the title of the *Gentoo Code*. A generation later this had been superseded by the *Digest* of Colebrooke, who was at once a sound lawyer and a Sanskrit scholar. The influence of such works, however, was to invest ancient Sanskrit texts with an authority which perhaps they had never before enjoyed, for the changes made by customary and local use were wholly ignored. The pundits who were attached to each court as expounders of Hindu law were also inclined to stand upon their texts and to dispute the validity of custom where the latter differed from the former. In northern India this tendency was in part counteracted by the growing practice of taking evidence of prevalent usage; but in the south the text locally recognised—the commentary on Yajnavalkya known as the *Mitakshara* compiled in the eleventh century A.D.—long continued to enjoy absolute authority.

These texts confronted English lawyers with principles of ownership wholly strange to them. In England ownership was "simple, independent, and unrestricted". But in the Hindu world this was an exceptional condition. Property of all kinds normally vested, not in the individual, but in the joint family; and though each male member could at any time demand his share, which would become his sole property, it would almost at once become the joint property of a new family composed of the owner and his descendants. Thus individual rights were in a perpetual state of flux, and, although they could be determined for the instant by a division, such temporary settlement would be at once upset by the birth of children. The individual was thus seldom entitled to alienate on his own behalf any specific piece of property. This system, while in general recognised and maintained by English courts, has in modern times been modified in two respects. The individual has been invested with rights to sell or charge his share in joint property and to dispose by will of property which he has acquired independently, and with which under Hindu law he could deal by gift.

The growth of commerce rendered the first of these changes almost indispensable. Economic activity would be greatly stimu-

lated by allowing a man to deal with his share in family property.
Between 1855 and 1872 the courts came to hold that a creditor
might recover a judgment debt by bringing to sale a debtor's
share in family property, the purchaser becoming entitled to the
items representing that share when ascertained by a division. In
the west and south it then came to be held that the individual
himself might sell what might be sold under a decree against him.
In the north and east, however, this logical development was not
followed. In the matter of wills the pundits, following their texts,
considered such a right as an innovation which should not be
permitted. But as against this was the fact that from 1758 Hindus
began in increasing numbers to make wills. In Bengal the right
was formally acknowledged in 1792 in regard to property of
which a man could dispose by gift in his lifetime. In Bombay an
anomalous position developed. In the presidency town, under
the influence of English legal ideas, such wills received effect,
but elsewhere in the province they did not. In Madras the
sadr court had at first been inclined to follow the precedents
established in Bengal. But a regulation of 1829, declaring that
wills of Hindus should have no force save in so far as they
might be valid under Hindu law, produced an entire change of
attitude. Such wills, therefore, remained wholly inoperative till
1862, when the High Court at last recognised their validity,
following a decision of the Privy Council in 1856. Later legislation of 1870 and 1881 applied to such wills certain general
conditions regarding the exercise of testamentary power.

In certain other directions the enactment of the codes and the
reorganisation of the superior courts produced important consequences. They led for instance to the disappearance of the main
differences between the regulation and non-regulation provinces.
Those had consisted in the methods of legislation and the modes of
district organisation. Law in the non-regulation provinces had
been provided by executive order; and the district officer had
united in his own hands executive and judicial functions. In a
province like the Panjab a large body of law was in force; but,
unlike the enactments prevalent in the older provinces, it had not
been the work of the legislative council, and was not distinguished
by special legislative form. It consisted in the orders of the
governor-general, under whose personal direction the new provinces had been administered, and the orders of the principal

authorities whom he had set up. One disadvantage was that the lack of legislative form gave rise to uncertainty, since, as Maine noted, it was not always easy to discern which orders were, and which were not designed to have legislative effect. Another was the dubious legality of the system. It had been called in question by Sir Barnes Peacock, chief justice of the Supreme Court at Calcutta. The Councils Act of 1861 therefore included a section declaring valid the rules actually in force, although they had not been made in the manner laid down by the statutes. This necessitated an enquiry as to what rules actually were in force in Oudh or in the Panjab; and thenceforward legislative methods followed the statutory processes. The union also of executive and judicial power was modified, and district administration, in part at least, was assimilated to the typical organisation elsewhere. The deputy-commissioner, as the head of a district was called in the non-regulation provinces, had originally exercised the combined authority of revenue collector, head of the police, and chief civil and criminal judge within his district, while the commissioner in charge of a division or group of districts supervised his executive and revenue work and heard appeals from his judicial decisions. Gradually these judicial functions were transferred to separate officials. The deputy-commissioner retained as magistrate a limited criminal jurisdiction, but he was gradually relieved of the task of hearing civil suits save those arising between landlord and tenant; the commissioner's jurisdiction in like manner was transferred to divisional judges, who came in course of time to correspond closely with the district and sessions judges of the regulation provinces. Thus the personal administration which had been the mark of the non-regulation provinces came to an end and was replaced by much the same rule of law as had been established elsewhere. The principal surviving distinction was that the higher administrative posts long continued to be open to men who were not members of the covenanted civil service.

However, though personal rule vanished from wide areas as a whole, it was neither practicable nor desirable for it to disappear altogether. There were numerous tracts in the various provinces, consisting of hilly or jungly regions, inhabited by primitive tribes wholly unaccustomed to regular administration. Earlier governments had ignored their existence except when raids of the hill-men upon the plains had called for punishment. The Santhāl

parganas in Bengal, the Mahī Kanta in Bombay, the hill tracts
of the Northern Circars, and many other areas, were all unsuited
for the elaborate system of government which had been established
in the older provinces, with their separation of functions, complicated laws, and endless series of appeals from court to court.
Where primitive tribesmen, as in the Santhāl *parganas*, had been
subjected to the general plan of government, the plain dwellers
had taken advantage of this to exploit the hill tribes, with injustice and rebellion as the consequence. A statute of 1870 and an
Indian act of 1874 permitted a certain elasticity in the system.
The first permitted the secretary of state to "schedule" tracts
within which the governor-general in council should have authority to make binding regulations. The second enabled the government to declare in cases of doubt the law in force in such "scheduled
tracts". In these restricted areas the system of personal rule and
united powers which had characterised the non-regulation provinces persisted in all its force, despite its disappearance as a mode
of provincial government.

In its main principles the mode of district administration had
been already settled, and, except for the modification in the newer
non-regulation provinces already noted, the formal changes made
in the period after the Mutiny were not great. The collector or
deputy-commissioner continued to be the chief agent of government in his district; he continued to be responsible for its general
order and well-being. But as time passed, those objects came to
be pursued in a different manner and by changed methods, which,
in the restricted area of the district, corresponded with the assimilation of non-regulation to regulation provinces. Government
was becoming more a matter of method, of statistics, of general
rules pressed into force over ever-widening areas, than of personal
judgment and influence. The district officer gradually came to
pass more of his time at headquarters, less on tour. Tours themselves became more hurried, as the motor car superseded horse
and ox-cart and elephant. The telegraph cut down the collector's
discretionary powers, just as it cut down the local governor's and
even the governor-general's.

The elaboration of public business led to the division of administration among a number of new departments, usually of a highly
specialised nature, tending to absorb part of the duties for which
the district officer had been exclusively responsible. Public works,

for instance, acquired a new importance. Before the Mutiny, except for the building and repair of public offices and the maintenance of the few public roads, little had been done. But the new period was one of great expansion. Especially in the Panjab, new irrigation works on a large scale were planned and carried out, bringing under the plough wide areas which till then had lain barren and uninhabited. New roads were cut; new bridges made; railways were built. These new activities demanded a technical knowledge which could be acquired only by special training, and so the control which the collector had formerly exercised over the public works of his district was in part replaced by that of a Public Works Department, composed of engineers, military and civil, and represented in each district by an official called the executive engineer, who was responsible to the provincial head of the department. The collector was still consulted about operations in his district, for they would certainly affect the important question of revenue; and his opinion continued to carry great weight on all questions of general policy within the district; but there had come into existence an organised department owing obedience to another authority.

Much the same happened with the forests. Till the time of Dalhousie hardly anything had been attempted in the way of conservation, and great areas had been damaged or destroyed by indiscriminate cutting and grazing. In 1856 Brandis was invited from Germany to advise on the policy to be followed in the Burmese forests, and he with two other German experts organised the Forest Department, formed in 1869. A conservator of forests was appointed in each province, with deputies in charge of the "circles" into which the forest lands were divided. Under acts passed in 1865 and 1878 the forest lands were classified as "reserved", "protected" and "unclassed". The first are maintained under strict rules of scientific forestry; the second are subject only to rules designed to increase their value to the neighbouring inhabitants or to permit their subsequent reservation if that should become desirable; the third are virtually open. The chief difficulties which arose in this branch of administration resulted from the uncertain and ill-defined rights of user which the neighbouring inhabitants, whether settled villagers or primitive tribes, claimed to possess. The extension of cultivation in the course of the nineteenth century absorbed in certain provinces lands which had lain waste and had been employed for pasture. This led to a growing pressure upon forest areas, threatening widespread destruction, with the accompaniment of a diminished rainfall and extensive denudation. The act of 1878 therefore laid down methods by which public and private rights in forest lands were to be determined, and provided for the extinction of private rights by compensation or exchange where they endangered areas which it was judged necessary to "reserve". As was the case with public works, these forest operations also closely affected the interests of the agricultural population; while, then, the technical operations of the forest conservators were withdrawn from the collector's management, rules for the control of grazing or the levy of fees required his approval.

A further development intimately touching the welfare of the rural population was the appearance of an agricultural department. From the early days of the company's rule sporadic efforts had been made to improve agriculture and introduce new and profitable crops. At the end of the eighteenth and the beginning of the nineteenth centuries attempts were made to introduce cinnamon from Ceylon and cloves from Amboyna. Cotton seed was imported from Bourbon. Prickly pear was planted to feed the insect which produces cochineal. At Madras an experimental farm was instituted in 1865, developing later into an agricultural school, and in 1886 into an agricultural college. In 1882 an agricultural expert was appointed to advise the officers concerned with the land-revenue settlements. At Bombay and elsewhere departments of land records and agriculture were formed between 1880 and 1884. But these attempts led to little, mainly because such experts as there were lay under the control of the non-expert revenue department. Curzon, however, inaugurated a most fruitful change. In 1901 he appointed an inspector-general of agriculture with a small staff of experts. This was followed in 1905 and 1906 by the organisation of provincial departments. Agricultural colleges were opened; research was undertaken; methods of exterminating pests were discovered and recommended; the improvement of crops was zealously sought after. Here as elsewhere development required the supersession of non-expert by expert control.

The organisation of the provincial departments of education worked in the same direction. The collector in early days had exercised a paternal if vaguely informed supervision over the schools maintained within his district, occasionally visiting them and questioning teachers and pupils. When the educational departments were formed in 1856, this work was taken over by the inspectors of schools and their subordinates. But beyond the appearance in the districts of a new official responsible not to the collector but to the head of the department, the change scarcely affected the collector's position because the rural population took and continued to take no interest in education, since it was, even in its simplest and most elementary forms, in no wise connected with the daily business and vital concerns of agriculturists.

For a different reason the reorganisation of the police departments also affected but little the collector's position. An act of 1861 introduced extensive reforms in the provincial police, which had been entirely controlled by the collectors and deputy-commissioners in their capacity as district magistrates acting under the orders of the provincial governments. The district officers had in fact insufficient leisure to maintain an adequate control over the police of their district, and investigation had brought to light cases in which Indian police officials had employed the methods familiar to earlier Indian governments but inconsistent with western ideas. No one under the rule of the nawab of Arcot had been astonished or shocked when a prisoner was stood in the sun with a heavy stone on his head to make him confess to a crime which he was thought to have committed. But such practices assumed a different complexion under the Presidency of Madras. The police of each province were therefore placed under an inspector-general, with deputy-inspectors-general in charge of areas corresponding with the revenue divisions. In each district a superintendent was placed in charge of the local police establishments. But the maintenance of public order was too important a matter to be withdrawn from the head of the district. The district superintendents were therefore placed under a dual control. They were responsible to their departmental authorities for the internal management and discipline of their police-force; but in regard to its distribution, the preservation of peace and the suppression of crime, they followed the directions of the district magistrates, so that the authority of the collector was little affected. The change certainly produced improvement. But the pay and qualifications, especially of the lower Indian ranks, remained poor; and the police commission appointed by Curzon recommended numerous reforms which were gradually introduced as financial conditions permitted.

The net result of all these changes was to set up within the district agents of numerous departments owing but a limited obedience to the collector, whereas in the past he had been the channel by which all government orders had been carried into operation. This did not greatly affect his pre-eminence within the area of his authority, but it enormously increased his office-work. Matters which would previously have been settled by the drafting of an order to the appropriate official became the subjects of voluminous correspondence, not merely with the district representatives of the various new departments, but also, in consequence of proposals submitted by the heads of these new departments, with the provincial government itself. This certainly reduced the capacity of the collector to deal directly and personally with the affairs of his district. Government was becoming a matter of memoranda, minutes, letters and statistics instead of personal inspection and decision. The change involved greater method, greater regularity, a tighter control by the central bodies, a more efficient administration. But it also carried with it the loss of that close personal touch between the head of the district and the villagers in which had lain the real strength of the company's government in every province but Bengal.

In some respects this more systematic government carried with it great advantages. General measures adapted to the special needs of various provinces, were taken to protect the interests and rights of the cultivators. In Bengal they had been most grievously neglected. The zamindars and their agents had succeeded in hiding the agrarian position. Cornwallis had hoped that the operation of his new courts would disentangle a problem which he thought too intricate for executive solution; but the advantage which his elaborate judicial procedure and its freedom of appeal from court to court bestowed on the rich land-holder as against the poor cultivator, had completely falsified his expectations. The zamindars claimed under the permanent settlement to be entitled to the fee simple of their estate except where tenants could prove customary rights; and the large class of customary tenants had undergone grievous diminution. In 1859 the first act was passed to remedy this injustice. This declared that certain classes of tenants were entitled to occupy their holdings at fixed rentals, and that occupancy rights should be presumed where tenants had held the same lands for twelve years or more, while it also limited the zamindars' powers of distraint upon the ryot. But the burden of proof still lay upon the latter, and no provision was made to ascertain and record existing rights. In 1872 agrarian trouble arose out of the additional demands made upon the cultivators in certain districts. After long discussions a new tenancy act was passed in 1885. This checked the practice, introduced after 1859, of moving tenants from holding to holding in order to prevent their securing occupancy rights, and enabled a survey and a record of rights to be prepared in any area by direction of the Government of India, or in any estate where either the zamindar or the ryots petitioned the provincial government for such action. In this way after the lapse of three generations part of the injustice of the permanent settlement was undone.

The problem of occupancy rights had been far more acute in Bengal than in any of the other provinces, because there alone a system of large estates coincided with a permanent zamindari settlement. But questions of tenant-right emerged in the Āgra or North-Western Provinces, in Oudh, and in the Panjab. In the first the Bengal act of 1859 applied until it was replaced by special acts of 1873 and 1881,-which maintained the same general principles but also gave to the collectors and subordinate revenue officials the power of settling disputes between tenants and their landlords. In Oudh, where the talukdari settlement had recognised subordinate rights, by acts of 1868 and 1886 such occupancy rights were admitted as had been enjoyed within thirty years of the annexation, and non-occupancy tenants were protected against any increase of rent at intervals of less than seven years. In the Panjab, where the prevalent land-tenures were different, an act of 1868, passed after much controversy, defined the classes of tenant entitled to occupancy rights but abolished future acquisition by mere lapse of time.

Economic development led to evils of a different kind. One of the major consequences of the stability of British rule and the growing precision of rights over the soil was a great rise in the marketability of land. A buyer could rely, in a degree which had never before existed, on knowing what rights he was purchasing and on finding full legal support for the rights he had acquired.

At the same time the development of the world-markets for Indian produce, the expansion of the legal profession, the rise of a middle class possessed of great wealth, produced a large number of individuals ready to lend money on landed security or to buy land outright as the safest of all possible investments. What had happened in England in the half-century following on the confusion of the Wars of the Roses happened in India in the second half of the nineteenth century. The mortgage and sale of land increased with extraordinary rapidity. In so far as this affected the landlord class, it mattered comparatively little. But over great tracts the land was divided out into the tiny holdings of peasant proprietors. Their extrusion from their holdings and their reduction from the position of land-holders to that of agricultural labourers was a matter which could not be viewed with unconcern. In 1875 considerable agrarian trouble broke out in the Bombay Deccan; riots took place; the village money-lenders and grain-dealers were attacked, their houses burnt, their accounts destroyed. In Madras a large amount of land gradually passed out of the possession of the non-Brāhman peasant into that of the Brāhman professional class. In the Panjab the cultivating class was being ousted by traders and money-lenders. In order to meet this social evil two remedies, direct and indirect, were gradually applied. The direct remedy lay in legislation. In consequence of the Bombay troubles, and the recommendations of a commission appointed to investigate their causes, an act was passed to prevent money-lenders from acquiring land by fraudulent claims. But, as this failed to attain its object, a different principle was adopted in the Panjab, where an act of 1900 placed under severe restrictions all transfers of land from the ownership of the agricultural into that of the non-agricultural classes of the province. The indirect method consisted in the establishment and development of a system of co-operative credit. The value of this, both moral and economic, would be hard to exaggerate.

India has suffered for untold generations from two economic vices. One has been the reluctance of all but the banking and commercial castes to employ savings in any productive way. They have been either hidden in the ground or spent upon the purchase of personal ornaments of gold or silver. The consequence has been that a great proportion of the wealth of the country has increased only in arithmetical instead of geometrical progression.

This medieval characteristic has been accompanied by another even more injurious. Social custom has been allowed to dictate the expenditure of relatively huge sums on the ceremonial occasions of marriage and death. Expenses amounting to two or three years' entire income have been virtually inevitable at such times, because individuals feared lest their fellow-villagers or caste-men would despise them if they kept their outlay below the customary standard. But since their actual savings often would not cover such extravagance, the aid of the money-lender was sought. Indian capital being scarce and ill-organised (another condition which assimilates India to medieval Europe), the rate of interest was usurious, and would run from 18 to 24 per cent. per annum. These peculiarities explain why the Indian cultivator was remarkable among all the peasant proprietors of the world for the extent of his indebtedness.

A real remedy for this evil demanded not only the provision of cheaper credit but also a measure of practical economic education. Cheaper credit by itself would be a mere palliative. Men needed to learn the practical disadvantages of borrowing for even the most solemn of religious rites, the practical advantages of borrowing and lending for productive purposes. In 1904 Curzon resolved to apply to India methods which had produced most fruitful results in not dissimilar conditions in Germany and Italy—the methods of co-operative credit. An act of that year provided for the establishment of co-operative credit societies under due supervision. In 1912 the law was revised in the light of Indian experience and widened so as to include societies for co-operative purchase and marketing. The local societies are managed by committees of the villagers themselves; their funds are in part provided by the subscriptions and deposits of the villagers. Under due supervision and control the movement, which has spread steadily, carries with it the most valuable educative influences; and the act of 1904 will perhaps rank with the organisation of the agricultural department as the most enduring and valuable monument of Curzon's rule in India.

The definition of landed rights and the provision of co-operative credit formed two developments of great importance to the peasantry of India. A third was the formation of regular and systematised methods of dealing with famine. The failure of the periodic rains in India had much the same effect within the area concerned as a prolonged general strike would have in the industrial countries of the West. The ryot could not till his land or feed his cattle. The cities ceased to receive their accustomed supplies of food. The industries lacked their raw materials. Everyone was thrown out of work. Inland transport ceased, for pack-oxen could not be fed and watered. At intervals of a generation or so this terrific calamity had fallen upon wide tracts of India, leaving them wasted, impoverished, dispeopled. The traditional methods of relieving famine had consisted in forbidding the export of grain, in suspension of the revenue demand, in making advances to distressed cultivators, and (in extreme cases) in the bestowal of charity by the ruler and his chief officers. Similar methods were adopted by the company's government. But they were obviously inadequate. When in 1837 the upper provinces were smitten with famine, the Āgra government laid down the principle that the state should find work for the able-bodied, but that charity must provide for those incapable of working. The result was the same in 1837 as it had always been. Many perished.

The change in general conditions, however, permitted the development of more effectual methods of dealing with famines, while the extension of humanitarian ideas made such a development a matter of urgency. The areas liable to famine were con-tracted by the new irrigation works, begun by the company's government and continued with ever-growing vigour and more liberal finance by its successor. The building of railways aided the solution of the problem with even greater power, though in another manner, for it solved the problem of transporting food-stuffs into the afflicted regions. The Orissa famine of 1866–67 laid a sharp emphasis on this aspect of the matter. The Orissa districts were notably lacking in means of land transport, and the coast was inaccessible after the breaking of the south-west monsoon. The consequences were exaggerated by the ignorance in which the Bengal system of administration had involved the local govern-ment. The magistrate of Cuttack was almost starved within a few days of reporting that no need for anxiety existed. In the ensuing famine a quarter of the population was believed to have perished; and though, as is usual in such cases, the estimate probably ex-ceeded the fact, the suffering was great. However, a committee was appointed to enquire into the causes of the failure to anticipate and remedy the evil. Under the acute and vigorous guidance of George Campbell, its report led to a great development of policy. When famine appeared again in 1868 Lawrence, then governor-general, declared that the district officers would be held responsible for seeing to it that no preventable deaths occurred. In 1873 the Bihar famine exhibited the opposite extreme. Relief was extravagant. Famine was acute in two districts only; but 6½ millions was spent on relief and 800,000 tons of unneeded grain were carried into the affected area. After the lack of preparation for the Orissa famine and the excessive relief of the Bihar famine, policy took on a more exact and foreseeing character. A severe famine raged in 1876-8, caused by the failure of two successive monsoons, and covering an area stretching from Madras northwards as far as the North-Western Provinces and Oudh. The governor-general, Lytton, toured through the famine-stricken districts, closely observing the methods of relief in force. He found great divergencies. In Bombay, for instance, a greater saving of life had been secured than in Madras, though Madras had spent ten millions as against Bombay's four. He therefore appointed a commission, under Sir Richard Strachey as chairman, to examine into the whole question. Its report, which appeared in 1880, laid the basis of a new and efficient famine policy.

The main points of the report dealt with the need of properly compiled statistical information on the condition of agriculture, with the preparation of local schemes of relief-works which would absorb such proportion of the population as would probably be thrown out of employment, and with the financial measures necessary as a regular annual provision against the possibility of famine. This led to the preparation of a Famine Code issued in 1883 and to the appearance in the Indian Budget of a head called "Famine Relief and Insurance". Under the famine code schemes were to be prepared for relief-works, the larger ones by the Public Works Departments, the smaller ones by the district officials, so that, whenever famine appeared, there should be a maturely considered programme of suitable projects ready to be put into immediate operation. As regards finance, it was reckoned that famine had cost in recent years an average of a crore and a half of rupees. It was therefore resolved to budget for this sum as part of the regular expenditure. In normal times it was to be employed either on schemes of irrigation designed to protect areas specially liable to famine against its occurrence, or on the construction of railways and canals which would otherwise have been financed by loans.

This new system was bitterly tested by two great famines in 1896-7 and 1899-1900, in which devoted efforts were made by the whole power of the administration to minimise suffering. Each was followed by a commission of enquiry; and while both generally endorsed the findings of Lytton's former commission, the second suggested a number of points in which the methods of combating famine might be improved, laying particular emphasis on the importance of a more careful preparation of district schemes and on the early announcement of suspensions of the land revenue and of the grant of advances. The changes then introduced by Curzon were put to the test of experience in 1907-8 when famine again visited the United Provinces. The failure of the autumn and spring harvests was as great as it had been in 1896-7. But its effects were far smaller. Railway extensions, canal extensions, a higher range of prices and wages, a growing variety of employment, a more mobile population, had at last enabled the efforts of policy successfully to cope with the strain of famine, and in this most important respect medieval conditions had disappeared in India.

The organisation of the civil servants of the government still remains to be described. In 1854 they were classified into two groups—the covenanted and the uncovenanted servants. The first formed the administrative aristocracy. They and they alone could legally fill any civil office in the regulation provinces that carried a salary of £800 a year and upwards. They had been the personal nominees of the directors of the company. But in 1853 Macaulay succeeded in carrying into effect the plan, which seems to have been first proposed by Lord Grenville in 1813, to provide for their future appointment by open literary competition. Macaulay's skilful pleading persuaded almost everyone that the change was a great and unassailable reform. It had many advantages, especially in that it prevented dull or vicious lads being thrust into the covenanted service by family interest. It also ensured that future entrants would be quick-brained, well-read, good pen-and-ink men, like Macaulay himself. After a little while the same system of recruitment was applied to the civil services in England, and its undeniable success in the public offices of London was thought to confirm the suitability of such selections for the public offices of Calcutta, and the head-quarters of every district in British India. But in fact the principal duties of the higher civil service in England and of the covenanted service, or Indian civil service as it came to be called, were fundamentally different. In England the civil servant is the servant of the political head of his department, in whose name and by whose orders alone he communicates with the general public. His responsibility is limited, his discretionary powers small. The English administration is, and has always been, controlled in part by the politicians of Westminster, in part by prominent local men, justices of the peace, county councillors, borough and district councillors, and the like. Such amateurs have benefited incalculably by the clever and trustworthy assistants provided for them by competitive methods. But, although the civil servants have always believed it, it is not at all certain that the country would have been better governed had they been entrusted with the whole power and responsibility of administration. For centuries a like method of recruitment had been in force in China, where men who had competed successfully in difficult literary examinations were entrusted with the principal offices of the state.

The defects of this system as applied to India were three-fold. Engrafted on a bureaucratic government, it ensured a supply of clever men, while bureaucracy ensured that the cleverest should rise speedily and constantly into the secretariats and thence into the councils. But the qualities which India required of her foreign rulers were not mere cleverness. Her own people were not lacking in quickness and subtlety of mind. On that side Britain had nothing to contribute. What was wanted was honesty of purpose, independence of judgment, freedom from the disturbing influence of caste and creed, absence of self-seeking. But the men possessed of these were not those whom the system raised most readily into high places. The best men remained long in the districts and only rose with difficulty or by good fortune to high office. On the whole the system probably improved the district administration, improved the secretariats, but did not improve the general control.

The second defect of the new system lay in its weakening family connections with the Indian administration. It was all to the good that when a young man arrived in India he should find friends, both English and Indian, ready-made, that he should carry out with him the intimate tradition of family service and be inspired by obligation not only to the people of the country but also to his father and grandfather. He came to India not as a stranger to a strange land, but as one fulfilling an ancestral destiny. The competitive system weakened this beneficent influence and often replaced it by feelings of mere personal advantage.

The third defect was that pointed out by Lord Stanley, though quite fruitlessly, in the debates of 1853. The competitive examination was based on western knowledge. Though Indians might be eligible to compete, they could not compete on anything like equal terms. Their schools, their traditions, their family life, all forbade their acquiring such a knowledge of Latin and Greek as would allow them to rival English competitors. The examinations were held in London; and Indian candidates were thus required to undertake a long and expensive voyage, to live among people of utterly different habits, and to endure the quick changes of a different and most volatile climate. They could not but break solemn rules of caste if they came to England. They might fall sick amid the fogs of London. And even when they had run all these social and personal risks, they would still have hardly the faintest chances of success. It is true that the rules of the examination were later on modified so as to include Sanskrit, Persian and Arabic, and to permit Indian candidates to offer them instead of the classical languages of the West. Other oriental languages were introduced. But the fact remained that, unless an Indian boy spent several years in an English school and college, far from home, and incurring what in India was considered an enormous expense, his chances of success were very poor. The system ensured that the higher posts of the British-Indian government should be filled by Englishmen or Indians of English training, so as to preserve the English character of the administration. But this object, valuable as it was, was secured by a side-wind. It was secured by a system which professed to offer an equal opportunity to all. Indians therefore resented it with a bitterness which would not have been provoked by the creation of a *corps d'élite* publicly declared to consist of Englishmen alone. In 1914 only twenty-six Indians competed out of 183 candidates. The remedy demanded by Indian political bodies such as the National Congress was that simultaneous examinations should be held in India and England.

But to this there was a great obstacle. In the existing state of education it was certain that Hindus alone would succeed among the Indian competitors, and that large and powerful sections of the population, such as the Muslims and the Sikhs, would remain completely excluded; the proposal was therefore rejected, until the reorganisation of recruitment following on the reforms of 1919, and even then it was still apparent that the principle of open competition could not be applied without restriction.

In view of the practical working of the competitive system, a number of experiments had been made in order to modify the virtual exclusion of Indians from the posts open to members of the Indian civil service. The first was a proposal by Lawrence to establish a number of state-scholarships, in order to enable Indians to pursue their studies in England. But almost as soon as this scheme began to work, it was suspended by the Duke of Argyll, then secretary of state. He desired a completer plan, and in 1870 passed an act through parliament enabling the Government of India with the secretary of state's approval to make rules under which Indians might be appointed to posts usually reserved for covenanted civilians. The subject was then actively discussed, but nothing was done till Lytton framed a scheme for the nomination of Indians to one-sixth of the reserved posts. His hope was that the nominees would consist mainly of young Indians of distinguished family, and that the " Statutory Civil Service " (as the new group was to be called) would bring the old Indian aristocracy into closer and more effective relations with the administrative machine. These expectations were not realised. The provincial governments, in recommending persons for the governor-general's nomination, found themselves obliged to choose between young men of good family but of meagre educational attainments, and older men of the professional groups qualified by administrative experience. Their recommendations came to be more and more limited to persons of the latter class.

Below the covenanted service was a large subordinate service recruited in India and known as the "Uncovenanted Service". In the regulation provinces its members could not rise to superior posts, and in the non-regulation provinces they were seldom suffered to do so. They included men of pure and mixed English blood, and Indians; and they provided most of the persons nominated to the Statutory Civil Service. In consequence of the report of the Public Services Commission appointed in 1886, it was resolved to abolish this long-standing classification. For it was substituted an imperial service, recruited in England, and two others, one provincial and the other subordinate, recruited in India. No more appointments were to be made to the Statutory Civil Service; but specially recommended members of the provincial civil services were to be eligible for appointment to a fixed proportion of the posts reserved for the Indian civilians.

A similar organisation was adopted for the services employed under the specialised departments which had come into existence. Here too, as in general civil employment, the chief posts had been usually reserved for persons recruited in England, while the remainder were filled in India. However, special circumstances had demanded special treatment. The Public Works Department, for instance, had been staffed partly by officers of the Royal Engineers, partly by civil engineers selected in London, and partly by men who had qualified at the Indian engineering colleges—Rūrkī, Poona, and Madras. In 1871, however, the Royal Engineering College at Cooper's Hill was established to provide civil engineers, and a fixed proportion was adopted, Cooper's Hill providing half, the Indian colleges three-tenths, and the Royal Engineers one-fifth of the recruits to the department. For a while too Cooper's Hill provided a training for the candidates selected as probationers in the Forest Department.

The general system adopted all through the administration was thus Indian agency under English supervision. This persisted in spite of a slow infiltration of Indians into offices of superior rank, and undoubtedly produced a government more honest and efficient than had previously existed in India. The price paid for this development was discontent, growing with the spread of education in India, at the exclusion of Indians from the higher grades.

CHAPTER XIV

Central Asia and the Routes to India

In a previous chapter some attempt has been made to sketch the growing importance of Central Asia and the Mediterranean avenues of approach to India. The other ways to India were securely held by the British navy, with its outposts at the Cape of Good Hope to the west, and at Singapore to the east. But the eastern ends of the Mediterranean routes were less completely held; Gibraltar closed the western entrance to the Mediterranean itself, and Malta lay full in the path of French fleets aimed, as Napoleon had aimed them, at Alexandria. But French influence was strong in Egypt; and Russian predominance at Constantinople had been avoided only at the cost of the Crimean War. If the long-discussed project of cutting through the isthmus of Suez were ever realised, then both France and Russia might find entrance through the Red Sea into Indian waters; and though Aden had been occupied in 1839, it could not seal up the southern exit. If the Suez Canal were cut, the duties of the British navy would be greatly increased, and a more effective control over Egypt would become indispensable to the security of India. And besides these considerations the Crimean War had brought the understanding between England and Russia about Central Asia to an end. Unless some influence could be found to make abstention worth Russia's while, she would almost certainly renew the policy which had alarmed Great Britain in the 'thirties, either extending her influence in Persia or advancing her frontier towards Afghanistan, or following both lines of development. In the middle of the nineteenth century these were the problems dominating the external policy of the Government of India. From the British point of view, was British foreign policy to become liable to deflection by Russian pressure on India? From the Indian point of view, was India to remain secure from external attack or were the conditions of the past to be revived? These considerations had already led to one ill-calculated and mismanaged war. They were now to produce fierce controversy and violent alternations of policy. Moreover, in this more than in any other aspect of policy was the growing control of the home government to receive its fullest effect. Auckland had entered on the First Afghan War in the belief that he was pursuing the desires of the English ministry, and Hobhouse boasted that he had dictated the conduct of the governor-general. This boast had not been wholly true; but within forty years it was to be realised, and a governor-general was to resign because he disliked the foreign policy of the secretary of state. The world was in fact shrinking, and action which in the past would have produced a mere local disturbance was now liable to bring about important reactions in all the capitals of Europe. India could no longer have a foreign policy of its own.

The annexation of the Panjab had at least simplified the position, for it had brought British India into direct contact with the area from which invaders had ever been wont to set out for the conquest of the country. In 1855 a treaty of friendship had been made with Dost Muhammad, the amir of Kābul, who had been driven into alliance with his former enemy, the Government of India, by the renewed ambitions of the shah of Persia. In 1852 the latter had seized Herat and had relinquished it only under British threats. In 1856 he again attacked Herat and boasted that he would conquer Kandahār as well. This led at once to war. An expedition was despatched from Bombay under the command of Outram; and aid in arms and money was sent to Dost Muhammad. These vigorous measures soon brought the Persians to terms. In the course of the next six years Dost Muhammad was busy consolidating his position in eastern and southern Afghanistan. In 1862 he resolved to add Herat, then under an independent Sadozai prince, to his dominions. Elgin, the governor-general, protested against this action, and recalled the Muslim agent whom the Government of India had maintained at Kābul since 1857. But Dost Muhammad persisted, and in the next year captured the place, but died shortly after at the age of eighty. His death involved the country in a long and confused war of succession. It lasted from 1864 to 1868. First one son and then another gained the upper hand; and each party applied to the Government of India for assistance. But John Lawrence, who was then governor-general, refused to take any part in the matter. He belonged to the generation which had drawn natural but mistaken conclusions from the lamentable war of 1839. He held strongly that Britain had no interests beyond the line which the Sikhs had formerly held, and that the defence of India should be based on the Indus. He had tried to prevent the conclusion of the treaty with Dost Muhammad; he had, in the crisis of the Mutiny, proposed to give away Peshāwar to the Afghans; and now when he had attained to power, he persisted in his former views. He assured each applicant that if he could establish himself as the ruler of Afghanistan, he should be recognised by the Government of India. This attitude, which its friends described unwisely as "the policy of masterly inactivity", was well calculated to induce the rival claimants to seek aid elsewhere. They approached Persia and Russia. This brought the policy of Lawrence to a hasty end. He at once gave a subsidy to Shīr 'Alī, whom Dost Muhammad had formerly designated as his heir; and with this help Shīr 'Alī soon succeeded in establishing himself as the ruler of Kābul, Kandahār, and Herat. But great harm had been done. Shīr 'Alī believed that "the English look to nothing but their interests and bide their time". Everyone had come to regard the English as unreliable friends and impotent enemies.

While Lawrence had been looking on at the Afghan situation, the Russians had been advancing swiftly in Central Asia. Their expansion had begun soon after the Crimean War. In 1864 they touched on the borders of Khokand, Bukhāra, and Khiva. In 1865 they occupied Tashkent. In 1867 they formed the new province of Russian Turkestan and reduced Bukhāra to the position of a vassal state. In 1873 the same fate befell Khiva. The ostensible motives for this advance were the difficulties which were always arising with the Turkmān tribes, the need of suppressing the slave-trade, and the encouragement of commerce. English opinion was divided between the acceptance and the rejection of these explanations. But we now know from undeniable Russian authority that the real motive was political. The imperial Russian government argued that since Britain could attack Russia through continental alliances, as had happened in the Crimean War, Russia should secure in Turkestan "a military position strong enough to keep England in check by the threat of intervention in India". Against this action England had two possible remedies. One was to occupy advanced stations in Central Asia and secure a commanding influence in Afghanistan, in order to convince Russia of the futility of advance in that direction. The other, which Lawrence recommended, was to reach a diplomatic agreement. If that could have been attained, it might have proved to be the cheaper way. But it was liable to one disadvantage. Russia clearly would not assent to any such proposals unless they were beneficial to herself; and the only bribe which Great Britain could offer would have been British support for Russian interests on the continent. But neither of the great English political parties would have dreamed of pursuing such a policy. What in fact happened was that diplomatic discussions were conducted without ever bringing the matter near a real settlement. The utmost that emerged from the conversations between Clarendon and Gortchakoff were Russian assurances of pacific intentions.

Meanwhile in India endeavours were made to form a closer union between Britain and Afghanistan, in order to preclude the establishment of Russian influence there. In accordance with the later policy of Lawrence, his successor, Lord Mayo, had a conference with Shīr 'Alī at Ambāla in 1869. But the net result was small. The amir only received a letter couched in encouraging but non-committal terms. In 1873, after the absorption of the khanates on the Oxus by Russia, Shīr 'Alī made an endeavour to secure a real alliance with Great Britain. He sent an agent to Simla, and proposed to Lord Northbrook that the British government should promise him help in case of any unprovoked aggression on the part of his northern neighbour. Northbrook was willing to accede to this request. But the Duke of Argyll, then secretary of state for India in Mr Gladstone's first cabinet, would allow him to go no further than to declare that "we shall maintain our settled policy in Afghanistan". To Shīr 'Alī this could mean nothing but a continuation of the Lawrence policy of helping those who no longer needed assistance. Argyll's decision marks a turning point in the development of the Central Asia question. Its ill effects were accentuated by two other events. The British government had agreed to arbitrate on the long-standing disputes between Afghanistan and Persia on their boundaries in Seistān. The decision in some points went against the amir, who complained bitterly of its injustice. In the circumstances it would have been wiser to allow the Persians and Afghans to settle the matter as best they could than to indispose both parties by a decision which if just would displease both. The second was the request of Shīr 'Alī for British recognition of 'Abdullāh Jān, whom he had installed as his heir. The answer which was sent to this proposal was intentionally phrased in the same terms as had been used in 1858 when Dost Muhammad had sent a similar request on behalf of Shīr 'Alī himself. From this Shīr 'Alī must have drawn the conclusion that his son would be recognised as amir only when he had destroyed or exiled every possible rival.

In these circumstances Shīr 'Alī seems to have concluded that for his own security he must make terms with Russia. General Kaufmann, the governor-general of Turkestan, was delighted at this development, which fitted in admirably with the purposes of the Russian Foreign Office. In 1870 he had opened a correspondence by assuring Shīr 'Alī that 'Abdur Rahmān, his nephew who had taken refuge at Tashkent, would receive no help to wage war against his uncle. This letter had been forwarded by Shīr 'Alī to the Government of India for advice regarding the answer which he should return. The latter merely informed him that "such letters should be looked on as an additional ground of confidence". When Shīr 'Alī asked for the recognition of 'Abdullāh Jān by the British, he made the same request to the Russians, who, instead of reminding him of his own struggles to secure his succession, blandly stated that "such nominations tend to the comfort and tranquillity of the kingdom". From 1875 the exchange of letters between Kābul and Tashkent became frequent. Such as transpired were mere letters of compliment; but no one in India knew what the others might contain. London suggested to St Petersburg that the correspondence might be brought to an end; but St Petersburg ignored the request. Yet, as the Government of India asked, what would have been thought at St Petersburg had the British entered into similar relations with the khans of Khiva or Bukhāra?

While affairs were thus developing in Central Asia, the position in the Mediterranean had been transformed. After long delays, and in defiance of all the obstacles which the British Foreign Office under Lord Palmerston could put forward, de Lesseps had obtained support and approval for his plan to cut the Suez Canal. That great work had been carried through, and was at last opened in 1869. Almost immediately afterwards the telegraph line which had been erected by way of Persia and Asia Minor was replaced by a submarine cable running from Bombay to Aden, thence up the Red Sea, and so to England through the Mediterranean. This cut out the long delays which the despatch of messages through several foreign jurisdictions had involved, and placed India in direct communication with London. For the first time the India Office could telegraph its orders to Calcutta or Simla in the certainty that they would arrive in time to be acted upon. From that moment the home government's control of foreign policy became unquestioned, and the discretional authority which the governor-general of India had long enjoyed began to disappear.

In 1874 also the Gladstone government was replaced by the first Disraeli ministry, with Lord Salisbury at the India Office. The new government was eager to redeem what it regarded as the great errors committed by its predecessor in the matter of foreign policy. In particular it thought that Gladstone's government had acquiesced far too easily in the explanations of Central Asia policy which had been offered by the imperial Russian government. Salisbury feared that unless something were done, Great Britain might suddenly find herself in a position of great strategic and political disadvantage. At Kābul the Government of India was represented only by a Muslim agent, who wrote (Salisbury thought) just what the amir chose to tell him, and whose reports did not tally with other reports received. The India Office therefore proposed that the amir should be invited to receive a British agent who should be stationed at Herat, in order that full and accurate information should be available regarding developments on the Russo-Afghan frontier. The governor-general, Lord Northbrook, disliked this proposal, and virtually refused to give effect to it. Soon afterwards he resigned his office and was succeeded by Lord Lytton, who was specially charged to carry out Salisbury's policy.

The new plan was not so unreasonable as has been supposed. It was based upon the terms which Shīr 'Alī had been willing to concede in 1873 in return for a conditional guarantee. It was asserted that Shīr 'Alī had never given any formal promise to receive a British agent at Herat. That was true, but it was not the whole truth. Northbrook himself was driven to admit that the amir "had appeared to consent", in return for the agreement which Argyll had compelled Northbrook to refuse but which Salisbury was now prepared to give, together with the acknowledgement of his son 'Abdullāh Jān as his heir. The real trouble was not that the proposals were bad but that they came too late.

What Shīr 'Alī would have given in 1873 he would not give in 1876, when his relations with Kaufmann had become closer and more intimate. At the same time Salisbury authorised a movement of great importance, the occupation of Quetta. This step had long been advocated by men like Jacob, Rawlinson, and Frere, who argued that the defence of India could not be conducted adequately without a strong post on the farther side of the hills separating Afghanistan from India. The line of the Indus was impossible partly from the defects of a river as a line of defence, partly from the political consequences which would follow immediately on the invasion of India by a foreign enemy. The administrative line, which roughly followed the boundary which the British had inherited from the Sikhs, possessed no military value whatever, and was, like most Indian frontiers, more likely to provide subjects of dispute than to secure a clear-cut division of interests between two neighbouring states. The advocates of an advance therefore claimed that the proper course was to occupy Quetta, under the existing treaty with the khan of Kalāt. This step would open the road to Kandahār, and permit the outflanking of any enemy seeking to advance against India by way of the northern passes. So long as Lawrence's influence had been supreme, this course had been reprobated as improper. But the advance of Russia and the growing correspondence between Shīr 'Alī and Kaufmann had led many to change their views. In 1876, therefore, a new treaty was made with the khan of Kalāt, and shortly afterwards Quetta was occupied. In a military sense the step had everything to recommend it. For the first time since the days of Aurangzīb the Indian frontier was no longer liable to attack with all the advantages on the side of the assailant. In a political sense also it was sound, although at the time it was regarded with much misgiving. It was said that it would alarm Shīr 'Alī and drive him into the arms of Russia. But that judgment ignored the fact that Shīr 'Alī had already been alienated by the policy of Argyll, and was already in communication with Russia. The occupation of Quetta was undoubtedly regarded by him as a threat. But it was the sort of threat which, had he not been deceived by the attitude of Mr Gladstone's government, should have made him think twice before committing himself to the friendship of Russia. Unless Great Britain was willing to allow the establishment of Russian predominance in Afghanistan, and concede to Russia the power of intervening in India at moments of European crisis, she was obliged to take action, and the conduct of Salisbury and Lytton, while certainly aggressive, compelled Shīr 'Alī either to give up his relations with Kaufmann or to embark on war in a position of relative disadvantage.

Therefore for the first time Shīr 'Alī found himself confronted by a British government which recognised that its own political interests were involved in Central Asia. He did not, however, understand the position in which he stood. He was probably much misled both by the past conduct of the Government of India and by the attitude of the Russian authorities. He seems to have hoped that he could balance between the two rivals, committing himself to neither, and protecting himself from inconvenient entanglements by their common fears. Long negotiations, lasting from October, 1876, to March, 1877, regarding Salisbury's proposed mission led to no conclusion. The chief argument against agreeing to this proposal was that if a British mission were accepted, the amir would be unable to avoid receiving a Russian mission, were one despatched. This argument was most unlucky, for almost at once a crisis arose in Europe. Rebellions broke out in European Turkey: Russian and British policies were antagonistic; and when Russia went to war with the sultan, the British attitude became definitely hostile to Russia. Both parties sought to employ every possible means of limiting and controlling the action of the other. Indian troops were sent to Malta. The Russians demanded of Shīr 'Alī a specific treaty of alliance. In these circumstances Shīr 'Alī's hopes of being able to follow a policy of balance were doomed to disappointment.

In June, 1878, Kaufmann wrote to the amir informing him that his external relations required "deep consideration" and that he was sending a Russian officer "to inform you of all that is hidden in my mind". He calculated wisely that Shīr 'Alī was unlikely to turn his mission back at the frontier. His envoy, Stolietoff, bore with him a draft treaty, offering much the same terms as Lytton had just offered, the recognition of 'Abdullāh Jān as heir and assistance against any foreign aggression. At the same time three columns of troops marched from Tashkent towards points on the Afghan frontier, and, in case by chance Shīr 'Alī refused the offer, Kaufmann entered into discussions with 'Abdur Rahmān, the amir's fugitive nephew, with a view to a possible revolution at

Kābul. On the border Stolietoff met half-hearted orders forbidding his admission into Afghan territory. These he of course ignored, and moved on to Kābul, where he arrived on July 22. In the course of the next four weeks he negotiated a treaty with the amir ready for signature and ratification.

Lytton was well informed of these events. He had learnt of Stolietoff's mission before that officer had actually left Tashkent. It seemed to him that the time had come to recall to the amir's mind the arguments which he had so lately used against accepting a British mission. Having received a Russian envoy, he could hardly refuse to receive a British one without displaying a marked hostility which no one could mistake. With the English cabinet's approval, therefore, Lytton wrote demanding that an English mission should be received. His letter reached Kābul on August 17. No answer was returned, on the score of the death of 'Abdullāh Jān, who died that same day; but the letter was read in durbar and Stolietoff's advice taken. He urged that the answer should be delayed, that if any British mission were sent it should be stopped by force, while he would hasten to Tashkent to communicate with the Russian authorities, who would compel the English to withdraw their demands. The amir followed this advice to the letter. He delayed giving any answer, and when Neville Chamberlain was sent as envoy from Peshāwar, he was met with threats of being fired on if he attempted to pass 'Ali Masjid.

Shīr 'Ali would hardly have done this but for the trust which he placed in the promises of the Russians. But the latter had shown more zeal than discretion. Kaufmann, perhaps on the orders of the Russian War Office, had acted as though war were certain between Great Britain and his own country. But the expected war did not come to pass. Instead of that the Congress of Berlin reached a peaceful settlement. Kaufmann had received this news while Stolietoff was still on his way to Kābul, and seems to have written warning him to give the amir no specific promises of help against the English; at the same time he recalled the columns which had set out from Tashkent. But the mischief had been done. Lytton had been given the best possible excuse for demanding the reception of an English mission; and Shīr 'Ali had been encouraged to defy the English. The Russians had thus fallen into the trap which they had set for others. All Kaufmann could say in reply to the amir's urgent demands for help was to advise him to come to terms with the English as best he could. One is reminded of the fate of the Indian princes who in the previous century had been encouraged by French intrigues to give overt proofs of their hostility to the East India Company.

The cabinet in London viewed the swift development of the Afghan crisis with some alarm. Salisbury, who had been moved to the Foreign Office, feared lest the Russians might find in it an excuse for not withdrawing their troops from Turkish territory in accordance with the Treaty of Berlin. He and the prime minister, Lord Beaconsfield, blamed Lytton for sending his envoy by the Khaibar Pass, where he was not unlikely to be stopped, instead of by the Bolān Pass, where such an event was more improbable. Attempts were made to smooth over matters for a while. But these plans failed through the strong defence which Lord Cranbrook, the new secretary of state for India, made on behalf of Lytton. On November 2, therefore, with the cabinet's reluctant assent, an ultimatum, expiring on the 20th, was sent to Kābul. No answer being received before that date, British forces invaded Afghan territory. Lytton had succeeded in taking full advantage of the Russian blunder.

The Second Afghan War opened by an advance through the Kurram and the Khaibar Passes. A month later Shīr 'Alī issued a farmān in which he recounted the innumerable victories which he had achieved over the invaders and announced his retirement into Russian territory. Negotiations were opened with his son Ya'kūb, with whom in May, 1879, the British signed the Treaty of Gandammak. Ya'kūb assigned the districts of Kurram, Pishīn, and Sibi to the British; he agreed to conduct his foreign relations in accordance with the governor-general's advice; and he accepted a permanent English agent who was to be established at Kābul. The Second Afghan War was as successful in its first stage as the first had been. But inevitable difficulties loomed ahead: The new amir was believed to be fickle and weak. Nor was the establishment of the agent at Kābul entirely in accordance with English desires. Herat had been the place where they thought an agent would be most useful. But Ya'kūb had urged Kābul so strongly that it had been felt undesirable to insist on the other course. Cavagnari was therefore selected as envoy. He was an active, energetic man, who had conducted the Gandammak negotiations to a successful conclusion; but he was scarcely tactful enough for a post demanding great delicacy. He reached Kābul in July, 1879, and though well received, was regarded from the first with great suspicion. He found himself isolated. No nobles were allowed to visit him. He tried to counter this restriction by setting up a dispensary to serve as a cover for persons who wished to communicate with him. But this device was of doubtful advantage. Early in September a real or pretended mutiny broke out among the troops at Kābul. The residency was attacked, and its inhabitants massacred. Ya'kūb's complicity was and still remains uncertain. Roberts believed, probably with reason, that he knew of and favoured the projects of a mutiny, in the hope that it would allow him to represent to the Government of India the difficulties which the presence of a British resident involved and would enable him to request the agent's withdrawal. Indeed some such ideas may well have underlain the proposal to station the envoy at Kābul instead of at Herat. But it is not likely that Ya'kūb either expected or desired the death of Cavagnari. His Afghan advisers, however, probably did.

This event led to a re-opening of the war. Once more a brilliant opening had been followed by the murder of the unfortunate man chosen to represent British policy at a ferocious capital. But now the sequence of events was to diverge sharply from the earlier example. Roberts promptly occupied Kābul, where he established himself securely, and throughout the following winter resisted with ease the attempts of the tribesmen to expel him. Ya'kūb himself had abandoned his precarious position and joined the English camp, declaring that he would rather be a grass-cutter with them than attempt to rule the ungovernable Afghans. He was sent down into British India, where he lived on a government pension till his death in 1923. But his disappearance left for a while no satisfactory candidate for the government of the country. In these circumstances the British authorities turned naturally towards partition. The Foreign Office even began to discuss with Teherān the terms on which Persia might be allowed to occupy Herat; and a member of the old ruling Sadozai family was recognised as ruler of Kandahār. Such arrangements would, it was thought, make it a small matter what became of Kābul.

At this moment, however, a new candidate stood forward. 'Abdur Rahmān, who had been living under Russian protection, thought the time had come to claim the succession of his uncle

Shīr 'Alī, who had died soon after his flight into Russian territory. 'Abdur Rahmān was now a man of forty, and had inherited much of the vigour and ferocity of his grandfather, Dost Muhammad. In 1880, after long discussions with the Russian governor-general, he was allowed to return to his native country. The Russians undoubtedly hoped by this to embarrass the English and to secure a friend at Kābul to replace the dead amir. But in this they miscalculated. 'Abdur Rahmān had seen much of them, and had meditated long on the causes of his uncle's fate. He had come to the conclusion that friendship with the English was worth having, thus reversing the sentiments with which he had fled to Tashkent sixteen years earlier. As soon as Lytton heard of his appearance, he sent orders to the English agent to enter into discussions with him. But at that moment negotiations were interrupted by the arrival of a new governor-general, Lord Ripon.

In the spring of 1880 a general election had taken place in which the foreign policy of the Beaconsfield government both in Turkey and Afghanistan had become the object of violent and indeed dishonest attack. Mr Gladstone's success led at once to the resignation of Lytton and the appointment of Ripon, pledged to carry out a policy of withdrawing altogether from beyond the hills. With this policy Ripon had been in the fullest possible agreement. But after his arrival in India, he found that much more was to be said for the late Conservative policy than he had imagined. Indeed he came speedily to the conclusion that the execution of the policy of withdrawal which had been promised in the queen's speech at the opening of the new parliament would infallibly lead to a new war, and insisted with a covert threat of resignation that Pishīn and Sibi should be retained. Meanwhile he took up the discussions with 'Abdur Rahmān at the point at which Lytton had left them. 'Abdur Rahmān had already given proof of his desire to be friends with the English. When Ayūb Khān, Shīr 'Alī's son, inflicted a sharp defeat on the English at Maiwand, 'Abdur Rahmān had materially assisted Roberts in the great march which the latter made on Kandahār, leading to the complete overthrow of Ayūb Khān's forces. Ripon therefore reached an understanding with him, by which he was to be allowed to establish his authority over the whole of Afghanistan, Pishīn and Sibi being retained by the British, and soon afterwards 'Abdur Rahmān agreed in return for an annual subsidy to place the conduct of his foreign relations under British control. Thus the settlement at which Lytton had aimed was largely secured. The hostile amir had been replaced by one friendly to Great Britain; the fear of having an ally of Russia on the immediate frontier of India was removed; the control of the amir's external relations was secured; and above all a position was obtained on the further side of the hills from which any hostile advance towards India might be met and checked before the Indian territories were reached. The main point which still awaited settlement was the delimitation of the new amir's dominions. Except towards Persia they were as yet undefined. Between them and Russian Turkestan on the north, and British India on the east, lay belts of territory under no settled government. This was a not uncommon feature of political Asia. It carried with it what had long been regarded as a distinct advantage, a standing pretext for a declaration of war. Until that question had been cleared up, Central Asia was still likely to give ground for international dispute.

The matter became the more urgent because the Russian government speedily began to take advantage of the numerous difficulties in which Mr Gladstone was involved by his conduct of foreign policy. Russian documents (for instance the correspondence of the Baron de Staal who was the Russian ambassador at London at this period) prove how greatly Russia valued his tenure of office as providing a favourable opportunity of extending its power in Central Asia. The Merv oasis formed the first step. It was a region the importance of which had been exaggerated. It was, however, not far from Herat, and the Russians had repeatedly disclaimed all intentions of advancing thither. But while the Russian foreign minister was seeking to reassure the British ambassador on this point, Russian agents were urging and bribing the chiefs of Merv to submit themselves to the emperor. At last in 1884, when Mr Gladstone was embarrassed by the Sudan question, the allegiance of the chiefs was formally accepted and the Russian War Office prepared a map showing the new Russian boundary stretching south to touch the Hari-rūd near Herat. Fresh remonstrances led to a proposal that the Russo-Afghan boundary should be defined and laid down. The British ministry eagerly took up the idea, and at once appointed a commission to act with the Russians in the matter. It was suggested that the two missions should meet at Sarakhs on October 1, 1884. But the

Russian advance had not yet been sufficiently developed to make so early a meeting convenient. A general was therefore named head of the Russian mission, but he was at the same instant smitten with sickness, and it was evident that his diplomatic recovery would be followed by a lengthy period during which he would be diligently studying the problem and the Russian forces would be occupying the posts on which the Russians desired their frontier to rest. The chief point at which they aimed was Panjdeh, which the English had always regarded as lying well within the amir's territories. The Afghans sought to defend the place. Early in 1885 the respective forces were face to face. The English boundary commission was also present. On March 30, when the only line of telegraph by Mashhad was conveniently interrupted, the Russians took advantage of an incautious movement of the Afghan troops to attack and expel them from Panjdeh.

This news did not reach London till April 9. The Irish question was acute. The ministry's policy in the Sudan and the death of Gordon had involved it in deep unpopularity. The Afghan question also had excited much attention; and acceptance of the Russian action would be deemed a new humiliation. In these trying circumstances Mr Gladstone found it necessary to make a show of spirit. He called up the reserves and moved a vote of credit for special military preparations. De Giers, the Russian foreign minister, had reckoned on carrying his point by bluff. He had even ordered the ambassador to inform the English cabinet that the Afghan commandant admitted that he would have retired but for the pressure of the English boundary commission. But the vote of credit looked too like business and he at once cancelled his instructions to de Staal. The Russians wanted two things. They wished to avoid war; and they wished Mr Gladstone to retain office. A suggestion was put about that the matter might be referred to arbitration. The cabinet eagerly snatched at the idea, hoping that the German emperor might be named arbitrator. The Russians refused emphatically to submit the conduct of their general to discussion; but were willing to arbitrate on the question whether they had kept their engagements with Great Britain, provided that the arbitrator was the king of Denmark. These points were conceded, and the Russians, having obtained their main point, permitted the delimitation of the frontier, which took place in the course of the following year. The arbitration lapsed, indeed it had never been more than a pretext under cover of which Mr Gladstone might retire from his bellicose position. After somewhat similar though less provocative events, the boundary through the Pāmirs was formally laid down.

In Afghanistan itself, the amir had been gradually building up his position. He was excellently fitted for the difficult office which he held. He ruled the Afghans with a rod of iron. Rebellions were crushed with traditional vigour and commemorated by the erection of great pyramids of skulls. 'Abdur Rahmān's administration of justice was personal, and marked by the fantastic but striking methods of Jahāngīr in Mughal India. He was perhaps the most absolute ruler of his day. His rigid orthodoxy carried with it the support and sympathy of the mullahs; and he enjoyed a great and deserved reputation in the world of Islam. With the English he maintained generally good relations. But the later part of his reign was marked by periods of coolness, of distrust, and frontier intrigue. Indeed the incident of Panjdeh seems to have given him a lesson. Misled by the experience of Shīr 'Alī and the assurances of the boundary commission, he seems to have believed that the Russians would never dare to attack his territory so long as he was sheltered by British arms. At the moment at which the incident occurred, he was paying a visit to Lord Dufferin at Rawulpindi. The governor-general had at once assured him of arms, ammunition, and possibly money should war with Russia follow. But Great Britain evidently had thought Afghanistan not worth going to war over. 'Abdur Rahmān probably concluded with wisdom that just as Russia had not been willing to fight for Shīr 'Alī, so, too, England would not fight for him. He could hardly be expected to relish the position of his country as the region in which the security of India from invasion was to be defended.

However, the chief difficulties arose not out of any leanings towards Russia but out of questions of frontier policy. The frontier problem was exceedingly complicated. It involved political, military, and administrative questions. The political question was to define the proper division of rule between India and Afghanistan; the military to find the line from which India might best be defended; and the administrative to determine the point to which control of the frontier tribesmen should be assumed. The military question had already been determined by the Second Afghan

War. Quetta was occupied and developed; it was linked up with the Indian railways; it was designed to permit the speedy occupation of Kandahār, in order to meet and repel any attack, whether Russian or Afghan, coming from the north-west. The political question still had to be answered. Along what line was the authority of the amir on the one side and of the governor-general on the other to terminate? The British had inherited from the Sikhs an undefined border beyond which lay a tangle of great hills, cut by deep winding valleys, and occupied by a great number of tribes. Further to the south, where the conquest of Sind had carried British authority on to the edge of Balūchistān, the political position was much the same. But the whole frontier had fallen under two provincial authorities. The Sind frontier was under Bombay, the Pathān frontier under the Panjab. This fact had led to the development of two distinct methods of administering the frontier and conducting relations with the trans-border tribes. On the Sind frontier, where the valleys were broader and less tortuous than in the Panjab and where the cultivated land pressed less closely on the tribal areas, the "closed frontier system" was in force. Under this, the frontier was patrolled, and no tribesman from beyond was allowed to enter British territory without a pass. The Panjab frontier was an "open frontier". Its protection was based upon forts and garrisons. In the fruitless hope of winning the tribesmen to forsake their immemorial habits of plunder, they were encouraged to trade within British territory. Raids, however, were frequent, and the only practicable punishment consisted in punitive expeditions. The frontier officials were strongly discouraged from visiting the tribal region. Down to about 1890 the Sind system was working incomparably better than that of the Panjab.

This result, however, was due to local circumstances rather than to anything else. The physical differences of the two frontiers have already been noted. But there existed political differences as well. Major Sandeman, who was appointed to the Balūchistan agency in 1877, was able to enter into comparatively close and friendly relations with the principal Balūch chiefs, and Lytton withdrew the prohibition which had limited the activities of English agents to British India. But Sandeman's success was only possible in a region such as the Balūch region, where the chiefs possessed a high degree of influence over their fellow tribesmen.

The Pathān tribes were real democracies. The *jirga*, or tribal council, in the Balūch country was a small group of leaders; in the Pathān country it might consist of the whole tribe. Agreements with the Pathān chiefs therefore did not and could not possess the value which agreements with the Balūch chiefs carried. All attempts to extend Sandeman's methods to the Pathān tribes were foredoomed to failure. While then Sandeman could establish a vastly improved order in the south by agreeing with chiefs for the guarding of the passes and the execution of the decisions of the *jirgas*, in return for the grant of allowances, Bruce's attempt to introduce the same plan into British relations with the Mahsud tribesmen proved useless.

The early history of the Panjab frontier was thus a series of raids interspersed with expeditions into tribal territory intended to bring the tribesmen to reason and teach them that raids were disadvantageous. At the same time a tendency existed towards the extension of British authority. After difficult negotiations in 1893, Durand induced the amir to accept a formal boundary, known as the Durand line, intended to mark out the political jurisdiction of the amir on the one side and of the British on the other. The British government was disposed to take its new responsibilities seriously. The Chitrāl campaign of 1895, the extensive frontier risings of 1897, were the result, assisted by the intrigues of the amir, who might have agreed to renounce his authority over certain tribes but who was not willing to honour his pledges. Lord Curzon did more than any other individual to bring order into the confusion of frontier politics. In the first place, despite the protests of the Panjab government, he created the North-West Frontier Province, reaching from one end of the frontier to the other, and replacing the divided authority which had till then existed by the power of a single group of individuals. In the second place he withdrew the British troops whom he had found established in forward positions, where they were not only exposed to tribal attacks but also were a constant source of irritation to the tribes. Instead of regulars, he set up groups of *khassidars*, or militiamen, drawn from the tribes themselves, and supported by regular troops who were concentrated in positions in the rear, and enabled by new roads and railways to move laterally with a speed till then impossible. These changes greatly improved the situation; but the temper of the tribes still remained uncertain, owing partly to their fanatical religious ideas, partly to the efforts of the amir, who hoped that if he induced the tribes to give sufficient trouble the English sooner or later would cease to dominate them and leave them to his management.

Meanwhile troubles had arisen with the scarcely known and seldom-visited state of Tibet. This country was nominally a dependency of China, Chinese troops having been invited in to save it from Gurkha occupation. But by the close of the nineteenth century this dependence was scarcely more than nominal. The Chinese maintained a resident, the *amban*, at Lhasa, and demanded that all Indo-Tibetan relations should be conducted through him. But he had become virtually powerless, and was most unwilling to do anything which would reveal his impotency to the external world. The country was really controlled by a council of regency, acting in the name of the Dalai Lama, one of the two religious heads of Buddhism in Tibet. The Dalai Lama was regarded as an incarnation of the Buddha, an emanation of whose spirit was thought, immediately on the lama's death, to be reincarnate in some child born at the same moment. But throughout the greater part of the century successive lamas had perished on approaching maturity, and the iniquity of man had thus limited the abode of the divinity to a person incapable of exercising government. Towards the close of the century, however, the existing Dalai Lama had come of age instead of being quietly put to death. This change of policy was probably due to the influence of a Russian Buriat named Dorjieff. This man seems to have persuaded the council that Russia was a Buddhist country, and that, if matters were rightly handled, the Dalai Lama might become head of a consolidated Buddhist church under the military protection of the Russian emperor.

The relations of this region with British India had been scanty. The roads leading into it were difficult and unfrequented, and, although in the eighteenth and early nineteenth centuries British agents had been received at Lhasa, the Chinese spread distrust of the motives and policy of the rulers of British India. In 1886 a commercial mission had been dispatched, but recalled in deference to Chinese protests, and its withdrawal had been at once followed by a Tibetan invasion of the protected state of Sikkim. Two years later, after numerous efforts to induce the Chinese government to compel the invaders to withdraw, the Tibetans were expelled by force, and in 1893 a trade agreement was adopted. But every article of it was ignored by the Tibetans. It had been negotiated with the Chinese alone, and their dependents destroyed the Indian boundary-pillars, and again invaded Sikkim. These causes of offence were emphasised by reports of Tibetan missions to Russia. These were sent in 1898, 1900, and again in 1901, when Dorjieff was received in audience by the emperor. Rumours spread that China had been induced to cede to the emperor her rights over Tibet; and, although the Russians emphatically denied that the Tibetan missions had any political significance or that they had negotiated with China about Tibet, none but the simplest-minded Briton could give full credit to such assertions. Lord Curzon, then governor-general, resolved that the position could be cleared up only by the dispatch of a mission to Lhasa. After prolonged discussions with the home government, and a most provocative complaint from Russia against British intervention in Tibet, Colonel Younghusband was sent at the head of a mission. The Tibetans attempted to prevent his advancing into the country; but their efforts were brushed aside with considerable loss to them, and the mission advanced, first to Gyantse, and then to Lhasa; the Dalai Lama fled; and at last an agreement was negotiated with the Tibetans themselves, who agreed to open trading-posts and to pay an indemnity, much reduced by the decision of the home government. Thus in Tibet, as in Afghanistan, British-Indian interests had been protected at the cost of military action.

In the early years of the present century the various branches of policy here reviewed underwent considerable changes. German policy was becoming particularly active, seeking to set up definite communications with the near and middle east. Of the German projects the most notable was the construction of a railway to link up Constantinople with the Persian Gulf. This was regarded with the greatest suspicion by the Russians, who thought it designed to dispute with them access to India. The English attitude was less hostile. at all events in official circles; but none the less agreement on joint action proved to be impossible, and the whole plan was found to involve too much international jealousy to be executed. With this should be set the attempts of various powers, Russia, France, and Germany, to secure bases on the Persian Gulf. These attempts were sharply resisted by Great Britain, and Lord Lansdowne, when foreign minister, declared that any such acquisition, in the light of special British interests in the Persian Gulf, would be considered an unfriendly action. It was fortunate for India that neither the Berlin-Baghdad railway, nor the desired German base on the Persian Gulf, had come into existence when war broke out in 1914, for they would have greatly complicated the problems of the defence of the country.

The development of these German views, coupled with the disappearance of the understanding between that country and Russia which had enabled the latter to play so large a part in Central Asia at an earlier time, greatly modified Anglo-Indian policy. The home government, finding Britain menaced by the expansion of the German navy, set to work to clear away ancient misunderstandings with France and Russia. With the first, agreement was reached on the subject of the Burma frontier; with the second, a convention was signed dealing with the Asiatic interests of the two empires. This was exclusively the work of the government in London. Any agreement with Russia was regarded by Lord Minto, who was then governor-general, as likely to produce danger rather than security. But despite his protests, the convention was signed in 1907, without giving him any opportunity to secure the assent of the amir of Afghanistan. By this convention Russia recognised for the first time in any formal document that Afghanistan lay beyond her sphere of interests. At this time the ruler of Kābul was Habībullāh, who had succeeded his father, 'Abdur Rahmān, in 1901. He himself was inclined to friendly relations with Great Britain; but he found difficulties in the activity and influence of his very orthodox brother, Nasrullāh. He refused therefore to recognise the convention, which was unpopular in the world of Islam owing to the division of Persia into spheres of influence, generally but mistakenly thought to portend a real partition of that country. But, so long as the entente between Great Britain and Russia lasted, no ruler of Afghanistan could venture to break with British India. The effects of the convention were therefore less than Minto had expected. Even the outbreak of the war with Germany in 1914, and the attempts which were made to use Kābul as the starting point of an attack on British India, proved failures. But the revolution which broke out in Russia in 1917, and the consequent disappearance of the friendliness which had marked Anglo-Russian relations since 1907, transformed the position. In 1919 the amir was murdered, and his successor, Amānullāh, thought he might strengthen his position by an attack on British India. Thus the Third Afghan War came about. This attempt to invade Indian territory showed at once the need of strong defences on the frontier, and the difficulty of controlling Afghan policy so long as Russia and Great Britain remained enemies. The peace which concluded the war in 1921 restored to Afghanistan freedom of conducting its foreign relations, and it still remains precariously perched between two great states, much as was the case in the days of Shīr 'Alī.

The kingdom of Burma offered a notable instance of the difficulty of maintaining friendly relations (in the European sense of the term) with an Asiatic state. The diplomatic traditions of the kingdom had been formed by its relations with the empire of China and its age-long rivalry with the neighbouring Siam. The decay of Chinese imperial pretensions in practice if not in theory, coupled with the successes which the rulers of Burma had obtained against the Siamese, had firmly established the belief that Burma was great and powerful. Nor had that belief been much shaken by the first, badly managed, war between Burma and the East India Company. When a new king, Tharrawaddy, ascended the throne in 1837, he had refused to recognise the Treaty of Yandabo as binding, since in accordance with general Asiatic tradition he regarded treaties as mere personal agreements between sovereigns which lapsed with the death of either signatory. Nor would he even receive the English resident in his representative character, since the latter was commissioned by a dependent government instead of the sovereign of Great Britain. In consequence the resident had been withdrawn in 1840.

No local means remained to smooth away the difficulties which arose from time to time at the port of Rangoon. The Burmese governor there in 1850 was a man given to liquor, who in his cups would threaten to behead the whole population of the city. According to Burmese custom, he regarded his government as his estate, to be made the most of while he continued to hold it. He extorted 1005 rupees from the commander of one British-owned barque on a false charge of throwing his pilot overboard, and 700 from another with threats of flogging and beheading on an equally false charge of murdering a lascar. Dalhousie therefore sent a queen's frigate, *Fox*, under Commodore Lambert, to seek reparation—the removal of the governor and the payment of compensation. Pagān, who had become king in 1845, was quite willing to accommodate matters. He despatched a new governor to Rangoon with orders to arrange a settlement. Lambert, who knew little of eastern uses, quarrelled with the new governor on a point of etiquette. He blockaded Rangoon and seized one of the king's vessels. In return the Burmese batteries opened fire on the *Fox*. Dalhousie very reluctantly sent an ultimatum. The Burmese court ignored it, and the Second Burmese War began on April 1, 1852, when Dalhousie's forces under Admiral Austen and General Godwin reached Rangoon.

Their organisation was good. Dalhousie had paid special attention to matters of transport, commissariat and medical supplies, taking prudent warning by the difficulties of the former war. Rangoon and Mārtabān were taken in a fortnight. Bassein followed. Then Prome was captured and Pegu occupied. The Burmese had gathered together 30,000 men to oppose the 8000 British troops, but they only succeeded in killing and wounding 377. Pagān was not in fact vigorously supported by his people. The Shāns refused to send levies, the delta population welcomed the English, the Talaings rebelled against their Burmese king. As the Burmese court refused to come to terms, and Dalhousie had occupied as much territory as he thought prudent, Pegu was declared by proclamation on December 20, 1852, to be British territory and a letter was written to Pagān warning him that if he provoked another war it would end "in the ruin and exile of yourself and your race".

Almost immediately afterwards Pagān was deposed and imprisoned by his brother Mindōn, who ruled the remaining Burmese territories from 1853 to 1878. Like Tharrawaddy, in 1837, he refused to accept the consequences of his predecessor's foolish management. But he made no attempt to disturb the new frontier. In 1854 he sent agents to request of Dalhousie the rendition of Pegu. Despite Dalhousie's emphatic answer that the new province should never be restored, Mindōn next endeavoured, though in vain, to induce the missionaries to intervene; but when the Mutiny broke out, he would not listen to the advice of his court, that the time had come when Pegu might be recovered by force. His political conduct was thus notably peaceful and conciliatory. His great interests in life were trade and religion. He summoned a Buddhist council to his new capital at Mandalay in 1871, and presented a new spire, plated with gold and set with precious stones, to the Shwēdagōn Pagoda at Rangoon in the same year. As a trader he not only enforced the customary royal monopolies, but was the largest dealer in all kinds of produce in his kingdom. He encouraged English merchants, partly in the hope that they would succeed in developing the trade with the neighbouring Chinese province of Yunnan. He sent envoys to Europe in order to open direct relations with the west; and though disappointed by the refusal of the English ministry to deal with him except through the Government of India, he welcomed the governor-general's agents when the residency was re-established in 1862. The Burmese court had always insisted that the residents should comply with local etiquette, and appear before the king kneeling and unshod. But in 1876 the governor-general forbade the continuance of this practice, on the ground that Burmese had gone to Europe, had witnessed the ceremonies of European courts, and knew that it was not customary to exact humiliating ceremonial. This attitude might be supported by much argument, but it involved many regrettable results. Mindōn refused to give way. The resident was no longer admitted to the king's presence; he transacted business merely with the ministers; and the English influence at once began to decline.

Among other political defects the Burmese kingdom suffered from ill-regulated customs of succession. The king was entitled to nominate his successor from among his sons or brothers. Mindōn had forty-eight sons, and shrank from nominating any for fear that the favoured one would be immediately poisoned. At last, on his death-bed, he nominated three who were to divide the kingdom between them. The ministers disliked this decision, and rightly, because it would have meant civil war. They therefore supported a project of the queen dowager, to set up a younger son, Thibaw, who was married to her daughter, Supayālat. All the other sons and daughters were imprisoned, and for the traditional act of allegiance was substituted a new oath promising obedience, no longer to the king alone, but to the king acting with the *Hlutdaw*—the council of ministers.

However, this attempt to borrow western political ideas speedily collapsed. The custom of ministerial obedience was too strong to be abandoned. Thibaw was a feeble creature, much given to strong liquor; but he was ruled, not by the wisdom of the *Hlutdaw* but by the wiles of Supayālat. Under her influence the new king refused to marry the numerous queens regarded as the necessary appendages of royal state; and then, fearing a movement in favour of one of the other princes, Thibaw ordered seventy members of the royal family to be put to death. In the middle of February, 1879, these unfortunate persons were strangled or beaten to death, and their bodies flung into a trench within the palace enclosure. Although this practice had not been followed in the previous four reigns, there were numerous good precedents for the massacre from the thirteenth century onwards, nor did it shock Burmese sentiment. The ministerial view was that it was better for the princes to perish than that the country should be laid waste by rebellion and dacoity. After much indecision, it was resolved to withdraw the British resident, lest he too should be murdered. In any case he exercised no influence and could do little good.

British policy in the years immediately following was markedly unsteady. Four of Thibaw's brothers had escaped from Burma, and sought to raise rebellions. One or other would have succeeded in overthrowing the king but for the action of the Government of India in interning them whenever it could lay hands on them. Commercial and especially missionary opinion ran strongly in favour of annexation. In 1884 English and Chinese merchants in Rangoon joined in subscribing funds to assist one of the princes, Myingun, to invade Burma by way of Siam; while the English chief commissioner considered that in view of Thibaw's misrule another prince, Nyaungyan, should be assisted to set himself up as king. But the Calcutta government, torn between moral disapproval of Thibaw and moral disapproval of intervention, would do nothing.

The French were less squeamish. They had in recent years established an empire in Indo-China and desired to extend their influence into Upper Burma. From the time of Mindōn the Burmese court had been seeking an alliance with a first-class European power. In 1885 Ferry, who was pursuing an aggressive policy, signed a commercial treaty with the envoys whom Thibaw had sent to Europe, and at the same time gave them a letter agreeing, though reluctantly, to permit the import of arms through Tonkin as soon as order was regularly established there. He had assured the British ambassador that he would never allow the import of arms, and had insisted that his discussions merely related to trade. Six months later, in July, the British chief commissioner at Rangoon procured a copy of Ferry's letter. The falsity of Ferry's assurances led the Government of India to regard French policy in Upper Burma with much suspicion; and it was further alarmed by the activity of French finance in that country. The French government had established a consul at Mandalay. Through him and a Burmese envoy at Paris a number of important concessions were negotiated. The French were to establish a bank at Mandalay, to build railways, to place a fleet of steamers on the Irawadi, to manage the royal monopolies of teak and petroleum. These projects, however, overran the policy of the state. Great Britain had repeatedly and publicly claimed special interests in Upper Burma. On her remonstrances the French disavowed their consul's acts, while reverses in Tonkin at once restricted the French power, and cooled their desire, to interfere in Burma. As had happened in the previous century, the unconsidered policy of the French had encouraged an eastern prince in hostility to England, had persuaded him that French help would be forthcoming in the event of trouble, and so had nourished a policy which they were unable or unwilling to support by force of arms.

Thibaw undoubtedly fancied that French friendship would relieve him of all need to conciliate the English, and he unwisely proceeded to give them an opportunity of action. His finances were shamelessly mismanaged. The revenues were misappropriated. The royal jewels were pledged. State lotteries were tried and failed. Loans were raised from all willing to advance money. At this time the Bombay-Burma Trading Corporation was the largest English firm established in Burma. It drove a great trade in teak which it cut and sold under a royal concession. It had already advanced Thibaw £100,000. He demanded a further advance of twice that amount. The company refused. It was then accused before the *Hlutdaw* of not paying its employees and of cheating Thibaw of his royalties The *Hlutdaw* condemned the company to pay a fine exceeding the amount originally demanded as a loan, cancelled its leases, and prepared to grant new ones to French merchants. On this the governor-general, Lord Dufferin, demanded that the case should be submitted to his arbitration. The Burmese court refused. On October 19, 1885, an ultimatum reached Rangoon to be forwarded to Mandalay. It required the reception of a permanent resident, with free access to the king without humiliating ceremonies, the submission of the Bombay-

Burma Corporation's case to the viceroy's arbitration, the management of Burmese foreign relations through the Government of India, and assistance in developing the trade with Yunnan. On November 9 Thibaw's rejection was received. Three weeks later he was a prisoner.

Annexation was the only practicable course. Thibaw's massacres had destroyed most of the possible claimants to the throne, and the only survivor thought to possess the necessary character was under French influence. But annexation involved, as had been expected, great and prolonged difficulties. The country was disorganised and demoralised. Dacoity had long been prevalent. The troops whom Thibaw assembled to repel the English scarcely fired a shot, but disbanded and joined the dacoits. They could hardly ever be brought to action, and spent their time evading the British troops and plundering their own countrymen. Their reduction took five years, and at one time 32,000 men were employed against them.

The annexation of Upper Burma was the last example, in the expansion of British India, of the misfortunes which have commonly followed on a refusal to intervene at the appropriate moment. It was generally agreed that a small amount of countenance and help would have permitted one of the rival princes to overthrow Thibaw early in his ill-starred reign. There would then have possibly arisen a friendly Burmese state under acknowledged British protection, and that would have offered the best solution of the Burmese problem, for the country would have been spared the consequences of unskilful endeavours to treat it as an Indian province. The refusal in 1887 to accept the assistance voluntarily offered by the heads of the Buddhist priesthood was perhaps the greatest blunder that was committed, for it not only threw away a most valuable link between the people and the government but also led to the disintegration of the ecclesiastical organisation.

CHAPTER XVI

The Crown and the Indian States

The change in the form of government in 1858, although leaving the relations of the British government with the Indian states seemingly untouched, laid the foundation of the considerable developments which were to follow in the latter half of the nineteenth century. The act transferring the functions of the East India Company to the crown expressly confirmed all the treaties which the company had made; and the proclamation in which the queen announced her assumption of control declared that she held herself bound by those obsolescent documents. These announcements seem to have been made without due consideration. Taken literally, they appeared to mean that the treaties were to possess a force which they had long lost, and that the princes were to enjoy the status of equal allies of the British crown. But it was not the intention of either the home authorities or the Government of India to introduce any such revolutionary change into Indian political relations. The queen and the ministry meant that the princes should be treated fairly; the governor-general meant that the government should, as he expressly declared, continue to exercise the power of interference when needed to prevent abuses. Moreover, the government of the crown was not averse, as the company's government had been, from recognising its responsibility for India as a whole. In that respect a marked change took place. Responsibility was asserted firmly and consistently. The queen was regarded as the sovereign, not merely of the possessions formerly held by the East India Company, but of the whole country. The princes were expected to show her not friendship alone but also allegiance. The change was indicated by new phrases which appear in the documents relating to the states. They were expected to show "loyalty to the British crown", which the *sanads* of adoption lay down as a condition of the privilege which they conferred, and "allegiance to Her Majesty" which was an express condition of the rendition of Mysore. The princes were thus deemed to have become members of an empire, whose boundaries were no longer limited to the provinces directly administered from Calcutta. The assumption of the new title of Empress of India, announced at the great durbar of 1876, was an outward sign of the change which had taken place. So was the assumption of the power of bestowing orders and titles upon the princes. In 1861 a new order, the Star of India, was created specially to provide a means by which the crown could reward the princes for their services during the Indian Mutiny. As Canning, the governor-general, said, "There is a reality in the suzerainty of the sovereign of England which has never existed before, and which is not only felt but is eagerly acknowledged by the chiefs".

Nor were the latter without good reason for acknowledging and acquiescing in this change, despite the effects which it was to have upon the theory, and the practice, of the predominant power in India. Under the company the states had been threatened with extinction. A failure of heirs, a decadent administration, a quarrelsome resident, might involve any of them in annexation. But such a fate was now formally, explicitly, and effectually ruled out. The queen's proclamation of 1858 declared, in striking contrast to the declaration of the East India Company in 1832, that "we desire no extension of our present territorial possessions". These were mere words. But they were speedily followed by a measure which set the hearts of many princes at rest. In 1860 a number of special grants were issued under the name of "*sanads* of adoption." The chiefs to whom they were addressed were informed that "the doctrine of lapse" had been brought to an end. The *sanads* ran in two forms, one for the Hindus, the other for the Muslims. The first were assured that adoptions on a failure of natural heirs would be recognised and confirmed; the second that successions in accordance with Muslim law would be upheld. If then the princes had in fact lost their status as separate and individual sovereigns, if they had become subordinate members of an empire, they had also been recognised, not as transitory, but as permanent members of that empire.

But annexation was the only point in which the crown receded from the position of the company. In all other matters it accepted and developed the position to which it succeeded. Though annexation on a failure of natural heirs had been abjured, successions remained subject to the confirmation of the Government of India. "No succession is valid until recognition has been given." The military strength of the states was still closely watched. For this the company had had two motives. One was the fear, needless in fact, of any prince becoming inconveniently powerful; the other was the desire to prevent princes from wasting on unnecessary military display money which was more urgently required for administrative improvements. Under the crown this second motive certainly became much more powerful than the first; yet perhaps it was not the dominant factor when in the 'sixties Jayaji Rāo Sindhia was required to reduce his forces to the limits laid down by treaty; and even Lord Kitchener's re-organisation of the Indian Army took into account the possibility of troubles from the Indian states as well as external invasion or internal disturbance. No relaxation in the control of political relations was made; nor was the isolation of the individual states modified until the formation of the Chamber of Princes in 1921.

While in these respects the crown maintained the practice established by the company, in the matter of internal interference usages grew up far exceeding those of the former régime. The company had refrained from accepting a general responsibility for the whole of India. The government of the crown did not. On the contrary it emphasised its responsibility. In the face of the administrative disorder of the Nizām's dominions Dalhousie had formally disclaimed all concern for the administrative well-being of Hyderabad. But the later governors-general assumed a different attitude. Elgin, for example, in 1862, observed, "If we lay down the rule that we will scrupulously respect the right of the chiefs to do wrong, ... we may find that it may carry us somewhat far— possibly to annexation, the very bug-bear from which we are seeking to escape". Accordingly, from the first, the former hesitation to interfere vanished. The rule of the mahārāja of Alwar was replaced by a council of regency after he had provoked his nobles into rebellion. The nawab of Tānk was deposed for being concerned in an affray in which the family of one of his dependent chiefs was almost exterminated. The nawab of Kalāt was deposed for inflicting barbarous punishments. But the leading example was afforded by the case of the Gaekwar of Baroda. Malhar Rāo, who had succeeded in 1870, was a man of low character and mean intellect. He had on his accession imprisoned and destroyed the chief agents of the late ruler. He had provoked great discontent among the subjects of his state, and within three years the Government of India appointed a commission of enquiry to examine into his administration. Malhar Rāo was required to introduce a number of reforms. He did nothing, but instead quarrelled with the resident, a man of small judgment and little tact. Finally he was accused of attempting to poison the resident. A new commission was then appointed. On this occasion the political department was represented by only one member. The others were the chief justice of Bengal, another judge, two ruling princes, and Sir Dinkar Rāo, who had shown great ability in re-organising the administration of Indore. The Gaekwar was arrested and placed on his trial before this body. After hearing voluminous evidence and the prolonged addresses of counsel, all the members agreed that an attempt had been made to poison the resident by two members of his household, and that the guilty men had been in communication with the Gaekwar; but the Indian members found the charge against the Gaekwar himself unproven, while the two judges and the political official considered that it had been established. On this report, the Government of India concluded that, although the commission had not found the Gaekwar guilty of attempted murder, yet the presumptive evidence was so strong, coupled with his previous misconduct, as to render him impossible as a ruling prince. It decided therefore to depose him, and to recognise as his successor a young member of the family, not directly descended from the accused man. During his minority the state was placed under the management of a council of regency over which a distinguished Indian administrator, Sir Madhava Rāo, presided. Some such decision had been a foregone conclusion. But the procedure adopted had been unprecedented. Till then the decisions of the Government of India had been taken in the secrecy of the political department; and this was the first attempt to constitute anything like a judicial tribunal to decide on an accusation against a ruling chief. This action was possibly due to the views which Queen Victoria had formerly expressed in regard to cases concerning the princes of India, and it is closely similar to the procedure laid down for future guidance in 1921. It clearly marked a great advance on previous practice. But it was an advance in more directions than one. It promised to the princes the advantage of not having the Government of India acting as judge and party in the same suit; but it also manifested in an unmistakable manner the suzerainty claimed on behalf of the crown. But for the policy of the crown in refraining from annexation, such a step would perhaps have provoked great discontent on the part of the princes as a whole. Holkar, who had been invited to serve on the commission of enquiry but had declined, probably expressed the general view of his fellows when he said, "The person for the time being is little; the state with its rights is the point for consideration". Under the company Malhar Rāo would not have been brought to public trial; but none the less he would have been deposed, and in all probability his state would have been added to the British dominions.

The rendition of Mysore furnished another striking illustration of the new policy of the crown. The state had fallen under British administration in 1831. The mahārāja, who had then been removed from the exercise of authority, had survived till 1868. He had repeatedly sought permission to adopt a son, but this had been consistently refused; and at one time it had been generally expected that on his death the state would pass formally under British sovereignty. So in fact it did, but not in the expected manner. After the mahārāja's death, it was resolved that after all the son whom he had adopted to carry on the religious rites of the family and to inherit his private estate should be recognised as his political heir and be invested with the government of the state, provided that on coming of age the boy gave promise of becoming a satisfactory ruler. In accordance with this decision the state was made over to him in 1881. But it was not made over absolutely. The instrument of transfer did not confer sovereignty. That word, where used, refers to the sovereignty of Queen Victoria. The prince is given "possession" of the territories. He is to "administer" them. He is to "remain faithful in allegiance and subordination to Her Majesty". The state coinage is not to be revived. Its military forces are not to exceed the limits fixed by the Government of India. The law in force in 1881 is not to be changed without the approval of the governor-general in council. Lands needed for railway development are to be made over free of charge, and the Government of India is to enjoy full jurisdiction over them. Thus the state of Mysore is clearly not an independent state, even in regard to internal administration. It is a province of the empire of India. The administrative policy of its ruler must correspond with the policy of the country as a whole. Its prince exercises a trust on behalf of the British crown; and although his rights depend on an agreement between himself and the crown, instead of on statutes passed by the British parliament, his position is not dissimilar from that formerly enjoyed by the East India Company. He exercises sovereign powers, but his exercise of them is liable to control, and he is politically dependent on a superior authority.

The differences between this settlement of 1881 and the treaty by which the state was constituted by Wellesley in 1799 are most instructive. Under Wellesley's treaty Mysore was undoubtedly dependent. The company could garrison at its pleasure any fortress within its borders; any advice which it offered the prince was under an obligation to observe; it maintained a large force within his territory; it entirely regulated his foreign relations; and it had the right of re-entering on the territory and assuming the administration if the payments to which the prince was bound fell into arrears. The prince was thus a dependent ally of the East India Company. But the duties which he owed to it could hardly be brought under the term of allegiance. Wellesley's treaty in fact was mainly designed to secure two purposes. One was the adequate protection of the state from attack; the second was the maintenance of a stable financial system. Those had ceased to be the main purposes to be secured by the instrument of transfer. External danger was no longer to be feared. Financial stability had merged in the wider question of the maintenance of a sound system of administration. The suzerainty of the crown had to be placed beyond doubt or question.

The cases of the Gaekwar and of Mysore thus exhibited in a strong light the policy inaugurated in 1858. In both opportunities of annexation were deliberately passed by; in both the suzerainty of the crown was asserted in a striking manner. The terms on which the Mysore state was given back to princely rule offer a clear example of what the government of the crown considered should be the relations between itself and the princes of India. Moreover at this time a tendency prevailed for similar ideas to be applied in some degree to all the other states. The main cause lay in the higher consciousness of responsibility in the imperial as opposed to the company's government. But many other causes concurred. The development of communications within the country, the spread of railways and the swiftly-growing use of the telegraph, coupled with the growth of education and of the public press, brought news to the Government of India much more rapidly than had formerly been the case, and increased the amount of news which it received. Under the company a chief might cut off a delinquent's hand or foot, but such an episode might never come to the ears of the government, or only reach them weeks after the punishment had been inflicted. Interference would then either be impossible or appear useless. When, however, the government might be informed of the chief's intention before it had been carried out, interference was not only possible but beneficial. Then, too, the standpoint of government in regard to administrative misconduct changed greatly. Standards of judgment rose. Uses which had been tolerated in the old days were now rigorously prohibited. The custom of the country, which had once been a universal excuse for misconduct, was now no longer admitted. Princes whose private conduct had been regarded as exclusively a matter of their own concern were now liable to paternal advice. At the close of the century the ruling chiefs were circularised with an expression of the governor-general's opinion of the inexpediency of their making prolonged and repeated visits to Europe. The same governor-general, Lord Curzon, claimed them as his partners and colleagues, adding that they could not be at once loyal subjects of Her Majesty and frivolous or irresponsible despots. The prince "must be the servant as well as the master of his people".

Under the pressure of these moral considerations, the Government of India began to formulate a series of precedents which would normally be followed in certain cases with the Indian states. Some provisions in certain treaties were stressed, others were suffered to fall into oblivion. A body of rules was emerging for the coherent management of the relations with Indian India. Despite the variations in the terms of the treaties, a uniformity of treatment was beginning to emerge. The practice of "reading the treaties together" was coming into vogue. The result was that at the end of the century Lord Curzon could speak of the relations with the states as having "grown up under widely differing historical conditions", but having in process of time "gradually conformed to a single type". The objections to such a practice are clear. It tends to invalidate individual treaties; and if the states are regarded as really possessing an international status, the impropriety is unquestionable. But states which have surrendered either

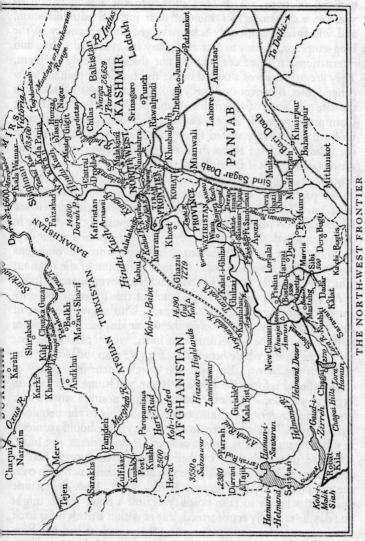

THE NORTH-WEST FRONTIER

— Durand and Outer Boundary of India
——— Other Boundaries
-·-·-· Russo-Afghan and Russo-Persian Frontier
xxxxxxxx Scientific Frontier
ooooooo Sandeman Line
——— Railways

by formal grant or acquiescence all power of control over their external relations, which have submitted for a long period of years to a constant supervision of their internal administration, and which have constantly acknowledged the supremacy of the king-emperor, do not in fact enjoy any international status, and international rules of conduct do not therefore apply to them. They are provinces of a united India; and from that point of view general rules, however cautiously applied, are indispensable. Even the late advocate of the rights of the princes before the Butler Committee found it impossible to avoid admitting that certain uniform rights were vested in the British crown; yet, it seems, the validity of those rights must rest upon cessions made by the greater states. But if the rights of small states can be modified by cessions made by larger ones, it is difficult to argue that a cession on the part of one large state cannot affect the rights of another large one. The fact is that a position has gradually developed which finds no place in treaties framed a century or more ago in circumstances differing completely from those of the present day. Nothing can be more idle than to attempt to restore the conditions of 1818. What is really needed is a new definition of the relations which shall exist between the states and the Government of India.

As a matter of fact the importance of this question has only emerged in comparatively recent times. Until about the close of the century the princes were on the whole disposed to acquiesce in the action of the Government of India, wisely perceiving that they were on the whole benefiting far more than suffering by the policy of the crown. But with the development of a policy of constitutional reform the position began to change. The princes began to ask themselves what would be their position when a new government might come into being responsible to the people of British India. They could see no reason why they should acquiesce in subordination to any Indian cabinet. It was Britain, not India, who had deprived them of their former sovereignty. Left to themselves they might well have established their own rule over the regions which had become British India. Thus democratic possibilities began to raise hostility against a body which might one day be radically transformed, just as within British India itself like hopes and fears excited an antagonism such as had not been known for generations between the Muslim and the Hindu.

It is noteworthy that the same period brought a reversal, in at least, of the policy of uniformity which had been actively pursued until the close of Lord Curzon's administration. Lord Minto deliberately changed the emphasis of British policy when he declared that he would avoid the issue of general instructions. But even he recognised that the treaties had to be interpreted in the light of actual fact and established usage, and did nothing to detract from that paramountcy of the crown which had gradually grown up.

Thus the course of policy since 1858 has been marked by two great changes, the first being the maintenance of the states and abstention from annexation, the second the extension of the practice of interference in matters of internal administration. But two other important changes have to be noted as well. One was in regard to the military forces of the states. The suspicion with which the princes were regarded by the company's government gradually gave place to a well-founded confidence. They had been looked on as allies who had been driven reluctantly into an alliance by the force of circumstances. But in times of external danger, when for instance the Panjdeh crisis threatened a war with Russia and when war broke out with Germany in 1914, the princes gave striking evidence of their desire to stand side by side with their suzerain. No observer could doubt that their alliance had ceased to be a galling bond which they desired to break at the first favourable opportunity. Sir Mortimer Durand, who was secretary of the Foreign Department in 1885, strongly urged the expediency of finding employment and recognition for the state troops. He discussed the question with the commander-in-chief, Sir Frederick Roberts, with the lieutenant-governor of the Panjab, with Lord Dufferin, the governor-general. The result of his persuasive advocacy was the formation of the Imperial Service Troops. Certain bodies of the state forces were to be placed for training under British officers, but were to remain entirely under the control of the states which raised them and were only to fall under the orders of the commander-in-chief when they were employed on active service. The maintenance of such bodies was a matter entirely at the discretion of the princes themselves, the chief condition being that they should always be kept effective and ready to serve whenever called for. They were first employed in the Hunza campaign in 1893. In 1914 they numbered 22,000; in 1923 they had risen to 27,000 men. This new policy offers a most remarkable contrast to that of Wellesley, who sought to hold the states in check by imposing on them bodies of foreign troops paid for by the princes but controlled by the company. It indicates a clear departure even from the policy of 1867 when Sindhia had been required to reduce his forces.

The other great change was the relaxation of the policy of keeping the states in strict isolation. Every treaty had placed the management of foreign affairs in the hands of the governor-general. No two states could communicate except through the Foreign Department. No two princes could converse on matters of common interest save through the agency of that department. The object of this had been to prevent as far as possible the formation of any league hostile to British supremacy in India. This practice persisted until a surprisingly late date. Lytton was the first governor-general to propose any relaxation. His general policy was directed towards securing a more active co-operation of the Indian aristocracy with the British government. That was the purpose underlying the formation of his Statutory Civil Service; that was the purpose of his proposed Indian Privy Council. He was eager to announce at the great durbar at which Queen Victoria was to be proclaimed Empress of India the creation of a council to be composed of a certain number of the greater chiefs, to consult with the governor-general on matters of common interest. Had this proposal been accepted, it would have led necessarily to the disappearance of the old isolation to which the princes had been politically condemned. But the project was viewed in England as dangerous, and the only step taken was to bestow the empty title of "councillors of the empress" on some of the princes. Curzon and Minto were the next to revive the idea. The latter desired the reforms of 1908 to be accompanied by the formation of a council on which the princes were to be represented. But the opposition of the home government and other influences defeated the proposal. Nevertheless, the same governor-general did begin a new practice, that of collective consultation. Lord Hardinge followed the practice and widened it. At last the Montagu-Chelmsford Report of 1918 recommended the formation of machinery for a regular collective consultation between the Government of India and the states, and this led to the establishment of the Chamber of Princes inaugurated in 1921. This brought to a close a stage in the development of the relations between the princes and the central government of British India. For the first time the princes were linked up with the central government by something more definite than a series of treaties which had in some respects lapsed into disuse almost as soon as they had been signed. It was a constitutional, not a diplomatic, link. It was a sign-post pointing to a united India as the goal of British policy, and thus formed a natural sequence to the course of events which has made the paramountcy of the king-emperor the outstanding feature of the last sixty years.

CHAPTER XVII

Educational and Political Development, 1858–92

Although the financial disorder brought about by the Mutiny had of necessity cut down the resources of the government, the development of educational policy continued unchecked. With a constancy of spirit as noble as that with which the defenders of the Delhi Ridge were holding their own against the mutineers' ceaseless attacks, Canning in the latter part of 1857 introduced and passed through his legislative council a bill establishing universities at Calcutta, Bombay, and Madras. Regular educational departments were organised in each province under a director of public instruction, who on the one hand corresponded direct with the provincial government and on the other controlled a swiftly growing establishment. This comprised inspecting and teaching officials, who were soon classified into superior or "graded" and subordinate or "ungraded". The first were normally Englishmen, the second Indians and Eurasians. At first the superior posts had been filled by covenanted servants, chaplains, military officers, or any other officials thought likely to prove competent. But in 1859 the secretary of state had laid it down that educational appointments should usually be filled by persons not members of the covenanted or military services. Although the rates of pay were much lower than those of covenanted servants, a number of distinguished men, such as Edwin Arnold, were attracted to the new service.

The universities which had been set up in 1857 had been intended to supervise and control higher education by means of examinations and courses of study conducted and laid down by the universities themselves. The faith thus placed in examinations as a method of testing ability and educational progress proved the dominion still exercised by the ideas which in 1834 had replaced Sanskrit and Arabic by English and twenty years later had established open competition as the sole method of admission to the covenanted service. The university bodies consisted of vice-chancellors and senates, mainly filled by government servants, which drew up regulations subject to the approval of government.

The three universities divided the whole of India between them. The university of Calcutta was supposed to be responsible for northern India, the Central Provinces, and British Burma, as well as for the Presidency of Bengal. Those of Bombay and Madras were limited to their own presidencies. To these bodies were affiliated a growing number of colleges, maintained by government itself, by missionary societies, and by private bodies; all these were devoted to literary or legal studies except a couple of engineering and three medical colleges. Many of the colleges were really schools which had formed classes for instruction in the subjects required for the lower university examination; and admission to a university class was limited to students who had passed the matriculation examination conducted by the universities. This unfortunate system took too much for granted. In 1854 it had been suggested that a number of university chairs should be established. Dalhousie had opposed this on the ground that the universities would be ill-qualified to supervise actual teaching. Yet functions of a far wider kind—the supervision of widespread groups of colleges—were actually confided to them. No steps were taken to secure adequate staffs, a sufficient rate of pay, classes of not more than manageable size, class-rooms well-lit and ventilated, libraries well equipped for the study of the subjects taught. Colleges dignified their chief lecturers with the title of professor, with small regard to attainments or salary; so that there came into being a multitude of professors whose work was judged solely by the percentage of students whom they managed to squeeze through the university examinations. This evil was accentuated by two others. Only through the matriculation examination could the universities influence the high schools from which all candidates for university learning were drawn, so that here the universities were as educationally noxious as the colleges. And only through university examinations could aspirants for government service secure success. This involved extraordinary pressure on the schools and colleges teaching for university examinations. Ill-qualified students besieged these institutions for admission and crowded the university examination-halls. When they were rejected, loud outcries arose against the authorities. Against the ceaseless pressure for a lowering of standards never high, no existing authority was able to oppose a firm enough resistance.

The colleges and high schools, forming a closely connected group and exposed to similar influences, had been designed to spread a knowledge of the English language and of western culture. But the students whom they attracted were drawn from narrowly defined classes of society. The castes with literary traditions—Brāhmans and Kayāsths in Bengal and northern India, Brāhmans elsewhere—showed the same eagerness to learn English as under Mughal rule they had already shown to learn Persian. In great part this zeal was due to the fact that English formed an indispensable qualification not only for government employment but also for professional work—the law, medicine, the press, education itself. In part, especially in Bengal, this interested motive was reinforced by a real and lively interest in western knowledge. In Bengal too, where the literary castes were interwoven with the class of landowners to a far greater degree than elsewhere, English education came to be widely diffused. But the structure of Indian society opposed an obstacle, which should have been foreseen but had in fact been ignored, in the way of "filtration". It had been hoped that western knowledge would gradually but surely penetrate downwards by way of the middle classes. It threatened, however, to become the monopoly of certain castes, just as Sanskrit had done. The castes without literary traditions, the castes whose *dharma* did not include study, took small interest in the movement. Very few girls were educated. Muhammadan boys were seldom to be found in schools or colleges.

The cause of this lay very largely in the literary and non-practical form which this education assumed. English language and literature, philosophy, history, politics, economics, mathematics, were the subjects mainly taught and studied. Science was almost entirely ignored; technical education was neglected. What nine-tenths of the educated classes learned was in fact useless for all the practical purposes of life except conducting public business in English and pleading in the courts of law. How partial the effects of the educational system were is shown by the fact that at the close of the century among the castes ranked as clean Sudras, who formed about half the Hindu population, only one in fifty could read and write, while of the polluting castes, who formed a quarter of the Hindu population, hardly one in a thousand was literate.

While higher and secondary education had made rapid progress, elementary education had languished. At first the officials of the education departments had been expected to induce villagers to promise the contributions without which elementary schools were not to be opened; but this task had been difficult and invidious. The villagers were poor and set small store by school-learning. If one of them wished to write a letter he would hire a scribe; if he wished to prosecute a law-suit he could retain a pleader. In 1883 an inspector in the United Provinces claimed with reason that the elementary education provided was useless to such a man. Most of the pupils, he said, in less than ten years after leaving school could neither read, write, nor cipher. "Having nothing to read, having no occasion to write, and no accounts to keep, they gradually forget whatever they learn." Nor did it offer any real avenue of escape from the degraded position marked out by ancient social custom for the polluting castes. An inspector found a boy of the "sweeper" caste, in an essay on the compara-tive advantages of trade and service as an occupation, preferring trade. "Yet", he asks, "who would enter into mercantile rela-tions with a sweeper, even if a man of that caste could be started in such a calling? Everything that he touches would be considered as polluted." Moreover, the greatest difficulties were raised by the higher-caste Hindus against the admission of the lower castes to the schools at all.

In 1882 a commission was appointed to enquire into the means by which elementary education could be extended and improved. This body, which consisted of both Indian and European mem-bers under the presidency of Sir William Hunter, recommended that in future elementary education should possess "an almost exclusive claim" upon provincial and local revenues, and that, while in future secondary schools should be opened only where local co-operation could be found, elementary schools should be established wherever they were judged necessary without requir-ing private co-operation as a preliminary. Secondary schools ought, it was thought, to be made over wherever possible to private control. The commission also recommended the intro-duction of a text-book embodying "the fundamental principles of natural religion" and the delivery of lectures upon civic duties. The last eccentric proposal was rejected by the government; the others were in the main adopted. But the results were bad. The withdrawal of control from secondary schools led to the multiplication, especially in Bengal, of private schools conducted in the hope of profit, thus increasing the pressure upon the existing frail defences of sound education; and the increase in the number of elementary schools was idle, so long as they continued to teach nothing which the villagers valued.

Meanwhile under the wise inspiration of Sayyid Ahmad Khān some provision had been tardily made for Muslim education. He induced a number of prominent Muslims of the United Provinces to join with him in a campaign to break down Muslim antipathy to western knowledge. Mayo, the governor-general, sympathised with and promoted the projects. Funds for a Muslim college were collected; in 1875 a high school for Muslims was founded at Aligarh; and in 1878 the high school was developed into a college teaching up to the university intermediate examination. The college was divided into two departments, English and Oriental. In the former English was the language of instruction with Arabic or Persian as a second language; in the latter Urdu was the language of instruction, with Arabic or Persian literature as the chief subject, and English as a second language. But here as elsewhere the popular branch was that most likely to be of practical use, and the Oriental branch attracted few students as compared with the English branch.

Desultory beginnings were also made with female education. In Bengal a member of council, Bethune, had established a girls' school with funds privately subscribed. In Madras missionary societies had led the way. In Bombay the same had been done, and there the missionaries had found a greater response than elsewhere, the cause being taken up by the Parsis and the Gujarātis. But even in Bombay not one girl in fifty of those of a school-going age was being educated in 1882, and elsewhere the proportion was even lower. The purdah system, the marriage system, the lack of economic motive in a country where prostitution offered women the only means of independent livelihood, were the principal obstacles. But there was also the difficulty of gathering together a sufficient staff of female teachers. An unmarried woman was in the opinion of orthodox Hindu society suspect and almost certainly disreputable.

Little had thus been done to counteract the unbalanced tendencies of the system set up in 1854. New universities, but of the old pattern, were established in the Panjab in 1882 and at Allāhābād in 1887. But the University of Calcutta, in spite of this relief, was still overburdened with a multitude of students. In the last fifteen years of the century the number of students in colleges rose from 11,000 to 23,000, and of pupils in secondary schools from 429,000 to 633,000. But while numbers were rising, the quality of the education was tending to fall. English, for instance, was being taught by an ever-increasing proportion of men to whom it was a foreign tongue. Students were relapsing into the ancient Hindu mode of study, memorising their text-books as pandits of old had memorised the Vedas. Elementary education was not progressing, and, instead of carrying useful knowledge to the masses, was only enabling a few of the more intelligent boys of the villages to earn a scanty living by clerical drudgery in the cities.

In 1901, nearly three years after his arrival as governor-general, Curzon resolved on introducing reforms, and convened a conference of the principal educational officials, to whom he pointed out the chief defects as he saw them—the predominance of examinations, the lack of university organisation, the unpopularity of primary schools, the neglect of technical and vocational instruction. He also called deserved attention to an important social aspect of the matter. A large number of students in the great cities lived in miserable lodgings, amid insanitary and undesirable surroundings, and untouched by the corporate influences which form a large and most important element in school and university education. As regards general policy he suggested that central control had been inadequate, that the provincial governments had been left too much to their own devices, that expert direction was needed, that the subject had been approached with too little consideration. It must be remembered, he said, that they were "handling the life-blood of future generations". After this conference reforms began. Enlarged grants were made to the provincial governments for educational purposes. An agricultural college was opened at Pūsa. An inspector-general of education was appointed, to tour the provinces and advise the Government of India on matters of policy. A universities commission was appointed to inspect the working of both universities and colleges, and on its recommendations was framed the Universities Act of 1904.

The aim of the new act was to strengthen the control over and raise the standards of university education. The senates were to include majorities of educationalists, and to be responsible for courses of studies, text-books, and standards of examination. Colleges were to be inspected and certified as competently housed, equipped, and staffed, before they were affiliated. Vice-chancellors would in future be appointed by government. Moreover, the universities themselves should provide post-graduate instruction, and to that extent at least become teaching bodies, setting up new and higher standards of attainment and thus exercising a new and most necessary influence upon higher education as a whole. As regards secondary schools the senates were to recommend to government the conditions under which high schools should be allowed to prepare boys for admission to colleges.

These reforms were in themselves most desirable. The tightening of control and the raising of educational standards were long over-due. The development of scientific and technical instruction was urgently needed to promote the search for occupations other than an over-crowded bar and press. Higher literary education had far out-run the economic development of the country, and there were no means of absorbing the numerous arts graduates who poured annually from the colleges. Bengal had as many university students as England, without a tenth of the posts to offer them. Nor had Indian public opinion proved itself capable of wisely influencing educational policy. That public opinion was the opinion of the literary castes, apparently eager that every boy born in them should secure the dubious advantages of a university degree. Curzon had even been urged to commemorate Queen Victoria's reign by a general lowering of examination standards. If matters were to be mended, government must of necessity exercise more direction and control. But unfortunately the proposals came at least a generation too late. Could the clear, incisive mind of Curzon have replaced the cloudy and confused ideas of Ripon, and had the commission in 1882 been set on its way with an allocution as direct, poignant, and unmistakable as that which Curzon delivered twenty years later, a real turn for the better might then have been taken. As it was, his proposals met a most bitter opposition. It was feared that his underlying purpose was to curb the political activity of the educated classes, to lessen their numbers, to diminish their importance. The owners of private schools and colleges in Bengal felt that their interests were threatened, which was indeed the fact. The partition of Bengal created an angry atmosphere in which the real interests of education vanished.

The result was that in spite of the desperate efforts of individuals, both Indian and English, to give reality to Curzon's educational proposals, they produced comparatively small results. Education continued to expand and to deteriorate. Expenditure from public and private funds was more than doubled, while the numbers of students went on rising. Persevering efforts were made to broaden the educational basis by establishing new agricultural colleges, and by opening technical schools for weaving, for carpentry, for commerce. But these efforts were frustrated by the lack of sound training in the primary and secondary schools.

It is not difficult to find the fundamental defects from which modern Indian education has suffered. Government has almost always pursued the idle hope of producing a good system with cheap and often inefficient instruments. For decade after decade swelling numbers have been hailed as proof of progress. Yet the multiplication of pupils meant that the demand for efficient teachers was out-running the supply. In founding a new educational system the provision of teachers should have been the first consideration. Normal schools should have engaged the closest attention of government. Suitable men should have been attracted by good prospects of pay and promotion; and the schools recognised and supported by government should have been kept down to the level at which it was possible to staff and equip them adequately. This would have placed secondary education on a sound basis, and have permitted the gradual development of universities above them and of elementary schools below. But instead of this government complied with the public demand for English education, irrespective of quality. Educational salaries were kept low in order to make education cheap. Secondary schools multiplied and worsened. They sent up ill-prepared students to the colleges. College standards fell as numbers rose. So the vicious circle was completed. The ablest students naturally preferred well-paid administrative to ill-paid teaching work. The schools could not be improved owing to the lack of a sufficient number of able teachers; the colleges could not be improved because of the overwhelming numbers of ill-taught students pressing up to them. Nor did the influence of the educational departments counteract this unfortunate tendency. Everyone soon came to be over-worked, while the failure to divide the departments into distinct teaching and administrative sections emphasised the consequences. The ideal recruit, from the departmental point of view, was not the specialist but the man of all work, who could be sent to inspect schools, or to teach English in a college, or at a pinch to teach science or mathematics. The result was that the outstanding personalities in the world of Indian education were missionaries rather than government servants; and the Europeans who rose to eminence from the ranks of the educational service, like the talented Indians who emerged from the system of education itself, could only achieve this after overcoming grave and needless disadvantages.

The general position was well summed up by the recent Interim (Education) Report of the Statutory Commission. The difficulties of developing elementary education still persisted. It was easy to increase the number of pupils in primary schools; but few remained long enough to attain any certain and well-established literacy. The majority either never attained literacy, or else, under the conditions of rural life and owing to the lack of suitable vernacular literature, speedily relapsed. The secondary schools and colleges were still overcrowded with students not naturally gifted for literary education, as was shown by "the immense numbers of failures at matriculation and in the other university examinations". In spite of the recent movement to make the universities real teaching bodies, the theory was still generally held that they existed mainly to pass students through examinations, instead of training men to become "broad-minded, tolerant, and self-reliant citizens". But, as Curzon himself pointed out, the severest critics must recognise the important results that followed from the working of this imperfect educational system. It brought a large number of persons into pregnant contact with western ideas. Of late years it has been asserted by the extremer nationalists that it produced (and was intended to produce) a "slave-mentality". But in so far as a slave-mentality is discernible among the educated classes of India, it would seem to be inherited from the past rather than inspired by modern conditions and methods. Under favourable conditions western education emancipated rather than enslaved. It inspired a habit of questioning that the ancient culture had lost, and it set up assimilation as the purpose of study instead of the traditional memorisation. It also gave to the social classes peculiarly associated with it a common language and a common stock of ideas.

From this certain social and political tendencies inevitably flowed. The broad basis on which Hindu society had rested for many centuries was silent, undoubting acquiescence in the customary. The whole influence of religion, the idea of transmigration, the system of caste, all made in the same direction. It was the business of one group of castes to fight, of another to propitiate the gods, of a third to till the fields. He who held the sword not only ruled, but was entitled to rule so long as he upheld ancient custom. The prudent Indian ruler might have grievous cause to dread his neighbours, but not to fear his subjects. But it was certain that if a neighbouring prince invaded his territory and overthrew his army, the people would submit and accept the new dominion as submissively as the peasants of Aquitaine accepted the dominion of Edward III. But western education rudely disturbed these medieval conditions. The activity of missionaries in early educational enterprise led naturally to the earliest movements occurring in the closely related social and religious spheres. In Bengal Rām Mohun Roy founded the *Brāhmo Samāj*. This was a deist sect inspired largely by the free-thought of the eighteenth century, which had been propagated in Calcutta by David Hare. The *Brāhmo Samāj* exhibited its social tendencies by supporting the abolition of sati. At a later time it was sharply divided over the question of tolerating other Hindu usages and customs vigourously attacked by Keshub Chandra Sen. Finally the latter was expelled from the society, and established a new body which championed the reform of the marriage-system, and advocated female education.

The spirit of criticism spread inevitably from social to political questions about the middle of the nineteenth century. The writings of Burke, overloaded with image and simile, for that very reason appealed to a people whose literature had been almost exclusively poetic, who were still in the process of developing a prose style, and who in general preferred a striking metaphor to a sound argument. English history, especially as represented by Whig theorists, and the political writings of the younger Mill abounded in suggestions that the natural development of political societies was from despotism to liberty. The career and writings of Mazzini, equally widely studied, offered an example of a nationalist movement directed to the overthrow of foreign dominion. Under these western influences small groups of educated Indians began to set before themselves as an ideal the transformation of the basis of government and the gradual extrusion of foreign control.

This was far from having been entirely unforeseen. Munro, Elphinstone, Malcolm, Lord Hastings, and others who had thoughtfully surveyed the prospects of the Indian empire which their generation had consolidated, had all looked forward to the day when it would be expedient for Great Britain to withdraw from the task of administering that great and perplexing dependency. But their anticipations had not taken all the factors into account. They had expected their successors to be called upon to deliver Indian rule back to the princes, the nobles, the warriors, whom they regarded as the natural leaders of the country. But the nationalist spirit was developing, not among these but among castes which, with a few notable exceptions, had always held a subordinate place in Indian governments, and among races which had been notably unwarlike. Could these new claimants impose themselves on grounds of intellectual superiority alone upon classes which in the past had relied upon the judgment of the sword and the shrewd manipulation of purely material factors?

The distrust thus inspired by the new movement was emphasised naturally if irrationally by the eccentricities of style in which the claims of the educated class were being advocated. Just as true Persians had mocked the phraseology and pronunciation which had passed for Persian in India, just as in medieval Europe the French of London had been a marked and inferior variety of the language spoken at Paris, so now Indian English had developed peculiarities of its own. The misuse of subtle English idiom, the appearance in English dress of idiom borrowed from Indian vernaculars, the use of grandiloquence on quite ordinary occasions, the laborious research for the poetic and the resonant, afforded easy subjects of ridicule. Englishmen doubted whether western ideas had been any better apprehended than the usages of English speech, and whether the democratic ideals of universal equality could be sincerely adopted by a society founded on the principles of caste. The administration considered that it was being invited to deliver over its functions to a minority scarcely more considerable than the civil services, and incapable of maintaining itself in power except by the constant support of British troops.

The political movement had originated in Bengal, where the literary castes were stronger, wealthier, and more widely affected by English teaching than elsewhere. The zamindars for instance set up the British Indian Association to support their interests, menaced by what they regarded as infractions of the Permanent Settlement, such as the levy of additional cesses for local purposes and the protection of tenants by the Bengal Tenancy Act. Then Surendranāth Banerji, who had taken up educational work, set out (as he says) "to kindle in the young the beginnings of public spirit and to inspire them with a patriotic ardour, fruitful of good to them and to the Motherland". In 1876 he founded the Indian Association, intended to spread the same spirit through the middle classes as a whole. When the age of admission to the Indian Civil Service examination was lowered from 22 to 19, delegates were sent to northern India, to Bombay and to Madras, to obtain signatures for a memorial declaring the change to be hurtful to Indian competitors and praying for the restoration of the former age-limit and for simultaneous examinations to be held in England and in India. The delegates were also to establish branch-associations wherever this could be done. These endeavours to introduce changes by argument and persuasion were accompanied (as is usually the case) by attempts of the more angry and hasty to spread hatred of the government by charging it with injustice and tyranny. The vernacular press, which had sprung up in the third quarter of the century, consisted of a large number of very ephemeral periodicals, often edited by college students who found in their columns an opportunity of practising their talents for invective. In 1878 the Vernacular Press Act was passed in order to restrain these activities. It empowered the government to demand securities from such vernacular journals as were thought to calumniate the administration. About the same time, in connection it would appear with alarms concerning the revival of Wahhabī activity among the Muslims, an Arms Act was passed to limit the possession of fire-arms. These measures provided the occasion for further criticisms of government policy.

In 1880 Lytton was succeeded by Ripon and policy was

sharply reversed. He repealed the Vernacular Press Act, announced his intention of developing the system of local self-government, and thus secured great personal popularity. Towards the close of his government this was enormously increased by his unintentionally becoming involved in the Ilbert Bill controversy. The Indians who had competed successfully for the Indian Civil Service had generally been posted to the judicial branch of the administration, and the more senior had reached the stage where they were eligible for appointment as district and sessions judges. But as the law stood, such Indians would not be capable, in their magisterial capacity, of hearing charges against Europeans residing in their districts. The anomaly of the position was emphasised by the fact that an Indian already held the office of presidency magistrate at Calcutta, where he could hear charges against Europeans, a power which he would lose on promotion elsewhere. A bill, diafted by the law member, Ilbert, was therefore introduced to confer on Indian district judges the same powers as were enjoyed by their British colleagues. Against this measure a strong agitation arose among the indigo and tea-planters, who feared that the change would expose them to unfounded or exaggerated charges; and after prolonged discussion the bill was amended by government so as to give Europeans, accused of criminal offences in the mofassal, the right of demanding trial by jury. But while thus partially successful, the agitation proved to have been singularly ill-judged. It provoked strong resentment among the Indian middle-classes, who regarded it as casting a slur on their integrity, and it therefore gave a most powerful impetus to the attempts which Surendranāth Banerji and his friends were making to establish an effective political organisation.

Already in 1883 a conference had been held at Calcutta attended by delegates from other parts of India. In the next year a group of men, brought together at Madras by the annual convention of the Theosophical Society, resolved to set up a body which should embrace all the provinces of India. In 1885 the first Indian National Congress met at Poona. The goal which these early organisers proposed was the establishment of representative government, and they hoped that the congress would develop into an Indian parliament. Their early demands included the enlargement of the legislative councils, the inclusion in them of elected members, the grant of the power to discuss the budget and to ask questions on all administrative matters, the abolition of the secretary of state's council, and the formation of a standing committee of the House of Commons to consider protests made by the legislative councils in matters in which their recommendations had been over-ruled by the executive governments.

From 1885 the National Congress held annual meetings. At first it was not easy to gather together any considerable number of delegates, and the rules were correspondingly loose. For some years delegates could be chosen by any kind of association and indeed at any public meeting convened by any person. Gradually these easy conditions were tightened up, and a general organisation came into being, supported by a considerable proportion of the middle classes in the larger cities. But the movement which it represented remained predominantly Hindu. Few Muslims had at first joined it; and although efforts were made to attract Muslim co-operation, although a Muslim was chosen president at the third meeting, and a resolution adopted at the fourth banning all proposals peculiarly unacceptable to either community, the Muslims continued to hold aloof. In this they were strongly influenced by the criticisms of Sayyid Ahmad, the founder of Aligarh. He disliked the proposals aimed at extending the selection of officials by competitive examination, which would unduly favour the Bengali Kayāsth at the expense of the Rājput and the Muslim. He disliked the proposals for the introduction of elected members, since this would be likely to exclude Muslims. He doubted too whether elected bodies would be willing to impose taxation even if they had the power.

While the leaders of the Hindu middle-classes were thus seeking the reconstruction of the government, and the Muslim leaders were resolving that such a change threatened many disadvantages, the government itself had been seeking to provide a school of political training by the extension of local self-government. Under past empires the villages of India had always been left to do, or leave undone, many things for themselves. Muslim and Hindu emperors alike had been sternly bent upon gathering in the land revenue, but had troubled the villages little otherwise. Local police, local education, local roads, had been supplied by the villagers' own efforts where such things were desired; and the only spur to their activity had been the responsibility of making good losses of travellers by robbery. In most provinces the villages had head-men, who were at once the local representatives of the government and the mouthpieces of village opinion. These head-men had associated with them a group of village servants, to help them in carrying out their duties, and could always convene meetings of the village notables, who would discuss at extra-ordinary length matters laid before them until unanimity was reached or at all events until opposition was silenced. In such regions as in Bengal where large land-holders had come into existence, the village organisation had tended to decay, for their functions generally had devolved upon the great man of the neighbourhood. But elsewhere the villages had remained largely self-dependent. The establishment of the British government had, however, affected this village-system deeply. It was far more completely organised than any of its predecessors. Nothing like its regular chain of law-courts, for example, had ever before been seen in India. Then too the conception of law which it brought with it was at once more definite and more comprehensive than either the Hindu law, which had been largely a matter of fluctu-ating and variable custom, or the Muslim law which, though definite in character, had been narrowly limited in scope. Furthermore, its conception of the functions of government embraced many things which its predecessors had been content to ignore—education, for example, and roads. Under the pressure of these new influences the old village-system, weakened by a century of political chaos, had collapsed. The new courts absorbed the judicial functions which the village panchayats had exercised. The new precision of the law forced the villager to employ the professional aid of pleaders and attorneys. The new activity of the district officials confronted him with new proposals which at best were but half-understood.

The tendencies thus brought into play were scarcely affected by early and imperfect efforts to preserve village institutions. Munro at Madras, Elphinstone in Bombay, attempted to preserve the judicial panchayats. But their endeavours were not followed up, and the origins of the British system of local self-government in India are to be found in the districts and in the larger towns rather than in any development of village-organisation. The earliest specific instance of this policy is found in the action taken in Bengal under regulations of 1816 and 1819. It was then decided that public ferries should be managed by the officers of the government, and that the surplus proceeds should be spent on roads, bridges, and other conveniences for travellers. Local committees were appointed in each district, with the district magistrate as secretary, to advise the government on the needs of the locality. This association of the district officials with the local gentry not only showed the former what works were considered most needful, but also led the latter to subscribe the funds needed for local roads which could not be constructed out of the inconsiderable surpluses available from the local tolls. In other provinces the district officials often levied a cess on the land revenue, to be expended on local purposes with the advice of local committees, and, though these cesses had no legal basis beyond the sanction of custom, they were paid readily. This was, however, a mere temporary phase. In Madras such cesses were legalised by an act of 1865; and in Bombay four years later an act authorised the appointment of district and taluk committees, to advise the district officials on the expenditure of local funds. The form of local self-government thus coming into existence differed from that long established in England. In England powerful officials of the central government had vanished with the decay of the sheriff's authority, and local self-government had thus come to be the business of local magnates working through a staff of their own. In India the collector, with his large executive staff, was the natural and most efficient agent by which local as well as provincial work could be executed; and his prominence and importance in the district necessarily meant that he would dominate the local committees instead of being their servant.

In 1870 Mayo had issued a resolution designed to place the existing incoherent and irregular state of affairs on a definite footing. The policy of the Government of India was two-fold. It hoped to provide for growing expenditure (especially on roads and education) by legalising the development of local taxation which would be better understood and more willingly borne if devised and voted by local men for local objects. It also hoped thus to associate more closely Indians and Europeans in the administration of affairs. Under this resolution a large number of provincial acts were passed, legalising, and in Bengal establishing for the first time, the collection of local cesses. But in the latter province much opposition was offered by the land-owners, on the ground that cesses were a violation of the permanent settlement.

In the legislative council Indian members declared that no more roads were wanted, although the recent famine in Orissa had just demonstrated the terrible insufficiency of land transport.

In the country towns affairs had followed a similar but easier course. As in the districts of many provinces, the magistrate had associated himself in early days with the principal merchants and householders; such informal committees had resolved by what means money for local purposes should be raised, and on what objects it should be spent; and the inhabitants were willing enough to contribute small sums by way of octroi-duties or house-rates to maintain night-watchmen and to keep the streets clean. This voluntary municipal system flourished especially in the Panjab, where in 1855 drainage had been provided in all the larger cities and quite elaborate projects formed for Lahore, Amritsar and Ambāla. In 1850 a municipal act had been passed, permitting the formal establishment of municipalities where the inhabitants petitioned for their introduction. This operated in a curiously uneven way. In Bombay the district officers had small difficulty in securing the necessary petitions from many towns and large villages. By 1856 as many as 292 municipalities had been created in the Satāra district alone, though many of them proved to be short-lived. But in Madras and the Panjab the people showed great reluctance to introduce the act. Between 1864 and 1868 municipal legislation—commonly of a vague form—was adopted by the provincial councils of Bengal, Madras, and the Panjab. In Oudh the Panjab act was followed. In Bombay a municipal act was adopted in 1873. In Madras municipal taxation was limited to an amount approved by the government for each municipality, which was increased by a government grant of 25 per cent. on the amount of the local rates. But in most places no legal limits were set to municipal taxation. The favourite mode of raising money was by the establishment of octroi-duties, in accordance with long-standing practice. Almost everywhere except in Lucknow (where a special act of 1864 had sanctioned the election of nineteen out of twenty-five municipal commissioners) the committees were appointed by the provincial government on the recommendation of the district officers. There was thus little "responsible" government, although there was much association of the principal local people with the officials in the administration of the towns. At the time there was small demand for election and popular control, and rich merchants and land-owners preferred to seek government nomination rather than the people's suffrage.

The three presidency cities stood in a class by themselves, owing to their numerous European population, their relative size, and their superior wealth. At the close of the eighteenth century a British statute, passed in consequence of the disagreeable discovery that taxation by executive order was illegal within these little domains of English law, empowered the governor-general in council to appoint in each a number of justices of the peace, and enabled the latter to appoint watchmen and scavengers and to levy rates for their payment. But, although this enactment was based on English precedent, it failed to include provision for the punishment of malversation. In early days the justices' finances were assisted by the promotion of lotteries, the profits of which were laid out on public buildings, roads, and drains. But the assessments never sufficed for the due maintenance of roads and conservancy; at Bombay alone was any additional taxation imposed; and the justices as a body took small interest in their duties. Attempts were made to set up an elective body at Calcutta, but produced such gross abuses as to discredit the system of direct election for years. At Bombay in 1845 administration was entrusted to a committee—the Conservancy Board—consisting of two European and three Indian members elected by the justices, with the senior magistrate of police as chairman. In 1856 acts were passed vesting the administration of each city in three commissioners. But this plan too was unsatisfactory. The commissioners had no power to raise the necessary funds, they were not subject to due audit control, and they were in no way associated with the inhabitants. Between 1863 and 1867 therefore further changes were made. From this point local methods began to diverge, but the immediate general tendency was to concentrate executive power in the hands of a single man. At Calcutta, while general control was restored to the justices, 120 in number, their chairman, appointed by the provincial government, alone possessed executive authority. At Bombay, where the justices formed a body of 500, much the same was done, the executive official being designated the Municipal Commissioner. At Madras a municipal council of 32 members was created, but it could act only through its president. On the whole this new plan proved much more efficient than the former ones. Hogg at Calcutta and

Crawford at Bombay introduced great improvements in drainage, water-supply, and general sanitation. But it was felt that a dictatorship could not be more than a temporary expedient. The next move was in the direction of elective councils, less unwieldy in number than the justices had become, and invested with financial control over the executive official. This was first done at Bombay. In 1872 a council of sixty-four replaced the five hundred justices, one-quarter nominated by government, one-quarter chosen by the justices, and a half elected directly by the rate-payers. The commissioner's accounts were to be audited weekly by a standing committee of the council, and monthly by paid auditors. At Calcutta in 1876 and 1882 the municipal body was reduced from one hundred and twenty to seventy-two, with a majority elected by the rate-payers and audit provision imitated from that adopted at Bombay. But, while the Bombay scheme worked well, at Calcutta large committees were formed which sought to exercise a minutely detailed control over the executive until definite limits to such interference were laid down by an act of 1899. At Madras, where the municipal body had already been cut down, first half and then two-thirds of the members became elective.

In 1882 experiments over three-quarters of a century had thus been conducted with a view to the development of local self-governing bodies. But these had by no means conformed to the English pattern. Direct election had been generally unsuccessful outside the presidency towns; local bodies had been overshadowed by the power, knowledge, and energy of the executive officials; little had been achieved in the nature of political education, or in the actual transference of control in local matters from official into unofficial hands. In 1882, however, Ripon, the governor-general, issued a resolution defining a new policy. This aimed at avoiding the defects of past attempts. The English machinery of the ballot-box was to be introduced; and with the English machinery it was hoped that the English spirit of real local self-government would come. By learning to manage local affairs men would qualify themselves for wider political action. Local organisation would form a solid foundation for constitutional reform. It did not greatly matter if at first local affairs were mismanaged. People would learn from their mistakes. The great object should be to teach the use of the vote, to build up electorates, to form a class accustomed not merely to discuss but to manage public affairs in a spirit of public responsibility.

In consequence of this resolution it was decided to establish under the existing district committees a series of boards, chosen wherever possible by election, with private persons instead of officials in executive charge. Some attempts were made to connect the new boards with the villages. In the Central Provinces village head-men grouped together were to choose members of the subordinate boards, while the latter were to choose members of the district boards. A somewhat similar plan was adopted in Bombay. In Madras village panchayats were recognised as electors for the taluk boards. But the district officials continued to provide the executive agency for both taluk and district boards, so that control was still exercised from within. In Bengal a most interesting experiment was proposed. A bill was introduced in 1883 to set up boards in each revenue sub-division, with a central board of supervision for the whole of the province, the members of the subordinate boards being chosen by village committees. When the bill had passed the provincial legislature and was awaiting the sanction of the home government, experimental elections of village committees were conducted. There was no secret ballot. The villagers were assembled and chose their representatives after open discussion. But this most hopeful plan was vetoed by the secretary of state, who insisted on setting up district boards, with the magistrate and collector at their head, to control and conduct local work within each district. Thus a measure, which would have gone far to put into practice the ideas of Ripon, was negatived, not by the hostility of the official world, but by the secretary of state's lack of comprehension. The net result in the districts was a very limited introduction of the ballot-box, elections in which no one took real interest, and the establishment of boards dependent upon the executive for the performance of their duties. Their apathy was shown by their neglect of means to increase the funds at their disposal. Their normal income was derived from cesses assessed and collected by the district officials. The district was far too large an area to be entrusted to elected members, who knew their own villages and the immediate neighbourhood but were ignorant of all the rest save perhaps the district head-quarters. Even the revenue sub-division, the *taluk* or *tahsil*, was too large to permit local patriotism and a sense of common interests to develop in an effective degree.

Municipal developments were similarly disappointing in character. In every province acts were passed requiring a large proportion—a half or three-quarters—of the municipal boards to be elected, permitting an elective member to be appointed chairman, and sometimes allowing boards to choose a chairman for themselves. But elective members were not often appointed by government, or chosen by the boards, to the chairman's office. The fact was that the district officer could promote the interests and defend the rights of the municipality far better than any private person. Little interest was taken in the elections. Seats were often uncontested, and voters did not trouble to exercise their powers. Except in some of the larger towns where individuals of strong personality emerged, the municipal executives remained under official control. In 1915 in the Panjab only ten out of eighty-three municipalities entitled to elect their chairmen chose non-officials. In Bombay and the United Provinces the number of non-official chairmen was increased only by constant official pressure. Finance offered perpetual difficulties. Octroi-dues formed the traditional and popular means by which money could be raised for municipal purposes. But since this obstructed the general movement of trade, strong efforts were made from 1868 onwards to induce municipalities to replace the octroi by direct taxation. This was exceedingly unwelcome. Even where assessments were imposed, the elected members were most reluctant to insist on their regular collection and prompt payment. In Bengal at the close of the period a quarter of the municipalities collected less than a rupee per head. Insanitary conditions were preferred to strict administration, and progress in water-supply and drainage was largely dependent on occasional doles from the provincial governments.

On the whole the local self-government policy must be adjudged a failure. It did not train an electorate, it elicited the services of only a few active and patriotic men, it increased instead of diminishing the duties of the district officials. The popular reasons which have been usually adduced to explain this failure are the closeness of official control, the small extent of powers accorded to the municipal and rural boards, and the inadequate funds provided out of provincial revenues for the development of local self-government. These reasons undoubtedly explain why the leaders of the Indian political movement preferred to exhibit their eloquence at the Congress meetings, in public assemblies, and in the columns of the press, rather than in the humble and laborious sphere of local administration. With certain notable exceptions, such as Gokhale, they shirked the exacting political school out of which the English system of self-government had been painfully elaborated, judging that quick minds and ready argument could make good the lack of practical political experience. But although the limitation of powers and the demand that local finance should be provided mainly out of local funds explain why many prominent Indians refused to co-operate actively in the field of local self-government, this is far from providing any complete explanation of the failure. Other more important factors were at work. Sufficient allowance was perhaps never made for the difference of conditions in England and India—the difference between a system of responsible government in a small and homogeneous country, and a system of highly centralised autocracy in a sub-continent fissured by every kind of religious and social division. The strong, well-organised administrative machine of the latter would be bound to dominate local institutions even more completely in India than it did under the centralised governments of Europe. In another way the experiment had been incomplete. The mechanism of ballot-box and voting-paper had been borrowed from England, but not the vital, educative basis of the English system. In India control was exercised through official supervision; in England it was exercised through financial responsibility. In the latter a local board which improperly expended public money, or neglected to gather in at the due time the rates which it had imposed, would find itself surcharged and the members would be collectively and individually liable to make good the public loss out of their private estates. But neither in the corporations established in the presidency towns, nor in the rural and municipal boards, was this most salutary provision applied. The men who accepted nomination or sought election to these bodies accepted no personal financial responsibility with their seats, and consequently membership was neither so selective nor so formative as it might have been. Herein certainly lies one of the fundamental reasons why local self-government worked so disappointingly. Lastly, in the rural areas, the system was never properly connected with the villages, where alone effective local life was to be found. The nearest approach was made by the vetoed Bengal scheme of 1883. Experiments along those lines might have produced a really active spirit, a true electorate uncursed by voting-papers, and boards filled with men who were looked up to as the natural leaders of their neighbourhood and who would not have been diverted from local duties by the thought that the sphere was incommensurate with their dignity and importance.

While these attempts were being made to provide elementary schools of political education by means of local self-government, the demands of the National Congress and of the Indian press led to certain changes in the structure of the legislative councils. Lord Dufferin, who succeded Ripon as governor-general in 1884, possessed not only great personal charm but also a large measure of political sagacity. In 1883 he had prepared a plan for the gradual introduction of popular influence into the despotic government of Egypt, where fundamental conditions were similar to those of India though the political situation was less complicated. In 1886 he wrote a very important minute on the question of political development. In this he dwelt on the importance of giving quickly without the appearance of coercion whatever concessions it might be judged right to make. The particular measures which he had in view were the enlargement of the legislative councils, and the introduction of some method of electing part of the non-official members. These changes would provide the Government of India and the provincial governments with independent Indian advice; but, since he proposed to maintain official majorities in the councils, the responsibility to the home government would be in no way impaired. These proposals, however, went much farther than the home government would go. In 1890 a bill was introduced into parliament to enlarge the councils, but Dufferin's elective proposals were completely suppressed, and the Irish crisis led to the abandonment of the bill, after debates in the House of Lords on the practicability of establishing the elective principle, which was supported by both Ripon and Northbrook. Not until 1892 was a measure enlarging the Indian councils passed into law. This contained a clause designedly wide enough to permit the application of the elective principle, but not prescribing it. "It would be a great evil", said Lord Salisbury in debate, "if, in any system of government which we gradually develop, the really strong portions of Indian society did not obtain that share in the government to which their natural position among their own people traditionally entitled them." It was, however, clearly understood that the new rules which the Government of India were to frame would recognise the elective principle.

The result of the act was to increase materially the provincial councils, and to provide that a number of members should be nominated on the recommendation of the municipalities and rural boards; while four new members were to be recommended for the imperial council by the non-official members of the existing provincial councils and a fifth by the Bengal Chamber of Commerce. In future too the budgets were to be laid before the councils for discussion, and the right of interpellation was granted to the members. Although it was solemnly declared that the changes were not intended to represent any movement towards responsible government, they evidently involved important principles and were not mere matters of form. The councils established in 1861 had been exclusively legislative in character. No business save changes in the law could be laid before them. But now members could ask questions touching administrative and executive business, and they were given the first elements of that financial power on which responsible government has always rested. These concessions, linked with the introduction of free choice into the selection of members, naturally appeared to the Congress leaders as definite steps towards the liberalisation of Indian institutions. They began indeed to hope that they would succeed in securing for themselves in the name of the people the supreme control of the machine, regardless of the development of political experience among the populace. In political reform, as in education, the results of British policy were to raise the super-structure before the foundations had been laid.

CHAPTER XVIII

The Morley-Minto Reforms

While the Congress was planning the capture of the government machine by constitutional agitation, and while the government was seeking to lay the foundations of a broad political advance by developing local institutions, an extremist party was growing up among Indians advocating the use of violence. In this respect matters were following a normal course. The Italian *risorgimento*, the Russian movement, the Irish Home Rule movement, had likewise developed an external propaganda, professing more or less moderate aims by more or less moderate methods, and these too had been accompanied by the formation of subterranean societies, with revolutionary objects, for the perpetration of political crime. In India as elsewhere the precise relation between the secret and the avowed branches was obscure. But moderate leaders almost always hope to be carried towards success by the efforts of the extremists, almost always hope to make political capital out of crimes the preparation of which they prefer to ignore, and almost always forget that he who rides a tiger cannot dismount. In India, however, an ill-judged policy enabled the extremists to appear more openly and exert more control over the moderate organisation than was the normal case elsewhere. The Austrians in Italy, the imperial government in Russia, did not permit the extremists openly to spread their propaganda among the people at large. The British government in India did. This resulted from the fundamental conflict between the British position in India and British political ideas. In Great Britain the press was free, and political life based upon open discussion. But India presented the political monstrosity of a free press and an autocratic government. The position had been created by Metcalfe in 1835 when he withdrew all press restrictions on the ground that this was necessary to promote western knowledge in India. The measure probably reflects the influence of Bentinck and Macaulay; it was certainly opposed to the views of the best and ablest company's servants of the period. Neither Mountstuart Elphinstone nor Thomas Munro can justly be called men of illiberal views; both looked forward to the time when the British, in the interests of both Indians and themselves, would withdraw from the control of the Indian government; but both were emphatic in declaring that the immediate liberty of the press would weaken the existing government before any other was ready to replace it. Their expectations were fulfilled. As the Indian press developed, a section of it devoted its energies to attacking the British government. In 1857 Canning had found it necessary to limit for a year its freedom of comment and perversion. In 1878 Lytton had laid restrictions on the vernacular press. In 1882 Ripon had repealed this act. Press attacks seem to have been regarded as a safety-valve. This curious example of argument by analogy seems to have missed the point that press attacks were more likely to increase than reduce the political pressure. In any case Ripon's policy was inconsistent with itself. He strove, as has been shown, to establish schools of political education in his rural boards and municipalities. But he judged the time far indeed from ripe for any fundamental political reform. He would not have dreamed of setting up responsible government, yet he restored freedom to the press as though he considered the days of autocracy almost run. The error was the more considerable since the British government in India was ill-constructed to resist the constant fret of newspaper criticism and attack. It rested, and had always rested, upon nothing firmer than popular acquiescence and the respect which the east has always paid to successful force. The people cherished a traditional respect for the commands of government, not because they were good but because they were thought to be backed by irresistible power. The religious basis on which a despotism may long rest as upon a rock had never existed. The popular basis on which self-government rests had never existed. The economic basis on which a well-organised oligarchy has often rested had never existed. Anything which lowered the readiness with which the government was obeyed, which taught the people to question the orders which might be issued, struck at the very roots of government in India. Full freedom of the press should therefore have been deferred until the autocrat was ready to abdicate. Ripon's measure might suitably have accompanied the reforms of 1919. But to couple it with the local self-government resolution of 1882 was to condemn the one or the other as an anachronism.

After this release the section of the Indian press devoted to invective became the more extreme; while the section which had inclined to argument rather than to abuse became the more abusive. The Ilbert Bill agitation provided matter for a multitude of leading articles. The early Congress meetings also served to stimulate press campaigns in favour of the changes advocated by the Congress leaders. But the appearance of a real extremist group of newspapers may be dated from the passing of the Age of Consent Act in 1891. The death of a Hindu child-wife at Calcutta had led to the prosecution of her husband for culpable homicide. The case excited considerable and unfavourable comment, and the legislature decided to prohibit cohabitation until the wife should be at least twelve years of age. As in the case of sati, many Hindus of Calcutta professed to see an attack on their religion in this beneficent if modest piece of social reform. One Calcutta newspaper was prosecuted for sedition on account of its comments on the new act. But the chief opposition came from the other side of India. At Bombay a considerable number of educated Indians coupled their demands for an increasing share in the government of the country with a strong advocacy of reforms within the structure of Indian society itself. But on the latter there was small agreement. The orthodox Hindus, who had hitherto held aloof from the congress-men as tainted with the falsities of western education, would clearly become more than ever hostile to the political movement if it were identified with social reform; and this would demonstrate to every foreign observer that the Congress could not claim to speak for Hinduism as a whole. None saw this so clearly as Bāl Gangadhar Tilak. He was a Chitpāvan Brāhman, the caste that had produced the family of the great Pēshwās. He was a man of outstanding personality—decided, eloquent, learned; and soon became a man of note at the Congress. He seems to have conceived the plan of bringing the orthodox Hindu under the banner of the National Congress, in order to reinforce the political discontent of himself and his fellows by any religious discontent that could be promoted. His Marāthi journal, the *Kēsari*, therefore denounced the Age of Consent bill as violating religious duties and bitterly attacked every Hindu supporter of it as a traitor to his faith. Rightly regarding youth as the most impressionable age, he took special pains to bring school-boys and college-students under his influence. He organised gymnastic societies, and developed a cult of Sīvajī as the national hero of the Marātha people. All the evils of India, he taught, had been brought upon her by foreigners—first the Muslims and then the British. In this he was but echoing the ideas which theosophical lecturers had been spreading for years. But, while Colonel Olcott and his companions had lectured in English, Tilak's vigorous Marāthi carried his words among the populace of a region where historical events had created more of a true national feeling than existed anywhere else in India.

Moreover, fortune favoured Tilak in his campaign, or, rather, he was on the alert to seize every opportunity. In 1896 famine disposed men to murmur. Then bubonic plague appeared in Bombay. There was no special reason why this in itself should have led to trouble. From time to time it had swept men away by whole families in every eastern port. It had ever been accepted as a decree of an inscrutable providence. But western men, obsessed with the hope of mastering some at least of the more unpleasant manifestations of nature, deemed it their duty to attempt to stay its ravages. No one yet knew the method by which bubonic plague was propagated. It was generally thought that stricken men communicated it directly to their fellows. Every effort was therefore made to segregate the victims. Houses were searched. At Poona British troops were employed as search-parties. Measures of so extraordinary a nature did much to transform the prevailing panic into popular resentment. They were very easily misrepresented. The Marāthi press abounded in complaint. Tilak's journal accused the government of deliberate oppression. In one article he described the horror with which Sīvajī, the national hero, must regard the condition of his people —impoverished, famine-stricken, diseased, and persecuted, the sacred Brāhman polluted with imprisonment among low castes, and veiled women insulted and dragged into the public view. In another he defended the conduct of Sīvajī in killing Afzal Khān by treachery. Great men, he said, were above the common rules of conduct. There was no sin in killing for the benefit of others, and his readers were exhorted to consider how unrightful was the position of the foreigner in India and to ponder the actions of the great. The hint was quickly taken. Two young Chitpāvans murdered a military officer and the India civilian in charge of plague-prevention at Poona. They were duly tried and executed.

Tilak himself was tried for sedition and imprisoned for eighteen months.

This experiment in instigating political crime was imitated in Bengal. There too religious motives were brought into play. There too school-boys were organised into gymnastic societies for political agitation. There too was worshipped the national hero whose successors had laid waste the province with fire and sword. In 1902 a small band of revolutionary conspirators had already been formed. Their efforts were aided by the Japanese victories over Russia, by the unpopularity of Curzon's educational reforms, but above all by the resentment against the partition of Bengal. That measure excited alarm among influential sections of the educated class. The Calcutta lawyers feared that the creation of a new province would mean the establishment of a court of appeal at Dacca and diminish the business of their own High Court. Journalists feared the appearance of new provincial news-papers which would restrict the circulation of the Calcutta press. The change seemed thus to endanger existing interests and was assured of powerful opposition. But this was intensified to an extraordinary degree by sentimental and political considerations. In Bengal the worship of Kāli, wife of Siva, had always been very popular. She there possessed a two-fold character. She delighted in bloody sacrifices; but she was also venerated as the Great Mother. This mingling of attributes, destructive and generative, recalls the deities of ancient civilisations of whom she is perhaps the last representative. Associated with her worship was yet another conception—Bengal as the mother-land. This conception, vague and cloudy as it was, offered a far better basis for the support of political desires by religious excitement than the cult of Sīvajī or the indefensible hostility to the Age of Consent Act. A great revival of Kāli-worship took place. At her temple in Calcutta thousands of goats were slaughtered, while the partition was described as the rending in pieces of the revered mother by impious foreign hands. On the political side the partition meant the creation of a province in which the Muslims would form a clear majority of the population. It was therefore represented as the designed subjection of Hindus to Muslim interests. In support of the excitement thus called up was organised the *swādeshi* movement. This was designed to secure a boycott of foreign goods and their replacement by native—*swādeshi*—articles.

Students and school-boys were employed to picket shops; would-be purchasers of English cloth were abused and intimidated; shop-keepers who stocked it were threatened; and when in the new province Muslims resisted these endeavours to make them buy what they did not want, communal riots became frequent.

Under cover of this violent agitation, the revolutionary group formed secret societies, collected arms, prepared bombs, and scattered abroad newspapers and leaflets designed to vilify the government and inflame the people. It was a religious duty to get rid of the foreigner. The man who was executed for murdering an Englishman should be regarded as a martyr to his motherland. Miserly and luxurious men who refused to contribute subscriptions to the cause should be made to give by force. The doctrine fell on ready ears. Prices were rising, and with them the cost of living was increasing. But large numbers of the educated class lived on fixed salaries as clerks and school-masters. Their discontent rose as the purchasing power of their monthly pay fell. Then, too, the province was full of men who had failed in the various university examinations and who blamed the examiners and the government for the blight that had descended on their exaggerated hopes. Many even of those who had passed found themselves without the government posts which they had sought, or starving at the over-crowded bar, or teaching at miserably low pay in schools. These, and especially the last, became the eager disciples of the revolutionary movement, which through its adherents among teachers found a ready way into the classes of both schools and colleges. The result was a long series of political crimes. The terrorist associations attacked both the officials of government and their own countrymen. Within four months, in the cold weather of 1907–8, the lieutenant-governor's train was derailed, a former district magistrate of Dacca was shot at and wounded, and two Englishwomen were killed by a bomb thrown into their carriage. About the same time began a series of political dacoities. Dacoity had always been the characteristic crime of Bengal; but whereas in the past it had been the work of specific criminal castes, it was now conducted by groups of young *badralog* —middle-class people. Their methods were the same. Evidence was silenced by intimidation and murder. Sometimes the money and valuables stolen were devoted to the personal use of the robbers. But the ostensible purpose always was to provide funds for the revolutionary movement.

These two movements, centring respectively at Poona and Calcutta, formed the most active branches, both characterised by the union of political and religious excitement. In the Panjab the latter was lacking. There advantage was taken of agrarian discontent arising out of legislation affecting the canal colonies. The leaders, Lājput Rai and Ajīt Singh, sought to revive memories of Sikh rule, bitterly attacking as traitors those who served the government in the police or the army.

It has often been asserted that this unrest was basically due to the growing misery of the population under the depressing influences of British rule. Such statements lack both the support of evidence and any degree of inherent probability. So far as evidence goes, the population of India was more prosperous at the close of the nineteenth century than it had been at the beginning. Nor do men ponder rebellion when ground down by misery. A wholly wretched population is docile. When all the energies of a man are needed to save himself and his family from starvation, he has no time left for politics. Political discontent emerges, not among men who have always been destitute, but among men who find themselves worse off than they formerly were. This was predominantly the case with the professional and educated classes. Their growing numbers having exceeded the public demand for their services, and the rise in prices having reduced the value of the salaries they could command, they were all ready for political activity.

Blame also has been laid on the personality and policy of the governor-general who retired in 1905, Lord Curzon. In such matters contemporary judgment often lays too heavy a responsibility on individuals, and neglects the relentless pressure of general conditions. In like manner Dalhousie was blamed for bringing about the Indian Mutiny. But while the consequences of Dalhousie's and of Curzon's policy may be observed clearly in the developments which followed on their rule, the responsibility of both lay in failing to see what indirect and unexpected tendencies their conduct would call into action, and in the fact that their measures were timed unluckily rather than in themselves ill-considered. Curzon's reforming zeal, his partition of Bengal, his educational reforms, the douches of cold common-sense which he poured from time to time on political enthusiasm, his strong and well-founded admiration of the change which a century of British government had produced in India, intensely annoyed the educated classes who claimed that this tutelage was out-of-date, and who were eager to grasp authority in their own hands. To this extent he certainly exasperated the Congress and facilitated the extension of extremist influence. But though a more conciliatory attitude might have smoothed away some part of the moderates' hostility, nothing short of complete abdication could have satisfied the irreconcilable elements.

This was exhibited clearly by the course of events under Curzon's successor, Lord Minto. Minto's aim was twofold. He desired to rally to the government the moderate group which had been antagonised by his predecessor, and to bring forward into active political life the large land-owners of the country. In this respect Minto's attitude was much more realistic than either that of his predecessor or that of the secretary of state with whom he found himself yoked to the plough of government. Minto's appointment as governor-general had been made in 1905, when the Balfour ministry was approaching its termination. In January 1906 a Liberal cabinet came into office, with Campbell-Bannerman as prime minister and John Morley as secretary of state for India. Morley's selection had been one of those accidents which characterise the working of responsible government. He possessed no special fitness for the office. He had never studied Indian affairs. But he was a convinced and obstinate defender of the party-creed, who had held subordinate offices in past administrations, with a deserved reputation for incisive speech and a character of greater honesty than is usual among politicians. His intellect was, however, narrowly doctrinaire. All his life had been passed among writers and speakers; outside the sphere of party-management his practical experience was small; he suffered therefore from all the disabilities which afflict the *intelligentsia* in every age and every region. He exaggerated the importance of the political arena. He exaggerated the importance of the spoken and written word. He was essentially a critic, and a better critic of books and speeches than of action and policy. Minto presented a strong contrast. He was a Conservative in politics, but had never been a violent party-man. He had seen active service in the army. He had managed landed estates. He loved fair play with all the earnestness of the true sportsman, and would no more have done a dirty thing than he would have shot a bird sitting or pulled his horse in a steeple-chase. He had little of Morley's width of reading, or vigour of phrase; but he had learnt to read men if not books, and to manage men if not to manage periods. He had never been guilty of a calculated ambiguity. He had just served a term of office as governor-general of Canada with remarkable success, and had been reckoned the very man to handle with tactful skill the difficult situation which Curzon had left behind. In accordance with well-established custom he continued in office under the new Liberal ministry.

The problem which confronted him and the secretary of state was two-fold. To maintain ordered government the efforts of the revolutionary societies had to be met and checked; but it was equally essential to restrict the sources of discontent by associating with the government influential Indians drawn not only from among the urban middle-classes but also from among the land-owners in close touch with the rural districts. Action against the revolutionaries and the newspapers which favoured their designs was made difficult by the reluctance of Morley to associate himself and the ministry with a policy of repression. The Radicals persistently denied the serious character of the situation, claiming that the newspaper reports were exaggerated and that the bureaucratic government was attempting to evade reform under cover of the revolutionary bogey. But after long delay Morley was induced publicly to confess that "You may put picric acid in the ink and pen, just as much as in any steel bomb". Meetings held to promote hatred against the government were prohibited first by a temporary ordinance and then by a permanent act. An act was passed limiting the conditions under which persons might possess explosive substances. In June, 1908, the Newspapers (Incitement to Offences) Act was passed. Under this the most inflammatory of the Calcutta newspapers—the *Jugantar* or New Era—was suppressed. In 1910 a further act was passed. Prosecutions and other repressive measures followed. Tilak for instance had seized the occasion of the murder of the two Englishwomen in Bengal to assert that their death was due to the unbearable oppression of the government. He was tried and sentenced by an Indian judge to six years' transportation. Other leaders who were believed to be deeply concerned in promoting the revolutionary movement were deported under an old regulation of 1818.

In all these matters the policy clearly originated with Minto; Morley's view was that such measures would do more to discourage the moderates than to check the extremists. But here practical wisdom lay rather with the man of affairs than with the politician. The moderates were bound to express loud public disapproval of repression. They could not without endangering their position declare open war upon the party of violence. But they were in fact alarmed at the extent to which the revolutionary movement was spreading. The cleavage had already produced notable effects in the National Congress. In 1905 under the presidency of Gokhale, the Congress had supported the Bengal boycott. Gokhale had complained of the repression of the educated classes, and compared Curzon's policy with that of Aurangzīb, as if the partition of Bengal and the Universities Act had been akin in spirit to the emperor's calling out his elephants to crush a path for him from the Delhi palace to the Jama Masjid through the Hindu throng appealing against the re-establishment of the infidel poll-tax. But in 1906 difficulties within the Congress were evaded only by one of those devices favoured by embarrassed politicians. A formula was found vague enough to conceal the widening gap between moderate and extremist. *Swarāj* was declared to be the goal of Indian progress; and that convenient catchword was accepted by all—by moderates in the sense of responsible parliamentary government, by extremists in the sense of absolute independence. In 1907 violence emerged. A preliminary meeting of the organising committee at Nāgpur, where the Congress was to have met, was forcibly broken up by a body of extremists. At Surat, where the Congress finally sat, the two parties came to blows again; the extremists were driven out; and then the Congress purged itself of irreconcilables like Tilak from Poona and Arabindo Ghose from Bengal. This was mainly due to the influence of two men, Gokhale and Surendranāth Banerji. Gokhale, the ablest and probably the most far-seeing of the moderates, had been and still remained an earnest advocate of social reform. He was therefore fundamentally separated from his fellow-casteman, Tilak, by his conceptions of both political method and political objects. Moreover, he was honest as well as courageous. A free and often severe critic of the existing administration, he would also declare unpalatable truths to his own people, reminding them that Indian troubles sprang less from foreign dominion than from internal defects, that British rule had been a great instrument of progress, that the average degree of knowledge, energy, and self-sacrifice among Indians remained far below that of the western self-governing nations, and that real political progress depended far less on political concessions than on a raising of the average Indian capacity.

Surendranāth Banerji had long been in the forefront of agitation in Bengal. He had led the anti-partition movement. He had followed Tilak in seeking to reinforce the political agitation by religious zeal, and to enlist the young enthusiasm of students and school-boys in spreading his views among the people. At one time he had verged closely upon the irreconcilable extremist attitude. But he had been alarmed by the anarchical developments which had arisen in Bengal, and in 1908 swung back decisively into the moderate camp.

Meanwhile proposals for political reform, which Minto deemed the natural correlative to the repression of violence, had been under serious debate. Here again the views of the governor-general and the secretary of state differed profoundly. Morley's ideas were based upon the proposals which had been put forward by the National Congress, designed in the main to secure a large measure of the political machinery existing in England. To Minto, on the contrary, the enlargement of the legislative councils, the extension of elective methods, and the widening of the powers of the councils, seemed of far less moment than certain other considerations which did not necessarily affect the actual political structure. The numberless and deep divisions of the population seemed to him completely to rule out the establishment of real representative government. "We cannot move far in that direction", he wrote on May 16, 1907, "and any move we make is merely a sop to impossible ambitions." But these words were far from indicating any reluctance to undertake important reforms. The essence of the matter, as he saw it, was to bridge over the gulf between Indian and Englishman, which had been at once concealed and widened by the spreading use of the English language in India. "I cannot admit", he wrote at the close of 1906, "that we have only the aspirations of the so-called advanced party to deal with....I believe that we have something much bigger in front of us—the desire of a largely increasing class of well-educated and loyal men to possess a greater share in the government of India. Since I have been in India I have talked with many such men, chiefs, land-owners and others; and I have found them almost universally...opposed to an increase of representative government, but strongly pressing the claims and capabilities of their countrymen to share in the highest executive councils of their country."

This thought perpetually recurred in his letters. "The more I see, the more convinced I am", he wrote in the following year, "that we cannot continue to govern India with any hopes of tranquillity till we give her educated classes a chance of a greater share in the government of the country." But this was to be sought not by a mere mechanical widening of the elective elements in the legislative councils, but by rendering them more truly representative, and above all by a considerable increase in th high executive offices open, in practice as well as in theory, to men of Indian birth. "The only way we can save India from a tremendous convulsion", he declared, "...is in recognising the right of the Indian gentleman, loyal at the present moment, to a greater share in the government of the country."

While therefore he was quite willing to accept such changes in the direction of parliamentary government as Morley desired, he was far from regarding them as the essential part of the plans which he was elaborating. While Morley, despite disclaimers alike in his correspondence with Minto and in his speeches in parliament, considered the enlargement of the legislative councils and the establishment of elective methods as leading directly towards the establishment of western institutions, Minto busied himself with bringing into the scheme of reforms changes which would demonstrate his principles of associating Indians with the business of administration and of providing large but unorganised masses with the means of self-expression. His share in the formation of the changes introduced by the act of 1909 was therefore far more personal than that of the secretary of state, who hardly did more than adopt current ideas. The statement may surprise those conversant only with the published documents. With studied egotism Morley's *Recollections* tacitly claim a wholly disproportionate share of credit for the measure with which his name and Minto's are connected, and his private correspondence more than once suggested that the official communications of the Government of India should be so drafted as to make its dependence on the home government appear more evident. In fact his autocratic temperament and his doctrinaire ideas led him to consider the governor-general as his agent rather than as his colleague. Minto, however, succeeded to a great extent in defending the government over which he presided. He was particularly anxious that the Indian public should have no reason to think that reform was being forced on him from London, and refused altogether to allow "the Government of India to give a blank cheque, so to speak, to be filled in for us at home".

Minto's special contributions to the reform scheme of 1909 were three in number—the proposed advisory council, the provision of special representation for certain classes, and the inclusion of Indians in the executive councils. The first of these came to nothing, but is interesting as illustrating the ideas by which he was inspired. The proposal sprang out of a suggestion of Curzon's that a council of princes should be set up. Minto thought this by itself inadvisable, but turned his attention to the possibility of forming a council of land-owners, ruling chiefs, and men of influence outside the legislative council, to be summoned from time to time and consulted regarding projected changes in law or policy. The special advantage which he hoped thus to secure was to ascertain the views of rural India, scarcely represented by congresses or elected members of an exclusively urban character. As the discussions progressed, this proposal was developed—it appears, by the secretary of state's council—into a scheme for an advisory council consisting of both ruling princes and territorial magnates. This was designed to represent the views "of the hereditary leaders of the people, both in British India and in the principal nativ states". But in this form the proposal proved impracticable. Ruling chiefs refused to sit as equals beside the zamindars of British India; and Minto himself concluded that his purpose could be better achieved by other methods. The proposal was therefore abandoned.

The provision for an improved representative system in the legislative councils, though a difficult matter, was however, developed. The scheme adopted under the act of 1892 had worked very much in one direction. The members recommended for appointment by the local boards had consisted in the main of lawyers. The district municipalities had recommended forty lawyers out of a total of forty-three members; and even the district boards, which might have been expected to possess a more rural complexion, had nominated nearly four times as many lawyers as land-owners. Direct nomination had done something to set this right, but lawyers had succeeded in obtaining over a third of the seats on the provincial councils, while lawyers and school-masters between them had formed 40 per cent. of the imperial council. Minto and his council did not deny "that the professional classes are entitled to a share of representation proportioned not merely to their numbers, which are small, but to their influence, which is large and tends continually to increase. But they are not prepared to allow them a virtual monopoly of the power exercised by the councils, and they believe that the soundest solution of the problem is to be found in supplying the requisite counterpoise...by creating an additional electorate recruited from the landed and moneyed classes".

The over-representation of urban interests was not the only problem to be considered. The Muslims demanded a larger proportion of seats than they had been able to secure in the past. They formed about a quarter of the population of British India, but had not secured an eighth of the seats filled by recommendation in the imperial council. These results were necessarily displeasing to the leaders of the community, who feared that further advances in the direction of self-government would result in an increasing political predominance of the Hindu professional classes. The fact was, as Sir Valentine Chirol pointed out at the time, that "the more we delegate of our authority in India to the natives of India, the more we must necessarily in practice delegate it to the Hindus who form the majority". The whole question of constitutional change was therefore viewed by Muslims with great apprehension. They had besides been exasperated by the Hindu opposition to the creation of a predominantly Muslim province in Eastern Bengal. Thus the long-standing social and religious division of India into Hindu and Muslim was sharpened into bitter hostility by political fears and projects. Hindu politicians have usually sought to represent this revival of a deep-seated and long existing jealousy as the work of government, seeking to ease the burden of rule by division, and encouraging Muslim hopes in order to set one community against the other. But Muslim anxiety was in part the product of circumstances, in part th product of Hindu policy. Any movement towards self-gover ment suggested to a great minority the growing need of fortifying its position; and the conduct of the Hindu politicians had shown no sympathy whatever with the Muslim position. When the Hindus could not bear Muslim influence to be predominant in a single province, when journalists like Tilak classed the Muslims with the British as the tyrants and despoilers of India, what might not be expected if ever political power really fell into Hindu hands? Muslim distrust of a possible Hindu rule was a source of great annoyance to the Hindu leaders, for it showed too plainly that they could not claim to speak for the country as a whole. Naturally therefore they sought to minimise the importance and sincerity of Muslim demands by accusing the government of inspiring a fictitious movement. But, however well Hindu and Muslim had dwelt together under a common subjection, the idea of self-government was more than enough to revive irreconcilable bitterness between groups whose social and religious practices were mutually repugnant.

As soon therefore as it was known that the Government of India had a reform schéme under consideration, a Muslim deputation, headed by the Aga Khān, waited upon Minto to urge the necessity of special provision to safeguard Muslim interests. The governor-general, whose great aim was to secure an improved degree of representation, was in natural sympathy with the demand that the existing lack of electoral provision for minorities should be amended. He agreed that their position should be estimated not merely by their numerical strength but also by their political importance and the services they had rendered to the empire.

In the circular despatch issued in August, 1907, for the purpose of eliciting both public opinion and official views, considerable emphasis was laid upon the need of giving the widest possible representation to the various classes, races and interests of the country. The creation of special electorates for the landed class and Muslims was suggested; and a scheme (which was in fact over-elaborated) was published, proposing to assign specific numbers of seats to each race, caste, and religion, with special electorates in each case. This detailed proposal was abandoned. But the Government of India, like the Decentralisation Commission which was sitting at this time, concluded "that representation by classes and interests is the only practicable method of embodying the elective principle in the constitution of the Indian legislative councils". Special provision was therefore proposed; landed and Muslim constituencies should be established, and means taken to secure for each important class in the country at least one member well acquainted with its views.

While Morley was induced to agree that general territorial constituencies on the English pattern could not be trusted to reflect adequately the numberless cross-divisions by which India was seamed, he attempted to overcome the difficulties raised by special electorates by putting forward an alternative plan. This had been mainly prepared by MacDonnell, a retired Indian civilian who had had an unusually distinguished career alike in India and after his retirement in London. This contemplated a system of indirect elections. The primary electors might choose electoral colleges, which should include minority representatives in numbers proportioned to the strength of the various minorities; and this, it was hoped, might obviate the need of securing representation by nomination. This plan, however, met with much criticism, especially among the Muslims, and was judged unworkable. The statute which was finally passed by parliament directed the Government of India to prepare rules for the constitution of the legislative councils; and the rules which were at last issued with the secretary of state's approval provided for the creation of special land-holders' and Muslim constituencies in the principal provinces.

Minto's other individual contribution to the reforms of 1909 was the inclusion of Indian members in the executive councils. The idea of such appointments was far from new, but difficulties of various kinds had always prevented their serious consideration. It had been suggested that a ruling prince should be included in the governor-general's council; but this would have had the disadvantage of giving mortal offence to all the others; nor was it easy to find among the great land-owners, whom Minto and more than one of his predecessors had wished to bring forward, men who possessed at once sufficient knowledge of affairs and a sufficient grasp of English. This had indeed been the chief practical obstacle to the inclusion of some of the distinguished men who had emerged in the Indian states. Knowledge of English had, however, spread rapidly in the last quarter of the nineteenth century, and at the opening of the twentieth Minto was convinced that the time was ripe for a convincing demonstration of good-will. The appointment of Indian members had had a place in his earliest projects of reform, and seemed to him of the utmost importance both from their probable effect on Indian opinion and from their expected influence on government policy. As the law stood, such action was only possible within certain narrow limitations. Indian members of the Indian Civil Service were eligible to all the seats in the governors' councils at Bombay and Madras, and to most of the seats in the governor-general's council. But the Indians of the service had mostly chosen the judicial rather than the executive line of employment, and, what was of more importance, had been debarred by their occupation from taking a part in Indian politics or securing a following in the Congress world. While their appointment to council might then have flattered Indian sentiment, the advantage would for the most part have been sentimental only. Their judicial experience would have been of small use, and their appointment would have conciliated few but the members of their own families. Prominent Indians outside the service were not eligible at all for seats in the subordinate councils or for most of the seats in the governor-general's council.

While this was the legal and practical position, Minto busied himself in 1906–7 in raising the question in his own executive council. Though he met with small encouragement, he resolved at last to recommend on his own responsibility the appointment of an Indian to his council. One cynical adviser suggested the creation of a special educational portfolio, on the ground that the educational departments had few friends. But the office of the law member was the most suitable for such a departure, both because it required no change in the existing law and because it opened the field to a very active and influential class. Serious opposition emerged against this proposal in England. It had only been supported in the governor-general's council by a single member besides Minto himself. Morley was unable to induce the Council of India to agree to the measure. He then laid it before the cabinet, where the opposition of Lord Ripon was decisive. For the moment therefore the project dropped, and all that immediately followed was the nomination of two Indians to the Council of India, appointments to which lay within the statutory powers of the secretary of state. Morley himself admitted that this step would hardly have been taken but for the firm stand which Minto had made in favour of including Indians in the executive council.

Though foiled for the moment, Minto persisted in his advocacy of appointing Indian members to council. "The best reply", he thought, "that can be made to the unrest that is in the air would be the appointment of a native member to the viceroy's council." In consequence of his persistence, it was at last resolved to adopt his advice, to appoint an Indian member to his council, to enlarge the two presidency councils by one member each so as to permit the same being done at Bombay and Madras, and to take powers to create executive councils in the other provinces.

These reforms, so far as was necessary, were embodied in the Government of India Act, 1909, and the regulations made under it by the Government of India. The legislative councils were enlarged, their powers were increased, and they were authorised to adopt resolutions on matters of administrative and financial policy; elective methods of choice were at last formally introduced; the higher governments lost that exclusive character which had marked them from the inception of British rule; and special provision was made to secure in the enlarged legislatures representation of numerous and important classes without reducing the representation of those classes specially associated with the National Congress. "Regarding the scheme as a whole," the Government of India wrote, "we consider ourselves justified in claiming for it that it will really and effectively associate the people of India with the government in the work, not only of occasional legislation, but of actual every-day administration."

This claim was well substantiated. The existing councils were enlarged from a total of 124 to a total of 331 members; elected members increased from 39 to 136; and though the official majority was retained in the imperial council, it disappeared from the provincial legislatures. The original proposals had included the retention of the official majority—i.e. the retention of full executive control over legislation—in all the councils. This was regarded as a legitimate and necessary consequence of the nature of the Indian government, nor was it seriously attacked except by men of extremist leanings. However, as a result of discussions with the provincial governments, and, on consideration of the views expressed in the Indian journals and elsewhere, the Government of India finally proposed not to create an official majority in the various councils but only to retain the power of calling one into existence if necessary. "We propose to work normally with a minority but to reserve power in the last resort to transform it into a majority." It was in this connection that Morley made his particular and individual contribution to the reform scheme as finally adopted. The limited powers of the provincial legislatures and the effective powers of veto exercised by the executive authorities seemed to him to render the retention in them of official majorities unnecessary. Moreover, the Bombay government had for some years worked without an official majority, and did not desire one. He therefore decided that the official majority should be discontinued in these bodies. But in respect of the imperial council he was not prepared to go as far as Minto. The essential condition of "liberalising" the provincial councils was "that the imperial supremacy shall be in no degree compromised". The Government of India, he held, must always be so constituted as to be able to carry out the orders, executive or legislative, which it might receive from Whitehall. In no circumstances must its dependence be impaired. "I am convinced", he wrote, "that a permanent official majority...is absolutely necessary."

The Morley-Minto reforms, enacted in 1909, and brought into force in the following year, did not bring political crime to an end, as Morley seems to have expected. As soon as his bill was brought into the House of Commons, he began to demand the release of the deportees. But Minto was resolved to move more cautiously, holding the view that the political purpose of the reforms was to rally the moderates to the government, not to conciliate the irreconcilables. In this he proved to have judged aright. The moderates under Gokhale's leadership, while sharply criticising the provisions to secure the representation of classes other than those composing the *intelligentsia*, wisely accepted the reforms as a substantial move towards associating Indians with the government of their country. Pandit Moti Lāl Nehru, for example, in a presidential address to a social congress held at Āgra in 1909, reminded his audience that even self-government on the colonial model could not convert Indians into a united nation until they purged themselves of "the many social diseases that your body politic suffers from". In 1910, when a new regulation was introduced to control newspaper incitement to political crime by requiring presses to deposit security which might be forfeited,

Gokhale supported the measure, which was passed by the imperial council without a division, and with only two members rising to speak against it. This notable success, which indicated in how great a degree Minto had secured the confidence of the moderate congress-men, was followed at once by the release of the persons who had been deported under the regulation of 1818. Minto had in fact succeeded by mingled tact and firmness in turning a nasty political corner. It may justly be said that the unanimity with which the leading Indian politicians supported the government on the outbreak of war in 1914 was due in no small degree to the conciliating effects of his reforms, coupled as they were with the firm repression of political crime and of those who instigated it.

CHAPTER XIX

Political Developments, 1910–19

The new press act of 1910 has been already mentioned. The earlier act had proved ineffective in preventing incitement to political crime, and sober minds were beginning to question the universal expedience of an unrestricted press. Further legislation had been recommended by the Indian princes. In the House of Lords in 1908 Lord Cromer recanted his former defence of Ripon's repeal of the Vernacular Press Act and admitted that the policy of complete freedom had failed alike in Egypt and in India. The earlier act too had led to the ostensible conduct of journals by mere nominees who went to prison for illegal publications one after another while the persons really responsible kept securely in the background. The new act was designed to make incitement to crime expensive as well as illegal. New presses were required to deposit security which might be forfeited if the press published illegal matter; forfeiture entailed the closing of the press which might be required to double the security if its owners desired to reopen it; and a second offence might entail not only forfeiture of the increased deposit but also confiscation of the press itself. Similar powers were granted over newspapers. An appeal against an order of forfeiture was allowed to the High Courts. The principles of this measure were approved by Gokhale, were accepted by the imperial council without a division, and indeed were attacked by only two of its members.

This act did much to check the open dissemination of revolutionary doctrines. But secret societies, especially in Bengal, continued their activity. Murders and dacoities continued. In the latter part of 1910 six occurred round Dacca, and sixteen more in 1911, although after a prolonged trial a number of men were convicted of conspiring to wage war against the king. The secret societies concerned in these and similar outbreaks found great advantage in the political immunities of French territory at Chandernagore. Pondichery also served as a refuge for political agitators in southern India. A newspaper which had been closed down at Madras was republished in the French settlement, and

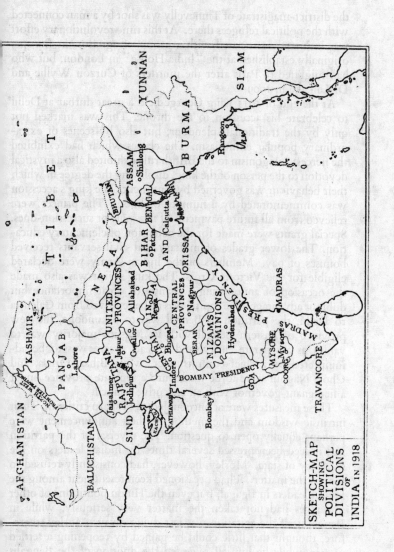

SKETCH-MAP SHOWING POLITICAL DIVISIONS OF INDIA IN 1918

the district-magistrate of Tinnevelly was shot by a man connected with the political refugees there. At this time revolutionary effort was intimately associated with a group of agitators in Europe, originally established at the "India House" in London, but who had migrated to Paris after the murders of Curzon Wyllie and Dr Lalkaka in 1909.

At the end of 1911 King George held a great durbar at Delhi to celebrate his accession to the throne. This was marked not only by the traditional splendour, but also by scenes of extraordinary popular enthusiasm. The classes which had exhibited the fiercest antagonism to the British rule exhibited also a mystical devotion to the person of the king, displaying the degree in which their behaviour was governed by sentiment. The king's accession was commemorated by a number of boons. The princes were relieved from all future payments of *nazarāna* or succession-dues. Special grants were made for the extension of elementary education. The lower grades of military and civil servants received bonuses of pay. Members of the Indian Army were declared eligible for the Victoria Cross. The king's visit was also made the occasion of announcing a change of great importance but dubious advantage. The capital was to be removed from Calcutta to Delhi, the partition of Bengal was to be undone, the new province of Eastern Bengal with its Muslim majority was to vanish as a separate entity, and instead Assam was to be administered by a chief commissioner, while Bihar, Orissa, and Chota Nāgpur were to be made into a separate province under a lieutenant-governor with an executive council.

These measures were at once subjected to sharp criticism. Their intrinsic wisdom and the method of their announcement were perhaps equally open to question. The reversal of the partition had indeed been pressed several times by Indian leaders on the secretary of state. Morley, however, had consistently refused to reopen the matter. It had occasioned keen resentment among the Hindu leaders in Bengal, but even the Hindu politicians of other provinces had not taken the matter very seriously, while in Bengal itself the agitation was fast dying away. Morley, therefore, thought that little could be gained by reopening a settled matter, while he himself regarded the division of the Bengalis into two groups as expedient rather than otherwise. In 1910 he retired from office and was succeeded by Lord Crewe, while

Edwin Montagu retained his former position as under-secretary. The change probably invested Montagu with a greater degree of influence than he had previously enjoyed. He had always been disposed to emphasise the predominance of the India Office in Indian affairs. He had ventured in defiance of the facts to describe the reforms of 1909 as entirely the work of the secretary of state and publicly to refer to the governor-general as the secretary of state's agent. He was a man of high ideals, sharp perceptions, but uncertain judgment; and preferred the spectacular to the cautious in the way of political action. He probably had much to do with the adoption of this policy by Lord Crewe and with the method chosen for its promulgation. The objections to the reversal of the partition were numerous. Eastern Bengal had always been a much neglected area so long as it had been administered from Calcutta, and its separation therefore seemed expedient. Again, if the transference of authority into Indian hands was to continue, it was well that there should be provinces predominantly Muslim, since in most the Muslims would form a minority. Thirdly the reversal of an administrative measure in the face of objections which were mainly sentimental in character, for which no solid reasons could be adduced, which had been made the pretext for an outburst of political crime, was politically unwise. It suggested that clamour alone, irrespective of reason, could secure concessions. Besides this, to cancel the partition when the opposition to it was sinking involved government in all the odium of an unpopular measure without securing the advantages of a timely acceptance of popular opinion. Lastly, while the Hindus of Bengal felt they had gained a victory for which they owed thanks to the efforts of none but themselves, the Muslims felt they had been deserted and must make the best terms they could with the rival party. The transference of the capital to the city renowned throughout the world as the centre of Mughal rule had been intended to off-set this Muslim reaction. It certainly carried with it an appeal to Muslim sentiment. But it was unlikely that any good Muslim would respond deeply. Why should Muslims be moved by the establishment of the infidel capital in a centre of Muslim glory? It was quite as likely to wound as to conciliate. The building of a new city would be enormously expensive, even though this might be partly concealed by the modesty of initial estimates. It was widely felt that Calcutta, created, as it had been, by English enterprise and Indian co-operation, still remained the most appropriate capital for British India, and that little would be gained by removal to a city whose traditions were essentially those of oriental despotism. The main advantage which could be claimed for the move was that it would shift the seat of government from the agitated atmosphere of Bengal. The whole project appears to have been formulated in London without any formal consultation with the Government of India, while official discussion or protest seems to have been designedly avoided by the method of announcement. The arguments which might have been sent in reply to an official despatch could not be urged against a measure announced by the king in person. The procedure illustrates in a striking way the degree in which the authorities at the India Office had come to regard themselves as the real executive government of India. This tendency, which had come into being in 1858, and had been greatly strengthened by the character and ideas of Morley, was destined to reach its peak under the influence of Montagu.

The futility of this endeavour to conciliate revolutionary leaders was displayed by the events of the next few years. Lord Hardinge, who had succeeded Minto in 1910, narrowly escaped being killed by a bomb thrown at him in Delhi in 1912. In Bengal murder and dacoity continued unchecked. Bengali influence extended to Benares, where revolutionary societies were formed. In the Panjab a movement arose that was to develop under Parisian, American and Bengali guidance, into the *Ghadr* (Mutiny) Movement.

More ominous, however, than this continuance of political crime was the change in the Muslim attitude. Attempts were made to reduce the antagonism of the Hindu and Muslim leaders by holding a conference. Any results that might have followed from this were cast away by a Hindu member of the imperial legislative council who insisted on moving a resolution demanding the abolition of the special Muslim electorates. But although an alliance between Hindu and Muslim leaders proved impossible, the Muslim attitude to the government lost the friendliness which had marked it in recent years. Sayyid Ahmad had died in 1898, and no one of his school of thought could exercise the same degree of influence over the Muslim community. It was much excited by the development of foreign affairs. The Italian seizure of Tripoli, the Anglo-Russian agreement in Persia, and the Balkan War all made it fear that soon no independent Muslim state would survive. The question too of the caliphate began more and more to exercise the minds of Indian Muslims. When the Turkish sultan assumed the title of caliph in 1517, his spiritual authority was not recognised in India. The Mughal emperors themselves assumed the same rank and style, and down to the Indian Mutiny and the final disappearance of the forms of empire from Delhi, no Indian Muslim seems to have looked to Constantinople for leadership or regarded the sultan with any special respect. With the disappearance of the shadowy Indian caliph, however, a new position emerged. For a time Indian Muslims were much perplexed. Whose name was to replace that of Bahādur Shāh in the Friday prayers? In the Panjab some are stated to have followed the extraordinary course of substituting the name of Queen Victoria. But after a period of considerable confusion, it was generally agreed that the sultan's name should be used in the *khūtba*. To the more vehement followers of Islam this meant a formal transference of allegiance; but the majority continued in the passive obedience which they had generally shown to the British power in India, while some, under the leadership of Sayyid Ahmad, held that the caliphate had lapsed with the Mongol destruction of the 'Abbāsids in 1258 and had never truly been revived. Early in the present century, however, when the sultan found himself pressed on the one hand by the European powers and on the other by the agnostic, cosmopolitan group known as the Young Turks, he hoped to strengthen his position by emphasising his claim to the spiritual leadership of Islam. His agents spread to India, and Indian interest deepened considerably. When the Balkan War broke out in 1912, Indian Muslims equipped a medical mission, subscribed to the Red Crescent Fund, and formed the society called "The Servants of the Ka'aba", the object of which was the maintenance of Turkish integrity. The excitement aroused by this propaganda was illustrated by events at Cawnpore. In the course of street improvements it had been decided to demolish a Hindu temple and a room and platform which had been added to a small mosque. When it was found possible to spare the temple, the Muslims at once demanded that these additions should also be spared. A wild agitation arose, fostered from without; the police were attacked; lives were lost; and the matter gained importance enough for Lord Hardinge to visit the place and personally arrange a settlement. In the past whole mosques had been removed without the least complaint being raised.

In two respects the reforms of 1909 had produced unexpected results in actual working. It was found necessary to prevent attacks on government measures by official members of the new councils, and to prevent provincial governments from evading obedience to the orders of the secretary of state on the score of opposition by the non-official majority. The latter also began to influence the course of policy and legislation much more directly than had till then been the case. Down to 1917 not quite half the resolutions moved in the imperial council had been followed by official action in the sense desired, but the power of putting questions was too often used to demand information which was already published or of small public value. Important changes were often made in government bills in the course of discussions in select committee, which proved more useful than the formal debates, where non-official members aimed less at persuading the government than at addressing the outside public.

The act of 1909 had given powers to extend the council form of executive government from Bombay and Madras to the other major provinces. In 1910 this was carried into effect in Bengal, where the lieutenant-governor was replaced by a governor with a council of four members. When in the next year the province of Bihar was formed, the new lieutenant-governor was provided with an executive council, on the ground that the province, when part of Bengal, had already been under council-government. But this was the only instance in which an executive council was set up in a lieutenant-governor's province, although proposals were made to establish one in the United Provinces by resolutions moved in the imperial legislative council in 1911 and in the provincial council in 1913. Indian opinion favoured such changes partly because government by council was reckoned a form of government superior to the individual government of a lieutenant-governor, partly because council-government would favour the appointment of heads of provinces from among public men in England, and partly because they would increase the number of high offices available for Indian politicians. On the first occasion the lieutenant-governor, Sir John Hewitt, opposed the change on the ground that the volume of work to be done would not justify the creation of such a body, and that it would be difficult to select Indians with a sufficient knowledge of public work. On the second occasion, Sir James (now Lord) Meston was lieutenant-governor. He held much the same views as his predecessor as regards the need of a council, but on the whole advised compliance as the demand would certainly grow and have to be conceded sooner or later. After a prolonged discussion, this recommendation was accepted by the Government of India and the secretary of state. But when in 1915 a draft proclamation was laid before parliament in accordance with the act of 1909, the House of Lords voted an address to the crown opposing it, and the matter therefore dropped.

The most embarrassing question, however, of the years immediately preceding the outbreak of war in 1914 was that raised by the status of Indians in the South African colonies. Indians had gone to South Africa in considerable numbers as indentured coolies, to work on the semi-tropical plantations. On the expiry of their term of service many had settled down as small shop-keepers and pedlars. The growth of their numbers led to the appearance of a much smaller group of Indian professional men, lawyers and doctors. The same neglect of sanitation as characterises Indian villages made the poorer and much larger section of the immigrants unwelcome neighbours; and their unpopularity was strengthened by the strong colour-sense of the South African colonists, especially among the large Dutch element, which was disposed to class the Indians with the native inhabitants. In the two Dutch republics special regulations were directed against them. From the Orange Free State they were completely excluded. In the Transvaal they could not acquire land or reside outside certain defined areas. This produced many complaints in India and formed indeed one of the grievances alleged against the Dutch republics before the outbreak of the South African War. But the absorption of the republics at the end of the war produced no improvement. The new authorities were primarily anxious so far as possible to conciliate Dutch sentiment; while the formation of the Union of South Africa in 1909 deprived the home government of all powers of direct interference. At the same time restrictions tended to increase. Indians were best off in the Cape Colony. In Natal they had to pay a licence tax if they remained beyond the term of their indentures. They lost their franchise for the state legislature; and they were threatened with the loss of the municipal franchise. Mr M. R. Gāndhi first came into prominence in connection with these restrictions. He was a Gujarāti lawyer who had gone to South Africa in 1893 and had remained with the object of obtaining some improvement in the status of his countrymen. Inspired by the nonconformist resistance to payment of the educational rates under the Education Act of 1902, he organised a passive resistance movement. The Government of India supported the demands, but could not deal direct with the South African governments, while the home government, though favouring the Indian claims, was hampered by its long-standing and deliberate acceptance of the rights of self-governing colonies. However, milder legislation was introduced in 1911 and passive resistance ceased. But long delays occurred in the passing of the bills. The governor-general spoke publicly and severely of Indian grievances in the Union. Passive resistance revived and this time led to acts of violence; riots were followed by vigorous prosecutions; and at last a commission of enquiry followed which produced a temporary settlement of the question.

Although the crisis of 1907 had on the whole eased considerably in the following years, there remained many points of difficulty, when, in August, 1914, war broke out in Europe and at once involved all the major powers. The effect in India was remarkable. German propagandists had claimed that war in Europe would be followed by a general Indian revolt, comparable only with the Mutiny. Instead, all the great princes offered their personal services and all the resources of their states. In British India private individuals and political associations wrote and telegraphed declaring their support of the British cause. When the imperial legislative council met in September, the nonofficial members agreed unasked that India should contribute to the heavy financial burden of the war. Often before had Great Britain been involved in desperate struggles, but the only deep feeling which Indians had exhibited had been a general apprehension, tempered by a cautious calculation of probabilities.

This unexpected enthusiasm permitted the Government of India to make a far larger contribution to the struggle in men, services

and munitions than had ever been dreamt of. Only a year earlier
it had been resolved, in accordance with the findings of the Indian
Army Committee, that the duties of the Indian Army were
limited to meeting local aggression and resisting any attack by a
great power until reinforcements could arrive from England.
India, it was laid down, "is not called upon to maintain troops
for the specific purpose of placing them at the disposal of the
home government for wars outside the Indian sphere". It had
been computed that in favourable circumstances the Indian Army
could spare for service outside the Indian frontiers two divisions.
But at once four divisions, two infantry and two cavalry, with
four artillery brigades in excess of establishment, were sent to
France to take part in the bitter fighting of the autumn of 1914.
Troops were sent to East Africa. Two divisions of Indian infantry
and a brigade of cavalry were sent to Egypt. When no less than
eight divisions had either been sent abroad or were posted on
guard on the north-west frontier, it was resolved to embark on
a campaign in Mesopotamia, whither by January, 1915, two
whole divisions had been sent. As the war went on, the area of
operations constantly expanded; and before peace was made,
Indian soldiers had fought all over the near and middle east,
besides many parts of Africa, North China, and France. Whereas
in normal times the rate of combatant recruitment had been
about 15,000 men a year, during the war-years it was raised to
200,000, of whom about a quarter came from the Panjab. Whereas
in 1914 the total establishment of British officers with the Indian
Army was only 2500, more than 23,000 were sent overseas in the
course of the war.

This tremendous effort was achieved at a great, and indeed
disproportionate, cost. The Indian Army had been called quite
without preparation to undertake tasks which its organisation
had never anticipated. Its leaders had contemplated wars, perhaps even a great and serious struggle, upon the frontier; but
they had never guessed that the pick of the Indian troops would
be sent to France, and that then the remainder, with the aid of
newly raised battalions from England, would be required to
conduct campaigns in Africa, in 'Irak, in Palestine. The effects
of this situation were exaggerated by the early exhaustion of
munitions, and by the excessive burden placed upon the commander-in-chief. The magazines had been emptied in order to

equip the divisions sent to France, and existing conditions of manufacture and supply prevented their being restocked with the quantities needed for the further conduct of the war, until a new system had been built up from the foundation. The commander-in-chief found himself, as Kitchener had insisted he should be, sole head of the Indian Army, and responsible alike for the training and discipline of the forces and for the technical departments without which a modern army is helpless. Kitchener had never supposed that the commander-in-chief would be called upon to bear so heavy a strain. But the system which he had set up was clearly over-centralised. The results appeared most clearly and disastrously in the early campaign in Mesopotamia. Failure of supplies, failure of medical attentions, failure of staff-organisation, failure of superior control were all revealed by the enquiries of a commission which public uneasiness had made necessary. But the blame seems due, far less to individual shortcomings than to the inevitable failure of an organisation required in a time of sudden crisis to carry out duties far more extensive than ever had been anticipated.

The task of government was rendered the more difficult during the period 1914-18 by the aid which external events lent to the revolutionary movements within India itself. German propaganda, Muslim anxiety produced by the entrance of Turkey into the war as an ally of Germany, Bolshevik propaganda following on the downfall of the imperial Russian government in 1917, the uncertain position on the north-west frontier where peace or war all along depended on whether the amir Habībullāh could or could not hold his people in check, encouraged the revolutionaries to redoubled efforts. Shortly after the outbreak of the war there arrived at Calcutta a ship-load of Sikhs who had been recruited and carried to Vancouver for the express purpose (as it would seem) of being refused admission into British Columbia and then sent back to India to excite discontent. On arrival they refused to enter the special train designed to convey them back to their native province; a riot ensued; the returned emigrants proved to have been provided with revolvers; men were shot on both sides; and those Sikhs who escaped capture joined groups of dacoits and committed a series of violent crimes. In December, 1914, a Bombay Brāhman was employed to concert a joint-rebellion in Bengal and the Panjab. A general rising was planned for the following February, but was frustrated by the betrayal of the plan. In consequence of these efforts, the Defence of India Act was passed, under which revolutionists could be tried by a bench of judges with no preliminary commitment and no power of appeal, and suspects against whom actual crime could not be juridically proved might be interned.

In 1915 came the unfortunate *Khiláfat* movement. Muslim uneasiness at the war with Turkey was exploited in order, if possible, to produce rebellion. The cry raised was that the Holy Places of Islam were in danger. Many unfortunate peasants were persuaded to sell their land and emigrate into Afghanistan. Muslim students from the Lahore colleges were induced to join fanatical groups in the tribal territory. A Turco-German mission at Kābul busied itself in seeking to promote open rebellion and in nominating a government to replace the British government on its overthrow. Other attempts were made by the *Ghadr* party in America to raise trouble in Burma, where Muslim agents were employed to instigate an Indian regiment to mutiny.

As the event showed, these attempts were adequately watched and forestalled by the secret intelligence of the government. Probably greater anxiety was occasioned by the changed attitude of many Indian leaders as the war drew on. The early enthusiasm of August and September, 1914, did not hold. This should have surprised nobody. The fickleness of popular feeling is the tritest of political commonplaces. Nor was much done to keep enthusiasm alive. It needed constant tending. Associations for voluntary work might have done much to keep it alive with the stimulus of emulation. But, except by Lord and Lady Willingdon at Bombay, little was done in this direction. As the first warmth of feeling cooled, as the burdens of war grew heavier, and the issue became less certain, the politicians began to change their tone. Something of this must be ascribed to the unbalanced praise and strong exaggeration of the part which India had played. English newspapers and politicians alike wrote and spoke as though India had saved the empire, and as though her effort, great as it was, had been really comparable with the efforts of the allied states, involved in as desperate a struggle as any that stands upon record. The effect of such language was unfortunate. It was naturally argued in Indian circles that Indian services would be acknowledged in the only way that could be acceptable to

Indian leaders, by the concession of substantial political changes; and when the cabinet, immersed in the overwhelming business of the hour, gave no sign of having considered the expected reorganisation of the empire, the early enthusiasm of political circles gave way to growing disappointment and suspicion. The calamitous mismanagement of Irish affairs seemed to indicate that the British government could be squeezed. New relations between Great Britain and the self-governing dominions too seemed to be in process of development; President Wilson, with headlong ineptitude, proposed "self-determination" as the goal to be attained on the conclusion of the war, while other leaders held out hopes that the war then raging was destined to be the last and that the dominion of armed force was drawing to its end. The new world thus foreshadowed, when the western powers should have attained to victory, the pathetic and delusive hopes spread abroad to encourage disheartened and weary combatants, seemed to promise the advent of an age when power and interests would be subordinated to argument and ideals. In these circumstances the Home Rule Movement was launched by Tilak and Mrs Besant. It was well calculated to attract wide support. Even the Muslims were for a while drawn into alliance with the extremer Hindu leaders. Forgetting the manifest dangers of their position in the excitement aroused by the Khilāfat movement, a considerable section of them agreed to accept a scheme hurriedly prepared as the basis of demands which were to be made in the name of a united India. In order to facilitate propaganda, Indian leaders in 1917 demanded the repeal of the Press Act of 1910. It was stigmatised as being at once ineffectual and oppressive. In fact while 143 newspapers had been formally warned under its provisions, in only three cases had the security been declared forfeit; while fifty-five presses had been warned, thirteen had forfeited their first security and only one its second. No forfeiture had been set aside by the High Courts, and the number of newspapers and presses had increased greatly, despite the existence of the act. The demand was therefore refused. Meanwhile Tilak and Mrs Besant succeeded in arousing a vigorous agitation. The government viewed this as undesirable and untimely, at a moment when the need of recruits, combatant and non-combatant alike, was great and growing. But unfortunately the views of the government were divided, its policy irresolute, its action half-hearted. Mrs Besant was first restrained from entering Bombay and the Central Provinces, and then interned in the pleasant seclusion of the Nilgiris. But the agitation only redoubled under acts sharp enough to sting but not severe enough to hurt. The same ideas which in Indian minds were fostering agitation were in British minds shaking the strong confidence which had prevailed ever since the Mutiny in the British mission to the Indian peoples.

At last the war-worn British cabinet decided on making a pronouncement on the goal of British policy in India. The subject had long been under discussion. When Lord Chelmsford became governor-general in 1916, he had immediately invited his executive council to consider two questions. The first was, "What is the goal of British rule in India?" The conclusion reached was that the goal was "the endowment of British India as an integral part of the British Empire with self-government". The second question was, "What are the steps on the road to that goal?" But here greater difficulties of definition were found. The lines of advance which had been urged from time to time by the National Congress were provincial autonomy, further expansion and reform of the legislative and executive councils, the development of local self-government, and the abolition or at least the reform of the Council of India, which, it was claimed, had long laid the dead hand of obsolete experience on the constitutional development of India.

The gradual release of provincial administrations from the detailed control of the Government of India and of the secretary of state certainly formed an obvious line of advance. So early as 1911 it had been commended by the Government of India to the secretary of state. Sound policy, it wrote, appeared to lie in giving gradually to the provinces "a larger measure of self-government, until at last India would consist of a number of administrations, autonomous in all provincial affairs, with the Government of India above them all, and possessing power to interfere in cases of misgovernment, but ordinarily restricting their functions to matters of imperial concern". But the secretary of state refused to take any decision on this important proposal.

When Lord Chelmsford again raised the question, the government's conclusions were more specific than they had been in 1911. It was felt that self-government within the empire could not be well attained by any blind imitation of dominion models. The social structure of India was too different to admit the adoption of colonial constitutions. But (as Lord Zetland has stated) a larger measure of control by Indians was desirable. This "would ultimately result in a form of self-government . . . differing possibly in many ways from that enjoyed by other parts of the empire, but evolved on lines which had taken into account India's past history and the special circumstances and traditions of her component peoples". It was therefore proposed to develop the existing local self-governing bodies, to increase the number of Indians appointed to high administrative posts, and to enlarge the elective element in the provincial legislatures so as to prepare for an extension of their constitutional powers. Sir Austen Chamberlain, then secretary of state, did not wish to go further at the moment than declare "an intention to foster the gradual development of free institutions". Montagu, who succeeded him in 1917, proposed a similar formula, which was finally recast by Curzon as the result of cabinet discussions into the words read by Montagu in the House of Commons on August 20, 1917. It ran, "The policy of His Majesty's government, with which the Government of India are in complete accord, is that of the increasing association of Indians with every branch of the administration, and the gradual development of self-governing institutions, with a view to the progressive realisation of responsible government in India as an integral part of the British Empire". Such progress, it was added, could be achieved only by successive stages, to be determined by the British Government and the Government of India in accordance with the degree of success secured.

Meanwhile Indians had been busily devising constitutions. A body known as the "Madras Parliament", connected with Mrs Besant's Home Rule League, drew up one. Nineteen of the elected members of the imperial legislative council prepared another. A third was produced, in November, 1916, by representatives of the Hindu National Congress and of the Muslim League, and this was formally adopted by both bodies at meetings held in Lucknow in the following month. This proposed the direct election of four-fifths of all the members of the provincial legislatures, and a similar proportion of elected members in the imperial council, though the elective members of the latter were to be chosen in part by the elective members of the provincial councils, and only in part by a direct vote. Apart from certain items of receipt and expenditure which were to be reserved as imperial, the provincial authorities were to become financially independent, subject to a vague general supervision. At the head of each province was to be a governor who in general was not to be a member of any service, with an executive council, half of which was to be chosen by the elective members of the legislative council. Resolutions of the latter were to be binding unless vetoed by the governor-in-council, and in the latter case, when repeated after a fixed interval, were to become absolute. Muslims were to have separate electorates, with a proportion of numbers considerably in excess of their numerical claims, but were no longer to be free to contest other seats; and any bill or resolution opposed by three-quarters of either the Hindu or the Muslim members as injurious to their community was not to be further proceeded with.

Another scheme was propounded by Mr Lionel Curtis and a group of his associates, who included Anglo-Indian officials of high rank. Mr Curtis was a leading member of the Round Table group, which had played a not inconsiderable part in bringing about the union of South Africa in 1909. They were convinced believers in the sobering effects of frank and informal discussion. In South Africa they believed that the formation of study-circles to discuss the conflicting outlooks of Briton and Dutchman had done much to moderate antagonism, and hoped that a like procedure might be followed by like results in India. Mr Curtis reached India in the latter half of 1916 and attempted to set this plan in operation. But advanced Indian opinion was from the first hostile to him, perhaps owing to his South African associations, perhaps also because it was reluctant to defend itself in an arena where rhetoric and invective would be idle weapons. A chance phrase in a private letter of his which was stolen, and published, was deliberately distorted in order to wreck his plan. But he persisted in his study of the Indian problem with the aid of such as were willing to work with him, seeking especially to test the possibility of a plan of devolution suggested by Sir William Duke early in 1916 when a member of the Council of India. The essence of this proposal lay in a projected division of the functions of government. Granted that a step was to be taken towards the establishment of responsible government without abandoning the essential matters for which the paramount power felt itself peculiarly responsible, why should it not be possible to transfer to responsible ministers the other duties of government? Mr Curtis persuaded himself that this conception might really solve the difficulty of a gradual transference of power from English into Indian hands. Early in 1917, in his *Letter to the People of India*, he advocated the development of responsible government (in the dominion sense of the term) by this evolutionary method. He urged the formation of smaller provinces with a much higher degree of homogeneity than existed in the old ones, which had grown up largely by chance and often embraced peoples of diverse languages. In each province should be established elective assemblies, with a ministry in each dependent on commanding a majority of votes. These ministries and executive councils of the old pattern would form two parallel executives under the common control of a governor, who would deal with certain departments of business in consultation with the responsible ministers, and with the other departments in consultation with the non-responsible councillors. It was suggested that public works, local self-government, and primary education might be transferred to the management of the proposed ministers, leaving the remaining functions of government under official control as before. Gradually, and by degrees varying in different provinces in proportion as the transferred departments were worked successfully, the whole of the duties of the provincial governments might thus pass under the control of popular assemblies.

This ingenious plan was much discussed. A number of Europeans and Indians presented an address to government commending it in its general outlines. The National Congress, however, rejected it in favour of the plan of reform which it had already put forward; it thought that this should be introduced at once, and that a definite time should be laid down within which full responsible government was to be established.

Meanwhile Montagu resolved to visit India, ostensibly to consult with the Government of India and Indian leaders, actually in order to press the adoption of the scheme for dividing government into two parts—responsible and non-responsible. He was accompanied by a small committee, in which the original inventor of the scheme, Sir William Duke, had a place. He rapidly toured India, interviewed a large number of politicians, exhibited great impatience with persons whose views differed from his own, and within six months of his arrival he and Lord Chelmsford signed the joint report in which dyarchy (as Sir William Duke's scheme had come to be called) was formally recommended for adoption. The report was drawn with great skill and persuasiveness. The first part of it was devoted to an historical exposition of the various endeavours which had been already made to modify the inherited autocracy of government in India. The second part discussed the methods by which the process might best be continued. The authors held that the sole practical solution lay in the development of responsible parliamentary government. The process, it was admitted, must be gradual, and the Congress proposals for the immediate establishment of full provincial autonomy were premature. It was also objected that such a legislative control over finance as Congress desired was impossible until the executives should become wholly responsible to the legislatures. Mr Curtis's plan to place certain departments of government under the legislatures, with executives responsible to the latter, was also rejected as likely to produce friction. The report agreed that the duties of provincial government should be divided into two groups, conducted respectively by an executive council and by a group of ministers chosen by the governor from the elected members of the legislature; but it recommended that the two halves should act as far as possible in union, that they should cultivate a habit of joint deliberation, and that the governor should remain free to reject the advice of his ministers in regard to their departments where he judged acceptance of it would produce serious disadvantages. It recommended a great increase in the number of non-official members in the legislatures, chosen wherever possible by direct election. It condemned the principle of communal representation as inconsistent with democracy; but reluctantly recognised the necessity of continuing it in the case of the Muslims.

All these schemes, whether produced by Indian politicians, by the Round Table group, or by the secretary of state and the governor-general, attached primary importance to the development of parliamentary government, and relegated "the increasing association of Indians with every branch of the administration" to a secondary place. It was evident that the establishment of the former would at once secure the concession of the latter. Indian politicians very naturally, therefore, set the former in the foreground and devoted every effort to securing it. It was natural too that English politicians should consider the reorganisation of political institutions as more important than a mere matter of personnel. "Englishmen", once said Thomas Munro, "are as great fanatics in politics as Moslems in religion." He was thinking of the manner in which Cornwallis had forced English administrative and legal ideas upon Bengal. But in like manner Metcalfe had given India a free press; and so in the twentieth century Morley and Montagu had been seeking to prepare for a free parliament. This was in notable contrast with Minto's view, in which greater importance was attached to the administrative co-operation of Indian and Englishman. Montagu was disposed to assume that co-operation would automatically follow upon constitutional reform. Seldom has political dogmatism been more evident in the formulation of a scheme of government.

The Montagu-Chelmsford report was published in the middle of 1918. The more moderate politicians were inclined to approve, and so were the land-owners, provided they might retain the special rights of representation which they enjoyed. But the advanced party began at once to denounce the new proposals, declaring that they would accept nothing short of full provincial autonomy. The official world also was strongly critical, on the ground that the transferred departments would be ill-managed and that the new oligarchy which would be set in power would not work harmoniously with their official colleagues. The heads of provinces were summoned to Delhi to discuss possible alternatives. The principal criticism put forward was that as yet the men who on political grounds would have the best claims to selection as ministers lacked sufficient administrative experience; and that the best course would be to increase the association of Indians with the administration before making any move towards parliamentary government. Lord Ronaldshay and Sir Edward Gait considered that any delay in introducing constitutional reform would be regarded as a breach of faith. Others, however, recommended an alternative scheme in line with their objections to dyarchy. They proposed that in the first instance executive councils should be appointed containing an equal number of officials and non-officials. The governor would be free to distribute the charge of departments as he thought best, and the official and non-official members would act together as a single government. The line of development which these proposals were designed to assist lay in the gradual increase in the number of non-official members, the extension of the functions entrusted to them, and the disuse of the governor's powers of overruling his council. The advantage which was claimed for this scheme was that it did not threaten to impair the efficiency of the administrative machine, and that it manifested equally with Minto's most characteristic measure a sincere desire no longer to engross, but to share power. Although it would involve no immediate constitutional change, it would provide an ever-growing number of men practised in administration in the highest fields, and thus prepare and train the responsible ministers of the future if constitutional changes, at a later time and in a less heated atmosphere, should still appear to be desirable.

In at least one respect this alternative proposal promised some advantage over the dyarchic scheme adopted by the secretary of state and the governor-general. The successful working of dyarchy presupposed conditions which it was in fact unwise to take for granted. For the two halves of the provincial governments to work smoothly together, compromise and tolerance would be needed. These commonplace virtues of English political life could not be assumed in a country where representative government was in its infancy. Again if ministers were to fulfil their functions properly, they would have not only to display ability in the conduct of business unfamiliar to them, but also to command a stable majority in the legislative councils. But whence was such a majority to be drawn? There were no political parties. These would have to be built up from the foundations. Communal groups would doubtless form themselves, divided by narrow communal interests; but these would tend either to hamper or pervert ministerial action. Ministers would have for a long time to rely upon a personal following; they would probably be driven to employ their ministerial power to keep that following together; in proportion as they succeeded in favouring their own group they would exasperate the rest; so that their careers were likely to be short and fitful. Above all their acceptance of office would mark them out as targets of attack by the extreme party whose complete hostility was in any case assured. Neither among the ministers nor in the legislative councils was there any guarantee of the cordial co-operation without which the scheme must inevitably fail. The proposals of the heads of provinces, on the contrary, promised a much more workable system. The unity of the government would check eccentricity on the part of non-official members. They would be chosen from among the men who were disposed to work with government; and the unextended powers of the legislatures would not permit an embarrassing interference with the conduct of administration. As against the advantage of not weakening the mechanism of government had to be set the disadvantage of alienating those who insisted on the need of constitutional change. But the latter would perhaps have been a lesser evil than was thought, for appointments on the councils would have conciliated moderate leaders, while extremist leaders were resolved in no circumstances to be conciliated.

The secretary of state and the governor-general had, however, already decided in favour of the scheme to which they had set their hands, and the proposals of the heads of provinces were rejected. A committee, over which Lord Southborough presided, was then sent to India to frame proposals for the regulation of the franchise and the formation of constituencies. In the middle of 1919 a bill was introduced. It was referred to a joint-committee of both Houses, and passed into law on December 23. The new system established governors and executive councils in five provinces in the place of lieutenant-governors. The branches of government were divided into central and provincial, and the latter head again into "transferred" and "reserved" subjects. To deal with transferred subjects the governor was empowered to appoint ministers from the elected members of his legislative council. In accordance with a preponderance of Indian political opinion, the funds available for the transferred and for the reserved subjects were to be drawn from a joint purse, instead of being (as the Government of India had desired) definitely allocated between the two halves of government. This proved an unfortunate decision, and the more so by reason of the financial stringency which affected the Indian governments just at the critical time when the new arrangements were coming into operation. Budgets were to be passed by the legislative councils, but the governors were authorised to restore grants for reserved subjects, where these were reduced or rejected by the legislatures. The councils were doubled in size, and were not to include more than 20 per cent. of officials, while 70 per cent. was to consist of elected members. The franchise and arrangement of constituencies varied greatly from province to province. The demand for separate, communal electorates, the principle of which had been condemned by the Montagu-Chelmsford report, proved widespread and vehement. Not only did the Muslims insist on retaining the special protection which they enjoyed, but numerous other bodies brought forward similar claims. In the Panjab, for example, the Sikhs claimed it with success; and in southern India the non-Brāhmans, though forming a large numerical majority, insisted that they required special seats to be reserved for them, owing to the superior education and organisation of the Brāhmans.

Although the Government of India was not split in two after the manner of the provincial governments, large changes were made in it also. The legislature was made bi-cameral, a new body, the Council of State, being established with a membership of sixty, of whom not more than twenty might be officials. The imperial legislative council, thenceforth to be known as the Legislative Assembly, was enlarged to one hundred and forty members, of whom one hundred were to be elective and only twenty-six officials. The official majority, which had vanished from the provincial councils in 1909, was thus withdrawn from the central legislature as well. Presidents were to be appointed in each chamber, in place of the executive head who had presided till then, and the legislature was entrusted with the obligation of adopting as well as discussing the budget. Executive control over the legislature thus disappeared from the central government. But it was still thought necessary to reserve means by which in the last resort the executive could ensure such legislation and grants of supply as it judged imperative. A bill rejected by the assembly might be "certified" by the governor-general as essential to the peace, order, or good government of the country; it could then be introduced into the council of state and when passed there need not be referred back to the assembly. In like manner a grant of supplies which was refused or proposed new taxation which was rejected, might be made operative by certification.

Such fundamental changes in the structure of the Indian governments involved a necessary reduction in the influence of the secretary of state. Till 1919 the legal authority of the home government had always been supreme in so far as supreme authority could at any given moment be exercised from so great a distance. But the extension of the powers and influence of the Indian legislatures and their release from executive control, would evidently diminish the moral authority which Whitehall had claimed over a purely bureaucratic administration. This had been recognised by the select committee. The legal position, it held, could not as yet be modified, but it hoped that the secretary of state would interfere only in exceptional circumstances in matters "of purely Indian interest, where the government and the legislature of India are in agreement". The recommendation applied with special force to provincial subjects classified as "transferred" and placed under the management of ministers. Henceforth too the secretary of state was to be paid from British, and no longer from Indian revenues, while the functions which he discharged were reduced by the creation of a high commissioner, with duties akin to those of the dominion high commissioners, under the orders of the Government of India.

The passing of the act was signalised by the issue of a proclamation which may well challenge comparison with Queen Victoria's proclamation of 1858. It dwelt on the greatness of the changes and the demands which they would make upon all concerned in their operation. "There will be need of perseverance and mutual forbearance between all sections and races of my people in India. ... I rely on the new popular assemblies to interpret wisely the wishes of those whom they represent. ... I rely on the leaders of the people ... to face responsibility and endure misrepresentations, to sacrifice much for the common interest of the state. ... Equally do I rely upon my officers to respect their new colleagues, and to work with them in harmony and kindliness, to assist the people and their representatives in an orderly advance towards free institutions; and to find in these new tasks a fresh opportunity to fulfil, as in the past, their highest purpose of service to my people."

Chapters XX to XXIV
(1919—1968)

by
V. D. MAHAJAN

CHAPTER XX

Constitutional Development (1919—50)

The Government of India Act, 1919 is a great landmark in the constitutional development of India. It was in this Act that the first step was taken on the road to responsible Government in pursuance of the policy enunciated in the August Declaration of 1917. The Preamble of the Act was in these words:

"Whereas it is the declared policy of the Parliament to provide for the increasing association of Indians in every branch of Indian administration, and for gradual development of self-governing institutions, with a view to the progressive realisation of responsible government in British India as an integral part of the Empire;

"And whereas progress, in giving effect to this policy, can only be achieved by successive stages, and it is expedient that substantial steps in this direction should now be taken;

"And whereas the time and manner of each advance can be determined only by Parliament upon whom responsibility lies for the welfare and advancement of the Indian people;

"And whereas the action of Parliament in such matters should be guided by the cooperation received from those on whom new opportunities of service will be conferred, and by the extent to which it is found that confidence can be reposed in their sense of responsibility;

"And whereas concurrently with the development of self-governing institutions in the Provinces of India, it is expedient to give to those provinces in provincial matters the highest measure of independence of the Government of India, which is compatible with the due discharge by the latter of its own responsibilities."

Formerly, the Secretary of State for India used to be paid out of the Indian revenues. The new Act provided that in future he was to be paid out of the British revenues. Some of his functions were taken away from him and given to the High Commissioner for India who was to be appointed by the Government of India and paid by the Government of India. He was to act as the agent of the Governor-in-Council.

He was to be incharge of the Stores Department, the Indian Students Department, etc. The control of the Secretary of State was reduced in the provincial sphere in so far as the Transferred Departments were concerned, but it remained as complete as before in so far as the reserved departments were concerned. The Secretary of State was to possess and exercise the power of superintendence, direction and control over the affairs of India and it was the duty of the Government of India to carry out his orders.

The Act set up a bicameral legislature at the Centre in place of the Imperial Legislative Council. The names of the two Houses were the Council of State and Central Legislative Assembly. The Council of State consisted of 60 members out of which 33 were elected and 27 nominated by the Governor-General. The Assembly consisted of 145 members out of which 103 were elected and the rest were nominated. Out of the nominated members, 25 were officials and the rest non-officials. Out of the 103 elected members, 51 were elected by the general constituencies, 32 by communal constituencies (30 by the Muslims and 2 by the Sikhs) and 20 by special constituencies (7 by landholders, 9 by Europeans and 4 by Indian Commerce). The life of the Central Assembly was 3 years and that of the Council of State 5 years. However, the same could be extended by the Governor-General. As a matter of fact, the last Assembly sat for 11 years. The first Speaker of the Assembly was nominated by the Government but the subsequent Speakers were elected by the members of the Assembly. The Governor-General was given the power to summon, prorogue and dissolve both Houses of the Legislature. He was given the authority to address the members of both Houses of the Central Legislature.

The Franchise Committee recommended a system of indirect elections to the Central Assembly on the ground that direct elections, though preferable, were impracticable on account of the unwieldy character of the constituencies. However, the Government of India decided in favour of direct elections for both Houses of the Central Legislature. The franchise was very much restricted. In 1920, the total number of voters for the Council of State was 17,364 and for the Central Assembly 9,09,874.

The Central Legislature was given very wide powers. It could make laws for the whole of British India, for the subjects of His Majesty and Services of the Crown in other parts of India, for the Indian subjects of His Majesty wherever they may happen to be and for all persons employed in His Majesty's defence forces. It could also repeal or amend laws for the time being in force in British India or applicable to persons mentioned in the preceding sentence. However, the previous sanction of the Secretary of State-in-Council was required to pass any legislation abolishing any High Court. The Central Legislature had no power to amend or repeal any Parliamentary statute relating to British India or to do anything affecting the authority of Parliament or the written laws or constitution of the United Kingdom. The previous sanction of the Governor-General was also required to introduce bills concerning the public debt or public revenues of India, religion or religious rites and usages of the British subjects in India, discipline or maintenance of His Majesty's military, naval and air forces, relations of the Government of India with foreign states or Indian states and any measure which repealed or amended any Act of a Legislature or any ordinance made by the Governor-General, etc. The Governor-General was also given the power of preventing the consideration, at any stage, of a bill or a part of a bill in either Chamber of the Central Legislature if in his opinion it "affects the safety or tranquillity of British India or any part thereof". The Governor-General was given the power to enact laws which were considered essential for the safety, tranquillity or interests of British India or any part thereof if either Chamber refused or failed to pass them. Every Act so passed required the assent of His Majesty. The Governor-General was given the power of making and promulgating ordinances for the peace and quiet Government of British India in case of emergency. An ordinance issued by the Governor-General was to have the same force of law as a law passed by the Central Legislature and was to last for 6 months. The Governor-General was given the power of returning any measure passed by the two Houses of Central Legislature for reconsideration before signifying his assent or dissent. The assent of the Governor-General was essential before a bill passed by the Legislature could become law. He was given the power to give his assent or reserve a Bill for approval by His Majesty. The Crown was given the power of disallowing any Act made by the Central Legislature or the

Governor-General. The power of veto was not only in theory but was actually exercised by the Governor-General on many occasions.

The members of both houses of the Central Legislature were given the right of putting interpellations and supplementary questions and moving resolutions and motions of adjournment according to rules. They were also given the right of freedom of speech. The Government was to submit proposals for appropriations, in the form of demands, for the vote of the Central Assembly. However, there were certain non-votable items in the budget which were not open to discussion in either Chamber "unless the Governor-General otherwise directs". All other items of expenditure were to be submitted to the vote of the Assembly which "may assent or refuse its assent to any demand or may reduce the amount referred to in any demand by a reduction of the whole grant". If the Governor-General was satisfied that any demand which had been refused by the Assembly was essential for the discharge of his responsibilities, he could restore the grant even if it was rejected by the Assembly. In cases of emergency, the Governor-General was given the power "to authorise such expenditure as may, in his opinion, be necessary for the safety and tranquillity of British India or any part thereof". It is obvious that the Central Legislature was helpless before the Governor-General who was not only independent of the Legislature, but was also given the power of over-riding it in almost all respects.

It is rightly pointed out that the Government of India Act, 1919 introduced responsive and not responsible Government at the Centre. The members of the Executive Council of the Governor-General were nominated members and the people had neither any hand in their appointment nor in their removal. No vote of no-confidence by Legislature could turn them out. However, as a matter of fact, the members of the Executive Council did respond to the wishes of the members of the Central Legislature and through them to the people of the country. Some of the members of the Central Legislature were members of the Standing Committees such as Finance Committee, Committee on Public Accounts, etc., and in that capacity they had an opportunity to influence the Government. The members could expose the Government by putting them questions, supplementary questions and moving motions of adjournment. They could reject the budget and move and pass resolutions against the Government. It is these factors which made the Government respond to the wishes of the members of the Legislature. Even the most irresponsible Executive Councillors could not afford to ignore the wishes of the members of the Legislature. Thus it was that although the Executive was independent of the Legislature, the latter could influence its decisions to a certain extent. The large majority given to the elected members of the Central Assembly made things hot for the Government and the only way to improve matters was to carry on the administration according to the wishes of the people.

The Government of India Act, 1919 provided for two lists of subjects: Central List and Provincial List. The principle underlying this division of subjects was that matters in regard to which uniformity in legislation was necessary or desirable for the whole of India or in more than one province were given to the centre and matters in which the provinces in general were interested were given to the Provinces. The items included in the Central List were defence, foreign and political relations, public debt, tariffs and customs, posts and telegraphs, patents and copyright, currency and coinage, communications, commerce and shipping, civil and criminal law and procedure, major ports, etc. The Provincial subjects were local self-government, public health and sanitation and medical administration, education, public works, water supply and irrigation, land revenue administration, famine relief, agriculture, forests, cooperative societies, law and order, etc. The residuary subjects were divided between the centre and the provinces on the same principle on which the Lists were drawn. The division was not clear-cut or definite. There was a lot of over-lapping. While subjects like commerce and law regarding property were placed in the Central List, important subjects like excise and laws regarding land revenue were given to the provinces. Although all subjects in the Provincial List were provincial for purposes of administration, that was not the case in legislation. Certain parts of them in regard to which uniformity in legislation was considered desirable, were made "subject to legislation by the Indian Legislature". Those were borrowing and taxing powers of local self-governing bodies, infectious and contagious diseases of men, animals and plants, water supply and irrigation, industrial matters including factories, electricity, settlement of labour disputes, control of newspapers, printing presses, etc.

The size of the provincial Legislative Council was considerably enlarged. While about 70% of the members of the provincial Legislatures were elected, about 30% were nominated by the Governor. Some of the nominated members were officials and the others were non-officials. The life of the Council was fixed at 3 years, but the same could be extended. The members were given the right of asking questions and supplementary questions. They were also given the power of rejecting the budget although the Governor was given the power of restoring the same.

Dyarchy was introduced in the provinces. The subjects given in the Provincial List were divided into two parts, reserved and transferred subjects. The reserved subjects were to be administered by the Governor as before with the help of the Executive Council. The change now made was that the transferred subjects were to be dealt with by the Governor in future with the help of his ministers. While the members of the Executive Council were nominated by the Governor, the ministers were chosen by him from the members of the Legislature. The reserved subjects were the administration of justice, police, irrigation and canals, drainage and embankments, water storage and water power, land revenue administration, land improvement and agricultural loans, famine relief, control of newspapers, books and printing presses, prisons and reformatories, borrowing money on the credit of the province, forests except in Bombay and Burma, factory inspection, settlement of industrial disputes, industrial insurance and housing. The transferred subjects were local self-government including matters relating to municipal corporations and district boards, public health, sanitation and medical administration including hospitals and asylums and provision for medical education, education of Indians with some exceptions, public works including roads, bridges and municipal tramways, but excluding irrigation, agriculture and fisheries, cooperative societies, excise, forests in Bombay and Burma only, development of industries including industrial research and technical education. The Governor was not to act as a constitutional head. He was given special responsibilities. He was given the authority to over-rule his ministers and the members of the Executive Council if that was considered necessary for the discharge of his responsibilities. The Governor was expected to encourage joint deliberations between the ministers and the members of the Executive Council. Provision was made for the temporary administration of transferred subjects in case of an emergency. If no minister was incharge of a transferred subject, the Governor himself assumed temporary charge of it till a minister was appointed. The Governor-General-in-Council, with the previous sanction of the Secretary of State in Council, could revoke or suspend the transfer of all or any subjects in a province and in that case those were to be administered by the Governor in Council.

The system of dyarchy was worked in the provinces from 1921 to 1937, but it did not work satisfactorily. The very principle of dyarchy was faulty. Any division of administration into two parts, each independent of the other, is opposed to political theory and the practice of government. The state is like an organism and the two parts cannot be separated completely. However, the actual division of subjects was the most defective. There would not be a worst division than the one actually attempted. Sir K. V. Reddy, a minister of Madras, says: "I was a minister for development without forests. I was the minister for agriculture without irrigation. As minister of agriculture, I have nothing to do with the administration of the Madras Agriculturists' Loans Act or the Madras Land Improvement Loans Act.... Famine relief, of course, could not be touched by the minister for agriculture, efficacy and efficiency of a minister for agriculture without anything to do with irrigation, agricultural loans, land improvement loans and famine relief is better imagined than described. Then again, I was a minister for industries without factories, boilers, electricity and water power, mines or labour, all of which were reserved subjects." While education was a transferred subject, the education of Europeans and the Anglo-Indians was made a reserved subject. Sir C. Y. Chintamani, a minister of U.P., has given some examples of the manner in which dyarchy was actually worked. In 1921, an enquiry was started in the Department of Agriculture on the question of the fragmentation of lands. When the report was submitted in 1922, it was felt that the question should have been dealt with by the Revenue Department and the case was transferred to that Department. In 1924, it was decided that the case should be sent to the Cooperative Department to which it related. Similar examples could be multiplied.

There was no harmony between the two halves of the provincial Government. While the ministers were the representatives of the people, the members of the Executive Council belonged to the bureaucracy. Ordinarily, they did not pull together. There was constant friction. Occasionally, the ministers and the Executive Councillors condemned each other openly in the public. The result was that the work of the administration suffered. As a rule, the Governor backed the members of the Executive Council because he himself belonged to the service to which they belonged.

The position of the ministers was very weak. They had to serve two masters, viz., the Governor and the Legislative Council. A minister could be appointed by the Governor and dismissed at his will. He was responsible to the Legislature for the administration of his Department. He could be turned out by the Legislature by a vote of no-confidence. However, from the point of view of practical politics, the ministers cared more for the Governor than for the Legislature. There were no strong political parties in the provincial legislatures on whom the ministers could rely upon for their support. No minister had a majority in the Legislature to back him in office. He had always to depend upon the support of the official bloc in the Legislature. While the elected members of the Provincial Legislature were divided into many groups on the basis of various religions, the support of the official bloc which always voted under instructions from the Governor, was always available to a minister who cared for the goodwill and support of the Governor. No wonder, the ministers always looked up to the Governor and were dependent upon him. The Raja of Panagal openly used to say in the Madras Legislative Council that he was responsible only to the Governor and none else. In certain cases, the ministers hoped to become Executive Councillors after the expiry of their term of office as ministers. The result of all this was that the ministers sank to the position of glorified secretaries. C. Y. Chintamani rightly says that the ministers had no power. "The power is with the Governor and not with the ministers". The Governor could interfere in any matter under any minister. Kelkar says that he was allowed to have his way in matters of policy but was constantly over-ruled in matters of detail. To quote him, "For instance, I could not picture myself how a Governor could support my policy of non-interference with a Municipal Committee who wanted to hoist national flag on the municipal office and how the same Governor could ask me to uphold an order of a Deputy Commissioner who had suspended a Committee's resolution to the effect that its servants should put on Khaddar dress".

The Governor did not care to encourage the principle of joint responsibility among the ministers. The ministers never worked as a team. They were always quarrelling among themselves. In the case of the Calcutta Municipal Bill, the Nawab Sahib and Sir Surendranath Banerjee openly canvassed against each other in the Legislative Council. In 1928, Sir Feroz Khan Noon publicly criticized and condemned the action of his Hindu colleague. It is to be noted that the dismissal or resignation of a minister did not affect his colleagues. The Governor dealt with every minister individually.

The position of the permanent services created many difficulties. The appointment, salary, suspension, dismissal and transfer of the members of the All-India services were under the control of the Secretary of State for India. Those persons continued to be under the control of the Secretary of State for India even if they worked in the Transferred Departments. No wonder, they did not care for the ministers. The ministers had no power to choose their own subordinates. Vacancies occurred in their Departments. Most of the important jobs were reserved for the members of the All-India services. In the case of Madras, when the post of the Surgeon-General fell vacant, the minister concerned could not get his nominee appointed. An I.M.S. officer was sent to fill the post. Although the minister desired to encourage the Indian system of medicine, the Surgeon-General did not care for his views. Even if there were certain superfluous jobs, the minister concerned had no power to abolish them. In the case of U.P., a District Officer refused to apply for appeal in an excise case as required by the minister and he was supported by a member of the Executive Council. As a general rule, the Governors could be expected to support the members of the civil services against the ministers.

According to the rules of executive business, if a minister differed from the opinion of the Permanent Secretary or the Head of the Department or the Commissioner of a Division, the matter had to be submitted to the Governor for final orders. Both the Permanent Secretary and the Head of the Department had direct access to the Governor. The Secretary had a weekly interview with the Governor and he could discuss everything about his Department with the Governor. That must have weakened the position of the ministers. Sometimes, the Governor knew more things about a Department than the minister who was incharge of that Department.

Another cause of the failure of dyarchy was the reservation of the Finance Department in the hands of a member of the Executive Council. While all the nation-building Departments were given to the ministers, they were given no money for the same. The result was that the ministers had to depend upon the sweet-will of the Finance Secretary. As a member of the Indian Civil Service, the Finance Secretary had no sympathy with the aspirations of the Indians as represented by the ministers. He cared more for the needs of the Reserved Departments than for the Transferred Departments. C. Y. Chintamani says: "A Finance Member was certainly more anxious to see that his Reserved Departments got all the money they required before other Departments got what they wanted". In certain cases, the Finance Department refused even to examine any scheme on the ground that no money was likely to be available. In the case of U.P., the Finance Department issued a circular to all the Heads of the Departments directing them not to send proposals involving expenditure. When actually money was found available, it was contended by the Finance Department that no money could be granted as proposals had not been put in for examination at the right time. Many a time, the reply of the Finance Department was that the proposals were not "worth spending money on". Even when schemes were approved, ways and means were found to defeat them or delay them till the end of the financial year which compelled the minister concerned to start from the very beginning once again. C. Y. Chintamani says: "I am prepared to state this without any exaggeration that it was the general experience of both the ministers in the United Provinces that they had to contend with great difficulties when they went to the Finance Department, that pretty frequently they had to go before the Governor, pretty frequently the Governor did not side with them and pretty frequently they could only gain their point in the end by placing their offices at the disposal of the Governor".

There was another hindrance in the way of the successful working of dyarchy. It was born under an unlucky star. The political atmosphere in the country was surcharged with suspicion and distrust on account of the happenings in the Punjab and the attitude of the British Government towards Turkey. The monsoons failed in 1920 and added to the misery of the people. Slump also came in the market. The result was that the finances of both the Central and Provincial Governments were upset. The favourable balance of trade of India was upset. Under the Meston Award, the Provincial Governments were required to make certain annual contributions to the Government of India. On account of the financial crisis, the Government of India demanded full contributions from the provincial governments which themselves were in a very bad condition. Dyarchy could not be expected to work without finances.

The man in the street knew that the reforms of 1919 were in the nature of a half-way house. It was known that the Indians were going to get more in the future. The result was that the people were not in a mood to give the reforms a fair trial.

Regarding the working of dyarchy, Sir Harcourt Butler says: "In India, it has almost become a term of abuse. I have heard one man shouting to another: 'You are a dyarchy'. 'I will beat you with a dyarchy', said one Indian boy to another and when questioned as to what dyarchy was, replied 'a new kind of tennis racket'. I have been received in a Burma village by 'a dyarchy band' braying against a Home Rule band with all the vigour of village faction neither having the least idea of what Home Rule or dyarchy meant".

Dr. Appadorai in "Dyarchy in Practice" observes: "Dyarchy was introduced with high hopes and it must be said that, on a theoretical analysis and if worked under ideal conditions, it is not without merits. It is the strictly logical solution of a situation in which it is desired to base the authority of Government in different matters on two different sources—a situation in which a complete transfer of responsibility is considered impossible by a ruling power. It is thus a bridge between autocracy and responsibility. It is educative in the sense that it gives men an opportunity to show what they can do, as it proceeds on the basis of proved results; it would put everybody on their mettle.....In practice, largely because, I think, the conditions it postulates are too difficult to obtain, its achievements are much more modest. It is a trite remark that where it succeeded it succeeded only because the principle of dyarchy was largely ignored. But this much may be said: under dyarchy many persons have been brought in touch with problems of administration, and with the difficulties of a responsible form of government. This is a valuable asset, especially if the same people have an opportunity of working later under a system of full responsible government. And another good result is that the ideas of 'transferred subjects' and 'popular control' have brought about a concentration of public interest on certain beneficial activities of government —the nation building departments".

The estimate of Coupland is in these words: "The Government of India Act, 1919 was by far the most important measure of Indian policy adopted by the British Parliament since the process of constitutional development began in 1861, for it crossed the line between legislative and executive authority. Previous measures had enabled Indians increasingly to control their legislatures, but not their Governments. Some Indians, it is true, had been members of those Governments but they had been officially appointed and were responsible, like their colleagues, to the Secretary of State and Parliament. Now Indians were to govern, so to speak, on their own. They were to take charge of great departments of Provincial administration, not as official nominees but as the leaders of the elected majorities in their Legislatures and responsible only to them. Limited and checked though it might be, this was a genuine transfer of power, and it was the appointment of these Ministers, more than anything else, that brought home the fact that the abdication of the British Raj had actually begun".

Thompson and Garratt observe that the Reforms were far from being a complete failure. Useful work was done in the provinces by the Indian Ministers and there was no breakdown during the first three years. The process of Indianisation within the Government was proceeding quickly if unostentatiously (British Rule in India, p. 615). P. E. Roberts is of the opinion that dyarchy was the best transitional mechanism that appeared after a prolonged examination of alternatives (British India, p. 589).

Constitutional Development from 1919 to 1935

The Reforms of 1919 were considered to be utterly inadequate by the Indians. The Indian National Congress at its annual session held in 1919 characterised the Reforms as "inadequate, unsatisfactory and disappointing". While it asked the British Government to take early steps to establish full responsible Government in India in accordance with the principle of self-determination, it resolved to work the Reforms "so far as may be possible" with a view to bring about the early establishment of responsible Government in India. The Indians were not in an uncompromising mood but certain events spoiled the political atmosphere in the country. On the Report of a Committee presided over by Mr. Justice J. Rowlatt, two Bills were introduced in the Imperial Legislature in February 1919 and passed into law by the official majority in respect of the opposition from the people. Mahatma Gandhi appealed to the people of India to offer Satyagraha against the oppressive laws. Hartals were held all over the country. Disturbances took place at various places. Martial Law was declared in the Punjab. On the Baisakhi day (April 13, 1919), there occurred the Jallianwala Bagh tragedy. General Dyer ordered the opening of fire on a peaceful crowd at Amritsar. 1,650 rounds were fired and about 400 persons were killed and 1,200 wounded. The people were subjected to great humiliations. The "crawling order" was most resented. The people were required to pass through a street like four-footed animals. The Punjab leaders were put in jails. At many places in the Punjab, bombs were thrown on innocent persons. All this resulted in resentment against the Government. Certain events brought the Congress and the Muslims together. The Muslims of India protested against the harsh terms imposed on Turkey after the First World War. Mahatma Gandhi joined hands with the Muslims and started his non-violent Non-Cooperation Movement for the redress of the Khilafat and the wrongs of the Punjab and the establishment of Swarajya in India. The Calcutta session of the Congress in September 1920 endorsed the policy of Mahatma Gandhi and called upon the people to give up their titles and honorary offices and also boycott schools, law courts, Legislative councils and British goods. The movement was very strong for two years. However, the events of Chauri Chaura in U.P.

where 22 policemen were burnt alive by a mob, made Mahatma Gandhi suspend the movement. The Mahatma was himself arrested in March 1922 and the movement collapsed.

Although the Moderates "were prepared to do everything in their power to make the new Constitution a success", they were themselves not satisfied with it. It was felt that the Reforms did not go far enough. On September 23, 1921, a resolution was moved in the Central Assembly by Rai Jadunath Mozumdar Bahadur for the establishment of autonomy in the provinces and introduction of responsibility in the Central Government. To that resolution, an amendment was moved by Mr. Jamnadas Dwarkadas in which he asked the Governor-General-in-Council "to appoint a Committee consisting of officials and non-officials, including members of Indian Legislatures, to consider the best way of bringing about provincial autonomy in all the Governors' Provinces and of introducing responsibility in the Central Government and to make recommendations". Sir William Vincent, the Home Member, suggested the following formula which was adopted by the Assembly: "That this Assembly recommends to the Governor-General-in-Council that he should convey to the Secretary of State for India the views of this Assembly that the progress made by India on the path of responsible Government warrants a re-examination and revision of the Constitution at an earlier date than 1929".

The Government of India submitted a Report of its debates to the Secretary of State for India for necessary action. The latter was of the opinion that the possibilities of the new Constitution had not been exhausted. He maintained that progress was possible under the existing Constitution. The merits and capabilities of the electorate had not been tested by time and experience. The new constitutional machinery had still to be tested in its working as a whole. The reply of the Secretary of State was followed by a resolution moved in the Assembly by Diwan Bahadur Rangachariar in February 1923 expressing extreme dissatisfaction with it. Another resolution was moved by Dr. Hari Singh Gour in July 1923 which recommended to the Governor-General to move the Secretary of State for India to carry out his suggestions with regard to further reforms possible under the Constitution.

At this stage, the Swarajists appeared on the scene. So far, the Indian National Congress had followed a policy of non-co-operation. However, certain of its leaders led by Sarvashri C. R. Dass and Motilal Nehru turned to a new method of embarrassing the Government. That method was "of wrecking legislatures from within". The members of the Swarajist party took the pledge of "uniform, continuous and sustained obstruction with a view to making the Government through the Assembly and the Council impossible" and they had great success in the elections.

In the newly elected Assembly, Diwan Bahadur Rangachariar moved a resolution recommending to the Governor-General-in-Council that he be pleased to take, at a very early date, the necessary steps (including, if necessary, appointment of a Royal Commission) for revising the Government of India Act so as to secure for India full Self-Governing Dominion Status within the British Empire and provincial autonomy in the provinces. The Government opposed the resolution but proposed to make a serious attempt to investigate justifiable complaints against the working of the scheme in practice, to assess the causes and to examine the necessary remedies. Neither the original resolution nor the proposal of the Government was acceptable to the Swarajist Party and consequently Pt. Motilal Nehru, leader of the Swarajist Party, moved the following amendment and the same was carried:—

"This Assembly recommends to the Governor-General-in-Council to take steps to have the Government of India Act revised with a view to establish full responsible Government in India and for the said purpose—

"(a) to summon at an early date a representative Round Table Conference to recommend with due regard to the protection of the rights and interests of important minorities the scheme of a Constitution for India"; and

"(b) after dissolving the Central Legislature to place the said scheme for approval before a newly elected Indian Legislature for its approval and submit the same to the British Parliament to be embodied in a statute".

Muddiman Committee Report

Although the Government of India did not accept the resolution of the Central Assembly, it set up a Committee under the chairmanship of Sir Alexander Muddiman

"(1) to enquire into the difficulties arising from or defects inherent in the working of the Government of India Act and the Rules thereunder in regard to the Central Government and the Governments of Governors' provinces; and

(2) to investigate the feasibility and desirability and of securing remedies for such difficulties or defects, consistent with the structure, policy and purpose of the Act;

(a) by action taken under the Act and the Rules, or

(b) by such amendments of the Act as appear necessary to rectify any administrative imperfections".

The Muddiman Committee did not submit a unanimous Report. The majority view was that the existing Constitution was working in most provinces and was affording valuable political experience. As the new Constitution had been in existence only for a short period, it was not possible to say definitely as to whether it would succeed ultimately or not. Detailed recommendations were made for improving the machinery of the Government. The minority view was that dyarchy had completely failed and could not succeed at all in future. It was only a fundamental change of the Constitution which could improve matters. To quote, "It has been urged that an advance could be made by action under S. 19A of the Act and without any radical amendment of the Act itself. With all respect to those who maintain this view, we entirely differ from it. In the first place, it is obvious that under S. 19A, the Secretary of State can only 'regulate and restrict' the exercise of the powers of superintendence, direction and control vested in him. In the second place, such a regulation and restriction of powers must be with a view to give effect to the purposes of the Government of India Act. These purposes are defined in the Preamble and we think that even if the Secretary of State felt so disposed, he could not, by the mere exercise of his powers under this section, abolish dyarchy. In the third place, reading the second and third parts of S. 19A with the first part, it seems to us that the relaxation of the control contemplated by S. 19A can only be with regard to provincial Governments and cannot have any relation to the Central Government.... We also think that the relaxation of control provided by this section cannot mean the same thing as divestment."

In September 1925, the Report of the Muddiman Committee

was discussed in the Central Assembly. The Government of India proposed to accept the principle underlying the majority report and proceeded with the consideration of its recommendations. Shri Motilal Nehru moved the following amendment which was carried in the Assembly in spite of opposition from the Government:

"That immediate steps should be taken to move "His Majesty's Government to make a declaration in the Parliament embodying such fundamental changes in the Constitution of India as would make Government fully responsible; and that Round Table Conference or Convention of representatives of all interests should be held to frame a detailed scheme which should be placed before the Legislative Assembly for approval and afterwards submitted to the British Parliament to be embodied in a statute."

The Simon Commission

In November 1927 was appointed the Simon Commission. Different views have been expressed as to why the Statutory Commission was appointed earlier than what was stipulated in the Government of India Act, 1919. One view is that the British Government was forced to appoint the Commission earlier on account of the agitation carried on in India. However, the real reason seems to have been different. In December 1925, Lord Birkenhead, Secretary of State for India in the Conservative Ministry, referred to the possibility of accelarating the Commission. The whole object of Lord Birkenhead and the Conservative Government was not to leave the Commission to be appointed by the Labour Government which, it was felt, would almost certainly come to power at the next general elections. Another object was to use the appointment of the Commission as a bargaining counter and to disintegrate the Swarajist Party.

The Commission consisted of 7 members and was presided over by Sir John Simon. All of its members were Englishmen. The Commission was boycotted by the Indians on the ground that it had no Indian member. The Commission was boycotted not only by the Congress and other representative organisations but by other distinguished leaders of India. Resolutions were passed condemning the composition of the Commission. To quote, "We have come to a deliberate conclusion that the exclusion of the Indians from the Commission is fundamentally wrong. The underlying principle of the scheme that Indians are to have no authoritative voice either in the collection of proper materials and evidence or in taking of decisions by way of recommendations of the Commission to Parliament is of such a character that India cannot, without any self-respect, acquiesce in it. Unless a commission on which British and Indian statesmen are invited to sit on equal terms is set up, we cannot conscientiously take any part or share in the work of the Commission as at present constituted". The excuse put forward for not appointing any Indian on the Commission was that the intention of the framers of the Government of India Act, 1919 was to confine the Commission to members of Parliament. However, the Act did not lay down any such restriction. But even if the British Government wanted to restrict the nomination to members of the British Parliament, there were two Indian members at that time. Lord Sinha was a member of the House of Lords and Mr. Shapurji Saklatwala was in the House of Commons. Lord Sinha had been closely associated with the various stages of constitutional reforms in India. His presence on the Commission would have been very valuable. The real reason seems to be that the Conservative Government did not want any Indian to be on the Commission.

The Simon Commission was appointed "for the purpose of inquiring into the working of the system of Government, the growth of education and development of representative institutions in British India and matters connected therewith and reporting" as to whether and to what extent it is desirable to establish the principle of responsible government or to extend, modify or restrict the degree of responsible government then existing therein, including the question whether the establishment of second chambers of the local legislatures, is or is not desirable." As the enquiry was coming to a close, the members of the Commission "were increasingly impressed by the impossibility of considering the constitutional problems of British India without taking into account the relations between British India and the Indian States." With the approval of the British Government, the Commission also considered the relations between British India and the Indian states.

The day on which the Commission landed in India, there was a Hartal all over the country. Wherever the members of the Commission went, they were greeted with black flags and cries of "Simon go back". The Central Assembly was invited to set up a committee to cooperate with the Commission but it refused to do so. A large number of persons were arrested and prosecuted. However, the prosecutions did not damp the enthusiasm of the people against the Commission.

The Nehru Report

The Indians had condemned the appointment of the all-White Simon Commission and Lord Birkenhead, while justifying the exclusion of Indians from the Commission, challenged the latter to produce an agreed constitution and submit the same to the British Parliament for consideration. The challenge was accepted by the Indians and an All-Parties Conference was held in Bombay on May 9, 1928 under the Presidentship of Dr. M. A. Ansari. The Conference appointed a Committee with Pandit Moti Lal Nehru as Chairman to consider and determine the principles of a constitution for India. Sir Tej Bahadur Sapru, Sir Ali Imam, Shri M. S. Aney, Sardar Mangal Singh, Shri Shuaib Qureshi, Shri G. R. Pradhan and Shri Subhash Chandra Bose were its members. The Committee produced a report which has gone down in history as the Nehru Report. The recommendations of the Report were unanimous except in regard to the basis of the constitution. While the majority favoured Dominion Status not only as a distant goal but as "the next immediate step", it gave liberty of action to all those groups and parties which made complete independence their goal. Although the report envisaged a future linking up of the Indian states with the rest of India in a federal polity, it confined itself to British India.

It was provided in the report that all treaties made between the East India Company and the Indian States and all such subsequent treaties so far as they were in force, would be binding on the Commonwealth of India which would exercise the same right in relation to and discharge the same obligations towards the Indian states as the Government of India exercised and discharged previously. In case of differences between the Commonwealth and the Indian states on any matter arising out of treaties, engagements, Sanads or similar other documents, the Governor-General-in-Council may, with the consent of the state concerned, refer such matters to the Supreme Court for its decision.

As regards the communal question, many basic recommendations were made. Joint electorates with reservation of seats for minorities on population basis with the right to contest additional seats were recommended. No seats were to be reserved for any community in the Punjab and Bengal. Full protection was to be given to the religious and cultural interests of the Muslim community. New provinces on linguistic basis were to be created with a view to the "planning of Muslim majority provinces against Hindu majority provinces".

The Report enumerated 19 fundamental rights which were to be embodied in the statute. It was to be declared that all powers of the Government and all authority were derived from the people. No person shall be deprived of his liberty, nor shall his dwelling or property be entered, sequestered or confiscated, save in accordance with law. Freedom of conscience and free profession and practice of religion shall be guaranteed to all. The right of free expression of opinion and the right to assemble peacefully and without arms and to form associations or unions shall be guaranteed for purposes not opposed to public order or morality. All citizens shall have the right to free elementary education. All citizens shall be equal before law and possess equal civic rights. There shall be no penal law of a discriminatory nature. No person shall be punished for any act which is not punishable under the law at the time it is committed. No corporal punishment or other punishment involving torture of any kind shall be lawful. Every citizen shall have the right to a writ of Habeas Corpus. There shall be no state religion for the Commonwealth of India or for any province nor shall any state endow any religion or give preference to any religion. No person attending any school receiving state aid or other public money shall be compelled to attend religious instruction that may be given in the school. No person shall, by reason of his religion, caste or creed, be prejudiced in any way in regard to public employment, office of power or honour and the exercise of any trade or calling. All citizens shall have an equal right of access to and use of public roads, public wells and all other places of public resort. Freedom of combination and association for maintenance and improvement of labour and economic conditions shall be guaranteed to every one. All agreements and measures tending to restrict or obstruct such freedom shall be illegal. No breach of contract of service or abetment shall be made a criminal offence. Parliament shall make suitable laws for the maintenance of health and fitness for work of all citizens, securing of a living wage for every worker, the protection of motherhood, welfare of children and the economic consequences of old age, infirmity and unemployment. Every citizen shall have the right to keep and bear arms in accordance with the regulations made for that purpose. Men and women shall have equal rights as citizens.

The report provided for a Parliament of two houses: the Senate and House of Representatives. The Governor-General was to be appointed by the British Government but paid out of the Indian revenues. His salary was not to be altered during his continuance in office. The Senate was to consist of 200 members elected by the Provincial Councils. The House of Representatives was to consist of 500 members. It was to be elected on adult franchise basis. The life of the Senate was to be seven years and that of the House of Representatives five years.

The Governor-General was to act on the advice of the Executive Council. The Prime Minister was to be appointed by the Governor-General and the other ministers were to be appointed on the advice of the Prime Minister. The Executive Government was to be collectively responsible to Parliament. The Governor-General-in-Council was to appoint High Commissioners and other foreign representatives similar to those appointed by Canada and other Dominions. The Governor-General was also to appoint the Auditor-General of India.

The Governors of the provinces were to be appointed by the King of England. They were to be paid out of the provincial revenues. Provision was to be made for a Legislative Council elected on an adult franchise basis. The Provincial Legislative Council was to sit for 5 years but could be dissolved earlier by the Governor. The latter was also given the authority to extend its life under special circumstances. Provision was also made for a President and a Vice-President of the Legislative Council. The Governor was to act on the advice of the Provincial Executive Council whose number was not to exceed 5. The Governor was to select the Chief Minister but the other members of the Executive Council were to be appointed by him on the advice of the Chief Minister.

Provision was made for a Supreme Court of India which was to consist of Lord President and other Justices. The Judges of the Supreme Court were to be appointed by the

Governor-General-in-Council and were not liable to be removed from office except on an address from both Houses of Parliament praying for such removal on the ground of misbehaviour or incapacity. The Supreme Court was to have both original and appellate jurisdiction. Provision was also made for the taking of appeals to the King-in-Council under certain circumstances.

The Governor-General-in-Council was to appoint a Committee of Defence consisting of the Minister of Defence, Minister of Foreign Affairs, Commander-in-Chief, Commander of Air Forces, Commander of Naval Forces, Chief of the General Staff and two other experts. The Prime Minister was to be the Chairman of the Committee. The functions of the Committee were to advise the Government and the various Departments concerned on question of defence and general policy.

As regards the Civil Services, all officers of public services at the time of the establishment of the Commonwealth were to become the officers of the Commonwealth. The Governor-General was to appoint a Public Service Commission. All officers of the Army Services were to retain all their existing rights regarding their salaries, allowances and pensions. They were also to get compensation for any loss incurred by them.

The Nehru Report was submitted on August 10, 1928 and the All Parties Conference met at Calcutta on December 22, 1928 to consider it. As regards the communal question, Mr. Jinnah, on behalf of the All-India Muslim League, moved amendments to the Report. The first amendment was that 1/3rd of the elected representatives of both the Houses of the Central Legislature should be Muslims but the amendment was rejected. The second amendment was that in the event of an adult franchise not being established in the Punjab and Bengal, there should be reservation of seats for the Muslims on population basis for 10 years subject to re-examination after that period, but the Muslims should have no right to contest additional seats. This amendment was also rejected. The third amendment moved by Mr. Jinnah was that the residuary powers should vest in the provinces. This amendment was also not accepted. Another amendment moved by him was that no amendment of the Constitution should be made unless it was first passed by both Houses of Parliament separately by a majority of four-fifths and was approved by a similar mojority of both the Houses in joint session. This amendment was unanimously accepted. Sir Tej Bahadur Sapru pressed the Conference to accept this amendment with a view to secure a settlement. To quote him, "The simple position is that for the sake of settlement, you are invited by Mr. Jinnah, however illogical and unreasonable, to agree to this proposition which I consider not inconsistent with the Nehru Report. Speaking for myself, I would like you to picture Mr. Jinnah whom I have known intimately for 15 years as a spoilt child. If he is a spoilt child, naughty child, I am prepared to say, give him what he wants and be finished with it. I am not going to ask him to be reasonable; but we must, as practical statesmen, try to solve the problem and not be misled by arithmetical figures". It is worthy of notice that Shri M. R. Jayakar who represented the Hindu point of view, was opposed to the demands of Mr. Jinnah. A session of the All-India Muslim League was convened in March, 1929 and the Subject Committee of the Muslim League which met on March 31, 1929 approved of the Nehru Report by a majority subject to certain specified safeguards which Mr. Jinnah had advocated at the Calcutta meeting. At the open session of the League also, the resolution was adopted by a majority.

Jinnah's Fourteen Points (1929)

At a meeting of the All-India Muslim League held in Delhi in 1929, Mr. Jinnah put forward the following 14 points as the minimum Muslim demands for any political settlement:—

1. The form of the future constitution should be federal with the residuary powers vested in the provinces.

2. A uniform measure of autonomy shall be granted to all provinces.

3. All legislatures in the country and other elected bodies shall be constituted on the definite principle of adequate and effective representation of minorities in every province without reducing the majority in any province to a minority or even equality.

4. In Central Legislature, Muslim representation shall be one-third.

5. Representation of communal groups shall continue to be separate electorates as at present, provided it shall be open to any community, at any time, to abandon its separate electorate in favour of joint electorates.

6. Any territorial re-distribution that might at any time be necessary shall not in any way affect the Muslim majority in the Punjab, Bengal and North-West Frontier Province.

7. Full religious liberty, i.e., liberty of belief, worship and observance, propaganda, association and education shall be guaranteed to all communities.

8. No bill or resolution or any part thereof shall be passed in any legislature or any elected body if three-fourths of the members of any community in that particular body oppose such a bill, resolution or part thereof on the ground that it would be injurious to the interests of that community, or in the alternative such other method is devised as may be found possible and practicable to deal with such cases.

9. Sind should be separated from the Bombay Presidency.

10. Reforms should be introduced in the N.W.F. Province and Baluchistan on the same footing as in other provinces.

11. Provision should be made in the constitution giving Muslims an adequate share along with other Indians in all the services of the State and in local self-government bodies having due regard to the requirements of efficiency.

12. The constitution should embody adequate safeguards for the protection of Muslim culture and for the promotion of Muslim education, language, religion, personal laws and Muslim charitable institutions and for their due share in the grants-in-aid given by the State and by the self-governing bodies.

13. No Cabinet, either central or provincial, should be formed without there being a proportion of at least one-third Muslim Ministers.

14. No change shall be made in the constitution of the Central Legislature except with the concurrence of the States constituting the Indian Federation.

There was a change of Government in England and the Labour Party headed by Ramsay MacDonald came to power. High hopes were entertained regarding the future of India. That was partly due to the fact that while in opposition Ramsay MacDonold had always sympathised with the Indian aspirations and advocated their cause. Lord Irwin, the then Governor-General and Viceroy of India, was convinced that it was not possible to maintain an irresponsible Government at the Centre for long. He paid a hasty visit to England to confer with the new Labour Government and on his return issued the following statement on October 31, 1929: "In view of the doubts which have been expressed both in Great Britain and in India regarding the interpretation to be placed on the intentions of the British Government in enacting the statute of 1919, I am authorised on behalf of His Majesty's Government to state clearly that in their judgment, it is implicit in the declaration of 1917 that the natural issue of India's constitutional progress as there contemplated is the attainment of the Dominion Status". He also stated that the Simon Commission had suggested to His Majesty's Government and the latter has accepted the suggestion that after the publication of their Report and before its examination by the Joint Parliamentary Committee, they should summon a Conference "in which His Majesty's Government meet the representatives both of British India and of the States for the purpose of seeking the greatest possible measure of agreement for the final proposals which it would later be the duty of His Majesty's Government to submit to Parliament". It is pointed out that whatever may be thought about the statesmanship of this declaration, it should not have been made until the Commission had concluded its labours. It left that unfortunate body in the air and at the same time stole its thunder. Moreover, the phrase "Dominion Status" was unhappily so ambiguous that it could be given various interpretations. The Government of India seems to have used the phrase in the sense in which it was employed in the Preamble to the Government of India Act, 1919 as applicable to the Constitution of a dependency enjoying responsible Government. The Congress leaders were not satisfied with the limited scope and purpose of the Round Table Conference. What they demanded was the convening of a Constituent Assembly for the purpose of drafting a Constitution for India. It was obvious that the views of the people of India and the British Government differed radically from each other. In spite of it, an interview was arranged between Mahatma Gandhi and Lord Irwin with a view to exploring the possibility of a compromise. The interview failed to achieve its object. The result was that when the Indian National Congress met at Lahore in December 1929 under the presidentship of Pt. Jawaharlal Nehru, it passed resolutions boycotting the Round Table Conference, declaring the object of the Indian National Congress the demand of Swarajya or complete independence for India and authorising the All-

India Congress Committee to start Civil Disobedience Movement. January 26, 1930 was observed as Independence Day and the Civil Disobedience Movement was started in March 1930. Mahatma Gandhi started his historic march to Dandi to violate the Salt laws. Thousands of people all over the country violated certain laws of the country and courted arrest. There were Lathi charges by the police. Repression was in full swing. Ordinances were issued in quick succession by the Government to meet the situation. Editors and proprietors of newspapers and printing presses were arrested and fined. Their presses were confiscated in many cases. There seemed to be a complete breach between the Government and the leaders of the Nationalist Movement in the country.

The Simon Commission's Report (1930)

The Report of the Simon Commission was published in May, 1930. First of all, the Report considered as to what should be the ultimate constitutional framework of India and what should be the place of the provinces in that framework. The Report declared that the framework could not be of a unitary type. That must be federal, not merely in response to the growth of provincial loyalties but primarily because it must embrace all India. It was only in a federation that Indian States could be expected in course of time to unite with British India.

The Report recommended that dyarchy should be abolished in the provinces and the whole field of provincial administration should be entrusted to Ministers responsible to their Legislatures. "Each province should, as far as possible, be the mistress in her own house". It was pointed out that the retention of reserved subjects implied the continuance of control over that part of the provincial administration by the Central Government and the Secretary of State for India and that was not a desirable thing. In the new provincial set up, the Ministries were not to be formed entirely on the British model. The Governor was to be allowed to select those Ministers who commanded a majority in the Legislature. He was not to appoint a Ministry on the advice of the Prime Minister or the Chief Minister. In all legislation and administration, Ministers were to be free from interference by the Governor except for such stated vital reasons as the maintenance of the safety of the province or the protection of the minorities. It was recommended that franchise should be extended and the legislature be enlarged.

The Report recommended that the question of making Sind and Orissa as separate provinces should be given further expert examination. However, it should be decided forthwith to separate Burma from India. The North-Western Frontier Province was considered to be ripe for the first step in constitutional advancement. That province should be given a Legislative Council and its representation in the Central Legislature should be strengthened.

The Report made certain recommendations which aimed at preparing the way for an All-India Federation. The Central Legislature was to be refashioned on the federal principle. The members of the Federal Assembly were to be representatives not of sections of the people of India at large but of the provinces. They were to be elected by the Provincial Councils. The elections and nominations to the Council of State were also to be on a provincial basis. The distribution of seats amongst the various provinces for the Federal Assembly was to be roughly on population basis. Each province was to have 3 members on the Council of State.

So far as the Central Executive was concerned, there was a note of "gradualness" in the Report. No substantial change was recommended. There was to be no responsible Government at the centre. There was to be no dyarchy even at the centre. It was pointed out that there was the need of keeping the Centre strong and stable "while the provincial Councils were learning by experience to bear the full weight of new and heavy responsibilities". The reason given for this was not the immediate need of the political situation in India, but the ultimate needs of the Federation. It was stated that the provinces must find themselves before the nature of their participation in a federal government could be determined. To quote, "It is necessary to take a long view of the development of Indian self-government.... A pre-mature endeavour to introduce a form of responsible government at the centre before the conditions for its actual practice have emerged, would in the end result not in advance but in retrogression."

An All-India Federation was to be set up in the distant future. The idea that "the Federation of Greater India can be artificially hastened or that when it comes, it will spring into being at a bound", was rejected. For the present, only one new step was recommended. In order to "foster the sense of need for further developments and bring more nearly within the range of realisation other steps which are as yet too distant and too dime to be entered upon and described", a Council for Greater India should be set up, representing both British India and the Indian States. That Council should have authority to discuss in a consultative capacity all matters of common concern which were to be drawn up in the form of a list and given as a Schedule. The preamble of the new Act should record the desire to bring about a closer association between the two parts of India.

The Government of India Act, 1919 had provided for setting up a Commission after every 10 years for enquiring into the working of the reforms and the naming of the recommendations for the future. The Report recommended that the method of periodical enquiry should be given up. The new constitution should be so elastically framed as to enable it to develop by itself. The Provincial Legislatures should have power to modify their own composition and procedure and self-government should grow not by making laws but by usages and conventions.

The view of P. E. Roberts is that the Simon Commission Report "will always stand out as one of the greatest of India State Papers. The impressive unanimity of the commissioners who from their known party antecedents must clearly have sacrificed all but their deepest convictions to attain it, ought to have commended their sagacious and temperately worded conclusions to men of goodwill (British India, page 598). However, the Report was condemned by the Indians. The British Government itself had also partly forestalled it and ultimately side-tracked it, although some of its recommendations were ultimately embodied in the Government of India Act, 1935. Dr. A. B. Keith observes: "It was probably foolish of Indian opinion to repudiate the Report out and out. If it had been accepted, the British Government could hardly have failed to work on it and responsible government could in the provinces have been achieved much earlier than it could be under any later scheme. Moreover, the pressure of such Governments on the Centre would doubtless have operated strongly in the direction of inducing the British Government to aim at federation and the states to come to terms with the Indian political leaders." (Constitutional History of India, p. 293).

Round Table Conferences (1930-31)

After the publication of the Simon Commission Report and its condemnation by the people of India, the British Government called the first Round Table Conference in London. The conference met in November 1930. As the Congress leaders were in jail, the Government appointed safe men belonging to other parties, communities and interests to represent India. Representatives from the Indian states were also invited to participate in the deliberations and included men like Sir Mirza Ismail, Sir Akbar Hydari and the Maharaja of Bikaner. There were lengthy discussions on the question of the future form of the Government of India. Ultimately, three basic principles were settled and accepted by the British Government. The form of the new Government of India was to be an All-India Federation in which the British India provinces and the Indian states were to join. Subject to special reservations and safeguards as might be considered necessary for the transitional period, the Federal Government was made responsible to the Federal Legislature. Provinces were to be given autonomy in their own affairs. At the end of the first Round Table Conference, Prime Minister Ramsay MacDonald made the following important statement: "The view of His Majesty's Government is that responsibility for the Government of India should be placed upon legislatures, Central and Provincial, with such provisions as may be considered necessary to guarantee, during period of transition, the observance of certain obligations and to meet other special circumstances, and also with such guarantees as are required by minorities to protect their political liberties and rights. In such statutory safeguards as may be made for meeting the needs of the transitional period, it will be a primary concern of His Majesty's Government to see that the reserved powers are so framed and exercised as not to prejudice the advance of India through the new Constitution to full responsibility for her own Government. Pledge after pledge had been given to India that British Raj was there not for perpetual domination. Why did we put facilities for education at your disposal? Why did we put in your hands text-books from which we draw political inspiration? If we meant that the people of India should for ever be silent and negative, subordinated to our rule, why have our Queens and Kings given you pledges? Why has our Parliament given you pledges? Finally, I hope, and trust, and I pray that by our labours together India will come to possess the only thing which she now lacks, to give her the status of a Dominion amongst the British Commonwealth of Nations— what she now lacks for that—the responsibilities and the cares, the burdens and difficulties, but the pride and the honour of responsible self-government."

As it was not considered advisable to proceed with the work of the final form of the future constitution of India in the absence of the representatives of the Indian National Congress, it was decided to call a second Round Table Conference and in the meanwhile, efforts were to be made to bring about a reconciliation between the Congress and the Government. The efforts of Sir Tej Bahadur Sapru and M. R. Jayakar were crowned with success and the famous Gandhi-Irwin Pact was signed in March 1931. The Government released all the political prisoners. Mahatma Gandhi withdrew the civil disobedience movement. An atmosphere of goodwill having been created, Mahatma Gandhi left for London to attend the Second Round Table Conference as the sole representative of the Congress. In spite of magnetic personality of Mahatma Gandhi and his devotion to the work in hand, the communal tangle could not be solved. Mahatma Gandhi gave a **carta blanche** to Mr. M. A. Jinnah but all efforts for a settlement failed on account of the uncompromising attitude of Mr. Jinnah and the part played by Sir Samuel Hoare, the then Secretary of State for India, in persuading Mr. Jinnah not to come to any settlement with Mahatma Gandhi by offering him better terms. Realising the failure of his mission, Mahatma Gandhi left England in disgust and was arrested on his arrival in India.

It is true that as a result of the economic crisis in the world and especially in England, the Labour Government of Ramsay MacDonald had been replaced by a National Government, but Ramsay MacDonald managed to follow his previous policy with regard to India at the Second Round Table Conference. Many problems were considered, but the members could not come to any definite conclusion. Consequently, the work was referred to various committees which were required to submit detailed reports. As regards the question of communal representation, Ramsay MacDonald made it clear that if the various communities in India did not come to any definite settlement, the British Government would be forced to give its own award regarding the same.

Communal Award (1932)

As the Indians could not arrive at any settlement, Ramsay MacDonald gave his famous award known as the Communal Award on August 16, 1932. The scope of the Award was purposely confined to the arrangements to be made for the representation of British Indian communities in the Provincial Legislatures, consideration of representation to the Central Legislature being deferred for the time being as that involved the question of the representation of the Indian states which needed further discussion. The hope was expressed that once a pronouncement was made upon questions of the method and proportions of representation, the communities themselves may find it possible to arrive at a **modus vivendi** on the communal problem. If before the passing of the Government of India Act, the Government was satisfied that the communities concerned were mutually agreed upon any alternative scheme, they would be prepared to recommend to Parliament the substitution of the alternative scheme for the Communal Award. "His Majesty's Government wish it to be most clearly understood that they themselves can be no parties to any negotiations which may be initiated with a view to revision of their decision and will not be prepared to give consideration to any representation aimed at securing modification of it which is not supported by all parties affected. ... If before the new Government of India Act has passed into law they are satisfied that the communities who are concerned are mutually agreed upon a practical alternative scheme either in respect of any one or more of Governors' provinces or in respect of the whole of British India, they will be prepared to recommend to Parliament that the alternative scheme should be adopted."

According to the Award, elections to the seats allotted to the Muslim, European and Sikh constituencies were to be by voters voting for separate communal electorates covering between them the whole area of a province. Special provisions were made for excluded areas. Provision was to be made in the new constitution of India to allow the revision of electoral arrangements after the lapse of 10 years with the assent of the communities affected, for the ascertainment of which suitable means were to be devised. All qualified voters who were not voters in Muslim, Sikh, Indian Christian, Anglo-Indian and European constituencies were entitled to vote in a general constituency. 7 seats were reserved for the Marathas in certain selected plural-member general constituencies in Bombay. The members of the depressed classes who were qualified to vote, were to vote in a general constituency. However, special seats were to be reserved for them. Those seats were to be filled up by election from special constituencies in which only the members of the depressed classes electorally qualified were to be entitled to vote. Any person voting in such a special constituency was also to be entitled to vote in a general constituency. These constituencies were to be formed in those selected areas where the depressed classes were most numerous and except in Madras, those were not to cover the whole of the area of a province. In the case of Bengal, in some general constituencies, the majority of the voters belonged to the depressed classes. Consequently, no special number was to be fixed for their seats in that province. However, they were not to get less than 10 seats in Bengal. The maximum duration of the depressed classes constituencies was to be 20 years, provided those were not abolished earlier. The election of the Indian Christians was to be by voters voting in separate communal constituencies. It was felt that practical difficulties would prevent the formation of the Indian Christian constituencies covering the whole area of a province and consequently special Indian Christian constituencies were to be formed in one or two selected areas in a province. The Indian Christian voters in those areas were not to vote in a general constituency. Outside those areas, they were to vote in a general constituency. Special arrangements were to be made in Bihar and Orissa where a large number of Indian Christians belonged to the original tribes. The Anglo-Indians were also to vote on communal lines. The intention was that the Anglo-Indian constituencies were to cover the whole of the area of a province and postal ballot was to be used for that purpose.

Women were also given special representation on communal lines. The electors of a particular community were to elect their own quota. Special seats were to be allotted to commerce and industry, mining and planting, to be filled up by election through the Chambers of Commerce and other associations. The details were to be worked out later on. The seats allotted to the landholders were to be filled up by the landholders' constituencies.

It was stated that the work of the determination of the constituencies was to begin soon. The Government reserved to itself the right of making slight variations in the number of seats given to various communities with a view to facilitate the work of the delimitation of constituencies. However, the proportion was not to be materially changed. The composition of the second chambers in the provinces was not to disturb in any essential the balance between the communities resulting from the composition of the lower house.

Poona Pact (1932)

Mahatma Gandhi in his letter written in March 1932 to Sir Samuel Hoare, Secretary of State for India, had warned him that he would resist with his life the grant of separate communal electorates to the depressed classes. When the Communal Award was published and it was found that the British Government was determined to give separate communal representation to the depressed classes, Mahatma Gandhi wrote to Ramsay MacDonald that the matter was "one of pure religion" with him and he asked: "Do you realise that, if your decision stands and the constitution comes into being, you arrest the marvellous growth of the work of the Hindu reformers who have dedicated themselves to the uplift of their suppressed brethren in every walk of life?" Mahatma Gandhi's letter had no effect on the Prime Minister of England who took the matter light-heartedly and would not have bothered even if the Mahatma had died. When the British Government refused to move in the matter and the condition of Mahatma Gandhi became serious on account of his fast unto death, the Indian leaders made up their minds to get the Award modified by mutual agreement. Negotiations took place with Dr. Ambedkar and Rajah and ultimately the Poona Pact was signed in September 1932 and was accepted by the Government.

The Poona Pact reserved seats for depressed classes out of the general electoral seats in provincial legislatures as follows: Madras 30, Bombay with Sind 15, Punjab 8, Bihar and Orissa 18, C.P. 20, Assam 7, Bengal 30 and U.P. 20. The total of the reserved seats for the depressed classes was 148. As regards the procedure for elections to these seats by joint electorates, all members of the depressed classes registered in the general electoral roll in a constituency were to form an electoral college which was to elect a panel of 4 candidates belonging to the depressed classes for each of the reserved seats by the method of single vote. The 4 persons getting the highest number of votes in the primary election were to be candidates for election by the general electorate. The depressed classes were to have representation in the Central Legislature on the principle of joint electorates and seats were to be reserved for them in the same way as in the case of the provinces. 18% of the general seats for British India were to be reserved for the depressed classes. The system of primary elections to a panel of candidates for election to Central and Provincial Legislatures was to be abolished after 10 years or earlier, if an agreement to that effect was made. The depressed classes were to be given fair representation in the local bodies and public services subject to educational qualifications. In every educational grant in the provincial budget, an adequate sum was to be earmarked for the education of the depressed classes. The procedure to be adopted for election of the representatives of the depressed classes to the Central Legislature was postponed as that involved the whole system of representation at the Centre.

Third Round Table Conference

The Third Round Table Conference was called by the British Government rather reluctantly as it was of the opinion that the rest of the work could be done in India. The result was that the session of the Third Round Table Conference lasted from November 17, 1932 to December 24, 1932. The Labour Party did not participate in the deliberations and the Indian National Congress was unrepresented. The delegates of the Conference merely discussed the reports of the various committees appointed by the Second Round Table Conference and decided a few more points.

The White Paper (1933)

When the whole scheme regarding the future constitution of India was thrashed out, the British Government issued in March 1933 a small document known as the White Paper. It gave in detail the working basis of the new Indian Constitution with dyarchy at the Centre and a responsible Government in the provinces. As was to be expected, the White Paper was condemned by the Indian public opinion, but the British Government went on with its programme.

In April 1933, a Joint Select Committee was appointed to examine and report on the Government proposals as contained in the White Paper. The Committee consisted of 16 members each from the House of Commons and House of Lords and its Chairman was Lord Linlithgow. The Committee invited representatives from British India and Indian States. After examining many witnesses and going through the memoranda received from the Indian Association, the British India delegations, Sir Tej Bahadur Sapru, Shri M. R. Jayakar and other prominent individuals, the Joint Select Committee submitted its report on November 22, 1934. Although it did not alter the fundamentals as given in the White Paper, it recommended many changes in the structure of the Provincial and Federal Legislatures and other matters also.

When the Reforms scheme was thoroughly discussed and given the shape by the Joint Select Committee, a Bill was drafted on those lines and introduced in the House of Commons on February 5, 1935. Sir Samuel Hoare, Secretary of State for India, was in-charge of the Bill which was severely criticised by the Labour Party for its limited scope. The Labour members tried to amend the Bill in such a way as to recommend explicitly India's right to Dominion Status. The diehards led by Winston Churchill tried to introduce reactionary elements into the Bill. However, the Government went on with its own scheme which was passed by the House of Commons on June 4, 1935. The Bill was introduced in the House of Lords on June 6, 1935 and was passed in July, 1935. Here also the efforts of the Labour members to liberalise the Bill failed. As the Government had made many amendments in the Bill at this stage, the Bill had to be sent back to the House of Commons which accepted the proposed amendments. The Bill received the Royal assent on August 2, 1935 as the Government of India Act, 1935.

Government of India Act, 1935

The Act provided for an All-India Federation. The question of a federation for India had presented a peculiar problem on account of the disparity between the Indian States and the provinces of British India. The Indian States were under the complete control of Political Department of the Government of India. On the other hand, the provinces had some sort of a democratic Government. The Act provided that all the provinces were to join the Indian Federation automatically. Entry into the Federation was to be a voluntary act on the part of the ruler of each State, however small and insignificant that State might be. At the time of joining the Federation, the ruler of the State was to execute an Instrument of Accession in favour of the Crown. On the acceptance of that Instrument, the State was to become a unit of the Federation. The Crown was forbidden to accept an Instrument of Accession if its terms appeared to be inconsistent with the scheme of the Federation. While the provinces were to be alike in respect of the position and quantum of legislative and executive powers in the Federation, the States were to differ regarding the extent of their powers in the Federation. The scope of the federal jurisdiction in the States was to depend solely upon the transfers made by their respective rulers through their Instrumen of Accession. The Instrument was to authorise the various federal authorities to exercise their respective functions under the Act in relation to a particular State. It was to be the duty of the ruler of the State to see that due effect was given within his State to the provisions of the Act in so far as those provisions were made applicable by virtue of the Instrument. The ruler was authorised to extend the functions of the federal authority in respect of his State by another Instrument, but no subsequent Instrument could decrease the scope of the authority of the Federation as provided by the original Instrument of Accession.

The Indian States were to send 125 members to the Federal Assembly and 104 members to the Council of State. The provinces were to send 250 members to the Federal Assembly and 156 members to the Council of State. The members from the Indian States were to be nominated by the rulers but those from the provinces were to be elected on communal lines. The functions of the Crown with regard to Indian States were to be performed in India by his representative who was the Viceroy himself.

The Indian Federation as provided by the Government of India Act, 1935 was different from the other federal system. There was no simple division of powers between the Centre and the units. The Act provided for 3 Lists: Federal List, Provincial List and Concurrent List. The Federal Government was authorised to pass laws on the subjects given in the Federal List. The subjects given in the Provincial List were within the exclusive jurisdiction of the Provincial Legislature. As regards the Concurrent List, both the Federal Legislature and the Provincial Legislatures could pass laws on the subjects given in that List. However, if a law was passed by the Federal Legislature on any subject given in the Concurrent List, the Federal legislature could not make laws on the same subject afterwards. As regards the residuary powers, the Governor-General in his discretion was given the power to decide as to which of the 3 Lists a particular subject was to be allotted.

The Act provided for dyarchy at the Centre. Certain federal subjects were reserved in the hands of the Governor-General to be administered by him with the assistance of not more than 3 Counsellors to be appointed by him. Those subjects were Defence, External Affairs, Ecclesiastical Affairs and the administration of tribal areas. In the administration of other federal subjects, the Governor-General was to be aided and advised by a Council of Ministers whose number was not to exceed 10. The federal ministry was to administer all the federal departments except the above mentioned reserved departments. The federal ministry was to be formed on the usual cabinet lines except that it was to include the representatives of the important minorities. The Governor-General was instructed by means of an Instrument of Instructions to secure such representation to the best of his ability. In spite of the composite character of the ministry, responsibility was to be collective. The ministry was to be responsible to the federal legislature.

The Governor-General was required to act in three different capacities. Ordinarily, he was to act on the advice of his ministers with regard to all subjects other than the reserved subjects. When he acted on the advice of the ministers, he acted as a constitutional head. He was also required to act in his individual judgment. When he did so, he was required to consult his ministers but it was not binding on him to act upon their advice. The Governor-General acted in his individual judgment while performing his special responsibilities. Those were the safeguarding of the financial stability and credit of India, prevention of any grave menace to the peace and tranquillity of India or any part of India, safeguarding of the legitimate interests of the minorities, the legitimate rights of the public servants and their dependents and the interests of the Indian States and the dignity of their rulers, prevention of commercial discrimination and discriminatory taxation against goods of British origin or Burmese origin and the securing of the due discharge of his discretionary powers.

While acting in his discretion, the Governor-General was not required even to consult his ministers and the question of acting upon their advice did not arise at all. While doing so, he could act in an arbitrary manner. The Governor-General acted in his discretion while administering the reserved departments of Defence, External Affairs, Ecclesiastical Affairs and the tribal areas. He also acted in the same capacity while appointing the 3 Counsellors. He appointed and dismissed his ministers and presided over their meetings in his discretion. In the same capacity, he was authorised to issue two kinds of ordinances. One type of ordinance could be issued by him at any time and that lasted for 6 months. The other type of ordinance was to be issued only when the Legislature was not sitting. The Governor-General was given the power to issue what were known as Governor-General's Acts. But those Acts had to be forwarded to the Secretary of State. The previous sanction of the Governor-General in his discretion was required for the introduction of certain bills in the federal Legislature and the Provincial Legislature. He was authorised to stop the discussion of any Bill at any time by the Legislature. He could withhold his assent to a bill passed by the Legislature or send the same back for reconsideration or reserve the same for the consideration of His Majesty. He was given control over about 80% of the federal budget. The non-votable items of the budget formed a major part of the budget. He could, in his discretion, send any instructions to the Governors and it was the special responsibility of the Governors to carry them out. He could suspend the Constitution in his discretion. He was given the authority to summon, prorogue or dissolve the Federal Assembly. He could summon both Houses for a joint sitting. He could address the Legislature or send messages regarding a certain bill.

The Federal Legislature was to be bicameral consisting of the Federal Assembly and the Council of State. The Federal Assembly was to have a life of 5 years from the date of its first meeting. On the expiry of that period, it was automatically dissolved. However, the Governor-General was given the power to extend its life. The Council of State was to be a permanent body of which 1/3rd members were to retire after every 3 years. The members from the States were to be nominated by the rulers. The representatives from British India were to be elected. The Hindu, Muslim and Sikh members were to be elected on communal lines. While the members of the Council of State were to be directly elected, those of the Federal Assembly were to be indirectly elected.

The powers of the Indian Legislature were severely restricted. There were certain subjects on which neither the Federal Legislature nor the Provincial Legislatures could legislate. The Indian Legislatures was debarred from making any law affecting the Sovereign or the Royal family or the succession to the throne or suzerainty of the Crown over any part of India or law of British nationality or the Army Act, the Air Force Act or the law of Prize Courts. The Indian Legislatures could not make any law amending any of the provisions of the Government of India Act, 1935 or any Order-in-Council made under it or any rules made thereunder by the Secretary of State or the Governor-General or a Governor in his discretion or in the exercise of his individual judgment. It could not make any law affecting the prerogative right of the Crown to grant special leave to appeal to the Privy Council except in so far as that was expressly permitted by the Act. It could not pass any legislation which discriminated against the British interests in commercial and other spheres. There were a large number of subjects of vital importance on which initiation of legislation required previous sanction of the Governor-General. There were many non-votable items in the Budget over which the Federal Legislature had absolutely no control. If any item of the budget was rejected by the Federal Assembly, the same could be put before the Council of State if the Governor-General so directed. If the two Houses of the Federal Legislature differed with respect to any demand, the Governor-General was required to summon a joint sitting for voting on that demand and the decision of the majority was to prevail. The Governor-General was given the power to summon a joint sitting of the two Houses of the Federal Legislature, when a bill passed by one House was rejected by the other or was amended in a form to which the first House was not agreeable.

After a bill was passed by both the Houses of Federal Legislature, the Governor-General, in his discretion, could assent to it or veto it or send it back for reconsideration or reserve it for His Majesty's consideration. The Act assented to by the Governor-General could be disallowed within a year by the King-in-Council.

The Act provided for the establishment of a Federal Court of India with jurisdiction over the States and the provinces. The Court was to consist of a Chief Justice and two puisne Judges. It was given both original and appellate powers. It was the duty of the Federal Court to interpret the Constitution and to see that the provinces and the Federal Legislature acted within the spheres reserved for them by the Act. However, the last word in that matter was to be said by the Privy Council sitting in London.

The Act abolished the India Council of the Secretary of State. This body had been set up in 1858 to assist the Secretary of State for India in the discharge of his duties. However, there had been a lot of criticism about its composition and its actual role and consequently the same was abolished by the new Act. The Secretary of State was to be assisted in future by an advisory body consisting of not less than 3 and not more than 6 advisers. At least half of those advisers were to be those persons who had held offices in India for at least 10 years and who had not left India for more than 2 years at the time of their appointment. They were to hold office for 5 years only. They could not sit in Parliament. Their function was advisory and as a rule, the Secretary of State was required to secure the concurrence of at least one-half of the advisers. The Act provided that "It shall be in the discretion of the Secretary of State whether or not he consults his advisers in any matter, and if so, whether he consults them individually and whether or not he acts in accordance with any advice given to him by them."

The position of the Governor under the new Act resembled that of the Governor-General although it differed a little on account of the introduction of provincial autonomy. The Governor-General was required to act in 3 different capacities. Ordinarily, he was to act according to the advice of his ministers. When he did so, he acted as a constitutional head and his position could be compared to the Lieutenant-Governor of a Canadian province. He was also authorised to act in his individual judgment. While doing so, he had to listen to the advice of his ministers but it was up to him to accept their advice or not. He acted in his individual judgment while performing his special responsibilities which were the prevention of any grave menace to the peace and tranquillity of the province or any part of it, safeguarding the rights and legitimate interests of the public servants and their dependents, the rights and interests of the Indian states and the dignity of their rulers and the legitimate interests of the minorities, administration of partially excluded areas, prevention of commercial discrimination against Englishmen and their goods and the execution of the orders and directions of the Governor-General issued by him in his discretion. It was the duty of the Governor of C.P. to see that a reasonable share of the provincial revenues was spent for the benefit of the people of Berar. Likewise, it was the duty of the Governor of Sind to secure the proper administration of the Lloyd Barrage and Canals' Scheme.

The Governor was to act in his discretion in the following cases. He was to appoint and dismiss ministers. This was a very substantial power and it was actually exercised by the Governors of Bengal and the North-West Frontier Province to exclude a party and keep the other party in power. He was to preside over the meetings of the Council of Ministers. While doing so, he could influence the deliberations and conclusions of the ministers. That was particularly due to his great administrative experience. He could issue two kinds of ordinances. One kind of ordinance could be issued by him at any time and that lasted for 6 months. The other type of ordinance was to be issued only when the Legislature was not sitting. The Governor could also issue what were known as Governor's Acts. In certain cases, the previous sanction of the Governor was required for the introduction of certain bills in the Provincial Legislature. He could stop the discussion of any bill in the Legislature at any time. Even when the bill was passed, he could veto the same or send the same back for reconsideration by the Legislature. He could reserve a bill for the assent of the Governor-General. He appointed the members of the provincial Public Service Commission. He was given many powers regarding the police force and also the authority to suppress the terrorists. The Governor was to decide which items of expenditure were to be regarded as "expenditure charged upon revenues of the province". Those items were taken out of the control of the legislature. The non-votable items formed about 40% of the budget. If the whole or any part of the budget was rejected, the Governor was given the authority to restore the same. Under section 93 of the Act, a Governor could suspend the Constitution and take over the administration of the province in his own hands.

The position of the provincial ministers under the new Act was certainly superior to that under the old Act. There were no reserved Departments and the Governor was expected to carry on the administration of the province according to the advice of the ministers. It was laid down in the Instrument of Instructions that the Governor was to summon that person to form the ministry who could be expected to command a majority in the Provincial Legislature. The other ministers were to be appointed by the Governor on the advice of the Chief Minister. It was the duty of the Governor to see that minorities were given representation in the ministry. If a person was not a member of the Legislature at the time of his appointment, he was to get himself elected within 6 months of his appointment. The Governors were instructed to encourage collective responsibility among the ministers. They were allowed to preside over the meetings of the Council of Ministers.

However, it cannot be denied that the powers of the ministers were limited. They did not enjoy complete autonomy in the provincial field. The enormous powers of the Governor were responsible for the weakness of the position of the ministers. The Governor had many legislative powers and those powers restricted the legislative control of the ministers. He may not allow a particular bill to be introduced in the Legislature. He may veto a bill which had been passed by the Legislature on the initiative of the ministry. He may stop the discussion of any bill at any time. The issuing of ordinances and Governor's Acts also limited the legislative scope of the ministers. The same could be said about finance. The ministers were not given a free hand in the matter of proposing new taxes. A Governor may not give his sanction to a bill for that purpose. The ministers had no control over 40% of the budget which was non-votable. A Governor could dismiss the ministers and that was actually done in many cases. Fazl-ul-Haq, the Chief Minister of Bengal, was unceremoniously dismissed by the Governor in 1943. Alla Bux, the Chief Minister of Sind, was dismissed because he gave up the title of Khan Bahadur. The Governor of the Punjab dismissed Shaukat Hayat Khan.

Different views were expressed regarding the position of the ministers under the Act of 1935. The view of Lord Zetland was: "Let it not be supposed that the field of Government is to be divided into two parts, in which the Governor and the ministry operate separately at the risk of clashes between them. The essence of the new constitution is that the initiative and responsibility for the whole of the Government of province, though in form vesting in the Governor, passes to the ministry as soon as it takes office." Sir Maurice Hallet, Governor of U.P., says: "After all, the relations of a Governor with his ministers were not those of a master and his servants; rather they are partners in a common enterprise—the good government of the province." The true position was that the actual position of the ministry depended upon its party strength in the Legislature and the personality of the members who constituted the ministry. In the last analysis, much depended upon the personal equation.

The Government of India Act, 1935 did not set up Provincial Legislatures of a uniform pattern. The six provinces of Assam, Bengal, Bihar, U.P., Madras and Bombay were given two chambers each, while the legislatures of the Punjab, Sind, North-West Frontier Province, Orissa and C.P. had only one chamber. Where there were two chambers, their names were the Provincial Legislative Assembly and Provincial Legislative Council. Where there was only one house, it was merely the Provincial Legislative Assembly. While all the members of the Assembly were elected, some of the members of the Council were nominated. The size of the Provincial Assemblies varied from province to province. It was 215 for Madras, 175 for Bombay and Punjab, 250 for Bengal, 228 for U.P., 152 for Bihar, 112 for C.P. and Berar, 108 for Assam, 50 for North-West Frontier Province and 60 each for Orissa and Sind. The seats in the various provinces were distributed according to the Communal Award as amended by the Poona Pact. Some seats were known as general seats out of which some were reserved for the scheduled castes. Separate representation on communal lines was given to the Muslims, Sikhs, Anglo-Indians, Europeans and the

Indian Christians. Some seats were reserved for commerce, industry, mining and plantation, land-holders, labour and universities. Europeans in Bengal were given the highest representation. The land-holders both in U.P. and Madras got 6 seats each. 90 seats were given in Bengal to commerce, industry, mining and plantation. In Bengal, out of a total of 78 seats given to the Hindus, 30 were reserved for the scheduled casts. The life of the Assembly was fixed at 5 years but the same could be dissolved earlier. It could also be extended beyond the period of 5 years. The first general elections were held in 1937 and the next elections were held not earlier than 1945. The maximum number of seats for a provincial Legislative Council was 56 in Madras, 30 in Bombay, 65 in Bengal, 60 in U.P., 30 in Bihar and 22 in Assam. Out of a total of 56 seats in Madras, 10 were filled up by the Governor through nomination. The general seats for Madras, Bombay, Bengal, U.P., Bihar and Assam were 35, 20, 10, 34, 9 and 10 respectively. The Muslims were given 17 seats each in Bihar and U.P. 27 and 12 seats respectively in Bengal and Bihar were filled by the Legislative Assemblies of those provinces. Some seats were reserved for Europeans and Indian Christians. The Provincial Legislative Council was a permanent body. The tenure of office of members was 9 years and one-third of them were to retire after every 3 years.

The age qualification for the membership of the Provincial Legislative Assembly was fixed at 25 and for Legislative Council 30. No person could become a member of both the Houses of the Legislature. Residence in the constituency for a certain number of days, usually 180 or 120, was necessary for franchise. The voting qualifications varied from province to province. In the case of the Punjab, the right of voting was given to those who paid an income tax or a direct municipal tax amounting to not less than Rs. 50 per year, those who paid land revenue amounting to not less than Rs. 5 per year, those who owned or occupied immovable property of the rental value of Rs. 60 per year and those who possessed educational qualifications up to the primary standard.

It is true that the provincial autonomy as introduced by the Government of India Act, 1935 was a definite improvement on the system set up by the Government of India Act, 1919, but it is not correct to presume that provincial autonomy was intended to establish a full-fledged responsible government in the provinces. If that had been the intention, the authors of the Government of India Act, 1935 would have chosen to use a different terminology. The fact is that the British Government did not intend to give full responsible Government in the provinces. This is clear from the large number of discretionary powers given to the Governors. The same intention becomes clear when we consider the nature and extent of the special responsibilities of the Governors. If the Governors were expected to play the role of the guardians of the British interests and other vested interests in India, that was bound to affect adversely the position of the ministers. Lord Zetland who was the Secretary of State for India in 1937, has rightly pointed out that the British Parliament reserved to itself a potential measure of control in a certain limited and clearly defined sphere. While performing their special responsibilities, the Governors were responsible to the British Parliament for acts of commission and omission. It was pointed out by critics that provincial autonomy was merely a farce and far from a living reality. It has also been characterised as merely a sham.

The Government of India Act, 1935 had many defects. The Indians were not given control over the Government of their country. They could not change or amend their constitution. The Whitehall framed the policy which was followed by the Government of India. The Indians detested control from London. They also detested the dyarchical form of Government at the centre. It was rightly pointed out that the evils of dyarchy which were found in the provinces were bound to be repeated at the centre also. The inauguration of the All-India Federation depended upon the condition that a specified number of states joined the Federation. The Act gave the Indian States the option to join or not to join the Federation. The result was that the federal part of the Act could not be enforced at all. The Indian states were given a privileged position under the Act. The representation given to them both in the Council of State and the Federal Assembly was more than what was due to them on the basis of their territory, population or the contributions to be made by them to the revenues of the Federal Government. While the members from British India were to be elected by the people, Indian princes were allowed to nominate their quota. It was well-known that the Indian princes were absolutely under the control of the Political Department of the Government of India and they did what they were directed to do by the Viceroy who was incharge of the Political Department. They could not dare to vote against their masters. It was rightly feared that the nominees from the Indian states would be used by the British Government in India to serve their own interests and stop the progress of the country. The system of indirect elections to the Federal Assembly was resented. That was against the very spirit of democracy and also of the times. The control to be exercised by the Secretary of State for India over the Indian Civil Service, the Indian Police Service and other All-India Services was also resented. The Indian army got the lion's share out of the Indian revenues but the Indians were not given any control over the Defence part of the budget as the same was kept as a reserved subject. The seats in the Legislatures were to be filled on the basis of the Communal Award and hence the constitution became communalism-ridden. The Communal Award cut at the very roots of Indian nationalism and solidarity and was rightly considered to be most dangerous. It was feared that longer the period for which the Communal Award worked, the greater will be the difficulty in keeping the unity of the country. The powers of the Provincial Legislatures and the Federal Legislature were very much restricted and did not give enough of scope to the ministers concerned. The rulers of the Indian states criticized the Federal scheme on the ground that it did not give them any power or authority to leave the federation after joining it once. The federation was given the power of coercing them. The representatives from British India were bound to dominate the Federal Legislature and Federal executive and thereby influence the Viceroy to take steps which might impair their sovereignty. The discretionary powers of the Governors reduced provincial autonomy to a farce. Those powers and responsibilities "combine, crib and confine" the powers of the Provincial Legislatures and executive. Some of those powers and responsibilities were so vaguely defined that those could be interpreted to mean anything according to the exigencies of the situation. The Governor was made the sole judge to decide whether any particular matter fell within the scope of its discretionary powers or not or affected any of his special responsibilities. He could become a virtual dictator of the province within the letter of the law.

The Indian National Congress condemned the federal scheme on many grounds. The scheme did not envisage any real transfer of power into the hands of the Indians. The Federal Legislature was saddled with an element of conservatism in the form of the nominated representatives of the states. The constitutional advancement of India was wholly at the mercy of the Indian states.

The view of Dr. A. B. Keith was that the Federal scheme was not satisfactory. The units of which it was composed were too disparate to be joined suitably together. On the British side, the scheme was favoured in order to provide an element of pure conservatism in order to combat any dangerous elements of democracy contributed by British India. On the side of the rulers, their essential pre-occupation was with the effort to secure immunity from pressure in regard to the improvement of internal administration of their states. Particularly unsatisfactory was the effort made to obtain a definition of paramountcy which would acknowledge the right of the ruler to mis-govern his state as he was assured of British support while putting down any resistance to his regime. The federation was largely cooked by the desire to evade the issue of extending responsible government to the Central Government of British India. The withholding of Defence and External Affairs from federal control rendered the alleged concession of responsibility all but meaningless. Sir Shanmukham Chetty, at one time the Speaker of the Central Assembly under the Government of India Act, 1919 and later on the Finance Minister in post-independence India, made the following observation in this connection: "It is indeed a far cry between the Government Act and the Dominion Status. The principle of Dominion Status asserts that the Dominion should have the right to the same measure of autonomy in external affairs as in internal matters and that it is the duty of the British Government to give effect to the doctrine accepted. But India has neither control in the internal nor in the external affairs. The internal administration shall be under the guidance of the Governor-General and the Governors who are vested with tremendous powers; the external affairs shall be under the guidance of Parliament, the Crown and the Secretary of State. Indians shall not be able to work out their own destiny. The safeguards, reservations, special powers of the Governor-General and the Governors, the weakness of the

Indian Legislatures, and the ministers in the Federal and the Provincial Governments with no Central responsibility and weak provincial autonomy, the Communal Award, the States' representation bought at the expense of British Indians, the financial and other economic drawbacks, half measures of the Indianisation of the Army with no control over the Defence—all these things show that Indians shall not be having Dominion Status."

The new Indian constitution was described by Pandit Jawahar Lal Nehru as a "machine with strong brakes and no engine." The view of Pandit Madan Mohan Malaviya was: "The new Act has been thrust upon us. It has a somewhat democratic appearance outwardly, but it is absolutely hollow from inside." C. Rajagopalachariar described the new constitution as worse than dyarchy. Mr. M. A. Jinnah described the scheme of 1935 as "thoroughly rotten, fundamentally bad and totally unacceptable". C. Y. Chintamani described the Government of India Act, 1935 as the anti-India Act and the government as "against" India. Mr. Fazl-ul-Huq, Chief Minister of Bengal, observed that under the Government of India Act, 1935, there was to be neither Hindu Raj nor Muslim Raj but British Raj.

Constitutional Development from 1937 to 1950

The whole of the Government of India Act, 1935 was not introduced at once. The part dealing with provincial autonomy came into force on April 1, 1937. The Federal Court of India was also set up. The Indian National Congress took part in the provincial elections held in 1937 and got a clear majority in 6 provinces. Later on, the number rose to 7. To begin with, there was a deadlock on account of the differences between the Government of India and the Indian National Congress which was not satisfied with the intentions of the British Government. There were prolonged negotiations and when the Viceroy gave an undertaking that the Governors would not interfere in the day to day affairs of the provincial administration, the Congress ministries were formed and they remained in office till 1939 when they resigned on account of their differences with the British Government after the outbreak of the World War II (1939-45). Throughout the War, many attempts were made by the British Government to win over the cooperation of the people of India. With that object in view, the famous **August Offer** was made in 1940 by Lord Linlithgow, the then Victory of India. The August Offer was in the form of a statement made by the Viceroy on behalf of the British Government. It was pointed out that though the differences which prevented national unity remained un-bridged in India, the expansion of the Executive Council of the Governor-General and the establishment of an Advisory War Council should not be postponed any longer. In view of the doubts as to whether the position of the minorities would be sufficiently safeguarded in any future constitutional change or not, the British Government reaffirmed its desire that full weight would be given to minority opinion. To quote the words of the Viceroy, "It goes without saying that they could not contemplate transfer of their present responsibilities for the peace and welfare of India to any system of Gov-ernment whose authority is directly denied by large and powerful elements of India's national life. Nor could they be parties to the coercion of such elements into submission to such a Government." Subject to the fulfilment of their obli-gations—an allusion to such questions as defence, minority rights, the treaties with the states and the position of the Secretary of State Services—, the British Government concur-red in the Indian desire that the framing of the new constitu-tion should be "primarily the responsibility of Indians them-selves and should originate from Indian conceptions of the social, economic and political structure of the Indian life". Constitutional issues could not be decided at "a moment when the national life is engaged in a struggle for existence", but after the War, a representative Indian body would be set up to formulate the new constitution. In the meantime, the British Government would welcome and assist any efforts to reach agreement as to the form and operation of this con-stitution-making body and as to the principles of the constitu-tion. In the interval, the British Government hoped that all parties and communities in India would cooperate in India's war effort and by thus working together pave the way for India's attainment of free and equal partnership in the British Commonwealth of Nations. Nothing came out of this offer on account of the attitude of the Indian National Congress and the offer was simply rejected.

Cripps Proposals (1942)

The deadlock in Indian politics continued. While the British Government refused to come to terms with the Congress, the latter refused to cooperate with the former. During this period, the second World War was going on. The international situation began to deteriorate. In December 1940, Japan joined the War against the United States and Great Britain. The Japanese armies advanced rapidly all over the South-East Asia. The tide of their conquest rolled at a tremendous pace towards Burma and India. When Singapore fell in February 1942, the security of India was threatened. Rangoon fell on March 7, 1942. Colombo was bombarded. Some bombs fell on the eastern coast of India. Calcutta was threatened and refugees began to leave that city. In spite of this threatening situation, the attitude of the Indian leaders did not change. The Congress was as hostile as ever. It was not prepared to help the British Government against anybody. It was prepared to help only if India was given independence. The Muslim League was more concerned with the partition of India than its immediate salvation from the Japanese conquest.

It was under these circumstances that Sir Stafford Cripps, the Leader of the House of Commons, came to India in March 1942 with certain proposals on behalf of the British Government. The following is the text of the Draft Declaration of the British Government:

"(a) Immediately upon cessation of hostilities, steps shall be taken to set up in India, in the manner described hereafter, an elected body charged with the task of framing a new constitution for India.

"(b) Provision shall be made, as set out below, for participation of Indian States in the constitution-making body.

"(c) His Majesty's Government undertake to accept and implement forthwith the constitution so framed subject only to:

"(i) The right of any province of British India that is not prepared to accept the new constitution to retain its present constitutional position, provision being made for its subsequent accession if it so decides.

"With such non-acceding provinces, should they so desire, His Majesty's Government will be prepared to agree upon a new constitution giving them the same full status as the Indian

Union and arrived at by a procedure analogous to that here laid down.

"(ii) The signing of a treaty which shall be negotiated between His Majesty's Government and the constitution-making body. This treaty will cover all necessary matters arising out of the complete transfer of responsibility from British to Indian hands; it will make provision, in accordance with undertakings given by His Majesty's Government, for the protection of the racial and religious minorities, but will not impose any restriction on the power of the Indian Union to decide in future its relationship to other member-States of the British Commonwealth.

"Whether or not an Indian State elects to adhere to the constitution, it will be necessary to negotiate a revision of its treaty arrangements so far as this may be required in the new situation.

"(d) The constitution-making body shall be composed as follows unless the leaders of Indian opinion in the principal communities agree upon some other form before the end of hostilities:

"Immediately upon the result being known of provincial elections which will be necessary at the end of hostilities, the entire membership of the Lower Houses of Provincial Legislatures shall as a single electoral college proceed to the election of the constitution-making body by the system of proportional representation. This new body shall be in number about 1/10th of the number of the electoral college.

"Indian States shall be invited to appoint representatives in the same proportion to their total population as in the case of representatives of British India as a whole and with the same powers as British Indian members.

"(e) During the critical period which now faces India and until the new constitution can be framed, His Majesty's Government must inevitably bear the responsibility for and retain the control and direction of the defence of India as part of their world war effort but the task of organizing to the full the military, moral and material resources of India must be the responsibility of the Government of India with the co-operation of the people of India. His Majesty's Government desire and invite the immediate and effective participation of the leaders of the principal sections of the Indian people in the counsels of their country, of the Commonwealth and of the

United Nations. Thus they will be enabled to give their active and constructive help in the discharge of a task which is vital and essential for the future freedom of India."

Sir Stafford had a very busy time in India. He met the leaders of the various parties and did his level best to persuade them to accept the proposals. His mission was a very difficult one. The Indian leaders were prepared to accept what was being promised to them in the future, but they were not satisfied with what was being offered to them at once. What they wanted was a say in the matter of the participation of India in the war. This Sir Stafford Cripps was not able to give them and no wonder his mission failed and he had to go back empty-handed.

It is true that the proposals of Cripps were an advance on the August Offer in many respects. They conceded to the projected Indian Union the liberty to secede from the British Commonwealth, if so desired. The framing of the new constitution was to rest not primarily but solely in Indian hands. However, its acceptance was made subject to the fulfilment of British obligations. If the Indians could not become free as a single unit, they could become free as two or more units. Disagreement among the Indians was not to give the British Government an excuse to perpetuate their rule in India. The August Offer had invited the Indian leaders to start discussing the principles of the new constitution and the method of framing it. The Cripps Proposals contained a plan for a constitution-making body to be adopted if no Indian plan was agreed upon before the cessation of the hostilities. The Cripps Proposals went farther than the August Offer as regards the character of the interim system of the Government. The offer had provided for the inclusion of a certain number of representative Indians in the Executive Council. The Cripps Proposals invited the leaders of the principal sections of the Indian people to participate in the counsels of India, the Commonwealth and the United Nations.

However, the Cripps Proposals were criticized by all the interested parties in India. Each party criticized the proposals from its own point of view. The objection of the Congress was not so much to the long-term arrangement as to the interim arrangement. The Congress acted on the principle that one bird in hand was better than two in the bush. Cripps had given an understanding to the Congress that with the exception of the Defence Department, other Departments would be completely in the hands of Indians and the Governor-General would act as a constitutional head. However, at a later stage, he withdrew that offer. That made the Congress suspicious regarding the honesty of the British Government. The Congress wanted the Executive Council of the Governor-General to work as a cabinet but the British Government was not prepared to make such a concession. The Congress also objected to the veto power of the Viceroy. It was also opposed to the acceptance of the novel principle of the non-accession of the provinces. It appeared to them that this provision brought in Pakistan by the back door.

The Hindu Mahasabha opposed the Cripps proposals on two grounds. It was opposed to the freedom given to the provinces to leave the Indian union and set up separate governments of their own. It also objected to the elections on the basis of the Communal Award which was anti-national and un-democratic. The Sikhs also opposed the provisions relating to the non-accession of the provinces. They declared: "We shall resist by all possible means the separation of the Punjab from All India Union." The depressed classes denounced the proposals on the ground that the necessary safeguards were not provided for their interests. The Muslim League opposed the creation of a single Indian Union. It was feared that if one single Union was created, the creation of another might become impossible. The League also opposed the system of election by a single electoral college by proportional representation. This was not in accordance with the system of communal representation which enabled the Muslims to send their own representatives. The League also objected to the method and procedure for non-accession of the Indian provinces. Their intention was that the provinces of India were created for administrative convenience and not on any logical basis. They demanded the redistribution of the provinces. They opposed the plebiscite by the whole of the adult population of India. They demanded the inherent right of self-determination for the Muslims alone. The scheme was not acceptable to the League because Pakistan was not conceded unequivocally and the right of Muslim self-determination was denied, although the recognition given to the principle of partition was appreciated.

Mahatma Gandhi was not at all impressed by the proposals

brought by Cripps. He is stated to have told him thus: "Why did you come if this is what you have to offer? If this is your entire proposal to India, I would advise you to take the next plane home". Sir Stafford's reply was: "I will consider that".

It is pointed out that there were snags in the proposals brought by Cripps. One was the repetition of the August Offer of 1940 and the addition of the explanation that "the present declaration is intended—not to supersede, but to clothe these general declarations with precision and to convince the people of India of the War Cabinet's sincere resolve." This created suspicion in the minds of the people. It indicated a resolve on the part of the British Government to safeguard its prestige. The second snag was that there was no indication in the proposals that the British Government was prepared to part with power. Another defect in the scheme was that it had either to be accepted as a whole or rejected as a whole. There was no scope for any internal adjustment. Sir Stafford Cripps had been placed in a very tight corner by Sir Winston Churchill and his associates. The failure of his mission was a foregone conclusion.

After the failure of the Cripps Mission there was a lot of discontentment in the country. The Congress leaders were convinced that they could not expect anything from the British Government in the near future. It is under these circumstances that the Indian National Congress passed the famous "Quit India" resolution on August 8, 1942. In March 1944, Mr. C. Rajagopalachariar put forward his formula to resolve the political deadlock in the country. However, his proposals were not accepted by Mr. Jinnah. In January 1945, the Desai-Liaquat Formula saw the light of the day but nothing came out of it. On June 14, 1945, Lord Wavell, the then Governor-General and Viceroy of India, gave a broadcast to the people of India. After that, he called at Simla a conference of the Indian leaders to end the deadlock. His proposals were not accepted and he made a public confession of his failure.

Cabinet Mission Scheme (1946)

When the Labour Party came to power in England in 1945, it ordered the holding of elections in the provinces. After that, the Labour Government sent the famous Cabinet Mission to India in March 1946. Prolonged discussions took place between the members of the Mission and the leaders of the

Indian National Congress and the Muslim League. However, the two main political parties could not come to any mutual understanding. The result was that the members of the Mission had to put forward their own formula for solving the constitutional deadlock. That formula was embodied in a joint statement issued by the Cabinet Mission and Lord Wavell on May 16, 1946.

After pointing out the impracticability of the Pakistan scheme, the statement of May 16 recommended that the new constitution of India should take the following basic form:—

"(1) There should be a Union of India, embracing both British India and the States which should deal with the following subjects: Foreign Affairs, Defence and Communications, and should have the powers necessary to raise the finances required for the above subjects.

"(2) The Union should have an Executive and a Legislature constituted from British India and States representatives. Any question raising a major communal issue in the Legislature should require for its decision a majority of the representatives present and voting of each of the two major communities as well as a majority of all the members present and voting.

"(3) All subjects other than the Union subjects and all residuary powers should vest in the Provinces.

"(4) The States will retain all subjects and powers other than those ceded to the Union.

"(5) Provinces should be free to form Groups with executives and legislatures, and each Group could determine the Provincial subjects to be taken in common.

"(6) The constitutions of the Union and of the Groups should contain a provision whereby any Province could, by a majority vote of its Legislative Assembly, call for a reconsideration of the terms of the constitution after an initial period of 10 years and at 10 yearly intervals thereafter."

As regards the constitution-making machinery, it was provided that the Legislative Assemblies of the provinces would elect the members of that body on the basis of one representative for one million of the population. The Sikh and Muslim legislators were to elect the quota of their communities, determined on the population basis. Others were to elect the representatives for the rest of the population. The representatives from the provinces were to divide themselves into three sections, A, B and C. Section C was to consist of the representatives of Bengal and Assam, Section B of the Punjab, Sind and North-West Frontier Province and Section A of the rest of the provinces of India. "These Sections shall proceed to settle the Provincial Constitution for the Provinces included in each Section, and shall also decide whether any Group Constitution shall be set up for these provinces and, if so, with what provincial subjects the Groups should deal." The representatives of the Sections of the Indian States were then to re-assemble and settle the Union Constitution.

TABLE OF REPRESENTATION

Section A

Province	General	Muslim	Total
Madras	45	4	49
Bombay	19	2	21
United Provinces	47	8	55
Bihar	31	5	36
Central Provinces	16	1	17
Orissa	9	0	9
Total	167	20	187

Section B

Province	General	Muslim	Sikh	Total
Punjab	8	16	4	28
N.-W. Frontier Province	0	3	0	3
Sind	1	3	0	4
Total	9	22	4	35

Section C

Province	General	Muslim	Total
Bengal	27	33	60
Assam	7	3	10
Total	34	36	70

Total for British India		292
Maximum for States		93
	Total	385

The Provinces of India were given the power to opt out of the Groups by a decision of their Legislature after the general elections under the new Constitution. The Resolutions of the Union Constituent Assembly regarding major communal issues were to require a majority of the representatives present and voting of each of the two major communities. The Chairman of the Constituent Assembly was to decide which resolution raised major communal issues and was to consult the Federal Court before giving his decision. A plan for the interim Government was also envisaged in the Scheme of May 16, 1946.

The Cabinet Mission declared that the British Government could not and would not in any circumstances transfer paramountcy to an Indian Government. However, it was made clear that when a new self-governing Government or Governments came into being in British India, it would not be possible for the British Government to carry out the obligations of paramountcy. In that case, all the rights surrendered by the states to the paramount power were to return to the Indian states. "Political arrangements between the states on the one hand and the British Crown and British India on the other will thus be brought to an end. The void will have to be filled either by the states entering into a federal relationship with the successor Government or Governments in British India or, failing this, entering into particular political arrangements with it or them." This policy has been described as a "political scorched-earth policy."

The great merit of the Cabinet Mission scheme was that the Constituent Assembly was to be constituted on the democratic principle of population strength. The principle of weightage was to be discarded altogether. The democratic method of the decision of issues by a simple majority was adopted in the case of communal issues. However, safeguards were provided for the minorities. The scheme also provided for an Indian Union of provinces and states and rejected the idea of Pakistan completely. The Cabinet Mission scheme was the last attempt made by British statesmen to save India from division and disaster. Some of the anomalies of the scheme were due to the desire of the members of the Cabinet Mission to save Indian unity at any cost. The scheme required that all the members of the Constituent Assembly were to be Indians. Neither the British Government nor non-official Europeans in

India were to be given any representation in the Constituent Assembly. The European members of the Provincial Assemblies were to absent themselves from voting. It was to be provided that there was to be no interference with the work of the Constituent Assembly either by the British Government or by its officials. Within the framework of the scheme, the Constituent Assembly was to be its own master.

As regards its demerits, while the scheme protected the rights of the Muslim minority, the same principle was not applied to the Sikhs in the Punjab. The proposals of the Cabinet Mission with regard to the grouping of the provinces were not clear. Both the Congress and the Muslim League interpreted the provisions differently. The Muslims regarded the compulsory grouping of the provinces as one of the cornerstones of the Cabinet Mission Scheme and were not prepared to come to a compromise on that question. The Congress stand was that the making of the groups was optional for the provinces and the latter were free to join or not to join any group. As a matter of fact, Mahatma Gandhi asked the people of Assam not to join the group if they did not approve of it. To solve this difficulty, it was suggested that the provinces might join provisionally, but later on freedom might be given to them to leave it if they so desired. The Congress suggested that the matter be referred to the Federal Court of India for decision. However, the British Government gave its verdict in favour of the compulsory grouping of the provinces. The Muslim League won and the Congress lost its point. Another defect of the scheme was the order in which the Union and Sectional Assemblies were to meet and work and draft their constitutions. It looked ridiculous first to form the constitutions of the groups and the provinces and then to frame the constitution of the Union. It was like putting the cart before the horse. This practical difficulty would have been experienced if the whole scheme would have been worked out in actual practice.

As regards the events after May 16, 1946, the All India Muslim League passed a resolution on June 6, 1946 by which it accepted the Cabinet Mission scheme in its entirety. On June 26, 1946, the Working Committee of the Indian National Congress passed a resolution by which it accepted the scheme partially. The part accepted by it related to constitution-making. The view of the Working Committee was that the grouping of the provinces was not to be compulsory. The Congress rejected the interim Government scheme on the ground that the clarifications given were not acceptable. The resolution of the Working Committee was ratified by the All India Congress Committee. The Sikhs rejected the scheme completely on the ground that the compulsory grouping of the provinces as contemplated by the scheme was suicidal to their interests.

Before the members of the Cabinet Mission left India, they issued a statement along with Lord Wavell in which they expressed their satisfaction that the work of the making of the constitution would proceed with the consent of the major political parties in India. They regretted that an interim Government consisting of the various political parties could not be formed on account of certain difficulties. It was hoped that after the elections to the Constituent Assembly were over, negotiations would be started for the formation of an interim Government consisting of the representatives of the various political parties.

Mr. Jinnah who had accepted the scheme in its entirety, was annoyed at the decision of the British Government to postpone the formation of the interim Government. He accused Lord Wavell of his having gone back on his promise. He was so much angry that the Muslim League, under his leadership, passed another resolution on July 29, 1946 by which it withdrew its former acceptance of the Cabinet Mission scheme. Mr. Jinnah was not contented with this negative action. The Muslim League passed the famous Direct Action Resolution by which both the Congress and the British Government were condemned for their breach of faith with the Muslims. It was declared that the time had come for the Muslim League to resort to direct action to achieve Pakistan. The resolution authorised the Working Committee of the Muslim League to prepare a programme of direct action at once. August 16, 1946 was fixed as the Direct Action Day. On that day, Hindu-Muslim riots took place in Calcutta on an unprecedented scale. There was a lot of bloodshed. There was an enormous loss of life and property. The British Government did nothing to stop this wholesale massacre. Mr. Suhrawardy, the Chief Minister of Bengal, at that time was himself in the control room to direct and protect the rioters.

Lord Wavell invited Pandit Jawahar Lal Nehru, the President of the Indian National Congress, to form the interim Government. He took office on September 2, 1946. To begin with, the Muslim League refused to join the interim Government, but on October 13, 1946 it decided to join. On October 15, 1946, 5 members of the Muslim League were included in the interim Government. This interim Government remained in office till the partition of India in August 1947.

Elections to the Constituent Assembly took place in July 1946 and the Constituent Assembly met for the first time in New Delhi on December 9, 1946 under the Presidentship of Dr. Sachidanand Sinha. The Muslim League refused to participate in its deliberations and boycotted it. In February 1947, Mr. Attlee, Prime Minister of England, declared that the British would leave India before June 1948 even if no agreement was made between the Muslim League and the Congress. In March 1947, Lord Mountbatten was appointed the Governor-General of India. After prolonged negotiations with the Congress and the Muslim League, he put forward his famous June 3 Plan in which he suggested the partition of the country into India and Pakistan. The scheme was accepted both by the Congress and the Muslim League. The proposals were put in the form of a bill which was passed by the British Parliament on July 18, 1947 as the Indian Independence Act, 1947.

The Indian Independence Act (1947)

The object of this Act was to give effect to June 3 Plan of Lord Mountbatten. It merely legalised what had already been promised to the people of India. The Act provided for the partition of India and the establishment of two Dominions of India and Pakistan from the appointed day (August 15, 1947). It also provided for the legislative supremacy of the two Dominions. The legislatures of the two Dominions were given full power to make laws having extra territorial jurisdiction. The British Government was to have no control over the affairs of the Dominions, provinces or any part of the Dominions after August 15, 1947. Until a new constitution was framed for each Dominion, the Act made the existing Constituent Assemblies the Dominion Legislatures for the time being. The Assemblies were to exercise all the powers which were formerly exercised by the Central Legislature in addition to its power regarding the framing of a new constitution. Pending the framing of a new constitution, each of the Dominions and all the provinces were to be governed in accordance with the Government of India Act, 1935. Each Dominion was authorised to make modifications in the Government of India Act, 1935. The Governor-General was given the power to modify or adapt the Government of India Act, 1935 as might be considered necessary till March 31, 1948. After that date, it was open to the Constituent Assembly to modify or adapt the old Government of India Act, 1935. The right of the King to veto laws or to reserve laws for his pleasure was given up. This right was given to the Governor-General. He was given the full right to assent in the name of His Majesty to any law of the Dominion Legislature made in the ordinary legislative capacity. The Act provided for the termination of the size-rainty of the Crown over the Indian States. All treaties, agreements and functions exercisable by His Majesty with regard to the states and their rulers were to lapse from August 15, 1947. The existing arrangements between the Government of India and the Indian states were to continue pending the detailed negotiations between the Indian states and the new Dominions. Agreements with the tribes of the North-West Frontier Province of India were to be negotiated by the successor Dominion. The office of the Secretary of State for India was to be abolished and his work was to be taken over by the Secretary of State for Commonwealth Affairs. The title of Emperor of India was to be dropped from the royal style and titles of the King of England. The Act terminated British authority over India and set up two independent Dominions, each with full authority to make its own constitution. Both the Dominions were given full freedom. They could leave the British Commonwealth of Nations if they so pleased. The Indian Independence Act was a great landmark in the Anglo-Indian relations. It marked the end of the British rule in India. The one unfortunate result of this Act was the partition of India into two parts: India and Pakistan.

Partition of India

The partition of India in 1947 was the outcome of many forces, although the main cause was the isolationist policy of the Muslims in India. Under the influence of Sir Syed Ahmed Khan, the Muslims in India began to think and dream separately from the Hindus. They started feeling that their interests were different from those of the Hindus and they had nothing in common with them. They went to the extent of saying that their interests were opposed to those of the Hindus. If India was given a responsible government, Hindu majority was bound to dominate the Muslims in India who were in a minority in the whole country. The Muslims also felt that they were educationally backward and consequently could not compete with the Hindus. With the passage of time, they drifted more and more away from the Hindus. The Muslim League ideology also estranged the Muslims from the Hindus. Sir Mohammad Iqbal and Mr. Jinnah also played their part in taking the Muslims away from the Hindus. Particularly after 1940, the Muslims insisted that they wanted a separate homeland and they were not prepared to come to any compromise with the Hindus. This isolationist policy of the Muslims ultimately led to the partitioning of India.

There is no denying the fact that the Muslims were helped immensely by the British Government in India. After the revolt of 1857, the Government of India was in search of allies in the country to stabilize its position against those who were out to drive them away and they found the Indian princes, zamindars and the Indian Muslims ready to cooperate with them. The Government of India followed a policy of "divide and rule" and kept on favouring the Muslims even at the cost of other communities in India. Bengal was partitioned in 1905 to please the Muslims. In 1909, the Muslims were given separate representation. They were given weightage in the legislatures. Seats were reserved for them on the Indian Council and the Governor General's Executive Council. Whatever was offered by the Congress to win over the Muslims, the Government of India and the British Government was always ready to offer them more. Under the circumstances, the Muslims of India began to look to the British Government for everything and were not in a mood to come to any compromise with the Congress or the Hindus. This is what happened on the occasion of the Second Round Table Conference and on many other occasions. The British bureaucracy was determined to have its revenge against Hindus who were clamouring for the liberation of their country. They were determined to crush the nationalist movement in India and if they failed in their effort, they were determined to divide the country in such a way that it was not worthwhile for the Hindus to have their freedom. It was this attitude which was responsible for the partition of India. It is a well-known fact that the British bureaucracy in India helped the Muslim League agitation in 1946 and 1947. As a matter of fact, it was this encouragement that helped the Muslim Leagues to hold their demonstrations without any interference or oppression from the side of the Government. This attitude may be compared with the treatment meted out to the Hindu agitators who were not only beaten mercilessly but also actually shot dead on many occasions.

It is pointed out that the Indian National Congress was also partly responsible for the partition of India. Dr. Lal Bahadur says: "It (Congress) adopted an attitude of appeasement towards the Mussalmans and thus encouraged them, withow wishing it, to go on adding to their unreasonable claims. In its passion to woo the Mussalmans, it frequently made sacrifices of principles. The communal malady grew into unproportioned height and ultimately led to the division of India. The Congress unfortunately never tried to understand the Muslim character of isolation and aggression and, to the end, continued to dally with the false hopes that somehow or other some turn of event would remove communal problem". The same author points out that even in the hour of the division of India, the Congress preferred to indulge in self-deception. "The All India Congress Committee trusted that when present passions subsided, India's problems would be viewed in their proper perspective and the false doctrine of **two** nations would be discredited and discarded by all." The initial mistake was made by the Indian National Congress in 1916 when it signed the Lucknow Pact. It ought not to have conceded separate electorates to the Muslims. It ought not to have agreed to give the Muslims a fixed percentage of representatives in the legislatures. The Congress attitude towards the Communal Award of 1932 also helped the isolationist policy of the Muslims. Nobody doubts the patriotism of the Congressmen but the fact remains that the Congress policy of appeasement of the Muslims ultimately led to the partitioning of India.

It is true that the Cabinet Mission scheme ruled out the idea of Pakistan and made provision for a Constituent Assembly which was to frame a constitution for free India. However, certain events helped the Muslim League. The Muslim League was allowed to join the Interim Government without agreeing to take part in the deliberations of the Constituent Assembly. Its members in the Interim Government refused to cooperate with the other members. They proclaimed their loyalty to the Viceroy whose appointees and nominees they considered themselves to be. They openly talked of carving out a Pakistan.

The division among the members of the Interim Government was reflected in the whole administrative machinery. According to the Report of the General Secretaries of the Indian National Congress, "If the Civil Services, the police and the army became divided in their loyalty and their members functioned on communal lines, nothing but mischief and chaos in the administration could result. And this was happening.... for the League, this situation was in the nature of pressure tactics for its demand for Pakistan." The Muslim League members of the Interim Government removed the Hindu and Sikh officers from the key positions in their Departments and put in their places Muslims who could be depended upon to help the cause of Pakistan.

It was during the period of the Interim Government that communal riots took place on a very large scale. "The ever-increasing and ever deepening chain of communal disturbances involving mass murder, arson or loot accompanied by unthinkable atrocities and horrors obliged the Working Committee of the Indian National Congress to consider the whole communal and political situation afresh." The only way out of the difficulty appeared to be the partitioning of India. Jawaharlal Nehru referred to this fact in these words on June 3, 1947: "There has been violence, shameful, degrading and revolting violence, in various parts of this country. This must end." The Congress was not happy about the partitioning of the country as it had consistently fought for the liberation of united India. The following words of Jawaharlal Nehru give an idea of the working of his inner mind: "For generations we have dreamt and struggled for a free and independent, united India. The proposal to allow certain parts to secede, if they so will, is painful for any of us to contemplate".

The announcement of the British Government in February 1947 that it was determined to put power into the hands of the Indians at a very early date worsened the communal situation in the country and helped the cause of Pakistan. While making the declaration, "His Majesty's Government had hoped that it would be possible for the major parties to cooperate in the working out of the Cabinet Mission's Plan of May 1946 and evolve for India a constitution acceptable to all concerned." However, that hope was not fulfilled as no pressure was put on the Muslim League to take part in the deliberations of the Constituent Assembly. The British Government also accepted the point of view of the Muslim League that the grouping of the provinces under the Cabinet Mission scheme was compulsory. It appears that it was felt by the Congress leaders in the month of May 1947 that the partition of India was absolutely inevitable. "The Congress had to choose between partition and continuance of a state of affairs which was becoming more and more intolerable." According to Sardar Patel, "I felt that if we did not accept partition, India would be split into many bits and would be completely ruined. My experience of office for one year convinced me that the way we have been proceeding would lead us to disaster. We would not have had one Pakistan but several. We would have had Pakistan cells in every office." Again, "It was then that I was made fully conscious of the extent to which our interests were being prejudiced everywhere by the machination of the Political Department, and came to the conclusion that the best course was to hasten the departure of these foreigners even at the cost of the partition of the country. It was also then that I felt that there was the unification of the rest of India."

Prof. Percival Spear says: "Was partition inevitable? In my opinion it was as soon as Jinnah resorted to direct action in 1946, for the only alternatives then were the frightful excesses of civil commotion and anarchy. But the die was probably cast much earlier, when the Congress failed to realize the new strength of the League in 1945 or to take office under the Cripps proposals of 1942. The Simla talks in 1945 were probably the last chance of getting the League to accept something short of full Pakistan; the Cripps offer of 1942 the last chance for the Congress to smother the League before it became a formidable mass movement. But there is another point to remember before too much regret is felt for the lost unity of India. The federal provisions of the Cripps and later proposals so reduced the powers of the Central Government that it is very doubtful if the great developments of Nehru's India would have been possible under them. It is probable that the centre would have been weak, and political energy spent by the communities in jostling for position instead of re-organising the country. Industrial development would have waited on party tactics, and five-year plans on political polemics. Only a joint directorate of the two parties could have achieved the kind of development which has actually occurred, and of this there was never any sign. However much partition may be regretted in principle, it was perhaps necessary, on this account, in the larger interests of the country." The views of Dr. Lal Bahadur are: "The partition of India was an event of great importance. It ushered in an era of independence, though the enthusiasm for it was somewhat diminished due to division. But even the partition is not without advantage. Had India remained a united whole, the Mussalmans would surely have dominated and would have shared in the amenities of life more than their due. Right traditions could never have developed as at every step special claims of the Mussalmans would have been advanced. They would have taken roots only if homage were not paid to Muslim appeasement. But seeing the history of the Indian National Congress this would have been impossible......But as it never understood Muslim mind and character, it also never adhered to principles in its dealing with Mussalmans. Expediency always came in operation in its treatment with the Muslims. The territorial integrity of India could be a benefit to the country only in the event of equal treatment to all and in the absence of Muslim appeasement policy. Since the Congress was incapable of doing it, the division of the country cannot be seriously lamented. It was choosing between the two evils—Muslim domination over the whole of the country and vivisection of Mother India—and in accepting the latter position, perhaps a better evil was chosen." (The Muslim League, p. 345).

On August 15, 1947, India became free. The Constituent Assembly which had met in New Delhi in December 1946, minus the members of Pakistan continued its work after the independence of India. Many committees were set up to do spadework and ultimately the draft constitution was published in January 1948. The people of India were given 8 months to discuss it and make their suggestions. It was on November 4, 1948 that the general discussion on the draft constitution started in the Constituent Assembly and the same continued till November 9, 1948. Between November 15, 1948 and

October 17, 1949 the draft was thoroughly discussed clause by clause. As many as 7,635 amendments were proposed and 2,473 were actually discussed by the Constituent Assembly. The draft was given the third reading from November 14, 1949 to November 26, 1949. The Constitution of India was adopted on November 26, 1949 and the same was signed by Dr. Rajendra Prasad as the President of the Constituent Assembly. In all, there were 11 sessions of the Constituent Assembly. It sat for two years, 11 months and 18 days. The consideration of the draft constitution took 114 days. The Constitution came into force on January 26, 1950.

The Constitution of India (1950)

The new Constitution of India consists of 395 Articles and 9 Schedules. It is divided into twelve parts. Between 1950 and 1968, there have been 21 amendments of the Constitution. The last amendment took place in April 1967.

The Constitution of India contains a Preamble which secures to all its citizens justice, social, economic and political, liberty of thought, expression, belief, faith and worship and equality of status and opportunity. It also aims at creating in all its citizens the feelings of fraternity and also assures the dignity of the individual and the unity of the nation. It also sets up in the country a sovereign democratic republic.

To begin with, there were four kinds of states under the Constitution, viz., Part A states, Part B states, Part C states and Part D states. Part A States were previously the Governors' provinces. Part B States were previously ruled by the Indian princes. Part C states were those which were formerly under the Chief Commissioners and Lieutenant-Governors. As a result of the Seventh Amendment of the Constitution made in 1956, the old distinction among the states was abolished. At present (1968), there are only 17 states and five Union Territories. The number of States has fluctuated from time to time on account of agitations from various quarters.

Persons born or domiciled in India, refugees who have migrated to India from Pakistan and the Indians overseas who apply for Indian citizenship, are Indian citizens. The Constitution has adopted the principle of a single citizenship for the whole of India.

The constitution provides for a large number of fundamental rights which are guaranteed to every citizen of India. Those rights are to be found in Articles 12 to 35 of the Constitution. The Supreme Court of India and the High Courts have been appointed the guardians of those fundamental rights and it must be admitted that they have performed their duty faithfully. This is conclusively proved by the judgment of the Supreme Court in the case of Golak Nath v. State of Punjab (A.I.R. 1967 S.C. 1643). The fundamental rights guaranteed by the Constitution are: right to equality before law, prohibition of discrimination on grounds of religion, race, caste, colour, sex or place of birth, equality of opportunity in matters of public employment, abolition of untouchability, right to freedom of speech and expression, right to assemble peacefully and without arms, the right to form associations and unions, the right to move freely throughout the territory of India, the right to reside and settle in any part of India, the right to acquire, hold and dispose of property, the right to practise any profession or to carry on any occupation, trade or business, the right to life and personal liberty, the right to freedom from arrest and detention in certain cases, the prohibition of traffic in human beings and forced labour, the prohibition of employment of children in any factory or mine or in any other hazardous work, the right to freedom of conscience and free profession, practice and propagation of religion, the freedom to manage religious affairs, freedom as to payment of taxes for promotion of any particular religion, freedom as to attendance at religious instruction or religious worship in certain educational institutions, protection of interests of minorities, right of minorities to establish and administer educational institutions, right to property with certain limitations and the right to constitutional remedies. It is worthy of notice that Article 32 which gives the right to move the Supreme Court for the enforcement of the fundamental rights is itself a fundamental right. Article 33 gives the Parliament power to modify the fundamental rights in their application to the Armed Forces or the forces charged with the maintenance of public order.

The constitution of India also contains what are known as the Directive Principles of State Policy. These principles relate to those matters which the Government of India is required to keep in view for the welfare of the people of the country. It is true that these cannot be enforced by a court of law but no Government can afford to ignore them. Articles 36 to 51 of the Constitution contain these Directive Principles of State

Policy. Article 38 provides that the state shall strive to promote the welfare of the people by securing and protecting as effectively as it may a social order in which justice, social economic and political shall inform all the institutions of the national life. The state shall, in particular, direct its policy towards securing that the citizens, men and women equally, have the right to adequate means of livelihood, that the ownership and control of the material resources of the community are so distributed as best to subserve the common good, that the operation of the economic system does not result in the concentration of wealth and means of production to the common detriment, that there is equal pay for equal work for both men and women, that the health and strength of workers, men and women, and the tender age of children are not abused and that the citizens are not forced by economic necessity to enter avocations unsuited to their age or strength and that childhood and youth are protected against exploitation and against moral and material abandonment. It shall take steps to organise village Panchayats and endow them with powers and authority to enable them to function as units of self-government. It shall make effective provision for securing the right to work, to education, and to public assistance in cases of unemployment, old age, sickness and disablement and any other cases of undeserved want. It shall make provision for securing just and humane conditions of work and for maternity relief. It shall endeavour to secure to all workers a living wage, conditions of work ensuring a decent standard of life and full enjoyment of leisure and social and cultural opportunities. It shall endeavour to promote cottage industries on an individual or cooperative basis in rural areas. It shall endeavour to secure for the citizens a uniform civil code throughout the territory of India. It shall endeavour to provide for free and compulsory education for all children until they complete the age of 14. It shall promote with special care the educational and economic interests of the weaker sections of the people. It shall raise the level of nutrition and the standard of living and improve public health. It shall endeavour to organise agriculture and animal husbandry on modern and scientific lines. It shall protect monuments and places and objects of national importance. It shall take steps to separate the judiciary from the executive. It shall endeavour to promote international peace and security, maintain just and honourable relations between nations, foster respect for international law and treaty obligations in the dealings of organised peoples with one another and encourage settlement of international disputes by arbitration.

The constitution provides for a President of the Indian Republic. He is to be elected indirectly by an electoral college consisting of the elected members of both houses of Parliament and Legislatures of the States. The President must be a citizen of India. He must have completed the age of 35 and he must be qualified for election as a member of Lok Sabha or House of the People. He is not eligible for election if he holds a job under the Government. He holds office for five years but he can be re-elected. He gets a salary of Rs. 10,000/- in addition to other allowances. He can be impeached for the violation of the constitution. The constitution provides a special procedure for the impeachment of the President. The President has been given a large number of powers in the executive, legislative and judicial fields. He is authorised to act in times of emergency. He is expected to act as constitutional head like the King of England.

The Vice-President of India is the ex-officio Chairman of the Council of States. Any citizen of India who is 35 years of age or more and who is qualified for the membership of Rajya Sabha or Council of States can be elected to this office by both the Houses of Parliament. When the President is ill or resigns or dies or is removed or is absent for any other reason, his place is taken over by the Vice-President of India for the time being.

The constitution provides for a Council of Ministers to assist the President. The President is to appoint the Prime Minister, but the other ministers are to be appointed by him on the advice of the Prime Minister. All the ministers are collectively responsible to the House of the People. It is the duty of the Prime Minister to communicate to the President all the decisions arrived at in the Cabinet. The Prime Minister is the link between the President and the Cabinet. His position is the same as that of the Prime Minister of England.

The Indian Parliament consists of two Houses: Lok Sabha and Rajya Sabha. Lok Sabha or House of the People consists of 525 members who are elected by the voters in the States and the Union Territories. Every adult or grown up citizen of India has been given the right to vote. The life of

Lok Sabha is five years. Lok Sabha has a Speaker and a Deputy Speaker. Rajya Sabha is a permanent body of 250 members. 238 members are elected by States and Union Territories and 12 members are nominated by the President on the ground of their having special knowledge or practical experience in respect of literature, science, art and social service. A member of Rajya Sabha must be a citizen of India and he must be not less than 30 years of age.

The constitution provides for Supreme Court of India consisting of Chief Justice of India and not more than 7 other judges. However, the number can be increased by an Act of Parliament and the same has actually been done. An Act of 1956 fixed the number at 10 but 3 more judges were added by an Act of 1960. All the judges of the Supreme Court are appointed by the President. They hold office during good behaviour till the age of 65. Provision has also been made for the appointment of **ad hoc** judges of the Supreme Court. The Supreme Court has been given both original and appellate jurisdiction. As regards its original jurisdiction, it can try any dispute between the Government of India and one or more States or between the Government of India and any State or States on one side and one or more States on the other, or between two or more States if and in so far as the dispute involves any question, whether of law or fact, on which the existence or extent of a legal right depends. The Supreme Court has the power to issue directions or orders in the nature of writs of Habeas Corpus, mandamus, prohibition, quo warranto and certiorari or any of them for the enforcement of fundamental rights. The appellate jurisdiction of the Supreme Court is of three kinds: constitutional, civil and criminal. An appeal can be taken from a High Court to the Supreme Court if a case involves a substantial question of law with regard to the interpretation of the constitution. In civil cases, an appeal lies to the Supreme Court if the value of the subject-matter of the dispute is not less than Rs. 20,000. In criminal cases, an appeal lies to the Supreme Court if the High Court on appeal reverses an order of acquittal of an accused person and sentences him to death. An appeal also lies if the High Court tries the accused and sentences him to death. Provision is made for the increase of its powers in criminal cases by Parliament. The Supreme Court has also advisory jurisdiction. It advises the President on questions of law and fact.

It has the power to grant special leave to appeal in certain cases. It has the power of review.

The constitution provides for a High Court for every Stat It is to consist of a Chief Justice and such other judges as the President of India may from time to time think fit. Every judge is required to retire at the age of 62. Every High Co has control over all the courts subordinate to it throughout the territory under its control except any courts constituted for the Armed Forces of India. Every High Court has both original and appellate jurisdiction. It can issue writs of the type issued by the Supreme Court. It also hears appeals in civil and criminal cases. Appointments, promotions and postings of the District Judges are made by the Governor in consultation with the Chief Justice of the High Court and the Chief Justice of India.

The constitution provides for a Union Public Service Commission and also State Public Service Commissions. Two or more States can have a joint Public Service Commission. The main functions of the Public Service Commissions are to recommend candidates for appointment and also to conduct examinations for recruitment to the services.

The constitution provides for a Comptroller and Auditor-General of India. He is to be appointed by the President to perform duties and exercise powers relating to the accounts of the Union and the States. His main duty is to keep a careful watch on the finances of the Union and the States and especially to see that the expenses voted by the Parliament or the Legislature of a State and laid down in the Appropriation Act are not exceeded or varied.

The constitution provides for the distribution of powers between the Union and the States. The Union List contains those subjects on which laws can be passed by the Indian Parliament. The State List contains those subjects on which laws can be made only by a State Legislature. The concurrent list contains those subjects on which laws can be passed both by the Union Parliament and the State Legislatures. However, if a law is passed by the Union Parliament on a subject in the concurrent list, any state law on that subject is superseded to the extent it is repugnant to the Union law. The residuary powers are given to the Union Parliament. There has been a lot of discussion in recent times with regard to the Union-State relations. It is emphasized that these relations must be reviewed in the light of the experience gained during the last few years as there is a possibility of a conflict between the two.

The constitution provides for the appointment of a Governor of the State by the Central Government. However, a demand is being made that the State Government concerned should be consulted by the Central Government before making the appointment. The Governor holds office during the pleasure of the President. A Governor has the power to grant pardons, reprieves, respites or remissions of punishment, or to suspend, remit or commute sentences in certain cases. The Governor appoints the Chief Minister but the other ministers are appointed by him on the advice of the Chief Minister. The ministers are collectively responsible to the Legislative Assembly of the State. The Governor appoints an Advocate-General for the State. His duty is to give advice to the Government upon legal matters and to perform other duties which are given to him by the Governor.

In the States of Andhra Pradesh, Bihar, Madhya Pradesh, Madras, Maharashtra, Mysore, Punjab, Uttar Pradesh and West Bengal, the State Legislatures have two houses known as the State Legislative Council and State Legislative Assembly. In other States, there is only one house consisting of the State Legislative Assembly. Provision has also been made for the abolition or creation of Legislative Councils in the States. Every Legislative Assembly has a Speaker and a Deputy Speaker and every Legislative Council has a Chairman and a Deputy Chairman.

The constitution provides for an Election Commission consisting of the Chief Election Commissioner and such number of other Election Commissioners as the President may from time to time fix. The superintendence, direction and control of the preparation of the electoral rolls for, and the conduct of, all elections to Parliament and to the Legislatures of every State and of elections to the offices of the President and the Vice-President held under the constitution vest in this Commission.

The constitution provides that the official language of the Indian Union shall be Hindi in Devnagri script. For a period of 15 years from the commencement of the Constitution, the English language shall continue to be used for all the official purposes of the Union for which it was being used immediately before its commencement. The President may, during the said period, by order authorise the use of Hindi language in addition to the English language. Notwithstanding anything in Article 343, Parliament may by law provide for the use, after the said period of 15 years, of the English language for such purposes as may be specified in the law. This has actually been done by an Act of Parliament on account of an agitation by the people of South India who demand the retention of the English language.

Provision has also been made for the amendment of the constitution. The constitution is amended when the President gives assent to any bill after it is passed in each House of Parliament by a majority of not less than two-thirds of the members of the House present and voting. Exception is made in the case of amendments of certain particular provisions in which amendments require ratification by not less than one-half of the State legislatures. The constitution was amended very frequently as the Congress had an overwhelming majority both at the Centre and in the States. It appears that such a thing is not going to be in the future as the Congress majority at the centre at present is very small and the Congress has practically no control over most of the States. It will be a herculean task in the future to amend the constitution. The emergence of a large number of political parties is going to give a lot of headache.

Suggested Readings

Alexander, H.	:	*India Since Cripps* (1944).
Alexandrowicz, C. H.	:	*Constitutional Developments in India* (1957).
Appadorai, A.	:	*Dyarchy in Practice*.
Banerjee, A. C. (Ed.)	:	*Indian Constitutional Documents*.
Campbell-Johnson	:	*Mission with Mountbatten* (1961).
Chatterji, A.	:	*The Constitutional Development of India* (1937-47).
Coupland, R.	:	*The Indian Problem* (1805-1935).
Coupland, R.	:	*The Cripps Mission*.
Cowell, H.	:	*History and Constitution of the Courts and Legislative Authorities in India*.
Curtis	:	*Dyarchy*.
Keith, A. B.	:	*Constitutional History of India*.
Lumby, W. E. R.	:	*The Transfer of Power in India*.

Mahajan, V. D.   :   *Constitutional History of India.*
Masaldan, P. N.   :   *Evolution of Provincial Autonomy in India* (1953).
Menon, V. P.   :   *Story of the Wavell Plan.*
Menon, V. P.   :   *The Transfer of Power in India.*
Munshi Papers   :   *Indian Constitutional Documents (Bhartiya Vidya Bhavan).*
Report of the Indian Statutory Commission.
Shelat, J. M.   :   *The Spirit of the Constitution.*

CHAPTER XXI

The Nationalist Movement in India

The nationalist movement which culminated in the achievement of independence in 1947, was not the result of a few agitators. It was the outcome of a large number of factors and the most important among them was British imperialism. It was British imperialism which brought about the unification of the country and enabled the people to think as one nation. Before the coming of the English to India, the people of the South were usually separated from the rest of India except for some short intervals. British imperialism made the people of India think themselves as one nation. Prof. Moon rightly observes: "British imperialism in India gave her a political unity under a third party in spite of the many discordant elements in Indian society". British rule in India brought the Indians into intimate contact with European countries and they were very much influenced by that contact. The 19th century in Europe was the century of nationalism and liberalism and the Indians learnt their lessons in nationalism and liberalism from the Europeans. It was argued by the Indians that if Germany and Italy could achieve their independence and unity, the Indians could also do likewise. The practical examples of those countries created a new spirit among the Indians to fight for the liberation of their country. Lord Ronaldshay points out that the new wine of western learning went into the heads of the young Indians. They drank deep from the source of liberty and nationalism and their whole outlook underwent a revolution. Coupland says that the Indians learnt from British history that British liberalism had backed the cause of the nations struggling to be free in South America, in the Balkans, in Italy and in Ireland. They found that Britain was not only the most powerful champion of popular government in the West but had also evolved a particular form of it which seemed the best of all possible forms. They also learnt that that particular form of Government could be transplanted in India.

The improvements in the means of transport and communication also quickened the pace of the nationalist movement in the country. The Indian leaders found themselves in a position to carry on their propaganda in every nook and corner of the country. Without those means of communication and transport, such a thing would have been unthinkable. The frequent meetings of the leaders among themselves and their personal contact with the people in different parts of the country gave a momentum to the nationalist movement.

Many scholars, poets and religious reformers contributed towards the progress of the nationalist movement. The study and republication of the ancient Indian literature by the Asiatic Society of Bengal and scholars like Max Muller, Monier Williams, Colebrooke, Ranade, Har Prasad Sastri, R. G. Bhandarkar, Rajendra Lal Mitra, etc., revealed to the people of India the majesty of the Sanskrit language and also inculcated among them a feeling of pride in their past and their faith in the future.

The religious and social reformers like Raja Ram Mohan Roy, Devendra Nath Tagore, Kishor Chandra Sen, P. C. Sarkar, Ishwar Chandra Vidyasagar, Swami Dayanand Saraswati, Ramkrishan Paramhans, Vivekanand, etc., presented a glorious picture of India's past and appealed to the people of India to bring back those good days once again. Col. Olcott rightly points out that Swami Dayanand exercised "great nationalising influence upon his followers". Mrs. Annie Besant says: "It was Dayanand Saraswati who proclaimed India for the Indians". It was Dayanand who proclaimed that good Government was no substitute for self-Government. Regarding the influence of Vivekanand, Nivedita says that "the queen of his adoration was the motherland". Like Dayanand, Vivekanand taught young India self-confidence and self-reliance. Mrs. Annie Besant also helped the cause of Indian nationalism by her writings and life-long work in various fields.

The Indian press and literature, both English and vernacular, also aroused national consciousness. Great was the influence of the papers like the Indian Mirror, Bombay Samachar, The Hindu Patriot, The Amrita Bazar Patrika, The Hindu, The Kesari, The Bengalee, etc., on the political life of the country. The writings of Dinbandhu Hemchandra Banerjee, Navin Chandra Sen, Bankim Chandra Chatterjee, R. C. Dutt and Rabindra Nath Tagore also affected the minds of the people. The Anand Math of Bankim Chandra Chatterjee has rightly been called "the Bible of modern Bengalee patriotism". Tagore and D. L. Roy gave us a lot of national poetry, songs and music. The writings of Indian patriots brought about a revolution in the minds of the Indians and those revolutionary minds were responsible for the growth of Indian nationalism.

There was a lot of discontentment in the country on account of many causes and that discontentment gave a stimulus to the growth of the nationalist movement in the country. The masses suffered from economic troubles. The middle classes suffered from the bugbear of unemployment. All the intelligent Indians felt and bewailed the economic exploitation of their country. The British officials working in India were a very heavy drain on the Indian resources. The economic system of India was adjusted to the needs of the people of England. The interests of the Indians were completely ignored. Blunt rightly points out that the vice of Indian finance was that the Finance Minister of India looked more to the interests of Great Britain than to those of India. Sir Henry Cotton condemned the economic exploitation of India and the consequent miseries of the people of the country. The Indians resented the attitude of the Englishmen towards them. The Europeans in India were arrogant. They had a very low opinion of the Indian character. They took pleasure in calling the Indians the creatures of an inferior breed, "half Gorilla, half Negro". They ridiculed the Indian black heathens "worshipping stocks and stones and swinging themselves on bamboo trees like bees". The European masters regarded the Indians as the "helots of the land, the hewers of wood and the drawers of water". Travelling in the upper class railway compartment was not for the Indians. Even the ruling Chiefs while travelling in the upper classes were bullied into unlacing the boots and shampooing the weary legs of the Sahibs just back from hunting excursions. Assaults on Indians by Europeans were frequent. As the Europeans were tried by juries consisting of Europeans, they very often escaped scot free. The administration of criminal justice in such cases was "a judicial scandal". Garrat says: "There was the long succession of murders and brutalities perpetrated by Englishmen upon the Indians which either went unpunished or in which, at the demand of the whole European community, only a small penalty was exacted. This scandal of which there were many flagrant instances in the sixties, has continued till recent times". (**An Indian Commentary,** pp. 116-17). Sir

Theodore Morrison, a member of the Indian Civil Service, wrote thus in 1890: "It is an ugly fact which it is no use to disguise that the murder of the natives by Englishmen is no infrequent occurrence". The Europeans had certain maxims about the Indians. "The first was that the life of one European was worth those of many Indians. The second was that the only thing that an oriental understood was fear. The third was that England had been forced to lose many lives and spend many millions to hold India and did she not merit some more substantial recompense than the privilege of governing India in a spirit of wisdom and unselfishness"? Such an attitude was bound to create a lot of bitterness between the rulers and the ruled. Edward Thompson observes: "Right at the back of the mind of many an Indian, the Mutiny flits as he talks with an Englishman—an unavenged, an unappeased ghost". (**The Other Side of the Medal**, p. 30).

The free trade policy of the Government of India stood in the way of the development of the country. Lala Murlidhar of the Punjab observed thus in 1891: "Free trade, fair-play between nations, how I hate the sham? What fair-play in trade can there be between impoverished India and the bloated capitalist England?" Again, "what are all these chandeliers and lamps and European-made chairs and tables and smart clothes and hats, English coats and bonnets and frocks and silver-mounted canes and all the luxurious fittings of your houses but trophies of India's misery, mementoes of India's starvation?" D. E. Wacha points out that the economic condition of the people of India deteriorated under the British Rule. 40 millions of Indians had to be contented with one meal a day. That was due to the tribute exacted by England from the starving peasantry and "exported to fructify there and swell still further the unparalleled wealth of these distant isles".

There was a lopsided development of the Indian economy. While Indian handicrafts and industries were allowed to starve, Indian agriculture was encouraged with a purpose. Most of the raw materials were produced in the country so that those could be used to feed the industries in England. That policy made India dependent on England. The free trade policy helped the British manufacturers and sacrificed the interests of India. The public debt increased tremendously. After 1858, the Crown took over the entire debt of 70 millions from the English East India Company. Between 1858 and 1876, the public debt was practically doubled. Out of the additional debt, only about 24 millions were spent on the construction of railways and irrigation works. No proper use of the money was made while constructing the railways. Those who constructed them were given more than what was due to them. It is rightly pointed out that the first 6,000 miles of railways cost more than £100 millions or £16,000 a mile. To quote W. N. Massey, "Enormous sums were lavished and the contractors had no motive for economy. All the money came from the English capitalist and so long as he was guaranteed 5% on the revenues of India, it was immaterial for him whether the funds he lent were thrown into the Hooghly or converted into bricks or mortar". L. H. Jenks points out that the expenses which increased the public debt of India were "the cost of the Mutiny, the price of the transfer of Company's rights to the Crown, the expenses of simultaneous wars in China and Abyssinia, every governmental item in London that remotely related to India down to the fees of the char-woman in the India Office and the expenses of ships that sailed but did not participate in hostilities and the cost of the Indian regiments for 6 months' training at home before they sailed.... The Sultan of Turkey visited London in 1868 in state and his official ball was arranged at the India Office and the Bill was charged to India. A lunatic asylum in Ealing, gifts to members of a Zanzibar Mission, the Consular and diplomatic establishments of Great Britain in China or in Persia, part of the permanent expenses of the Mediterranean fleet and the entire cost of a line of telegraph from England to India had been charged to the Indian treasury". (**The Migration of British Capital,** pp. 223-24). The net result of all these factors was that there was great misery in India. There was a lot of resentment and unrest. There were frequent famines in the country. There were as many as 24 famines during the second half of the 19th century and it is estimated that more than 28 millions died. The export of foodgrains from India to Great Britain during the years of famine added to the bitterness among the people. No wonder, Mr. Blunt, a British journalist touring India in 1882, observed that when Lord Lytton left India, India was on the verge of a revolution.

Before the outbreak of the Mutiny in 1857, there were many Englishmen who honestly believed and worked for the good of India. However, during the Mutiny days a lot of blood was shed on both sides. The Europeans wreaked their vengeance on the helpless and innocent Indians after the Mutiny. It was the policy of oppression and repression which added to the discontent of the country. The Indians were completely excluded from the legislatures in the country and also from the key posts in the administration. Zacharias says: "The blight of distrust had begun to fall upon England's relations with India; these people had mutineed once and committed dreadful atrocities—how could one trust them not to plan further sedition?" Another writer points out that "the old sympathy with India changed to a feeling of repugnance—the old spirit of content with life and work in India, the old inclination to regard things in an Indian rather than an English light, gave place to a reluctance to stay in India longer than needs must, and a disposition to judge things by an emphatically English standard". Garrat observes: "The English killed their prisoners without trial and in a manner held by all Indians to be the height of barbarity. They massacred thousands of the civilian population. Genl. Neil gave orders to his lieutenants that certain villages were marked out for destruction and all the men inhabiting them were slaughtered and the indiscriminate burning of their inhabitants occurred wherever our English armies moved".

The English language played a very important part in the growth of nationalism in the country. It acted as the **lingua franca** of the intelligentsia of India. Without the common medium of the English language, it would have been out of the question for the Madrasis, Bengalees and the Punjabis to sit at one table and discuss the common problems facing the country. The English language also made the Indians inheritors of a great literature which was full of great ideas and ideals. Tagore says: "We had come to know England through her glorious literature, which had brought new inspiration into our young lives. The English authors, whose books and poems we studied, were full of love for humanity, justice, and freedom. This great literary tradition had come down to us from the revolution period. We felt its power in Wordsworth's sonnets about human liberty. We gloried in it even in the immature production of Shelley written in the enthusiasm of his youth when he declared against the tyranny of priestcraft and preached the overthrow of all despotisms through the power of suffering bravely endured. All this fired our youthful imaginations. We believed with all our simple faith that even if we rebelled against foreign rule, we should have the sympathy of the West. We felt that England was on our side in wishing to gain our freedom." Sardar K. M. Panikkar has pointed out in **Asia and Western Dominance** that the introduction of the English language helped the cause of unity in the country and without it India would have been split into as many different units as there are languages in India and would have repeated the pattern of Europe with its conglomeration of mutually hostile units within the same Christian community (p. 332).

The ground was ready and the acts of omission and commission in the time of Lord Lytton accelerated the nationalist movement. The period from 1876 to 1884 has been called the seed-time of Indian nationalism. Lord Lytton held his famous Delhi Durbar in 1877 at a time when the people of South India were suffering terribly from the destruction brought about by famine. They wondered at the callousness of Lytton. An appropriate comment was made in these words: "Nero was fiddling while Rome was burning". The second Afghan War cost the Indian treasury a lot. No wonder, the Indians criticised Lytton mercilessly. In order to gag the Indian public opinion, Lytton passed the notorious Vernacular Press Act in 1878. The discriminatory provisions of this Act were universally condemned by the people belonging to all walks of life. Sir Erskine Perry points out that the Act was "a retrograde and ill-conceived measure injurious to the future progress of India". It was called the Gagging Act. Lytton passed the Arms Act in 1878 which made an invidious distinction between the Indians and the Europeans. While the Europeans were allowed to keep arms freely, the Indians could not do so without a licence. In the words of Surendra Nath Banerjee, the Arms Act "imposed upon was a badge of racial inferiority". Such a measure was derogatory to the self-respect of the people of India. Lord Lytton removed the import duty on cotton manufactures with a view to help the British manufacturers and this was resented by the Indians. It is true that Lord Ripon tried to remove some of the grievances of the Indians, but before he could do so, the Ilbert Bill controversy came to the fore. On that occasion, the Europeans behaved in such a manner that the Indians lost their faith in them. They refused to be tried by Indian officers. It became clear that the Indians could not expect any justice or fair-play from the Englishmen when their own interests were involved. Surendra Nath Banerjee observes: "No self-respecting Indian could sit idle under the fierce light of that revelation. It was a call to high patriotic duty to those who understood its significance". Before the effect of the Ilbert Bill controversy was over, the Indians had already organised themselves into the so-called Indian National Conference which met for the first time in December 1883 under the leadership of Surendra Nath Banerjee. This Conference was the fore-runner of the Indian National Congress which was founded in 1885.

The initiative for the foundation of the Indian National Congress came from Mr. A. O. Hume who was a retired British civilian. Hume has universally been acknowledged as the Father of the Congress. During his official career in India, Hume had formed strong views in favour of an early attainment of self-Government by India and when he retired in 1882, he began to evolve a definite scheme for creating a united public opinion in the country. His original idea was to bring together the leading Indian public men to discuss the social matters of the country. It was Lord Dufferin who changed his original scheme and suggested to him that the proposed organisation should perform the functions which Her Majesty's Opposition performed in England. Lord Dufferin wanted the "Indian politicians to meet yearly and point out to the Government in what respects the administration was defective and how it could be improved". Hume changed his original scheme according to the wishes of Lord Dufferin. The Congress was to act as a safety-valve for popular discontentment. It was to provide a peaceful and constitutional channel for the expression of Indian unrest so that it might not drift towards terrorism. It is sometimes stated that the object of Hume was to save the British Empire from disruption. However, the Congress was not expected to act as a bulwark of the British Empire in India. Hume was not a henchman of British imperialism. He had a passion for liberty. He wanted the Congress to serve the people of India.

On March 1, 1883, Hume issued a circular letter to the graduates of the Calcutta University in which the following passage occurs: "Constituting as you do a large body of the most highly educated Indians, you should, in the natural order of things, constitute also the most important source of all mental, moral, social and political progress in India. Whether in the individual or the nation, all vital progress must spring from within and it is to you, her most cultured, enlightened minds, her most favoured sons that your country must look for initiative. In vain, many aliens like myself love India and her children, as well as the most loving of these; in vain, may they, for her and their good, give time and trouble, money and thought; in vain may they struggle and sacrifice; they may assist with advice and suggestions; they may place their experience, abilities and knowledge at the disposal of the workers, but they lack the essential of nationality, and the real work must ever be done by the people of the country themselves." He proposed that a beginning should be made with a body of 50 founders who were to act as a mustard seed of future growth. "If only 50 men, good and true, can be found to join as founders, the thing can be established and the future development would be comparatively easy".

The appeal did not fall on deaf ears. The required number of persons did come forward from all parts of India and the first meeting of the Indian National Union which was subsequently renamed Indian National Congress was arranged to be held at Poona in December 1885. However, its venue had to be shifted to Bombay. W. C. Bonnerji, a leading barrister of Calcutta, was elected its President. A large number of delegates came from different parts of the country and the most important among them were Pherozeshah Mehta, Dadabhai Naoroji, K. T. Telang, Dinshaw Wacha, etc. The meeting was truly a national gathering consisting of leading men from all parts of India. In his presidential address, Mr. Bonnerji laid down the following as the objects of the Congress:

1. "The promotion of personal intimacy and friendship amongst all the more earnest workers in our country's cause in the various parts of the Empire.

2. "The eradication by direct friendly personal intercourse of all possible race, creed or provincial prejudices amongst all lovers of the country, and the fuller development and consolidation of those sentiments of national unity that took their origin in our beloved Lord Ripon's ever memorable reign.

3. "The authoritative record of the matured opinions of the educated classes in India on some of the more important and pressing of the social questions of the day.

4. "The determination of the methods by which during the next twelve months it is desirable for native politicians to labour in public interest."

The second meeting of the Indian National Congress was held in 1886 at Calcutta. Lord Dufferin invited the members of the Congress as "distinguished visitors" to a garden party at the Government House. A similar welcome was given by the Governor of Madras in 1887. However, a change took place in the attitude of the Government. After the Madras Session in 1887, an aggressive propaganda was started among the masses. Hume published a pamphlet entitled "An Old Man's Hope" in which he appealed to the people of England in these words: "Ah Men! well fed and happy! Do you at all realize the dull misery of these countless myriads? From their births to their deaths, how many rays of sunshine think you chequer their 'gloom-shrouded paths'? Toil, Toil, Toil; hunger, hunger, hunger; sickness, suffering, sorrow; these alas, alas, alas are the key-notes of their short and sad existence."

Hume made arrangements in England for propaganda in the press in favour of India. He was also able to enlist the support of a few members of the British Parliament. In April 1888, he made a vigorous speech at Allahabad in which he advocated propaganda among the masses of India in the same way as the Anti-Corn Law League had done in England. That was not liked by the British bureaucracy in India and it was suggested that the Indian National Congress be suppressed and Hume be deported to England. In October 1888, Sir A. Colvin, Lieutenant-Governor of the North-Western Provinces, addressed a letter to Hume covering 20 printed pages and warned him of the consequences of his action. Hume's reply covered 60 pages. On account of the attitude of bureaucracy, it became difficult to hold the session at Allahabad in December 1888, but Sir Luchmesher Singh, Maharajadhiraj of Darbhanga, came to its rescue by purchasing the property known as Lowther Castle where the session was held. Andrew Yule, a European magnate of Calcutta, presided over the Allahabad Session. The next session was held at Bombay in December 1889 under the presidentship of Sir William Wedderburn. It was attended by Charles Bradlaugh, a member of the British Parliament. Bradlaugh spoke in such a loud and clear voice that he was heard not only in every corner of the pandal but also by the people outside. He declared: **"For whom should I work if not for the people? Born of the people, trusted by the people, I will die for the people."**

Dadabhai Naoroji, a member of the British House of

Commons, was elected the President of the Lahore Session of the Congress held in December 1893. His travel from Bombay to Lahore presented the spectacle of a procession. Citizens of the various places on the way presented him addresses. At the Sikh Golden Temple of Amritsar, he was invested a robe of honour. Dadabhai brought the following message from the Irish members of the British Parliament: "Don't forget to tell your colleagues at the Congress that every one of the Ireland's Home Rule members in Parliament is at your back in the cause of the Indian people." The next session was held at Madras in 1894 under the presidentship of Alfred Webb, an Irish member of the British Parliament. The next session at Poona was presided over by Surendra Nath Banerjee in 1895. The President had such a memory that without looking at the printed address, he was able to repeat orally, word for word, the whole of his address for two hours. Gokhale presided over the Banaras session in 1905. The next session was held in Calcutta in 1906 under the presidentship of Dadabhai Naoroji. On that occasion, Dadabhai unfurled the flag of Swarajya for India and the following resolution was passed: "Resolved that having regard to the fact that the people of this country have little or no voice in its administration and that their representations to the Government do not receive due consideration, this Congress is of opinion that the boycott movement inaugurated in Bengal, by way of protest against the partition of the Province, was, and is, legitimate."

The next session was to be held at Nagpur but the venue was shifted to Surat on account of the unfavourable atmosphere at Nagpur. Tilak was opposed to the policy of the Congress at that time. He did not want the Congress to go back on its resolution of 1906 at the instance of the Moderates. On December 23, 1907, he declared thus at Surat: "We have not come to cause a split in the Congress; we did not want to hold a separate Congress; we want to see that the Congress does not go back. We solemnly say that we want to see the Congress moving with the times. But the people who brought the Congress to Surat, although Nagpur was willing to have it, are going to drag the Congress back. They have no moral courage. They are against the word boycott though they are for Swadeshi. When you profess to accept Swadeshi, you must boycott Videshi (foreign) goods: without boycott Swadeshi cannot flourish. The fight is between two principles:

(1) earnestly doing what is right, and (2) doing it but not displeasing the Government. I belong to the party which is prepared to do what it thinks right whether the Government is pleased or displeased. We are against the policy of mendicancy. Many young gentlemen in Bengal have gladly suffered for this attitude. No one has any authority to make the Congress recede from its ideal. We do not come here to embarrass the Moderates; but we are determined not to allow the Congress to retrograde. If they are not prepared to brave the dangers, let them be quiet, but they should not ask us to retrograde. We have come here to fight out constitutionally; we will behave as gentlemen even if our opponents do not do so. Our opponents create rowdyism when they fear defeat. We are fighting against foreign autocracy. Why should we allow this home autocracy? The Congress is an organisation of all people and the voice of the people should predominate. The policy of the Moderates is destructive. I don't want you to follow it; we want to progress."

All attempts on the part of Tilak and his colleagues failed to bring about a compromise between the Moderates and the Extremists before the open session of the Congress. Although the agenda of the Congress session was not distributed among the delegates, Tilak happened to get a copy of the draft of the proposed constitution as prepared by Gokhale. A perusal of the draft showed that there was clearly a change in the objective of the Congress different from the one declared at Calcutta in 1906. This was too much for Tilak. He pointed out that the proposed constitution was a direct attempt to tamper with the ideal of self-government on the lines of self-governing colonies and to exclude the Extremists from the Congress by making the acceptance of the new creed a condition precedent for Congress membership. He declared that if he and his colleagues were assured that no sliding back of the Congress would be attempted, opposition to the election of the President would be withdrawn. He agreed to a Joint Committee representing the points of view of the two sides to settle the question in dispute. However, the Moderates were not willing to compromise. They were determined to have things in their own way. The reaction of the Extremists was: "The retrogression of the Congress was a serious step not to be decided upon only by a bare accidental majority of any party, either in the Subjects Committees or in the whole Congress (as at present constituted) simply because its session happens to be held in a particular place or province, in a particular year; and the usual unanimous acceptance of the President would have, under such exceptional circumstances, greatly weakened the point and force of the opposition".

When the Congress met on December 27, 1907, the atmosphere was surcharged and there were all kinds of rumours. The name of Dr. Rash Behari Ghosh was proposed for the Presidentship. When Surendra Nath Banerjee got up to second the proposition, attempts were made to shout him down and pandemonium prevailed in the Pandal. The meeting had to be adjourned. The next day, Dr. Ghosh was elected the President, but when he got up to deliver his presidential address, Tilak ascended the platform, stood in front of the President and demanded that he be allowed to address the audience. He refused to submit to the ruling of the chair that he could not be allowed to address at that stage. While this tussle was going on, the rank and file of the Extremists created trouble and there were clashes. All efforts to persuade Tilak failed. He stood with folded arms and refused to go to his seat unless he was bodily removed. Some persons from Nagpur and Poona rushed to the platform with Lathies in their hands. A shoe was hurled from the audience and it struck Pherozeshah Mehta. Pandemonium prevailed. Chairs were thrown at the dais and sticks were freely used. The session had to be suspended.

On December 28, 1907, a convention of the Moderates was held in the Congress Pandal from which the Extremists were excluded, although some of them were ready and willing to sign the necessary declaration. Those who did not wish to go back from the position taken at the Calcutta Congress met at a separate place to consider what steps were to be taken to continue the work of the Congress. It was in this way that the Surat session of the Congress ended. After the Surat fiasco, it was clear that the Moderates were not prepared to yield to the Extremists. They knew that once the plant of extremism was planted, it was bound to grow. They were not prepared for any compromise. Tilak was ridiculed, abused and called a traitor. The Moderate press wrote such things as the following: "Tilak has been feeding the flames which have burnt the Congress to ashes. He is not a patriot, but a traitor to the country, and has blackened himself. May God save us from such patriots." In spite of the attacks from the Moderates, Tilak was prepared to accommodate them. He wrote thus in the Kesari: "It is a mistake to suppose that a difference of opinion as to ultimate ideals should prevent Indians from cooperating with one another, for gaining a common end. We see that Radicals, Socialists, Democrats and others, though labouring for widely different ideals, are able to cooperate with one another in Parliament for advancing the interests of their country as a whole. With this example before our eyes, does it not betake a lack of liberality to insist that the representatives of a certain school of Indian politicians should alone be admitted to the National Congress. The duty that lies before our politicians is not to seek to eradicate all differences of opinion but to secure the cooperation of men holding divergent views for the accomplishment of common ends. Whatever our difference may be about the ideals, we Moderates and Extremists should unite in carrying on the work of the National Congress. The rise of a new Party necessarily produces friction with the old but it is the duty of the wise men not to make much of this friction but to carry on national work in cooperation with the new Party."

In 1908, a change was made in the constitution of the Indian National Congress. Under the new constitution, delegates to the Congress were to be elected only by the Congress Committees and Associations affiliated to the Congress and not by other bodies or public meetings. The result was that the Extremists were excluded from the Congress and Tilak and his followers remained outside till 1915 when a compromise was brought about.

Rise of Extremism

Many factors were responsible for the rise of extremism in the Congress. The Indian Councils Act, 1892 did not satisfy the aspirations of even the Moderates. It was contended that the policy of appeals and prayers had brought forth no result. The Government of India considered that policy as a sign of weakness. To quote Tilak, "Political rights will have to be fought for. The Moderates think that these can be won by persuasion. We think that they can only be obtained by strong pressure." The constant economic drain on the resources of the country due to foreign domination added to the discontentment in the country. The writings of men like Dinshaw Wacha, R. C. Dutt and Dadabhai Naoroji proved that the impoverishment of the people of India was largely due to the deliberate policy of the British Government. The policy of the Government of India sacrificed the industries of India in the interests of British manufacturers. There seemed to be no prospects for Indian industries.

Another cause was the discontent created by the outbreak of famine in 1897. It affected about 20 million people and 70,000 square miles of Indian territory. The attitude of the Government of India was rather unhappy. While the people were in the grip of famine, the Government was busy in celebrating the Jubilee Celebrations of Queen Victoria. The money which was required for the relief of the people was being wasted on needless celebrations. This was interpreted as an attitude of callousness on the part of the Government.

The outbreak of the Bubonic Plague in Bombay Presidency also added to the discontentment among the people. It is true that the Government of India adopted certain measures to check the spread of the disease but the methods adopted by it were unfortunate. No consideration was shown for the sentiments of the people. Mr. Rand, the Plague Commissioner of Poona, was most ruthless in his operations. To quote Ram Gopal, "Rand moved with a regular army of coolies and Policemen at his heels, pulled down infested dwellings, had the inmates forcibly removed to segregation camps. At many places beddings and clothes were burnt with the object of destroying plague germs. This would have been tolerated had the denuded people been provided germ-free clothes but this was not done. Similarly, essential articles of life were destroyed, leaving the owners thereof weeping and destitute. Rand entered any part of the house, even the kitchen or the room where the family idols were kept. Locks were freely picked to see if any plague cases were concealed in the closed houses. Armed Indian Police and European soldiers, with revolvers in their hands, rushed into the women's apartments. From the unlocked houses, household effects were sometimes removed, never to be returned. Huts were burnt down. Some soldiers employed in such parties broke open the cash boxes and safes of shopkeepers. Others believed that sewing machines could not in any way be disinfected and must be burnt. Another party thought it necessary to burn glass chandeliers, which they found in a house where a case had occurred. The whole proceedings resembled the sacking of a conquered town by the enemy." (**Lokmanya Tilak,** p. 137). Such a state of affairs could not be tolerated by the people and no wonder the plague policy of the Government was attacked vigorously by the critics of the Government, particularly Tilak. The resentment was so great that Mr. Rand and one of his associates were shot dead when they were returning from the Government House from Bombay after taking part in the Jubilee Celebrations of Queen Victoria.

Another cause was the revival of Hinduism. Swami Vivekananda attended in 1893 the Parliament of Religions at Chicago and explained to his audience the greatness of Hindu religion. The Swami had faith in the spiritual mission of India and it was felt that the same was not possible without the independence of the country. Aurobindo Ghosh declared: "Independence is the goal of life and Hinduism alone will fulfil this aspiration of ours." Tilak was also the product of Hindu revival and, no wonder, he put great emphasis on the Hindu festivals and the consolidation of the Hindus for the emancipation of India. The Theosophical Society also made its contribution in this direction. Sir Valentine Chirol says: "The advent of the Theosophists headed by Madame Blavatski, Col. Olkott and Mrs. Besant gave a fresh impetus to the revival and certainly no Hindu has so much organised and consolidated the movement as Mrs. Besant, who in her Central Hindu College at Banaras and her Theosophical Institution at Adyar near Madras has openly proclaimed the superiority of the whole Hindu system to the vaunted civilisation of the West. Is it surprising that the Hindus should turn their heads back upon our civilisation when a European of highly intellectual power and with an extraordinary gift of eloquence, comes and tells them that it is they who possess and have from all times possessed the key to supreme wisdom, that their gods, their philosophy, their morality, are on a higher plane of thought than the West has ever reached?"

The exclusion of the intelligentsia of India from all the big jobs in the country created bitterness. The anti-Indian policy of Lord Curzon added to the discontentment. The view of Lord Curzon was that "the highest ranks of civil employment must, as a general rule, be held by Englishmen." He emphasised that it was only the Englishmen who by their birth and training were fit to rule India, and not the Indians. According to him, Providence had selected the Englishmen to rule over

India and to give freedom to India was against the will of God. Such a theory of divine right to rule could not be palatable to the Indians who were learning to demand the right to govern themselves. Lord Curzon was a bureaucrat **par excellence** and he put the greatest emphasis on efficiency. He had no sympathy with the aspirations of the people of India. As a matter of fact, he ignored them altogether. He acted unmindful of the reactions of the people. He regarded the administration as a machine and acted only in the interests of the efficiency of the machine, although the people were adversely affected by the machine. His reign was full of "missions, omissions and commissions." In 1899, he passed the famous Calcutta Corporation Act which completely officialised the Calcutta Corporation. The total number of the members of the Calcutta Corporation was reduced from 75 to 50. The 25 members who were eliminated were those persons who were the representatives of the people of Calcutta. The result of this measure was that there was a European majority in the Corporation. No wonder, the measure was vehemently condemned. In 1904 was passed the Indian Universities Act. This law reduced the size of the Syndicates, Senates and Faculties with a view to giving prominence to the Europeans. The result of this law was that the Indian Universities became the most officialised universities in the world. They were practically left with no autonomy. In 1904 was also passed the famous Official Secrets Act. The definition of the term "sedition" was widened. The Official Secrets Acts of 1889 and 1898 related to the disclosure of only military secrets. The Act of 1904 covered also the official secrets relating to the civil affairs and newspaper criticism which were likely to bring the government into suspicion or contempt. Unmindful of the reactions of the people, Lord Curzon partitioned Bengal into two parts in 1905. His object was to create a Muslim majority province. The people of Bengal characterised the partition as a "subtle attack on the growing solidarity of Bengal nationalism". The view of A. C. Mazumdar is that the object of Lord Curzon in partitioning Bengal "was not only to relieve the Bengali administration but to create a Mohammedan Province where Islam could be predominant and its followers in ascendancy." The people of Bengal felt that they had been humiliated, insulted and tricked. There was a vigorous agitation for the repeal of the partition and the same was cancelled in 1911.

The treatment of the Indians in British colonies was another source of discontentment. Particularly in South Africa, the Indians were regarded as pariahs. Meaningless restrictions were imposed on their movements. They could not walk on footpaths, or travel in first class railway carriages, or travel without passes or go out after 9 p.m. It was felt that the humiliating treatment of the Indians was due to the slavery of India and the only way to end that tyranny was the independence of India. Certain international events also had their repercussions on India. In the Russo-Japanese War of 1904-5, Japan defeated Russia. This was interpreted as a symbol of the rise of the East. The Indians could take inspiration from that event. It was felt that if a European nation could be defeated by an Asiatic power, it was also possible for the Indians to drive away the Englishmen from their country. A similar inference was drawn from the defeat of Italy by Abyssinia in the battle of Adowa in 1896.

The methods of extremists were boycott, Swadeshi and national education. Boycott was directed primarily against the foreign goods but it also included the boycott of Government services, honours and titles. Both boycott and Swadeshi movements had great success. **The Englishman** of Calcutta wrote thus: "It is absolutely true that Calcutta warehouses are full of fabrics that cannot be sold. Many Marwari firms have been absolutely ruined, and a number of the biggest European houses have had either to close down their piece-goods branch, or to put up with a very small business. In boycott, the enemies of Raj have found a most effective weapon for injuring British interests in the country." About the methods of the extremists, Lala Lajpat Rai wrote thus: "We desire to turn our faces away from the Government Houses and turn them to the huts of the people. We want to stop our mouth so far as an appeal to the Government is concerned and open our mouth with a new appeal to the masses of our people. This is the psychology, this is the ethics, this is the spiritual significance of the boycott movement." The same writer declared thus: "An Englishman hates or dislikes nothing like beggary. I think a beggar deserves to be hated. Therefore, it is our duty to Englishman that we are no longer beggars." The same view was expressed by Tilak in these words: **"Our motto is self-reliance and not mendicancy."** Desai points out that

"Extremist leaders revive the memory of the Vedic past of the Hindus, the great phase of the reigns of Asoka and Chandragupta, the heroic deeds of Rana Pratap and Shivaji, the epic patriotism of Laxmi Bai, the queen of Jhansi and leaders of 1857." The worship of Durga, Kali, Bhawani and other Hindu gods and goddesses was revived and it was believed that they alone could give inspiration that was necessary for the emancipation of the country.

B. C. Pal spoke of so organising the forces of the nation as to "compel the submission to our will of any power that may set itself against us." Again, "If the Government were to come and tell me today, 'Take Swaraj', I would say 'Thank you' for the gift but I will not have that which I cannot acquire by my own hands." Regarding the boycott movement, B. C. Pal addressed his audiences in these words: "You may get a High Court judgeship here, a membership of the Legislative Council there, possibly an executive membership of the Council. Do you want a larger number of Indians in the Civil Service? The whole Civil Service might be Indian; but the Civil Servants have to carry out orders. The supplanting of Europeans by Indian agencies will not make for self-government in this country. They say, 'Can you boycott all the Government offices?' Who ever said we want? What we can do is this. We can make the Government impossible without entirely making it impossible for them to find people to serve them. The administration may be made impossible in a variety of ways."

In his whirlwind tour of the country, Tilak declared that the Moderates could not deliver the goods and the people should look up to the Extremists for the liberation of their country. The repetition of resolutions full of prayers to the Government could not bring any results. The remedy was not petitions but boycott. To quote him, "We are not armed and there is no necessity for arms either. We have a strong weapon, a political weapon in boycott. The whole of this administration which is carried on by a handful of Englishmen is carried on with our assistance. We are in subordinate service. We are clerks and willing instruments of our own oppression in the hands of an alien Government and the Government is ruling over us not by its innate strength but by keeping us in ignorance and blindness to the perception of this fact. Every Englishman knows that they are a mere handful in this country and it is the business of every one of them to fool you into believing that you are weak and they are strong. What the New Party wants you to do is to realise the fact that your future rests entirely in your hands."

After the Surat session, Tilak had no rest. Singlehanded, he started a many-sided struggle and spread the fire of patriotism in every nook and corner of the Bombay Presidency. He went on tours and collected a lot of money for the various national causes. He asked his audiences to work for Swaraj and get ready for sufferings which alone could bring Swaraj. In one of his meetings, he declared: "We are at present clamouring for Swaraj and therefore the Shivaji festival is the most fitting one for us to celebrate. If Shivaji was able to establish Swarajya two centuries ago, we too may expect to achieve it some day. Swarajya belongs to us by birthright. The Moderates can be compared to Shivaji's father Shahji who always used to advise his son not to take up arms against the mighty Mohammedan monarchs of the Deccan. But Shivaji, who can be compared to the Extremists of the present day, gave a new turn to events. **We are masters of our fortunes and can govern them if we only make up our minds to do so. Swarajya is not far off from us. It will come to us the moment we learn to stand on our own legs."** His slogan at the meetings was: **"Swarajya is my birthright; I will have it."** As was to be expected, the Government of India regarded the growth of Extremism with apprehension and danger. No stone was left unturned to suppress the advocates of Extremism. They were arrested and imprisoned. Sections 124-A and 153-A were added to the Indian Penal Code to deal with the situation. By another law, the authorities were authorised to ban political organisations suspected of subversive tendencies and to conduct the summary trials of the political offenders. Two laws were passed in 1908 and 1910 to crush the Indian press. In 1907, Lord Minto promulgated the Regulation of Meetings Ordinance which curtailed the right of the people to hold public meetings.

Between the passing of the Indian Councils Act of 1909 and the starting of the Home Rule Movement by Tilak and Mrs. Annie Besant, there was not much of bitterness between the Congress on the one hand and the Government of India on the other. There were many factors responsible for this change. The Extremists were out of the political field and the Moderates were incharge of the Congress. Lord Hardinge followed a sympathetic policy towards the Congress. He expressed his feelings of sympathy for the national aspirations of the people of India. He wept with them in the matter of the treatment of the Indians in South Africa. It was during his regime that the partition of Bengal was cancelled. The result was that the Congress adopted a policy of conciliation. With regard to the visit of George V to India and the holding of the Delhi Durbar in 1911, Shri Ambika Charan Mazumdar declared: "Every heart is beating in unison with reverence and devotion to the British Crown, overflowing with revived confidence in and gratitude towards British statesmanship. Some of us never faltered—not even in the darkest days of our trials and tribulations—in our hope, in our conviction and in our faith in the ultimate triumph and vindication of British justice." We are told that when the Governor of Madras visited the Pandal of the Congress, the whole House cheered the Governor and a resolution was passed expressing the loyalty of the Congress to the British throne. In his speech delivered at Poona in July 1909, Gokhale asked for loyal cooperation with the British Government in India for two reasons: "One that, considering the difficulties of the position, Britain had done very well in India; the other that there was no alternative to British rule and could be none for a long time....They could proceed in two directions: first, towards an obliteration of distinctions, on the ground of race, between individual Indians and individual Englishmen and secondly, by way of advance towards the form of government enjoyed in other parts of the Empire. The latter is an ideal for which the Indian people have to qualify themselves, for the whole question turns on character and capacity and they must realise that their main difficulty lies with themselves." In October of the same year, he addressed the students at Bombay in these words: "The active participation of students in political agitation really tends to lower the dignity and the responsible character of public life and impair its true effectiveness." Tilak was out of Indian politics from 1908 to 1914 on account of his long imprisonment in the Mandlay jail in Burma. During his absence, the politics of the country was dull. The Moderates were happy that their opponent was in jail. However, things changed after the release of Tilak in 1914. Tilak was not in a mood to precipitate matters. He was willing to have a compromise with the Moderates. It is true that when Gokhale started negotiations with Tilak for a compromise, Pherozeshah Mehta disapproved of them and the result was that the negotiations broke down. Pherozeshah Mehta decided to have the next session of the Congress at Bombay so that he may be able to maintain his hold over the Congress. Sir Satyendra Sinha who later on became Lord Sinha, was selected as the President of the Bombay session but unfortunately Pherozeshah Mehta died a few weeks before the Congress session. Gokhale also died. On account of their old age, Dinshaw Wacha and Chandravarkar were not active. S. N. Banerjee was not in tune with the new surroundings. Madan Mohan Malaviya was not in a position to lead the Congress on the Moderate lines.

The speech of Sir Satyendra Sinha, the Congress President at the Bombay session in 1915, came as a shock to the progressive elements in India. He is said to have observed thus: "Even if the English nation were willing to make us an immediate free gift of full self-government, I take leave to doubt whether the boon would be worth having as such, for it is a commonplace of politics that nations like individuals must grow into Freedom and nothing is so baneful in political institutions as prematurity; nor must we forget that India free can never be ancient India restored." The right of the Extremists to enter the Congress was admitted at the Bombay session of the Congress and the constitution of the Congress was suitably amended. Although Tilak was not present at the Bombay session, enough of heat was created by the Home Rule Proposals of Mrs. Annie Besant. Her speeches and writings in 1915 had given a rude shock to the Moderates. The Bombay session was the announcement of the ascendancy of the politicians of the Extremist School and the decline of the influence of the Moderates. The citadel of the Moderates was successfully attacked. The adoption of the resolution on self-government was interpreted as having converted the Congress into an Extremist league. The ground was prepared for Tilak and his colleagues.

Home Rule Movement

Mrs. Annie Besant and Tilak started the Home Rule Movement in 1916. There was nothing original or revolutionary about this movement. Annie Besant was not the enemy of the British Empire. She merely wanted to awaken the people of India out of their slumber. She declared: "I am an Indian

Tom Tom, waking up all the sleepers so that they make wake and work for their motherland." Her plan was "to disentangle the nationalist Extremists from their compromising alliance with the revolutionaries, to reconcile them to a position with the Empire and to bring them with the Moderates into line in the united Congress." She herself wrote thus: "In political reform, we aim at the building up of complete self-government from village councils, through District and Municipal Boards and Provincial Legislative Assemblies to a National Parliament, equal in its powers to the Legislative Bodies of the Self-Governing Colonies, by whatever name they may be called, also at the direct representation of India to the Imperial Parliament when that body shall contain representatives of the self-Governing States of the Empire."

Mrs. Annie Besant made it clear that home rule was the birthright of the people of India and they were not prepared to take it as a reward for their services for the British Empire and their loyalty to the British Crown. She wrote thus: "India does not chaffer with the blood of her sons and the proud tears of her daughters in exchange for so much liberty, so much right. India claims the right, as a Nation, to justice among the peoples of the Empire. India asked for this before the War, India asked for it during the War; India will ask for it after the War, but not as reward but as a right does she ask for it."

The Home Rule Movement reached its high watermark in 1917. It was in that year that the Government of India took strong action against the leaders of the movement. Mrs. Annie Besant was interned. There was a lot of agitation for her release. Tilak threatened to start passive resistance. The atmosphere of the country was surcharged with enthusiasm. It was at this time that the Secretary of State for India made in August 1917 his historic declaration which promised responsible government to the people by stages. By slow degrees, the Home Rule Movement died out. Mrs. Annie Besant was elected the President of the Congress in 1917. The Secretary of State for India visited this country in 1917. He went on tours of the country and met the representatives of the people. The joint Report was published in 1918 and the Government of India Act was passed in 1919.

Terrorist and Revolutionary Movements

Terrorism was one of the phases of militant nationalism although it differed radically from the political Extremists represented by Tilak. The revolutionaries did not believe in the methods of appeal, persuasion and peaceful struggle. They were convinced that without violence it was impossible to uproot an imperialism imposed and maintained by brute force. The reactionary and repressive policy of the British Government exasperated them. They believed in violent action with a view to demoralise the administration and its Indian collaborators. They had no scruples to resort to armed raids and dacoities to help their movement.

The earliest storm centre of revolutionary nationalism was Maharashtra and the name of Vasudeo Balwant Phadake stands foremost in that connection. Shri Vasudeo was born in 1845. He was profoundly influenced by the ideas of Ranade. He was bitter against Englishmen who were drawing fat salaries at the expense of the starving Indians. When famine broke out in Poona in 1876, the Government, instead of organising relief work, levied heavier taxes from the people. Vasudeo resigned his government job and undertook a tour of Maharashtra. He went from place to place to organise the people against the Government. He started collecting arms and ammunition to turn out the English from the country and for that purpose he had no hesitation in plundering the moneylenders. For some time, he created a reign of terror in the seven districts of Maharashtra. The Government announced a reward for his arrest and he was captured by Major Daniel on July 20, 1879. He was put up for trial, convicted and sentenced to life imprisonment. His conviction was upheld by the High Court and he was sent to Aden Jail. In October 1880, he made an attempt to escape but he was pursued and caught after 17 miles of pursuit. He died in February 1883. He made the following statement at the time of his conviction by the Sessions Court: "The Indian people are today standing on the threshold of death. The British bureaucracy and the Government machinery has so ground down the common masses that have been already harassed by famines and food scarcities. We, the sons of Bharat, are made the object of intense hatred and contempt. Wherever you cast your glance, you witness only such sights, hear such words, as no Hindu or Muslim whose necks have been straight so long with self-respect can do anything but bend his head in shame. Death would have been more honourable for us all than this disgraceful slavery. Had I but succeeded in my design, I would have accomplished a great task. It was my ambition to establish a Republic of free India. I have always preached in my lectures that our bliss lies in killing the British people. I told my audience a number of times that if they did not help me in this task, then the British rulers will destroy them root and branch. **Oh citizens of India! Why should I not suffer like the great sage Dadheechi? If by my sacrifice and total surrender, I can help your resurrection from slavery, why should I not make effort?** Accept this my last bow."

Damodar Chapekar was another hero of the same type. Although he was essentially a soldier, he took up the profession of Kirtan as the Brahmins were not eligible for recruitment in the army. He began to hate British administration in India. On one occasion, he observed thus: "Mere recalling the mighty deeds of Shivaji will not deliver the goods. If we want freedom, we shall have to plunge in action like our idols— Shivaji and Baji Rao. My young friends! The time has come to sharpen our swords in order to behead the enemies. Let us take a pledge to fight till the last breath and die bravely but not without tainting the earth red with English blood. Be not idle; be not a lifeless burden on the country. Be up and doing; be a hero in the strife. Is it not shameful that we call our country Hindustan (the land of the Hindus) but let it be ruled over by the Englishmen?" When Mr. Rand the Plague Commissioner of Poona and Mr. Ayerst were coming back from the Government House, they were shot dead by Damodar Chapekar. The result was that he and a few others were hanged by the Government.

It appears that Mr. Shyamji Krishna Varma was connected with the murder of Rand but he managed to escape to London. He was a Sanskrit scholar and he had been the Dewan of Udaipur and Junagarh States. He delivered a few lectures at the Oxford University and he impressed every one by his learning. He took to business and earned a lot of money. He started a monthly journal entitled The Indian Sociologist. With the help of Rana, six lecturerships of Rs. 1,000 each and three travelling scholarships for Rs. 2,000 each were offered to Indian students to go abroad for training themselves as national missionaries. One of the students who went to London was V. D. Savarkar. He was a youngman when Chapekar was hanged. It is said that on that occasion, he took the following vow before his family deity: "I will raise the banner of an armed revolution to achieve the freedom of my motherland till I die fighting the enemy. I will spare no breath in performing this sacred pledge." In 1900, he started an association known as Mitra Mela. Its members were young-men who were prepared to lay down their lives for the sake of their country. The name of this association was changed to Abhinava Bharat in 1904. Every member was required to take the following pledge: "In the sacred name of Chatrapati Shivaji, in the name of my sacred religion, for the sake of my beloved country, invoking my fore-fathers, I swear that my nation will be prosperous only after freedom, full freedom is achieved. Convinced of this, I dedicate all my health, wealth and talents for the freedom of my country and for her total uplift. I will work hard to my utmost capacity till my breath. I will not spare myself or slacken in this mission. I will never disclose anything about the organisation."

Savarkar was very much loved by Shyamji Krishna Varma. A new life was put into the residents of India House by him. By the end of 1906, he completed his book entitled 'Joseph Mazzini—Biography and Politics'. He also wrote a book on the rising of 1857 in India and gave it the name of Indian War of Independence.

Savarkar sent a parcel containing 20 Browning Automatic Pistols with ammunition to Bombay concealed in the false bottom of a box forming part of the luggage of one Chatur-bhuj Amin who was working as a cook in the India House. The pistols were to be used by the members of Abhinava Bharat which was working under the direction of Ganesh Savarkar, the brother of V. D. Savarkar. Before the parcel reached India, Ganesh Savarkar had already been arrested on the charge of waging war against the Government and sentenc-ed to transportation for life. The members of Abhinava Bharat decided to murder Jackson, District Magistrate of Nasik, as he had convicted Ganesh Savarkar. Jackson actually was shot dead on December 21, 1909. Anant Laxman Kanhere was arrested and put up for trial. In his statement, Kanhere declared: "I have performed my part. Ganesh Damodar Savarkar is being sentenced to transportation for life in your administration whereas your Executive Engineer Mr. Williams who caused the death of an Indian cartman, is being rewarded with life. It is for this that I have killed Jackson. I have no desire to run away." The details of the Nasik Conspiracy were divulged by one Ganu Vaidya who was a member of the Nasik branch of Abhinava Bharat. Acting on the information supplied by him, the Police rounded up 37 youngmen. Three of them were hanged and the others were sentenced to varying terms of imprisonment.

It is stated that Mr. Jackson arrested Ganesh Savarkar on the instigation of Sir Curzon Willie who had laid a ring of spies around the India House to watch the activities of the Indian students. He also dictated the British policies concerning India. At the instigation of V. D. Savarkar, Sir Curzon Willie was shot dead on July 1, 1909 by one Madan Lal Dhingra. When he was arrested, a chit was recovered from his pocket and it read as follows: "I attempted to shed English blood intentionally and with purpose as a humble protest against the inhuman transportation and hanging of Indian youth." At the time of his trial, he made the following statement: "I admit the other day I attempted to shed English blood as an humble revenge for the inhuman happenings and deportations of the Indian patriotic youths. And in this I have consulted with none but my own conscience. I have conspired with none but with my own duty. I believe that a nation held in bondage with the help of bayonets, is in a state of perpetual war and since the guns are denied to me, I drew forth my pistol and attacked by surprise. **What could a son poor in wealth and intellect like me offer to the Mother except my own blood! My only prayer to God is that I may again return to the same Mother and die in the same cause till the Mother is freed for the service of humanity and glory of God.** Vande Mataram." Madan Lal was sentenced to death and hanged on August 16, 1909. In November 9, 1909 an attempt was made to blow up the carriage in which Lord and Lady Minto were driving through the city of Ahmedabad. Two cocoanut bombs were thrown but they did not explode in time.

When all this was happening, V. D. Savarkar was in Paris and he decided to go back to London to resume his work. Shyamji Krishna Varma and Lala Hardayal and Madame Cama tried to dissuade him from taking the risk but he refused to accept their advice and went to London. As soon as he reached London, he was arrested on March 13, 1910. Apprehending his death to be near, Savarkar wrote the following letter to his brother's wife: "We had taken a solemn pledge to free our country from political slavery. We are proud to lay down our lives one by one to attain our goal. It is a great day for me—the day of the fruition of all my aspirations. I am extremely glad that I have done my bit to free my mother from the shackles of bondage. **Oh my Motherland! I have already offered at your feet my youth, my pleasures, my sweet home, my purse and my brother and sister. Here am I ready to offer my body. Thanked be they who have dedicated their lives to the service of the nation.** Dear sister-in-law, entertain such thoughts and hold on to your pledge and add lustre to the fair name of the family." The view of the Government of India was that V. D. Savarkar had a hand in the Nasik Conspiracy and consequently orders were passed for his removal to India. He tried to escape when his ship was near the Port of Marseilles. He jumped into the sea and successfully reached the shore but was illegally caught by British officers on the French soil. On reaching India, he was put up for trial. He was convicted and sentenced to 50 years' imprisonment and transportation on March 22, 1911. He was sent to the Andamans at the age of 28. It is stated that when the Jailor came to know that he was put in Jail for 50 years, he exclaimed: "Oh God! Fifty years". The reply of Savarkar was "why worry! Fifty years. Is the British rule going to survive these fifty years?" In 1924, Savarkar was brought to India along with his brother Ganesh. He was released in 1937 when the Congress Ministry came to power.

Sardar Singh Rana was closely associated with the editing of the papers like the Vande Mataram, Indian Freedom and Talwar. He gave money when Hem Chandra was sent to Russia by the revolutionaries to learn the technique of making the bomb. He was responsible for the smuggling of twenty automatic shining pistols and bullets into India and one of those bullets was used for killing Jackson. During the First World War, he was sent to a remote Island from where he was released after the end of the war.

Madame Cama also made her contribution towards the cause of India's freedom. She attended the International Socialist Conference held in Germany in 1907 along with Sardar Singh Rana and there unfurled the National flag of

India. She urged all the freedom-loving nations of the world to help the cause of India's freedom. In December 1908, she moved a resolution for the boycott of foreign goods. In 1914, she was arrested and deported. She came to India in 1934 but died in 1936.

Revolutionary propaganda was carried on in Bengal by Barindra Kumar Ghosh, the younger brother of Aurobindo, and Bhupendra Nath Dutt, the brother of Swami Vivekanand. To begin with, Barindra Kumar tried to preach "the cause of Independence as a political missionary." However, later on he was convinced that purely political propaganda was not enough. He started the Yugantar and through its columns carried on the work of educating the masses. In an article, he expounded his revolutionary gospel in these words: "Shri Krishna had said in Gita that whenever there is a decline of righteousness and a rise in unrighteousness, there shall be a reincarnation of God to rescue the good, to destroy the wrong-doer and to establish righteousness." Again, "At the present time, righteousness is declining and unrighteousness is springing up in India. A handful of alien robbers are ruining the crores of the people of India by robbing the wealth of India. Through the hard grinding of their servitude, the ribs of the countless people are being broken to pieces. Fear not, Oh Indians, God will not remain inactive. He will keep His word. Placing firm reliance on the promises of God, invoke His power. When the lightning of Heaven flashes in their hearts, men perform impossible deeds."

A programme was chalked out and it consisted of six items. Hatred was to be created in the minds of the educated people of India against servitude by vigorous propaganda in the press. The fear of unemployment and starvation was to be removed from the minds of the Indians and love of freedom and of the Motherland was to be inculcated in them. That was to be done by "soul-stirring music and theatrical performances glorifying the lives of heroes and their great deeds in the cause of freedom and by patriotic songs." The Government was to be kept busy by means of Bande Mataram processions, Swadeshi conferences and boycott meetings. Youngmen were to be recruited, organized in small bands and trained in physical exercises and use of weapons and were to be taught absolute obedience to rules and the leaders. Weapons were to be manufactured, purchased from foreign countries and smuggled into the country or manufactured in the country itself. Money was to be raised for the Terrorist Movement by means of raids and dacoities. The belief was that "the law of the English is established on brute force and if to liberate ourselves we too must use brute force, it is right that we should do so". An appeal was made to the youngmen of Bengal in these words: "Will the Bengali worshipper of Shakti shrink from the shedding of blood? The number of Englishmen in this country is not above one lac and a half, and what is the number of English officials in each district? If you are firm in your resolution, you can in a single day bring British rule to an end. **Lay down your life, but first take a life**. The worship of the goddess will not be consummated if you sacrifice your lives at the shrine of Independence without shedding blood."

As a result of the efforts made by Barindra Kumar Ghosh and Bhupendra Nath Dutt and their associates, a number of revolutionary societies were set up and one of them was the Anusilan Samiti or Society for the Promotion of Culture and Training. The Society had its branches in Calcutta and Dacca. It was modelled on the same line as the secret societies of Italy and Russia. It embarked upon a programme of wholesale terrorism. On December 6, 1907 an attempt was made to blow up the train in which the Lieutenant-Governor was travelling. On December 23, 1907, Mr. Allen who was formerly the District Magistrate of Dacca, was shot in the back but the injury did not prove to be fatal. On April 30, 1908 Mrs. and Miss Kennedy were murdered. The facts were that Mr. Kingsford was hated by the terrorists on account of the heavy punishments inflicted by him on the Swadeshi workers. What was resented particularly was the infliction of corporal punishment on respectable youngmen. Susil Sen, a boy of fifteen, was flogged in public for the offence that he was mixed up in a Police fracas. The terrorists decided to murder him and a clever device was prepared to achieve the objective. What was done was that the middle portions of the leaves of a book borrowed from Mr. Kingsford were cut out and a bomb was put into the hollow thus created. It was thought that when Mr. Kingsford would open the book, the bomb would burst and kill him. The scheme was not successful as Mr. Kingsford did not require the book immediately and the same was never opened. Another device was thought of to murder Kingsford. Khudi Ram Bose and Profulla Chakie were deputed for that purpose. When both of them were going to the Bungalow of Mr. Kingsford, they saw a carriage coming from that direction. They thought that the occupant of the carriage was Mr. Kingsford and they threw the bomb into the carriage. What happened was that Mrs. and Miss Kennedy were killed by the bomb. Profulla Chakie shot himself but Khudi Ram Bose was arrested, tried and hanged. Khudi Ram became a martyr and a hero. Students and many others put on mourning for him. Schools were closed for two or three days as a tribute to his memory. His photographs had an immense sale. By and by, the youngmen began to wear Dhoties with Khudi Ram Bose's name woven into the borders of garments.

The Government was able to unearth a conspiracy in Calcutta and also captured some bombs, dynamite, cartridges and the correspondence which led to the arrest and trial of about 39 persons including Aurobindo Ghosh, Bhupendra Nath Dutt, Hem Chandra Das and Narinder Gosain. Kanai Lal Dutt and S. N. Bose were separately tried and executed. Heavy punishments were inflicted on the remaining 36 accused. Narinder Gosain became an approver, but he was shot dead by his companions in the jail. Nand Lal, the Sub-Inspector who had arrested Khudi Ram Bose, was murdered. Ashutosh Biswas who had acted as Public Prosecutor in the Gosain Murder case and the Alipore case was shot dead. Shams-ul-Alam, Deputy Superintendent of Police, who was connected with the Alipore case, was also shot dead. On November 7, 1908, an attempt was made to shoot Sir Andrew Frazer, the Lieutenant Governor of Bengal, but the attempt failed. The terrorists of Bengal did not spare the Police officers, Magistrates, Prosecuting Lawyers, hostile witnesses, traitors, betrayers and approvers. One and all, they were all shot. The consequences were absolutely immaterial to the revolutionaries.

In 1907, B. C. Pal toured the Madras Presidency and preached the gospel of Swaraj. He was imprisoned for six months for his refusal to give evidence against Shri Aurobindo. When he was released, two of his admirers from Madras celebrated his release by holding a public meeting, hoisting the flag of Swaraj and pledging to boycott everything foreign. Both of them were arrested by the Government and that led to a riot at Tinnevelly. The Sedition Committee Report says: "It was marked by wholesale and deliberate destruction of Government property in open defiance of the constituted authority. Every public building in Tinnevelly, except the Sub-Registrar's Office, was attacked. The furniture and records of these buildings set on fire as well as portions of the buildings themselves: the municipal office was gutted. Twenty-seven were convicted and sentenced for participation in the riot.

Pondicherry was also the centre of revolutionary work. M. P. Tiruhal Acharya and V. V. S. Aiyer were the guiding spirits. Aiyer prepared the youngmen at Pondicherry by giving them training in the use of revolvers. One of the trainees was Vanchi Aiyer who shot Mr. Ashe, the District Magistrate of Tinnevelly, on June 17, 1911. He was arrested, tried and executed. His companions were also arrested, tried and executed in the Tinnevelly Conspiracy case.

Lord Hardinge decided to shift the capital of India from Calcutta to Delhi. When he was entering in the city of Delhi in a procession, a bomb exploded. It injured the Viceroy and killed his A.D.C. The bomb was thrown by Ras Bihari Bose. There was a lot of confusion and Ras Bihari managed to escape. The Government did its level best to find out the culprit. A reward of Rs. 7,500 was announced for the arrest of Ras Bihari Bose. He was chased from place to place but every time he managed to escape. He went away to Japan under a fictitious name. He played an important role in organising the Indian National Army in Japan. He died in 1945.

Delhi Conspiracy Case

The action taken by the Government in connection with the bomb thrown on Lord Hardinge is known as the Delhi Conspiracy Case. Thirteen persons had been arrested in that connection. The names of some of them were Master Amir Chand, his adopted son Sultan Chand, Dina Nath, Bhai Balmukund, Bal Raj Bhalla, Basant Kumar and Avadh Bihari. Two of them were sentenced to seven years' imprisonment and four of them were hanged. Dina Nath became an approver. During the trial in 1914, the Police produced in the Court a letter written by Master Amir Chand and that letter contained the following passage: "Constitutional struggles and agitations have borne no fruit. The only effective and unfailing means to liberate our country is that of armed revolution. History testifies to the fact that the rulers never offer independence on a silver platter. They surrender it to the threat of sword." It is stated that when Avadh Behari was going to be hanged, an Englishman asked him as to what was his last wish. His reply was: "The end of the British Rule". When the Englishman advised him to die peacefully, Avadh Behari replied: "Peace? I wish that a conflagration may break out in the country gutting the British rule. Let my country emerge out of this fire like pure gold."

February 21, 1915 was fixed for an all-India revolt and vigorous preparations were made for that purpose. Ras Bihari Bose, Suchindra Sanyal, Ganesh Pingale and Bagi Kartar Singh prepared a master plan for that purpose. Bomb factories were set up at Ludhiana, Amritsar, etc. Indian troops were contacted and persuaded to revolt on that date. Some revolutionaries raided the Moga Treasury in the Punjab. Two revolutionaries were killed and several were arrested. They were also hanged. The all-India revolt failed because one Kirpal Singh passed on all the secret plans to the Government. Many places were raided and bombs were recovered. Secret papers were also captured by the Government. Most of the ring leaders of the Punjab fell into the hands of the Police. Luckily, Ras Bihari Bose, Ganesh Pingale and Bagi Kartar Singh escaped. Ganesh Pingale got down at Meerut and was handed over to the government by a Muslim Inspector with whom he stayed. He was hanged on November 16, 1915. His last words were: "Oh God! May the task left incomplete by me be executed by you. My only wish is that my country may be free." Kartar Singh was also caught later on and sentenced to death along with Jagat Singh, Bhai Parmanand, Man Singh and Udham Singh. Many others were transportated for life. The death sentence of Bhai Parmanand was later on commuted to life imprisonment. It is stated that Chief Justice was inclined to commute the death sentence of Kartar Singh also. but the latter said: **"I prefer gallows to life sentence. I wish I were born again to unfetter my motherland. I shall be glad to be hanged every time I am reborn till my country achieves independence."**

Lala Hardayal was a great philosopher and a powerful orator. In 1913, he called a rally of revolutionary workers in a town of California. He started an independent press and brought out a paper known as "The Gadar". It was published in English, Hindi, Urdu, Bengali, Marathi and Gurmukhi. The copies of this newspaper were sent to all those countries where Indians lived. There was a great demand for this paper in Japan, China, Singapore, Germany and Canada. The newspaper condemned the mis-deeds of the British Government in India and also explained the objects of the Gadar Movement.

In 1913, a few thousand Indians lived in Canada and most of them were Sikhs. They were subjected to all kinds of indignities. The Canadian Government did not like their presence in their country and was anxious to stop their flow. With that object in view, a law was passed by which only those Indians were allowed to land in Canada who were direct passengers from Calcutta. The Canadian Government knew full well that there were no direct services from India to Canada and hence indirectly the immigration of Indians into Canada would stop. Baba Gurdit Singh who was a very rich Indian in Canada, came forward to help the Indians. He floated a shipping company known as the Guru Nanak Navigation Company and hired a Japanese ship called Komagata Maru. The ship reached Calcutta and was able to accommodate 500 Indian passengers. When the ship reached the Port of Vancouver on May 22, 1914, the Canadian authorities did not allow her to enter the harbour. The passengers were not allowed to land even on the shore. The ship was not allowed even to unload the goods. The Canadian authorities acted in a very cruel manner. Although the passengers were suffering terribly, the Canadian Government was not moved by their plight. An effort was made by the Canadian authorities to throw boiling water on the passengers. Finally, the Canadian Government sent two warships to sink the Komagata Maru. After about two months of stay in the Canadian waters, the Komagata Maru started on his return voyage on July 23, 1914. The passengers had to suffer even on the return journey as the British Government did not allow the ship to enter the harbours of Hongkong and Singapore. On September 26, 1914, the ship reached the Budge Budge harbour near Calcutta. The Government of India ordered the passengers of the ship to enter the special train which was kept ready to take them away. As the passengers refused to get into the train, they were forcibly dragged and put in the train. Some of the passengers resisted and while doing so used American revolvers. 18

Sikhs were killed and many more were wounded. Although Baba Gurdit Singh was injured, he managed to escape. The occurrences connected with the Komagata Maru created a lot of bitterness among the Indians in general and the Sikhs in particular. Bhai Bhag Singh and Bhai Vatan Singh led an agitation against the Canadian authorities for the repeal of the law against the immigration of the Indians. Mr. Hopkins who was the chief of the Immigration Section of Canada, became the target and he was killed by one Mewa Singh. The Gadar Party also intensified its propaganda against the Government of India. In the issue of August 18, 1914, the Gadar Party gave the following instructions: "Spread the literature of revolution; help and encourage all resistance, armed and passive; destroy the railway lines, withdraw all your funds from British Banks and inspire the Indian army to strike on every point against the Firangis."

Lala Hardayal went to Germany to negotiate with William II, the German Emperor. He sent thousands of recruits and a lot of explosive materials to India. Raja Mahendra Pratap set up a provisional government at Kabul. It was agreed that the Muslims of Iran, Arabia, Iraq and Afghanistan would take up arms against the British Government after getting help from Germany and Turkey. The Sikhs of the Punjab were also to revolt. Unfortunately, the whole plan for the revolt of 1915 leaked out and nothing came out.

The Kakori Case

The revolutionaries were in great need of money for the manufacture of bombs and consequently a few revolutionaries boarded the train on August 9, 1915 on the Lucknow-Saharanpur line. The revolutionaries had with them revolvers and cartridges. After the departure of the train from Kakori Railway station, one of the revolutionaries pulled the alarm chain of the train. When the train stopped, the revolutionaries tried to take away the money from the Iron Box in the train which was broken open with great effort with hammer-blows by Ashfaq. Unfortunately, the revolutionaries were able to get Rs. 5,000 only. The Government took action and arrested about 40 persons and sent them for trial. That case is known as the Kakori case. The trial concluded on April 7, 1927. It was a mere farce. Pt. Ram Parsad Bismil, Roshan Singh and Rajindra Lahri were given death sentence. Manmath Nath Gupta got 14 years and many others got death sentences. Ashfaq and Suchendra Nath Bakhshi were caught later on and were given death sentence and transportation for life respectively. Ram Parsad Bismil was hanged on December 19, 1927. His mother is said to have observed thus about her son: **"I am greatly proud to have given birth to a soldier of freedom who laid down his life at the feet of his motherland.** Your country has greater claim on you than I have. You have fallen for a noble cause and I see no reason to feel sorry." A little before his death, Ashfaq Ullah gave the following message to his countrymen: "We have played our role on the political stage of our country. Right or wrong all our actions were motivated by the lofty object of securing independence. I know my actions will elicit praise from some quarters and criticism from the other, but as a true revolutionary I am indifferent to such remarks. One thing I beg to clarify before I die. It never had been our object to create terror in the country. Our trial has lasted for such a long time but tell me if ever we tried to shoot down an approver or a prosecution witness. That is not in our line. My only wish is that my country-men may, irrespective of their religion or creed, unite like a solid bloc to smash the citadel of British rule. The British are the common enemies of all the religious sections of our country. It is the moral duty of every Indian to dig the grave of the British bureaucracy. I am far from being a murderer as has been established by the prosecution. I am rather proud of being the first Musalman to lay down my life at the altar of India's freedom."

The people of India had boycotted the Simon Commission but in spite of that the Commission visited Lahore on October 20, 1928. The Hindustan Socialist Republican Party took out a huge procession against the Simon Commission. The processionists were shouting: "Simon, go back". Lala Lajpat Rai was leading the procession. One Mr. I. P. Saunders gave blows on the head and chest of Lala Lajpat Rai with his baton and thereby caused grievous injuries on his person. While addressing the public meeting in the same evening at the Bradlaugh Hall, Lahore, Lala Lajpat Rai declared: "The Government which attacks its own innocent subjects has no claim to be called a civilized Government. Bear in mind, such a Government does not survive long. **I declare that the blows struck at me will be the last nails in the coffin of British rule in India".** Lala Lajpat Rai died on November 17, 1928 as a result of the injuries received by him. That was too much for the people of India and nobody who had inflicted those injuries on Lalaji could be forgiven. Addressing a public meeting, Shrimati Basanti Debi, the wife of C. R. Das, observed thus: "My blood boils with rage to think that Lalaji, who had been so aged and so dear to his countrymen, has been beaten to death by that brute English police officer. It is a challenge to the youth and manliness of 300 million Indians. **On behalf of the women of India, I want a reply to my question whether Indian youths are dead or alive. Is there nobody from the young generation of India to step forward and respond to my question?"** The reply was given by Sardar Bhagat Singh and his companions. It was decided to kill Mr. Scott who had ordered the lathi charge and Mr. Saunders who had killed Lalaji. On December 17, 1928, when Saunders was approaching the police gate on his bicycle, he was shot by Rajguru and he was followed by Bhagat Singh who tore the head of Saunders to pieces by pistol shots. All the revolutionaries took refuge in the D.A.V. College, Lahore and then managed to slip away to Simla.

Within 5 days of the incident, the following posters were found on the walls of the city of Lahore:

"Hindustan Socialist Republican Party

NOTICE

BEWARE BUREAUCRACY

"This killing of I. P. Saunders was only to avenge fully the murder of Lala Lajpat Rai. It was indeed a sad and shameful episode that so mean a fellow like I. P. Saunders should dare to deliver blows on the chest of the old and most respected person worshipped by a nation of thirty-five crores of Indians. That was indeed an affront to the nation. By that insult of the Indian Nation, the foreign power had as if thrown a challenge to the self-respecting and brave sons of the soil. This reply will surely convince the people and the foreign power that the Indian Nation is indeed not yet dead or spiritless to bear such insults. The people of Bharat have fresh blood flowing in their veins. Young India is up and ready to guard the honour of the nation even at the stake and sacrifice of life.

"Beware, you, Tyrant of Government!

"Do not hereafter try to touch the provoked feelings of

the people that are already exploited and harassed. Hold your devilish hands! Remember that in spite all your laws and endeavours to keep us disarmed a flood of pistols and revolvers will always flow into the hands of the youth of the country. Though it may be admitted that no armed revolution can be accomplished with a sprinkling of arms yet they will indeed be enough to wreak vengeance for the repeated national insults which the administration indulges in from time to time. Our so-called national leaders may condemn and reproach our actions, and the foreign Government may try their utmost to crush our organisation. But we want to make it clear here that we shall ever be ready to safeguard our national honour and to teach lessons to all the foreign aggrandisers. We shall never permit the cry of revolution to languish even under the encirclement of oppression and suppression all around; bear in mind that even with the noose knot of death round our necks, we shall always shout and cheer 'Long Live Revolution.'

"We are really sorry that we had to kill a human being. But the man whom we had to shoot down was a part and parcel of such a cruel, mean and unjust administration of a foreign power that we had no alternative but to overthrow him. This man is killed only in his capacity as a representative of the British power in India. British Power is undoubtedly the most tyrannical one in the world.

"We again repeat that we are sorry that we had to shed human blood. But it becomes inevitable to shed blood on the altar of revolution, which will end all exploitation of man at the hands of man.

"Long Live Revolution.

Sd/- (BALRAJ)

18th December, 1928.   Commander: Punjab HSRA."

Another incident took place on April 8, 1929. After the question hour was over in the Central Legislative Assembly in New Delhi, Sardar Bhagat Singh threw a bomb on the wall which exploded with a thundering boom. Two bullets were fired to frighten the Speaker of the House. When the smoke ended, Sardar Bhagat Singh threw leaflets into the hall and those read thus: "Bombs are needed to let the deaf hear". Sardar Bhagat Singh could have run away but he surrendered himself to the police. Sardar Bhagat Singh and his companions were put up for trial and ultimately condemned to death. In the course of his lengthy statement in the court, Sardar Bhagat Singh observed thus: "Our sole object was to warn the listless and to wake up the deaf. Many others are thinking just like us. The bombs which were thrown were intentionally so manufactured as to cause insignificant damage, and they were thrown also in such a clear place as to produce the least injury to anybody. Under the apparent calm on the surface of the Indian mind there is a ceaseless terrible seething discontent on the point of bursting into a storm. Our action is merely a danger-signal to those who are rushing ahead thoughtlessly without caring for the serious consequences before them. We have, as if, heralded the end of the era of non-violence, the idealist dream, about whose utter failure the young generation is now doubtlessly convinced. We have adopted this course of striking a warning purely out of our love and good-will for humanity to ward off the unheard of harassments and hardships. The new spirit, notice of whose dawn has been just given by us, is really inspired by the idealism of Guru Govind Singh, Shivaji, Mustafa Kamal Pasha, Raza Khan, Washington, Garibaldi, Lafayette and Lenin. It was because the Government and the Indian leaders had closed their eyes and ears that we had to sound that warning to attract their attention......

"It will be readily accepted that we had no personal prejudice or hatred against any individual in the House or against any one who had received minor injuries. On the other hand, we emphatically reassert that we hold all human life as sacred beyond description. **Instead of inflicting injuries on any one else, we are ready to offer ourselves to be sacrificed for the sake of humanity.** The mental attitude of mercenary soldiers in the Imperial armies trained to mercilessly kill the humanity is not in our character. When we surrendered, it was purely out of the sole thought to suffer the atonement of our actions. We wanted to warn the Imperialist exploiters that they could never destroy the truth by crushing a few individuals. A whole nation cannot be suppressed by doing away with a couple of persons. Bastile could not prevent the French Revolution. Exiles in Siberia could not liquidate the Russian Revolution. The bloody Sundays could not arrest the course of Irish struggle for Independence. How could then these atrocious measures extinguish the flame of freedom burning bright in the Indian mind?......

"The opponents of revolution mistakenly believe that revolution means violence with arms, weapons and such other means. But revolution is not confined to this process. It may be that these are used as instruments but it should not be forgotten that behind them is the solid strength and spirit of the revolution and that strength is the will, the aspiration of the people to demand and get a change, a revolution in the current economic structure, the shape and form of political Government of the nation. Our idea of revolution has never been simply the bloodshed of some individuals. It is to end the present regime of exploitation of man by man and to secure for our nation absolute right of self-determination. That is the ultimate objective of our idea of revolution. Freedom is the birth-right of man. We welcome any amount of suffering and sacrifice that might fall to our lot for this idealism and devotion to it. Long live that Revolution."

The Tribunal which tried Sardar Bhagat Singh and his companions gave its decision on October 7, 1930 and Sardar Bhagat Singh, Raj Guru and Sukhdeo were hanged at Lahore on March 23, 1931. Unfortunately, the dead bodies of these heroes were taken by the Government to Ferozepore and an attempt was made to burn them on the banks of the river Sutlej. However, the people came to know of it and were able to recover the half-burnt dead bodies. Those were taken to Lahore and cremated there with great honours.

A reference must be made to the work of Chandra Shekhar Azad, Bhagwati Charan and Yash Pal. Azad was a fearless person who was determined to liberate his country even at the cost of his life. He had a hand in the Kakori conspiracy case but he managed to escape. He helped Sardar Bhagat Singh in his attack against Saunders. His efforts to take Sardar Bhagat Singh out of the jail failed. Efforts were also made to persuade the Viceroy to condone the death sentence passed on Sardar Bhagat Singh and his companions. When all that failed, Chandra Shekhar Azad and Yash Pal chalked out a plan to blow up the train carrying Lord Irwin. When on December 23, 1929, the train carrying the Viceroy left the Nizamuddin Railway Station near New Delhi, a bomb exploded and the train was derailed. The dining car was shattered to pieces. However, Lord Irwin escaped unhurt.

On February 27, 1931, Chandra Shekhar Azad, Yash Pal and Surendra Pandey assembled at Allahabad to finalize their plans for getting help from Russia for fighting India's battle for freedom. Yash Pal and Surendra Pandey left Azad in the Alfred Park to meet another revolutionary. While Azad was still in that Park, he found himself surrounded by armed police. He fought bravely against the police party with revolvers in his both hands. His body was punctured with bullets. While he used the other bullets on his enemies, the last bullet he used on himself and thus died a great man who could have helped to solve free India's problems.

Yash Pal was selected the Commander-in-Chief of the Hindustan Socialist Republican Army after the death of Azad. The Government announced big rewards for information leading to his arrest. He re-organized the Revolutionary Army and made a declaration of a general revolt. He was caught by the police because his revolver did not work. He was sentenced to 14 years' rigorous imprisonment but was released by the Congress Ministry in March, 1938.

Sir Michael O'Dwyer had been the Lieutenant-Governor of the Punjab and it was during his regime that General Dyer murdered innocent Indians in the Jallianwala Bagh at Amritsar. Sir Michael had also been responsible for various other atrocities on the people of the Punjab. It was felt that he must be taught a lesson. Sardar Udham Singh was a great revolutionary. He went to London in 1919 and waited for full 20 years to have revenge against Sir Michael. On March 13, 1940, while Sir Michael was leaving the Caxton Hall, London, Sardar Udham Singh fired at him and killed him with his second bullet. He was put up for trial and sentenced to death. He made the following statement in the court: "I have seen my starving countrymen being trampled under the jackboots of British imperialism. I am not at all sorry for having registered my protest in this manner......I am not the least afraid of death. What after all is the use in prolonging life till dotage. **There is bravery in dying young, in sacrificing life for the country.**"

There were many causes for the decline of the revolutionary movement in India. It was confined to a small circle of youngmen and there was no public backing. The terrorist movement had no central organization to direct its activities. The upper middle class leadership was not sympathetic towards the movement. Leaders like Sir Asutosh Mukherjee and S. N. Banerjee asked the government to take drastic measures against the terrorists. The emergence of Mahatma Gandhi as the leader of Indian Nationalist Movement also led to gradual decline of the revolutionary movement. The Gandhian technique of non-cooperation, civil disobedience and non-violence appealed more to the people of India than the activities of the terrorists. No wonder, they went into the background. However, the Hindustan Socialist Republican Party tried to meet the terrorism of government "with an even greater terrorism." Sardar Bhagat Singh, Jitendra Nath Das and Chandra Shekhar Azad were the revolutionaries who staked their lives for the sake of the country. The terrorists also played their part during the revolt of 1942, the mutiny of the Royal Indian Navy and the crusade of the Indian National Army of Subhash Chandra Bose.

India and World War I (1914-18)

When the war started, there was great enthusiasm in the country. The people of India were willing to serve the government in every possible way. After Marne, there was an increasing demand for Indian troops outside India. When Turkey joined the Central Powers in October 1914, Indian troops garrisoned the Suez Canal and repulsed a Turkish attack. Indian troops fought through the long campaigns of Macedonia and German East Africa. They played an important part in the Iraq campaign leading to the capture of Baghdad in 1917. In this way, they helped to found the present State of Iraq. They were in the allied army which took Jerusalem in 1917. All this involved a great effort in India itself. Eight lakhs of men were recruited for the fighting forces, together with four lakhs of non-combatants. This resulted in a great expansion in the Military machine, a greater mixture of classes and a stronger feeling of self-confidence all around. Indian self-confidence grew when the magnitude of their effort and the extent to which it depended upon Indians themselves, were realised.

In the administrative sphere, the British government made a mistake in allowing the British civilian officers to serve the forces during the war. Many of them never returned and those who returned found themselves in a strange new mental world to which it was difficult to adapt themselves. When times grew difficult towards the end of the war, the Government had only an ageing and tired cadre of officers to rely upon.

In the economic sphere, the first effect of the war was one of stimulus. The industrial development of modern India owes a good deal to the demands of World War I. However, increasing demands and expenditure led to rise in prices and ultimately enthusiasm was turned into discontent. Englishmen could be expected to put up with inconveniences because they felt that they were fighting for their very existence and their victory was likely to add to their glory. The same could not be said about the Indians for whom the War was merely an external affliction. No doubt, they became not only exhausted and war-weary but also sour, discontented and resentful.

The attitude of India towards Europe and its people was altered radically and permanently. The Indians gave up the feeling that the Europeans were superior to them morally and technically. They were regarded now at best as more powerful. The first War casualty in India was the idol of Western superiority.

The Russian Revolution of 1917 also had a profound influence on the minds of the Indians. They felt that if the people of Russia could overthrow an imperialist regime, the same could be done by the Indians in their own country. The Fourteen Points of President Wilson had great influence on the Indians. They also demanded the rights of national freedom and self-determination of peoples. No wonder, the Indians demanded self-government in the name of the fundamental principles accepted by the Allied Powers.

As regards the effect of war on Muslims, they were very unhappy. They did not approve of the dismemberment of Turkey, which was regarded as the sword of Islam. They also did not like the treatment given to the Arabs who were considered to be rebels against the Turkish Khalifa. Their princes were regarded as stooges of the infidel.

When the war started, the Congress was still a middle-class body of Westernised professionals with some commercial and industrial backing. It was firmly under the control of Gokhale and the Moderates. However, all this was changed during the war. Tilak came back from jail and became a leader of all-India importance. Tilak gave up the old policy of making prayers to the British Government. His contention was that every Indian had the birthright to be free. He laid the foundations for the great anti-government movement led by Gandhiji in the next few years.

The World War I ended in 1918. The Indians had helped the British Government both with men and money. They had done everything in their power to further the war efforts of the British Government. However, they suffered on account of high prices, low wages and shortage of supplies. Plague and influenza took a heavy toll. The liberty of the people was restricted on account of the working of the Defence of India Rules. The people put up with the acts of high-handedness of British officers in the matter of recruitment and the collection of war-funds. After having done all that, the people were not at all happy at what was given to them by the Report of 1918. Mrs. Annie Besant rightly stated that the scheme was "ungenerous for England to offer and unworthy for India to accept." When India was in this mood, the Government of India passed the infamous Rowlatt Act in 1918 in spite of opposition from all quarters. The result was that a wave of anger spread all over India and even the Moderates joined hands with other Indians. The Act was a very drastic one. It gave the Government power to crush popular liberties, to arrest and detain suspected persons without warrant and to imprison them without regular trial. Mahatma Gandhi who had been loyal to the British Government throughout the World War I came to the fore-front and asked the people to offer Satyagraha against the Act. There was great enthusiasm throughout the country. Hartals were observed with great success. The Hindus and Muslims co-operated with one another. However, Mahatma Gandhi, all of a sudden, suspended the Satyagraha movement as there was a clash in Delhi and disturbances at other places. Later on, Mahatma Gandhi admitted that he made a "Himalayan miscalculation", but the mischief had been done.

Great atrocities were committed in the Punjab during the regime of Sir Michael O'Dwyer, Lieutenant-Governor of the Punjab. Sir Michael was known as the iron man of the Punjab. He had no faith in political reforms and consequently had no sympathy with the political agitators. He refused Tilak and B. C. Pal to enter the Punjab. The methods adopted by Sir Michael to raise war loans and to find recruits were very often unauthorised and oppressive. When the agitation against the Rowlatt Act started, Sir Micheal gave on April 7, 1919 the following warning to the people of the Punjab: "The Government of this Province is and will remain determined that public order, which was maintained so successfully during the time of war, shall not be disturbed in times of peace. Action has, therefore, already been taken under the Defence of India Act against certain individuals at Lahore and Amritsar. The recent puerile demonstrations against the Rowlatt Act in both Lahore and Amritsar indicate how easily the ignorant and the credulous people can be misled. Those who only want to mislead them incur a serious responsibility. Those who appeal to ignorance rather than to reason have a day of reckoning in store for them." Amritsar observed Hartal peacefully both on 30th March and 6th April. However, on 9th April, 1919, the Government of the Punjab passed orders for the deportation of Dr. Satyapal and Dr. Kitchlew and their internment at Dharmsala under the Defence of India Act. On 10th April, 1919, they were removed by the police from Amritsar. When the people came to know of it, complete Hartal was declared in the city. The people marched in a procession to the residence of the Deputy Commissioner to demand the release of their leaders. They had no sticks or lathis with them. However, they were checked by the police at the railway level-crossing and there was firing. This infuriated the mob and there was wholesale burning of whatever fell in their way. Europeans were assaulted. Buildings were burnt and godowns were looted. When the troops appeared in the city, the mob disappeared. On 11th April, 1919, the people were allowed to arrange for the funerals of the dead bodies.

On April 12, 1919, a proclamation was issued by General Dyer, who had taken charge of the troops the day before, that no meetings or gatherings of the people were to be held. However, no steps were taken to see that the proclamation was brought to the notice of the people living in the various localities of the city. The result was that it was announced on 12th evening that there would be a public meeting on 13th April, 1919, at 4.30 p.m. in the Jallianwala Bagh. Neither General Dyer nor other authorities took any action to stop the meeting. The meeting started at the right time and there were about 6,000 to 10,000 people present in the meeting. All of them were practically unarmed and defenceless. The Jallianwalla Bagh is closed practically on all sides by walls except one entrance. General Dyer entered the Jallianwala Bagh with armoured cars and troops. Without giving any warning to the people to disperse, he ordered the troops to fire and he continued to do so till the whole of the ammunition at his disposal was exhausted. Hundreds of people were killed. Lala Girdhari Lal gave the following account of the tragedy before the Hunter Enquiry Committee: "I saw hundreds of persons killed on the spot. The worst part of the whole thing was that firing was directed towards the gates through which the people were running out. There were small outlets, four or five in all, and bullets actually rained over the people at all these gates and many got trampled under the feet of rushing crowds and thus lost their lives. Blood was pouring in profusion. Even those who lay flat were shot. No arrangements were made by the authorities to look after the dead or wounded. I then gave water to the wounded and rendered such assistance as was possible. I went round the people and saw almost everybody lying there. There were heaps of them at different places. The dead bodies were of grown up people and young boys also. Some had their heads cut open, others had eyes shot and nose, chest, arms or legs shattered. I think there must have been over 1,000 dead bodies in the garden then. I saw people were hurrying up and many had to leave their dead and wounded because they were afraid of being fired upon again after 8 p.m." The contention of Gen. Dyer was that he wanted to teach the people a lesson so that they might not laugh at him. He would have fired and fired longer, he said, if he had the required ammunition. He had only fired 1,600 rounds because his ammunition had run out. The regime of Gen. Dyer saw some unthinkable punishments. The water and electric supply of Amritsar were cut off. Public flogging was common. However, the "Crawling Order" was the worst of all. One Miss Sherwood was attacked by the people when she was cycling in a lane, and Gen. Dyer ordered that everyone passing through that lane must crawl with belly on the ground. All who lived in the said lane had to obey that order, although Miss Sherwood was protected by the people themselves. The issue of third-class tickets on the railway was prohibited and common people could not travel. More than two persons were prohibited from marching together on side-walks or pavements. Bicycles, other than those owned by the Europeans, were commandeered. Those who had closed their shops were forced to open them or had to suffer severe penalties. Prices of commodities were fixed by military authorities. A public platform for whipping was constructed near the fort. A number of triangles for flogging were constructed in various parts of the city. Martial Law Commissioners tried 298 persons at Amritsar. 51 persons were sentenced to death, 46 to transportation for life, 2 to imprisonment for seven years, 10 for five years, 13 for three years and 11 for a lesser period. 105 persons were convicted under Martial Law by the Civil Magistrates.

The administration of Martial Law was more intensive at Lahore than elsewhere. The curfew order was enforced and the people who went out after 8 p.m. were liable to be shot, flogged, fined or imprisoned or otherwise punished. Those who closed their shops were ordered to open them and the alternatives were either to be shot or have the shops publicly opened and their contents distributed free to the public. Occupiers of the premises on whose walls Martial Law notices were pasted were ordered to protect them and they were liable to punishment if those were defaced or torn in any way, although they could not stay out to watch them. Students of the colleges were ordered to report themselves four times a day to the military authorities. Langars or public kitchens opened by public spirited people were ordered to be closed. Motor cars and motorcycles belonging to the Indians were ordered to be delivered to the military authorities for the use of the officials. Electric fans and other electric things belonging to the Indians were commandeered for the use of the British soldiers. Public conveyances were ordered to report themselves daily at places which were far from the city. 300 tonga drivers were commandeered. Those who were allowed to ply for hire were ordered to report themselves at different places at different times. A Martial Law notice was torn from one of the walls of a college and the result was that the whole of the staff of the college, including the principal, was arrested and taken to the Fort where they were kept for three days in military custody.

There was bombing at Gujranwala. Major Carbey who was responsible for the bombing, has given the account in these words: "The crowd was running away and he fired to disperse them. As the crowd dispersed, he fired the machine-gun into the village itself. He supposed some shots hit the houses. He could make no discrimination between the innocent and the guilty. He was at a height of 200 feet and could see perfectly what he was doing. His object was not accomplished by the firing of bombs alone. The firing was not intended to do damage alone. It was in the interests of the villagers themselves. By killing a few, he thought he would drive the people from collecting again. This had a moral effect. After that he went over the city, dropping bombs, and fired at the people who were trying to get away." Gujranwala, Kasur and Shekhupura had their curfew order, prohibition of travelling for Indians, public and private flogging, wholesale arrests and punishments by summary courts and Special Tribunals.

The action of General Dyer was approved by Sir Michael in these words "Your action correct. Lieutenant Governor approves." However, there was condemnation of his action from all quarters. Sir Rabindra Nath Tagore was so much distressed by the happenings in the Punjab that he gave up his knighthood which had been conferred on him by the Government of India. In his letter addressed to the Viceroy on that occasion, he observed thus: "The accounts of the insults and sufferings undergone by our brothers in the Punjab have trickled through the gagged silence reaching every corner of India and the universal agony of indignation roused in the hearts of our people has been ignored by our rulers, possibly congratulating themselves for imparting what they imagine salutary lessons...knowing that our appeals have been in vain and that the passion of vengeance is blinding, the noble vision of statesmanship in our Government, which could so easily afford to be magnanimous as befitting its physical strength and moral traditions, the very least I can do is to take all consequences on myself in giving voice to the protest of the millions of my countrymen suppressed into a dumb anguish of terror.

"The time has come when badges of honour make our shame glaring in their incongruous context by humiliation, and I, for my part, wish to stand short of all special distinction by the side of those of my countrymen who, for their so-called insignificance, are liable to suffer a degradation not fit for human beings, and these are the reasons which have painfully compelled me to ask Your Excellency with due deference and regret, to release me of my title of knighthood."

Non-Cooperation Movement

Under the leadership of Mahatma Gandhi, the Indian National Congress decided in 1920 to start the Non-Cooperation Movement. It was truly a revolutionary step. It was for the first time that the Congress decided to follow a policy of direct action. Many factors were responsible for this change. Mahatma Gandhi had so far believed in the justice and fairplay of the British Government. He had given his full cooperation to the Government during the World War I in spite of opposition from men like Tilak. However, the tragedy of the Jallianwalla Bagh, the Martial Law in the Punjab and the findings of the Hunter Committee destroyed his faith in the good sense of the Englishmen. He felt that the old methods must be given up. After the withdrawal of the Moderates, the Extremists were in complete control of the Congress and it was possible for the Congress to adopt a revolutionary programme. The terms of the Treaty of Sevres which was entered into between Turkey and the Allies were very severe and were resented by the Muslims of India. The Muslims tried to persuade the British Government to show leniency towards Turkey but they got a flat refusal. That resulted in resentment among them against the British Government. The Muslims started the Khilafat Movement and Mahatma Gandhi identified himself with them in that movement. The result was that Mahatma Gandhi was sure of Muslim support if the Congress started the Non-Cooperation Movement.

A special session of the Congress was held at Calcutta in September 1922 under the Presidentship of Lala Lajpat Rai and Mahatma Gandhi himself moved the non-cooperation resolution. There was a lot of opposition, particularly from C. R. Das, B. C. Pal, Annie Besant, Jinnah and M. M. Malaviya but the resolution was carried by a majority of 1855 against 873. The programme of the Non-Cooperation Movement was clearly stated in the non-cooperation resolution. It involved the surrender of titles and honorary offices and resignation from nominated posts in the local bodies. The non-cooperators were not to attend Government Levies, Darbars and other official and semi-official functions held by the Government officials or in their honour. They were to withdraw their children gradually from schools and colleges and establish national schools and colleges. They were to boycott gradually the British courts and establish private arbitration courts. They were not to join the army as recruits for service in Mesopotamia. They were not to stand for election to the Legislatures and they were also not to vote. They were to use Swadeshi cloth. Hand spinning and hand weaving were to be encouraged. Untouchability was to be removed as there could be no Swaraj without this reform. Mahatma Gandhi promised Swaraj within one year if people conducted his programme sincerely and whole-heartedly. Ahimsa or non-violence was to be strictly observed by the non-cooperators. They were not to give up Satya or truth under any circumstances.

The Non-Cooperation Movement captured the imagination of the people. Both the Hindus and Muslims participated in it. There was wholesale burning of foreign goods. Many students left schools and colleges and the Congress set up such national educational institutions as the Kashi Vidyapeeth, Banaras Vidyapeeth, Gujarat Vidyapeeth, Bihar Vidapeeth, Bengal National University, National College of Lahore, Jamia Millia of Delhi and the National Muslim University of Aligarh. Seth Jamna Lal Bajaj declared that he would give Rs. one lakh a year for the maintenance of non-practising lawyers. Forty lakh volunteers were enrolled by the Congress. Twenty thousand Charkhas were manufactured. The people started deciding their disputes by means of arbitration. Mahatma Gandhi gave up the title of Kaisar-i-Hind and his example was followed by others. When the Prince of Wales landed in Bombay on November 13, 1921, a complete Hartal was observed in the city on that day. A similar Hartal was observed at Calcutta when he visited that city in December 1921. The Government followed a policy of repression to crush the movement. There was indiscriminate beating of the non-cooperators and the dispersal of their meetings with the help of force. The Seditious Meetings Act was passed and thousands of persons were arrested. All the Congress leaders, with the exception of Mahatma Gandhi, were arrested. Mahatmaji was not arrested because the government was afraid of the consequences of his arrest. It is estimated that the total number of arrested persons was about 25,000.

The Congress reaction to this "virulent repression unworthy of a civilised government" was its decision at the Ahmedabad Session of the Congress in 1921 to start individual and mass civil disobedience. Mahatma Gandhi was appointed the "sole executive authority". On 1st February, 1922, Mahatma Gandhi informed the Governor-General of India of his intention to start mass civil disobedience in Bardoli and to sanction the no-tax campaign in Guntur which was in progress since 12th January, 1922. However, he was "prepared to advise post-ponement of civil disobedience of an aggressive character" if all non-violent non-cooperating persons were released and the government announced non-interference with all non-violent activities. He gave seven days to the Government to accept his demands. However, before the period of seven days was over, the tragedy of Chauri Chaura occurred which "changed the course of Indian history." What actually happened was that a mob of 3,000 persons killed 21 policemen and one inspector, some of whom were burnt alive in the police station. This was too much for Mahatma Gandhi who stood for complete non-violence. The result was that Mahatma Gandhi gave orders for the suspension of the Non-Cooperation Movement at once. As soon as the movement was suspended, there was a lot of criticism of Mahatma Gandhi and the Government of India finding him in disgrace, decided to arrest him and pro-secute him. He was sentenced to six years' imprisonment al-though he was released in February 1924 on grounds of health.

The action of Mahatma Gandhi in suspending the movement was severely criticised from many quarters. According to Dr. Pattabhi Sitaramayya, "Long letters were written from be-hind the bars by Pt. Motilal Nehru and Lala Lajpat Rai. They took Gandhi to task for punishing the whole country for the sins of a place." According to Subhash Chandra Bose, C. R. Dass was "beside himself with sorrow." To quote Bose, "To sound the order of retreat just when public enthusiasm was reaching the boiling point was nothing short of a national cala-mity." According to Jawaharlal Nehru, "We in prison learnt to our amazement and consternation that Gandhi had stopped the aggressive aspect of our struggle, that he had suspended civil disobedience." According to C. R. Dass, "The Mahatma opens a campaign in a brilliant fashion, he works it up with skill, he moves from success to success still he reaches the zenith of his campaign but after that he loses his nerve and begins to falter." According to Polak, "The Muslims wilted under the blow and it was never again possible to restore the confidence and fraternity that had united the two communities during this brief period of alliance."

However, Pt. Jawaharlal Nehru justified the action of Mahatma Gandhi later on, on ground of practical politics. The incident of Chauri Chaura was not a solitary one. It was only the last straw. There was practically no discipline among the volunteers. There were frequent cases of violence. As practically all the leaders of the Congress were in jail with the exception of Mahatma Gandhi, it was not possible to lead the movement on the right lines. Towards the end of 1921, there had occurred the Moplah rising in Malabar with the object of establishing a Khilafat State. However, it took a communal turn and the Moplahs slaughtered not only a few British officials but far more Hindu neighbours. If the movement had not been stopped by Mahatma Gandhi, there was every possibility of more violence in the country and that would have given the government a chance to crush the same with a lot of cruelty. To quote Jawaharlal Nehru, "This would have been crushed by the government in a bloody manner and a reign of terror established which would have thoroughly demoralised the people." It was the action of Mahatma Gandhi that saved the people from that danger. According to Romain Rolland, "It is dangerous to assemble all the forces of a nation, and to hold the nation panting, before a prescribed movement to lift one's arm to give the final command and then, at the last moment, let one's arm drop and thrice call a halt just as the formidable machinery has been set in motion."

As regards the shortcomings and achievements of the Non-Cooperation Movement, the movement apparently failed to achieve its object of securing the redress of Khilafat and Punjab wrongs. The Swaraj was not attained in one year as promised by Mahatma Gandhi. According to Subhash Chandra Bose, "The promise of Swaraj within one year was not only unwise but childish." The Congress ought not to have identified itself with the Khilafat Movement. According to Polak, the Khilafat Movement "rested on a wrong foundation. While Indian Muslims were reviving the romantic, old world tradition of an Islamic theocracy, the Turks in whose interest they believed they were acting, were tossing it aside as medieval lumber." Under Kamal Pasha, Turkey became a secular State and the institution of the Khilafat was abolished in 1922 and the Khalifa himself was exiled. The sudden suspension of the movement increased Hindu-Muslim tension. There started "a series of communal riots which raged, with brief intervals, for many years and surpassed in bitterness the records of the past."

However, there is a lot to be said in favour of the achievements of the Non-Cooperation Movement. According to Subhash Chandra Bose, "The year 1921 undoubtedly gave the country a highly organized party organization. Before that the Congress was a constitutional party and mainly a talking body. The Mahatma not only gave it a constitution and a nation-wide basis, but what is more important converted it into a revolutionary organization. Uniform slogans were repeated everywhere and uniform policy and ideology gained currency from one end of India to the other. The English language lost its importance and the Congress adopted Hindi as the lingua franca for the whole country. Khadi became the official uniform for all Congressmen." According to Coupland, "He (Gandhi) had done what Tilak had failed to do. He had converted the national movement into a revolutionary movement. He had taught it to pursue the goal of India's freedom not by constitutional pressure on the government, still less by discussion and agreement, but by force, none the less force because it was meant to be non-violent. And he had not only made the national movement revolutionary, he had also made it popular. It had hitherto been confined to the urban intelligentsia; it had made no appeal to the country folk. Gandhi's personality had deeply stirred the countryside." According to Pt. Jawaharlal Nehru, "The old feeling of oppression and frustration was completely gone. There was no whispering, no round-about legal phraseology to avoid getting into trouble with the authorities. We said what we felt and shouted it out from the house-tops." According to A. R. Desai, "With the section of workers and peasants participating in it, the nationalist movement which was restricted to the upper and middle-classes till 1917, got a mass basis for the first time." The Non-Cooperation Movement added to the self-reliance of the people. They were no more afraid of the strength of the British Government. The prisons lost their terror and became places of pilgrimage for the liberation of the country. Swadeshi became popular. Khadi became the uniform of the Indian patriots. The Congress became a mass movement."

The Swarajist Party

Under the leadership of C. R. Das and Motilal Nehru, the Swarajist Party was set up. Its object was the same as that of the Congress, viz., the establishment of Swaraj or Dominion Status within the British Empire. However, its methods were different. The Swarajist Party was to follow the policy of "uniform, continuous and consistent obstruction." Obstruction was the keynote of the creed of the Party. It wanted to wreck the Legislatures from within. It wanted to put up "resistance to the obstruction placed in their path to Swaraj by the bureaucratic government." It wanted to carry non-cooperation "into the very aisles and chancel of the bureaucratic church." Within the legislative bodies, its members were to throw out budgets. They were to reject all proposals for legislative enactments by which the bureaucracy proposed to consolidate its position. They wanted to introduce all those resolutions, measures and bills which were necessary for the healthy growth of the national life of India and the consequent displacement of the bureaucracy. They were to follow a definite economic policy to prevent the drain of public wealth from India by checking all activities leading to exploitation. Outside the legislatures, they were to give whole-hearted support to the constructive programme of Mahatma Gandhi and work that programme unitedly through the Congress organization. They were to supplement the work of the Congress by helping the labour and peasant organizations throughout the country. They declared that if they found that it was impossible to meet the selfish obstinacy of the bureaucracy without civil obedience, they would place themselves without any reservation under the guidance of Mahatma Gandhi.

It cannot be denied that the Swarajist Party rendered a very useful service to the national cause. It whipped up the enthusiasm of the people, who were suffering from a sense of frustration on account of the abrupt suspension of the Non-Cooperation Movement. By throwing out budgets and bills introduced by the Government, they were able to create interest among the people in the work of the Government. They were also able to discredit the Government in the eyes of the world. The spirit of resistance was maintained among the people against the foreign Government. The passing of the Swarajist Resolution in February 1924 led to the appointment of the Muddiman Committee by the Government of India to report on the working of dyarchy in the country. The Simon Commission was appointed two years earlier on account of the activities of the Swarajist Party. H. N. Brailsford observes: "To my thinking the tactics of obstruction were justified for they convinced even the British Conservatives that the system of dyarchy was unworkable."

There was a lot of agitation in the country when the Simon Commission visited India. At the Calcutta session of the Congress held in 1928 it was intended to pass a resolution declaring complete independence as the goal of India. However, Mahatma Gandhi intervened and Dominion Status was declared to be the goal of India. Mahatma Gandhi gave the assurance that he himself would lead the movement for independence if by the end of 1929 the British Government did not confer Dominion Status on India. It is true that Lord Irwin declared in October 1929 that Dominion Status was the goal of the British Government in India, but a mere declaration was not considered to be enough. Hence, under the Presidentship of Pandit Jawaharlal Nehru, the following Independence Resolution was passed at the Lahore session of the Congress on the banks of the river Ravi on December 31, 1929: "This Congress endorses the action of the Working Committee in connection with the manifesto signed by party leaders, including Congressmen, on the Viceregal pronouncement of October 31, relating to Dominion Status, and appreciates the efforts of the Viceroy towards a settlement of the national movement for Swaraj. The Congress, however, having considered all that has since happened and the result of the meeting between Mahatma Gandhi, Pandit Motilal Nehru and other leaders, and the Viceroy, is of opinion that nothing is to be gained in the existing circumstances by the Congress being represented at the proposed Round Table Conference. This Congress, therefore, in pursuance of the resolution passed at its Session at Calcutta last year, declares that the word 'Swaraj' in Article of the Congress Constitution shall mean Complete Independence, and further declares the entire scheme of the Nehru Committee's Report to have lapsed, and hopes that all Congressmen will henceforth devote their exclusive attention to the attainment of complete independence for India. As a preliminary step towards organising a campaign for independence, and in order to make the Congress policy as consistent as possible with the change of creed, this Congress calls upon Congressmen and others taking part in the national movement to abstain from participating directly or indirectly in future elections, and directs the present Congress members of the legislatures and committees to resign their seats. This Congress appeals to the nation zealously to prosecute the constructive programme of the Congress and authorises the All-India Congress Committee, whenever it deems fit, to launch upon a programme of civil disobedience, including non-payment of taxes, whether in selected areas or otherwise and under such safeguards as it may consider necessary."

January 26, 1930 was declared the Independence Day and the following pledge was taken on that day by the people of India and the same was repeated year after year: "We believe that it is the inalienable right of the Indian people to have freedom and enjoy the fruits of their toil and have the necessities of life, so that they may have full opportunities of growth.

"We believe also that if any Government deprives the people of their rights and oppresses them the people have a further right to alter it or abolish it. The British Government in India has not only deprived the Indian people of their freedom but has based itself on the exploitation of the masses and has ruined India economically, culturally and spiritually.

"We believe, therefore that India must sever the British connection and attain Purna Swaraj or Complete Independence.

"We recognize that the most effective way of gaining freedom is not through violence.

"India has gained strength and self-reliance and marched a long way to Swaraj following peaceful and legitimate methods and it is by these methods that our country will attain independence.

"We believe that non-violent action in general and preparation of non-violent direct action in particular requires the successful working of the programme of Khadi, communal harmony and removal of untouchability. We shall seek every opportunity to spread goodwill among the fellowmen without distinction of caste or creed. We shall endeavour to raise from ignorance and poverty those who have been neglected and to advance in every way the interests of those who are considered to be backward and suppressed."

The civil disobedience programme was prepared and launched. Mahatma Gandhi started his famour **Dandi March** on March 12, 1930 from Sabarmati Ashram. Thousands of Congress volunteers were sent to jail. The Government used all kinds of repressive methods to crush the nationalist movement but failed in its objective. The Congress boycotted the First Round Table Conference held in London in 1930, but M. R. Jayakar and Sir Tej Bahadur Sapru intervened and in March 1931, the famous Gandhi-Irwin Pact was signed. Mahatma Gandhi described the Pact as a victory for both the sides. Both Mahatma Gandhi and Lord Irwin sincerely wanted a settlement and the Pact was a victory for both. However, the Pact was criticized by Pandit Jawaharlal Nehru and Subhas Chandra Bose.

Mahatma Gandhi attended the Second Round Table Conference as the sole representative of the Congress. It is true that his visit to London had profound effect on the people of that country, but the immediate object of his visit was not served on account of the attitude adopted by Mr. Jinnah and Sir Samuel Hoare. Mahatma Gandhi had to leave the Round Table Conference in disgust. As soon as he reached India, he was arrested by the orders of Lord Willingdon. Wholesale arrests of Congress volunteers were ordered. Leaders were put behind the bars. The Congress did not participate in the Third Round Table Conference held in 1932. General Elections were held in 1934 to the Central Assembly and the Congress was able to win a large number of seats. When the elections were held for the Provincial Legislatures under the Government of India Act, 1935, the Congress was able to secure majority in a large number of provinces. There was a deadlock between the Congress and the Government on the question of the formation of ministries, but after some time, the Government gave an undertaking that the Governors would not interfere in the day to day affairs of the Provincial Governments and the Congress Ministries would be given a free hand. The Congress formed ministries in July 1937 and those ministries continued till November 1939 when they resigned after the declaration of the World War II. The

Congress Ministries did a lot of useful work in the provinces on account of their devotion to work and the spirit of sacrifice.

Quit India Movement

After the beginning of the Second World War, Lord Linlithgow made his offer to the Congress in August 1940 but the same was rejected. In March 1942, Sir Stafford Cripps came to India with his proposals which gave the people of India the right of making their constitution after the ending of the World War. He was prepared to transfer into the hands of the Indians all the Departments of the Government of India except that of Defence. The Congress was willing to accept the long-term scheme but not the interim scheme. The Congress did not like the attitude of "Take it or leave it" adopted by Cripps. It was after the failure of the talks with Cripps that the All-India Congress Committee passed the famous Quit India Resolution on August 8, 1942. The Resolution declared "that the immediate ending of British rule in India was an urgent necessity, both for the sake of India and for the success of the cause of United Nations. The continuation of that rule is degrading and enfeebling India and making her progressively less capable of benefiting herself and of contributing to the cause of world freedom. The ending of British rule in this country was thus a vital and immediate issue on which depends the future of the war, and the success of freedom and democracy. The All-India Congress Committee, therefore, repeats with all emphasis the demand for the withdrawal of the British power from India. The Committee resolves, therefore, to sanction for the vindication of India's inalienable right to freedom and independence, the starting of a mass struggle on non-violent lines on the widest scale possible. Such a struggle must inevitably be under the leadership of Mahatma Gandhi and the Committee requests him to take the lead and guide the nation in the steps to be taken." Many reasons have been given for starting the mass movement of 1942. The first was the growing threat of Japanese invasion of India. Gandhiji wanted to save India from that attack and his view was that if the British Government withdrew from India, the Japanese might not attack India. Another reason was the defencelessness of the British position in India and their easy defeat in Singapore. The view of Mahatma Gandhi was that India also would meet the same fate if the

British did not withdraw from India. The Mahatma also believed that the British Government left the people of Malaya and Burma neither to God nor to anarchy but to the Japanese. To quote Gandhiji, "Don't repeat that story here. Don't leave India to Japan but leave India to Indians in an orderly manner." Another cause was the alarming growth of Axis propaganda which was having its effect on the minds of the people of India. This was particularly so because Subhash Chandra Bose, the former President of the Indian National Congress, was himself broadcasting from Berlin in the Indian languages. Another cause was that the mind of Gandhiji was revolting against racial discrimination shown in the process of evacuation from Burma. The British provided separate routes for evacuation for Europeans and Indians. The White Road was meant for Europeans and the Black Road for Indians. The result was that the Indian evacuees had to undergo too many hardships on the way. The late Mr. M. S. Aney who was at that time a member of the Executive Council of the Viceroy incharge of the Indian Overseas Department observed: "Indian refugees are treated in such a way as to humiliate them and make them feel that they belong to an inferior race." In the words of Gandhiji, "The admitted inequality of treatment of Indian and European evacuees and the manifestly overbearing behaviour of the troops are adding to the distrust of British intentions and declarations." There was a lot of resentment in the country when the people heard of the sufferings of the Indians and this contributed to the decision of Gandhiji to start the Quit India Movement. Another cause was the sufferings of the people on account of the scorched earth policy followed by the British Government in India. The lands belonging to the people of India were destroyed for military purposes and they were not given adequate compensation. They were deprived of their means of livelihood. To quote Gandhiji, "For a Bengali to part with his Canoe, is like parting with his life." A lot of harshness was used by the Government while getting the houses of the peasants evacuated for the military. The inefficient and ineffective controls and transportation muddles added to the sufferings of the people. Prices rose in those months. The people lost their faith in the paper currency issued by the Government. There was a lot of discontentment among the people and Gandhiji decided to take advantage of it.

The immediate effect of the passing of the Quit India Resolution was the arrest of Mahatma Gandhi and all the members of the All India Congress Working Committee. The Indian National Congress was banned and its offices were taken possession of by the Police. The Government did all that it could to crush the Congress and the movement. The people also hit back. They revolted against the tyranny and oppression of the Government. Gandhiji had not unfolded his strategy before his arrest. After the passing of the resolution, Gandhiji intended to carry on negotiations with the British Government. As he was arrested all of a sudden, the people were left without any plan and no wonder the movement was carried on by the people in any way they could. When the Government resorted to violence and shot innocent men, women and children, the people also resorted to violence. The result was that in some parts of the country, British authority completely collapsed. It was with great difficulty that the British Government was able to restore law and order in the country.

The movement did not have the support of the upper classes of India consisting of rich merchants, landlords and princes and also a part of labour. The Muslim League, under the leadership of Mr. Jinnah, asked the Muslims to keep aloof from the movement. It was declared that the movement was directed to coerce the British Government to hand over to the Hindus the administration of the country. The Muslim League raised the slogans of "Divide and Quit" and "Bat Ke Rahega Hindustan" (Hindustan will have to be divided). The Police and the bureaucracy remained loyal throughout. Churchill praised "the loyalty and steadfastness of the brave Indian Police as well as Indian official class generally." The Hindu soldiers were not trusted to put down the rioters and the Gurkhas, Baluchis and White soldiers were usually employed for that purpose. Those who actually participated in the movement were the lower middle classes and peasants from whom also come most of the students and labour. The processions were composed of small shopkeepers, milk vendors, street hawkers, petty traders, students and workers in small establishments and mills. Shops remained closed for many days in spite of the threats of the Government to fine the shopkeepers and also imprison them. The peasants of India also made great sacrifices. Collective fines were imposed on them and also realised. This was particularly so in Bihar, Uttar Pradesh, Andhra, Gujarat and Maharashtra. The movement of 1942 can appropriately be called a student-peasant-middle class rebellion. The students provided the leadership and the peasantry the fighting strength.

The revolt of 1942 had significance not only for India but the whole world. Its reactions were widespread. "The abnormal times in which it took place, the low fortunes of England and the United Nations at the time of the occurrence, the importance of India as a base of operation against Japan and as controlling the supply line to China—the South-Eastern and Burma routes having been conquered by Japan—and the danger of an immediate Japanese move into India, all combined to make the widespread phenomenon of an uprising a matter of concern to the entire United Nations. The fortunes of India were closely bound up with it. The Axis Powers were not less interested as they found in the revolt much to capitalize on."

Dr. Amba Prasad rightly points out that the failure of the movement of 1942 was more marked than was the case with the movements of 1921 and 1930. "The earlier movements had been in the nature of preparatory training for a final struggle. They were intended to create a national consciousness in the masses who had been emasculated through centuries of subjection to a foreign rule. The movement of 1921 was intended to revive the spirit of self-respect among the people by removing the fear of going to jail for the love of the country. The object of self-government was there but it was realized that there was still a distant goal. The movement of 1930 was a further stage in the direction of independence. It was sought to remove the fear of loss of property and thereby to create a spirit of sacrifice. The objective of independence was there but there was a realization that still more sacrifices were needed. The movement of 1942, however, was intended to be the last stage in that struggle and, therefore, the supreme sacrifice of one's life was required to attain independence. The call was 'do or die' and the mass slogan was 'we shall do or die.' It is for this reason that the word failure was more appropriately applicable to the revolt of 1942 than it was to the earlier movements, which had constituted preparatory stages for the goal of independence."

The failure of the revolt of 1942 was due to many causes.

The first was the tactical mistakes of organization and planning. The arrest of Mahatma Gandhi and the Congress leaders left the people without any leadership or guidance. No wonder, they made mistakes and were ultimately crushed. To quote Jai Prakash Narain, "The lack of organization was so considerable that even important Congressmen were not aware of the progress of the revolt and, till late in the course of the rising, it remained a matter of debate in many Congress quarters whether what the people were doing was really in accordance with the Congress programme." There was no co-ordination and no strategy. Those who led, the movement were divided in their views on the course of action. Nobody knew what to do. The loyalty of the services and the superior physical strength of the Government succeeded in crushing the revolt. To quote Dr. Amba Prasad, "Thus it was the superior physical power of the Government which succeeded in putting down the revolt. On the one side were large unarmed masses, unorganised, leaderless, hesitating in their minds whether what they were doing would be approved by Gandhiji or not; on the other side was the power of the uniformed, disciplined policeman and soldier, armed with rifles and guns, and the power of law and the use of all means of communications. If necessary, the machine-gunning would be done from the aeroplanes. In such a situation, the revolt could only succeed, if it were a simultaneous rising which would have paralysed the administrative machinery in the shortest possible time. At its best it was a satyagraha or mass movement; at its worst, it was an unorganised revolt of a violent character and, in the latter form, it gave the Government a good excuse to crush down with force."

As regards the gains of the revolt of 1942, Dr. Amba Prasad observes thus: "Though the revolt of 1942 failed at the time, it prepared the ground for independence in 1947. When people have reached a stage where they can demonstrate that they can lay down their lives for national independence, it becomes impossible for a foreign power to continue to impose its will on them for any length of time. The revolt of 1942 made the British nation realize, supreme realists as they have been, that their rule was no longer wanted by India. Woodrow Wyatt, who was adviser to the Cabinet Mission to India throughout their negotiations, was of the opinion in 1946 that 'if the British fail to find soon a way of handing over smoothly, there may first be a revolution to drive them out. There was a deep and wide-spread anti-British feeling existing after 1942, mostly created by the revolt of that year'."

The Congress leaders remained in jail till the end of the Second World War in 1945. Many attempts were made to find a solution to the political tangle in the country but all of them failed. The Muslim League was adamant on getting Pakistan and ultimately the Indian Independence Act, 1947 was passed and thus India became independent on August 15, 1947.

India Becomes Independent

There were many reasons which forced the British Government to grant independence to India and the most important was the strength of the nationalist movement. That movement under the leadership of Mahatma Gandhi had become so strong that the grant of independence could not be postponed for long. The Quit India Movement showed that the people of India could go to any length to bring to an end the British Raj in the country. The people made tremendous sacrifices to paralyse the administrative machinery. The British Government was not ignorant of the slogans: "Do or Die" and "Now or Never." The organization of the Indian National army under Subhash Chandra Bose and the cry of "Dilli Chalo" made the British Government realise the folly of resisting the demand of the people of India for independence. Another reason which forced the Government to grant independence was that it found itself unable to keep India under her control with the help of sheer force. Great Britain became a second rate power after World War II. She became so weak that it became difficult for her to keep India under her control. While Great Britain gave independence to Burma, she gave independence to India also. The strike of the naval officers and ratings in Bombay in 1945 convinced the British Government that it was no longer possible to rule India and power must be transferred into the hands of the Indians without further delay. After World War II, all the three branches of the defence forces were inspired by the new spirit of patriotism and the revolt of the naval officers was of special significance in the context of the existing circumstances. It was for the first time after 1857 that a section of the defence forces openly revolted against the British Government on a political issue. The rebellion was not an isolated event. The Indian National Army which had been formed out of the prisoners of war had attacked India. After the surrender of Japan, many officers of the Indian National Army were captured and publicly tried in the Red Fort. There was a lot of public excitement and enthusiasm and in the end, all of them were released. All these developments convinced the British Government that they could not rely upon the armed forces in holding the country against the wishes of the people.

Another cause was a conviction in the minds of those who ruled India that it was no longer profitable to keep India in chains. It was felt that Great Britain could gain more by giving India independence. This has actually been found to be true as there is more trade between India and Great Britain today than it was before her independence. The grant of independence to India was facilitated by the fact that the Labour Party came to power in England in 1945. The members of the Labour Party had always been the advocates of independence for India and they actually gave the same to her when they themselves came to power. Things would have been certainly more tedious and the grant of independence would have been delayed if a person like Winston Churchill was in power in 1945-47. Another factor which helped the grant of independence was the acceptance by the Congress of the Muslim League demand for the establishment of Pakistan. The situation was so serious that if the Congress had not agreed to partition India, it would not have been possible for the British Government to hand over the administration of India into the hands of the Indian leaders. By dividing India and giving the Muslim League a separate state of Pakistan, the British rulers must have felt that they had avoided a bloody civil war. The American Government also played its part. It is well known that during World War II, President Roosevelt put a lot of pressure on the British Government to grant independence to India. That pressure continued even after the death of Roosevelt in 1945. The British Government which depended upon American Government for help after 1945, could not resist the pressure of public opinion in America in favour of the grant of independence to India.

Suggested Readings

Amba Prasad	:	*The Indian Revolt of 1942.*
Argov, Daniel	:	*Moderates and Extremists in the Indian Nationalist Movement.*
Bose, Subhas Chandra	:	*The Indian Struggle.*
Bose, Subhas Chandra	:	*Netaji Memorial Volume*, 1948.
Brailsford, H. N.	:	*Rebel India* (1931).
Chatterji, A. C.	:	*India's Struggle for Freedom* (1947).
Chintamani, C. Y.	:	*Indian Politics Since the Mutiny.*
Chirol, Valentine	:	*Indian Unrest.*
Chirol, Valentine	:	*India, Old and New*, London, 1921.
Hans, Kahn	:	*A History of Nationalism in the East.*
Jones, G. E.	:	*Tumult in India*, 1946.
Lovett, Sir, Varney	:	*A History of the Indian Nationalist Movement* (1600-1919).
Mazumdar, A. C.	:	*Indian National Evolution.*
Mukerjee, Hiren	:	*India's Struggle for Freedom.*
Mukerjee, Shyama Prasad	:	*A Phase of the Indian Struggle.*
Munshi, K. M.	:	*Pilgrimage to Freedom.*
Nevinson	:	*The New Spirit in India.*
Rao, U. R.	:	*Quit India* (1942).
Rosinger, L. K.	:	*Restless India* (New York, 1946).
Raghuvanshi, V. P. S.	:	*Indian Nationalist Movement.*
Sahai, G.	:	*42 Rebellion* (Delhi, 1947).
Singh, G. N.	:	*Landmarks in Indian Constitutional and National Development (1600-1919)*, Banaras, 1930.
Sitaramayya, P.	:	*History of the Indian National Congress*, Vols. I and II.
Smith, William	:	*Nationalism and Reforms in India.*
Satya Pal and Prabodh Chandra	:	*Sixty Years of Congress*, 1946.
Tara Chand	:	*History of the Freedom Movement*, Vols. I & II.
Zacharias, H.	:	*Renascent India (From Ram Mohan Roy to Mohan Das Gandhi)* London, 1933.
Zetland, Lord (Ronaldshay)	:	*The Heart of Aryavarta* (1925).

CHAPTER XXII

Establishment of Pakistan

The tendencies which ultimately resulted in the establishment of Pakistan in 1947 were already there before 1919. It was in the year 1886 that Sir Syed Ahmed Khan set up the Annual Muslim Education Conference. In 1893 was set up the Mohammedan Defence Association of Upper India with the object of preventing the Muslims from joining the Indian National Congress. Sir Syed was successful in alienating the Muslims from the Hindus and he was helped in his task by the British bureaucracy which hated the Hindu agitators who were demanding the establishment of democratic institutions in the country.

In 1905, Lord Curzon partitioned Bengal with the ulterior object of separating the Muslims from the Hindus by creating a separate Muslim province of East Bengal. However, the partition was cancelled in 1911 as a result of a vigorous agitation led by the Congress. This was disliked by the Muslims who considered the cancellation as a weakness on the part of the Government. They started feeling that no trust could be placed in the utterances and actions of the Government.

When the Government of India made up their mind to give more concessions to India in the constitutional field about the year 1906, the Muslims put forward a demand for separate electorates for themselves. The demand was placed before Lord Minto by a Muslim deputation led by Sir Agha Khan, but everything was arranged by Archibold, Principal of the Aligarh College. The deputation was a command affair. Mr. Archibold wrote thus : "Colonel Dunlop Smith, Private Secretary of His Excellency, the Viceroy, informs me that His Excellency is agreeable to receive the Muslim deputation. He advises that a formal letter requesting permission to wait on His Excellency be sent to him. In this connection, I would like to make a few suggestions. The formal letters should be sent with the signatures of some representatives of Mussalmans. The deputation should consist of representatives of all the provinces. The third point to be considered

is the text of the address. I would here suggest that we
begin with a solemn assurance of loyalty. The Government's
decision to take a step in the direction of self-government
should be appreciated. But our apprehensions should be expressed that the principle of election, if introduced, would
prove detrimental to the interests of the Muslim minority. It
should respectfully be suggested that nomination or representation by religion be introduced to meet Muslim opinion.
We should also say that in a country like India due weight
must be given to the Zamindars. But in all these views, I
must be in the background. They must come from you...
I can prepare for you the draft of the address or revise it.
If it is prepared in Bombay, I can go through it. As you
are aware, I know how to phrase these things in proper language. Please remember that if we want to organise a powerful movement in the short time at our disposal, we must ex-
pedite matters."

Lord Minto received the deputation sympathetically and
gave the following reply: "The pith of your address, as I
understand it, is a claim that under any system of representation, whether it affects a municipality or a district board or
a legislative council, in which it is proposed to introduce or
increase an electoral organization, the Mohammedan community should be represented as a community. You point out
that in many cases electoral bodies as now constituted cannot
be expected to return a Mohammedan candidate, and if by
chance they did so, it could only be at the sacrifice of such
a candidate's views to those of a majority opposed to his community whom he would in no way represent; and you justly
claim that your position should be estimated not only in your
numerical strength, but in respect to the political importance
of your community and the service it has rendered to the
Empire. I am entirely in accord with you. Please do not
misunderstand me. I make no attempt to indicate by what
means the representation of communities can be obtained,
but I am as firmly convinced as I believe you to be that any
electoral representation in India would be doomed to mischievous failure which aimed at granting a personal enfran-
chisement regardless of the beliefs and traditions of the communities composing the population of this continent." Lady
Minto tells us in her Diary that Lord Minto described the
day on which the Muslim deputation met him as "an epoch

in Indian history."

Having committed himself to give separate electorates to the Muslims, Lord Minto took up the matter with Lord Morley, the Liberal Secretary of State for India. The latter was not in favour of the proposal of Lord Minto. However, the latter insisted that separate electorates alone could satisfy the Muslims of India and nothing else. The result was that ultimately Lord Morley accepted the point of view of Lord Minto. While doing so, he addressed Lord Minto in these words : "Please remember, in granting separate electorates, we are sowing dragon's teeth and the harvest will be bitter." Lord Morley wrote to Lord Minto again in December 1909 to the following effect : "I won't follow you again in our Mohammedan dispute. Only I respectfully remind you again that it was your early speech about their extra claims that started the (Muslim) hare. I am convinced my decision was best."

In December 1906 was established the All India Muslim League with a view to "support, whenever possible, all measures emanating from the Government, and to protect the cause and advance the interests of our co-religionists throughout the country, to controvert the growing influence of the so-called Indian National Congress, which has a tendency to misinterpret and subvert British rule in India, or which might lead to that deplorable situation, and to enable our young-men of education, who for want of such an association have joined the Congress, to find scope, according to their fitness and ability, for public life."

The relations between the Hindus and the Muslims were cordial for some time and the Congress and the Muslim League worked in collaboration. Many factors were responsible for it. One was the treatment of Turkey by the European Powers before 1914. The Balkan Wars of 1912-13 weakened Turkey in Europe. It appeared as if there was a kind of Crusade against the Muslims in Europe. That was resented by the Indian Muslims who regarded the Sultan of Turkey as the Head of Islam. Turkey was considered to be the symbol of the greatness of Islam. As the British Government did nothing to save Turkey, the Indian Muslims became bitter. The cancellation of the partition of Bengal disappointed the Muslims and they felt that they could not rely upon their British friends and they turned to the Congress.

Sir Agha Khan was forced to resign from the Presidentship of the Muslim League which came under the control of M. A. Jinnah. The result was that the sessions of the Muslim League and the Congress were held at the same place and at the same time for some years. In 1916, both the Congress and the Muslim League held their annual session at Lucknow. It was in an atmosphere of give and take that the Lucknow Pact was signed by the Muslim League and the Congress. The Pact provided that the provinces should be free as much as possible from the control of the Central Government in matters of finance and administration. Four-fifths of the Central and Provincial Legislative Councils should be elected and one-fifth nominated. The Central and Provincial Governments should be bound to act in accordance with the resolutions passed by their respective legislative councils, unless they were vetoed by the Governor-General-in-Council. The Central Legislative Council should have no power to interfere with the Government of India's direction of military affairs and the foreign and political relations of India including declaration of war and entering into treaties. The relations of the Secretary of State for India with the Government of India should be similar to those of the Colonial Secretary with the Governments of the Dominions.

The Congress leaders like Mahatma Gandhi and Madan Mohan Malaviya attended the sessions of the Muslim League in 1915, 1916 and 1917 and spoke from its platform in support of several resolutions. The Raja of Mahmudabad who presided over the Calcutta session of the Muslim League spoke thus : "The interests of the country are paramount. We need not try to argue whether we are Muslims first or Indians. The fact is we are both : to us the question of precedence has no meaning. The League has inculcated among the Muslims a spirit of sacrifice for their country as their own religion."

It is on account of this friendly atmosphere that both the Hindus and Muslims participated in the Non-Cooperation Movement. As the Khilafat Committee and the Jamiat-ul-Ulema-i-Hind came to have their hold on the Muslim masses, the Muslim League suffered an eclipse after 1920. However, many members of the Muslim League were patronized by the British Government and occupied important offices in the Government.

When the Non-Cooperation Movement was withdrawn by Mahatma Gandhi, Hindu-Muslim riots broke out in various parts of the country. This created bad blood between the Hindus and the Muslims. The programme of **Shudhi** and **Sangathan** of the Hindus also made the Muslims anti-Hindu. M. A. Jinnah took advantage of the atmosphere and tried to put new life into the Muslim League. However, he did not achieve much success. When the Simon Commission was appointed, the members of the Muslim League were divided on the question of their attitude towards the Commission. The result was that the two sections of the League held their sessions separately. The Nationalist Muslims like Hakim Ajmal Khan, Dr. Ansari, Dr. Kitchlew, Maulana Azad, Dr. Syed Mahmud and Asaf Ali formed themselves into a separate party. Jinnah found himself alone. He could not join the Congress whose programme of direct action he did not approve of. He decided to retire from Indian politics and went away to England to practise law. However, within a few years, most of the Muslim leaders of All-India status such as Fazl-i-Hussain, Ajmal Khan, Mohammad Shafi, Ansari and Mohammad Ali, died and Jinnah found a golden opportunity to be the leader of the Muslims. He came back from England and took up the leadership of the League.

When the general elections were held in 1937, the Muslim League did not do well in the Muslim-majority provinces. However, there were negotiations for cooperation between the Congress and the Muslim League. Mr. Jinnah proposed the establishment of coalition Governments between independent parties. To quote him, "There is really no substantial difference, now at any rate, between the League and the Congress. We shall always be glad to cooperate with the Congress in their constructive programme." The Congress invited the Muslim League to join ministries on certain terms which were found to be unacceptable to the League. In the case of U.P., the terms required that the Muslim League group should cease to function as a separate group. The existing members of the Muslim League party in the U.P. Assembly were to become a part of the Congress party and were also to be subject to the control and discipline of the Congress party. "The Muslim League Parliamentary Board in the United Provinces will be dissolved and no candidates will thereafter be set up by the said Board at any by-election."

The point of view of the Congress was that such terms were necessary for the purpose of maintaining discipline among the ministers. However, critics pointed out that the Congress was "drunk with victory." Mr. Jinnah considered the terms as "a direct rebuff" and declared that "the Muslims can expect neither justice nor fairplay under Congress Government." He attacked the Congress as a Fascist Hindu body which was out to crush all other parties in the country, particularly the Muslim League. The big Muslim land-owners got afraid of the agrarian policy of the Congress. They feared that if everything was to be given to the peasantry, that could be done only at their cost and no wonder they joined hands with the Muslim League to strengthen their position.

The middle class among the Muslims also foresaw a bleak future for themselves. They felt that they could not compete with the Hindus in industry, in professions and in public services. The only way out of the difficulty was to set up a separate State for the Muslims where there would be no competition from the Hindus. They were also sensitive to the educational policy of the Congress. They condemned the Congress scheme of primary education through handicrafts. It was maintained that the Congress educational policy was essentially a Hindu one. The Muslims complained that their culture was being attacked by the Congress which was tantamount to an attack on the very existence of the Muslims. There were other causes for the denunciation of the Congress by the Muslim League. According to Brailsford, "On the eve of the elections of 1937 in the United Provinces, a leading Muslim politician who had hitherto belonged to the Congress Party deserted it, because he thought he would be defeated and went over to the Muslim League with his following. He was mistaken; the Congress was victorious and formed the Ministry. This man asked to be taken back to the fold and also to be rewarded with a cabinet post. Very naturally, but perhaps unwisely, the Congress refused—as any British party in a like case would have done. The consequences were unfortunate and to the English mind outstanding. The Muslim League redoubled its attacks on the Congress and on the strength of this and similar cases accused it of being a totalitarian party which sought to monopolise power." (Subject India, p. 83).

Another factor which annoyed the Muslim League was the

mass contact movement of the Congress under the leadership of Pandit Jawaharlal Nehru. Its object was to bring the Muslim masses into the fold of the Congress. Such a movement was considered to be a challenge to the very existence of the Muslim League. Mr. Jinnah declared that the Congress movement was "calculated to divide and weaken and break the Mussalmans and to detach them from their accredited leaders." No wonder, the Muslim League raised the cry of "Islam in danger." It was declared that under the despotism of the Congress rule, the Muslims "were doomed to the fate of under-dogs."

As time passed, the Muslim League condemned from the house-tops the tyranny to which the Muslims were being subjected in those provinces in which the Congress ministries existed. In March 1938, the Muslim League appointed a Special Committee under the Raja of Pirpur to enquire into the "numerous complaints of oppression and ill-treatment meted out to Muslims in general and the workers of the League in particular." The Pirpur Report gave a list of the sufferings of the Muslims under the Congress regime and declared that "no tyranny could be so great as the tyranny of the majority." There was absolutely no substance in the charges of the Muslim League. According to Coupland, "The Congress Ministries had not lent themselves to a policy of communal injustice, still less of deliberate persecution." According to Sir Harry Haig, Governor of U.P., "The Congress Ministries dealt with the Muslims fairly and justly." The Congress President asked the Muslim League to submit the grievances of the Muslims under the Congress regime to an impartial tribunal, but the Muslim League refused to do so. It merely went on harping on the theme of persecution till the day the Congress Ministries resigned in 1939. During this period, it looked to the Governor-General for the redress of its grievances and after that nothing was heard of them. The Muslim League observed the Deliverance Day when the Congress Ministries resigned. The Muslim League was not concerned with the truth or untruth of the myth of persecution. Its technique worked well. Mr. Jinnah came to be recognised as the champion of the Muslims in India. He became the leader of the Muslim community and the Muslim League became the representative Muslim body. Between 1937 and 1942, the Muslim League got 47 seats in 61 by-elections to the

Muslim seats and the Congress got only four.

Sir Mohammad Iqbal is considered to be the father of the idea of Pakistan. At the Allahabad session of the Muslim League held in 1930, he declared that the "formation of a consolidated North-West India Muslim State appears to me to be the final destiny of Muslims at least of North-West India." However, Iqbal did not stand for a sovereign, independent State of the Muslims. According to Coupland, Iqbal stood for a loose federation of all-India, "the Central Federal Government only exercising those powers which are expressly vested in it by the free consent of the federal States." Iqbal is stated to have told Edward Thompson that "the Pakistan plan would be disastrous to the British Government, disastrous to the Hindu community and disastrous to the Muslim community."

In spite of this, some Muslim under-graduates at the Cambridge University were influenced by his ideas. Their leader was Rahmat Ali. In 1933, Rahmat Ali described the Indian Muslims as a nation and prepared a plan for the establishment of Pakistan which was to include the Punjab, Kashmir, Sind, Baluchistan and the N.W.F.P. He also referred to the establishment of Osmanistan of Hyderabad and Bang-i-Islam of Bengal and Assam. Rahmat Ali tried to propagate his ideas among the people. However, he did not meet with any encouragement. In August 1933, Sir Zafrullah Khan described the scheme as "chimerical and impracticable." Up to 1937, the Muslim League also did not approve of the idea of Pakistan. It was in 1938 that Mr. Jinnah demanded the division of India. In January 1940, he referred to the two nations of the Hindus and the Muslims in India.

Presiding over the Muslim League session at Lahore on March 22, 1940, Mr. Jinnah declared that the Mussalmans were not in minority and they were a nation by any definition. To quote him, "If the British Government are really in earnest and sincere to secure peace and happiness of the people of this sub-continent, the only course open to us all is to allow the major nations separate homelands by dividing India into autonomous national States. There is no reason why the States should be antagonistic to each other. On the other hand, the rivalry and the natural desire and efforts on the part of one to dominate the social order and establish political supremacy over the other in the Government of the country will disappear. It will lead more towards natural goodwill by international pacts between them, and they can live in complete harmony with their neighbours. This will lead further to a friendly settlement all the more easily with regard to minorities by reciprocal arrangements and adjustments between Muslim India and Hindu India which will far more adequately and effectively safeguard the rights and interests of Muslims and various other minorities.

"It is extremely difficult to appreciate why our Hindu friends fail to understand the real natures of Islam and Hinduism. They are not religions in the strict sense of the word, but are, in fact, quite different distinct social orders, and it is a dream that the Hindus and Muslims can ever evolve a common nationality, and this misconception of the Indian nation has gone far beyond the limits and is the cause of most of our troubles and will lead India to destruction if we fail to revise our notions in time. The Hindus and Muslims belong to two different religious philosophies, social customs and literatures. They neither inter-marry nor inter-dine and, indeed, they belong to two different civilisations which are based mainly on conflicting ideas and conceptions. Their aspects on life and of life are different. It is quite clear that Hindus and Mussalmans derive their inspirations from different sources of history. They have different epics, their heroes are different, and different episodes. Very often the hero of one is foe of the other and, likewise, their victories and defeats overlap. To yoke together two such nations under a single State, one as a numerical minority and the other as a majority, must lead to growing discontent and final destruction of any fabric that may be so built up for the government of such a State."

On March 23, 1940, the following resolution on Pakistan was passed by the All-India Muslim League at its Lahore Session: "Resolved that it is the considered view of this session of the All-India Muslim League that no constitutional plan would be workable in this country or acceptable to Muslims unless it is designed on the following basic principles, namely, that geographically contiguous units are demarcated into regions which should be so constituted, with such territorial readjustments as may be necessary, that the areas in which the Muslims are numerically in a majority as in the North-Western and Eastern Zones of India should be grouped to constitute 'Independent States' in which the constituent units shall be autonomous and sovereign.

"This adequate, effective and mandatory safeguard should be specifically provided in the constitution for minorities in these units and in these regions for the protection of their religious, cultural, economic, political, administrative and other rights and interests in consultation with them; and in other parts of India where the Mussalmans are in a minority, adequate, effective and mandatory safeguards shall be specifically provided in the constitution for them and other minorities for the protection of their religious, cultural, economic, political, administrative and other rights and interests in consultation with them.

"This session further authorises the Working Committee to frame a scheme or constitution in accordance with these basic principles providing for the assumption finally by the respective regions of all powers such as defence, external affairs, communications, customs and such other matters as may be necessary."

Dr. Lal Bahadur rightly points out that the Pakistan resolution was the highest culmination of Muslim aspirations roused by leaders from the times of Sir Syed Ahmad Khan. It gave the Muslim League a new ambition and a new programme. A renewed stress was laid on the two-nation theory and the communal differences were exaggerated with redoubled energy. The Pakistan resolution was a personal triumph for Mr. Jinnah and it established his dictatorial leadership beyond all possibility of over-throw. On account of the Second World War, the British Government began to rely more and more on the support of the Muslim League and Mr. Jinnah took full advantage of that fact. However, there were many ambiguities in the Pakistan resolution. The resolution did not explain the nature of the sovereignty to be enjoyed by the Muslim State. It did not state as to who was to frame the constitution, what was to be the nature of the constitution, what were to be the relations of the independent states with the British Empire and the non-Muslim zones, what territories were to be included in the Muslim States or State, and which authority was to be incharge of defence, external affairs, etc. In spite of all these shortcomings, Pakistan became the key-stone of the ideological arch of the Muslim League after 1940 and the Muslim League asserted its-determination to achieve the ideal of Pakistan at all costs. The Anglo-Indian bureaucracy encouraged Mr. Jinnah in his demand.

The Cripps' proposals of March 1942 also recognised the claim of the Muslim League for Pakistan. The proposals recognised "the right of any province of British India that is not prepared to accept the new constitution to retain its present position, provision being made for its accession if it so decides. With such non-acceding provinces, should they so desire, His Majesty's Government would be prepared to agree upon a new constitution, giving them the same full status as the Indian Union." A resolution of the Congress stated that "the acceptance before-hand of the novel principle of non-accession for a province is also a severe blow to the conception of Indian unity and an apple of discord likely to generate growing trouble in the provinces, and which may well lead to further difficulties in the way of the Indian States merging themselves in the Indian Union." The view of Dr. Shyama Prasad Mukerjee was that the Cripps' proposals were likely to "sound the death-knell of Indian unity and freedom. India will then become a veritable chess-board on which not only Indian provinces (constituted mainly on a religious basis) may fight with each other but interested foreign nations may find ample scope for fateful intrigues and dissessions." The view of Sir Bijoy Prasad Singh Roy was: "The Cripps Mission led to (1) the stiffening of the attitude of Mahatma Gandhi and the Congress; (2) the insistence of the demand by Mr. Jinnah and the Muslim League for Pakistan; (3) the dissociation of Mr. C. Rajagopalachari from the Congress with a number of his disciples in Madras; (4) the growth of a sense of frustration in non-Congress political parties." Dr. Lal Bahadur says that "the provision of non-accession provinces in Cripps' proposals was undoubtedly disastrous in this connection. It whetted the demand for Pakistan, and also raised dormant potentialities for its opposition. In Cripps' proposals lay the germs of strained relations between the two communities of India."

The Working Committee of the Muslim League passed the following resolution on April 11, 1942: "The Committee, while expressing their gratification that the possibility of Pakistan is recognised by implication by providing for the establishment of two or more independent unions in India, regret that the proposals of His Majesty's Government, embodying the fundamental, are not open to any modification and, therefore, no alternative proposals are invited." The history of the Muslim League after the return of the Cripps' Mission was one of ever-increasing demand for Pakistan. It was declared that "any scheme which seeks to torpedo the Pakistan demand of Muslim

India will be raised by the Muslim League and as such any political party which stands for the establishment of a democratic State in India can have no agreement with the Muslim League."

Many schemes were put forward in connection with Pakistan. Dr. Latif suggested that India should be divided into cultural zones and then those should be linked up by means of a federation. He was in favour of the transfer of populations on a large scale in order to make the zones homogeneous. In addition to the North-Western and Eastern States, two more states were to be created for the Muslims. The Muslims living in U.P. and Bihar were to be concentrated in a bloc extending in a line from eastern border of Patiala to Lucknow, rounding up Rampur on the way. This state was to be known as the Delhi-Lucknow state. To quote him, "The Muslims below the Vindhyas and Satpuras are scattered all over the North in colonies of varying sizes and exceed 12 millions in number. For them a zone is to be carved. Such a zone the Dominions of Hyderabad and Berar may provide with a narrow strip of territory resorted to them in the South, running down, viz., Kurnool and Cudappah to the city of Madras. There is a communal school of thought among the Muslims who prefer to have an opening to the western coast via., Bijapur. Such a strip with an opening to the sea will be found necessary to settle the large Muslim mercantile and marine community living for ages on the Coromondel and Malabar coast." Dr. Latif also contended that the ports of Calcutta and Madras be given to the Muslims.

The Aligarh scheme was prepared by Prof. Zafrul Hassan and Mohammad Afzal Hassan Qadri. Berar and Karnatak were to be restored to Hyderabad. All towns of India with a population of 50,000 or more were to have the status of a borough with a large measure of autonomy. After the partition of India, the Muslims were to be recognised in Hindustan as a separate nation and allowed to have their separate organization.

In 1944, Rajagopalachariar put forward his formula, with the consent of Mahatma Gandhi, to satisfy the demand of the Muslims for Pakistan. That formula accepted the principle of Pakistan. The Muslim League was to support the demand of the Congress for the independence of India. During the transitional period, the Muslim League was to join hands with the Congress in forming a provisional Government. After the War, a commission was to be appointed to demarcate those contiguous areas in North-West and North-East India in which the Muslims were in absolute majority. A plebiscite of all the inhabitants of those areas was to be taken to decide whether those areas wanted to be separated from Hindustan or not. If they decided to be separated, agreements were to be made for defence, communications, etc. These terms were binding on the parties only if the British Government transferred all control into the hands of the Indians for the administration of the country. Mr. Jinnah rejected the formula of Rajaji. He condemned the offer of a "maimed, mutilated and moth-eaten Pakistan." He declared that he would not accept anything less than the six provinces of Sind, Punjab, North-West Frontier Province, Baluchistan, Bengal and Assam subject only to the adjustment of their territories. He was also opposed to the non-Muslims living in the Muslim majority areas to vote along with the Muslims.

After the end of the Second World War, fresh elections were held in the provinces and the Muslim League was able to secure 446 seats out of a total of 495 Muslim seats. Mr. Attlee, Prime Minister of England, sent a delegation of the Cabinet Ministers to India to find a solution of the Indian problem. That came to be known as the Cabinet Mission. It reached India in March 1946. The members of the Mission met the leaders of the various political parties, but they failed to persuade them to come to an agreed settlement. On March 16, 1946, they published their own proposals. After a careful examination of the Muslim League demand for Pakistan, the Mission came to the conclusion that it was not practicable to set up a sovereign Muslim state. Pakistan was not an acceptable solution for the communal problem. It was under these circumstances that the Cabinet Mission made a proposal for a Federal Union of India in which the Union Government was to have very limited powers. Provision was made for the grouping of provinces. The view of the Congress was that the grouping of the provinces was voluntary while the Muslim League maintained that it was compulsory. The British Government gave its decision in favour of the League view.

Difficulties arose in connection with the formation of the interim Government as provided for in the Cabinet Mission Scheme. On June 16, 1946, Lord Wavell issued invitations to 6 representatives of the Congress, 5 representatives of the Muslim League and 3 representatives of the minorities. The

Congress demanded the right to include one nationalist Muslim in its list of 6 members. As this claim was rejected, the Congress refused to join the interim Government. The Muslim League demanded that it should be allowed to form the Government even without the Congress. Lord Wavell refused to oblige the Muslim League and appointed a care-taker Government of officials. Mr. Jinnah attacked the British Government and on July 29, 1946, the Muslim League withdrew its acceptance of the Cabinet Mission Scheme. It also decided to prepare a programme of Direct Action "to achieve Pakistan... and to get rid of the present slavery under the British and the contemplated future of Hindu domination."

On August 6, 1946, Lord Wavell invited the Congress to form the interim Government and that invitation was accepted. The Muslim League fixed August 16, 1946 as the Direct Action Day. To facilitate the action of the League, the League Ministry of Bengal declared 16th August, 1946, as a public holiday. On that day, there was a lot of bloodshed in Calcutta and Sylhet. The great Calcutta killing was followed by bloodshed in Noakhali and Tipperah. There were abductions, forced marriages, rapes, compulsory conversions to Islam and destitution of families.

On September 2, 1946, Lord Wavell administered the oath of allegiance to the members of the Interim Government. When this was being done inside, rival crowds were shouting outside the following slogans: "Victory to Hindustan; Long live Congress Committee" and "Death of Congress; Long live Pakistan." The Muslim League was anxious to enter the Interim Government with a view to hamper the work of the Congress members in the Government. Although the Muslim League refused to undertake to work in a spirit of cooperation, Lord Wavell took 5 nominees of the Muslim League into the Interim Government. The first meeting of the Constituent Assembly was held on December 9, 1946 but this was boycotted by the Muslim League. Riots took place in Bihar, Garhmukteswar, Lahore and Rawalpindi. The Muslims threatened to revive the days of Halaku and Chengiz Khan. Nothing was done to suppress the agitation of the Muslim League in the Punjab and law and order was allowed to collapse in that province. It was in that atmosphere of lawlessness that the Prime Minister of England declared that the British Government would transfer power into the hands of Indians by a date not later than June 1948. It was also declared that the British Government would have to consider to whom the powers of the Central Government in British India should be handed over on the due date, whether as a whole to some form of Central Government for British India or in some areas to the existing provincial Governments or in some such other way as may seem most reasonable in the best interests of the Indian people.

Lord Mountbatten was sent to India to carry out the new policy of the Government. He had lengthy discussions with the leaders of the different political parties and ultimately he announced his June 3 Plan which provided for the establishment of two separate dominions of India and Pakistan. The British Government was to withdraw from India on August 15, 1947. The provinces of Bengal and Punjab were to be partitioned. The Indian Independence Act was passed by the British Parliament in July 1947. Lord Mountbatten went to Karachi to inaugurate Pakistan on August 14, 1947, with Mr. Jinnah as the first Governor-General of Pakistan.

SUGGESTED READING

Ahmad, K. A.	:	*The Founder of Pakistan—Through Trial to Triumph.*
Ambedkar, B. R.	:	*Thoughts on Pakistan.*
Khaliquzzaman, Chaudhry	:	*Pathway to Pakistan.*
Rajendra Prasad	:	*Pakistan.*
Spear, T. G. P.	:	*India, Pakistan and the West* (London 1949).
Symonds, Richard	:	*The Making of Pakistan, 1951.*

CHAPTER XXIII

The Indian States

Before the independence of India, there were a large number
of States in the country. Some of them were big and others
small. Those were in various stages of development. The Government of India exercised paramountcy over them through its
Political Department. The result was that the Indian rulers
were left with practically no independence of action. They
were completely under the thumb of the Residents stationed in
their states. A Resident watched the British interests in the
state and offered friendly advice to the ruler. He acted as the
channel of communication between the State and the Paramount
Power. His advice was usually an order or a command. It
was correctly stated that the whisper of the Residency was the
thunder of the state and there was no matter on which a Resident did not feel qualified to give his advice. The British Government claimed the right to control and use of all titles,
honours and salutes and matters of precedent. No ruler could
accept any foreign title without the consent of the British Government. He also could not confer any title. The number of
salutes to which a ruler was entitled was fixed by the British
Government. The latter also asserted and exercised the right
of deposing princes or forcing them to abdicate in certain circumstances. The rulers were required to pay succession duties
which could be exempted by the British Government only on
special grounds. The subjects of the Indian States had to apply
to the Government of India for passports to go out of India.
The Government of India had complete control over the issue
of all licences for arms and ammunitions. The appointments
of the Diwans, Chief Ministers and other important officers of
the Indian States had to be approved by the Political Department of the Government of India. The latter also exercised
the right of establishing a regency whenever a prince was a
minor or the ruler of a state was temporarily suspended or
permanently exiled from the state. It also asserted the right
of wardship over minor princes including the right to control
their education. Lord Curzon insisted that it was the duty of
the Government of India to satisfy itself that "the young chief

has received the education and training that will qualify him to rule before he is vested with powers to govern the state". Important legislation in the state required the previous sanction of the Government of India. The latter had also the right to entertain petition from the subjects of Indian states against the state administration. The Paramount Power interfered only when the things reached a critical stage. The ruler was not allowed to deal directly with any foreign state or subjects of any foreign state. He could not employ Europeans without the consent of the British Government.

Such was the state of affairs when the Government of India Act, 1919 was passed. After some time, an announcement was made by the British Government for the establishment of the Chamber of Princes and the same was inaugurated in 1921. It consisted of 120 members in all. Out of those, 12 members represented 127 states and the remaining 108 were members in their own right. About 327 states were given no representation at all. Some important Indian rulers did not join it. Ordinarily, the Chamber of Princes met once a year and was presided over by the Viceroy. It elected its own Chancellor who presided over its meeting in the absence of the Viceroy. The Chancellor was the President of the Standing Committee of the Chamber of Princes. The Standing Committee met twice or thrice a year at Delhi to discuss the important questions facing the Indian States. Every year the Standing Committee submitted its report to the Chamber of Princes. The princes also had informal conferences among themselves when they went to Delhi to attend the session.

The Chamber of Princes was a deliberative, consultative, and advisory body. Its importance has been stated by the Simon Commission Report in these words: "The establishment of the Chamber of Princes marks an important stage in the development of relations between the Crown and the States, for it involves a definite breach in an earlier policy, according to which it was rather the aim of the Crown to discourage joint action and joint consultation between the Indian States and to treat each State as an isolated unit apart from its neighbours. That principle, indeed, has already been giving place to the idea of conference and co-operation amongst the ruling princes of India, but this latter conception was not embodied in permanent shape until the Chamber of Princes was established. The Chamber has enabled thorough inter-change of views to take place on weighty matters concerning relationship of the State with the Crown and concerning other points of contact with British India."

In 1927 was appointed the Butler Committee to enquire into the relationship between the Government of India and the Indian States and to make the necessary recommendations for their satisfactory adjustment. The Committee recommended that the Viceroy and not the Governor-General-in-Council should be the agent of the Crown in dealing with the states. The relations between the Crown and the Princes should not be transferred without the consent of the princes to a new Government in British India responsible to the legislature. The scheme regarding the creation of a State Council should be rejected. Intervention in the administration of a state should be left to the decision of the Viceroy. Special Committees should be appointed to enquire into disputes that may arise between the states and British India. A Committee should be appointed to enquire into the financial relations between the Indian States and British India. There should be separate recruitment and training of political officers drawn from the Universities of England.

The authors of the Butler Committee Report enunciated the theory of direct relationship between the Indian States and the British Crown. It was contended that the relationship of the Indian States was not with the Government of India but with the British Crown. This theory was put forward with a view to setting up a "Chinese Wall" between British India and Indian States. As a matter of fact, the theory of direct relationship was being gradually evolved from 1917 when the famous August Declaration was made to give India responsible Government by stages. Its first sign was to be seen in the transfer of the relationship of Indian States from the provinces to the Central Government. In an inspired letter, the Maharaja of Indore wrote that "His Highness's treaty relations are with the British Government maintained in India by His Excellency the Viceroy as a representative of His Majesty, the King Emperor." With "autonomous Government, British India can but occupy with regard to Indore the position of a sister state like Gwalior or Hyderabad each absolutely independent of the other and having His Majesty's Government as the connecting link between the two." The theory of direct relationship was also advocated by Dr. A. B. Keith and Sir Leslie Scott. According to

Dr. Keith, "It is important to note that the relations of the Indian States, however conducted, are essentially relations with the Crown and not with the Indian Government and that this fact presents an essential complication as regards the establishment of responsible Government in India. It is clear that it is not possible for the Crown to transfer its rights under a treaty without the assent of the Native States to the Government of India under responsible Government."

Sir Leslie Scott was an eminent lawyer and he was engaged by the Standing Committee of the Chamber of Princes to represent them before the Butler Committee. In an article contributed to the Law Quarterly Review, Sir Leslie laid down five propositions, some of which might be accepted as true, others palpably false and advanced to perpetuate British stranglehold of India and to keep the States out of a united constitution for ever. Two of these were that the contracts or treaties beween the princes and the Crown were between two sovereigns and not between the Company and the Government of British India, and that the princes in making those contracts or treaties gave their confidence to the British Crown and the Crown could not assign the contracts or treaties to any concerned party. The British Government, as paramount power, had undertaken the defence of all States and to remain in India with whatever military and naval forces might be requisite to enable it to discharge that obligation. The British Government could not hand over those forces to any other Government, to a foreign power such as France or Japan, or even to British India. The Indian princes were very much pleased with the theory which was intended to help them to exclude themselves from the control of the Government of India when it came into the hands of the Indians.

The recommendations of the Butler Committee were criticised by the Indians from all walks of public life. The view of Chintamani was: "The Butler Committee was bad in its origin, bad in the time chosen for its appointment, bad in its terms of reference, bad in its personnel and bad in its line of inquiry, while its report is bad in reasoning and bad in its conclusions." The view of Sir M. Visvesvarayya was: "In the Butler Committee Report, there is no hint of a future for the Indian States' people. Their proposals are unsympathetic, unhistorical, hardly constitutional or legal.... There is no modern conception in their outlook. Certainly nothing to inspire trust or hope."

On the occasion of the first Round Table Conference held in 1930 in London, the Indian princes accepted the proposal for the creation of an All-India Federation in which both the Indian provinces and the Indian States were to be combined. The Government of India Act, 1935, provided for such a Federation. Under this Act, the Indian States were given more representation in the Federal Legislature than was due to them on the basis of their population and area. While 250 seats were allotted to British India, the Indian States got 125 seats. In the Council of State, States were given the right to send 104 members out of a total of 260 members. While the representatives from the provinces were to be elected, those from the States were to be nominated by the rulers of the States concerned. While the inclusion of the provinces into the Federation was automatic or compulsory, the Indian States were given the option to join the Federation or not. While the control of the Federal Government over the provinces was to be uniform, it was to vary in the case of the Indian States according to the terms of the Instrument of Accession signed by the particular ruler at the time of joining the Federation and accepted by the Crown. The Federal scheme as provided for in the Act of 1935 was rejected both by the Muslim League and the Congress. The British Government also did not do much to enforce it. Moreover, the outbreak of the Second World War in 1939 shelved the whole scheme. Nothing was done throughout the War to deal with the question of Indian States. However, assurances were given from time to time to the Indian Princes that no agreement would be made with the Congress against their wishes. They would not be forced to join any Indian scheme of Government against their wishes. On May 12, 1946, the members of the Cabinet Mission declared that the British Government could not and would not in any circumstances transfer paramountcy to an Indian Government. However, it was made clear that when the new self-governing Government or Governments came into being in British India, it would not be possible for the British Government to carry out the obligations of paramountcy. In that case, all the rights surrendered by the States to the Paramount Power would return to the Indian States. "Political arrangements between the States on the one side and the British Crown and British India on the other will thus be brought to an end. The void will have to be filled either by the States entering into a federal relationship with the successor Government or Governments of British India, or failing this, entering into particular political arrangements with it or them."

The Cabinet Mission scheme did not deal with the details of the problem of the States. The representation of the States in the Constituent Assembly, the stage at which their representatives were to participate in its work, the position of the States in the future Union and other questions were left to be settled by negotiation in the future between the Princes on one hand and the Constituent Assembly and the major political parties in India on the other. The Committee set up by the Constituent Assembly to negotiate with the States and the negotiating Committee of the Princes were able to arrive at an arrangement on the method of choosing the representatives of States, the allocation of seats to the different States and other matters relating to their participation in the Constituent Assembly. In accordance with the decision, the representatives of the various States took their seats in the Constituent Assembly.

The Indian Independence Act, 1947 provided that "the suzerainty of His Majesty over the Indian States lapses, and with it all treaties and agreements in force on that date." As a result of this provision, the Indian States became completely independent and the Governments of India and Pakistan did not inherit the rights or authority of the former Government of India. The Act did not attempt a solution of the problem of the States and left the same to be tackled by the new Dominions. However, the authors of the Act did not contemplate that the Indian States would become independent States as such and thereby disrupt the unity of India. Sir Hartley Shawcross, Attorney-General of England, observed thus in Parliament: "We do not propose to recognize the States as separate international entities on August 15."

It was on June 15, 1947 that the All-India Congress Committee laid down its policy towards the Indian States. The princes who had not already joined the Constituent Assembly were invited to do the same and "co-operate in the building of the constitutional structure of free India in which the States will be equal and autonomous shares with other units of the Federation." The Congress also urged the States to hasten progress towards responsible Government "so as to keep in line with the fast changing situation in India and at the same time to produce contentment and self-reliance in their people." The

Congress rejected the claim of the Princes to become independent. It claimed for the people of the States the dominant voice in decisions concerning them. The Congress Resolution declared that All-India Congress Committee did not admit the right of any State in India to declare its independence and to live in isolation from the rest of India. That would be a denial of the course of Indian history and of the objectives of the Indian people today. Pt. Jawaharlal Nehru also declared that the claim of the States to independence could not be sustained as independence did not depend on a mere declaration by a State but rested fundamentally on recognition by other States. The lapse of paramountcy of the British Crown did not make the Indian States independent. To quote him, "I should like to say and other countries to know that we shall not recognise the independence of any State in India, further that any recognition of any such independence by any Foreign Power will be considered an unfriendly act."

The Congress was able to tackle the problem of the Indian States successfully and the credit goes to Sardar Patel, Lord Mountbatten and Mr. V. P. Menon. On the suggestion of Sardar Patel, the States Ministry was set up and he himself became its head. An Instrument of Accession was drawn up which was acceptable to the Princes. They were required to hand over to the Indian Union only the subjects of defence, foreign relations and communications. In other matters, their autonomy was to be scrupulously respected. Sardar Patel made it clear to the Princes that it was not the desire of the Congress "to interfere in any manner in the domestic affairs of the States." He also appealed to the patriotism of the Indian Princes thus: "We are at a momentous stage in the history of India. By common endeavour we can raise the country to a new greatness while lack of unity will expose us to fresh calamities. I hope the Indian States will bear in mind that the alternative to cooperation in the general interest is anarchy and chaos which will overwhelm great and small alike in common ruin if we are unable to act together in the minimum of common tasks. Let not the future generations curse us for having had the opportunity but failed to turn it to our mutual advantage. Instead, let it be our proud privilege to leave a legacy of mutually beneficial relationship which would raise this Sacred Land to its proper place among the nations of the world and turn it into an abode of peace and prosperity." Addressing the Chamber of

Princes on 25th July 1947, Lord Mountbatten also endorsed the appeal of Sardar Patel and advised the Indian States to accede to one or the other of the Dominions before 15th August, 1947. He pointed out that if nothing was put in the place of co-ordinated administration that had grown up under the British rule, only chaos would result and that was bound to hurt the States most. No State could live in isolation. The subjects which were proposed to be vested in the Federation were the subjects which the States could not handle themselves. The States had not administered their external relations or their defence and were not in a position to handle them in the future. Communications were a means of maintaining the lifeblood of the whole sub-continent. The three subjects were such which could be left to be handled on their behalf "for their convenience and advantage by a larger organisation." Lord Mountbatten also stressed the factors that were to be taken into consideration by the States while acceding to any Dominion. "There are certain geographical compulsions which cannot be evaded." "The vast majority of States were irretrievably linked up with India." He concluded his address thus: "I am not asking any State to make intolerable sacrifice of either its internal autonomy or independence. My scheme leaves you with all internal autonomy or independence. My scheme leaves you with all the practical independence that you can possibly use and makes you free of all those subjects which you cannot possibly manage of your own. You cannot run away from the Dominion Government which is your neighbour any more than you can run away from the subjects for whose welfare you are responsible."

The net result of all the efforts was that by 15th August, 1947, with the exception of Junagadh, Hyderabad and Kashmir, as many as 136 salute and fully jurisdictional States acceded to the Indian Union. On 15th August, Lord Mountbatten paid the following tribute to Sardar Patel; "Thanks to that far-sighted statesman, Sardar Vallabhbhai Patel, Minister-in-charge of the States Department, a scheme was produced which appeared to me to be equally in the interests of the States as of the Dominion of India. It is a great triumph for the realism and sense of responsibility of the rulers and the Government of the States as well as for the Government of India that it was possible to produce an Instrument of Accession, which was equally acceptable to both sides, and one moreover so simple and straightforward that within less than 3 weeks, practically all the States concerned had signed the Instrument of Accession."

Junagadh. Junagadh was a small State in Kathiawar. Its population was predominantly Hindu but its ruler was a Muslim. The result was that the Muslim ruler acceded to Pakistan on the eve of the transfer of power. The people of the State revolted against the ruler. Disturbances spread everywhere. The situation became so serious that the life of the ruler himself became unsafe and he left for Pakistan. The Muslim Diwan of the State was forced to invite the Government of India on 9th November, 1947 to intervene to restore order. A referendum was held in the State in February 1948 and that was in favour of accession to India. The representatives of the State decided to merge themselves with the Union of Kathiawar and the merger took place on 29th January 1949.

Hyderabad. Hyderabad was the largest Indian State with an area of 82,313 sq. miles and a population of 1.86 crores. Its population was predominantly Hindu (89%) but its ruler was a Muslim. The State was in the heart of the Indian Union and was surrounded by it on all sides. The Government of India invited the Nizam of Hyderabad to accede to the Dominion of India before 15th August, 1947. However, the Nizam was under the control of Razakars and the Ittehad-ul-Musalmeen led by Kasim Razvi. The result was that the invitation was rejected. However, the Nizam entered into a standstill agreement with the Government of India on 29th November, 1947. All kinds of efforts were made by Lord Mountbatten to find out a solution of the problem of Hyderabad but he failed. The Nizam was not prepared to listen to reason. He tried to raise an army to fight against the Indian Government. The result was that the Government of India decided to take action against the Nizam. The police action started on 13th September 1948 and within 3 days the Nizam surrendered. The Nizam was not deposed but the State was put under military administration for some time. On 1st November, 1948, Hyderabad acceded to the Indian Union. Later on, a democratic Government was set up in that State with the Nizam as a constitutional head.

Kashmir. As regards Kashmir, its area was 84,471 sq. miles and its population 44 lakhs. Three-fourths of its population was Muslim and the rest was Hindu, Sikh or Buddhist. The ruler of the State was a Hindu. The Maharaja did not join either of the two Dominions before 15th August, 1947, in spite of the advice of Lord Mountbatten to do so. Lord Mountbatten had advised the Maharaja not to accede to either Dominion "without first taking steps to ascertain the will of his people by referendum, plebiscite, election or even if these methods were impracticable, by representative public meetings." He had given an assurance that if he acceded to Pakistan, the Government of India will not consider that to be an unfriendly act. In spite of that, the ruler hesitated. He intended to enter into Standstill Agreements, both with India and Pakistan. Actually he entered into a Standstill Agreement only with Pakistan. In spite of that, border raids were organized against the State immediately after 15th August, 1947. When the tribal people were just going to capture Srinagar itself, the Maharaja requested the Government of India for help and signed the Instrument of Accession on 26th October, 1947. The Indian forces went to Kashmir and turned out the invaders from a major part of the State.

The problem of Kashmir is a complicated one. Kashmir still remains the bone of contention between India and Pakistan. All efforts to solve the problem have failed so far. In 1965, Pakistan first sent infiltrators into Kashmir to create trouble and then attacked the Chhamb area of Jammu and Kashmir State. There was a brief war but that failed to solve the problem. Tension continues to exist between the two countries.

Integration and Democratisation of States

The accession of States was only a partial solution of the problem of the States. The people of the States were restive and wanted to have a share in the administration. The Government of India was also favourably inclined towards their aspirations. The administration of the Indian States required to be modernised. The work of integration, democratisation and modernisation of the Indian States was done simultaneously. Integration involved the elimination of the small States by their merger with the neighbouring Provinces or States, or their consolidation into larger political units by means of the Unions of the States. By those means a few viable and sizeable units were to be created. Integration also involved the establishment of "a common Centre in the whole of India, able to function efficiently in the Provinces and States alike in matters requiring all-India action." In the words of the White Paper on the

States, "The aim was the integration of all elements in the country in a free, united and democratic India."

(1) As regards the merger of the smallest States into the neighbouring States or Provinces, the Orissa and Chattisgarh States were the first to be merged. Those States were 39 in number and had a population of 70 lakhs and an area of 56,000 sq. miles. Individually those States were too small for a modern system of administration. Their mergers were negotiated by Sardar Patel on 14th and 15th December, 1947. According to the Merger Agreements, the ruling Princes surrendered to the Dominion Government "full and exclusive authority, jurisdiction and power for and in relation to the governance" of their States and agreed to transfer their administration on 1st January, 1948. On 1st January, 1948, these States became a part of Orissa and Central Provinces. On 16th December, 1947, Sardar Patel observed thus: "It should be obvious to everyone, however, that even democracy and democratic institutions can function efficiently only where the units to which these are applied can subsist in a fairly autonomous existence. Where, on account of smallness of its size, isolation of its situation, the inseparable link with a neighbouring autonomous territory, be it a Province or a bigger State, in practically all economic matters of everyday life, the inadequacy of the resources to open up its economic potentialities, the backwardness of its people and sheer incapacity to shoulder a self-contained administration, a State is unable to afford a modern system of Government, both democratisation and integration are clearly and unmistakably indicated."

The next merger was that of the Deccan States numbering 17. They were merged with Bombay in March 1948. Kolhapur was merged later on. In this way, an area of 10,860 sq. miles and a population of 27 lakhs was merged in the Bombay Presidency. In June 1948, the Gujarat States numbering 289 were merged in Bombay Presidency. These States covered an area of 17,680 sq. miles and had a population of 27 lakhs. In May 1949, Baroda was merged in Bomaby Presidency. It had an area of 8,236 sq. miles and population of 30 lakhs. A few small States in the Punjab, the State of Banganapalli, Pudukotti and Sandur in Madras, Cooch-Behar in West Bengal, the Khasi Hills States in Assam and Tehri-Garhwal, Banaras and Rampur in U.P. were merged in the surrounding Provinces in 1948 and 1949.

The Merger Agreements of practically all the States were in identical terms. The merged States became part and parcel of the Provinces into which they were included. The people of the merged States were given representation in the Provincial Legislatures. The Government of India Act, 1935, as amended, was applied to them in the same way as was done to other Provinces of India.

(2) Another form of integration of States was the consolidation of States into Centrally administered areas. This was done in the case of Himachal Pradesh, Vindhya Pradesh, Kutch, Bilaspur, Bhopal, Tripura and Manipur. 21 States in East Punjab covering an area of 10,600 sq. miles with a population of about 10 lakhs were consolidated into the Union of Himachal Pradesh. This Union was inaugurated on 15th April, 1948. Vindhya Pradesh was created by consolidating the Bundelkhand and Bhagelkhand States numbering 35 with an area of 24,600 sq. miles and a population of 36 lakhs. Vindhya Pradesh was created into a States Union in April 1948 with a responsible ministry but later on its Government was taken over by the Government of India on 1st January, 1950. Kutch with an area of 17,249 sq. miles and a population of 5 lakhs was made a Chief Commissioner's Province in May 1948. The State of Bilaspur in the Punjab was taken over by the Government of India on 12th October, 1948. The State of Bhopal was taken over by the Government of India on 1st June, 1949. The State of Tripura was taken over by the Government of India on 15th October, 1949.

(3) Another form of integration of States was the formation of the States-Unions. These Unions were created "with due regard to geographical, linguistic, social and cultural affinities" of the people living in the States. Their rulers came to be known as Rajpramukhs.

On 15th February, 1948, the United States of Kathiwar (Saurashtra) was inaugurated. This Union had 222 States, estates and talukas. Its area was 21,451 sq. miles and its population was 41 lakhs. The important States of the Union were Nawanagar and Bhavanagar. According to the terms of the covenant, the States agreed to unite and integrate their territories into one State with a common executive, legislature and judiciary. There was to be a Council of Rulers with a Presidium of five members. The Rulers were to elect the President and Vice-President of the Presidium. The President was to be the Rajpramukh of the Union. All the executive powers were put in the hands of the Rajpramukh but he was to be aided and advised by a Council of Ministers. In other words, he was to act as a constitutional head. The covenant fixed the privy purses of the rulers and guaranteed their private property, personal privileges and the right of succession.

On 18th March, 1948 was created the United States of Matsya consisting of Alwar, Bharatpur, etc. The Union of Vindhya Pradesh was created on 4th April, 1948. The United States of Gwalior, Indore and Malwa or Madhya Bharat was inaugurated on 28th May, 1948. It had an area of 46,710 sq. miles and a population of 80 lakhs. The Patiala and East Punjab States Union (PEPSU) consisting of 7 big States such as Patiala, Nabha, Kapurthala, etc., was inaugurated on 20th August, 1948. It had an area of 10,999 sq. miles and a population of 35 lakhs. The United States of Rajasthan was created in three stages. The first United States of Rajasthan consisting of Mewar and nine other smaller Rajputana States was inaugurated on 18th April, 1948. The State was reconstituted to include Jaipur, Jodhpur, Jaisalmer and Bikaner. On 15th May, 1949, the United State of Matsya was incorporated into Rajasthan. The United State of Travancore-Cochin came into being on 1st July, 1949. Its total area was 9,155 sq. miles and its population was 93 lakhs.

Under the Indian Princes, the States had autocratic government. The people had absolutely no voice in the administration of the States. The Princes did whatever they pleased. There was practically no distinction between the public revenues and the private revenues of the ruling Princes.

However, such a state of things could not exist after the independence of India and the integration of the States. The people of the States were demanding a share in the administration and the Government of India had full sympathy with them. No wonder, when the Indian States were merged into the Provinces, the people of those States were put on the same footing as the people of the provinces concerned. When the Government of India created Centrally administered areas, the people of those States were also associated with the administration. When the Unions of the States were created, full-fledged responsible government was established in them. It is true that the people living within the Centrally-administered area were not given full control over their administration, but the people of other Indian States were given responsible government. Legislatures were set up in the States and the Ministries were made responsible to them. The Rajpramukhs were made constitutional heads.

The States Re-organisation Commission

For a long time, there was a demand for the re-organisation of the provinces of India on linguistic lines. It was contended that the existing provinces were not created by the British Government on any scientific principle. These were set up from time to time on grounds of expediency. In 1948, the Linguistic Provinces Committee known as the Dar Committee was set up to go into the matter. The Committee reported against the proposition. Its view was that nationalism and sub-nationalism were two emotional experiences which grew at the expense of each other. A Committee consisting of Jawaharlal Nehru, Sardar Patel and Dr. Pattabhi Sitaramayya was set up to examine the findings of the Dar Committee. As a result of the death of Sriramulu, the situation in Andhra became very tense and the Government of India appointed Mr. Justice Wanchoo (as he then was) to report on the matter. It was under these circumstances that the first linguistic State was set up in Andhra. This gave an impetus to the supporters of the idea of linguistic States and ultimately Prime Minister Nehru made a statement in Parliament on 22nd December, 1953, to the effect that a Commission would be appointed to examine "objectively and dispassionately" the question of the reorganisation of the States of the Indian Union "so that the welfare of the people of each constituent unit as well as the nation as a whole is promoted." The Commission was appointed under a resolution of the Government of India in the Ministry of Home Affairs. Mr. Fazl Ali was appointed the Chairman of the Commission and its two other members were Pandit Hridayanath Kunzru and Sardar K. M. Panikkar.

Para. 7 of the resolution mentioned above runs thus: "The Commission will investigate the conditions of the problem, the historical background, the existing situation and the bearing of all important and relevant factors thereon. They will be free to consider any proposal relating to such reorganisation. The Government expects that the Commission would, in the first instance, not go into the details, but make recommendations in regard to the broad principles which should govern the solution of this problem. The language and culture of an area have an undoubted importance as they represent a pattern of living which is common in that area. In considering a reorganisation of States, however, there are other important factors which have also to be borne in mind. The first essential consideration is the preservation and strengthening of the unity and security of India. Financial, economic and administrative considerations are almost equally important, not only from the point of view of each State, but for the whole nation. India is embarked upon a great ordered plan for the economic, cultural and moral progress. Changes which interfere with the successful prosecution of such a national plan would be harmful to the national interest."

The Commission submitted its report to the Government of India on 30th September, 1955 and it was released to the public on 10th October, 1955. According to the recommendations of the Commission, the Indian Union was to consist of 16 States as against the existing 27 and three Centrally-administered territories. The States that were to disappear were those of Travancore-Cochine, Mysore, Coorg, Saurashtra, Kutch, Madhya Bharat, Bhopal, Vindhya Pradesh, PEPSU, Himachal Pradesh, Ajmer and Tripura. In certain cases, the whole of the State and in certain others only a part was to be merged in a neighbouring State or States. PEPSU and Himachal Pradesh were to form part of the Punjab. All the Part 'C' States were to be abolished. The distinction between Part 'A' and Part 'B' States was to be done away with.

The Commission recommended the abolition of the institution of Rajpramukhs. Special safeguards were recommended for linguistic minorities. The minorities were given the right to have instruction in their mother-tongue at the primary school stage. In the interests of national unity and good administration, the Commission recommended the reconstitution of certain All-India Services, viz., the Indian Medical and Health Services. With the same object in view, the Commission recommended that as a general rule, 50% of the new entrants in the All-India Services should be from outside the State concerned and regular transfers to and from the Centre and the States should be arranged. At least one-third of the number of judges in a High Court should consist of persons recruited from outside that State so that the administration might inspire confidence and help in arresting parochial trends. The Commission put emphasis on the need for encouraging the study of Indian languages other than Hindi. It also recommended that for some time to come, English should continue to occupy an important place in universities and institutions of high learning, even after the adoption of Hindi and the regional languages for official and educational purposes.

According to the Commission, the linguistic complexion and the communicational needs of the Punjab did not justify the creation of a Punjabi-speaking State. The creation of such a State was likely to disrupt the economic life of the area. There was no case for a Punjabi-speaking State because it lacked the general support of the people inhabiting the area, and because it was not to eliminate any of the causes of friction from which the demand for a separate Punjabi-speaking State had arisen. The Punjabi Suba was to solve neither the language nor the communal problem. On the other hand, it might further exacerbate the existing feelings. PEPSU and Himachal Pradesh were too small to continue by themselves. Having regard to the economic and administrative links between PEPSU and the Himachal Pradesh on the one hand and the present Punjab State on the other, the merger of these two States in the Punjab was justified.

During its inquiry, the Commission received 152,250 memoranda, petitions and communications, travelled 38,000 miles and interviewed over 9,000 persons in an effort to get a complete cross-section of public opinion. The report of the Commission comprises 267 printed pages, including two minutes of dissent by the Chairman, Mr. Fazl Ali and Sardar K. M. Panikkar. The first opposed the merger of Himachal Pradesh in the new Punjab and the second objected to the retention of U.P. in undivided form.

There was a lot of agitation against the recommendations of the Commission. The interested parties tried to create a sort of chaos in the country. The Maharashtrians raised a lot of hue and cry over the city of Bombay. The Congress High Command declared that it was willing to make alterations in the recommendations of the Commission if all the interested parties agreed upon any alternative. Prolonged negotiations were held and many changes were made in the recommendations of the Commission but the problem of Bombay City gave headache to all. Even when the States Reorganisation

Bill was sent to Parliament, the Maharashtrians were absolutely dissatisfied. However, when the Bill was being discussed in Lok Sabha, better sense prevailed and it was decided to create the bi-lingual State of Bombay containing all the territories of Maharashtra and Saurashtra with Bombay as capital. The Bill was passed by the Lok Sabha and Rajya Sabha and received the assent of President on 31st August, 1956.

After the establishment of the composite State of Bombay by the States Reorganisation Act, 1956, there was a lot of agitation for the separation of Maharashtra from Gujarat. For a long time, the Government of India resisted the demand but the Marathas seemed to be very keen on having the same. There were riots on a large scale and ultimately the Government of India passed the Bombay Reorganisation Act, 1960. It separated the State of Gujarat from that of Maharashtra and also divided the assets between the two States.

In July 1960, the Government of India decided to set up a new State of Nagaland with Kohima as its capital. That was done to satisfy the dis-contented elements in that region. An Act was passed in 1962 to implement that decision.

SUGGESTED READINGS

Menon, V. P.   : The Story of the Integration of
                                    the Indian States, 1956.

Mukherjee and
Ramaswamy   : Reorganisation of Indian States.

Rao, V. Venkata   : The Political Map of India (The
                                    Indian   Journal   of   Political
                                    Science, 1956, pp. 176-204).

Report of the States Reorganisation Commission, 1955.

Report of the Linguistic Provinces Committee (1949).

Report of the Official Language Commission (1957).

White Paper on Indian States (1950).

CHAPTER XXIV

Political Developments Since 1919

Lord Chelmsford was the Governor-General and Viceroy of India in 1919 when the Government of India Act, 1919 was passed by the British Parliament and he continued to occupy that exalted position up to 1921. He was succeeded by Lord Reading (1921-26). It was during the Viceroyalty of Lord Chelmsford that the Jallianwala Bagh tragedy took place at Amritsar. Mahatma Gandhi also started his Non-Cooperation Movement during his regime. The Muslims of India organised the Khilafat Movement to protest against the treatment meted out to Turkey by the Allies in spite of the repeated promises and assurances to the Muslims of India. The Khilafat Movement stood for the maintenance of the integrity of the Turkish Empire. The Muslims also demanded the establishment of a Muslim State of Palestine. The Chamber of Princes was in-augurated in 1921.

Lord Reading was born in a poor family but he rose to the high position of Lord Chief Justice of England by dint of hard work. During his Viceroyalty, there was a lot of opposition to the Government. There were strikes and riots at many places. Those were the days of the Swarajists who entered the legislatures to wreck them from within. It was during his re-gime that the Muddiman Committee was set up to report on the working of the reforms of 1919 and the Report was also published during this period.

Under the Government of India Act, 1919, 47 subjects were declared to be central subjects and 52 subjects were included in the Provincial List. The distribution of the subjects involved a deficit for the Central Government and consequently a Com-mittee known as the Provincial Relations Committee was set up with Lord Meston as its President to make recommendations as to how the deficit could be met. The Committee recommended that the provinces should make contributions to the Govern-ment of India so that the budget could be balanced. It was estimated that the deficit was to be about Rs. 10 crores and the provinces were required to pay according to their capacity. A schedule gave the permanent and standard ratio at which each province was to be taxed in order to wipe out the Central deficit. The contributions made by the various provinces to the Central Government in 1921-22 were Madras Rs. 348 lacs, Bombay Rs. 56 lacs, Bengal Rs. 63 lacs, Punjab Rs. 175 lacs, United Provinces Rs. 240 lacs, Assam Rs. 15 lacs, Burma Rs. 64 lacs and C.P. and Berar Rs. 22 lacs.

When the British Government promised the establishment of responsible Government of India, the members of the public services were upset. Formerly, they used to rule the country and now they got worried about their position in the future. They demanded certain safeguards. It was suggested that the members of the All India Services, with a few exceptions, might be allowed to retire before they completed the service ordinarily required for earning pension and they should be given a pension proportionate to their actual service. About 345 All India service officers retired by 1924. The Government of India was faced with the problem that an adequate number of Englishmen and Europeans was not forthcoming for the All India Services and a Royal Commission on Superior Civil Services in India was appointed in 1923. It came to be known as the Lee Commission as Lord Lee was its Chairman. The Commission made many recommendations. As regards the Indian Civil Service, the Indian Police Service, the Indian Forest Service and the Irrigation Branch of the Service of Engineers on which public security mainly depended, the Secretary of State was allowed to continue to recruit. His control, with certain safeguards, was to be maintained. As regards the Indian Education Service, the Indian Veterinary Service and the Indian Medical Service (Civil) which operated mostly in the Transferred field, it was recommended that the control of the ministers was to be made effective by closing the recruitment on an All-India basis. The officers already in those services were to be allowed to retain their All-India status and privileges. However, the new recruits to those services were to be appointed in future by the Provincial Governments and they were to form a part of the Provincial Services. It was made clear that the change was not to apply to the Indian Medical Services. Each province was required to employ in its Medical Department a certain number of officers lent from the Medical Department of the Army in India. The Commission recommended an increased rate of Indianisation. For the Indian Civil Service, 10% of the superior posts were to be filled by the appointment of the provincial service officers to "listed" posts. Direct recruitment in future was to be on the basis of equal numbers between Europeans and Indians. It was estimated that within 15 years, half the recruits to the Indian Civil Service would be Indians and half Europeans. As regards the Indian Police Service, recruitment was to be in the proportion of five Europeans and three Indians, allowing their promotion from provincial services to fill up 20% of the vacancies. It was estimated that by 1949 the personnel of the police service would be half Europeans and half Indians. As regards the Indian Forest Service, the recruitment was to be in the ratio of 75% Indians and 25% Europeans. As regards the Irrigation Branch of the Indian Service of Engineers, there was to be direct recruitment of Indians and Europeans in equal numbers. As regards the Central Services, the Commission recommended that in the Political Department 25% of the total officers to be recruited annually should be Indians. In the Imperial Customs, not less than half the new entrants should be the natives of India. In the Superior Telegraph and Wireless Branch, 25% of the persons should be recruited in England and the rest in India. As regards State railways, recruitment in India was to be increased as soon as possible to 75%. 25% new entrants were to be recruited in England. The Commission also recommended an increase in the emoluments and privileges of the members of the civil service. The European members of the services were to be allowed to remit their overseas pay at the rate of 2s. for a rupee or to draw the same in London in sterling at that rate, although the actual rate of exchange was 1s. 5d. The European members of the Superior Civil Services and their wives were to receive four return passages and one single passage for each child during services. If any European member of a Civil Service died while serving in India, his family was to be repatriated at the expense of the Government of India. The pensions of the civil servants were considerably increased. Medical attendance by European officers was to be made available to them. Family pension funds were to be introduced. All future British recruits to the All-India Services were given the option to retire on proportionate pension in case they decided not to serve in India. The Commission also recommended that the Public Service Commission should be set up immediately.

Lord Irwin was the Governor-General and Viceroy of India

from 1926 to 1931. It was during his regime that the Simon Commission was appointed in 1927. The Indians protested against its all-White composition. There were Hartals and boycots all over the country. Lathi charges were common. In December 1928, the Indian National Congress at its Calcutta session passed a resolution asking the British Government to grant India dominion status within a year. In October 1929, Lord Irwin made a statement on behalf of the British Government that the goal of the British Government in India was to give dominion status to India but that declaration did not satisfy the Indian leaders and at its Lahore session held in December 1929, the Congress declared that its goal was full independence and not dominion status. January 26, 1930 was declared as Independence Day. Civil Disobedience Movement was started by Mahatma Gandhi under his own leadership. Thousands of men, women and children were arrested and punished. In many cases, their properties were confiscated. It was in that atmosphere that the Simon Commission submitted its Report and the First Round Table Conference met in London in 1930. Not much could be accomplished on account of the absence of the representatives of the Indian National Congress. Through the efforts of Sir Tej Bahadur Sapru and M. R. Jayakar, the Gandhi-Irwin Pact was signed on March 5, 1931. While the Government of India agreed to make certain concessions, the Congress agreed to withdraw the Civil Disobedience Movement. The boycott of the non-Indian goods was to be discontinued. Mahatma Gandhi was not to press for a public inquiry into the allegations against the conduct of the police in India. The Government of India was to withdraw the ordinances promulgated in connection with the Civil Disobedience Movement. Pending prosecutions were to be withdrawn. The prisoners were to be released and their properties restored. Fines which had not been realised were to be remitted. Immoveable property taken into possession by the Government was to be returned to their owners.

The Gandhi-Irwin Pact had a mixed reception. The people of the country welcomed it as a great victory for the Congress. The Congress was in a stronger position in future to fight against the Government. However, the agreement was condemned on the ground that Mahatma Gandhi was not able to save the lives of Sardar Bhagat Singh and his comrades. The result was that when Gandhiji went to attend the Karachi session of the Congress soon after the signing of the agreement, there were black flag demonstrations against him and there were shouts of "Down with Gandhi" and "Gandhi truce has sent Bhagat Singh to the gallows."

Lord Irwin was succeeded by Lord Willingdon (1931-36). Before his appointment as Governor-General, Lord Willingdon was the Governor of Bombay and Madras from 1913 to 1924. From 1926 to 1930, he was the Governor-General of Canada. It was during his Viceroylty that the Second Round Table Conference met in London in 1931. Nothing came out of this Conference as Mr. Jinnah refused to come to terms with Mahatma Gandhi and the Mahatma left the Conference in disgust. As soon as he came back from London, he was arrested and a reign of terror and repression was started in the country. The more the movement was suppressed, the stronger it became. The ordinances and the various laws passed by the Government to meet the situation proved to be ineffective and the spirit of the people was not crushed. In August 1932 was announced the famous Communal Award by Prime Minister Ramsay MacDonald. Mahatma Gandhi strongly protested against it and threatened to go on fast unto death if the clauses relating to the depressed classes were not changed. Ultimately, the Poona Pact was signed and that Pact altered the Communal Award with regard to the representation of the depressed classes. In 1932 was summoned the Third Round Table Conference in London. In March 1933 was issued the White Paper containing the proposals of the British Government with regard to the new constitution of India. In 1935 was passed the Government of India Act.

During the Viceroylty of Lord Willingdon, earthquakes took place in Bihar and Quetta. There was a terrible loss of life and property.

The Indian Press (Emergency Powers) Act, 1931, Foreign Relations Act, 1932 and Indian States (Protection) Act, 1934 were passed during the regime of Lord Willingdon. The object of the Indian Press (Emergency Powers) Act, 1931 was to provide against the publication of that matter which incited or encouraged murder or violence. Provision was made for the deposit of security by the keepers of printing presses. The provincial Government was given the power to forfeit the security of a press in certain cases. If a printer applied for a fresh declaration, he could be asked by a magistrate to deposit a security of the value of not less than Rs. 1,000 and not more than Rs. 10,000 as the magistrate might think fit. If, after the deposit of a new security, a newspaper published objectionable matter, the provincial Government could forfeit the new security also. Provisions which applied to keepers of printing presses applied equally to the publishers of newspapers. Section 11 penalised the keeping of printing presses and the publishing of newspapers without making the security deposit as required by the provincial Government or the magistrate. If a press did not deposit the security but continued to do its work, it could be forfeited to His Majesty and the declaration of the publisher was liable to be cancelled. Any police officer empowered for that purpose by the provincial Government could seize any unauthorised news sheets or unauthorised newspapers wherever found and the same could be ordered to be destroyed by a magistrate. The Government was given the power to seize and forfeit undeclared presses producing unauthorised news sheets and newspapers. The penalty for disseminating unauthorised news sheets and newspapers was imprisonment up to 6 months, with or without fine. The provincial Government was given the power to declare certain publications forfeited to His Majesty and also issue search warrants for the same. The Customs Officers were authorised to detain packages containing certain publications when imported into British India. No unauthorised news sheets or newspapers could be transmitted by post.

The powers conferred by the Act were undoubtedly sweeping in their nature and scope. Those were actually used by the Provincial Governments to prohibit the publication of the names and portraits of well-known leaders of the Civil Disobedience Movement as the publication of such pictures tended to encourage the movement. The other restraints included the prohibition of the publication of Congress propaganda of any kind including messages from the persons arrested, messages issued or purported to be issued from persons in jail, exaggerated reports of political events, notices and advertisements of meetings, processions and other activities tending to promote Civil Disobedience Movement or any other matter in furtherance of the same. Under this Act, the Government took action against many newspapers. The printers and publishers of the Bombay Chronicle were called upon to deposit Rs. 3,000 each for publishing an article by Mr. Horniman. The printer and publisher of he Anand Bazar Patrika each received demand for Rs. 1,000. A security of Rs. 6,000 was demanded from Amrit Bazar Patrika. Rs. 6,000 were deposited by The Liberty of Calcutta. A security of Rs. 6,000 was deposited by the Free Press Journal and later on forfeited by the Bombay Government. Similar actions were taken against other newspapers. There was virtually a reign of terror in the country.

The Foreign Relations Act, 1932 replaced an Ordinance of 1931. Its object was to penalise publications calculated to interfere with the maintenance of good relations between His Majesty's Government and friendly foreign states. The necessity of this law arose when the Indian newspapers criticised the administration in certain states adjoining the frontiers of India. The Act provided that where an offence under Chapter XXI of the Indian Penal Code was committed against the ruler of a State outside but adjoining India or against the consort or son of principal minister of such a ruler, the Governor-General-in-Council could make or authorise any person to make a complaint in writing of such an offence and any court competent in other respects to take cognizance of such offence could take cognizance of such a complaint. Any book, newspaper or other document containing defamatory matter which tended to prejudice the maintenance of friendly relations between His Majesty's Government and the Government of such State, could be detained in the same manner as seditious literature.

In January 1933, four Ordinances were promulgated which conferred certain powers on the Government for the maintenance of law and order and widened the operative section of the Indian Press (Emergency Powers) Act, 1931 so as to permit action against the publication of matter calculated to encourage the Civil Disobedience Movement.

The object of the Indian States (Protection) Act, 1934 was to prevent unreasonable attacks on the administration of the Indian States in the newspapers of British India and to provide the authorities in British India with powers to deal with bands or demonstrators organised on semi-military lines for the purpose of entering and spreading dis-affection in the territories of Indian States.

Lord Linlithgow came to India as Governor-General in 1936 and he continued to occupy that position till 1944. Before his appointment as Governor-General, he had a brilliant career. He was the Chairman of the Royal Commission on

Indian Agriculture. He was also the Chairman of the Joint Select Committee on Indian Constitutional Reforms. He had also a hand in the drafting of the Government of India Act, 1935. No wonder, he was sent to India to enforce the law in the making of which he had a hand. The Federal part of the Government of India Act, 1935 was not introduced at all. Only the Provincial Part was introduced. Elections were held in the beginning of 1937 and the Congress got a majority in many provinces. In spite of that, the Congress Party refused to form ministries in the provinces unless an assurance was given that the Governors would not interfere in the day-to-day affairs of the departments under the control of the Indian Ministers. There was a deadlock for some time. However, the Governor-General gave the assurance and the Congress Ministries were formed and they continued to function till 1939, when they resigned after the declaration of the second World War (1939-45).

There was a split in the Congress during this period. Subhash Chandra Bose got himself elected as the Congress President in 1938 and 1939. There arose differences between him on the one hand and Mahatma Gandhi and his followers on the other. Ultimately, Subhash Chandra Bose left the Congress and formed the Forward Bloc. During the War, he disappeared from India and ultimately was responsible for organising the Indian National Army.

In 1940, Lord Linlithgow made his famous August Offer but the same was rejected by the Congress. In March 1942, Sir Stafford Cripps came to India with a view to coming to an understanding with the Congress on the basis of the proposals brought by him. However, his mission was a failure. In August 1942, the Congress passed the famous Quit India Resolution and as a result of it, all the Congress leaders were arrested and they remained in jails throughout the World War II.

Lord Wavell came to India as the Governor-General in 1944 and he occupied that position up to 1947. He had a brilliant military career before his appointment as Governor-General and he brought to his task all the qualities of a great General. It was during his regime that there was a famine in Bengal and he tried his best to relieve the sufferings of the people in spite of the many handicaps arising out of the military operations. In June 1945, Lord Wavell called a Conference at

Simla with the object of coming to some sort of an agreement with the major political parties in the country. In spite of the sincere efforts of the Governor-General, the Simla Conference failed on account of the attitude of the Muslim League.

When the Labour Party came to power in England, fresh elections were ordered to be held for the provincial Legislatures in India. The Cabinet Mission came to India in March 1946. After long negotiations, the Cabinet Mission issued a scheme on May 16, 1946. The scheme provided for an Interim Government and also a procedure for the framing of a Constitution for India and also for the groups into which the provinces were to be combined. The Muslim League accepted the scheme but the Congress rejected it. Later on, the Congress accepted it and the Muslim League rejected it. There was the Calcutta killing in August 1946. On September 2, 1946, Pt. Jawaharlal Nehru formed the Interim Government but the same was boycotted by the Muslim League. However, its representatives joined it later on. The Constituent Assembly met in December 1946 at New Delhi but it was boycotted by the Muslim League.

Lord Mountbatten was appointed by the Labour Government as Governor-General and Viceroy of India in March 1947 and he was in India up to June 1948. Up to August 15, 1947, he was Governor-General and Viceroy of the whole of India. After the partition of India, he became the Governor-General of free India minus Pakistan. He was loved by the people of India for his qualities of head and heart.

When Lord Mountbatten reached India in March 1947, the situation was very critical. The Muslim League was carrying on its wear and tear campaign all over the country, especially in the Punjab. There were riots in March 1947. Lord Mountbatten felt that the only way to deal with the situation was to complete the work of the transfer of power into the hands of the Indians within as short a period as possible. With that object in view, he held consultations with the Indian leaders. He went to London in May 1947 to discuss the matter with the British Government. On his return, he announced his famous June 3 Plan by which he proposed to divide India into two parts, viz., the Dominion of India and the Dominion of Pakistan. Both the Dominions were to be given independence. The Plan was accepted both by the Muslim League and the Indian National Congress and the Indian Independence

Act, 1947 was passed to give effect to it. The division of the country took place on August 15, 1947.

After the declaration of India's independence on August 15, 1947, the State of Jammu and Kashmir was attacked by the tribal raiders. Kashmir acceded to India and the Indian forces were flown to Kashmir to protect her.

The division of India on communal lines presented insurmountable difficulties. A lot of heat was generated by the refugees on both sides. There was a lot of bloodshed both in India and Pakistan on account of the communal riots and the wholesale exodus of population from India to Pakistan and vice versa.

Lord Mountbatten did a lot of useful work in connection with the Indian States. There was the possibility of a large number of independent states coming into existence in the country after the extinction of British paramountcy in India. It goes to the credit of Lord Mountbatten that he was able to persuade most of the Indian States to join one or the other Dominion. The result was that a lot of complications which otherwise would have given headache to the rulers of both India and Pakistan were avoided. When Lord and Lady Mountbatten left India in June 1948, there was a general feeling that one who belonged to them was going to depart from their country.

Shri C. Rajagopalachariar was the Governor-General of India from June 1948 to January 1950. It was during his regime that police action was taken against the Nizam of Hyderabad. Kasim Razvi and his followers were defeated and Hyderabad became a part of the Indian Union. During this period, the Constituent Ascembly passed the new constitution of India which came into force on January 26, 1950. The relations between India and Pakistan were unsatisfactory. There was a lot of tension on account of the problem of Kashmir and evacuee property.

In 1948 was created the Press Trust of India Limited. This organisation took over the supply of news to and from India. This was done on the basis of an agreement with the Reuters. The agreement enabled the Indian press to get complete control over its internal news supply. The Press Trust of India is a non-profit making concern and its membership is open to all newspapers of India. It has now become independent of the Reuters.

The Government of India set up a Press Laws Enquiry Committee under the Chairmanship of Shri Ganganath Jha. The Committee was required to examine all the existing press laws of India and make its recommendations regarding the direction in which those should be modified. The Central Legislature nominated some members to the Committee. Three editors were also recommended by the Indian Newspapers Editors' Conference. The Committee recommended that an explanation should be added to Section 153-A of the Indian Penal Code to the effect that it did not amount to an offence under that Section to advocate a change in the social and economic order provided that advocacy did not involve violence. The Committee recommended the repeal of the Foreign Relations Act, 1932, the Indian States (Protection) Act, 1934 and the Indian Press (Emergency Powers) Act, 1931. However, it was suggested that certain provisions of the Indian Press (Emergency Powers) Act, 1931 which did not find a place in the ordinary law of the country, should be incorporated into that law at suitable places. Section 124-A of the Indian Penal Code should be amended in such a way as to apply only to those acts which either incite disorder or are intended or tend to incite disorder. Section 144 of the Code of Criminal Procedure should not apply to the press and separate provision should be made for dealing with the press in urgent cases of apprehended danger. Necessary provision should be made in the law to empower courts to order the closing down of a press for a special period in case of repeated violation of law.

In 1948, the Government of India appointed a University Commission under the Chairmanship of Sir S. Radhakrishnan. The terms of reference of the Commission were to consider and make recommendations on the aims and objects of University education and research in India, the changes considered necessary and desirable in the constitution, control, functions and jurisdiction of universities in India and their relations with the Government of India and the Provincial Governments, the finances of the universities, the courses of study in the universities and their duration, the standards of admission to university courses of study with special reference to the desirability of an independent university entrance examination and the avoidance of unfair demonstrations which militate against the fundamental rights, the medium of instruction in the universities, the provision for advanced study in Indian culture, history, literature, languages, philosophy and finance, the maintenance of the highest standards of teaching and examinations in the universities and the colleges under their control, the organisation of advanced research in all branches of knowledge in the universities and institutions of higher research in a well-coordinated fashion avoiding waste of efforts and re- sources, religious instruction in the universities, the quali- fications, conditions of service, salaries, privileges and functions of teachers and the encouragement of original research by teachers, the discipline of students, hostels and the organisation of tutorial work and any other matter which was germane and essential to a complete and comprehensive enquiry into all as- pects of university education and advanced research in India.

After touring the whole country, interviewing people and re- ceiving and considering memoranda from various quarters, the Commission made its recommendations in 1949. It recom- mended the establishment of rural universities with Shantinike- tan and Jamma Millia as their model. It criticised the al- location of small funds for education. It stressed the necessity of increasing considerably the grant of scholarships and stipends so that the poor students may not suffer. No college was to be allowed to admit more than 1,000 students. Where the mother tongue was the same as the federal language, the federal language was to be the medium of instruction. If the mother tongue and the federal language were identical, the students were required to take up any other Indian, classical or modern language. There was to be no hasty replacement of English as a medium of instruction for high academic standards. Co- education could be adopted in the secondary stage and in the college stage. A lot of emphasis was laid on improving the standards of the teaching profession. There were to be four classes of teachers, viz., Professors, readers, lecturers and ins- tructors. The promotion from one category to another was to be solely on the basis of merit.

The Constitution for free India came into force on January 26, 1950. It provided for a President of India in place of the Governor-General of India and Dr. Rajendra Prasad was elect- ed the First President and he continued to occupy that position up to 1962. He was a brilliant scholar. His nobility, devotion and sincerity were unequalled. He was succeeded by Dr. S. Radhakrishnan as President in 1962. Dr. Radhakrishnan is a

remarkable personality in many ways. He is a great Sanskrit
scholar. He was very near Prime Minister Nehru. Before be-
coming President, he was the Vice-President of India and the
Indian Ambassador in the Soviet Union. He retired in 1967
when Dr. Zakir Husain was elected the President. Pandit
Jawaharlal Nehru was the Prime Minister of India up to 1964.
He was succeeded by Lal Bahadur Sastri as Prime Minister and
Sastriji continued to occupy that position up to January 1965.
After his death at Tashkent, Mrs. Indira Gandhi became the
Prime Minister of India.

Indian leaders like Jawaharlal Nehru, Sardar Patel, and
Dr. Rajendra Prasad deserve credit for the manner in which
they dealt with the situation which faced them when India became free. Before leaving India, British bureaucracy had deliberately made the administrative machinery unworkable and
it was a problem to make it work smoothly for the good of the
country. The problem of law and order was a formidable one.
There were communal riots on a large scale. Caravans of refugees with horrible stories of murder, abductions and betrayals
came to India and created innumerable problems. They clamoured for revenge. They were badly in need of shelter and
food. The fury was so great that for some time the whole
thing collapsed but it must be said to the credit of those who
tackled the problem sympathetically and efficiently. Millions of
refugees were rehabilitated. They were given homes to live
in and food to eat. They were given money to start their
lives afresh. Undoubtedly, there were lapses at many places
but the problem was tackled to a great extent. The refugees
showed remarkable courage and facilitated the task of the
Government by self-help. Under the dynamic personality of
Jawaharlal Nehru, 3 Five-Year Plans were prepared and executed. A large number of canals were dug. Tubewells were
sunk in large numbers. Tractors were imported. Fertilizers
were secured. All that helped the cause of agriculture in spite
of corruption at various levels. Old industries were helped and
new ones were set up both in the public sector and private
sector. Undoubtedly, there has been a lot of industrial activity in the country. A big step has been taken on the road
to industrialisation. Inefficiency and corruption apart, there
has been no dearth of factories in the country. Big steel
plants have been set up in various states. Cement factories
have been multiplied. It cannot be denied that we have made
a lot of progress in this respect. But the price we have paid

is very high. It must be conceded that the country has not got the maximum for the money invested in agriculture and industry. While India owes more than Rs. 5,000 crores to foreign countries, the progress made is not adequate. A good bit of money has been wasted on account of corruption and inefficiency. As production in various fields has not kept pace with the growth of population in the country, prices have been continuously rising and with the exception of the rich, the condition of the man in the street is very unhappy. Freedom has not brought what the common man hoped and prayed for. Hartals and agitations have become the order of the day.

It cannot be denied that Prime Minister Nehru followed a vigorous foreign policy and as a result of it, the credit of India rose very high in the world. India was an un-aligned country and both the Soviet Bloc and the American Bloc did their best to woo her. Whenever there was any difficulty, the good offices of Prime Minister Nehru were sought for. India played an important part in bringing about peace in the Korean front. She was appointed the Chairman of the Commission which was set up for peace in Viet-Nam. When the Bandung Conference was held in 1955, the credit of India was very high. Her voice accounted.

However, it appears that the foreign policy of India failed even during the lifetime of Prime Minister Nehru. Mr. Nehru failed in his dealings with China. He made a mistake in allowing Red China to occupy Tibet. It was not realized that with millions of Chinese soldiers in Tibet, the security of India would be threatened. In 1954 was signed a treaty of friendship between India and China. By that treaty, India and China pledged themselves to follow 5 principles in their relations with each other. Those five principles were the mutual recognition of each other's territorial integrity and sovereignty, non-interference in each other's internal affairs, non-aggression, equality and mutual benefit and peaceful co-existence. Those principles came to be known as Panch-Shila. In spite of this treaty, the Chinese continued to violate the Indian border from time to time. A meeting was held at New Delhi in March 1960 and it was attended by Chou En-Lai. China wanted to strike a border deal. She was prepared to give up her claim to the disputed territory in the eastern sector provided India recognised her claim in the Ladakh area. The suggestion was not accepted by India. It was decided to set up a Committee of officials of both the countries to investigate the claims of each side and to submit a report by September 1960. However, nothing came out of the report of the Committee and China continued to occupy large chunks of Indian territory. It appears that the Indian Government did not attach due importance to the Chinese activities. It was naively pointed out that the "area occupied by the Chinese consisted of barren mountain tops, where not even a blade of grass grows". China claimed about 15,000 sq. miles of territory in Ladakh and NEFA. She also claimed Longju and Khinzemana. She also claimed Spiti, Shipki, Nilang, Jodhang, Lapthal and Barahoti. She also claimed about 2,000 sq. miles of territory of Bhutan and put forward her claim to negotiate directly with Bhutan.

The relations between India and China became very much strained after India gave political asylum to Dalai Lama. The Chinese attitude became very aggressive. When the attention of China was drawn to the activities of the Chinese soldiers on the Indian borders, Chou En-Lai wrote thus to Nehru : "I can assure Your Excellency that it is merely for preventing remnant armed Tibetan rebels from crossing the border back and forth to carry out harassing activities that the Chinese Government in recent months despatched guard units to be stationed in the south and eastern parts of Tibet region of China. This is obviously in the interest of ensuring the tranquillity of the border and will, in no way, constitute a threat to India". In spite of this assurance, the Chinese started trouble in the Ladakh area in July 1962. The Indian outpost in the Galwan valley was surrounded by the Chinese. The Chinese did not advance further as the Indian army was given orders to defend itself in case of further Chinese advance. On September 8, 1962, the Chinese launched a massive attack on the NEFA border. The Chinese crossed the Thagla Ridge and intruded into the Indian territory. On September 20, 1962, they again opened fire on Indian guards. On October 9, 1962, they attacked the Indian post on the side of the Thagla Ridge. They opened fire on Indian troops with 2″ mortars, automatic weapons and hand-grenades. On October 20, 1962 they occupied the post of Khinzemane and Dhola, south of the McMahon Line on the NEFA border. They also attacked Chip Chap area of Ladakh. The Indian troops were withdrawn from their posts. An Indian helicopter engaged in evacuating the injured and the dead Indian soldiers was fired upon. On October 31, 1962, the Chinese launched a massive attack. Twang fell into their hands. On November 19, 1962, the Indian forces suffered heavy reverses on the NEFA border at the hands of the Chinese. Walong, Sela and Bomdila fell into Chinese hands. On the Ladakh front also, Daulet Beg Oldi fell into their hands. Chushul was threatened and its airport was held under heavy enemy fire.

When the Government of India was under heavy fire from China and there was every possibility of Assam falling into the hands of the Chinese, Mr. Nehru requested the United States and Great Britain to help her. The response was a prompt one. There was a constant flow of arms to India from various quarters. Help also came from Canada, West Germany and Australia. It was this help which enabled the Indian troops to stand against the Chinese. When China found that the United States and Great Britain would help India to any extent, she declared a unilateral cease-fire on November 20, 1962. The Chinese Government declared that her frontier guards would withdraw to positions 12½ miles behind the lines of actual control which existed between China and India. China was to set up check posts on its own side of the MacMahon Line to forestall the activities of the saboteurs and to maintain order. However, on the Ladakh front, the Chinese were still controlling about 12,000 miles of Indian territory which included Aksai Chin area through which the Chinese had built a strategic road linking Sinkiang with Tibet. The occupation of that area provided the Chinese with an access to the Soviet Union, Kashmir and Pakistan.

The Chinese started withdrawing on both the fronts on December 1, 1962. They returned the sick and wounded Indian prisoners at Bomdila. They withdrew behind the MacMahon line on the NEFA front. They also withdrew from the Western sector but set up their own check posts in the area evacuated by them with a view to strengthen their position. Many efforts were made to solve the dispute between India and China. A Conference of the representatives of Cambodia, Burma, Indonesia, Ceylon, UAR and Ghana was held at Colombo from December 10, to December 12, 1962. The Conference put forward certain proposals for the settlement of the dispute. India accepted those proposals and the Indian Parliament endorsed them. However, those were rejected by the Chinese. The relations between the two countries have remained strained ever since. When Pakistan attacked India in 1965, China threatened to attack Kashmir in case certain of her frivolous demands were not conceded. The Pakistan war ended abruptly and China did not consider it desirable to attack India in 1965. However, the relations between the two countries have always remained strained. China is in occupation of Indian territory and there can be no compromise with her so long as she holds it.

The relations between India and Pakistan have never been happy. In October 1947, the tribal raiders backed by Pakistan attacked Kashmir which had acceded to India. The Indian forces were flown to Kashmir to meet the invasion and the raiders were successfully driven out of the Kashmir valley. However, the problem of Kashmir was not solved and it has been the bone of contention between the two countries. Various resolutions and missions of the United Nations have failed to solve the tangle. In 1965, Pakistan sent her infiltrators into Kashmir and later on attacked the Chhamb area of the Jammu province. As the attack was a sudden one, Pakistan was able to occupy a good bit of Jammu territory. However, the tables were turned against her when the Lahore front was opened by the Indian troops. Pakistan forces were driven out from the Kashmir Valley and defeated at many places and Pakistan was forced to fight on the defensive. There was enormous loss on both sides. The Security Council was able to bring about a cease-fire and both countries withdrew their forces in accordance with the terms of the Tashkent Declaration of January 10, 1966 which was arranged through the good offices of the Soviet Union.

India has friendly relations both with the United States and the Soviet Union. The American Government has given India billions of dollars with a view to help her to stand on her own legs. It is the American wheat that has saved the lives of millions of Indians. It was the American arms which helped India to stand against China in 1962. The Soviet Union also has given India a lot of military and economic help. The Soviet investment in India also runs to millions. When after 1965, the American Government refused to supply arms to India, the Soviet Union came to her help. Recently, the relations between India and the Soviet Union are under a strain on account of the Pro-Pakistan attitude of the Soviet Union. The Indian Government is not happy at the supply of Soviet arms to Pakistan.

The present position is that India finds herself in a difficult position. She does not belong to any camp. No world power can rely upon her. It is true that India has got and is getting help from both the blocs but experience has shown that such a policy has not been in the higher interests of the country. When she was attacked in 1962 by China, India found herself friendless and the same story was repeated in 1965 when she was attacked by Pakistan. Our leaders may defend a policy which is otherwise indefensible but it must be conceded that it has brought India neither security nor strength.

SUGGESTED READINGS

Appadorai, A. (Ed.)	:	*Indian Studies in Social and Political Development* (1947-1967).
Brecher, Michael	:	*Nehru.*
Brecher, Michael	:	*Struggle for Kashmir.*
Dean, Vera Micheles	:	*New Patterns of Democracy in India* (1959).
Gopal, Madan	:	*India As a World Power.*
Griffith, Sir P. J.	:	*Modern India* (London, 1957).
Gupta, Hari Ram	:	*India-Pakistan War*, 1965.
Jain, G. L.	:	*Panch-Sheel and After*, 1960.
Kundra, J. C.	:	*Indian Foreign Policy* (1947-54), 1965.
Malenbaum, Wilfred	:	*East and West in India's Development* (1959).
Mellor, A.	:	*India Since Partition.*
Moraes, Frank	:	*Jawaharlal Nehru* (New York, 1956).
Nehru, Jawaharlal	:	*Autobiography* (1937).
Nehru, Jawaharlal	:	*Discovery of India* (1946).
Parikh	:	*Patel.*
Planning Commission, Government of India.	:	*The New India: Progress through Democracy* (1958).
Rowland, John	:	*A History of Sino-Indian Relations* (1967).
Spear, Percival	:	*India, Pakistan and the West* (1958).
Spear, Percival	:	*India: A Modern History*, 1961 (Chapter 40).
Strachy, John	:	*The End of Empire.*
Zinkin, Maurice & Taya	:	*Britain and India*, 1964.

INDEX
(Index for Pages 1 to 908)

INDEX

(Index for Pages 909 to 1098)

Zane Grey Ohio River Trilogy

Betty Zane

The Spirit of the Border

The Last Trail

Zane Grey

This edition published in 2012

Zane Grey asserts the moral right to be identified as the author of this work.

Printed in the United States of America

ISBN: 1480220795
ISBN-13: 978-1480220799

DEDICATION

TO THE BETTY ZANE CHAPTER OF THE DAUGHTERS OF THE
REVOLUTION THIS BOOK IS RESPECTFULLY DEDICATED BY
THE AUTHOR

CONTENTS

NOTE

In a quiet corner of the stately little city of Wheeling, West Va., stands a monument on which is inscribed:

"By authority of the State of West Virginia to commemorate the siege of Fort Henry, Sept 11, 1782, the last battle of the American Revolution, this tablet is here placed."

Had it not been for the heroism of a girl the foregoing inscription would never have been written, and the city of Wheeling would never have existed. From time to time I have read short stories and magazine articles which have been published about Elizabeth Zane and her famous exploit; but they are unreliable in some particulars, which is owing, no doubt, to the singularly meagre details available in histories of our western border.

For a hundred years the stories of Betty and Isaac Zane have been familiar, oft-repeated tales in my family—tales told with that pardonable ancestral pride which seems inherent in every one. My grandmother loved to cluster the children round her and tell them that when she was a little girl she had knelt at the feet of Betty Zane, and listened to the old lady as she told of her brother's capture by the Indian Princess, of the burning of the Fort, and of her own race for life. I knew these stories by heart when a child.

Two years ago my mother came to me with an old note book which had been discovered in some rubbish that had been placed in the yard to burn. The book had probably been hidden in an old picture frame for many years. It belonged to my great-grandfather, Col. Ebenezer Zane. From its faded and time-worn pages I have taken the main facts of my story. My regret is that a worthier pen than mine has not had this wealth of material.

In this busy progressive age there are no heroes of the kind so dear to all lovers of chivalry and romance. There are heroes, perhaps, but they are the patient sad-faced kind, of whom few take cognizance as they hurry onward. But cannot we all remember some one who suffered greatly, who accomplished great deeds, who died on the battlefield—some one around whose name lingers a halo of glory? Few of us are so unfortunate that we cannot look backward on kith or kin and thrill with love and reverence as we dream of an act of heroism or martyrdom which rings down the annals of time like the melody of the huntsman's horn, as it peals out on a frosty

October morn purer and sweeter with each succeeding note.

If to any of those who have such remembrances, as well as those who have not, my story gives an hour of pleasure I shall be rewarded.

PROLOGUE

On June 16, 1716, Alexander Spotswood, Governor of the Colony of Virginia, and a gallant soldier who had served under Marlborough in the English wars, rode, at the head of a dauntless band of cavaliers, down the quiet street of quaint old Williamsburg.

The adventurous spirits of this party of men urged them toward the land of the setting sun, that unknown west far beyond the blue crested mountains rising so grandly before them.

Months afterward they stood on the western range of the Great North mountains towering above the picturesque Shenandoah Valley, and from the summit of one of the loftiest peaks, where, until then, the foot of a white man had never trod, they viewed the vast expanse of plain and forest with glistening eyes. Returning to Williamsburg they told of the wonderful richness of the newly discovered country and thus opened the way for the venturesome pioneer who was destined to overcome all difficulties and make a home in the western world.

But fifty years and more passed before a white man penetrated far beyond the purple spires of those majestic mountains.

One bright morning in June, 1769, the figure of a stalwart, broad shouldered man could have been seen standing on the wild and rugged promontory which rears its rocky bluff high above the Ohio river, at a point near the mouth of Wheeling Creek. He was alone save for the companionship of a deerhound that crouched at his feet. As he leaned on a long rifle, contemplating the glorious scene that stretched before him, a smile flashed across his bronzed cheek, and his heart bounded as he forecast the future of that spot. In the river below him lay an island so round and green that it resembled a huge lily pad floating placidly on the water. The fresh green foliage of the trees sparkled with glittering dewdrops. Back of him rose the high ridges, and, in front, as far as eye could reach, extended an unbroken forest.

Beneath him to the left and across a deep ravine he saw a wide level clearing. The few scattered and blackened tree stumps showed the ravages made by a forest fire in the years gone by. The field was now overgrown with hazel and laurel bushes, and intermingling with them were the trailing arbutus, the honeysuckle, and the wild rose. A fragrant perfume was wafted upward to him. A rushing creek bordered one edge of the clearing. After a long quiet reach of water, which could be seen winding back in the hills, the stream tumbled madly over a rocky ledge, and white with foam, it hurried onward as if impatient of long restraint, and lost its individuality in the broad Ohio.

This solitary hunter was Colonel Ebenezer Zane. He was one of those daring men, who, as the tide of emigration started westward, had left his friends and family and had struck out alone into the wilderness. Departing from his home in Eastern Virginia he had plunged into the woods, and after many days of hunting and exploring, he reached the then far Western Ohio valley.

The scene so impressed Colonel Zane that he concluded to found a settlement there. Taking "tomahawk possession" of the locality (which consisted of blazing a few trees with his tomahawk), he built himself a rude shack and remained that summer on the Ohio.

In the autumn he set out for Berkeley County, Virginia, to tell his people of the magnificent country he had discovered. The following spring he persuaded a number of settlers, of a like spirit with himself, to accompany him to the wilderness. Believing it unsafe to take their families with them at once, they left them at Red Stone on the Monongahela river, while the men, including Colonel Zane, his brothers Silas, Andrew, Jonathan and Isaac, the Wetzels, McCollochs, Bennets, Metzars and others, pushed on ahead.

The country through which they passed was one tangled, most impenetrable forest; the axe of the pioneer had never sounded in this region, where every rod of the way might harbor some unknown danger.

These reckless bordermen knew not the meaning of fear; to all, daring adventure was welcome, and the screech of a redskin and the ping of a bullet were familiar sounds; to the Wetzels, McCollochs and Jonathan Zane the hunting of Indians was the most thrilling passion of their lives; indeed, the Wetzels, particularly, knew no other occupation. They had attained a wonderful skill with the rifle; long practice had rendered their senses as acute as those of the fox. Skilled in every variety of woodcraft, with lynx eyes ever on the alert for detecting a trail, or the curling smoke of some camp fire, or the minutest sign of an enemy, these men stole onward through the forest with the cautious but dogged and persistent determination that was characteristic of the settler.

They at length climbed the commanding bluff overlooking the majestic river, and as they gazed out on the undulating and uninterrupted area of green, their hearts beat high with hope.

The keen axe, wielded by strong arms, soon opened the clearing and reared stout log cabins on the river bluff. Then Ebenezer Zane and his followers moved their families and soon the settlement began to grow and flourish. As the little village commenced to prosper the redmen became troublesome. Settlers were shot while plowing the fields or gathering the harvests. Bands of hostile Indians prowled around and made it dangerous for anyone to leave the clearing. Frequently the first person to appear in the early morning would be shot at by an Indian concealed in the woods.

General George Rodgers Clark, commandant of the Western Military Department, arrived at the village in 1774. As an attack from the savages was apprehended during the year the settlers determined to erect a fort as a defense for the infant settlement. It was planned by General Clark and built by the people themselves. At first they called it Fort Fincastle, in honor of Lord Dunmore, who, at the time of its erection, was Governor of the Colony of Virginia. In 1776 its name was changed to Fort Henry, in honor of Patrick Henry.

For many years it remained the most famous fort on the frontier, having withstood numberless Indian attacks and two memorable sieges, one in 1777, which year is called the year of the "Bloody Sevens," and again in 1782. In this last siege the British Rangers under Hamilton took part with the Indians, making the attack practically the last battle of the Revolution.

Betty Zane

CHAPTER I.

The Zane family was a remarkable one in early days, and most of its members are historical characters.

The first Zane of whom any trace can be found was a Dane of aristocratic lineage, who was exiled from his country and came to America with William Penn. He was prominent for several years in the new settlement founded by Penn, and Zane street, Philadelphia, bears his name. Being a proud and arrogant man, he soon became obnoxious to his Quaker brethren. He therefore cut loose from them and emigrated to Virginia, settling on the Potomac river, in what was then known as Berkeley county. There his five sons, and one daughter, the heroine of this story, were born.

Ebenezer Zane, the eldest, was born October 7, 1747, and grew to manhood in the Potomac valley. There he married Elizabeth McColloch, a sister of the famous McColloch brothers so well known in frontier history.

Ebenezer was fortunate in having such a wife and no pioneer could have been better blessed. She was not only a handsome woman, but one of remarkable force of character as well as kindness of heart. She was particularly noted for a rare skill in the treatment of illness, and her deftness in handling the surgeon's knife and extracting a poisoned bullet or arrow from a wound had restored to health many a settler when all had despaired.

The Zane brothers were best known on the border for their athletic prowess, and for their knowledge of Indian warfare and cunning. They were all powerful men, exceedingly active and as fleet as deer. In appearance they were singularly pleasing and bore a marked resemblance to one another, all having smooth faces, clear cut, regular features, dark eyes and long black hair.

When they were as yet boys they had been captured by Indians, soon after their arrival on the Virginia border, and had been taken far into the interior, and held as captives for two years. Ebenezer, Silas, and Jonathan Zane were then taken to Detroit and ransomed. While attempting to swim the Scioto river in an effort to escape, Andrew Zane had been shot and

1

killed by his pursuers.

But the bonds that held Isaac Zane, the remaining and youngest brother, were stronger than those of interest or revenge such as had caused the captivity of his brothers. He was loved by an Indian princess, the daughter of Tarhe, the chief of the puissant Huron race. Isaac had escaped on various occasions, but had always been retaken, and at the time of the opening of our story nothing had been heard of him for several years, and it was believed he had been killed.

At the period of the settling of the little colony in the wilderness, Elizabeth Zane, the only sister, was living with an aunt in Philadelphia, where she was being educated.

Colonel Zane's house, a two story structure built of rough hewn logs, was the most comfortable one in the settlement, and occupied a prominent site on the hillside about one hundred yards from the fort. It was constructed of heavy timber and presented rather a forbidding appearance with its square corners, its ominous looking portholes, and strongly barred doors and windows. There were three rooms on the ground floor, a kitchen, a magazine room for military supplies, and a large room for general use. The several sleeping rooms were on the second floor, which was reached by a steep stairway.

The interior of a pioneer's rude dwelling did not reveal, as a rule, more than bare walls, a bed or two, a table and a few chairs—in fact, no more than the necessities of life. But Colonel Zane's house proved an exception to this. Most interesting was the large room. The chinks between the logs had been plastered up with clay and then the walls covered with white birch bark; trophies of the chase, Indian bows and arrows, pipes and tomahawks hung upon them; the wide spreading antlers of a noble buck adorned the space above the mantel piece; buffalo robes covered the couches; bearskin rugs lay scattered about on the hardwood floor. The wall on the western side had been built over a huge stone, into which had been cut an open fireplace.

This blackened recess, which had seen two houses burned over it, when full of blazing logs had cheered many noted men with its warmth. Lord Dunmore, General Clark, Simon Kenton, and Daniel Boone had sat beside that fire. There Cornplanter, the Seneca chief, had made his famous deal with Colonel Zane, trading the island in the river opposite the settlement for a barrel of whiskey. Logan, the Mingo chief and friend of the whites, had smoked many pipes of peace there with Colonel Zane. At a later period, when King Louis Phillippe, who had been exiled from France by Napoleon, had come to America, during the course of his melancholy wanderings he had stopped at Fort Henry a few days. His stay there was marked by a fierce blizzard and the royal guest passed most of his time at Colonel Zane's fireside. Musing by those roaring logs perhaps he saw the radiant star of the Man of Destiny rise to its magnificent zenith.

One cold, raw night in early spring the Colonel had just returned from one of his hunting trips and the tramping of horses mingled with the rough voices of the negro slaves sounded without. When Colonel Zane entered the house he was greeted affectionately by his wife and sister. The latter, at the death of her aunt in Philadelphia, had come west to live with her brother, and had been there since late in the preceding autumn. It was a welcome sight for the eyes of a tired and weary hunter. The tender kiss of his comely wife, the cries of the delighted children, and the crackling of the fire warmed his heart and made him feel how good it was to be home again after a three days' march in the woods. Placing his rifle in a corner and throwing aside his wet hunting coat, he turned and stood with his back to the bright blaze. Still young and vigorous, Colonel Zane was a handsome man. Tall, though not heavy, his frame denoted great strength and endurance. His face was smooth, his heavy eyebrows met in a straight line; his eyes were dark and now beamed with a kindly light; his jaw was square and massive; his mouth resolute; in fact, his whole face was strikingly expressive of courage and geniality. A great wolf dog had followed him in and, tired from travel, had stretched himself out before the fireplace, laying his noble head on the paws he had extended toward the warm blaze.

"Well! Well! I am nearly starved and mighty glad to get back," said the Colonel, with a smile of satisfaction at the steaming dishes a negro servant was bringing from the kitchen.

"We are glad you have returned," answered his wife, whose glowing face testified to the pleasure she felt. "Supper is ready—Annie, bring in some cream—yes, indeed, I am happy that you are home. I never have a moment's peace when you are away, especially when you are accompanied by Lewis Wetzel."

"Our hunt was a failure," said the Colonel, after he had helped himself to a plate full of roast wild turkey. "The bears have just come out of their winter's sleep and are unusually wary at this time. We saw many signs of their work, tearing rotten logs to pieces in search of grubs and bees' nests. Wetzel killed a deer and we baited a likely place where we had discovered many bear tracks. We stayed up all night in a drizzling rain, hoping to get a shot. I am tired out. So is Tige. Wetzel did not mind the weather or the ill luck, and when we ran across some Indian sign he went off on one of his lonely tramps, leaving me to come home alone."

"He is such a reckless man," remarked Mrs. Zane.

"Wetzel is reckless, or rather, daring. His incomparable nerve carries him safely through many dangers, where an ordinary man would have no show whatever. Well, Betty, how are you?"

"Quite well," said the slender, dark-eyed girl who had just taken the seat opposite the Colonel.

"Bessie, has my sister indulged in any shocking escapade in my absence? I think that last trick of hers, when she gave a bucket of hard cider to that poor tame bear, should last her a spell."

3

"No, for a wonder Elizabeth has been very good. However, I do not attribute it to any unusual change of temperament; simply the cold, wet weather. I anticipate a catastrophe very shortly if she is kept indoors much longer."

"I have not had much opportunity to be anything but well behaved. If it rains a few days more I shall become desperate. I want to ride my pony, roam the woods, paddle my canoe, and enjoy myself," said Elizabeth.

"Well! Well! Betts, I knew it would be dull here for you, but you must not get discouraged. You know you got here late last fall, and have not had any pleasant weather yet. It is perfectly delightful in May and June. I can take you to fields of wild white honeysuckle and May flowers and wild roses. I know you love the woods, so be patient a little longer."

Elizabeth had been spoiled by her brothers—what girl would not have been by five great big worshippers?—and any trivial thing gone wrong with her was a serious matter to them. They were proud of her, and of her beauty and accomplishments were never tired of talking. She had the dark hair and eyes so characteristic of the Zanes; the same oval face and fine features: and added to this was a certain softness of contour and a sweetness of expression which made her face bewitching. But, in spite of that demure and innocent face, she possessed a decided will of her own, and one very apt to be asserted; she was mischievous; inclined to coquettishness, and more terrible than all she had a fiery temper which could be aroused with the most surprising ease.

Colonel Zane was wont to say that his sister's accomplishments were innumerable. After only a few months on the border she could prepare the flax and weave a linsey dresscloth with admirable skill. Sometimes to humor Betty the Colonel's wife would allow her to get the dinner, and she would do it in a manner that pleased her brothers, and called forth golden praises from the cook, old Sam's wife who had been with the family twenty years. Betty sang in the little church on Sundays; she organized and taught a Sunday school class; she often beat Colonel Zane and Major McColloch at their favorite game of checkers, which they had played together since they were knee high; in fact, Betty did nearly everything well, from baking pies to painting the birch bark walls of her room. But these things were insignificant in Colonel Zane's eyes. If the Colonel were ever guilty of bragging it was about his sister's ability in those acquirements demanding a true eye, a fleet foot, a strong arm and a daring spirit. He had told all the people in the settlement, to many of whom Betty was unknown, that she could ride like an Indian and shoot with undoubted skill; that she had a generous share of the Zanes' fleetness of foot, and that she would send a canoe over as bad a place as she could find. The boasts of the Colonel remained as yet unproven, but, be that as it may, Betty had, notwithstanding her many faults, endeared herself to all. She made sunshine and happiness everywhere; the old people loved her; the children adored her, and the broad shouldered, heavy footed young settlers were shy and silent, yet blissfully happy in her presence.

"Betty, will you fill my pipe?" asked the Colonel, when he had finished his supper and had pulled his big chair nearer the fire. His oldest child, Noah, a sturdy lad of six, climbed upon his knee and plied him with questions.

"Did you see any bars and bufflers?" he asked, his eyes large and round.

"No, my lad, not one."

"How long will it be until I am big enough to go?"

"Not for a very long time, Noah."

"But I am not afraid of Betty's bar. He growls at me when I throw sticks at him, and snaps his teeth. Can I go with you next time?"

"My brother came over from Short Creek to-day. He has been to Fort Pitt," interposed Mrs. Zane. As she was speaking a tap sounded on the door, which, being opened by Betty, disclosed Captain Boggs his daughter Lydia, and Major Samuel McColloch, the brother of Mrs. Zane.

"Ah, Colonel! I expected to find you at home to-night. The weather has been miserable for hunting and it is not getting any better. The wind is blowing from the northwest and a storm is coming," said Captain Boggs, a fine, soldierly looking man.

"Hello, Captain! How are you? Sam, I have not had the pleasure of seeing you for a long time," replied Colonel Zane, as he shook hands with his guests.

Major McColloch was the eldest of the brothers of that name. As an Indian killer he ranked next to the intrepid Wetzel; but while Wetzel preferred to take his chances alone and track the Indians through the untrodden wilds, McColloch was a leader of expeditions against the savages. A giant in stature, massive in build, bronzed and bearded, he looked the typical frontiersman. His blue eyes were like those of his sister and his voice had the same pleasant ring.

"Major McColloch, do you remember me?" asked Betty.

"Indeed I do," he answered, with a smile. "You were a little girl, running wild, on the Potomac when I last saw you!"

"Do you remember when you used to lift me on your horse and give me lessons in riding?"

"I remember better than you. How you used to stick on the back of that horse was a mystery to me."

"Well, I shall be ready soon to go on with those lessons in riding. I have heard of your wonderful leap over the hill and I should like to have you tell me all about it. Of all the stories I have heard since I arrived at Fort Henry, the one of your ride and leap for life is the most wonderful."

"Yes, Sam, she will bother you to death about that ride, and will try to give you lessons in leaping down precipices. I should not be at all surprised to find her trying to duplicate your feat. You know the Indian pony I got from that fur trader last summer. Well, he is as wild as a deer and she has

5

been riding him without his being broken," said Colonel Zane.

"Some other time I shall tell you about my jump over the hill. Just now I have important matters to discuss," answered the Major to Betty.

It was evident that something unusual had occurred, for after chatting a few moments the three men withdrew into the magazine room and conversed in low, earnest tones.

Lydia Boggs was eighteen, fair haired and blue eyed. Like Betty she had received a good education, and, in that respect, was superior to the border girls, who seldom knew more than to keep house and to make linen. At the outbreak of the Indian wars General Clark had stationed Captain Boggs at Fort Henry and Lydia had lived there with him two years. After Betty's arrival, which she hailed with delight, the girls had become fast friends.

Lydia slipped her arm affectionately around Betty's neck and said, "Why did you not come over to the Fort to-day?"

"It has been such an ugly day, so disagreeable altogether, that I have remained indoors."

"You missed something," said Lydia, knowingly.

"What do you mean? What did I miss?"

"Oh, perhaps, after all, it will not interest you."

"How provoking! Of course it will. Anything or anybody would interest me to-night. Do tell me, please."

"It isn't much. Only a young soldier came over with Major McColloch."

"A soldier? From Fort Pitt? Do I know him? I have met most of the officers."

"No, you have never seen him. He is a stranger to all of us."

"There does not seem to be so much in your news," said Betty, in a disappointed tone. "To be sure, strangers are a rarity in our little village, but, judging from the strangers who have visited us in the past, I imagine this one cannot be much different."

"Wait until you see him," said Lydia, with a serious little nod of her head.

"Come, tell me all about him," said Betty, now much interested.

"Major McColloch brought him in to see papa, and he was introduced to me. He is a southerner and from one of those old families. I could tell by his cool, easy, almost reckless air. He is handsome, tall and fair, and his face is frank and open. He has such beautiful manners. He bowed low to me and really I felt so embarrassed that I hardly spoke. You know I am used to these big hunters seizing your hand and giving it a squeeze which makes you want to scream. Well, this young man is different. He is a cavalier. All the girls are in love with him already. So will you be."

"I? Indeed not. But how refreshing. You must have been strongly impressed to see and remember all you have told me."

"Betty Zane, I remember so well because he is just the man you described one day when we were building castles and telling each other what

6

kind of a hero we wanted."

"Girls, do not talk such nonsense," interrupted the Colonel's wife who was perturbed by the colloquy in the other room. She had seen those ominous signs before. "Can you find nothing better to talk about?"

Meanwhile Colonel Zane and his companions were earnestly discussing certain information which had arrived that day. A friendly Indian runner had brought news to Short Creek, a settlement on the river between Fort Henry and Fort Pitt of an intended raid by the Indians all along the Ohio valley. Major McColloch, who had been warned by Wetzel of the fever of unrest among the Indians—a fever which broke out every spring—had gone to Fort Pitt with the hope of bringing back reinforcements, but, excepting the young soldier, who had volunteered to return with him, no help could he enlist, so he journeyed back post-haste to Fort Henry.

The information he brought disturbed Captain Boggs, who commanded the garrison, as a number of men were away on a logging expedition up the river, and were not expected to raft down to the Fort for two weeks.

Jonathan Zane, who had been sent for, joined the trio at this moment, and was acquainted with the particulars. The Zane brothers were always consulted where any question concerning Indian craft and cunning was to be decided. Colonel Zane had a strong friendly influence with certain tribes, and his advice was invaluable. Jonathan Zane hated the sight of an Indian and except for his knowledge as a scout, or Indian tracker or fighter, he was of little use in a council. Colonel Zane informed the men of the fact that Wetzel and he had discovered Indian tracks within ten miles of the Fort, and he dwelt particularly on the disappearance of Wetzel.

"Now, you can depend on what I say. There are Wyandots in force on the war path. Wetzel told me to dig for the Fort and he left me in a hurry. We were near that cranberry bog over at the foot of Bald mountain. I do not believe we shall be attacked. In my opinion the Indians would come up from the west and keep to the high ridges along Yellow creek. They always come that way. But of course, it is best to know surely, and I daresay Lew will come in to-night or to-morrow with the facts. In the meantime put out some scouts back in the woods and let Jonathan and the Major watch the river."

"I hope Wetzel will come in," said the Major. "We can trust him to know more about the Indians than any one. It was a week before you and he went hunting that I saw him. I went to Fort Pitt and tried to bring over some men, but the garrison is short and they need men as much as we do. A young soldier named Clarke volunteered to come and I brought him along with me. He has not seen any Indian fighting, but he is a likely looking chap, and I guess will do. Captain Boggs will give him a place in the block house if you say so."

"By all means. We shall be glad to have him," said Colonel Zane.

"It would not be so serious if I had not sent the men up the river," said Captain Boggs, in anxious tones. "Do you think it possible they might have

7

fallen in with the Indians?"

"It is possible, of course, but not probable," answered Colonel Zane. "The Indians are all across the Ohio. Wetzel is over there and he will get here long before they do."

"I hope it may be as you say. I have much confidence in your judgment," returned Captain Boggs. "I shall put out scouts and take all the precaution possible. We must return now. Come, Lydia."

"Whew! What an awful night this is going to be," said Colonel Zane, when he had closed the door after his guests' departure. "I should not care to sleep out to-night."

"Eb, what will Lew Wetzel do on a night like this?" asked Betty, curiously.

"Oh, Lew will be as snug as a rabbit in his burrow," said Colonel Zane, laughing. "In a few moments he can build a birch bark shack, start a fire inside and go to sleep comfortably."

"Ebenezer, what is all this confab about? What did my brother tell you?" asked Mrs. Zane, anxiously.

"We are in for more trouble from the Wyandots and Shawnees. But, Bessie, I don't believe it will come soon. We are too well protected here for anything but a protracted siege."

Colonel Zane's light and rather evasive answer did not deceive his wife. She knew her brother and her husband would not wear anxious faces for nothing. Her usually bright face clouded with a look of distress. She had seen enough of Indian warfare to make her shudder with horror at the mere thought. Betty seemed unconcerned. She sat down beside the dog and patted him on the head.

"Tige, Indians! Indians!" she said.

The dog growled and showed his teeth. It was only necessary to mention Indians to arouse his ire.

"The dog has been uneasy of late," continued Colonel Zane "He found the Indian tracks before Wetzel did. You know how Tige hates Indians. Ever since he came home with Isaac four years ago he has been of great service to the scouts, as he possesses so much intelligence and sagacity. Tige followed Isaac home the last time he escaped from the Wyandots. When Isaac was in captivity he nursed and cared for the dog after he had been brutally beaten by the redskins. Have you ever heard that long mournful howl Tige gives out sometimes in the dead of night?"

"Yes I have, and it makes me cover up my head," said Betty.

"Well, it is Tige mourning for Isaac," said Colonel Zane

"Poor Isaac," murmured Betty.

"Do you remember him? It has been nine years since you saw him," said Mrs. Zane.

"Remember Isaac? Indeed I do. I shall never forget him. I wonder if he is still living?"

"Probably not. It is now four years since he was recaptured. I think it would have been impossible to keep him that length of time, unless, of course, he has married that Indian girl. The simplicity of the Indian nature is remarkable. He could easily have deceived them and made them believe he was content in captivity. Probably, in attempting to escape again, he has been killed as was poor Andrew."

Brother and sister gazed with dark, sad eyes into the fire, now burned down to a glowing bed of coals. The silence remained unbroken save for the moan of the rising wind outside, the rattle of hail, and the patter of rain drops on the roof.

CHAPTER II.

Fort Henry stood on a bluff overlooking the river and commanded a fine view of the surrounding country. In shape it was a parallelogram, being about three hundred and fifty-six feet in length, and one hundred and fifty in width. Surrounded by a stockade fence twelve feet high, with a yard wide walk running around the inside, and with bastions at each corner large enough to contain six defenders, the fort presented an almost impregnable defense. The blockhouse was two stories in height, the second story projecting out several feet over the first. The thick white oak walls bristled with portholes. Besides the blockhouse, there were a number of cabins located within the stockade. Wells had been sunk inside the inclosure, so that if the spring happened to go dry, an abundance of good water could be had at all times.

In all the histories of frontier life mention is made of the forts and the protection they offered in time of savage warfare. These forts were used as homes for the settlers, who often lived for weeks inside the walls.

Forts constructed entirely of wood without the aid of a nail or spike (for the good reason that these things could not be had) may seem insignificant in these days of great nasal and military garrisons. However, they answered the purpose at that time and served to protect many an infant settlement from the savage attacks of Indian tribes. During a siege of Fort Henry, which had occurred about a year previous, the settlers would have lost scarcely a man had they kept to the fort. But Captain Ogle, at that time in charge of the garrison, had led a company out in search of the Indians. Nearly all of his men were killed, several only making their way to the fort.

On the day following Major McColloch's arrival at Fort Henry, the settlers had been called in from their spring plowing and other labors, and were now busily engaged in moving their stock and the things they wished to save from the destructive torch of the redskin. The women had their hands full with the children, the cleaning of rifles and moulding of bullets, and the thousand and one things the sterner tasks of their husbands had left them.

Major McColloch, Jonathan and Silas Zane, early in the day, had taken different directions along the river to keep a sharp lookout for signs of the enemy. Colonel Zane intended to stay in his oven house and defend it, so he had not moved anything to the fort excepting his horses and cattle. Old Sam, the negro, was hauling loads of hay inside the stockade. Captain Boggs had detailed several scouts to watch the roads and one of these was the young man, Clarke, who had accompanied the Major from Fort Pitt.

The appearance of Alfred Clarke, despite the fact that he wore the regulation hunting garb, indicated a young man to whom the hard work and privation of the settler were unaccustomed things. So thought the pioneers who noticed his graceful walk, his fair skin and smooth hands. Yet those who carefully studied his clearcut features were favorably impressed; the women, by the direct, honest gaze of his blue eyes and the absence of ungentle lines in his face; the men, by the good nature, and that indefinable something by which a man marks another as true steel.

He brought nothing with him from Fort Pitt except his horse, a black-coated, fine limbed thoroughbred, which he frankly confessed was all he could call his own. When asking Colonel Zane to give him a position in the garrison he said he was a Virginian and had been educated in Philadelphia; that after his father died his mother married again, and this, together with a natural love of adventure, had induced him to run away and seek his fortune with the hardy pioneer and the cunning savage of the border. Beyond a few months' service under General Clark he knew nothing of frontier life; but he was tired of idleness; he was strong and not afraid of work, and he could learn. Colonel Zane, who prided himself on his judgment of character, took a liking to the young man at once, and giving him a rifle and accoutrements, told him the border needed young men of pluck and fire, and that if he brought a strong hand and a willing heart he could surely find fortune. Possibly if Alfred Clarke could have been told of the fate in store for him he might have mounted his black steed and have placed miles between him and the frontier village; but, as there were none to tell, he went cheerfully out to meet that fate.

On this is bright spring morning he patrolled the road leading along the edge of the clearing, which was distant a quarter of a mile from the fort. He kept a keen eye on the opposite side of the river, as he had been directed. From the upper end of the island, almost straight across from where he stood, the river took a broad turn, which could not be observed from the fort windows. The river was high from the recent rains and brush heaps and logs and debris of all descriptions were floating down with the swift current. Rabbits and other small animals, which had probably been surrounded on some island and compelled to take to the brush or drown, crouched on floating logs and piles of driftwood. Happening to glance down the road, Clarke saw a horse galloping in his direction. At first he thought it was a messenger for himself, but as it neared him he saw that the horse was an

Indian pony and the rider a young girl, whose long, black hair was flying in the wind.

"Hello! I wonder what the deuce this is? Looks like an Indian girl," said Clarke to himself. "She rides well, whoever she may be."

He stepped behind a clump of laurel bushes near the roadside and waited. Rapidly the horse and rider approached him. When they were but a few paces distant he sprang out and, as the pony shied and reared at sight of him, he clutched the bridle and pulled the pony's head down. Looking up he encountered the astonished and bewildered gaze from a pair of the prettiest dark eyes it had ever been his fortune, or misfortune, to look into.

Betty, for it was she, looked at the young man in amazement, while Alfred was even more surprised and disconcerted. For a moment they looked at each other in silence. But Betty, who was scarcely ever at a loss for words, presently found her voice.

"Well, sir! What does this mean?" she asked indignantly.

"It means that you must turn around and go back to the fort," answered Alfred, also recovering himself.

Now Betty's favorite ride happened to be along this road. It lay along the top of the bluff a mile or more and afforded a fine unobstructed view of the river. Betty had either not heard of the Captain's order, that no one was to leave the fort, or she had disregarded it altogether; probably the latter, as she generally did what suited her fancy.

"Release my pony's head!" she cried, her face flushing, as she gave a jerk to the reins. "How dare you? What right have you to detain me?"

The expression Betty saw on Clarke's face was not new to her, for she remembered having seen it on the faces of young gentlemen whom she had met at her aunt's house in Philadelphia. It was the slight, provoking smile of the man familiar with the various moods of young women, the expression of an amused contempt for their imperiousness. But it was not that which angered Betty. It was the coolness with which he still held her pony regardless of her commands.

"Pray do not get excited," he said. "I am sorry I cannot allow such a pretty little girl to have her own way. I shall hold your pony until you say you will go back to the fort."

"Sir!" exclaimed Betty, blushing a bright-red. "You—you are impertinent!"

"Not at all," answered Alfred, with a pleasant laugh. "I am sure I do not intend to be. Captain Boggs did not acquaint me with full particulars or I might have declined my present occupation: not, however, that it is not agreeable just at this moment. He should have mentioned the danger of my being run down by Indian ponies and imperious young ladies."

"Will you let go of that bridle, or shall I get off and walk back for assistance?" said Betty, getting angrier every moment.

"Go back to the fort at once," ordered Alfred, authoritatively. "Captain

Boggs' orders are that no one shall be allowed to leave the clearing."

"Oh! Why did you not say so? I thought you were Simon Girty, or a highwayman. Was it necessary to keep me here all this time to explain that you were on duty?"

"You know sometimes it is difficult to explain," said Alfred, "besides, the situation had its charm. No, I am not a robber, and I don't believe you thought so. I have only thwarted a young lady's whim, which I am aware is a great crime. I am very sorry. Goodbye."

Betty gave him a withering glance from her black eyes, wheeled her pony and galloped away. A mellow laugh was borne to her ears before she got out of hearing, and again the red blood mantled her cheeks.

"Heavens! What a little beauty," said Alfred to himself, as he watched the graceful rider disappear. "What spirit! Now, I wonder who she can be. She had on moccasins and buckskin gloves and her hair tumbled like a tomboy's, but she is no backwoods girl, I'll bet on that. I'm afraid I was a little rude, but after taking such a stand I could not weaken, especially before such a haughty and disdainful little vixen. It was too great a temptation. What eyes she had! Contrary to what I expected, this little frontier settlement bids fair to become interesting."

The afternoon wore slowly away, and until late in the day nothing further happened to disturb Alfred's meditations, which consisted chiefly of different mental views and pictures of red lips and black eyes. Just as he decided to return to the fort for his supper he heard the barking of a dog that he had seen running along the road some moments before. The sound came from some distance down the river bank and nearer the fort. Walking a few paces up the bluff Alfred caught sight of a large black dog running along the edge of the water. He would run into the water a few paces and then come out and dash along the shore. He barked furiously all the while. Alfred concluded that he must have been excited by a fox or perhaps a wolf; so he climbed down the steep bank and spoke to the dog. Thereupon the dog barked louder and more fiercely than ever, ran to the water, looked out into the river and then up at the man with almost human intelligence.

Alfred understood. He glanced out over the muddy water, at first making out nothing but driftwood. Then suddenly he saw a log with an object clinging to it which he took to be a man, and an Indian at that. Alfred raised his rifle to his shoulder and was in the act of pressing the trigger when he thought he heard a faint halloo. Looking closer, he found he was not covering the smooth polished head adorned with the small tuft of hair, peculiar to a redskin on the warpath, but a head from which streamed long black hair.

Alfred lowered his rifle and studied intently the log with its human burden. Drifting with the current it gradually approached the bank, and as it came nearer he saw that it bore a white man, who was holding to the log with one hand and with the other was making feeble strokes. He concluded the man was either wounded or nearly drowned, for his movements were becoming slower and weaker every moment. His white face lay against the log and barely above water. Alfred shouted encouraging words to him.

At the bend of the river a little rocky point jutted out a few yards into the water. As the current carried the log toward this point, Alfred, after divesting himself of some of his clothing, plunged in and pulled it to the shore. The pallid face of the man clinging to the log showed that he was nearly exhausted, and that he had been rescued in the nick of time. When Alfred reached shoal water he slipped his arm around the man, who was unable to stand, and carried him ashore.

The rescued man wore a buckskin hunting shirt and leggins and moccasins of the same material, all very much the worse for wear. The leggins were torn into tatters and the moccasins worn through. His face was pinched with suffering and one arm was bleeding from a gunshot wound near the shoulder.

"Can you not speak? Who are you?" asked Clarke, supporting the limp figure.

The man made several efforts to answer, and finally said something that to Alfred sounded like "Zane," then he fell to the ground unconscious.

All this time the dog had acted in a most peculiar manner, and if Alfred had not been so intent on the man he would have noticed the animal's odd maneuvers. He ran to and fro on the sandy beach; he scratched up the sand and pebbles, sending them flying in the air; he made short, furious dashes; he jumped, whirled, and, at last, crawled close to the motionless figure and licked its hand.

Clarke realized that he would not be able to carry the inanimate figure, so he hurriedly put on his clothes and set out on a run for Colonel Zane's house. The first person whom he saw was the old negro slave, who was brushing one of the Colonel's horses.

Sam was deliberate and took his time about everything. He slowly looked up and surveyed Clarke with his rolling eyes. He did not recognize in him any one he had ever seen before, and being of a sullen and taciturn nature, especially with strangers, he seemed in no hurry to give the desired information as to Colonel Zane's whereabouts.

"Don't stare at me that way, you damn nigger," said Clarke, who was used to being obeyed by negroes. "Quick, you idiot. Where is the Colonel?"

At that moment Colonel Zane came out of the barn and started to speak, when Clarke interrupted him.

"Colonel, I have just pulled a man out of the river who says his name is Zane, or if he did not mean that, he knows you, for he surely said 'Zane.'"

"What!" ejaculated the Colonel, letting his pipe fall from his mouth.

Clarke related the circumstances in a few hurried words. Calling Sam they ran quickly down to the river, where they found the prostrate figure as Clarke had left it, the dog still crouched close by.

"My God! It is Isaac!" exclaimed Colonel Zane, when he saw the white face. "Poor boy, he looks as if he were dead. Are you sure he spoke? Of course he must have spoken for you could not have known. Yes, his heart is still beating."

Colonel Zane raised his head from the unconscious man's breast, where he had laid it to listen for the beating heart.

"Clarke, God bless you for saving him," said he fervently. "It shall never be forgotten. He is alive, and, I believe, only exhausted, for that wound amounts to little. Let us hurry."

"I did not save him. It was the dog," Alfred made haste to answer.

They carried the dripping form to the house, where the door was opened by Mrs. Zane.

"Oh, dear, another poor man," she said, pityingly. Then, as she saw his face, "Great Heavens, it is Isaac! Oh! don't say he is dead!"

"Yes, it is Isaac, and he is worth any number of dead men yet," said Colonel Zane, as they laid the insensible man on the couch. "Bessie, there is work here for you. He has been shot."

"Is there any other wound beside this one in his arm?" asked Mrs. Zane, examining it.

"I do not think so, and that injury is not serious. It is lose of blood, exposure and starvation. Clarke, will you please run over to Captain Boggs and tell Betty to hurry home! Sam, you get a blanket and warm it by the fire. That's right, Bessie, bring the whiskey," and Colonel Zane went on giving orders.

Alfred did not know in the least who Betty was, but, as he thought that unimportant, he started off on a run for the fort. He had a vague idea that Betty was the servant, possibly Sam's wife, or some one of the Colonel's several slaves.

Let us return to Betty. As she wheeled her pony and rode away from the scene of her adventure on the river bluff, her state of mind can be more readily imagined than described. Betty hated opposition of any kind, whether justifiable or not; she wanted her own way, and when prevented from doing as she pleased she invariably got angry. To be ordered and compelled to give up her ride, and that by a stranger, was intolerable. To make it all the worse this stranger had been decidedly flippant. He had familiarly spoken to her as "a pretty little girl." Not only that, which was a great offense, but he had stared at her, and she had a confused recollection of a gaze in which admiration had been ill disguised. Of course, it was that soldier Lydia had been telling her about. Strangers were of so rare an occurrence in the little village that it was not probable there could be more than one.

Approaching the house she met her brother who told her she had better go indoors and let Sam put up the pony. Accordingly, Betty called the negro, and then went into the house. Bessie had gone to the fort with the children. Betty found no one to talk to, so she tried to read. Finding she could not become interested she threw the book aside and took up her embroidery. This also turned out a useless effort; she got the linen hopelessly twisted and tangled, and presently she tossed this upon the table. Throwing her shawl over her shoulders, for it was now late in the afternoon and growing chilly, she walked downstairs and out into the Yard. She strolled aimlessly to and fro awhile, and then went over to the fort and into Captain Bogg's house, which adjoined the blockhouse. Here she found Lydia preparing flax.

"I saw you racing by on your pony. Goodness, how you can ride! I should be afraid of breaking my neck," exclaimed Lydia, as Betty entered.

"My ride was spoiled," said Betty, petulantly.

"Spoiled? By what—whom?"

"By a man, of course," retorted Betty, whose temper still was high. "It is always a man that spoils everything."

"Why, Betty, what in the world do you mean? I never heard you talk that way," said Lydia, opening her blue eyes in astonishment.

"Well, Lyde, I'll tell you. I was riding down the river road and just as I came to the end of the clearing a man jumped out from behind some bushes and grasped Madcap's bridle. Imagine! For a moment I was frightened out of my wits. I instantly thought of the Girtys, who, I have heard, have evinced a fondness for kidnapping little girls. Then the fellow said he was on guard and ordered me, actually commanded me to go home."

"Oh, is that all?" said Lydia, laughing.

"No, that is not all. He—he said I was a pretty little girl and that he was sorry I could not have my own way; that his present occupation was pleasant, and that the situation had its charm. The very idea. He was most impertinent," and Betty's telltale cheeks reddened again at the recollection.

"Betty, I do not think your experience was so dreadful, certainly nothing to put you out as it has," said Lydia, laughing merrily. "Be serious. You know we are not in the backwoods now and must not expect so much of the men. These rough border men know little of refinement like that with which you have been familiar. Some of them are quiet and never speak unless addressed; their simplicity is remarkable; Lew Wetzel and your brother Jonathan, when they are not fighting Indians, are examples. On the other hand, some of them are boisterous and if they get anything to drink they will make trouble for you. Why, I went to a party one night after I had been here only a few weeks and they played a game in which every man in the place kissed me."

"Gracious! Please tell me when any such games are likely to be proposed and I'll stay home," said Betty.

"I have learned to get along very well by simply making the best of it," continued Lydia. "And to tell the truth, I have learned to respect these rugged fellows. They are uncouth; they have no manners, but their hearts are honest and true, and that is of much greater importance in frontiersmen than the little attentions and courtesies upon which women are apt to lay too much stress."

"I think you speak sensibly and I shall try and be more reasonable hereafter. But, to return to the man who spoiled my ride. He, at least, is no frontiersman, notwithstanding his gun and his buckskin suit. He is an educated man. His manner and accent showed that. Then he looked at me so differently. I know it was that soldier from Fort Pitt."

"Mr. Clarke? Why, of course!" exclaimed Lydia, clapping her hands in glee. "How stupid of me!"

"You seem to be amused," said Betty, frowning.

"Oh, Betty, it is such a good joke."

"Is it? I fail to see it."

"But I can. I am very much amused. You see, I heard Mr. Clarke say, after papa told him there were lots of pretty girls here, that he usually succeeded in finding those things out and without any assistance. And the very first day he has met you and made you angry. It is delightful."

"Lyde, I never knew you could be so horrid."

"It is evident that Mr. Clarke is not only discerning, but not backward in expressing his thoughts. Betty, I see a romance."

"Don't be ridiculous," retorted Betty, with an angry blush. "Of course, he had a right to stop me, and perhaps he did me a good turn by keeping me inside the clearing, though I cannot imagine why he hid behind the bushes. But he might have been polite. He made me angry. He was so cool and—and—"

"I see," interrupted Lydia, teasingly. "He failed to recognize your importance."

"Nonsense, Lydia. I hope you do not think I am a silly little fool. It is only that I have not been accustomed to that kind of treatment, and I will not have it."

Lydia was rather pleased that some one had appeared on the scene who did not at once bow down before Betty, and therefore she took the young man's side of the argument.

"Do not be hard on poor Mr. Clarke. Maybe he mistook you for an Indian girl. He is handsome. I am sure you saw that."

"Oh, I don't remember how he looked," said Betty. She did remember, but would not admit it.

The conversation drifted into other channels after this, and soon twilight came stealing down on them. As Betty rose to go there came a hurried tap on the door.

"I wonder who would knock like that," said Lydia, rising "Betty, wait a moment while I open the door."

On doing this she discovered Clarke standing on the step with his cap in his hand.

"Why, Mr. Clarke! Will you come in?" exclaimed Lydia. "Thank you, only for a moment," said Alfred. "I cannot stay. I came to find Betty. Is she here?"

He had not observed Betty, who had stepped back into the shadow of the darkening room. At his question Lydia became so embarrassed she did not know what to say or do, and stood looking helplessly at him.

But Betty was equal to the occasion. At the mention of her first name in such a familiar manner by this stranger, who had already grievously offended her once before that day, Betty stood perfectly still a moment, speechless with surprise, then she stepped quickly out of the shadow.

Clarke turned as he heard her step and looked straight into a pair of dark, scornful eyes and a face pale with anger.

"If it be necessary that you use my name, and I do not see how that can be possible, will you please have courtesy enough to say Miss Zane?" she cried haughtily.

Lydia recovered her composure sufficiently to falter out:

"Betty, allow me to introduce—"

"Do not trouble yourself, Lydia. I have met this person once before to-day, and I do not care for an introduction."

When Alfred found himself gazing into the face that had haunted him all the afternoon, he forgot for the moment all about his errand. He was finally brought to a realization of the true state of affairs by Lydia's words.

"Mr. Clarke, you are all wet. What has happened?" she exclaimed, noticing the water dripping from his garments.

Suddenly a light broke in on Alfred. So the girl he had accosted on the road and "Betty" were one and the same person. His face flushed. He felt that his rudeness on that occasion may have merited censure, but that it had not justified the humiliation she had put upon him.

These two persons, so strangely brought together, and on whom Fate had made her inscrutable designs, looked steadily into each other's eyes. What mysterious force thrilled through Alfred Clarke and made Betty Zane tremble?

"Miss Boggs, I am twice unfortunate," said Alfred, tuning to Lydia, and there was an earnest ring in his deep voice "This time I am indeed blameless. I have just left Colonel Zane's house, where there has been an accident, and I was dispatched to find 'Betty,' being entirely ignorant as to who she might be. Colonel Zane did not stop to explain. Miss Zane is needed at the house, that is all."

And without so much as a glance at Betty he bowed low to Lydia and then strode out of the open door.

"What did he say?" asked Betty, in a small trembling voice, all her anger and resentment vanished.

"There has been an accident. He did not say what or to whom. You must hurry home. Oh, Betty, I hope no one has been hurt! And you were very unkind to Mr. Clarke. I am sure he is a gentleman, and you might have waited a moment to learn what he meant."

Betty did not answer, but flew out of the door and down the path to the gate of the fort. She was almost breathless when she reached Colonel Zane's house, and hesitated on the step before entering. Summoning her courage she pushed open the door. The first thing that struck her after the bright light was the pungent odor of strong liniment. She saw several women neighbors whispering together. Major McColloch and Jonathan Zane were standing by a couch over which Mrs. Zane was bending. Colonel Zane sat at the foot of the couch. Betty saw this in the first rapid glance, and then, as the Colonel's wife moved aside, she saw a prostrate figure, a white face and dark eyes that smiled at her.

"Betty," came in a low voice from those pale lips.

Her heart leaped and then seemed to cease beating. Many long years had passed since she had heard that voice, but it had never been forgotten. It was the best beloved voice of her childhood, and with it came the sweet memories of her brother and playmate. With a cry of joy she fell on her knees beside him and threw her arms around his neck.

"Oh, Isaac, brother, brother!" she cried, as she kissed him again and again. "Can it really be you? Oh, it is too good to be true! Thank God! I have prayed and prayed that you would be restored to us."

Then she began to cry and laugh at the same time in that strange way in which a woman relieves a heart too full of joy. "Yes, Betty. It is all that is left of me," he said, running his hand caressingly over the dark head that lay on his breast.

"Betty, you must not excite him," said Colonel Zane.

"So you have not forgotten me?" whispered Isaac.

"No, indeed, Isaac. I have never forgotten," answered Betty, softly. "Only last night I spoke of you and wondered if you were living. And now you are here. Oh, I am so happy!" The quivering lips and the dark eyes bright with tears spoke eloquently of her joy.

"Major will you tell Captain Boggs to come over after supper? Isaac will be able to talk a little by then, and he has some news of the Indians," said Colonel Zane.

"And ask the young man who saved my life to come that I may thank him," said Isaac.

"Saved your life?" exclaimed Betty, turning to her brother, in surprise, while a dark red flush spread over her face. A humiliating thought had flashed into her mind.

"Saved his life, of course," said Colonel Zane, answering for Isaac. "Young Clarke pulled him out of the river. Didn't he tell you?"

"No," said Betty, rather faintly.

"Well, he is a modest young fellow. He saved Isaac's life, there is no doubt of that. You will hear all about it after supper. Don't make Isaac talk any more at present."

Betty hid her face on Isaac's shoulder and remained quiet a few moments; then, rising, she kissed his cheek and went quietly to her room. Once there she threw herself on the bed and tried to think. The events of the day, coming after a long string of monotonous, wearying days, had been confusing; they had succeeded one another in such rapid order as to leave no time for reflection. The meeting by the river with the rude but interesting stranger; the shock to her dignity; Lydia's kindly advice; the stranger again, this time emerging from the dark depths of disgrace into the luminous light as the hero of her brother's rescue—all these thoughts jumbled in her mind making it difficult for her to think clearly. But after a time one thing forced itself upon her. She could not help being conscious that she had wronged some one to whom she would be forever indebted. Nothing could alter that. She was under an eternal obligation to the man who had saved the life she loved best on earth. She had unjustly scorned and insulted the man to whom she owed the life of her brother.

Betty was passionate and quick-tempered, but she was generous and tender-hearted as well, and when she realized how unkind and cruel she kind been she felt very miserable. Her position admitted of no retreat. No matter how much pride rebelled; no matter how much she disliked to retract anything she had said, she knew no other course lay open to her. She would have to apologize to Mr. Clarke. How could she? What would she say? She remembered how cold and stern his face had been as he turned from her to Lydia. Perplexed and unhappy, Betty did what any girl in her position would have done: she resorted to the consoling and unfailing privilege of her sex—a good cry.

When she became composed again she got up and bathed her hot cheeks, brushed her hair, and changed her gown for a becoming one of white. She tied a red ribbon about her throat and put a rosette in her hair. She had forgotten all about the Indians. By the time Mrs. Zane called her for supper she had her mind made up to ask Mr. Clarke's pardon, tell him she was sorry, and that she hoped they might be friends.

Isaac Zane's fame had spread from the Potomac to Detroit and Louisville. Many an anxious mother on the border used the story of his captivity as a means to frighten truant youngsters who had evinced a love for running wild in the woods. The evening of Isaac's return every one in the settlement called to welcome home the wanderer. In spite of the troubled times and the dark cloud hanging over them they made the occasion one of rejoicing.

Old John Bennet, the biggest and merriest man in the colony, came in and roared his appreciation of Isaac's return. He was a huge man, and when he stalked into the room he made the floor shake with his heavy tread. His honest face expressed his pleasure as he stood over Isaac and nearly crushed his hand.

"Glad to see you, Isaac. Always knew you would come back. Always said so. There are not enough damn redskins on the river to keep you prisoner."

"I think they managed to keep him long enough," remarked Silas Zane.

"Well, here comes the hero," said Colonel Zane, as Clarke entered, accompanied by Captain Boggs, Major McColloch and Jonathan. "Any sign of Wetzel or the Indians?"

Jonathan had not yet seen his brother, and he went over and seized Isaac's hand and wrung it without speaking.

"There are no Indians on this side of the river," said Major McColloch, in answer to the Colonel's question.

"Mr. Clarke, you do not seem impressed with your importance," said Colonel Zane. "My sister said you did not tell her what part you took in Isaac's rescue."

"I hardly deserve all the credit," answered Alfred. "Your big black dog merits a great deal of it."

"Well, I consider your first day at the fort a very satisfactory one, and an augury of that fortune you came west to find."

"How are you?" said Alfred, going up to the couch where Isaac lay.

"I am doing well, thanks to you," said Isaac, warmly shaking Alfred's hand.

"It is good to see you pulling out all right," answered Alfred. "I tell you, I feared you were in a bad way when I got you out of the water."

Isaac reclined on the couch with his head and shoulder propped up by pillows. He was the handsomest of the brothers. His face would have been but for the marks of privation, singularly like Betty's; the same low, level brows and dark eyes; the same mouth, though the lips were stronger and without the soft curves which made his sister's mouth so sweet.

Betty appeared at the door, and seeing the room filled with men she hesitated a moment before coming forward. In her white dress she made such a dainty picture that she seemed out of place among those surroundings. Alfred Clarke, for one, thought such a charming vision was wasted on the rough settlers, every one of whom wore a faded and dirty buckskin suit and a belt containing a knife and a tomahawk. Colonel Zane stepped up to Betty and placing his arm around her turned toward Clarke with pride in his eyes.

"Betty, I want to make you acquainted with the hero of the hour, Mr. Alfred Clarke. This is my sister."

Betty bowed to Alfred, but lowered her eyes instantly on encountering the young man's gaze.

"I have had the pleasure of meeting Miss Zane twice today," said Alfred.

"Twice?" asked Colonel Zane, turning to Betty. She did not answer, but disengaged herself from his arm and sat down by Isaac.

"It was on the river road that I first met Miss Zane, although I did not know her then," answered Alfred. "I had some difficulty in stopping her pony from going to Fort Pitt, or some other place down the river."

"Ha! Ha! Well, I know she rides that pony pretty hard," said Colonel Zane, with his hearty laugh. "I'll tell you, Clarke, we have some riders here in the settlement. Have you heard of Major McColloch's leap over the hill?"

"I have heard it mentioned, and I would like to hear the story," responded Alfred. "I am fond of horses, and think I can ride a little myself. I am afraid I shall be compelled to change my mind."

"That is a fine animal you rode from Fort Pitt," remarked the Major. "I would like to own him."

"Come, draw your chairs up and he'll listen to Isaac's story," said Colonel Zane.

"I have not much of a story to tell," said Isaac, in a voice still weak and low. "I have some bad news, I am sorry to say, but I shall leave that for the last. This year, if it had been completed, would have made my tenth year as a captive of the Wyandots. This last period of captivity, which has been nearly four years, I have not been ill-treated and have enjoyed more comfort than any of you can imagine. Probably you are all familiar with the reason for my long captivity. Because of the interest of Myeerah, the Indian Princess, they have importuned me for years to be adopted into the tribe, marry the White Crane, as they call Myeerah, and become a Wyandot chief. To this I would never consent, though I have been careful not to provoke the Indians. I was allowed the freedom of the camp, but have always been closely watched. I should still be with the Indians had I not suspected that Hamilton, the British Governor, had formed a plan with the Hurons, Shawnees, Delawares, and other tribes, to strike a terrible blow at the whites along, the river. For months I have watched the Indians preparing for an expedition, the extent of which they had never before undertaken. I finally learned from Myeerah that my suspicions were well founded. A favorable chance to escape presented and I took it and got away. I outran all the braves, even Arrowswift, the Wyandot runner, who shot me through the arm. I have had a hard time of it these last three or four days, living on herbs and roots, and when I reached the river I was ready to drop. I pushed a log into the water and started to drift over. When the old dog saw me I knew I was safe if I could hold on. Once, when the young man pointed his gun at me, I thought it was all over. I could not shout very loud."

"Were you going to shoot?" asked Colonel Zane of Clarke.

"I took him for an Indian, but fortunately I discovered my mistake in time," answered Alfred.

"Are the Indians on the way here?" asked Jonathan.

"That I cannot say. At present the Wyandots are at home. But I know that the British and the Indians will make a combined attack on the settlements. It may be a month, or a year, but it is coming."

"And Hamilton, the hair buyer, the scalp buyer, is behind the plan," said Colonel Zane, in disgust.

"The Indians have their wrongs. I sympathize with them in many ways.

We have robbed them, broken faith with them, and have not lived up to the treaties. Pipe and Wingenund are particularly bitter toward the whites. I understand Cornplanter is also. He would give anything for Jonathan's scalp, and I believe any of the tribes would give a hundred of their best warriors for 'Black Wind,' as they call Lew Wetzel."

"Have you ever seen Red Fox?" asked Jonathan, who was sitting near the fire and as usual saying but little. He was the wildest and most untamable of all the Zanes. Most of the time he spent in the woods, not so much to fight Indians, as Wetzel did, but for pure love of outdoor life. At home he was thoughtful and silent.

"Yes, I have seen him," answered Isaac. "He is a Shawnee chief and one of the fiercest warriors in that tribe of fighters. He was at Indian-head, which is the name of one of the Wyandot villages, when I visited there last, and he had two hundred of his best braves with him."

"He is a bad Indian. Wetzel and I know him. He swore he would hang our scalps up in his wigwam," said Jonathan.

"What has he in particular against you?" asked Colonel Zane. "Of course, Wetzel is the enemy of all Indians."

"Several years ago Wetzel and I were on a hunt down the river at the place called Girty's Point, where we fell in with the tracks of five Shawnees. I was for coming home, but Wetzel would not hear of it. We trailed the Indians and, coming up on them after dark, we tomahawked them. One of them got away crippled, but we could not follow him because we discovered that they had a white girl as captive, and one of the red devils, thinking we were a rescuing party, had tomahawked her. She was not quite dead. We did all we could to save her life. She died and we buried her on the spot. They were Red Fox's braves and were on their way to his camp with the prisoner. A year or so afterwards I learned from a friendly Indian that the Shawnee chief had sworn to kill us. No doubt he will be a leader in the coming attack."

"We are living in the midst of terrible times," remarked Colonel Zane. "Indeed, these are the times that try men's souls, but I firmly believe the day is not far distant when the redmen will be driven far over the border."

"Is the Indian Princess pretty?" asked Betty of Isaac.

"Indeed she is, Betty, almost as beautiful as you are," said Isaac. "She is tall and very fair for an Indian. But I have something to tell about her more interesting than that. Since I have been with the Wyandots this last time I have discovered a little of the jealously guarded secret of Myeerah's mother. When Tarhe and his band of Hurons lived in Canada their home was in the Muskoka Lakes region on the Moon river. The old warriors tell wonderful stories of the beauty of that country. Tarhe took captive some French travellers, among them a woman named La Durante. She had a beautiful little girl. The prisoners, except this little girl, were released. When she grew up Tarhe married her. Myeerah is her child. Once Tarhe took his wife to

Detroit and she was seen there by an old Frenchman who went crazy over her and said she was his child. Tarhe never went to the white settlements again. So you see, Myeerah is from a great French family on her mother's side, as this is old Frenchman was probably Chevalier La Durante, and Myeerah's grandfather."

"I would love to see her, and yet I hate her. What an odd name she has," said Betty.

"It is the Indian name for the white crane, a rare and beautiful bird. I never saw one. The name has been celebrated among the Hurons as long as any one of them can remember. The Indians call her the White Crane, or Walk-in-the-Water, because of her love for wading in the stream."

"I think we have made Isaac talk enough for one night," said Colonel Zane. "He is tired out. Major, tell Isaac and Betty, and Mr. Clarke, too, of your jump over the cliff."

"I have heard of that leap from the Indians," said Isaac.

"Major, from what hill did you jump your horse?" asked Alfred.

"You know the bare rocky bluff that stands out prominently on the hill across the creek. From that spot Colonel Zane first saw the valley, and from there I leaped my horse. I can never convince myself that it really happened. Often I look up at that cliff in doubt. But the Indians and Colonel Zane, Jonathan, Wetzel and others say they actually saw the deed done, so I must accept it," said Major McColloch.

"It seems incredible!" said Alfred. "I cannot understand how a man or horse could go over that precipice and live."

"That is what we all say," responded the Colonel. "I suppose I shall have to tell the story. We have fighters and makers of history here, but few talkers."

"I am anxious to hear it," answered Clarke, "and I am curious to see this man Wetzel, whose fame has reached as far as my home, way down in Virginia."

"You will have your wish gratified soon, I have no doubt," resumed the Colonel. "Well, now for the story of McColloch's mad ride for life and his wonderful leap down Wheeling hill. A year ago, when the fort was besieged by the Indians, the Major got through the lines and made off for Short Creek. He returned next morning with forty mounted men. They marched boldly up to the gate, and all succeeded in getting inside save the gallant Major, who had waited to be the last man to go in. Finding it impossible to make the short distance without going under the fire of the Indians, who had rushed up to prevent the relief party from entering the fort, he wheeled his big stallion, and, followed by the yelling band of savages, he took the road leading around back of the fort to the top of the bluff. The road lay along the edge of the cliff and I saw the Major turn and wave his rifle at us, evidently with the desire of assuring us that he was safe. Suddenly, on the very summit of the hill, he reined in his horse as if undecided. I knew in an instant what had happened. The Major had run right into the returning party of Indians, which had been sent out to intercept our reinforcements. In a moment more we heard the exultant yells of the savages, and saw them gliding from tree to tree, slowly lengthening out their line and surrounding the unfortunate Major. They did not fire a shot. We in the fort were stupefied with horror, and stood helplessly with our useless guns, watching and waiting for the seemingly inevitable doom of our comrade. Not so with the Major! Knowing that he was a marked man by the Indians and feeling that any death was preferable to the gauntlet, the knife, the stake and torch of the merciless savage, he had grasped at a desperate chance. He saw his enemies stealthily darting from rock to tree, and tree to bush, creeping through the brush, and slipping closer and closer every moment. On three sides were his hated foes and on the remaining side—the abyss. Without a moment's hesitation the intrepid Major spurred his horse at the precipice. Never shall I forget that thrilling moment. The three hundred savages were silent as they realized the Major's intention. Those in the fort watched with staring eyes. A few bounds and the noble steed reared high on his hind legs. Outlined by the clear blue sky the magnificent animal stood for one brief instant, his black mane flying in the wind, his head thrown up and his front hoofs pawing the air like Marcus Curtius' mailed steed of old, and then down with a crash, a cloud of dust, and the crackling of pine limbs. A long yell went up from the Indians below, while those above ran to the edge of the cliff. With cries of wonder and baffled vengeance they gesticulated toward the dark ravine into which horse and rider had plunged rather than wait to meet a more cruel death. The precipice at this point is over three hundred feet in height, and in places is almost perpendicular. We believed the Major to be lying crushed and mangled on the rocks. Imagine our frenzy of joy when we saw the daring soldier and his horse dash out of the bushes that skirt the base of the cliff, cross the creek, and come galloping to the fort in safety."

"It was wonderful! Wonderful!" exclaimed Isaac, his eyes glistening. "No wonder the Indians call you the 'Flying Chief.'"

"Had the Major not jumped into the clump of pine trees which grow thickly some thirty feet below the summit he would not now be alive," said Colonel Zane. "I am certain of that. Nevertheless that does not detract from the courage of his deed. He had no time to pick out the best place to jump. He simply took his one chance, and came out all right. That leap will live in the minds of men as long as yonder bluff stands a monument to McColloch's ride for life."

Alfred had listened with intense interest to the Colonel's recital. When it ended, although his pulses quickened and his soul expanded with awe and reverence for the hero of that ride, he sat silent. Alfred honored courage in a man more than any other quality. He marvelled at the simplicity of these bordermen who, he thought, took the most wonderful adventures and daring escapes as a matter of course, a compulsory part of their daily lives. He had already, in one day, had more excitement than had ever befallen him, and was beginning to believe his thirst for a free life of stirring action would be quenched long before he had learned to become useful in his new sphere. During the remaining half hour of his call on his lately acquired friends, he took little part in the conversation, but sat quietly watching the changeful expressions on Betty's face, and listening to Colonel Zane's jokes. When he rose to go he bade his host good-night, and expressed a wish that Isaac, who had fallen asleep, might have a speedy recovery. He turned toward the door to find that Betty had intercepted him.

"Mr. Clarke," she said, extending a little hand that trembled slightly. "I wish to say—that—I want to say that my feelings have changed. I am sorry for what I said over at Lydia's. I spoke hastily and rudely. You have saved my brother's life. I will be forever grateful to you. It is useless to try to thank you. I—I hope we may be friends."

Alfred found it desperately hard to resist that low voice, and those dark eyes which were raised shyly, yet bravely, to his. But he had been deeply hurt. He pretended not to see the friendly hand held out to him, and his voice was cold when he answered her.

"I am glad to have been of some service," he said, "but I think you overrate my action. Your brother would not have drowned, I am sure. You owe me nothing. Good-night."

Betty stood still one moment staring at the door through which he had gone before she realized that her overtures of friendship had been politely, but coldly, ignored. She had actually been snubbed. The impossible had happened to Elizabeth Zane. Her first sensation after she recovered from her momentary bewilderment was one of amusement, and she laughed in a constrained manner; but, presently, two bright red spots appeared in her cheeks, and she looked quickly around to see if any of the others had noticed the incident. None of them had been paying any attention to her and she breathed a sigh of relief. It was bad enough to be snubbed without having others see it. That would have been too humiliating. Her eyes flashed fire as she remembered the disdain in Clarke's face, and that she had not been clever enough to see it in time.

"Tige, come here!" called Colonel Zane. "What ails the dog?"

The dog had jumped to his feet and ran to the door, where he sniffed at the crack over the threshold. His aspect was fierce and threatening. He uttered low growls and then two short barks. Those in the room heard a soft moccasined footfall outside. The next instant the door opened wide and a tall figure stood disclosed.

"Wetzel!" exclaimed Colonel Zane. A hush fell on the little company after that exclamation, and all eyes were fastened on the new comer.

Well did the stranger merit close attention. He stalked into the room, leaned his long rifle against the mantelpiece and spread out his hands to the fire. He was clad from head to foot in fringed and beaded buckskin, which showed evidence of a long and arduous tramp. It was torn and wet and covered with mud. He was a magnificently made man, six feet in height, and stood straight as an arrow. His wide shoulders, and his muscular, though not heavy, limbs denoted wonderful strength and activity. His long hair, black as a raven's wing, hung far down his shoulders. Presently he turned and the light shone on a remarkable face. So calm and cold and stern it was that it seemed chiselled out of marble. The most striking features were its unusual pallor, and the eyes, which were coal black, and piercing as the dagger's point.

"If you have any bad news out with it," cried Colonel Zane, impatiently.

"No need fer alarm," said Wetzel. He smiled slightly as he saw Betty's apprehensive face. "Don't look scared, Betty. The redskins are miles away and goin' fer the Kanawha settlement."

CHAPTER III.

Many weeks of quiet followed the events of the last chapter. The settlers planted their corn, harvested their wheat and labored in the fields during the whole of one spring and summer without hearing the dreaded war cry of the Indians. Colonel Zane, who had been a disbursing officer in the army of Lord Dunmore, where he had attained the rank of Colonel, visited Fort Pitt during the summer in the hope of increasing the number of soldiers in his garrison. His efforts proved fruitless. He returned to Fort Henry by way of the river with several pioneers, who with their families were bound for Fort Henry. One of these pioneers was a minister who worked in the fields every week day and on Sundays preached the Gospel to those who gathered in the meeting house.

Alfred Clarke had taken up his permanent abode at the fort, where he had been installed as one of the regular garrison. His duties, as well as those of the nine other members of the garrison, were light. For two hours out of the twenty-four he was on guard. Thus he had ample time to acquaint himself with the settlers and their families.

Alfred and Isaac had now become firm friends. They spent many hours fishing in the river, and roaming the woods in the vicinity, as Colonel Zane would not allow Isaac to stray far from the fort. Alfred became a regular visitor at Colonel Zane's house. He saw Betty every day, but as yet, nothing had mended the breach between them. They were civil to each other when chance threw them together, but Betty usually left the room on some pretext soon after he entered. Alfred regretted his hasty exhibition of resentment and would have been glad to establish friendly relations with her. But she would not give him an opportunity. She avoided him on all possible occasions. Though Alfred was fast succumbing to the charm of Betty's beautiful face, though his desire to be near her had grown well nigh resistless, his pride had not yet broken down. Many of the summer evenings found him on the Colonel's doorstep, smoking a pipe, or playing with the children. He was that rare and best company—a good listener. Although he laughed at Colonel Zane's stories, and never tired of hearing of Isaac's experiences among the Indians, it is probable he would not have partaken of the Colonel's hospitality nearly so often had it not been that he usually saw Betty, and if he got only a glimpse of her he went away satisfied. On Sundays he attended the services at the little church and listened to Betty's sweet voice as she led the singing.

There were a number of girls at the fort near Betty's age. With all of these Alfred was popular. He appeared so entirely different from the usual young man on the frontier that he was more than welcome everywhere. Girls in the backwoods are much the same as girls in thickly populated and civilized districts. They liked his manly ways; his frank and pleasant manners; and when to these virtues he added a certain deferential regard, a courtliness to which they were unaccustomed, they were all the better pleased. He paid the young women little attentions, such as calling on them, taking them to parties and out driving, but there was not one of them who could think that she, in particular, interested him.

The girls noticed, however, that he never approached Betty after service, or on any occasion, and while it caused some wonder and gossip among them, for Betty enjoyed the distinction of being the belle of the border, they were secretly pleased. Little hints and knowing smiles, with which girls are so skillful, made known to Betty all of this, and, although she was apparently indifferent, it hurt her sensitive feelings. It had the effect of making her believe she hated the cause of it more than ever.

What would have happened had things gone on in this way, I am not prepared to say; probably had not a meddling Fate decided to take a hand in the game, Betty would have continued to think she hated Alfred, and I would never have had occasion to write his story; but Fate did interfere, and, one day in the early fall, brought about an incident which changed the whole world for the two young people.

It was the afternoon of an Indian summer day—in that most beautiful time of all the year—and Betty, accompanied by her dog, had wandered up the hillside into the woods. From the hilltop the broad river could be seen winding away in the distance, and a soft, bluish, smoky haze hung over the water. The forest seemed to be on fire. The yellow leaves of the poplars, the brown of the white and black oaks, the red and purple of the maples, and the green of the pines and hemlocks flamed in a glorious blaze of color. A stillness, which was only broken now and then by the twittering of birds uttering the plaintive notes peculiar to them in the autumn as they band together before their pilgrimage to the far south, pervaded the forest.

Betty loved the woods, and she knew all the trees. She could tell their names by the bark or the shape of the leaves. The giant black oak, with its smooth shiny bark and sturdy limbs, the chestnut with its rugged, seamed sides and bristling burrs, the hickory with its lofty height and curled shelling bark, were all well known and well loved by Betty. Many times had she wondered at the trembling, quivering leaves of the aspen, and the foliage of the silver-leaf as it glinted in the sun. To-day, especially, as she walked through the woods, did their beauty appeal to her. In the little sunny patches of clearing which were scattered here and there in the grove, great clusters of goldenrod grew profusely. The golden heads swayed gracefully on the long stems Betty gathered a few sprigs and added to them a bunch of warmly tinted maple leaves.

The chestnuts burrs were opening. As Betty mounted a little rocky eminence and reached out for a limb of a chestnut tree, she lost her footing and fell. Her right foot had twisted under her as she went down, and when a sharp pain shot through it she was unable to repress a cry. She got up, tenderly placed the foot on the ground and tried her weight on it, which caused acute pain. She unlaced and removed her moccasin to find that her ankle had commenced to swell. Assured that she had sprained it, and aware of the serious consequences of an injury of that nature, she felt greatly distressed. Another effort to place her foot on the ground and bear her weight on it caused such severe pain that she was compelled to give up the attempt. Sinking down by the trunk of the tree and leaning her head against it she tried to think of a way out of her difficulty.

The fort, which she could plainly see, seemed a long distance off, although it was only a little way down the grassy slope. She looked and looked, but not a person was to be seen. She called to Tige. She remembered that he had been chasing a squirrel a short while ago, but now there was no sign of him. He did not come at her call. How annoying! If Tige were only there she could have sent him for help. She shouted several times, but the distance was too great for her voice to carry to the fort. The mocking echo of her call came back from the bluff that rose to her left. Betty now began to be alarmed in earnest, and the tears started to roll down her cheeks. The throbbing pain in her ankle, the dread of having to remain out in that lonesome forest after dark, and the fear that she might not be found for hours, caused Betty's usually brave spirit to falter; she was weeping unreservedly.

In reality she had been there only a few minutes—although they seemed hours to her—when she heard the light tread of moccasined feet on the moss behind her. Starting up with a cry of joy she turned and looked up into the astonished face of Alfred Clarke.

Returning from a hunt back in the woods he had walked up to her before being aware of her presence. In a single glance he saw the wildflowers scattered beside her, the little moccasin turned inside out, the woebegone, tearstained face, and he knew Betty had come to grief.

Confused and vexed, Betty sank back at the foot of the tree. It is probable she would have encountered Girty or a member of his band of redmen, rather than have this young man find her in this predicament. It provoked her to think that of all the people at the fort it should be the only one she could not welcome who should find her in such a sad plight.

"Why, Miss Zane!" he exclaimed, after a moment of hesitation. "What in the world has happened? Have you been hurt? May I help you?"

"It is nothing," said Betty, bravely, as she gathered up her flowers and the moccasin and rose slowly to her feet. "Thank you, but you need not wait."

The cold words nettled Alfred and he was in the act of turning away from her when he caught, for the fleetest part of a second, the full gaze of her eyes. He stopped short. A closer scrutiny of her face convinced him that she was suffering and endeavoring with all her strength to conceal it.

"But I will wait. I think you have hurt yourself. Lean upon my arm," he said, quietly.

"Please let me help you," he continued, going nearer to her.

But Betty refused his assistance. She would not even allow him to take the goldenrod from her arms. After a few hesitating steps she paused and lifted her foot from the ground.

"Here, you must not try to walk a step farther," he said, resolutely, noting how white she had suddenly become. "You have sprained your ankle and are needlessly torturing yourself. Please let me carry you?"

"Oh, no, no, no!" cried Betty, in evident distress. "I will manage. It is not so—very—far."

She resumed the slow and painful walking, but she had taken only a few steps when she stopped again and this time a low moan issued from her lips. She swayed slightly backward and if Alfred had not dropped his rifle and caught her she would have fallen.

"Will you—please—for some one?" she whispered faintly, at the same time pushing him away.

"How absurd!" burst out Alfred, indignantly. "Am I then, so distasteful to you that you would rather wait here and suffer a half hour longer while I go for assistance? It is only common courtesy on my part. I do not want to carry you. I think you would be quite heavy."

He said this in a hard, bitter tone, deeply hurt that she would not accept even a little kindness from him. He looked away from her and waited. Presently a soft, half-smothered sob came from Betty and it expressed such utter wretchedness that his heart melted. After all she was only a child. He turned to see the tears running down her cheeks, and with a suppressed imprecation upon the wilfulness of young women in general, and this one in particular, he stepped forward and before she could offer any resistance, he had taken her up in his arms, goldenrod and all, and had started off at a rapid walk toward the fort.

Betty cried out in angry surprise, struggled violently for a moment, and then, as suddenly, lay quietly in his arms. His anger changed to self-reproach as he realized what a light burden she made. He looked down at the dark head lying on his shoulder. Her face was hidden by the dusky rippling hair, which tumbled over his breast, brushed against his cheek, and blew across his lips. The touch of those fragrant tresses was a soft caress. Almost unconsciously he pressed her closer to his heart. And as a sweet mad longing grew upon him he was blind to all save that he held her in his arms, that uncertainty was gone forever, and that he loved her. With these thoughts running riot in his brain he carried her down the hill to Colonel Zane's house.

The negro, Sam, who came out of the kitchen, dropped the bucket he had in his hand and ran into the house when he saw them. When Alfred reached the gate Colonel Zane and Isaac were hurrying out to meet him.

"For Heaven's sake! What has happened? Is she badly hurt? I have always looked for this," said the Colonel, excitedly.

"You need not look so alarmed," answered Alfred. "She has only sprained her ankle, and trying to walk afterward hurt her so badly that she became faint and I had to carry her."

"Dear me, is that all?" said Mrs. Zane, who had also come out. "We were terribly frightened. Sam came running into the house with some kind of a wild story. Said he knew you would be the death of Betty."

"How ridiculous! Colonel Zane, that servant of yours never fails to say something against me," said Alfred, as he carried Betty into the house.

"He doesn't like you. But you need not mind Sam. He is getting old and we humor him, perhaps too much. We are certainly indebted to you," returned the Colonel.

Betty was laid on the couch and consigned to the skillful hands of Mrs. Zane, who pronounced the injury a bad sprain.

"Well, Betty, this will keep you quiet for a few days," said she, with a touch of humor, as she gently felt the swollen ankle.

"Alfred, you have been our good angel so often that I don't see how we shall ever reward you," said Isaac to Alfred.

"Oh, that time will come. Don't worry about that," said Alfred, jestingly, and then, turning to the others he continued, earnestly. "I will apologize for the manner in which I disregarded Miss Zane's wish not to help her. I am sure I could do no less. I believe my rudeness has spared her considerable suffering."

"What did he mean, Betts?" asked Isaac, going back to his sister after he had closed the door. "Didn't you want him to help you?"

Betty did not answer. She sat on the couch while Mrs. Zane held the little bare foot and slowly poured the hot water over the swollen and discolored ankle. Betty's lips were pale. She winced every time Mrs. Zane touched her foot, but as yet she had not uttered even a sigh.

"Betty, does it hurt much?" asked Isaac.

"Hurt? Do you think I am made of wood? Of course it hurts," retorted Betty. "That water is so hot. Bessie, will not cold water do as well?"

"I am sorry. I won't tease any more," said Isaac, taking his sister's hand. "I'll tell you what, Betty, we owe Alfred Clarke a great deal, you and I. I am going to tell you something so you will know how much more you owe him. Do you remember last month when that red heifer of yours got away. Well, Clarke chased her away and finally caught her in the woods. He asked me to say I had caught her. Somehow or other he seems to be afraid of you. I wish you and he would be good friends. He is a mighty fine fellow."

In spite of the pain Betty was suffering a bright blush suffused her face at the words of her brother, who, blind as brothers are in regard to their own sisters, went on praising his friend.

Betty was confined to the house a week or more and during this enforced idleness she had ample time for reflection and opportunity to inquire into the perplexed state of her mind.

The small room, which Betty called her own, faced the river and fort. Most of the day she lay by the window trying to read her favorite books, but often she gazed out on the quiet scene, the rolling river, the everchanging trees and the pastures in which the red and white cows grazed peacefully; or she would watch with idle, dreamy eyes the flight of the crows over the hills, and the graceful motion of the hawk as he sailed around and around in the azure sky, looking like a white sail far out on a summer sea.

But Betty's mind was at variance with this peaceful scene. The consciousness of a change, which she could not readily define, in her feelings toward Alfred Clarke, vexed and irritated her. Why did she think of him so often? True, he had saved her brother's life. Still she was compelled to admit to herself that this was not the reason. Try as she would, she could not banish the thought of him. Over and over again, a thousand times, came the recollection of that moment when he had taken her up in his arms as though she were a child. Some vague feeling stirred in her heart as she remembered the strong yet gentle clasp of his arms.

Several times from her window she had seen him coming across the square between the fort and her brother's house, and womanlike, unseen herself, she had watched him. How erect was his carriage. How pleasant his deep voice sounded as she heard him talking to her brother. Day by day, as her ankle grew stronger and she knew she could not remain much longer in her room, she dreaded more and more the thought of meeting him. She could not understand herself; she had strange dreams; she cried seemingly without the slightest cause and she was restless and unhappy. Finally she grew angry and scolded herself. She said she was silly and sentimental. This had the effect of making her bolder, but it did not quiet her unrest. Betty did not know that the little blind God, who steals unawares on his victim, had marked her for his own, and that all this sweet perplexity was the unconscious awakening of the heart.

One afternoon, near the end of Betty's siege indoors, two of her friends, Lydia Boggs and Alice Reynolds, called to see her.

Alice had bright blue eyes, and her nut brown hair hung in rebellious curls around her demure and pretty face. An adorable dimple lay hidden in her rosy cheek and flashed into light with her smiles.

"Betty, you are a lazy thing!" exclaimed Lydia. "Lying here all day long doing nothing but gaze out of the window."

"Girls, I am glad you came over," said Betty. "I am blue. Perhaps you will cheer me up."

"Betty needs some one of the sterner sex to cheer her," said Alice, mischievously, her eyes twinkling. "Don't you think so, Lydia?"

"Of course," answered Lydia. "When I get blue—"

"Please spare me," interrupted Betty, holding up her hands in protest. "I have not a single doubt that your masculine remedies are sufficient for all your ills. Girls who have lost their interest in the old pleasures, who spend their spare time in making linen and quilts, and who have sunk their very personalities in a great big tyrant of a man, are not liable to get blue. They are afraid he may see a tear or a frown. But thank goodness, I have not yet reached that stage."

"Oh, Betty Zane! Just you wait! Wait!" exclaimed Lydia, shaking her finger at Betty. "Your turn is coming. When it does do not expect any mercy from us, for you shalt never get it."

"Unfortunately, you and Alice have monopolized the attentions of the only two eligible young men at the fort," said Betty, with a laugh.

"Nonsense there plenty of young men all eager for our favor, you little coquette," answered Lydia. "Harry Martin, Will Metzer, Captain Swearengen, of Short Creek, and others too numerous to count. Look at Lew Wetzel and Billy Bennet."

"Lew cares for nothing except hunting Indians and Billy's only a boy," said Betty.

"Well, have it your own way," said Lydia. "Only this, I know Billy adores you, for he told me so, and a better lad never lived."

"Lyde, you forget to include one other among those prostrate before Betty's charms," said Alice.

"Oh, yes, you mean Mr. Clarke. To be sure, I had forgotten him," answered Lydia. "How odd that he should be the one to find you the day you hurt your foot. Was it an accident?"

"Of course. I slipped off the bank," said Betty.

"No, no. I don't mean that. Was his finding you an accident?"

"Do you imagine I waylaid Mr. Clarke, and then sprained my ankle on purpose?" said Betty, who began to look dangerous.

"Certainly not that; only it seems so odd that he should be the one to rescue all the damsels in distress. Day before yesterday he stopped a runaway horse, and saved Nell Metzer who was in the wagon, a severe shaking up, if not something more serious. She is desperately in love with him. She told me Mr. Clarke—"

"I really do not care to hear about it," interrupted Betty.

"But, Betty, tell us. Wasn't it dreadful, his carrying you?" asked Alice, with a sly glance at Betty. "You know you are so—so prudish, one may say. Did he take you in his arms? It must have been very embarrassing for you, considering your dislike of Mr. Clarke, and he so much in love with—"

"You hateful girls," cried Betty, throwing a pillow at Alice, who just managed to dodge it. "I wish you would go home."

"Never mind, Betty. We will not tease anymore," said Lydia, putting her arm around Betty. "Come, Alice, we will tell Betty you have named the day for your wedding. See! She is all eyes now."

* * * * * * * * * * * * * * * *

The young people of the frontier settlements were usually married before they were twenty. This was owing to the fact that there was little distinction of rank and family pride. The object of the pioneers in moving West was, of course, to better their condition; but, the realization of their dependence on one another, the common cause of their labors, and the terrible dangers to which they were continually exposed, brought them together as one large family.

Therefore, early love affairs were encouraged—not frowned upon as they are to-day—and they usually resulted in early marriages.

However, do not let it be imagined that the path of the youthful swain was strewn with flowers. Courting or "sparking" his sweetheart had a painful as well as a joyous side. Many and varied were the tricks played on the fortunate lover by the gallants who had vied with him for the favor of the maid. Brave, indeed, he who won her. If he marched up to her home in the early evening he was made the object of innumerable jests, even the young lady's family indulging in and enjoying the banter. Later, when he come out of the door, it was more than likely that, if it were winter, he would be met by a volley of water soaked snowballs, or big buckets of icewater, or a mountain of snow shoved off the roof by some trickster, who had waited patiently for such an opportunity. On summer nights his horse would be stolen, led far into the woods and tied, or the wheels of his wagon would be taken off and hidden, leaving him to walk home. Usually the successful lover, and especially if he lived at a distance, would make his way only once a week and then late at night to the home of his betrothed. Silently, like a thief in the dark, he would crawl through the grass and shrubs until beneath her window. At a low signal, prearranged between them, she would slip to the door and let him in without disturbing the parents. Fearing to make a light, and perhaps welcoming that excuse to enjoy the darkness beloved by sweethearts, they would sit quietly, whispering low, until the brightening in the east betokened the break of day, and then he was off, happy and lighthearted, to his labors.

A wedding was looked forward to with much pleasure by old and young. Practically, it meant the only gathering of the settlers which was not accompanied by the work of reaping the harvest, building a cabin, planning an expedition to relieve some distant settlement, or a defense for themselves.

For all, it meant a rollicking good time; to the old people a feast, and the looking on at the merriment of their children—to the young folk, a pleasing break in the monotony of their busy lives, a day given up to fun and gossip, a day of romance, a wedding, and best of all, a dance. Therefore Alice Reynold's wedding proved a great event to the inhabitants of Fort Henry.

The day dawned bright and clear. The sun, rising like a ball of red gold, cast its yellow beams over the bare, brown hills, shining on the cabin roofs white with frost, and making the delicate weblike coat of ice on the river sparkle as if it had been sprinkled with powdered diamonds. William Martin, the groom, and his attendants, met at an appointed time to celebrate an old time-honored custom which always took place before the party started for the house of the bride. This performance was called "the race for the bottle."

A number of young men, selected by the groom, were asked to take part in this race, which was to be run over as rough and dangerous a track as could be found. The worse the road, the more ditches, bogs, trees, stumps, brush, in fact, the more obstacles of every kind, the better, as all these afforded opportunity for daring and expert horsemanship. The English fox race, now famous on three continents, while it involves risk and is sometimes dangerous, cannot, in the sense of hazard to life and limb, be compared to this race for the bottle.

On this day the run was not less exciting than usual. The horses were placed as nearly abreast as possible and the starter gave an Indian yell. Then followed the cracking of whips, the furious pounding of heavy hoofs, the commands of the contestants, and the yells of the onlookers. Away they went at a mad pace down the road. The course extended a mile straight away down the creek bottom. The first hundred yards the horses were bunched. At the ditch beyond the creek bridge a beautiful, clean limbed animal darted from among the furiously galloping horses and sailed over the deep furrow like a bird. All recognized the rider as Alfred Clarke on his black thoroughbred. Close behind was George Martin mounted on a large roan of powerful frame and long stride. Through the willows they dashed, over logs and brush heaps, up the little ridges of rising ground, and down the shallow gullies, unheeding the stinging branches and the splashing water. Half the distance covered and Alfred turned, to find the roan close behind. On a level road he would have laughed at the attempt of that horse to keep up with his racer, but he was beginning to fear that the strong limbed stallion deserved his reputation. Directly before them rose a pile of logs and matted brush, placed there by the daredevil settlers who had mapped out the route. It was too high for any horse to be put at. With pale cheek and clinched teeth Alfred touched the spurs to Roger and then threw himself forward. The gallant beast responded nobly. Up, up, up he rose, clearing all but the topmost branches. Alfred turned again and saw the giant roan make the leap without touching a twig. The next instant Roger went splash into a swamp. He sank to his knees in the soft black soil. He could move but one foot at a time, and Alfred saw at a glance he had won the race. The great weight of the roan handicapped him here. When Alfred reached the other side of the bog, where the bottle was swinging from a branch of a tree, his rival's horse was floundering hopelessly in the middle of the treacherous mire. The remaining three horsemen, who had come up by this time, seeing that it would be useless to attempt further efforts, had drawn up on the bank. With friendly shouts to Clarke, they acknowledged themselves beaten. There were no judges required for this race, because the man who reached the bottle first won it.

The five men returned to the starting point, where the victor was greeted by loud whoops. The groom got the first drink from the bottle, then came the attendants, and others in order, after which the bottle was put away to be kept as a memento of the occasion.

The party now repaired to the village and marched to the home of the bride. The hour for the observance of the marriage rites was just before the midday meal. When the groom reached the bride's home he found her in readiness. Sweet and pretty Alice looked in her gray linsey gown, perfectly plain and simple though it was, without an ornament or a ribbon. Proud indeed looked her lover as he took her hand and led her up to the waiting minister. When the whisperings had ceased the minister asked who gave this woman to be married. Alice's father answered.

"Will you take this woman to be your wedded wife, to love, cherish and protect her all the days of her life?" asked the minister.

"I will," answered a deep bass voice.

"Will you take this man to be your wedded husband, to love, honor and obey him all the days of your life?"

"I will," said Alice, in a low tone.

"I pronounce you man and wife. Those whom God has joined together let no man put asunder."

There was a brief prayer and the ceremony ended. Then followed the congratulations of relatives and friends. The felicitations were apt to be trying to the nerves of even the best tempered groom. The hand shakes, the heavy slaps on the back, and the pommeling he received at the hands of his intimate friends were as nothing compared to the anguish of mind he endured while they were kissing his wife. The young bucks would not have considered it a real wedding had they been prevented from kissing the bride, and for that matter, every girl within reach. So fast as the burly young settlers could push themselves through the densely packed rooms they kissed the bride, and then the first girl they came to.

Betty and Lydia had been Alice's maids of honor. This being Betty's first experience at a frontier wedding, it developed that she was much in need of Lydia's advice, which she had previously disdained. She had rested secure in her dignity. Poor Betty! The first man to kiss Alice was George Martin, a big, strong fellow, who gathered his brother's bride into his arms and gave her a bearish hug and a resounding kiss. Releasing her he turned toward Lydia and Betty. Lydia eluded him, but one of his great hands clasped around Betty's wrist. She tried to look haughty, but with everyone laughing, and the young man's face expressive of honest fun and happiness she found it impossible. She stood still and only turned her face a little to one side while George kissed her. The young men now made a rush for her. With blushing cheeks Betty, unable to stand her ground any longer, ran to her brother, the Colonel. He pushed her away with a laugh. She turned to Major McColloch, who held out his arms to her. With an exclamation she wrenched herself free from a young man, who had caught her hand, and flew to the Major. But alas for Betty! The Major was not proof against the temptation and he kissed her himself.

"Traitor!" cried Betty, breaking away from him.

Poor Betty was in despair. She had just made up her mind to submit when she caught sight of Wetzel's familiar figure. She ran to him and the hunter put one of his long arms around her.

"I reckon I kin take care of you, Betty," he said, a smile playing over his usually stern face. "See here, you young bucks. Betty don't want to be kissed, and if you keep on pesterin' her I'll have to scalp a few of you."

The merriment grew as the day progressed. During the wedding feast great hilarity prevailed. It culminated in the dance which followed the dinner. The long room of the block-house had been decorated with evergreens, autumn leaves and goldenrod, which were scattered profusely about, hiding the blackened walls and bare rafters. Numerous blazing pine knots, fastened on sticks which were stuck into the walls, lighted up a scene, which for color and animation could not have been surpassed.

Colonel Zane's old slave, Sam, who furnished the music, sat on a raised platform at the upper end of the hall, and the way he sawed away on his fiddle, accompanying the movements of his arm with a swaying of his body and a stamping of his heavy foot, showed he had a hearty appreciation of his own value.

Prominent among the men and women standing and sitting near the platform could be distinguished the tall forms of Jonathan Zane, Major McColloch and Wetzel, all, as usual, dressed in their hunting costumes and carrying long rifles. The other men had made more or less effort to improve their appearance. Bright homespun shirts and scarfs had replaced the everyday buckskin garments. Major McColloch was talking to Colonel Zane. The genial faces of both reflected the pleasure they felt in the enjoyment of the younger people. Jonathan Zane stood near the door. Moody and silent he watched the dance. Wetzel leaned against the wall. The black barrel of his rifle lay in the hollow of his arm. The hunter was gravely contemplating the members of the bridal party who were dancing in front of him. When the dance ended Lydia and Betty stopped before Wetzel and Betty said: "Lew, aren't you going to ask us to dance?"

The hunter looked down into the happy, gleaming faces, and smiling in his half sad way, answered: "Every man to his gifts."

"But you can dance. I want you to put aside your gun long enough to dance with me. If I waited for you to ask me, I fear I should have to wait a long time. Come, Lew, here I am asking you, and I know the other men are dying to dance with me," said Betty, coaxingly, in a roguish voice.

Wetzel never refused a request of Betty's, and so, laying aside his weapons, he danced with her, to the wonder and admiration of all. Colonel Zane clapped his hands, and everyone stared in amazement at the unprecedented sight Wetzel danced not ungracefully. He was wonderfully light on his feet. His striking figure, the long black hair, and the fancifully embroidered costume he wore contrasted strangely with Betty's slender, graceful form and pretty gray dress.

"Well, well, Lewis, I would not have believed anything but the evidence of my own eyes," said Colonel Zane, with a laugh, as Betty and Wetzel approached him.

"If all the men could dance as well as Lew, the girls would be thankful, I can assure you," said Betty.

"Betty, I declare you grow prettier every day," said old John Bennet, who was standing with the Colonel and the Major. "If I were only a young man once more I should try my chances with you, and I wouldn't give up very easily."

"I do not know, Uncle John, but I am inclined to think that if you were a young man and should come a-wooing you would not get a rebuff from me," answered Betty, smiling on the old man, of whom she was very fond.

"Miss Zane, will you dance with me?"

The voice sounded close by Betty's side. She recognized it, and an unaccountable sensation of shyness suddenly came over her. She had firmly made up her mind, should Mr. Clarke ask her to dance, that she would tell him she was tired, or engaged for that number—anything so that she could avoid dancing with him. But, now that the moment had come she either forgot her resolution or lacked the courage to keep it, for as the music commenced, she turned and without saying a word or looking at him, she placed her hand on his arm. He whirled her away. She gave a start of surprise and delight at the familiar step and then gave herself up to the charm of the dance. Supported by his strong arm she floated around the room in a sort of dream. Dancing as they did was new to the young people at the Fort—it was a style then in vogue in the east—and everyone looked on with great interest and curiosity. But all too soon the dance ended and before Betty had recovered her composure she found that her partner had led her to a secluded seat in the lower end of the hall. The bench was partly obscured from the dancers by masses of autumn leaves. "That was a very pleasant dance," said Alfred. "Miss Boggs told me you danced the round dance."

"I was much surprised and pleased," said Betty, who had indeed enjoyed it.

"It has been a delightful day," went on Alfred, seeing that Betty was still confused. "I almost killed myself in that race for the bottle this morning. I never saw such logs and brush heaps and ditches in my life. I am sure that if the fever of recklessness which seemed in the air had not suddenly seized me I would never have put my horse at such leaps."

"I heard my brother say your horse was one of the best he had ever seen, and that you rode superbly," murmured Betty.

"Well, to be honest, I would not care to take that ride again. It certainly was not fair to the horse."

"How do you like the fort by this time?"

"Miss Zane, I am learning to love this free, wild life. I really think I was made for the frontier. The odd customs and manners which seemed strange at first have become very acceptable to me now. I find everyone so honest and simple and brave. Here one must work to live, which is right. Do you know, I never worked in my life until I came to Fort Henry. My life was all uselessness, idleness."

"I can hardly believe that," answered Betty. "You have learned to dance and ride and—"

"What?" asked Alfred, as Betty hesitated.

"Never mind. It was an accomplishment with which the girls credited you," said Betty, with a little laugh.

"I suppose I did not deserve it. I heard I had a singular aptitude for discovering young ladies in distress."

"Have you become well acquainted with the boys?" asked Betty, hastening to change the subject.

"Oh, yes, particularly with your Indianized brother, Isaac. He is the finest fellow, as well as the most interesting, I ever knew. I like Colonel Zane immensely too. The dark, quiet fellow, Jack, or John, they call him, is not like your other brothers. The hunter, Wetzel, inspires me with awe. Everyone has been most kind to me and I have almost forgotten that I was a wanderer."

"I am glad to hear that," said Betty.

"Miss Zane," continued Alfred, "doubtless you have heard that I came West because I was compelled to leave my home. Please do not believe everything you hear of me. Some day I may tell you my story if you care to hear it. Suffice it to say now that I left my home of my own free will and I could go back to-morrow."

"I did not mean to imply—" began Betty, coloring.

"Of course not. But tell me about yourself. Is it not rather dull and lonesome here for you?"

"It was last winter. But I have been contented and happy this summer. Of course, it is not Philadelphia life, and I miss the excitement and gayety of my uncle's house. I knew my place was with my brothers. My aunt pleaded with me to live with her and not go to the wilderness. I had everything I wanted there—luxury, society, parties, balls, dances, friends—all that the heart of a girl could desire, but I preferred to come to this little frontier settlement. Strange choice for a girl, was it not?"

"Unusual, yes," answered Alfred, gravely. "And I cannot but wonder what motives actuated our coming to Fort Henry. I came to seek my fortune. You came to bring sunshine into the home of your brother, and left your fortune behind you. Well, your motive has the element of nobility. Mine has nothing but that of recklessness. I would like to read the future."

"I do not think it is right to have such a wish. With the veil rolled away could you work as hard, accomplish as much? I do not want to know the future. Perhaps some of it will be unhappy. I have made my choice and will cheerfully abide by it. I rather envy your being a man. You have the world to conquer. A woman—what can she do? She can knead the dough, ply the distaff, and sit by the lattice and watch and wait."

"Let us postpone such melancholy thoughts until some future day. I have not as yet said anything that I intended. I wish to tell you how sorry I am that I acted in such a rude way the night your brother came home. I do not know what made me do so, but I know I have regretted it ever since. Will you forgive me and may we not be friends?"

"I—I do not know," said Betty, surprised and vaguely troubled by the earnest light in his eyes.

"But why? Surely you will make some little allowance for a naturally quick temper, and you know you did not—that you were—"

"Yes, I remember I was hasty and unkind. But I made amends, or at least, I tried to do so."

"Try to overlook my stupidity. I will not give up until you forgive me. Consider how much you can avoid by being generous."

"Very well, then, I will forgive you," said Betty, who had arrived at the conclusion that this young man was one of determination.

"Thank you. I promise you shall never regret it. And the sprained ankle? It must be well, as I noticed you danced beautifully."

"I am compelled to believe what the girls say—that you are inclined to the language of compliment. My ankle is nearly well, thank you. It hurts a little now and then."

"Speaking of your accident reminds me of the day it happened," said Alfred, watching her closely. He desired to tease her a little, but he was not sure of his ground. "I had been all day in the woods with nothing but my thoughts—mostly unhappy ones—for company. When I met you I pretended to be surprised. As a matter of fact I was not, for I had followed your dog. He took a liking to me and I was extremely pleased, I assure you. Well, I saw your face a moment before you knew I was as near you. When you heard my footsteps you turned with a relieved and joyous cry. When you saw whom it was your glad expression changed, and if I had been a hostile Wyandot you could not have looked more unfriendly. Such a woeful, tear-stained face I never saw."

"Mr. Clarke, please do not speak any more of that," said Betty with dignity. "I desire that you forget it."

"I will forget all except that it was I who had the happiness of finding you and of helping you. I cannot forget that. I am sure we should never have been friends but for that accident."

"There is Isaac. He is looking for me," answered Betty, rising.

"Wait a moment longer—please. He will find you," said Alfred, detaining her. "Since you have been so kind I have grown bolder. May I come over to see you to-morrow?"

He looked straight down into the dark eyes which wavered and fell before he had completed his question.

"There is Isaac. He cannot see me here. I must go."

"But not before telling me. What is the good of your forgiving me if I may not see you. Please say yes."

"You may come," answered Betty, half amused and half provoked at his persistence. "I should think you would know that such permission invariably goes with a young woman's forgiveness."

"Hello, here you are. What a time I have had in finding you," said Isaac, coming up with flushed face and eyes bright with excitement. "Alfred, what do you mean by hiding the belle of the dance away like this? I want to dance with you, Betts. I am having a fine time. I have not danced anything but Indian dances for ages. Sorry to take her away, Alfred. I can see she doesn't want to go. Ha! Ha!" and with a mischievous look at both of them he led Betty away.

Alfred kept his seat awhile lost in thought. Suddenly he remembered that it would look strange if he did not make himself agreeable, so he got up and found a partner. He danced with Alice, Lydia, and the other young ladies. After an hour he slipped away to his room. He wished to be alone. He wanted to think; to decide whether it would be best for him to stay at the fort, or ride away in the darkness and never return. With the friendly touch of Betty's hand the madness with which he had been battling for weeks rushed over him stronger than ever. The thrill of that soft little palm remained with him, and he pressed the hand it had touched to his lips.

For a long hour he sat by his window. He could dimly see the broad winding river, with its curtain of pale gray mist, and beyond, the dark outline of the forest. A cool breeze from the water fanned his heated brow, and the quiet and solitude soothed him.

CHAPTER IV.

"Good morning, Harry. Where are you going so early?" called Betty from the doorway.

A lad was passing down the path in front of Colonel Zane's house as Betty hailed him. He carried a rifle almost as long as himself.

"Mornin', Betty. I am goin' 'cross the crick fer that turkey I hear gobblin'," he answered, stopping at the gate and smiling brightly at Betty.

"Hello, Harry Bennet. Going after that turkey? I have heard him several mornings and he must be a big, healthy gobbler," said Colonel Zane, stepping to the door. "You are going to have company. Here comes Wetzel."

"Good morning, Lew. Are you too off on a turkey hunt?" said Betty.

"Listen," said the hunter, as he stopped and leaned against the gate. They listened. All was quiet save for the tinkle of a cow-bell in the pasture adjoining the Colonel's barn. Presently the silence was broken by a long, shrill, peculiar cry.

"Chug-a-lug, chug-a-lug, chug-a-lug, chug-a-lug-chug."

"Well, it's a turkey, all right, and I'll bet a big gobbler," remarked Colonel Zane, as the cry ceased.

"Has Jonathan heard it?" asked Wetzel.

"Not that I know of. Why do you ask?" said the Colonel, in a low tone. "Look here, Lew, is that not a genuine call?"

"Goodbye, Harry, be sure and bring me a turkey," called Betty, as she disappeared.

"I calkilate it's a real turkey," answered the hunter, and motioning the lad to stay behind, he shouldered his rifle and passed swiftly down the path.

Of all the Wetzel family—a family noted from one end of the frontier to the other—Lewis was as the most famous.

The early history of West Virginia and Ohio is replete with the daring deeds of this wilderness roamer, this lone hunter and insatiable Nemesis, justly called the greatest Indian slayer known to men.

When Lewis was about twenty years old, and his brothers John and Martin little older, they left their Virginia home for a protracted hunt. On their return they found the smoking ruins of the home, the mangled remains of father and mother, the naked and violated bodies of their sisters, and the scalped and bleeding corpse of a baby brother.

Lewis Wetzel swore sleepless and eternal vengeance on the whole Indian race. Terribly did he carry out that resolution. From that time forward he lived most of the time in the woods, and an Indian who crossed his trail was a doomed man. The various Indian tribes gave him different names. The Shawnees called him "Long Knife;" the Hurons, "Destroyer;" the Delawares, "Death Wind," and any one of these names would chill the heart of the stoutest warrior.

To most of the famed pioneer hunters of the border, Indian fighting was only a side issue—generally a necessary one—but with Wetzel it was the business of his life. He lived solely to kill Indians. He plunged recklessly into the strife, and was never content unless roaming the wilderness solitudes, trailing the savages to their very homes and ambushing the village bridlepath like a panther waiting for his prey. Often in the gray of the morning the Indians, sleeping around their camp fire, were awakened by a horrible, screeching yell. They started up in terror only to fall victims to the tomahawk of their merciless foe, or to hear a rifle shot and get a glimpse of a form with flying black hair disappearing with wonderful quickness in the forest. Wetzel always left death behind him, and he was gone before his demoniac yell ceased to echo throughout the woods. Although often pursued, he invariably eluded the Indians, for he was the fleetest runner on the border.

For many years he was considered the right hand of the defense of the fort. The Indians held him in superstitious dread, and the fact that he was known to be in the settlement had averted more than one attack by the Indians.

Many regarded Wetzel as a savage, a man who was mad for the blood of the red men, and without one redeeming quality. But this was an unjust opinion. When that restless fever for revenge left him—it was not always with him—he was quiet and peaceable. To those few who knew him well he was even amiable. But Wetzel, although known to everyone, cared for few. He spent little time in the settlements and rarely spoke except when addressed.

Nature had singularly fitted him for his pre-eminent position among scouts and hunters. He was tall and broad across the shoulders; his strength, agility and endurance were marvelous; he had an eagle eye, the sagacity of the bloodhound, and that intuitive knowledge which plays such an important part in a hunter's life. He knew not fear. He was daring where daring was the wiser part. Crafty, tireless and implacable, Wetzel was incomparable in his vocation.

His long raven-black hair, of which he was vain, when combed out reached to within a foot of the ground. He had a rare scalp, one for which the Indians would have bartered anything.

A favorite Indian decoy, and the most fatal one, was the imitation of the call of the wild turkey. It had often happened that men from the settlements who had gone out for a turkey which had been gobbling, had not returned.

For several mornings Wetzel had heard a turkey call, and becoming suspicious of it, had determined to satisfy himself. On the east side of the creek hill there was a cavern some fifty or sixty yards above the water. The entrance to this cavern was concealed by vines and foliage. Wetzel knew of it, and, crossing the stream some distance above, he made a wide circuit and came up back of the cave. Here he concealed himself in a clump of bushes and waited. He had not been there long when directly below him sounded the cry, "Chug-a-lug, Chug-a-lug, Chug-a-lug." At the same time the polished head and brawny shoulders of an Indian warrior rose out of the cavern. Peering cautiously around, the savage again gave the peculiar cry, and then sank back out of sight. Wetzel screened himself safely in his position and watched the savage repeat the action at least ten times before he made up his mind that the Indian was alone in the cave. When he had satisfied himself of this he took a quick aim at the twisted tuft of hair and fired. Without waiting to see the result of his shot—so well did he trust his unerring aim—he climbed down the steep bank and brushing aside the vines entered the cave. A stalwart Indian lay in the entrance with his face pressed down on the vines. He still clutched in his sinewy fingers the buckhorn mouthpiece with which he had made the calls that had resulted in his death.

"Huron," muttered the hunter to himself as he ran the keen edge of his knife around the twisted tuft of hair and tore off the scalp-lock.

The cave showed evidence of having been inhabited for some time. There was a cunningly contrived fireplace made of stones, against which pieces of birch bark were placed in such a position that not a ray of light could get out of the cavern. The bed of black coals between the stones still smoked; a quantity of parched corn lay on a little rocky shelf which jutted out from the wall; a piece of jerked meat and a buckskin pouch hung from a peg.

Suddenly Wetzel dropped on his knees and began examining the footprints in the sandy floor of the cavern. He measured the length and width of the dead warrior's foot. He closely scrutinized every moccasin print. He crawled to the opening of the cavern and carefully surveyed the moss.

Then he rose to his feet. A remarkable transformation had come over him during the last few moments. His face had changed; the calm expression was replaced by one sullen and fierce: his lips were set in a thin, cruel line, and a strange light glittered in his eyes.

He slowly pursued a course lending gradually down to the creek. At intervals he would stop and listen. The strange voices of the woods were not mysteries to him. They were more familiar to him than the voices of men.

He recalled that, while on his circuit over the ridge to get behind the cavern, he had heard the report of a rifle far off in the direction of the chestnut grove, but, as that was a favorite place of the settlers for shooting squirrels, he had not thought anything of it at the time. Now it had a peculiar significance. He turned abruptly from the trail he had been following and plunged down the steep hill. Crossing the creek he took to the cover of the willows, which grew profusely along the banks, and striking a sort of bridle path he started on a run. He ran easily, as though accustomed to that mode of travel, and his long strides covered a couple of miles in short order. Coming to the rugged bluff, which marked the end of the ridge, he stopped and walked slowly along the edge of the water. He struck the trail of the Indians where it crossed the creek, just where he expected. There were several moccasin tracks in the wet sand and, in some of the depressions made by the heels the rounded edges of the imprints were still smooth and intact. The little pools of muddy water, which still lay in these hollows, were other indications to his keen eyes that the Indians had passed this point early that morning.

The trail led up the hill and far into the woods. Never in doubt the hunter kept on his course; like a shadow he passed from tree to tree and from bush to bush; silently, cautiously, but rapidly he followed the tracks of the Indians. When he had penetrated the dark backwoods of the Black Forest tangled underbrush, windfalls and gullies crossed his path and rendered fast trailing impossible. Before these almost impassible barriers he stopped and peered on all sides, studying the lay of the land, the deadfalls, the gorges, and all the time keeping in mind the probable route of the redskins. Then he turned aside to avoid the roughest travelling. Sometimes these detours were only a few hundred feet long; often they were miles; but nearly always he struck the trail again. This almost superhuman knowledge of the Indian's ways of traversing the forest, which probably no man could have possessed without giving his life to the hunting of Indians, was the one feature of Wetzel's woodcraft which placed him so far above other hunters, and made him so dreaded by the savages.

Descending a knoll he entered a glade where the trees grew farther apart and the underbrush was only knee high. The black soil showed that the tract of land had been burned over. On the banks of a babbling brook which wound its way through this open space, the hunter found tracks which brought an exclamation from him. Clearly defined in the soft earth was the impress of a white man's moccasin. The footprints of an Indian toe inward. Those of a white man are just the opposite. A little farther on Wetzel came to a slight crushing of the moss, where he concluded some heavy body had fallen. As he had seen the tracks of a buck and doe all the way down the brook he thought it probable one of them had been shot by the white hunter. He found a pool of blood surrounded by moccasin prints; and from that spot the trail led straight toward the west, showing that for some reason the Indians had changed their direction.

This new move puzzled the hunter, and he leaned against the trunk of a tree, while he revolved in his mind the reasons for this abrupt departure—for such he believed it. The trail he had followed for miles was the devious trail of hunting Indians, stealing slowly and stealthily along watching for their prey, whether it be man or beast. The trail toward the west was straight as the crow flies; the moccasin prints that indented the soil were wide apart, and to an inexperienced eye looked like the track of one Indian. To Wetzel this indicated that the Indians had all stepped in the tracks of a leader.

As was usually his way, Wetzel decided quickly. He had calculated that there were eight Indians in all, not counting the chief whom he had shot. This party of Indians had either killed or captured the white man who had been hunting. Wetzel believed that a part of the Indians would push on with all possible speed, leaving some of their number to ambush the trail or double back on it to see if they were pursued.

An hour of patient waiting, in which he never moved from his position, proved the wisdom of his judgment. Suddenly, away at the other end of the grove, he caught a flash of brown, of a living, moving something, like the flitting of a bird behind a tree. Was it a bird or a squirrel? Then again he saw it, almost lost in the shade of the forest. Several minutes passed, in which Wetzel never moved and hardly breathed. The shadow had disappeared behind a tree. He fixed his keen eyes on that tree and presently a dark object glided from it and darted stealthily forward to another tree. One, two, three dark forms followed the first one. They were Indian warriors, and they moved so quickly that only the eyes of a woodsman like Wetzel could have discerned their movements at that distance.

Probably most hunters would have taken to their heels while there was yet time. The thought did not occur to Wetzel. He slowly raised the hammer of his rifle. As the Indians came into plain view he saw they did not suspect his presence, but were returning on the trail in their customary cautious manner.

When the first warrior reached a big oak tree some two hundred yards distant, the long, black barrel of the hunter's rifle began slowly, almost imperceptibly, to rise, and as it reached a level the savage stepped forward from the tree. With the sharp report of the weapon he staggered and fell.

Wetzel sprang up and knowing that his only escape was in rapid flight, with his well known yell, he bounded off at the top of his speed. The remaining Indians discharged their guns at the fleeing, dodging figure, but without effect. So rapidly did he dart in and out among the trees that an effectual aim was impossible. Then, with loud yells, the Indians, drawing their tomahawks, started in pursuit, expecting soon to overtake their victim.

In the early years of his Indian hunting, Wetzel had perfected himself in a practice which had saved his life many tunes, and had added much to his fame. He could reload his rifle while running at topmost speed. His extraordinary fleetness enabled him to keep ahead of his pursuers until his rifle was reloaded. This trick he now employed. Keeping up his uneven pace until his gun was ready, he turned quickly and shot the nearest Indian dead in his tracks. The next Indian had by this time nearly come up with him and close enough to throw his tomahawk, which whizzed dangerously near Wetzel's head. But he leaped forward again and soon his rifle was reloaded. Every time he looked around the Indians treed, afraid to face his unerring weapon. After running a mile or more in this manner, he reached an open space in the woods where he wheeled suddenly on his pursuers. The foremost Indian jumped behind a tree, but, as it did not entirely screen his body, he, too, fell a victim to the hunter's aim. The Indian must have been desperately wounded, for his companion now abandoned the chase and went to his assistance. Together they disappeared in the forest.

Wetzel, seeing that he was no longer pursued, slackened his pace and proceeded thoughtfully toward the settlement.

* * * * * * * * * * * * * *

That same day, several hours after Wetzel's departure in quest of the turkey, Alfred Clarke strolled over from the fort and found Colonel Zane in the yard. The Colonel was industriously stirring the contents of a huge copper kettle which swung over a brisk wood fire. The honeyed fragrance of apple-butter mingled with the pungent odor of burning hickory.

"Morning, Alfred, you see they have me at it," was the Colonel's salute.

"So I observe," answered Alfred, as he seated himself on the wood-pile. "What is it you are churning so vigorously?"

"Apple-butter, my boy, apple-butter. I don't allow even Bessie to help when I am making apple-butter."

"Colonel Zane, I have come over to ask a favor. Ever since you notified us that you intended sending an expedition up the river I have been worried about my horse Roger. He is too light for a pack horse, and I cannot take two horses."

"I'll let you have the bay. He is big and strong enough. That black horse of yours is a beauty. You leave Roger with me and if you never come back I'll be in a fine horse. Ha, Ha! But, seriously, Clarke, this proposed trip is a hazardous undertaking, and if you would rather stay—"

"You misunderstand me," quickly replied Alfred, who had flushed. "I do not care about myself. I'll go and take my medicine. But I do mind about my horse."

"That's right. Always think of your horses. I'll have Sam take the best of care of Roger."

"What is the nature of this excursion, and how long shall we be gone?"

"Jonathan will guide the party. He says it will take six weeks if you have pleasant weather. You are to go by way of Short Creek, where you will help put up a blockhouse. Then you go to Fort Pitt. There you will embark on a raft with the supplies I need and make the return journey by water. You will probably smell gunpowder before you get back."

"What shall we do with the horses?"

"Bring them along with you on the raft, of course."

"That is a new way to travel with horses," said Alfred, looking dubiously at the swift river. "Will there be any way to get news from Fort Henry while we are away?"

"Yes, there will be several runners."

"Mr. Clarke, I am going to feed my pets. Would you like to see them?" asked a voice which brought Alfred to his feet. He turned and saw Betty. Her dog followed her, carrying a basket.

"I shall be delighted," answered Alfred. "Have you more pets than Tige and Madcap?"

"Oh, yes, indeed. I have a bear, six squirrels, one of them white, and some pigeons."

Betty led the way to an enclosure adjoining Colonel Zane's barn. It was about twenty feet square, made of pine saplings which had been split and driven firmly into the ground. As Betty took down a bar and opened the small gate a number of white pigeons fluttered down from the roof of the barn, several of them alighting on her shoulders. A half-grown black bear came out of a kennel and shuffled toward her. He was unmistakably glad to see her, but he avoided going near Tige, and looked doubtfully at the young man. But after Alfred had stroked his head and had spoken to him he seemed disposed to be friendly, for he sniffed around Alfred's knees and then stood up and put his paws against the young man's shoulders.

"Here, Caesar, get down," said Betty. "He always wants to wrestle, especially with anyone of whom he is not suspicious. He is very tame and will do almost anything. Indeed, you would marvel at his intelligence. He never forgets an injury. If anyone plays a trick on him you may be sure that person will not get a second opportunity. The night we caught him Tige chased him up a tree and Jonathan climbed the tree and lassoed him. Ever since he has evinced a hatred of Jonathan, and if I should leave Tige alone with him there would be a terrible fight. But for that I could allow Caesar to run free about the yard."

"He looks bright and sagacious," remarked Alfred.

"He is, but sometimes he gets into mischief. I nearly died laughing one day. Bessie, my brother's wife, you know, had the big kettle on the fire, just as you saw it a moment ago, only this time she was boiling down maple syrup. Tige was out with some of the men and I let Caesar loose awhile. If there is anything he loves it is maple sugar, so when he smelled the syrup he pulled down the kettle and the hot syrup went all over his nose. Oh, his howls were dreadful to hear. The funniest part about it was he seemed to think it was intentional, for he remained sulky and cross with me for two weeks."

"I can understand your love for animals," said Alfred. "I think there are many interesting things about wild creatures. There are comparatively few animals down in Virginia where I used to live, and my opportunities to study them have been limited."

"Here are my squirrels," said Betty, unfastening the door of a cage. A number of squirrels ran out. Several jumped to the ground. One perched on top of the box. Another sprang on Betty's shoulder. "I fasten them up every night, for I'm afraid the weasels and foxes will get them. The white squirrel is the only albino we have seen around here. It took Jonathan weeks to trap him, but once captured he soon grew tame. Is he not pretty?"

"He certainly is. I never saw one before; in fact, I did not know such a beautiful little animal existed," answered Alfred, looking in admiration at the graceful creature, as he leaped from the shelf to Betty's arm and ate from her hand, his great, bushy white tail arching over his back and his small pink eyes shining.

"There! Listen," said Betty. "Look at the fox squirrel, the big brownish red one. I call him the Captain, because he always wants to boss the others. I had another fox squirrel, older than this fellow, and he ran things to suit himself, until one day the grays united their forces and routed him. I think they would have killed him had I not freed him. Well, this one is commencing the same way. Do you hear that odd clicking noise? That comes from the Captain's teeth, and he is angry and jealous because I show so much attention to this one. He always does that, and he would fight too if I were not careful. It is a singular fact, though, that the white squirrel has not even a little pugnacity. He either cannot fight, or he is too well behaved. Here, Mr. Clarke, show Snowball this nut, and then hide it in your pocket, and see him find it."

Alfred did as he was told, except that while he pretended to put the nut in his pocket he really kept it concealed in his hand.

The pet squirrel leaped lightly on Alfred's shoulder, ran over his breast, peeped in all his pockets, and even pushed his cap to one side of his head. Then he ran down Alfred's arm, sniffed in his coat sleeve, and finally wedged a cold little nose between his closed fingers.

"There, he has found it, even though you did not play fair," said Betty, laughing gaily.

Alfred never forgot the picture Betty made standing there with the red cap on her dusky hair, and the loving smile upon her face as she talked to her pets. A white fan-tail pigeon had alighted on her shoulder and was picking daintily at the piece of cracker she held between her lips. The squirrels were all sitting up, each with a nut in his little paws, and each with an alert and cunning look in the corner of his eye, to prevent, no doubt, being surprised out of a portion of his nut. Caesar was lying on all fours, growling and tearing at his breakfast, while the dog looked on with a superior air, as if he knew they would not have had any breakfast but for him.

"Are you fond of canoeing and fishing?" asked Betty, as they returned to the house.

"Indeed I am. Isaac has taken me out on the river often. Canoeing may be pleasant for a girl, but I never knew one who cared for fishing."

"Now you behold one. I love dear old Izaak Walton. Of course, you have read his books?"

"I am ashamed to say I have not."

"And you say you are a fisherman? Well, you haste a great pleasure in store, as well as an opportunity to learn something of the 'contemplative man's recreation.' I shall lend you the books."

"I have not seen a book since I came to Fort Henry."

"I have a fine little library, and you are welcome to any of my books. But to return to fishing. I love it, and yet I nearly always allow the fish to go free. Sometimes I bring home a pretty sunfish, place him in a tub of water, watch him and try to tame him. But I must admit failure. It is the association which makes fishing so delightful. The canoe gliding down a swift stream, the open air, the blue sky, the birds and trees and flowers—these are what I love. Come and see my canoe."

Thus Betty rattled on as she led the way through the sitting-room and kitchen to Colonel Zane's magazine and store-house which opened into the kitchen. This little low-roofed hut contained a variety of things. Boxes, barrels and farming implements filled one corner; packs of dried skins were piled against the wall; some otter and fox pelts were stretched on the wall, and a number of powder kegs lined a shelf. A slender canoe swung from ropes thrown over the rafters. Alfred slipped it out of the loops and carried it outside.

The canoe was a superb specimen of Indian handiwork. It had a length of fourteen feet and was made of birch bark, stretched over a light framework of basswood. The bow curved gracefully upward, ending in a carved image representing a warrior's head. The sides were beautifully ornamented and decorated in fanciful Indian designs.

"My brother's Indian guide, Tomepomehala, a Shawnee chief, made it for me. You see this design on the bow. The arrow and the arm mean in Indian language, 'The race is to the swift and the strong.' The canoe is very light. See, I can easily carry it," said Betty, lifting it from the grass.

She ran into the house and presently came out with two rods, a book and a basket.

"These are Jack's rods. He cut them out of the heart of ten-year-old basswood trees, so he says. We must be careful of them."

Alfred examined the rods with the eye of a connoisseur and pronounced them perfect.

"These rods have been made by a lover of the art. Anyone with half an eye could see that. What shall we use for bait?" he said.

51

"Sam got me some this morning."

"Did you expect to go?" asked Alfred, looking up in surprise.

"Yes, I intended going, and as you said you were coming over, I meant to ask you to accompany me."

"That was kind of you."

"Where are you young people going?" called Colonel Zane, stopping in his task.

"We are going down to the sycamore," answered Betty.

"Very well. But be certain and stay on this side of the creek and do not go out on the river," said the Colonel.

"Why, Eb, what do you mean? One might think Mr. Clarke and I were children," exclaimed Betty.

"You certainly aren't much more. But that is not my reason. Never mind the reason. Do as I say or do not go," said Colonel Zane.

"All right, brother. I shall not forget," said Betty, soberly, looking at the Colonel. He had not spoken in his usual teasing way, and she was at a loss to understand him. "Come, Mr. Clarke, you carry the canoe and follow me down this path and look sharp for roots and stones or you may trip."

"Where is Isaac?" asked Alfred, as he lightly swung the canoe over his shoulder.

"He took his rifle and went up to the chestnut grove an hour or more ago."

A few minutes' walk down the willow skirted path and they reached the creek. Here it was a narrow stream, hardly fifty feet wide, shallow, and full of stones over which the clear brown water rushed noisily.

"Is it not rather risky going down there?" asked Alfred as he noticed the swift current and the numerous boulders poking treacherous heads just above the water.

"Of course. That is the great pleasure in canoeing," said Betty, calmly. "If you would rather walk—"

"No, I'll go if I drown. I was thinking of you."

"It is safe enough if you can handle a paddle," said Betty, with a smile at his hesitation. "And, of course, if your partner in the canoe sits trim."

"Perhaps you had better allow me to use the paddle. Where did you learn to steer a canoe?"

"I believe you are actually afraid. Why, I was born on the Potomac, and have used a paddle since I was old enough to lift one. Come, place the canoe in here and we will keep to the near shore until we reach the bend. There is a little fall just below this and I love to shoot it."

He steadied the canoe with one hand while he held out the other to help her, but she stepped nimbly aboard without his assistance.

"Wait a moment while I catch some crickets and grasshoppers."

"Gracious! What a fisherman. Don't you know we have had frost?"

"That's so," said Alfred, abashed by her simple remark.

"But you might find some crickets under those logs," said Betty. She laughed merrily at the awkward spectacle made by Alfred crawling over the ground, improvising a sort of trap out of his hat, and pouncing down on a poor little insect.

"Now, get in carefully, and give the canoe a push. There, we are off," she said, taking up the paddle.

The little bark glided slowly down stream at first hugging the bank as though reluctant to trust itself to the deeper water, and then gathering headway as a few gentle strokes of the paddle swerved it into the current. Betty knelt on one knee and skillfully plied the paddle, using the Indian stroke in which the paddle was not removed from the water.

"This is great!" exclaimed Alfred, as he leaned back in the bow facing her. "There is nothing more to be desired. This beautiful clear stream, the air so fresh, the gold lined banks, the autumn leaves, a guide who—"

"Look," said Betty. "There is the fall over which we must pass."

He looked ahead and saw that they were swiftly approaching two huge stones that reared themselves high out of the water. They were only a few yards apart and surrounded by smaller rocks, about high the water rushed white with foam.

"Please do not move!" cried Betty, her eyes shining bright with excitement.

Indeed, the situation was too novel for Alfred to do anything but feel a keen enjoyment. He had made up his mind that he was sure to get a ducking, but, as he watched Betty's easy, yet vigorous sweeps with the paddle, and her smiling, yet resolute lips, he felt reassured. He could see that the fall was not a great one, only a few feet, but one of those glancing sheets of water like a mill race, and he well knew that if they struck a stone disaster would be theirs. Twenty feet above the white-capped wave which marked the fall, Betty gave a strong forward pull on the paddle, a deep stroke which momentarily retarded their progress even in that swift current, and then, a short backward stroke, far under the stern of the canoe, and the little vessel turned straight, almost in the middle of the course between the two rocks. As she raised her paddle into the canoe and smiled at the fascinated young man, the bow dipped, and with that peculiar downward movement, that swift, exhilarating rush so dearly loved by canoeists, they shot down the smooth incline of water, were lost for a moment in a white cloud of mist, and in another they coated into a placid pool.

"Was not that delightful?" she asked, with just a little conscious pride glowing in her dark eyes.

"Miss Zane, it was more than that. I apologize for my suspicions. You have admirable skill. I only wish that on my voyage down the River of Life I could have such a sure eye and hand to guide me through the dangerous reefs and rapids."

"You are poetical," said Betty, who laughed, and at the same time blushed slightly. "But you are right about the guide. Jonathan says 'always get a good guide,' and as guiding is his work he ought to know. But this has nothing in common with fishing, and here is my favorite place under the old sycamore."

With a long sweep of the paddle she ran the canoe alongside a stone beneath a great tree which spread its long branches over the creek and shaded the pool. It was a grand old tree and must have guarded that sylvan spot for centuries. The gnarled and knotted trunk was scarred and seamed with the ravages of time. The upper part was dead. Long limbs extended skyward, gaunt and bare, like the masts of a storm beaten vessel. The lower branches were white and shining, relieved here and there by brown patches of bark which curled up like old parchment as they shelled away from the inner bark. The ground beneath the tree was carpeted with a velvety moss with little plots of grass and clusters of maiden-hair fern growing on it. From under an overhanging rock on the bank a spring of crystal water bubbled forth.

Alfred rigged up the rods, and baiting a hook directed Betty to throw her line well out into the current and let it float down into the eddy. She complied, and hardly had the line reached the circle of the eddy, where bits of white foam floated round and round, when there was a slight splash, a scream from Betty and she was standing up in the canoe holding tightly to her rod.

"Be careful!" exclaimed Alfred. "Sit down. You will have the canoe upset in a moment. Hold your rod steady and keep the line taut. That's right. Now lead him round toward me. There," and grasping the line he lifted a fine rock bass over the side of the canoe.

"Oh! I always get so intensely excited," breathlessly cried Betty. "I can't help it. Jonathan always declares he will never take me fishing again. Let me see the fish. It's a goggle-eye. Isn't he pretty? Look how funny he bats his eyes," and she laughed gleefully as she gingerly picked up the fish by the tail and dropped him into the water. "Now, Mr. Goggle-eye, if you are wise, in future you will beware of tempting looking bugs."

For an hour they had splendid sport. The pool teemed with sunfish. The bait would scarcely touch the water when the little orange colored fellows would rush for it. Now and then a black bass darted wickedly through the school of sunfish and stole the morsel from them. Or a sharp-nosed fiery-eyed pickerel—vulture of the water—rising to the surface, and, supreme in his indifference to man or fish, would swim lazily round until he had discovered the cause of all this commotion among the smaller fishes, and then, opening wide his jaws would take the bait with one voracious snap.

Presently something took hold of Betty's line and moved out toward the middle of the pool. She struck and the next instant her rod was bent double and the tip under water.

"Pull your rod up!" shouted Alfred. "Here, hand it to me."

But it was too late. A surge right and left, a vicious tug, and Betty's line floated on the surface of the water.

"Now, isn't that too bad? He has broken my line. Goodness, I never before felt such a strong fish. What shall I do?"

"You should be thankful you were not pulled in. I have been in a state of fear ever since we commenced fishing. You move round in this canoe as though it were a raft. Let me paddle out to that little ripple and try once there; then we will stop. I know you are tired."

Near the center of the pool a half submerged rock checked the current and caused a little ripple of the water. Several times Alfred had seen the dark shadow of a large fish followed by a swirl of the water, and the frantic leaping of little bright-sided minnows in all directions. As his hook, baited with a lively shiner, floated over the spot, a long, yellow object shot from out that shaded lair. There was a splash, not unlike that made by the sharp edge of a paddle impelled by a short, powerful stroke, the minnow disappeared, and the broad tail of the fish flapped on the water. The instant Alfred struck, the water boiled and the big fish leaped clear into the air, shaking himself convulsively to get rid of the hook. He made mad rushes up and down the pool, under the canoe, into the swift current and against the rocks, but all to no avail. Steadily Alfred increased the strain on the line and gradually it began to tell, for the plunges of the fish became shorter and less frequent. Once again, in a last magnificent effort, he leaped straight into the air, and failing to get loose, gave up the struggle and was drawn gasping and exhausted to the side of the canoe.

"Are you afraid to touch him?" asked Alfred.

"Indeed I am not," answered Betty.

"Then run your hand gently down the line, slip your fingers in under his gills and lift him over the side carefully."

"Five pounds," exclaimed Alfred, when the fish lay at his feet. "This is the largest black bass I ever caught. It is pity to take such a beautiful fish out of his element."

"Let him go, then. May I?" said Betty.

"No, you have allowed them all to go, even the pickerel which I think ought to be killed. We will keep this fellow alive, and place him in that nice clear pool over in the fort-yard."

"I like to watch you play a fish," said Betty. "Jonathan always hauls them right out. You are so skillful. You let this fish run so far and then you checked him. Then you gave him a line to go the other way, and no doubt he felt free once more when you stopped him again."

"You are expressing a sentiment which has been, is, and always will be particularly pleasing to the fair sex, I believe," observed Alfred, smiling rather grimly as he wound up his line.

"Would you mind being explicit?" she questioned.

Alfred had laughed and was about to answer when the whip-like crack of a rifle came from the hillside. The echoes of the shot reverberated from hill to hill and were finally lost far down the valley.

"What can that be?" exclaimed Alfred anxiously, recalling Colonel Zane's odd manner when they were about to leave the house.

"I am not sure, but I think that is my turkey, unless Lew Wetzel happened to miss his aim," said Betty, laughing. "And that is such an unprecedented thing that it can hardly be considered. Turkeys are scarce this season. Jonathan says the foxes and wolves ate up the broods. Lew heard this turkey calling and he made little Harry Bennet, who had started out with his gun, stay at home and went after Mr. Gobbler himself."

"Is that all? Well, that is nothing to get alarmed about, is it? I actually had a feeling of fear, or a presentiment, we might say."

They beached the canoe and spread out the lunch in the shade near the spring. Alfred threw himself at length upon the grass and Betty sat leaning against the tree. She took a biscuit in one hand, a pickle in the other, and began to chat volubly to Alfred of her school life, and of Philadelphia, and the friends she had made there. At length, remarking his abstraction, she said: "You are not listening to me."

"I beg your pardon. My thoughts did wander. I was thinking of my mother. Something about you reminds me of her. I do not know what, unless it is that little mannerism you have of pursing up your lips when you hesitate or stop to think."

"Tell me of her," said Betty, seeing his softened mood.

"My mother was very beautiful, and as good as she was lovely. I never had a care until my father died. Then she married again, and as I did not get on with my step-father I ran away from home. I have not been in Virginia for four years."

"Do you get homesick?"

"Indeed I do. While at Fort Pitt I used to have spells of the blues which lasted for days. For a time I felt more contented here. But I fear the old fever of restlessness will come over me again. I can speak freely to you because I know you will understand, and I feel sure of your sympathy. My father wanted me to be a minister. He sent me to the theological seminary at Princeton, where for two years I tried to study. Then my father died. I went home and looked after things until my mother married again. That changed everything for me. I ran away and have since been a wanderer. I feel that I am not lazy, that I am not afraid of work, but four years have drifted by and I have nothing to show for it. I am discouraged. Perhaps that is wrong, but tell me how I can help it. I have not the stoicism of the hunter, Wetzel, nor have I the philosophy of your brother. I could not be content to sit on my doorstep and smoke my pipe and watch the wheat and corn grow. And then, this life of the borderman, environed as it is by untold dangers, leads me, fascinates me, and yet appalls me with the fear that here I shall fall a victim to an Indian's bullet or spear, and find a nameless grave."

A long silence ensued. Alfred had spoken quietly, but with an undercurrent of bitterness that saddened Betty. For the first time she saw a shadow of pain in his eyes. She looked away down the valley, not seeing the brown and gold hills boldly defined against the blue sky, nor the beauty of the river as the setting sun cast a ruddy glow on the water. Her companion's words had touched an unknown chord in her heart. When finally she turned to answer him a beautiful light shone in her eyes, a light that shines not on land or sea—the light of woman's hope.

"Mr. Clarke," she said, and her voice was soft and low, "I am only a girl, but I can understand. You are unhappy. Try to rise above it. Who knows what will befall this little settlement? It may be swept away by the savages, and it may grow to be a mighty city. It must take that chance. So must you, so must we all take chances. You are here. Find your work and do it cheerfully, honestly, and let the future take care of itself. And let me say—do not be offended—beware of idleness and drink. They are as great a danger—nay, greater than the Indians."

"Miss Zane, if you were to ask me not to drink I would never touch a drop again," said Alfred, earnestly.

"I did not ask that," answered Betty, flushing slightly. "But I shall remember it as a promise and some day I may ask it of you."

He looked wonderingly at the girl beside him. He had spent most of his life among educated and cultured people. He had passed several years in the backwoods. But with all his experience with people he had to confess that this young woman was as a revelation to him. She could ride like an Indian and shoot like a hunter. He had heard that she could run almost as swiftly as her brothers. Evidently she feared nothing, for he had just seen an example of her courage in a deed that had tried even his own nerve, and, withal, she was a bright, happy girl, earnest and true, possessing all the softer graces of his sisters, and that exquisite touch of feminine delicacy and refinement which appeals more to men than any other virtue.

"Have you not met Mr. Miller before he came here from Fort Pitt?" asked Betty.

"Why do you ask?"

"I think he mentioned something of the kind."

"What else did he say?"

"Why—Mr. Clarke, I hardly remember."

"I see," said Alfred, his face darkening. "He has talked about me. I do not care what he said. I knew him at Fort Pitt, and we had trouble there. I venture to say he has told no one about it. He certainly would not shine in the story. But I am not a tattler."

"It is not very difficult to see that you do not like him. Jonathan does not, either. He says Mr. Miller was friendly with McKee, and the notorious Simon Girty, the soldiers who deserted from Fort Pitt and went to the Indians. The girls like him however."

"Usually if a man is good looking and pleasant that is enough for the girls. I noticed that he paid you a great deal of attention at the dance. He danced three times with you."

"Did he? How observing you are," said Betty, giving him a little sidelong glance. "Well, he is very agreeable, and he dances better than many of the young men."

"I wonder if Wetzel got the turkey. I have heard no more shots," said Alfred, showing plainly that he wished to change the subject.

"Oh, look there! Quick!" exclaimed Betty, pointing toward the hillside.

He looked in the direction indicated and saw a doe and a spotted fawn wading into the shallow water. The mother stood motionless a moment, with head erect and long ears extended. Then she drooped her graceful head and drank thirstily of the cool water. The fawn splashed playfully round while its mother was drinking. It would dash a few paces into the stream and then look back to see if its mother approved. Evidently she did not, for she would stop her drinking and call the fawn back to her side with a soft, crooning noise. Suddenly she raised her head, the long ears shot up, and she seemed to sniff the air. She waded through the deeper water to get round a rocky bluff which ran out into the creek. Then she turned and called the little one. The fawn waded until the water reached its knees, then stopped and uttered piteous little bleats. Encouraged by the soft crooning it plunged into the deep water and with great splashing and floundering managed to swim the short distance. Its slender legs shook as it staggered up the bank. Exhausted or frightened, it shrank close to its mother. Together they disappeared in the willows which fringed the side of the hill.

"Was not that little fellow cute? I have had several fawns, but have never had the heart to keep them," said Betty. Then, as Alfred made no motion to speak, she continued:

"You do not seem very talkative."

"I have nothing to say. You will think me dull. The fact is when I feel deepest I am least able to express myself."

"I will read to you." said Betty taking up the book. He lay back against the grassy bank and gazed dreamily at the many hued trees on the little hillside; at the bare rugged sides of McColloch's Rock which frowned down upon them. A silver-breasted eagle sailed slowly round and round in the blue sky, far above the bluff. Alfred wondered what mysterious power sustained that solitary bird as he floated high in the air without perceptible movement of his broad wings. He envied the king of birds his reign over that illimitable space, his far-reaching vision, and his freedom. Round and round the eagle soared, higher and higher, with each perfect circle, and at last, for an instant poising as lightly as if he were about to perch on his lonely crag, he arched his wings and swooped down through the air with the swiftness of a falling arrow.

Betty's low voice, the water rushing so musically over the falls, the great yellow leaves falling into the pool, the gentle breeze stirring the clusters of goldenrod—all came softly to Alfred as he lay there with half closed eyes.

The time slipped swiftly by as only such time can.

"I fear the melancholy spirit of the day has prevailed upon you," said Betty, half wistfully. "You did not know I had stopped reading, and I do not believe you heard my favorite poem. I have tried to give you a pleasant afternoon and have failed."

"No, no," said Alfred, looking at her with a blue flame in his eyes. "The afternoon has been perfect. I have forgotten my role, and have allowed you to see my real self, something I have tried to hide from all."

"And are you always sad when you are sincere?"

"Not always. But I am often sad. Is it any wonder? Is not all nature sad? Listen! There is the song of the oriole. Breaking in on the stillness it is mournful. The breeze is sad, the brook is sad, this dying Indian summer day is sad. Life itself is sad."

"Oh, no. Life is beautiful."

"You are a child," said he, with a thrill in his deep voice "I hope you may always be as you are to-day, in heart, at least."

"It grows late. See, the shadows are falling. We must go."

"You know I am going away to-morrow. I don't want to go. Perhaps that is why I have been such poor company today. I have a presentiment of evil I am afraid I may never come back."

"I am sorry you must go."

"Do you really mean that?" asked Alfred, earnestly, bending toward her "You know it is a very dangerous undertaking. Would you care if I never returned?"

She looked up and their eyes met. She had raised her head haughtily, as if questioning his right to speak to her in that manner, but as she saw the unspoken appeal in his eyes her own wavered and fell while a warm color crept into her cheek.

"Yes, I would be sorry," she said, gravely. Then, after a moment: "You must portage the canoe round the falls, and from there we can paddle back to the path."

The return trip made, they approached the house. As they turned the corner they saw Colonel Zane standing at the door talking to Wetzel.

They saw that the Colonel looked pale and distressed, and the face of the hunter was dark and gloomy.

"Lew, did you get my turkey?" said Betty, after a moment of hesitation. A nameless fear filled her breast.

For answer Wetzel threw back the flaps of his coat and there at his belt hung a small tuft of black hair. Betty knew at once it was the scalp-lock of an Indian. Her face turned white and she placed a hand on the hunter's arm.

"What do you mean? That is an Indian's scalp. Lew, you look so strange. Tell me, is it because we went off in the canoe and have been in danger?"

"Betty, Isaac has been captured again," said the Colonel.

"Oh, no, no, no," cried Betty in agonized tones, and wringing her hands. Then, excitedly, "Something can be done; you must pursue them. Oh, Lew, Mr. Clarke, cannot you rescue him? They have not had time to go far."

"Isaac went to the chestnut grove this morning. If he had stayed there he would not have been captured. But he went far into the Black Forest. The turkey call we heard across the creek was made by a Wyandot concealed in the cave. Lewis tells me that a number of Indians have camped there for days. He shot the one who was calling and followed the others until he found where they had taken Isaac's trail."

Betty turned to the younger man with tearful eyes, and with beseeching voice implored them to save her brother.

"I am ready to follow you," said Clarke to Wetzel.

The hunter shook his head, but did not answer.

"It is that hateful White Crane," passionately burst out Betty, as the Colonel's wife led her weeping into the house.

"Did you get more than one shot at them?" asked Clarke.

The hunter nodded, and the slight, inscrutable smile flitted across his stern features. He never spoke of his deeds. For this reason many of the thrilling adventures which he must have had will forever remain unrevealed. That evening there was sadness at Colonel Zane's supper table. They felt the absence of the Colonel's usual spirits, his teasing of Betty, and his cheerful conversation. He had nothing to say. Betty sat at the table a little while, and then got up and left the room saying she could not eat. Jonathan, on hearing of his brother's recapture, did not speak, but retired in gloomy silence. Silas was the only one of the family who was not utterly depressed. He said it could have been a great deal worse; that they must make the best of it, and that the sooner Isaac married his Indian Princess the better for his scalp and for the happiness of all concerned.

"I remember Myeerah very well," he said. "It was eight years ago, and she was only a child. Even then she was very proud and willful, and the loveliest girl I ever laid eyes on."

Alfred Clarke staid late at Colonel Zane's that night. Before going away for so many weeks he wished to have a few more moments alone with Betty. But a favorable opportunity did not present itself during the evening, so when he had bade them all goodbye and goodnight, except Betty, who opened the door for him, he said softly to her:

"It is bright moonlight outside. Come, please, and walk to the gate with me."

A full moon shone serenely down on hill and dale, flooding the valley with its pure white light and bathing the pastures in its glory; at the foot of the bluff the waves of the river gleamed like myriads of stars all twinkling and dancing on a bed of snowy clouds. Thus illumined the river wound down the valley, its brilliance growing fainter and fainter until at last, resembling the shimmering of a silver thread which joined the earth to heaven, it disappeared in the horizon.

"I must say goodbye," said Alfred, as they reached the gate.

"Friends must part. I am sorry you must go, Mr. Clarke, and I trust you may return safe. It seems only yesterday that you saved my brother's life, and I was so grateful and happy. Now he is gone."

"You should not think about it so much nor brood over it," answered the young man. "Grieving will not bring him back nor do you any good. It is not nearly so bad as if he had been captured by some other tribe. Wetzel assures us that Isaac was taken alive. Please do not grieve."

"I have cried until I cannot cry any more. I am so unhappy. We were children together, and I have always loved him better than any one since my mother died. To have him back again and then to lose him! Oh! I cannot bear it."

She covered her face with her hands and a low sob escaped her.

"Don't, don't grieve," he said in an unsteady voice, as he took the little hands in his and pulled them away from her face.

Betty trembled. Something in his voice, a tone she had never heard before startled her. She looked up at him half unconscious that he still held her hands in his. Never had she appeared so lovely.

"You cannot understand my feelings."

"I loved my mother."

"But you have not lost her. That makes all the difference."

"I want to comfort you and I am powerless. I am unable to say what— I—"

He stopped short. As he stood gazing down into her sweet face, burning, passionate words came to his lips; but he was dumb; he could not speak. All day long he had been living in a dream. Now he realized that but a moment remained for him to be near the girl he loved so well. He was leaving her, perhaps never to see her again, or to return to find her another's. A fierce pain tore his heart.

"You—you are holding my hands," faltered Betty, in a doubtful, troubled voice. She looked up into his face and saw that it was pale with suppressed emotion.

Alfred was mad indeed. He forgot everything. In that moment the world held nothing for him save that fair face. Her eyes, uplifted to his in the moonlight, beamed with a soft radiance. They were honest eyes, just now filled with innocent sadness and regret, but they drew him with irresistible power. Without realizing in the least what he was doing he yielded to the impulse. Bending his head he kissed the tremulous lips.

"Oh," whispered Betty, standing still as a statue and looking at him with wonderful eyes. Then, as reason returned, a hot flush dyed her face, and wrenching her hands free she struck him across the cheek.

"For God's sake, Betty, I did not mean to do that! Wait. I have something to tell you. For pity's sake, let me explain," he cried, as the full enormity of his offence dawned upon him.

Betty was deaf to the imploring voice, for she ran into the house and slammed the door.

He called to her, but received no answer. He knocked on the door, but it remained closed. He stood still awhile, trying to collect his thoughts, and to find a way to undo the mischief he had wrought. When the real significance of his act came to him he groaned in spirit. What a fool he had been! Only a few short hours and he must start on a perilous journey, leaving the girl he loved in ignorance of his real intentions. Who was to tell her that he loved her? Who was to tell her that it was because his whole heart and soul had gone to her that he had kissed her?

With bowed head he slowly walked away toward the fort, totally oblivious of the fact that a young girl, with hands pressed tightly over her breast to try to still a madly beating heart, watched him from her window until he disappeared into the shadow of the block-house.

Alfred paced up and down his room the four remaining hours of that eventful day. When the light was breaking in at the east and dawn near at hand he heard the rough voices of men and the tramping of iron-shod hoofs. The hour of his departure was at hand.

He sat down at his table and by the aid of the dim light from a pine knot he wrote a hurried letter to Betty. A little hope revived in his heart as he thought that perhaps all might yet be well. Surely some one would be up to whom he could intrust the letter, and if no one he would run over and slip it under the door of Colonel Zane's house.

In the gray of the early morning Alfred rode out with the daring band of heavily armed men, all grim and stern, each silent with the thought of the man who knows he may never return. Soon the settlement was left far behind.

CHAPTER V.

During the last few days, in which the frost had cracked open the hickory nuts, and in which the squirrels had been busily collecting and storing away their supply of nuts for winter use, it had been Isaac's wont to shoulder his rifle, walk up the hill, and spend the morning in the grove.

On this crisp autumn morning he had started off as usual, and had been called back by Col. Zane, who advised him not to wander far from the settlement. This admonition, kind and brotherly though it was, annoyed Isaac. Like all the Zanes he had born in him an intense love for the solitude of the wilderness. There were times when nothing could satisfy him but the calm of the deep woods.

One of these moods possessed him now. Courageous to a fault and daring where daring was not always the wiser part, Isaac lacked the practical sense of the Colonel and the cool judgment of Jonathan. Impatient of restraint, independent in spirit, and it must be admitted, in his persistence in doing as he liked instead of what he ought to do, he resembled Betty more than he did his brothers.

Feeling secure in his ability to take care of himself, for he knew he was an experienced hunter and woodsman, he resolved to take a long tramp in the forest. This resolution was strengthened by the fact that he did not believe what the Colonel and Jonathan had told him—that it was not improbable some of the Wyandot braves were lurking in the vicinity, bent on killing or recapturing him. At any rate he did not fear it.

Once in the shade of the great trees the fever of discontent left him, and, forgetting all except the happiness of being surrounded by the silent oaks, he penetrated deeper and deeper into the forest. The brushing of a branch against a tree, the thud of a falling nut, the dart of a squirrel, and the sight of a bushy tail disappearing round a limb—all these things which indicated that the little gray fellows were working in the tree-tops, and which would usually have brought Isaac to a standstill, now did not seem to interest him. At times he stooped to examine the tender shoots growing at the foot of a sassafras tree. Then, again, he closely examined marks he found in the soft banks of the streams.

He went on and on. Two hours of this still-hunting found him on the bank of a shallow gully through which a brook went rippling and babbling over the mossy green stones. The forest was dense here; rugged oaks and tall poplars grew high over the tops of the first growth of white oaks and beeches; the wild grapevines which coiled round the trees like gigantic serpents, spread out in the upper branches and obscured the sun; witch-hopples and laurel bushes grew thickly; monarchs of the forest, felled by some bygone storm, lay rotting on the ground; and in places the wind-falls were so thick and high as to be impenetrable.

Isaac hesitated. He realized that he had plunged far into the Black Forest. Here it was gloomy; a dreamy quiet prevailed, that deep calm of the wilderness, unbroken save for the distant note of the hermit-thrush, the strange bird whose lonely cry, given at long intervals, pierced the stillness. Although Isaac had never seen one of these birds, he was familiar with that cry which was never heard except in the deepest woods, far from the haunts of man.

A black squirrel ran down a tree and seeing the hunter scampered away in alarm. Isaac knew the habits of the black squirrel, that it was a denizen of the wildest woods and frequented only places remote from civilization. The song of the hermit and the sight of the black squirrel caused Isaac to stop and reflect, with the result that he concluded he had gone much farther from the fort than he had intended. He turned to retrace his steps when a faint sound from down the ravine came to his sharp ears.

There was no instinct to warn him that a hideously painted face was raised a moment over the clump of laurel bushes to his left, and that a pair of keen eyes watched every move he made.

Unconscious of impending evil Isaac stopped and looked around him. Suddenly above the musical babble of the brook and the rustle of the leaves by the breeze came a repetition of the sound. He crouched close by the trunk of a tree and strained his ears. All was quiet for some moments. Then he heard the patter, patter of little hoofs coming down the stream. Nearer and nearer they came. Sometimes they were almost inaudible and again he heard them clearly and distinctly. Then there came a splashing and the faint hollow sound caused by hard hoofs striking the stones in shallow water. Finally the sounds ceased.

Cautiously peering from behind the tree Isaac saw a doe standing on the bank fifty yards down the brook. Trembling she had stopped as if in doubt or uncertainty. Her ears pointed straight upward, and she lifted one front foot from the ground like a thoroughbred pointer. Isaac knew a doe always led the way through the woods and if there were other deer they would come up unless warned by the doe. Presently the willows parted and a magnificent buck with wide spreading antlers stepped out and stood motionless on the bank. Although they were down the wind Isaac knew the deer suspected some hidden danger. They looked steadily at the clump of laurels at Isaac's left, a circumstance he remarked at the time, but did not understand the real significance of until long afterward.

Following the ringing report of Isaac's rifle the buck sprang almost across the stream, leaped convulsively up the bank, reached the top, and then his strength failing, slid down into the stream, where, in his dying struggles, his hoofs beat the water into white foam. The doe had disappeared like a brown flash.

Isaac, congratulating himself on such a fortunate shot—for rarely indeed does a deer fall dead in his tracks even when shot through the heart—rose from his crouching position and commenced to reload his rifle. With great care he poured the powder into the palm of his hand, measuring the quantity with his eye—for it was an evidence of a hunter's skill to be able to get the proper quantity for the ball. Then he put the charge into the barrel. Placing a little greased linsey rag, about half an inch square, over the muzzle, he laid a small lead bullet on it, and with the ramrod began to push the ball into the barrel.

A slight rustle behind him, which sounded to him like the gliding of a rattlesnake over the leaves, caused him to start and turn round. But he was too late. A crushing blow on the head from a club in the hand of a brawny Indian laid him senseless on the ground.

When Isaac regained his senses he felt a throbbing pain in his head, and then he opened his eyes he was so dizzy that he was unable to discern objects clearly. After a few moments his sight returned. When he had struggled to a sitting posture he discovered that his hands were bound with buckskin thongs. By his side he saw two long poles of basswood, with some strips of green bark and pieces of grapevine laced across and tied fast to the poles. Evidently this had served as a litter on which he had been carried. From his wet clothes and the position of the sun, now low in the west, he concluded he had been brought across the river and was now miles from the fort. In front of him he saw three Indians sitting before a fire. One of them was cutting thin slices from a haunch of deer meat, another was drinking from a gourd, and the third was roasting a piece of venison which he held on a sharpened stick. Isaac knew at once the Indians were Wyandots, and he saw they were in full war paint. They were not young braves, but middle aged warriors. One of them Isaac recognized as Crow, a chief of one of the Wyandot tribes, and a warrior renowned for his daring and for his ability to make his way in a straight line through the wilderness. Crow was a short, heavy Indian and his frame denoted great strength. He had a broad forehead, high cheek bones, prominent nose and his face would have been handsome and intelligent but for the scar which ran across his cheek, giving him a sinister look.

"Hugh!" said Crow, as he looked up and saw Isaac staring at him. The other Indians immediately gave vent to a like exclamation.

"Crow, you caught me again," said Isaac, in the Wyandot tongue, which he spoke fluently.

"The white chief is sure of eye and swift of foot, but he cannot escape the Huron. Crow has been five times on his trail since the moon was bright. The white chief's eyes were shut and his ears were deaf," answered the Indian loftily.

"How long have you been near the fort?"

"Two moons have the warriors of Myeerah hunted the pale face."

"Have you any more Indians with you?"

The chief nodded and said a party of nine Wyandots had been in the vicinity of Wheeling for a month. He named some of the warriors.

Isaac was surprised to learn of the renowned chiefs who had been sent to recapture him. Not to mention Crow, the Delaware chiefs Son-of-Wingenund and Wapatomeka were among the most cunning and sagacious Indians of the west. Isaac reflected that his year's absence from Myeerah had not caused her to forget him.

Crow untied Isaac's hands and gave him water and venison. Then he picked up his rifle and with a word to the Indians he stepped into the underbrush that skirted the little dale, and was lost to view.

Isaac's head ached and throbbed so that after he had satisfied his thirst and hunger he was glad to close his eyes and lean back against the tree. Engrossed in thoughts of the home he might never see again, he had lain there an hour without moving, when he was aroused from his meditations by low guttural exclamations from the Indians. Opening his eyes he saw Crow and another Indian enter the glade, leading and half supporting a third savage.

They helped this Indian to the log, where he sat down slowly and wearily, holding one hand over his breast. He was a magnificent specimen of Indian manhood, almost a giant in stature, with broad shoulders in proportion to his height. His head-dress and the gold rings which encircled his bare muscular arms indicated that he was a chief high in power. The seven eagle plumes in his scalp-lock represented seven warriors that he had killed in battle. Little sticks of wood plaited in his coal black hair and painted different colors showed to an Indian eye how many times this chief had been wounded by bullet, knife, or tomahawk.

His face was calm. If he suffered he allowed no sign of it to escape him. He gazed thoughtfully into the fire, slowly the while untying the belt which contained his knife and tomahawk. The weapons were raised and held before him, one in each hand, and then waved on high. The action was repeated three times. Then slowly and reluctantly the Indian lowered them as if he knew their work on earth was done.

It was growing dark and the bright blaze from the camp fire lighted up the glade, thus enabling Isaac to see the drooping figure on the log, and in the background Crow, holding a whispered consultation with the other Indians. Isaac heard enough of the colloquy to guess the facts. The chief had been desperately rounded; the palefaces were on their trail, and a march must be commenced at once.

Isaac knew the wounded chief. He was the Delaware Son-of-Wingenund. He married a Wyandot squaw, had spent much of his time in the Wyandot village and on warring expeditions which the two friendly nations made on other tribes. Isaac had hunted with him, slept under the same blanket with him, and had grown to like him.

As Isaac moved slightly in his position the chief saw him. He straightened up, threw back the hunting shirt and pointed to a small hole in his broad breast. A slender stream of blood issued from the wound and flowed down his chest.

"Wind-of-Death is a great white chief. His gun is always loaded," he said calmly, and a look of pride gleamed across his dark face, as though he gloried in the wound made by such a warrior.

"Deathwind" was one of the many names given to Wetzel by the savages, and a thrill of hope shot through Isaac's heart when he saw the Indians feared Wetzel was on their track. This hope was short lived, however, for when he considered the probabilities of the thing he knew that pursuit would only result in his death before the settlers could come up with the Indians, and he concluded that Wetzel, familiar with every trick of the redmen, would be the first to think of the hopelessness of rescuing him and so would not attempt it.

The four Indians now returned to the fire and stood beside the chief. It was evident to them that his end was imminent. He sang in a low, not unmusical tone the death-chant of the Hurons. His companions silently bowed their heads. When he had finished singing he slowly rose to his great height, showing a commanding figure. Slowly his features lost their stern pride, his face softened, and his dark eyes, gazing straight into the gloom of the forest, bespoke a superhuman vision.

"Wingenund has been a great chief. He has crossed his last trail. The deeds of Wingenund will be told in the wigwams of the Lenape," said the chief in a loud voice, and then sank back into the arms of his comrades. They laid him gently down.

A convulsive shudder shook the stricken warrior's frame. Then, starting up he straightened out his long arm and clutched wildly at the air with his sinewy fingers as if to grasp and hold the life that was escaping him.

Isaac could see the fixed, sombre light in the eyes, and the pallor of death stealing over the face of the chief. He turned his eyes away from the sad spectacle, and when he looked again the majestic figure lay still.

The moon sailed out from behind a cloud and shed its mellow light down on the little glade. It showed the four Indians digging a grave beneath the oak tree. No word was spoken. They worked with their tomahawks on the soft duff and soon their task was completed. A bed of moss and ferns lined the last resting place of the chief. His weapons were placed beside him, to go with him to the Happy Hunting Ground, the eternal home of the redmen, where the redmen believe the sun will always shine, and where they will be free from their cruel white foes.

When the grave had been filled and the log rolled on it the Indians stood by it a moment, each speaking a few words in a low tone, while the night wind moaned the dead chief's requiem through the tree tops.

Accustomed as Isaac was to the bloody conflicts common to the Indians, and to the tragedy that surrounded the life of a borderman, the ghastly sight had unnerved him. The last glimpse of that stern, dark face, of that powerful form, as the moon brightened up the spot in seeming pity, he felt he could never forget. His thoughts were interrupted by the harsh voice of Crow bidding him get up. He was told that the slightest inclination on his part to lag behind on the march before them, or in any way to make their trail plainer, would be the signal for his death. With that Crow cut the thongs which bound Isaac's legs and placing him between two of the Indians, led the way into the forest.

Moving like spectres in the moonlight they marched on and on for hours. Crow was well named. He led them up the stony ridges where their footsteps left no mark, and where even a dog could not find their trail; down into the valleys and into the shallow streams where the running water would soon wash away all trace of their tracks; then out on the open plain, where the soft, springy grass retained little impress of their moccasins.

Single file they marched in the leader's tracks as he led them onward through the dark forests, out under the shining moon, never slacking his rapid pace, ever in a straight line, and yet avoiding the roughest going with that unerring instinct which was this Indian's gift. Toward dawn the moon went down, leaving them in darkness, but this made no difference, for, guided by the stars, Crow kept straight on his course. Not till break of day did he come to a halt.

Then, on the banks of a narrow stream, the Indians kindled a fire and broiled some of the venison. Crow told Isaac he could rest, so he made haste to avail himself of the permission, and almost instantly was wrapped in the deep slumber of exhaustion. Three of the Indians followed suit, and Crow stood guard. Sleepless, tireless, he paced to and fro on the bank his keen eyes vigilant for signs of pursuers.

The sun was high when the party resumed their flight toward the west. Crow plunged into the brook and waded several miles before he took to the woods on the other shore. Isaac suffered severely from the sharp and slippery stones, which in no wise bothered the Indians. His feet were cut and bruised; still he struggled on without complaining. They rested part of the night, and the next day the Indians, now deeming themselves practically safe from pursuit, did not exercise unusual care to conceal their trail.

That evening about dusk they came to a rapidly flowing stream which ran northwest. Crow and one of the other Indians parted the willows on the bank at this point and dragged forth a long birch-bark canoe which they ran into the stream. Isaac recognized the spot. It was near the head of Mad River, the river which ran through the Wyandot settlements.

Two of the Indians took the bow, the third Indian and Isaac sat in the middle, back to back, and Crow knelt in the stern. Once launched on that wild ride Isaac forgot his uneasiness and his bruises. The night was beautiful; he loved the water, and was not lacking in sentiment. He gave himself up to the charm of the silver moonlight, of the changing scenery, and the musical gurgle of the water. Had it not been for the cruel face of Crow, he could have imagined himself on one of those enchanted canoes in fairyland, of which he had read when a boy. Ever varying pictures presented themselves at the range, impelled by vigorous arms, flew over the shining bosom of the stream. Here, in a sharp bend, was a narrow place where the trees on each bank interlaced their branches and hid the moon, making a dark and dim retreat. Then came a short series of ripples, with merry, bouncing waves and foamy currents; below lay a long, smooth reach of water, deep and placid, mirroring the moon and the countless stars. Noiseless as a shadow the canoe glided down this stretch, the paddle dipping regularly, flashing brightly, and scattering diamond drops in the clear moonlight.

Another turn in the stream and a sound like the roar of an approaching storm as it is borne on a rising wind, broke the silence. It was the roar of rapids or falls. The stream narrowed; the water ran swifter; rocky ledges rose on both sides, gradually getting higher and higher. Crow rose to his feet and looked ahead. Then he dropped to his knees and turned the head of the canoe into the middle of the stream. The roar became deafening. Looking forward Isaac saw that they were entering a dark gorge. In another moment the canoe pitched over a fall and shot between two high, rocky bluffs. These walls ran up almost perpendicularly two hundred feet; the space between was scarcely twenty feet wide, and the water fairly screamed as it rushed madly through its narrow passage. In the center it was like a glancing sheet of glass, weird and dark, and was bordered on the sides by white, seething foam-capped waves which tore and dashed and leaped at their stony confines.

Though the danger was great, though Death lurked in those jagged stones and in those black waits Isaac felt no fear, he knew the strength of that arm, now rigid and again moving with lightning swiftness; he knew the power of the eye which guided them.

Once more out under the starry sky; rifts, shallows, narrows, and lake-like basins were passed swiftly. At length as the sky was becoming gray in the east, they passed into the shadow of what was called the Standing Stone. This was a peculiarly shaped stone-faced bluff, standing high over the river, and taking its name from Tarhe, or Standing Stone, chief of all the Hurons.

At the first sight of that well known landmark, which stood by the Wyandot village, there mingled with Isaac's despondency and resentment some other feeling that was akin to pleasure; with a quickening of the pulse came a confusion of expectancy and bitter memories as he thought of the dark eyed maiden from whom he had fled a year ago.

"Co-wee-Co-woe," called out one of the Indians in the bow of the canoe. The signal was heard, for immediately an answering shout came from the shore.

When a few moments later the canoe grated softly on a pebbly beach. Isaac saw, indistinctly in the morning mist, the faint outlines of tepees and wigwams, and he knew he was once more in the encampment of the Wyandots.

* * * * * * * * * * * * * *

Late in the afternoon of that day Isaac was awakened from his heavy slumber and told that the chief had summoned him. He got up from the buffalo robes upon which he had flung himself that morning, stretched his aching limbs, and walked to the door of the lodge.

The view before him was so familiar that it seemed as if he had suddenly come home after being absent a long time. The last rays of the setting sun shone ruddy and bright over the top of the Standing Stone; they touched the scores of lodges and wigwams which dotted the little valley; they crimsoned the swift, narrow river, rushing noisily over its rocky bed. The banks of the stream were lined with rows of canoes; here and there a bridge made of a single tree spanned the stream. From the camp fires long, thin columns of blue smoke curled lazily upward; giant maple trees, in them garb of purple and gold, rose high above the wigwams, adding a further beauty to this peaceful scene.

As Isaac was led down a lane between two long lines of tepees the watching Indians did not make the demonstration that usually marked the capture of a paleface. Some of the old squaws looked up from their work round the campfires and steaming kettles and grinned as the prisoner passed. The braves who were sitting upon their blankets and smoking their long pipes, or lounging before the warm blazes maintained a stolid indifference; the dusky maidens smiled shyly, and the little Indian boys, with whom Isaac had always been a great favorite, manifested their joy by yelling and running after him. One youngster grasped Isaac round the leg and held on until he was pulled away.

In the center of the village were several lodges connected with one another and larger and more imposing than the surrounding tepees. These were the wigwams of the chief, and thither Isaac was conducted. The guards led him to a large and circular apartment and left him there alone. This room was the council-room. It contained nothing but a low seat and a knotted war-club.

Isaac heard the rattle of beads and bear claws, and as he turned a tall and majestic Indian entered the room. It was Tarhe, the chief of all the Wyandots. Though Tarhe was over seventy, he walked erect; his calm face, dark as a bronze mask, showed no trace of his advanced age. Every line and feature of his face had race in it; the high forehead, the square, protruding jaw, the stern mouth, the falcon eyes—all denoted the pride and unbending will of the last of the Tarhes.

"The White Eagle is again in the power of Tarhe," said the chief in his native tongue. "Though he had the swiftness of the bounding deer or the flight of the eagle it would avail him not. The wild geese as they fly northward are not swifter than the warriors of Tarhe. Swifter than all is the vengeance of the Huron. The young paleface has cost the lives of some great warriors. What has he to say?"

"It was not my fault," answered Isaac quickly. "I was struck down from behind and had no chance to use a weapon. I have never raised my hand against a Wyandot. Crow will tell you that. If my people and friends kill your braves I am not to blame. Yet I have had good cause to shed Huron blood. Your warriors have taken me from my home and have wounded me many times."

"The White Chief speaks well. Tarhe believes his words," answered Tarhe in his sonorous voice. "The Lenapee seek the death of the pale face. Wingenund grieves for his son. He is Tarhe's friend. Tarhe is old and wise and he is king here. He can save the White Chief from Wingenund and Cornplanter. Listen. Tarhe is old and he has no son. He will make you a great chief and give you lands and braves and honors. He shall not ask you to raise your hand against your people, but help to bring peace. Tarhe does not love this war. He wants only justice. He wants only to keep his lands, his horses, and his people. The White Chief is known to be brave; his step is light, his eye is keen, and his bullet is true. For many long moons Tarhe's daughter has been like the singing bird without its mate. She sings no more. She shall be the White Chief's wife. She has the blood of her mother and not that of the last of the Tarhes. Thus the mistakes of Tarhe's youth come to disappoint his old age. He is the friend of the young paleface. Tarhe has said. Now go and make your peace with Myeerah."

The chief motioned toward the back of the lodge. Isaac stepped forward and went through another large room, evidently the chief's, as it was fitted up with a wild and barbaric splendor. Isaac hesitated before a bearskin curtain at the farther end of the chief's lodge. He had been there many times before, but never with such conflicting emotions. What was it that made his heart beat faster? With a quick movement he lifted the curtain and passed under it.

The room which he entered was circular in shape and furnished with all the bright colors and luxuriance known to the Indian. Buffalo robes covered the smooth, hard-packed clay floor; animals, allegorical pictures, and fanciful Indian designs had been painted on the wall; bows and arrows, shields, strings of bright-colored beads and Indian scarfs hung round the room. The wall was made of dried deerskins sewed together and fastened over long poles which were planted in the ground and bent until the ends met overhead. An oval-shaped opening let in the light. Through a narrow aperture, which served as a door leading to a smaller apartment, could be seen a low couch covered with red blankets, and a glimpse of many hued garments hanging on the wall.

As Isaac entered the room a slender maiden ran impulsively to him and throwing her arms round his neck hid her face on his breast. A few broken, incoherent words escaped her lips. Isaac disengaged himself from the clinging arms and put her from him. The face raised to his was strikingly beautiful. Oval in shape, it was as white as his own, with a broad, low brow and regular features. The eyes were large and dark and they dilated and quickened with a thousand shadows of thought.

"Myeerah, I am taken again. This time there has been blood shed. The Delaware chief was killed, and I do not know how many more Indians. The chiefs are all for putting me to death. I am in great danger. Why could you not leave me in peace?"

At his first words the maiden sighed and turned sorrowfully and proudly away from the angry face of the young man. A short silence ensued.

"Then you are not glad to see Myeerah?" she said, in English. Her voice was music. It rang low, sweet, clear-toned as a bell.

"What has that to do with it? Under some circumstances I would be glad to see you. But to be dragged back here and perhaps murdered—no, I don't welcome it. Look at this mark where Crow hit me," said Isaac, passionately, bowing his head to enable her to see the bruise where the club had struck him.

"I am sorry," said Myeerah, gently.

"I know that I am in great danger from the Delawares."

"The daughter of Tarhe has saved your life before and will save it again."

"They may kill me in spite of you."

"They will not dare. Do not forget that I saved you from the Shawnees. What did my father say to you?"

"He assured me that he was my friend and that he would protect me from Wingenund. But I must marry you and become one of the tribe. I cannot do that. And that is why I am sure they will kill me."

"You are angry now. I will tell you. Myeerah tried hard to win your love, and when you ran away from her she was proud for a long time. But there was no singing of birds, no music of the waters, no beauty in anything after you left her. Life became unbearable without you. Then Myeerah remembered that she was a daughter of kings. She summoned the bravest and greatest warriors of two tribes and said to them. 'Go and bring to me the paleface, White Eagle. Bring him to me alive or dead. If alive, Myeerah will smile once more upon her warriors. If dead, she will look once upon his face and die. Ever since Myeerah was old enough to remember she has thought of you. Would you wish her to be inconstant, like the moon?'"

"It is not what I wish you to be. It is that I cannot live always without seeing my people. I told you that a year ago."

"You told me other things in that past time before you ran away. They were tender words that were sweet to the ear of the Indian maiden. Have you forgotten them?"

"I have not forgotten them. I am not without feeling. You do not understand. Since I have been home this last time, I have realized more than ever that I could not live away from my home."

"Is there any maiden in your old home whom you have learned to love more than Myeerah?"

He did not reply, but looked gloomily out of the opening in the wall. Myeerah had placed her hold upon his arm, and as he did not answer the hand tightened its grasp.

"She shall never have you."

The low tones vibrated with intense feeling, with a deathless resolve. Isaac laughed bitterly and looked up at her. Myeerah's face was pale and her eyes burned like fire.

"I should not be surprised if you gave me up to the Delawares," said Isaac, coldly. "I am prepared for it, and I would not care very much. I have despaired of your ever becoming civilized enough to understand the misery of my sister and family. Why not let the Indians kill me?"

He knew how to wound her. A quick, shuddery cry broke from her lips. She stood before him with bowed head and wept. When she spoke again her voice was broken and pleading.

"You are cruel and unjust. Though Myeerah has Indian blood she is a white woman. She can feel as your people do. In your anger and bitterness you forget that Myeerah saved you from the knife of the Shawnees. You forget her tenderness; you forget that she nursed you when you were wounded. Myeerah has a heart to break. Has she not suffered? Is she not laughed at, scorned, called a 'paleface' by the other tribes? She thanks the Great Spirit for the Indian blood that keep her true. The white man changes his loves and his wives. That is not an Indian gift."

"No, Myeerah, I did not say so. There is no other woman. It is that I am wretched and sick at heart. Do you not see that this will end in a tragedy some day? Can you not realize that we would be happier if you would let me go? If you love me you would not want to see me dead. If I do not marry you they will kill me; if I try to escape again they win kill me. Let me go free."

"I cannot! I cannot!" she cried. "You have taught me many of the ways of your people, but you cannot change my nature."

"Why cannot you free me?"

"I love you, and I will not live without you."

"Then come and go to my home and live there with me," said Isaac, taking the weeping maiden in his arms. "I know that my people will welcome you."

"Myeerah would be pitied and scorned," she said, sadly, shaking her head.

Isaac tried hard to steel his heart against her, but he was only mortal and he failed. The charm of her presence influenced him; her love wrung tenderness from him. Those dark eyes, so proud to all others, but which gazed wistfully and yearningly into his, stirred his heart to its depths. He kissed the tear-wet cheeks and smiled upon her.

"Well, since I am a prisoner once more, I must make the best of it. Do not look so sad. We shall talk of this another day. Come, let us go and find my little friend, Captain Jack. He remembered me, for he ran out and grasped my knee and they pulled him away."

CHAPTER VI.

When the first French explorers invaded the northwest, about the year 1615, the Wyandot Indians occupied the territory between Georgian Bay and the Muskoka Lakes in Ontario. These Frenchmen named the tribe Huron because of the manner in which they wore their hair.

At this period the Hurons were at war with the Iroquois, and the two tribes kept up a bitter fight until in 1649, when the Hurons suffered a decisive defeat. They then abandoned their villages and sought other hunting grounds. They travelled south and settled in Ohio along the south and west shores of Lake Erie. The present site of Zanesfield, named from Isaac Zane, marks the spot where the largest tribe of Hurons once lived.

In a grove of maples on the banks of a swift little river named Mad River, the Hurons built their lodges and their wigwams. The stately elk and graceful deer abounded in this fertile valley, and countless herds of bison browsed upon the uplands.

There for many years the Hurons lived a peaceful and contented life. The long war cry was not heard. They were at peace with the neighboring tribes. Tarhe, the Huron chief, attained great influence with the Delawares. He became a friend of Logan, the Mingo chief.

With the invasion of the valley of the Ohio by the whites, with the march into the wilderness of that wild-turkey breed of heroes of which Boone, Kenton, the Zanes, and the Wetzels were the first, the Indian's nature gradually changed until he became a fierce and relentless foe.

The Hurons had sided with the French in Pontiac's war, and in the Revolution they aided the British. They allied themselves with the Mingoes, Delawares and Shawnees and made a fierce war on the Virginian pioneers. Some powerful influence must have engendered this implacable hatred in these tribes, particularly in the Mingo and the Wyandot.

The war between the Indians and the settlers along the Pennsylvania and West Virginia borders was known as "Dunmore's War." The Hurons, Mingoes, and Delawares living in the "hunter's paradise" west of the Ohio

River, seeing their land sold by the Iroquois and the occupation of their possessions by a daring band of white men naturally were filled with fierce anger and hate. But remembering the past bloody war and British punishment they slowly moved backward toward the setting sun and kept the peace. In 1774 a canoe filled with friendly Wyandots was attacked by white men below Yellow Creek and the Indians were killed. Later the same year a party of men under Colonel Cresop made an unprovoked and dastardly massacre of the family and relatives of Logan. This attack reflected the deepest dishonor upon all the white men concerned, and was the principal cause of the long and bloody war which followed. The settlers on the border sent messengers to Governor Dunmore at Williamsburg for immediate relief parties. Knowing well that the Indians would not allow this massacre to go unavenged the frontiersmen erected forts and blockhouses.

Logan, the famous Mingo chief, had been a noted friend of the white men. After the murder of his people he made ceaseless war upon them. He incited the wrath of the Hurons and the Delawares. He went on the warpath, and when his lust for vengeance had been satisfied he sent the following remarkable address to Lord Dunmore:

"I appeal to any white man to say if ever he entered Logan's cabin and he gave him not meat: if ever he came cold and naked and he clothed him not. During the course of the last long and bloody war Logan remained idle in his cabin, an advocate of peace. Such was my love for the whites that my countrymen pointed as they passed and said: 'Logan is the friend of the white man.' I had even thought to have lived with you but for the injuries of one man, Colonel Cresop, who, last spring, in cold blood and unprovoked, murdered all the relatives of Logan, not even sparing my women and children. There runs not a drop of my blood in the veins of any living creature. This called upon me for vengeance. I have sought it: I have killed many; I have glutted my vengeance. For my country I will rejoice at the beams of peace. But do not harbor a thought that mine is the joy of fear. Logan never felt fear; he could not turn upon his heel to save his life. Who is there to mourn for Logan? Not one."

The war between the Indians and the pioneers was waged for years. The settlers pushed farther and farther into the wilderness. The Indians, who at first sought only to save their farms and their stock, now fought for revenge. That is why every ambitious pioneer who went out upon those borders carried his life in his hands; why there was always the danger of being shot or tomahawked from behind every tree; why wife and children were constantly in fear of the terrible enemy.

To creep unawares upon a foe and strike him in the dark was Indian warfare; to an Indian it was not dishonorable; it was not cowardly. He was taught to hide in the long grass like a snake, to shoot from coverts, to worm his way stealthily through the dense woods and to ambush the paleface's trail. Horrible cruelties, such as torturing white prisoners and burning them at the stake were never heard of before the war made upon the Indians by the whites.

Comparatively little is known of the real character of the Indian of that time. We ourselves sit before our warm fires and talk of the deeds of the redman. We while away an hour by reading Pontiac's siege of Detroit, of the battle of Braddock's fields, and of Custer's last charge. We lay the book down with a fervent expression of thankfulness that the day of the horrible redman is past. Because little has been written on the subject, no thought is given to the long years of deceit and treachery practiced upon Pontiac; we are ignorant of the causes which led to the slaughter of Braddock's army, and we know little of the life of bitterness suffered by Sitting Bull.

Many intelligent white men, who were acquainted with the true life of the Indian before he was harassed and driven to desperation by the pioneers, said that he had been cruelly wronged. Many white men in those days loved the Indian life so well that they left the settlements and lived with the Indians. Boone, who knew the Indian nature, said the honesty and the simplicity of the Indian were remarkable. Kenton said he had been happy among the Indians. Col. Zane had many Indian friends. Isaac Zane, who lived most of his life with the Wyandots, said the American redman had been wrongfully judged a bloodthirsty savage, an ignorant, thieving wretch, capable of not one virtue. He said the free picturesque life of the Indians would have appealed to any white man; that it had a wonderful charm, and that before the war with the whites the Indians were kind to their prisoners, and sought only to make Indians of them. He told tales of how easily white boys become Indianized, so attached to the wild life and freedom of the redmen that it was impossible to get the captives to return to civilized life. The boys had been permitted to grow wild with the Indian lads; to fish and shoot and swim with them; to play the Indian games—to live idle, joyous lives. He said these white boys had been ransomed and taken from captivity and returned to their homes and, although a close watch has kept on them, they contrived to escape and return to the Indians, and that while they were back among civilized people it was difficult to keep the boys dressed. In summer time it was useless to attempt it. The strongest hemp-linen shirts, made with the strongest collar and wrist-band, would directly be torn off and the little rascals found swimming in the river or rolling on the sand.

If we may believe what these men have said—and there seems no good reason why we may not—the Indian was very different from the impression given of him. There can be little doubt that the redman once lived a noble and blameless life; that he was simple, honest and brave, that he had a regard for honor and a respect for a promise far exceeding that of most white men. Think of the beautiful poetry and legends left by these silent men: men who were a part of the woods; men whose music was the sighing of the wind, the rustling of the leaf, the murmur of the brook; men whose simple joys were the chase of the stag, and the light in the dark eye of a maiden.

If we wish to find the highest type of the American Indian we must look for him before he was driven west by the land-seeking pioneer and before he was degraded by the rum-selling French trader.

The French claimed all the land watered by the Mississippi River and its tributaries. The French Canadian was a restless, roaming adventurer and he found his vocation in the fur-trade. This fur-trade engendered a strange class of men—bush-rangers they were called—whose work was to paddle the canoe along the lakes and streams and exchange their cheap rum for the valuable furs of the Indians. To these men the Indians of the west owe their degradation. These bush-rangers or coureurs-des-bois, perverted the Indians and sank into barbarism with them.

The few travellers there in those days were often surprised to find in the wigwams of the Indians men who acknowledged the blood of France, yet who had lost all semblance to the white man. They lived in their tepee with their Indian squaws and lolled on their blankets while the squaws cooked their venison and did all the work. They let their hair grow long and wore feathers in it; they painted their faces hideously with ochre and vermilion.

These were the worthless traders and adventurers who, from the year 1748 to 1783, encroached on the hunting grounds of the Indians and explored the wilderness, seeking out the remote tribes and trading the villainous rum for the rare pelts. In 1784 the French authorities, realizing that these vagrants were demoralizing the Indians, warned them to get off the soil. Finding this course ineffectual they arrested those that could be apprehended and sent them to Canada. But it was too late: the harm had been done: the poor, ignorant savage had tasted of the terrible "fire-water," as he called the rum and his ruin was inevitable.

It was a singular fact that almost every Indian who had once tasted strong drink, was unable to resist the desire for more. When a trader came to one of the Indian hamlets the braves purchased a keg of rum and then they held a council to see who was to get drunk and who was to keep sober. It was necessary to have some sober Indians in camp, otherwise the drunken braves would kill one another. The weapons would have to be concealed. When the Indians had finished one keg of rum they would buy another, and so on until not a beaver-skin was left. Then the trader would move or when the Indians sobered up they would be much dejected, for invariably they would find that some had been wounded, others crippled, and often several had been killed.

Logan, using all his eloquence, travelled from village to village visiting the different tribes and making speeches. He urged the Indians to shun the dreaded "fire-water." He exclaimed against the whites for introducing liquor to the Indians and thus debasing them. At the same time Logan admitted his own fondness for rum. This intelligent and noble Indian was murdered in a drunken fight shortly after sending his address to Lord Dunmore.

Thus it was that the poor Indians had no chance to avert their downfall;

the steadily increasing tide of land-stealing settlers rolling westward, and the insidious, debasing, soul-destroying liquor were the noble redman's doom.

* * * * * * * * * * * * * *

Isaac Zane dropped back not altogether unhappily into his old place in the wigwam, in the hunting parties, and in the Indian games.

When the braves were in camp, the greatest part of the day was spent in shooting and running matches, in canoe races, in wrestling, and in the game of ball. The chiefs and the older braves who had won their laurels and the maidens of the tribe looked on and applauded.

Isaac entered into all these pastimes, partly because he had a natural love for them, and partly because he wished to win the regard of the Indians. In wrestling, and in those sports which required weight and endurance, he usually suffered defeat. In a foot race there was not a brave in the entire tribe who could keep even with him. But it was with the rifle that Isaac won his greatest distinction. The Indians never learned the finer shooting with the ride. Some few of them could shoot well, but for the most part they were poor marksmen.

Accordingly, Isaac was always taken on the fall hunt. Every autumn there were three parties sent out to bring in the supply of meat for the winter. Because of Isaac's fine marksmanship he was always taken with the bear hunters. Bear hunting was exciting and dangerous work. Before the weather got very cold and winter actually set in the bears crawled into a hole in a tree or a cave in the rocks, where they hibernated. A favorite place for them was in hollow trees. When the Indians found a tree with the scratches of a bear on it and a hole large enough to admit the body of a bear, an Indian climbed up the tree and with a long pole tried to punch Bruin out of his den. Often this was a hazardous undertaking, for the bear would get angry on being disturbed in his winter sleep and would rush out before the Indian could reach a place of safety. At times there were even two or three bears in one den. Sometimes the bear would refuse to come out, and on these occasions, which were rare, the hunters would resort to fire. A piece of dry, rotten wood was fastened to a long pole and was set on fire. When this was pushed in on the bear he would give a sniff and a growl and come out in a hurry.

The buffalo and elk were hunted with the bow and arrow. This effective weapon did not make a noise and frighten the game. The wary Indian crawled through the high grass until within easy range and sometimes killed several buffalo or elk before the herd became alarmed. The meat was then jerked. This consisted in cutting it into thin strips and drying it in the sun. Afterwards it was hung up in the lodges. The skins were stretched on poles to dry, and when cured they served as robes, clothing and wigwam-coverings.

The Indians were fond of honey and maple sugar. The finding of a hive of bees, or a good run of maple syrup was an occasion for general rejoicing. They found the honey in hollow trees, and they obtained the maple sugar in two ways. When the sap came up in the maple trees a hole was bored in the trees about a foot from the ground and a small tube, usually made from a piece of alder, was inserted in the hole. Through this the sap was carried into a vessel which was placed under the tree. This sap was boiled down in kettles. If the Indians had no kettles they made the frost take the place of heat in preparing the sugar. They used shallow vessels made of bark, and these were filled with water and the maple sap. It was left to freeze over night and in the morning the ice was broken and thrown away. The sugar did not freeze. When this process had been repeated several times the residue was very good maple sugar.

Isaac did more than his share toward the work of provisioning the village for the winter. But he enjoyed it. He was particularly fond of fishing by moonlight. Early November was the best season for this sport, and the Indians caught large numbers of fish. They placed a torch in the bow of a canoe and paddled noiselessly over the stream. In the clear water a bright light would so attract and fascinate the fish that they would lie motionless near the bottom of the shallow stream.

One cold night Isaac was in the bow of the canoe. Seeing a large fish he whispered to the Indians with him to exercise caution. His guides paddled noiselessly through the water. Isaac stood up and raised the spear, ready to strike. In another second Isaac had cast the iron, but in his eagerness he overbalanced himself and plunged head first into the icy current, making a great splash and spoiling any further fishing. Incidents like this were a source of infinite amusement to the Indians.

Before the autumn evenings grew too cold the Indian held their courting dances. All unmarried maidens and braves in the village were expected to take part in these dances. In the bright light of huge fires, and watched by the chiefs, the old men, the squaws, and the children, the maidens and the braves, arrayed in their gaudiest apparel, marched into the circle. They formed two lines a few paces apart. Each held in the right hand a dry gourd which contained pebbles. Advancing toward one another they sang the courting song, keeping time to the tune with the rattling of the pebbles. When they met in the center the braves bent forward and whispered a word to the maidens. At a certain point in the song, which was indicated by a louder note, the maidens would change their positions, and this was continued until every brave had whispered to every maiden, when the dance ended.

Isaac took part in all these pleasures; he entered into every phase of the Indian's life; he hunted, worked, played, danced, and sang with faithfulness. But when the long, dreary winter days came with their ice-laden breezes, enforcing idleness on the Indians, he became restless. Sometimes for days he would be morose and gloomy, keeping beside his own tent and not mingling with the Indians. At such times Myeerah did not question him.

Even in his happier hours his diversions were not many. He never tired of watching and studying the Indian children. When he had an opportunity without being observed, which was seldom, he amused himself with the papooses. The Indian baby was strapped to a flat piece of wood and covered with a broad flap of buckskin. The squaws hung these primitive baby carriages up on the pole of a tepee, on a branch of a tree, or threw them round anywhere. Isaac never heard a papoose cry. He often pulled down the flap of buckskin and looked at the solemn little fellow, who would stare up at him with big, wondering eyes.

Isaac's most intimate friend was a six-year-old Indian boy, whom he called Captain Jack. He was the son of Thundercloud, the war-chief of the Hurons. Jack made a brave picture in his buckskin hunting suit and his war bonnet. Already he could stick tenaciously on the back of a racing mustang and with his little bow he could place arrow after arrow in the center of the target. Knowing Captain Jack would some day be a mighty chief, Isaac taught him to speak English. He endeavored to make Jack love him, so that when the lad should grow to be a man he would remember his white brother and show mercy to the prisoners who fell into his power.

Another of Isaac's favorites was a half-breed Ottawa Indian, a distant relative of Tarhe's. This Indian was very old; no one knew how old; his face was seamed and scarred and wrinkled. Bent and shrunken was his form. He slept most of the time, but at long intervals he would brighten up and tell of his prowess when a warrior.

One of his favorite stories was of the part he had taken in the events of that fatal and memorable July 2, 1755, when Gen. Braddock and his English army were massacred by the French and Indians near Fort Duquesne.

The old chief told how Beaujeu with his Frenchmen and his five hundred Indians ambushed Braddock's army, surrounded the soldiers, fired from the ravines, the trees, the long grass, poured a pitiless hail of bullets on the bewildered British soldiers, who, unaccustomed to this deadly and unseen foe, huddled under the trees like herds of frightened sheep, and were shot down with hardly an effort to defend themselves.

The old chief related that fifteen years after that battle he went to the Kanawha settlement to see the Big Chief, Gen. George Washington, who was travelling on the Kanawha. He told Gen. Washington how he had fought in the battle of Braddock's Fields; how he had shot and killed Gen. Braddock; how he had fired repeatedly at Washington, and had killed two horses under him, and how at last he came to the conclusion that Washington was protected by the Great Spirit who destined him for a great future.

* * * * * * * * * * * * *

Myeerah was the Indian name for a rare and beautiful bird—the white crane—commonly called by the Indians, Walk-in-the-Water. It had been the name of Tarhe's mother and grandmother. The present Myeerah was the daughter of a French woman, who had been taken captive at a very early age, adopted into the Huron tribe, and married to Tarhe. The only child of this union was Myeerah. She grew to be beautiful woman and was known in Detroit and the Canadian forts as Tarhe's white daughter. The old chief often visited the towns along the lake shore, and so proud was he of Myeerah that he always had her accompany him. White men travelled far to look at the Indian beauty. Many French soldiers wooed her in vain. Once, while Tarhe was in Detroit, a noted French family tried in every way to get possession of Myeerah.

The head of this family believed he saw in Myeerah the child of his long lost daughter. Tarhe hurried away from the city and never returned to the white settlement.

Myeerah was only five years old at the time of the capture of the Zane brothers and it was at this early age that she formed the attachment for Isaac Zane which clung to her all her life. She was seven when the men came from Detroit to ransom the brothers, and she showed such grief when she learned that Isaac was to be returned to his people that Tarhe refused to accept any ransom for Isaac. As Myeerah grew older her childish fancy for the white boy deepened into an intense love.

But while this love tendered her inexorable to Isaac on the question of giving him his freedom, it undoubtedly saved his life as well as the lives of other white prisoners, on more than one occasion.

To the white captives who fell into the hands of the Hurons, she was kind and merciful; many of the wounded she had tended with her own hands, and many poor wretches she had saved from the gauntlet and the stake. When her efforts to persuade her father to save any one were unavailing she would retire in sorrow to her lodge and remain there.

Her infatuation for the White Eagle, the Huron name for Isaac, was an old story; it was known to all the tribes and had long ceased to be questioned. At first some of the Delawares and the Shawnee braves, who had failed to win Myeerah's love, had openly scorned her for her love for the pale face. The Wyandot warriors to a man worshipped her; they would have marched straight into the jaws of death at her command; they resented the insults which had been cast on their princess, and they had wiped them out in blood: now none dared taunt her.

In the spring following Isaac's recapture a very serious accident befell him. He had become expert in the Indian game of ball, which is a game resembling the Canadian lacrosse, and from which, in fact, it had been adopted. Goals were placed at both ends of a level plain. Each party of Indians chose a goal which they endeavored to defend and at the same time would try to carry the ball over their opponent's line.

A well contested game of Indian ball presented a scene of wonderful effort and excitement. Hundreds of strong and supple braves could be seen running over the plain, darting this way and that, or struggling in a yelling, kicking, fighting mass, all in a mad scramble to get the ball.

As Isaac had his share of the Zane swiftness of foot, at times his really remarkable fleetness enabled him to get control of the ball. In front of the band of yelling savages he would carry it down the field, and evading the guards at the goal, would throw it between the posts. This was a feat of which any brave could be proud.

During one of these games Red Fox, a Wyandot brave, who had long been hopelessly in love with Myeerah, and who cordially hated Isaac, used this opportunity for revenge. Red Fox, who was a swift runner, had vied with Isaac for the honors, but being defeated in the end, he had yielded to his jealous frenzy and had struck Isaac a terrible blow on the head with his bat.

It happened to be a glancing blow or Isaac's life would have been ended then and there. As it was he had a deep gash in his head. The Indians carried him to his lodge and the medicine men of the tribe were summoned.

When Isaac recovered consciousness he asked for Myeerah and entreated her not to punish Red Fox. He knew that such a course would only increase his difficulties, and, on the other hand, if he saved the life of the Indian who had struck him in such a cowardly manner such an act would appeal favorably to the Indians. His entreaties had no effect on Myeerah, who was furious, and who said that if Red Fox, who had escaped, ever returned he would pay for his unprovoked assault with his life, even if she had to kill him herself. Isaac knew that Myeerah would keep her word. He dreaded every morning that the old squaw who prepared his meals would bring him the news that his assailant had been slain. Red Fox was a popular brave, and there were many Indians who believed the blow he had struck Isaac was not intentional. Isaac worried needlessly, however, for Red Fox never came back, and nothing could be learned as to his whereabouts.

It was during his convalescence that Isaac learned really to love the Indian maiden. She showed such distress in the first days after his injury, and such happiness when he was out of danger and on the road to recovery that Isaac wondered at her. She attended him with anxious solicitude; when she bathed and bandaged his wound her every touch was a tender caress; she sat by him for hours; her low voice made soft melody as she sang the Huron love songs. The moments were sweet to Isaac when in the gathering twilight she leaned her head on his shoulder while they listened to the evening carol of the whip-poor-will. Days passed and at length Isaac was entirely well. One day when the air was laden with the warm breath of summer Myeerah and Isaac walked by the river.

"You are sad again," said Myeerah.

"I am homesick. I want to see my people. Myeerah, you have named me rightly. The Eagle can never be happy unless he is free."

"The Eagle can be happy with his mate. And what life could be freer than a Huron's? I hope always that you will grow content."

"It has been a long time now, Myeerah, since I have spoken with you of my freedom. Will you ever free me? Or must I take again those awful chances of escape? I cannot always live here in this way. Some day I shall be killed while trying to get away, and then, if you truly love me, you will never forgive yourself."

"Does not Myeerah truly love you?" she asked, gazing straight into his eyes, her own misty and sad.

"I do not doubt that, but I think sometimes that it is not the right kind of love. It is too savage. No man should be made a prisoner for no other reason than that he is loved by a woman. I have tried to teach you many things; the language of my people, their ways and thoughts, but I have failed to civilize you. I cannot make you understand that it is unwomanly—do not turn away. I am not indifferent. I have learned to care for you. Your beauty and tenderness have made anything else impossible."

"Myeerah is proud of her beauty, if it pleases the Eagle. Her beauty and her love are his. Yet the Eagle's words make Myeerah sad. She cannot tell what she feels. The pale face's words flow swiftly and smoothly like rippling waters, but Myeerah's heart is full and her lips are dumb."

Myeerah and Isaac stopped under a spreading elm tree the branches of which drooped over and shaded the river. The action of the high water had worn away the earth round the roots of the old elm, leaving them bare and dry when the stream was low. As though Nature had been jealous in the interest of lovers, she had twisted and curled the roots into a curiously shaped bench just above the water, which was secluded enough to escape all eyes except those of the beaver and the muskrat. The bank above was carpeted with fresh, dewy grass; blue bells and violets hid modestly under their dark green leaves; delicate ferns, like wonderful fairy lace, lifted their dainty heads to sway in the summer breeze. In this quiet nook the lovers passed many hours.

"Then, if my White Chief has learned to care for me, he must not try to escape," whispered Myeerah, tenderly, as she crept into Isaac's arms and laid her head on his breast. "I love you. I love you. What will become of Myeerah if you leave her? Could she ever be happy? Could she ever forget? No, no, I will keep my captive."

"I cannot persuade you to let me go?"

"If I free you I will come and lie here," cried Myeerah, pointing to the dark pool.

"Then come with me to my home and live there."

"Go with you to the village of the pale faces, where Myeerah would be scorned, pointed at as your captors laughed at and pitied? No! No!"

"But you would not be," said Isaac, eagerly. "You would be my wife. My sister and people will love you. Come, Myeerah save me from this bondage; come home with me and I will make you happy."

"It can never be," she said, sadly, after a long pause. "How would we ever reach the fort by the big river? Tarhe loves his daughter and will not give her up. If we tried to get away the braves would overtake us and then even Myeerah could not save your life. You would be killed. I dare not try. No, no, Myeerah loves too well for that."

"You might make the attempt," said Isaac, turning away in bitter disappointment. "If you loved me you could not see me suffer."

"Never say that again," cried Myeerah, pain and scorn in her dark eyes. "Can an Indian Princess who has the blood of great chiefs in her veins prove her love in any way that she has not? Some day you will know that you wrong me. I am Tarhe's daughter. A Huron does not lie."

They slowly wended their way back to the camp, both miserable at heart; Isaac longing to see his home and friends, and yet with tenderness in his heart for the Indian maiden who would not free him; Myeerah with pity and love for him and a fear that her long cherished dream could never be realized.

One dark, stormy night, when the rain beat down in torrents and the swollen river raged almost to its banks, Isaac slipped out of his lodge unobserved and under cover of the pitchy darkness he got safely between the lines of tepees to the river. He had just the opportunity for which he had been praying. He plunged into the water and floating down with the swift current he soon got out of sight of the flickering camp fires. Half a mile below he left the water and ran along the bank until he came to a large tree, a landmark he remembered, when he turned abruptly to the east and struck out through the dense woods. He travelled due east all that night and the next day without resting, and with nothing to eat except a small piece of jerked buffalo meat which he had taken the precaution to hide in his hunting shirt. He rested part of the second night and next morning pushed on toward the east. He had expected to reach the Ohio that day, but he did not and he noticed that the ground seemed to be gradually rising. He did not come across any swampy lands or saw grass or vegetation characteristic of the lowlands. He stopped and tried to get his bearings. The country was unknown to him, but he believed he knew the general lay of the ridges and the water-courses.

The fourth day found Isaac hopelessly lost in the woods. He was famished, having eaten but a few herbs and berries in the last two days; his buckskin garments were torn in tatters; his moccasins were worn out and his feet lacerated by the sharp thorns.

Darkness was fast approaching when he first realized that he was lost. He waited hopefully for the appearance of the north star—that most faithful of hunter's guides—but the sky clouded over and no stars appeared. Tired out and hopeless he dragged his weary body into a dense laurel thicket end lay down to wait for dawn. The dismal hoot of an owl nearby, the stealthy steps of some soft-footed animal prowling round the thicket, and the mournful sough of the wind in the treetops kept him awake for hours, but at last he fell asleep.

CHAPTER VII.

The chilling rains of November and December's flurry of snow had passed and mid-winter with its icy blasts had set in. The Black Forest had changed autumn's gay crimson and yellow to the somber hue of winter and now looked indescribably dreary. An ice gorge had formed in the bend of the river at the head of the island and from bank to bank logs, driftwood, broken ice and giant floes were packed and jammed so tightly as to resist the action of the mighty current. This natural bridge would remain solid until spring had loosened the frozen grip of old winter. The hills surrounding Fort Henry were white with snow. The huge drifts were on a level with Col. Zane's fence and in some places the top rail had disappeared. The pine trees in the yard were weighted down and drooped helplessly with their white burden.

On this frosty January morning the only signs of life round the settlement were a man and a dog walking up Wheeling hill. The man carried a rifle, an axe, and several steel traps. His snow-shoes sank into the drifts as he labored up the steep hill. All at once he stopped. The big black dog had put his nose high in the air and had sniffed at the cold wind.

"Well, Tige, old fellow, what is it?" said Jonathan Zane, for this was he.

The dog answered with a low whine. Jonathan looked up and down the creek valley and along the hillside, but he saw no living thing. Snow, snow everywhere, its white monotony relieved here and there by a black tree trunk. Tige sniffed again and then growled. Turning his ear to the breeze Jonathan heard faint yelps from far over the hilltop. He dropped his axe and the traps and ran the remaining short distance up the hill. When he reached the summit the clear baying of hunting wolves was borne to his ears.

The hill sloped gradually on the other side, ending in a white, unbroken plain which extended to the edge of the laurel thicket a quarter of a mile distant. Jonathan could not see the wolves, but he heard distinctly their peculiar, broken howls. They were in pursuit of something, whether quadruped or man he could not decide. Another moment and he was no longer in doubt, for a deer dashed out of the thicket. Jonathan saw that it was a buck and that he was well nigh exhausted; his head swung low from side to side; he sank slowly to his knees, and showed every indication of distress.

The next instant the baying of the wolves, which had ceased for a moment, sounded close at hand. The buck staggered to his feet; he turned this way and that. When he saw the man and the dog he started toward them without a moment's hesitation.

At a warning word from Jonathan the dog sank on the snow. Jonathan stepped behind a tree, which, however, was not large enough to screen his body. He thought the buck would pass close by him and he determined to shoot at the most favorable moment.

The buck, however, showed no intention of passing by; in his abject terror he saw in the man and the dog foes less terrible than those which were yelping on his trail. He came on in a lame uneven trot, making straight for the tree. When he reached the tree he crouched, or rather fell, on the ground within a yard of Jonathan and his dog. He quivered and twitched; his nostrils flared; at every pant drops of blood flecked the snow; his great dark eyes had a strained and awful look, almost human in its agony.

Another yelp from the thicket and Jonathan looked up in time to see five timber wolves, gaunt, hungry looking beasts, burst from the bushes. With their noses close to the snow they followed the trail. When they came to the spot where the deer had fallen a chorus of angry, thirsty howls filled the air.

"Well, if this doesn't beat me! I thought I knew a little about deer," said Jonathan. "Tige, we will save this buck from those gray devils if it costs a leg. Steady now, old fellow, wait."

When the wolves were within fifty yards of the tree and coming swiftly Jonathan threw his rifle forward and yelled with all the power of his strong lungs:

"Hi! Hi! Hi! Take 'em, Tige!"

In trying to stop quickly on the slippery snowcrust the wolves fell all over themselves. One dropped dead and another fell wounded at the report of Jonathan's rifle. The others turned tail and loped swiftly off into the thicket. Tige made short work of the wounded one.

"Old White Tail, if you were the last buck in the valley, I would not harm you," said Jonathan, looking at the panting deer. "You need have no farther fear of that pack of cowards."

So saying Jonathan called to Tige and wended his way down the hill toward the settlement.

An hour afterward he was sitting in Col. Zane's comfortable cabin, where all was warmth and cheerfulness. Blazing hickory logs roared and crackled in the stone fireplace.

"Hello, Jack, where did you come from?" said Col. Zane, who had just come in. "Haven't seen you since we were snowed up. Come over to see about the horses? If I were you I would not undertake that trip to Fort Pitt until the weather breaks. You could go in the sled, of course, but if you care anything for my advice you will stay home. This weather will hold on for some time. Let Lord Dunmore wait."

"I guess we are in for some stiff weather."

"Haven't a doubt of it. I told Bessie last fall we might expect a hard winter. Everything indicated it. Look at the thick corn-husks. The hulls of the nuts from the shell-bark here in the yard were larger and tougher than I ever saw them. Last October Tige killed a raccoon that had the wooliest kind of a fur. I could have given you a dozen signs of a hard winter. We shall still have a month or six weeks of it. In a week will be ground-hog day and you had better wait and decide after that."

"I tell you, Eb, I get tired chopping wood and hanging round the house."

"Aha! another moody spell," said Col. Zane, glancing kindly at his brother. "Jack, if you were married you would outgrow those 'blue-devils.' I used to have them. It runs in the family to be moody. I have known our father to take his gun and go into the woods and stay there until he had fought out the spell. I have done that myself, but once I married Bessie I have had no return of the old feeling. Get married, Jack, and then you will settle down and work. You will not have time to roam around alone in the woods."

"I prefer the spells, as you call them, any day," answered Jonathan, with a short laugh. "A man with my disposition has no right to get married. This weather is trying, for it keeps me indoors. I cannot hunt because we do not need the meat. And even if I did want to hunt I should not have to go out of sight of the fort. There were three deer in front of the barn this morning. They were nearly starved. They ran off a little at sight of me, but in a few moments came back for the hay I pitched out of the loft. This afternoon Tige and I saved a big buck from a pack of wolves. The buck came right up to me. I could have touched him. This storm is sending the deer down from the hills."

"You are right. It is too bad. Severe weather like this will kill more deer than an army could. Have you been doing anything with your traps?"

"Yes, I have thirty traps out."

"If you are going, tell Sam to fetch down another load of fodder before he unhitches."

"Eb, I have no patience with your brothers," said Col. Zane's wife to him after he had closed the door. "They are all alike; forever wanting to be on the go. If it isn't Indians it is something else. The very idea of going up the river in this weather. If Jonathan doesn't care for himself he should think of the horses."

"My dear, I was just as wild and discontented as Jack before I met you," remarked Col. Zane. "You may not think so, but a home and pretty little woman will do wonders for any man. My brothers have nothing to keep them steady."

"Perhaps. I do not believe that Jonathan ever will get married. Silas may; he certainly has been keeping company long enough with Mary Bennet. You are the only Zane who has conquered that adventurous spirit and the desire to be always roaming the woods in search of something to kill. Your old boy, Noah, is growing up like all the Zanes. He fights with all the children in the settlement. I cannot break him of it. He is not a bully, for I have never known him to do anything mean or cruel. It is just sheer love of fighting."

"Ha! Ha! I fear you will not break him of that," answered Col. Zane. "It is a good joke to say he gets it all from the Zanes. How about the McCollochs? What have you to say of your father and the Major and John McColloch? They are not anything if not the fighting kind. It's the best trait the youngster could have, out here on the border. He'll need it all. Don't worry about him. Where is Betty?"

"I told her to take the children out for a sled ride. Betty needs exercise. She stays indoors too much, and of late she looks pale."

"What! Betty not looking well! She was never ill in her life. I have noticed no change in her."

"No, I daresay you have not. You men can't see anything. But I can, and I tell you, Betty is very different from the girl she used to be. Most of the time she sits and gazes out of her window. She used to be so bright, and when she was not romping with the children she busied herself with her needle. Yesterday as I entered her room she hurriedly picked up a book, and, I think, intentionally hid her face behind it. I saw she had been crying."

"Come to think of it, I believe I have missed Betty," said Col. Zane, gravely. "She seems more quiet. Is she unhappy? When did you first see this change?"

"I think it a little while after Mr. Clarke left here last fall."

"Clarke! What has he to do with Betty? What are you driving at?" exclaimed the Colonel, stopping in front of his wife. His faced had paled slightly. "I had forgotten Clarke. Bess, you can't mean—"

"Now, Eb, do not get that look on your face. You always frighten me," answered his wife, as she quietly placed her hand on his arm. "I do not mean anything much, certainly nothing against Mr. Clarke. He was a true gentleman. I really liked him."

"So did I," interrupted the Colonel.

"I believe Betty cared for Mr. Clarke. She was always different with him. He has gone away and has forgotten her. That is strange to us, because we cannot imagine any one indifferent to our beautiful Betty. Nevertheless, no matter how attractive a woman may be men sometimes love and ride away. I hear the children coming now. Do not let Betty see that we have been talking about her. She is as quick as a steel trap."

A peal of childish laughter came from without. The door opened and Betty ran in, followed by the sturdy, rosy-checked youngsters. All three were white with snow.

"We have had great fun," said Betty. "We went over the bank once and tumbled off the sled into the snow. Then we had a snow-balling contest, and the boys compelled me to strike my colors and fly for the house."

Col. Zane looked closely at his sister. Her cheeks were flowing with health; her eyes were sparkling with pleasure. Failing to observe any indication of the change in Betty which his wife had spoken, he concluded that women were better qualified to judge their own sex than were men. He had to confess to himself that the only change he could see in his sister was that she grew prettier every day of her life.

"Oh, papa. I hit Sam right in the head with a big snow-ball, and I made Betty run into the house, and I slid down to all by myself. Sam was afraid," said Noah to his father.

"Noah, if Sammy saw the danger in sliding down the hill he was braver than you. Now both of you run to Annie and have these wet things taken off."

"I must go get on dry clothes myself," said Betty. "I am nearly frozen. It is growing colder. I saw Jack come in. Is he going to Fort Pitt?"

"No. He has decided to wait until good weather. I met Mr. Miller over at the garrison this afternoon and he wants you to go on the sled-ride to-night. There is to be a dance down at Watkins' place. All the young people are going. It is a long ride, but I guess it will be perfectly safe. Silas and Wetzel are going. Dress yourself warmly and go with them. You have never seen old Grandma Watkins."

"I shall be pleased to go," said Betty.

Betty's room was very cozy, considering that it was in a pioneer's cabin. It had two windows, the larger of which opened on the side toward the river. The walls had been smoothly plastered and covered with white birch-bark. They were adorned with a few pictures and Indian ornaments. A bright homespun carpet covered the floor. A small bookcase stood in the corner. The other furniture consisted of two chairs, a small table, a bureau with a mirror, and a large wardrobe. It was in this last that Betty kept the gowns which she had brought from Philadelphia, and which were the wonder of all the girls in the village.

"I wonder why Eb looked so closely at me," mused Betty, as she slipped on her little moccasins. "Usually he is not anxious to have me go so far from the fort; and now he seemed to think I would enjoy this dance to-night. I wonder what Bessie has been telling him."

Betty threw some wood on the smouldering fire in the little stone grate and sat down to think. Like every one who has a humiliating secret, Betty was eternally suspicious and feared the very walls would guess it. Swift as light came the thought that her brother and his wife had suspected her secret and had been talking about her, perhaps pitying her. With this thought came the fear that if she had betrayed herself to the Colonel's wife she might have done so to others. The consciousness that this might well be true and that even now the girls might be talking and laughing at her caused her exceeding shame and bitterness.

Many weeks had passed since that last night that Betty and Alfred Clarke had been together.

In due time Col. Zane's men returned and Betty learned from Jonathan that Alfred had left them at Ft. Pitt, saying he was going south to his old home. At first she had expected some word from Alfred, a letter, or if not that, surely an apology for his conduct on that last evening they had been together. But Jonathan brought her no word, and after hoping against hope and wearing away the long days looking for a letter that never came, she ceased to hope and plunged into despair.

The last few months had changed her life; changed it as only constant thinking, and suffering that must be hidden from the world, can change the life of a young girl. She had been so intent on her own thoughts, so deep in her dreams that she had taken no heed of other people. She did not know that those who loved her were always thinking of her welfare and would naturally see even a slight change in her. With a sudden shock of surprise and pain she realized that to-day for the first time in a month she had played with the boys. Sammy had asked her why she did not laugh any more. Now she understood the mad antics of Tige that morning; Madcap's whinney of delight; the chattering of the squirrels, and Caesar's pranks in the snow. She had neglected her pets. She had neglected her work, her friends, the boys' lessons; and her brother. For what? What would her girl friends say? That she was pining for a lover who had forgotten her. They would say that and it would be true. She did think of him constantly.

With bitter pain she recalled the first days of the acquaintance which now seemed so long past; how much she had disliked Alfred; how angry she had been with him and how contemptuously she had spurned his first proffer of friendship; how, little by little, her pride had been subdued; then the struggle with her heart. And, at last, after he had gone, came the realization that the moments spent with him had been the sweetest of her life. She thought of him as she used to see him stand before her; so good to look at; so strong and masterful, and yet so gentle.

"Oh, I cannot bear it," whispered Betty with a half sob, giving up to a rush of tender feeling. "I love him. I love him, and I cannot forget him. Oh, I am so ashamed."

Betty bowed her head on her knees. Her slight form quivered a while and then grew still. When a half hour later she raised her head her face was pale and cold. It bore the look of a girl who had suddenly become a woman; a woman who saw the battle of life before her and who was ready to fight. Stern resolve gleamed from her flashing eyes; there was no faltering in those set lips.

Betty was a Zane and the Zanes came of a fighting race. Their blood had ever been hot and passionate; the blood of men quick to love and quick to hate. It had flowed in the veins of daring, reckless men who had fought and died for their country; men who had won their sweethearts with the sword; men who had had unconquerable spirits. It was this fighting instinct that now rose in Betty; it gave her strength and pride to defend her secret; the resolve to fight against the longing in her heart.

"I will forget him! I will tear him out of my heart!" she exclaimed passionately. "He never deserved my love. He did not care. I was a little fool to let him amuse himself with me. He went away and forgot. I hate him."

At length Betty subdued her excitement, and when she went down to supper a few minutes later she tried to maintain a cheerful composure of manner and to chat with her old-time vivacity.

"Bessie, I am sure you have exaggerated things," remarked Col. Zane after Betty had gone upstairs to dress for the dance. "Perhaps it is only that Betty grows a little tired of this howling wilderness. Small wonder if she does. You know she has always been used to comfort and many young people, places to go and all that. This is her first winter on the frontier. She'll come round all right."

"Have it your way, Ebenezer," answered his wife with a look of amused contempt on her face. "I am sure I hope you are right. By the way, what do you think of this Ralfe Miller? He has been much with Betty of late."

"I do not know the fellow, Bessie. He seems agreeable. He is a good-looking young man. Why do you ask?"

"The Major told me that Miller had a bad name at Pitt, and that he had been a friend of Simon Girty before Girty became a renegade."

"Humph! I'll have to speak to Sam. As for knowing Girty, there is nothing terrible in that. All the women seem to think that Simon is the very prince of devils. I have known all the Girtys for years. Simon was not a bad fellow before he went over to the Indians. It is his brother James who has committed most of those deeds which have made the name of Girty so infamous."

"I don't like Miller," continued Mrs. Zane in a hesitating way. "I must admit that I have no sensible reason for my dislike. He is pleasant and agreeable, yes, but behind it there is a certain intensity. That man has something on his mind."

"If he is in love with Betty, as you seem to think, he has enough on his mind. I'll vouch for that," said Col. Zane. "Betty is inclined to be a coquette. If she liked Clarke pretty well, it may be a lesson to her."

"I wish she were married and settled down. It may have been no great harm for Betty to have had many admirers while in Philadelphia, but out here on the border it will never do. These men will not have it. There will be trouble come of Betty's coquettishness."

"Why, Bessie, she is only a child. What would you have her do? Marry the first man who asked her?"

"The clod-hoppers are coming," said Mrs. Zane as the jingling of sleigh bells broke the stillness.

Col. Zane sprang up and opened the door. A broad stream of light flashed from the room and lighted up the road. Three powerful teams stood before the door. They were hitched to sleds, or clod-hoppers, which were nothing more than wagon-beds fastened on wooden runners. A chorus of merry shouts greeted Col. Zane as he appeared in the doorway.

"All right! all right! Here she is," he cried, as Betty ran down the steps.

The Colonel bundled her in a buffalo robe in a corner of the foremost sled. At her feet he placed a buckskin bag containing a hot stone Mrs. Zane thoughtfully had provided.

"All ready here. Let them go," called the Colonel. "You will have clear weather. Coming back look well to the traces and keep a watch for the wolves."

The long whips cracked, the bells jingled, the impatient horses plunged forward and away they went over the glistening snow. The night was clear and cold; countless stars blinked in the black vault overhead; the pale moon cast its wintry light down on a white and frozen world. As the runners glided swiftly and smoothly onward showers of dry snow like fine powder flew from under the horses' hoofs and soon whitened the black-robed figures in the sleds. The way led down the hill past the Fort, over the creek bridge and along the road that skirted the Black Forest. The ride was long; it led up and down hills, and through a lengthy stretch of gloomy forest. Sometimes the drivers walked the horses up a steep climb and again raced them along a level bottom. Making a turn in the road they saw a bright light in the distance which marked their destination. In five minutes the horses dashed into a wide clearing. An immense log fire burned in front of a two-story structure. Streams of light poured from the small windows; the squeaking of fiddles, the shuffling of many feet, and gay laughter came through the open door.

The steaming horses were unhitched, covered carefully with robes and led into sheltered places, while the merry party disappeared into the house.

The occasion was the celebration of the birthday of old Dan Watkins' daughter. Dan was one of the oldest settlers along the river; in fact, he had located his farm several years after Col. Zane had founded the settlement. He was noted for his open-handed dealing and kindness of heart. He had loaned many a head of cattle which had never been returned, and many a sack of flour had left his mill unpaid for in grain. He was a good shot, he would lay a tree on the ground as quickly as any man who ever swung an axe, and he could drink more whiskey than any man in the valley.

Dan stood at the door with a smile of welcome upon his rugged features and a handshake and a pleasant word for everyone. His daughter Susan greeted the men with a little curtsy and kissed the girls upon the cheek. Susan was not pretty, though she was strong and healthy; her laughing blue eyes assured a sunny disposition, and she numbered her suitors by the score.

The young people lost no time. Soon the floor was covered with their whirling forms.

In one corner of the room sat a little dried-up old woman with white hair and bright dark eyes. This was Grandma Watkins. She was very old, so old that no one knew her age, but she was still vigorous enough to do her day's work with more pleasure than many a younger woman. Just now she was talking to Wetzel, who leaned upon his inseparable rifle and listened to her chatter. The hunter liked the old lady and would often stop at her cabin while on his way to the settlement and leave at her door a fat turkey or a haunch of venison.

"Lew Wetzel, I am ashamed of you." Grandmother Watkins was saying. "Put that gun in the corner and get out there and dance. Enjoy yourself. You are only a boy yet."

"I'd better look on, mother," answered the hunter.

"Pshaw! You can hop and skip around like any of then and laugh too if you want. I hope that pretty sister of Eb Zane has caught your fancy."

"She is not for the like of me," he said gently "I haven't the gifts."

"Don't talk about gifts. Not to an old woman who has lived three times and more your age," she said impatiently. "It is not gifts a woman wants out here in the West. If she does 'twill do her no good. She needs a strong arm to build cabins, a quick eye with a rifle, and a fearless heart. What border-women want are houses and children. They must bring up men, men to drive the redskins back, men to till the soil, or else what is the good of our suffering here."

"You are right," said Wetzel thoughtfully. "But I'd hate to see a flower like Betty Zane in a rude hunter's cabin."

"I have known the Zanes for forty year' and I never saw one yet that was afraid of work. And you might win her if you would give up running mad after Indians. I'll allow no woman would put up with that. You have killed many Indians. You ought to be satisfied."

"Fightin' redskins is somethin' I can't help," said the hunter, slowly shaking his head. "If I got married the fever would come on and I'd leave home. No, I'm no good for a woman. Fightin' is all I'm good for."

"Why not fight for her, then? Don't let one of these boys walk off with her. Look at her. She likes fun and admiration. I believe you do care for her. Why not try to win her?"

"Who is that tall man with her?" continued the old lady as Wetzel did not answer. "There, they have gone into the other room. Who is he?"

"His name is Miller."

"Lewis, I don't like him. I have been watching him all evening. I'm a contrary old woman, I know, but I have seen a good many men in my time, and his face is not honest. He is in love with her. Does she care for him?"

"No, Betty doesn't care for Miller. She's just full of life and fun."

"You may be mistaken. All the Zanes are fire and brimstone and this girl is a Zane clear through. Go and fetch her to me, Lewis. I'll tell you if there's a chance for you."

"Dear mother, perhaps there's a wife in Heaven for me. There's none on earth," said the hunter, a sad smile flitting over his calm face.

Ralfe Miller, whose actions had occasioned the remarks of the old lady, would have been conspicuous in any assembly of men. There was something in his dark face that compelled interest and yet left the observer in doubt. His square chin, deep-set eyes and firm mouth denoted a strong and indomitable will. He looked a man whom it would be dangerous to cross.

Little was known of Miller's history. He hailed from Ft. Pitt, where he had a reputation as a good soldier, but a man of morose and quarrelsome disposition. It was whispered that he drank, and that he had been friendly with the renegades McKee, Elliott, and Girty. He had passed the fall and winter at Ft. Henry, serving on garrison duty. Since he had made the acquaintance of Betty he had shown her all the attention possible.

On this night a close observer would have seen that Miller was laboring under some strong feeling. A half-subdued fire gleamed from his dark eyes. A peculiar nervous twitching of his nostrils betrayed a poorly suppressed excitement.

All evening he followed Betty like a shadow. Her kindness may have encouraged him. She danced often with him and showed a certain preference for his society. Alice and Lydia were puzzled by Betty's manner. As they were intimate friends they believed they knew something of her likes and dislikes. Had not Betty told them she did not care for Mr. Miller? What was the meaning of the arch glances she bestowed upon him, if she did not care for him? To be sure, it was nothing wonderful for Betty to smile,—she was always prodigal of her smiles—but she had never been known to encourage any man. The truth was that Betty had put her new resolution into effect; to be as merry and charming as any fancy-free maiden could possibly be, and the farthest removed from a young lady pining for an absent and indifferent sweetheart. To her sorrow Betty played her part too well.

Except to Wetzel, whose keen eyes little escaped, there was no significance in Miller's hilarity one moment and sudden thoughtfulness the next. And if there had been, it would have excited no comment. Most of the young men had sampled some of old Dan's best rye and their flushed faces and unusual spirits did not result altogether from the exercise of the dance.

After one of the reels Miller led Betty, with whom he had been dancing, into one of the side rooms. Round the dimly lighted room were benches upon which were seated some of the dancers. Betty was uneasy in mind and now wished that she had remained at home. They had exchanged several commonplace remarks when the music struck up and Betty rose quickly to her feet.

"See, the others have gone. Let us return," she said.

"Wait," said Miller hurriedly. "Do not go just yet. I wish to speak to you. I have asked you many times if you will marry me. Now I ask you again."

"Mr. Miller, I thanked you and begged you not to cause us both pain by again referring to that subject," answered Betty with dignity. "If you will persist in bringing it up we cannot be friends any longer."

"Wait, please wait. I have told you that I will not take 'No' for an answer. I love you with all my heart and soul and I cannot give you up."

His voice was low and hoarse and thrilled with a strong man's passion. Betty looked up into his face and tears of compassion filled her eyes. Her heart softened to this man, and her conscience gave her a little twinge of remorse. Could she not have averted all this? No doubt she had been much to blame, and this thought made her voice very low and sweet as she answered him.

"I like you as a friend, Mr. Miller, but we can never be more than friends. I am very sorry for you, and angry with myself that I did not try to help you instead of making it worse. Please do not speak of this again. Come, let us join the others."

They were quite alone in the room. As Betty finished speaking and started for the door Miller intercepted her. She recoiled in alarm from his white face.

"No, you don't go yet. I won't give you up so easily. No woman can play fast and loose with me! Do you understand? What have you meant all this winter? You encouraged me. You know you did," he cried passionately.

"I thought you were a gentleman. I have really taken the trouble to defend you against persons who evidently were not misled as to your real nature. I will not listen to you," said Betty coldly. She turned away from him, all her softened feeling changed to scorn.

"You shall listen to me," he whispered as he grasped her wrist and pulled her backward. All the man's brutal passion had been aroused. The fierce border blood boiled within his heart. Unmasked he showed himself in his true colors a frontier desperado. His eyes gleamed dark and lurid beneath his bent brows and a short, desperate laugh passed his lips.

"I will make you love me, my proud beauty. I shall have you yet, one way or another."

"Let me go. How dare you touch me!" cried Betty, the hot blood coloring her face. She struck him a stinging blow with her free hand and struggled with all her might to free herself; but she was powerless in his iron grasp. Closer he drew her.

"If it costs me my life I will kiss you for that blow," he muttered hoarsely.

"Oh, you coward! you ruffian! Release me or I will scream."

She had opened her lips to call for help when she saw a dark figure cross the threshold. She recognized the tall form of Wetzel. The hunter stood still in the doorway for a second and then with the swiftness of light he sprang forward. The single straightening of his arm sent Miller backward over a bench to the floor with a crashing sound. Miller rose with some difficulty and stood with one hand to his head.

"Lew, don't draw your knife," cried Betty as she saw Wetzel's hand go inside his hunting shirt. She had thrown herself in front of him as Miller got to his feet. With both little hands she clung to the brawny arm of the hunter, but she could not stay it. Wetzel's hand slipped to his belt.

"For God's sake, Lew, do not kill him," implored Betty, gazing horror-stricken at the glittering eyes of the hunter. "You have punished him enough. He only tried to kiss me. I was partly to blame. Put your knife away. Do not shed blood. For my sake, Lew, for my sake!"

When Betty found that she could not hold Wetzel's arm she threw her arms round his neck and clung to him with all her young strength. No doubt her action averted a tragedy. If Miller had been inclined to draw a weapon then he might have had a good opportunity to use it. He had the reputation of being quick with his knife, and many of his past fights testified that he was not a coward. But he made no effort to attack Wetzel. It was certain that he measured with his eye the distance to the door. Wetzel was not like other men. Irrespective of his wonderful strength and agility there was something about the Indian hunter that terrified all men. Miller shrank before those eyes. He knew that never in all his life of adventure had he been as near death as at that moment. There was nothing between him and eternity but the delicate arms of this frail girl. At a slight wave of the hunter's hand towards the door he turned and passed out.

"Oh, how dreadful!" cried Betty, dropping upon a bench with a sob of relief. "I am glad you came when you did even though you frightened me more than he did. Promise me that you will not do Miller any further harm. If you had fought it would all have been on my account; one or both of you might have been killed. Don't look at me so. I do not care for him. I never did. Now that I know him I despise him. He lost his senses and tried to kiss me. I could have killed him myself."

Wetzel did not answer. Betty had been holding his hand in both her own while she spoke impulsively.

"I understand how difficult it is for you to overlook an insult to me," she continued earnestly. "But I ask it of you. You are my best friend, almost my brother, and I promise you that if he ever speaks a word to me again that is not what it should be I will tell you."

"I reckon I'll let him go, considerin' how set on it you are."

"But remember, Lew, that he is revengeful and you must be on the lookout," said Betty gravely as she recalled the malignant gleam in Miller's eyes.

"He's dangerous only like a moccasin snake that hides in the grass."

"Am I all right? Do I look mussed or—or excited—or anything?" asked

Betty.

Lewis smiled as she turned round for his benefit. Her hair was a little awry and the lace at her neck disarranged. The natural bloom had not quite returned to her cheeks. With a look in his eyes that would have mystified Betty for many a day had she but seen it he ran his gaze over the dainty figure. Then reassuring her that she looked as well as ever, he led her into the dance-room.

"So this is Betty Zane. Dear child, kiss me," said Grandmother Watkins when Wetzel had brought Betty up to her. "Now, let me get a good look at you. Well, well, you are a true Zane. Black hair and eyes; all fire and pride. Child, I knew your father and mother long before you were born. Your father was a fine man but a proud one. And how do you like the frontier? Are you enjoying yourself?"

"Oh, yes, indeed," said Betty, smiling brightly at the old lady.

"Well, dearie, have a good time while you can. Life is hard in a pioneer's cabin. You will not always have the Colonel to look after you. They tell me you have been to some grand school in Philadelphia. Learning is very well, but it will not help you in the cabin of one of these rough men."

"There is a great need of education in all the pioneers' homes. I have persuaded brother Eb to have a schoolteacher at the Fort next spring."

"First teach the boys to plow and the girls to make Johnny cake. How much you favor your brother Isaac. He used to come and see me often. So must you in summertime. Poor lad, I suppose he is dead by this time. I have seen so many brave and good lads go. There now, I did not mean to make you sad," and the old lady patted Betty's hand and sighed.

"He often spoke of you and said that I must come with him to see you. Now he is gone," said Betty.

"Yes, he is gone, Betty, but you must not be sad while you are so young. Wait until you are old like I am. How long have you known Lew Wetzel?"

"All my life. He used to carry me in his arm, when I was a baby. Of course I do not remember that, but as far back as I can go in memory I can see Lew. Oh, the many times he has saved me from disaster! But why do you ask?"

"I think Lew Wetzel cares more for you than for all the world. He is as silent as an Indian, but I am an old woman and I can read men's hearts. If he could be made to give up his wandering life he would be the best man on the border."

"Oh, indeed I think you are wrong. Lew does not care for me in that way," said Betty, surprised and troubled by the old lady's vehemence.

A loud blast from a hunting-horn directed the attention of all to the platform at the upper end of the hall, where Dan Watkins stood. The fiddlers ceased playing, the dancers stopped, and all looked expectantly. The scene was simple strong, and earnest. The light in the eyes of these maidens shone like the light from the pine cones on the walls. It beamed soft and warm. These fearless sons of the wilderness, these sturdy sons of progress, standing there clasping the hands of their partners and with faces glowing with happiness, forgetful of all save the enjoyment of the moment, were ready to go out on the morrow and battle unto the death for the homes and the lives of their loved ones.

"Friends," said Dan when the hum of voices had ceased "I never thought as how I'd have to get up here and make a speech to-night or I might have taken to the woods. Howsomever, mother and Susan says as it's gettin' late it's about time we had some supper. Somewhere in the big cake is hid a gold ring. If one of the girls gets it she can keep it as a gift from Susan, and should one of the boys find it he may make a present to his best girl. And in the bargain he gets to kiss Susan. She made some objection about this and said that part of the game didn't go, but I reckon the lucky young man will decide that for hisself. And now to the festal board."

Ample justice was done to the turkey, the venison, and the bear meat. Grandmother Watkins' delicious apple and pumpkin pies for which she was renowned, disappeared as by magic. Likewise the cakes and the sweet cider and the apple butter vanished.

When the big cake had been cut and divided among the guests, Wetzel discovered the gold ring within his share. He presented the ring to Betty, and gave his privilege of kissing Susan to George Reynolds, with the remark: "George, I calkilate Susan would like it better if you do the kissin' part." Now it was known to all that George had long been an ardent admirer of Susan's, and it was suspected that she was not indifferent to him. Nevertheless, she protested that it was not fair. George acted like a man who had the opportunity of his life. Amid uproarious laughter he ran Susan all over the room, and when he caught her he pulled her hands away from her blushing face and bestowed a right hearty kiss on her cheek. To everyone's surprise and to Wetzel's discomfiture, Susan walked up to him and saying that as he had taken such an easy way out of it she intended to punish him by kissing him. And so she did. Poor Lewis' face looked the picture of dismay. Probably he had never been kissed before in his life.

Happy hours speed away on the wings of the wind. The feasting over, the good-byes were spoken, the girls were wrapped in the warm robes, for it was now intensely cold, and soon the horses, eager to start on the long homeward journey, were pulling hard on their bits. On the party's return trip there was an absence of the hilarity which had prevailed on their coming. The bells were taken off before the sleds left the blockhouse, and the traces and the harness examined and tightened with the caution of men who were apprehensive of danger and who would take no chances.

In winter time the foes most feared by the settlers were the timber wolves. Thousands of these savage beasts infested the wild forest regions which bounded the lonely roads, and their wonderful power of scent and swift and tireless pursuit made a long night ride a thing to be dreaded. While the horses moved swiftly danger from wolves was not imminent; but carelessness or some mishap to a trace or a wheel had been the cause of more than one tragedy.

Therefore it was not remarkable that the drivers of our party breathed a sigh of relief when the top of the last steep hill had been reached. The girls were quiet, and tired out and cold they pressed close to one another; the men were silent and watchful.

When they were half way home and had just reached the outskirts of the Black Forest the keen ear of Wetzel caught the cry of a wolf. It came from the south and sounded so faint that Wetzel believed at first that he had been mistaken. A few moments passed in which the hunter turned his ear to the south. He had about made up his mind that he had only imagined he had heard something when the unmistakable yelp of a wolf came down on the wind. Then another, this time clear and distinct, caused the driver to turn and whisper to Wetzel. The hunter spoke in a low tone and the driver whipped up his horses. From out the depths of the dark woods along which they were riding came a long and mournful howl. It was a wolf answering the call of his mate. This time the horses heard it, for they threw back their ears and increased their speed. The girls heard it, for they shrank closer to the men.

There is that which is frightful in the cry of a wolf. When one is safe in camp before a roaring fire the short, sharp bark of a wolf is startling, and the long howl will make one shudder. It is so lonely and dismal. It makes no difference whether it be given while the wolf is sitting on his haunches near some cabin waiting for the remains of the settler's dinner, or while he is in full chase after his prey—the cry is equally wild, savage and bloodcurdling.

Betty had never heard it and though she was brave, when the howl from the forest had its answer in another howl from the creek thicket, she slipped her little mittened hand under Wetzel's arm and looked up at him with frightened eyes.

In half an hour the full chorus of yelps, barks and howls swelled hideously on the air, and the ever increasing pack of wolves could be seen scarcely a hundred yards behind the sleds. The patter of their swiftly flying feet on the snow could be distinctly heard. The slender, dark forms came nearer and nearer every moment. Presently the wolves had approached close enough for the occupants of the sleds to see their shining eyes looking like little balls of green fire. A gaunt beast bolder than the others, and evidently the leader of the pack, bounded forward until he was only a few yards from the last sled. At every jump he opened his great jaws and uttered a quick bark as if to embolden his followers.

Almost simultaneously with the red flame that burst from Wetzel's rifle came a sharp yelp of agony from the leader. He rolled over and over. Instantly followed a horrible mingling of snarls and barks, and snapping of jaws as the band fought over the body of their luckless comrade.

This short delay gave the advantage to the horses. When the wolves again appeared they were a long way behind. The distance to the fort was now short and the horses were urged to their utmost. The wolves kept up the chase until they reached the creek bridge and the mill. Then they slowed up: the howling became desultory, and finally the dark forms disappeared in the thickets.

CHAPTER VIII.

Winter dragged by uneventfully for Betty. Unlike the other pioneer girls, who were kept busy all the time with their mending, and linsey weaving, and household duties, Betty had nothing to divert her but her embroidery and her reading. These she found very tiresome. Her maid was devoted to her and never left a thing undone. Annie was old Sam's daughter, and she had waited on Betty since she had been a baby. The cleaning or mending or darning—anything in the shape of work that would have helped pass away the monotonous hours for Betty, was always done before she could lift her hand.

During the day she passed hours in her little room, and most of them were dreamed away by her window. Lydia and Alice came over sometimes and whiled away the tedious moments with their bright chatter and merry laughter, their castle-building, and their romancing on heroes and love and marriage as girls always will until the end of time. They had not forgotten Mr. Clarke, but as Betty had rebuked them with a dignity which forbade any further teasing on that score, they had transferred their fun-making to the use of Mr. Miller's name.

Fearing her brothers' wrath Betty had not told them of the scene with Miller at the dance. She had learned enough of rough border justice to dread the consequence of such a disclosure. She permitted Miller to come to the house, although she never saw him alone. Miller had accepted this favor gratefully. He said that on the night of the dance he had been a little the worse for Dan Watkins' strong liquor, and that, together with his bitter disappointment, made him act in the mad way which had so grievously offended her. He exerted himself to win her forgiveness. Betty was always tender-hearted, and though she did not trust him, she said they might still be friends, but that that depended on his respect for her forbearance. Miller had promised he would never refer to the old subject and he had kept his word.

Indeed Betty welcomed any diversion for the long winter evenings. Occasionally some of the young people visited her, and they sang and danced, roasted apples, popped chestnuts, and played games. Often Wetzel and Major McColloch came in after supper. Betty would come down and sing for them, and afterward would coax Indian lore and woodcraft from Wetzel, or she would play checkers with the Major. If she succeeded in winning from him, which in truth was not often, she teased him unmercifully. When Col. Zane and the Major had settled down to their series of games, from which nothing short of Indians could have diverted them, Betty sat by Wetzel. The silent man of the woods, an appellation the hunter had earned by his reticence, talked for Betty as he would for no one else.

One night while Col. Zane, his wife and Betty were entertaining Capt. Boggs and Major McColloch and several of Betty's girls friends, after the usual music and singing, storytelling became the order of the evening. Little Noah told of the time he had climbed the apple-tree in the yard after a raccoon and got severely bitten.

"One day," said Noah, "I heard Tige barking out in the orchard and I ran out there and saw a funny little fur ball up in the tree with a black tail and white rings around it. It looked like a pretty cat with a sharp nose. Every time Tige barked the little animal showed his teeth and swelled up his back. I wanted him for a pet. I got Sam to give me a sack and I climbed the tree and the nearer I got to him the farther he backed down the limb. I followed him and put out the sack to put it over his head and he bit me. I fell from the limb, but he fell too and Tige killed him and Sam stuffed him for me."

"Noah, you are quite a valiant hunter," said Betty. "Now, Jonathan, remember that you promised to tell me of your meeting with Daniel Boone."

"It was over on the Muskingong near the mouth of the Sandusky. I was hunting in the open woods along the bank when I saw an Indian. He saw me at the same time and we both treed. There we stood a long time each afraid to change position. Finally I began to act tired and resorted to an old ruse. I put my coon-skin cap on my ramrod and cautiously poked it from behind the tree, expecting every second to hear the whistle of the redskin's bullet. Instead I heard a jolly voice yell: 'Hey, young feller, you'll have to try something better'n that.' I looked and saw a white man standing out in the open and shaking all over with laughter. I went up to him and found him to be a big strong fellow with an honest, merry face. He said: 'I'm Boone.' I was considerably taken aback, especially when I saw he knew I was a white man all the time. We camped and hunted along the river a week and at the Falls of the Muskingong he struck out for his Kentucky home."

"Here is Wetzel," said Col. Zane, who had risen and gone to the door. "Now, Betty, try and get Lew to tell us something."

"Come, Lewis, here is a seat by me," said Betty. "We have been pleasantly passing the time. We have had bear stories, snake stories, ghost stories—all kinds of tales. Will you tell us one?"

"Lewis, did you ever have a chance to kill a hostile Indian and not take it?" asked Col. Zane.

"Never but once," answered Lewis.

"Tell us about it. I imagine it will be interesting."

"Well, I ain't good at tellin' things," began Lewis. "I reckon I've seen some strange sights. I kin tell you about the only redskin I ever let off. Three years ago I was takin' a fall hunt over on the Big Sandy, and I run into a party of Shawnees. I plugged a chief and started to run. There was some good runners and I couldn't shake 'em in the open country. Comin' to the Ohio I jumped in and swum across, keepin' my rifle and powder dry by holdin' 'em up. I hid in some bulrushes and waited. Pretty soon along comes three Injuns, and when they saw where I had taken to the water they stopped and held a short pow-wow. Then they all took to the water. This was what I was waitin' for. When they got nearly acrosst I shot the first redskin, and loadin' quick got a bullet into the others. The last Injun did not sink. I watched him go floatin' down stream expectin' every minute to see him go under as he was hurt so bad he could hardly keep his head above water. He floated down a long ways and the current carried him to a pile of driftwood which had lodged against a little island. I saw the Injun crawl up on the drift. I went down stream and by keepin' the island between me and him I got out to where he was. I pulled my tomahawk and went around the head of the island and found the redskin leanin' against a big log. He was a young brave and a fine lookin strong feller. He was tryin' to stop the blood from my bullet-hole in his side. When he saw me he tried to get up, but he was too weak. He smiled, pointed to the wound and said: 'Deathwind not heap times bad shot.' Then he bowed his head and waited for the tomahawk. Well, I picked him up and carried him ashore and made a shack by a spring. I staid there with him. When he got well enough to stand a few days' travel I got him across the river and givin' him a hunk of deer meat I told him to go, and if I ever saw him again I'd make a better shot.

"A year afterwards I trailed two Shawnees into Wingenund's camp and got surrounded and captured. The Delaware chief is my great enemy. They beat me, shot salt into my legs, made me run the gauntlet, tied me on the back of a wild mustang. Then they got ready to burn me at the stake. That night they painted my face black and held the usual death dances. Some of the braves got drunk and worked themselves into a frenzy. I allowed I'd never see daylight. I seen that one of the braves left to guard me was the young feller I had wounded the year before. He never took no notice of me. In the gray of the early mornin' when all were asleep and the other watch dozin' I felt cold steel between my wrists and my buckskin thongs dropped off. Then my feet were cut loose. I looked round and in the dim light I seen my young brave. He handed me my own rifle, knife and tomahawk, put his finger on his lips and with a bright smile, as if to say he was square with me, he pointed to the east. I was out of sight in a minute."

"How noble of him!" exclaimed Betty, her eyes all aglow. "He paid his debt to you, perhaps at the price of his life."

"I have never known an Indian to forget a promise, or a kind action, or an injury," observed Col. Zane.

"Are the Indians half as bad as they are called?" asked Betty. "I have heard as many stories of their nobility as of their cruelty."

"The Indians consider that they have been robbed and driven from their homes. What we think hideously inhuman is war to them," answered Col. Zane.

"When I came here from Fort Pitt I expected to see and fight Indians every day," said Capt. Boggs. "I have been here at Wheeling for nearly two years and have never seen a hostile Indian. There have been some Indians in the vicinity during that time but not one has shown himself to me. I'm not up to Indian tricks, I know, but I think the last siege must have been enough for them. I don't believe we shall have any more trouble from them."

"Captain," called out Col. Zane, banging his hand on the table. "I'll bet you my best horse to a keg of gunpowder that you see enough Indians before you are a year older to make you wish you had never seen or heard of the western border."

"And I'll go you the same bet," said Major McColloch.

"You see, Captain, you must understand a little of the nature of the Indian," continued Col. Zane. "We have had proof that the Delawares and the Shawnees have been preparing for an expedition for months. We shall have another siege some day and to my thinking it will be a longer and harder one than the last. What say you, Wetzel?"

"I ain't sayin' much, but I don't calkilate on goin' on any long hunts this summer," answered the hunter.

"And do you think Tarhe, Wingenund, Pipe, Cornplanter, and all those chiefs will unite their forces and attack us?" asked Betty of Wetzel.

"Cornplanter won't. He has been paid for most of his land and he ain't so bitter. Tarhe is not likely to bother us. But Pipe and Wingenund and Red Fox—they all want blood."

"Have you seen these chiefs?" said Betty.

"Yes, I know 'em all and they all know me," answered the hunter. "I've watched over many a trail waitin' for one of 'em. If I can ever get a shot at any of 'em I'll give up Injuns and go farmin'. Good night, Betty."

"What a strange man is Wetzel," mused Betty, after the visitors had gone. "Do you know, Eb, he is not at all like any one else. I have seen the girls shudder at the mention of his name and I have heard them say they could not look in his eyes. He does not affect me that way. It is not often I can get him to talk, but sometimes he tells me beautiful thing about the woods; how he lives in the wilderness, his home under the great trees; how every leaf on the trees and every blade of grass has its joy for him as well as its knowledge; how he curls up in his little bark shack and is lulled to sleep by the sighing of the wind through the pine tops. He told me he has often watched the stars for hours at a time. I know there is a waterfall back in the Black Forest somewhere that Lewis goes to, simply to sit and watch the water tumble over the precipice."

"Wetzel is a wonderful character, even to those who know him only as an Indian slayer and a man who wants no other occupation. Some day he will go off on one of these long jaunts and will never return. That is certain. The day is fast approaching when a man like Wetzel will be of no use in life. Now, he is a necessity. Like Tiger he can smell Indians. Betty, I believe Lewis tells you so much and is so kind and gentle toward you because he cares for you."

"Of course Lew likes me. I know he does and I want him to," said Betty. "But he does not care as you seem to think. Grandmother Watkins said the same. I am sure both of you are wrong."

"Did Dan's mother tell you that? Well, she's pretty shrewd. It's quite likely, Betty, quite likely. It seems to me you are not so quick witted as you used to be."

"Why so?" asked Betty, quickly.

"Well, you used to be different somehow," said her brother, as he patted her hand.

"Do you mean I am more thoughtful?"

"Yes, and sometimes you seem sad."

"I have tried to be brave and—and happy," said Betty, her voice trembling slightly.

"Yes, yes, I know you have, Betty. You have done wonderfully well here in this dead place. But tell me, don't be angry, don't you think too much of some one?"

"You have no right to ask me that," said Betty, flushing and turning away toward the stairway.

"Well, well, child, don't mind me. I did not mean anything. There, good night, Betty."

Long after she had gone up-stairs Col. Zane sat by his fireside. From time to time he sighed. He thought of the old Virginia home and of the smile of his mother. It seemed only a few short years since he had promised her that he would take care of the baby sister. How had he kept that promise made when Betty was a little thing bouncing on his knee? It seemed only yesterday. How swift the flight of time! Already Betty was a woman; her sweet, gay girlhood had passed; already a shadow had fallen on her face, the shadow of a secret sorrow.

* * * * * * * * * * * * * *

March with its blustering winds had departed, and now April's showers and sunshine were gladdening the hearts of the settlers. Patches of green freshened the slopes of the hills; the lilac bushes showed tiny leaves, and the maple-buds were bursting. Yesterday a blue-bird—surest harbinger of spring—had alighted on the fence-post and had sung his plaintive song. A few more days and the blossoms were out mingling their pink and white with the green; the red-bud, the hawthorne, and the dog-wood were in bloom, checkering the hillsides.

"Bessie, spring is here," said Col. Zane, as he stood in the doorway. "The air is fresh, the sun shines warm, the birds are singing; it makes me feel good."

"Yes, it is pleasant to have spring with us again," answered his wife. "I think, though, that in winter I am happier. In summer I am always worried. I am afraid for the children to be out of my sight, and when you are away on a hunt I am distraught until you are home safe."

"Well, if the redskins let us alone this summer it will be something new," he said, laughing. "By the way, Bess, some new people came to the fort last night. They rafted down from the Monongahela settlements. Some of the women suffered considerably. I intend to offer them the cabin on the hill until they can cut the timber and run up a house. Sam said the cabin roof leaked and the chimney smoked, but with a little work I think they can be made more comfortable there than at the block-house."

"It is the only vacant cabin in the settlement. I can accommodate the women folks here."

"Well, we'll see about it. I don't want you and Betty inconvenienced. I'll send Sam up to the cabin and have him fix things up a bit and make it more habitable."

The door opened, admitting Col. Zane's elder boy. The lad's face was dirty, his nose was all bloody, and a big bruise showed over his right eye.

"For the land's sake!" exclaimed his mother. "Look at the boy. Noah, come here. What have you been doing?"

Noah crept close to his mother and grasping her apron with both hands hid his face. Mrs. Zane turned the boy around and wiped his discolored features with a wet towel. She gave him a little shake and said: "Noah, have you been fighting again?"

"Let him go and I'll tell you about it," said the Colonel, and when the youngster had disappeared he continued: "Right after breakfast Noah went with me down to the mill. I noticed several children playing in front of Reihart's blacksmith shop. I went in, leaving Noah outside. I got a plow-share which I had left with Reihart to be repaired. He came to the door with me and all at once he said: 'look at the kids.' I looked and saw Noah walk up to a boy and say something to him. The lad was a stranger, and I have no doubt belongs to these new people I told you about. He was bigger than Noah. At first the older boy appeared very friendly and evidently wanted to join the others in their game. I guess Noah did not approve of this, for after he had looked the stranger over he hauled away and punched the lad soundly. To make it short the strange boy gave Noah the worst beating he ever got in his life. I told Noah to come straight to you and confess."

"Well, did you ever!" ejaculated Mrs. Zane. "Noah is a bad boy. And you stood and watched him fight. You are laughing about it now. Ebenezer Zane, I would not put it beneath you to set Noah to fighting. I know you used to make the little niggers fight. Anyway, it serves Noah right and I hope it will be a lesson to him."

"I'll make you a bet, Bessie," said the Colonel, with another laugh. "I'll bet you that unless we lock him up, Noah will fight that boy every day or every time he meets him."

"I won't bet," said Mrs. Zane, with a smile of resignation.

"Where's Betts? I haven't seen her this morning. I am going over to Short Creek to-morrow or next day, and think I'll take her with me. You know I am to get a commission to lay out several settlements along the river, and I want to get some work finished at Short Creek this spring. Mrs. Raymer'll be delighted to have Betty. Shall I take her?"

"By all means. A visit there will brighten her up and do her good."

"Well, what on earth have you been doing?" cried the Colonel. His remark had been called forth by a charming vision that had entered by the open door. Betty—for it was she—wore a little red cap set jauntily on her black hair. Her linsey dress was crumpled and covered with hayseed.

"I've been in the hay-mow," said Betty, waving a small basket. "For a week that old black hen has circumvented me, but at last I have conquered. I found the nest in the farthest corner under the hay."

"How did you get up in the loft?" inquired Mrs. Zane.

"Bessie, I climbed up the ladder of course. I acknowledge being unusually light-hearted and happy this morning, but I have not as yet grown wings. Sam said I could not climb up that straight ladder, but I found it easy enough."

"You should not climb up into the loft," said Mrs. Zane, in a severe tone. "Only last fall Hugh Bennet's little boy slid off the hay down into one of the stalls and the horse kicked him nearly to death."

"Oh, fiddlesticks, Bessie, I am not a baby," said Betty, with vehemence. "There is not a horse in the barn but would stand on his hind legs before he would step on me, let alone kick me."

"I don't know, Betty, but I think that black horse Mr. Clarke left here would kick any one," remarked the Colonel.

"Oh, no, he would not hurt me."

"Betty, we have had pleasant weather for about three days," said the Colonel, gravely. "In that time you have let out that crazy bear of yours to turn everything topsy-turvy. Only yesterday I got my hands in the paint you have put on your canoe. If you had asked my advice I would have told you that painting your canoe should not have been done for a month yet. Silas told me you fell down the creek hill; Sam said you tried to drive his team over the bluff, and so on. We are happy to see you get back your old time spirits, but could you not be a little more careful? Your versatility is bewildering. We do not know what to look for next. I fully expect to see you brought to the house some day maimed for life, or all that beautiful black hair gone to decorate some Huron's lodge."

"I tell you I am perfectly delighted that the weather is again so I can go out. I am tired to death of staying indoors. This morning I could have cried for very joy. Bessie will soon be lecturing me about Madcap. I must not ride farther than the fort. Well, I don't care. I intend to ride all over."

"Betty, I do not wish you to think I am lecturing you," said the Colonel's wife. "But you are as wild as a March hare and some one must tell you things. Now listen. My brother, the Major, told me that Simon Girty, the renegade, had been heard to say that he had seen Eb Zane's little sister and that if he ever got his hands on her he would make a squaw of her. I am not teasing you. I am telling you the truth. Girty saw you when you were at Fort Pitt two years ago. Now what would you do if he caught you on one of your lonely rides and carried you off to his wigwam? He has done things like that before. James Girty carried off one of the Johnson girls. Her brothers tried to rescue her and lost their lives. It is a common trick of the Indians."

"What would I do if Mr. Simon Girty tried to make a squaw of me?" exclaimed Betty, her eyes flashing fire. "Why, I'd kill him!"

"I believe it, Betts, on my word I do," spoke up the Colonel. "But let us hope you may never see Girty. All I ask is that you be careful. I am going over to Short Creek to-morrow. Will you go with me? I know Mrs. Raymer will be pleased to see you."

"Oh, Eb, that will be delightful!"

"Very well, get ready and we shall start early in the morning."

Two weeks later Betty returned from Short Creek and seemed to have profited much by her short visit. Col. Zane remarked with satisfaction to his wife that Betty had regained all her former cheerfulness.

The morning after Betty's return was a perfect spring morning—the first in that month of May-days. The sun shone bright and warm; the mayflowers blossomed; the trailing arbutus scented the air; everywhere the grass and the leaves looked fresh and green; swallows flitted in and out of the barn door; the blue-birds twittered; a meadow-lark caroled forth his pure melody, and the busy hum of bees came from the fragrant apple-blossoms.

"Mis' Betty, Madcap 'pears powerfo' skittenish," said old Sam, when he had led the pony to where Betty stood on the hitching block. "Whoa, dar, you rascal."

Betty laughed as she leaped lightly into the saddle, and soon she was flying over the old familiar road, down across the creek bridge, past the old grist-mill, around the fort and then out on the river bluff. The Indian pony was fiery and mettlesome. He pranced and side-stepped, galloped and trotted by turns. He seemed as glad to get out again into the warm sunshine as was Betty herself. He tore down the road a mile at his best speed. Coming back Betty pulled him into a walk. Presently her musings were interrupted by a sharp switch in the face from a twig of a tree. She stopped the pony and broke off the offending branch. As she looked around the recollection of what had happened to her in that very spot flashed into her mind. It was here that she had been stopped by the man who had passed almost as swiftly out of her life as he had crossed her path that memorable afternoon. She fell to musing on the old perplexing question. After all could there not have been some mistake? Perhaps she might have misjudged him? And then the old spirit, which resented her thinking of him in that softened mood, rose and fought the old battle over again. But as often happened the mood conquered, and Betty permitted herself to sink for the moment into the sad thoughts which returned like a mournful strain of music once sung by beloved voices, now forever silent.

She could not resist the desire to ride down to the old sycamore. The pony turned into the bridle-path that led down the bluff and the sure-footed beast picked his way carefully over the roots and stones. Betty's heart beat quicker when she saw the noble tree under whose spreading branches she had spent the happiest day of her life. The old monarch of the forest was not one whit changed by the wild winds of winter. The dew sparkled on the nearly full grown leaves; the little sycamore balls were already as large as marbles.

Betty drew rein at the top of the bank and looked absently at the tree and into the foam covered pool beneath. At that moment her eyes saw nothing physical. They held the faraway light of the dreamer, the look that sees so much of the past and nothing of the present.

Presently her reflections were broken by the actions of the pony. Madcap had thrown up her head, laid back her ears and commenced to paw the ground with her forefeet. Betty looked round to see the cause of Madcap's excitement. What was that! She saw a tall figure clad in brown leaning against the stone. She saw a long fishing-rod. What was there so familiar in the poise of that figure? Madcap dislodged a stone from the path and it went rattling down the rock, slope and fell with a splash into the water. The man heard it, turned and faced the hillside. Betty recognized Alfred Clarke. For a moment she believed she must be dreaming. She had had many dreams of the old sycamore. She looked again. Yes, it was he. Pale, worn, and older he undoubtedly looked, but the features were surely those of Alfred Clarke. Her heart gave a great bound and then seemed to stop beating while a very agony of joy surged over her and made her faint. So he still lived. That was her first thought, glad and joyous, and then memory returning, her face went white as with clenched teeth she wheeled Madcap and struck her with the switch. Once on the level bluff she urged her toward the house at a furious pace.

Col. Zane had just stepped out of the barn door and his face took on an expression of amazement when he saw the pony come tearing up the road, Betty's hair flying in the wind and with a face as white as if she were pursued by a thousand yelling Indians.

"Say, Betts, what the deuce is wrong?" cried the Colonel, when Betty reached the fence.

"Why did you not tell me that man was here again?" she demanded in intense excitement.

"That man! What man?" asked Col. Zane, considerably taken back by this angry apparition.

"Mr. Clarke, of course. Just as if you did not know. I suppose you thought it a fine opportunity for one of your jokes."

"Oh, Clarke. Well, the fact is I just found it out myself. Haven't I been away as well as you? I certainly cannot imagine how any man could create such evident excitement in your mind. Poor Clarke, what has he done now?"

"You might have told me. Somebody could have told me and saved me from making a fool of myself," retorted Betty, who was plainly on the verge of tears. "I rode down to the old sycamore tree and he saw me in, of all the places in the world, the one place where I would not want him to see me."

"Huh!" said the Colonel, who often gave vent to the Indian exclamation. "Is that all? I thought something had happened."

"All! Is it not enough? I would rather have died. He is a man and he will think I followed him down there, that I was thinking of—that—Oh!" cried Betty, passionately, and then she strode into the house, slammed the door, and left the Colonel, lost in wonder.

"Humph! These women beat me. I can't make them out, and the older I grow the worse I get," he said, as he led the pony into the stable.

Betty ran up-stairs to her room, her head in a whirl stronger than the surprise of Alfred's unexpected appearance in Fort Henry and stronger than the mortification in having been discovered going to a spot she should have been too proud to remember was the bitter sweet consciousness that his mere presence had thrilled her through and through. It hurt her and made her hate herself in that moment. She hid her face in shame at the thought that she could not help being glad to see the man who had only trifled with her, the man who had considered the acquaintance of so little consequence that he had never taken the trouble to write her a line or send her a message. She wrung her trembling hands. She endeavored to still that throbbing heart and to conquer that sweet vague feeling which had crept over her and made her weak. The tears began to come and with a sob she threw herself on the bed and buried her head in the pillow.

An hour after, when Betty had quieted herself and had seated herself by the window a light knock sounded on the door and Col. Zane entered. He hesitated and came in rather timidly, for Betty was not to be taken liberties with, and seeing her by the window he crossed the room and sat down by her side.

Betty did not remember her father or her mother. Long ago when she was a child she had gone to her brother, laid her head on his shoulder and told him all her troubles. The desire grew strong within her now. There was comfort in the strong clasp of his hand. She was not proof against it, and her dark head fell on his shoulder.

* * * * * * * * * * * * * * *

Alfred Clarke had indeed made his reappearance in Fort Henry. The preceding October when he left the settlement to go on the expedition up the Monongahela River his intention had been to return to the fort as soon as he had finished his work, but what he did do was only another illustration of that fatality which affects everything. Man hopefully makes his plans and an inexorable destiny works out what it has in store for him.

The men of the expedition returned to Fort Henry in due time, but Alfred had been unable to accompany them. He had sustained a painful injury and had been compelled to go to Fort Pitt for medical assistance. While there he had received word that his mother was lying very ill at his old home in Southern Virginia and if he wished to see her alive he must not delay in reaching her bedside. He left Fort Pitt at once and went to his home, where he remained until his mother's death. She had been the only tie that bound him to the old home, and now that she was gone he determined to leave the scene of his boyhood forever.

Alfred was the rightful heir to all of the property, but an unjust and selfish stepfather stood between him and any contentment he might have found there. He decided he would be a soldier of fortune. He loved the daring life of a ranger, and preferred to take his chances with the hardy settlers on the border rather than live the idle life of a gentleman farmer. He declared his intention to his step-father, who ill-concealed his satisfaction at the turn affairs had taken. Then Alfred packed his belongings, secured his mother's jewels, and with one sad, backward glance rode away from the stately old mansion.

It was Sunday morning and Clarke had been two days in Fort Henry. From his little room in the block-house he surveyed the well-remembered scene. The rolling hills, the broad river, the green forests seemed like old friends.

"Here I am again," he mused. "What a fool a man can be. I have left a fine old plantation, slaves, horses, a country noted for its pretty women—for what? Here there can be nothing for me but Indians, hard work, privation, and trouble. Yet I could not get here quickly enough. Pshaw! What use to speak of the possibilities of a new country. I cannot deceive myself. It is she. I would walk a thousand miles and starve myself for months just for one glimpse of her sweet face. Knowing this what care I for all the rest. How strange she should ride down to the old sycamore tree yesterday the moment I was there and thinking of her. Evidently she had just returned from her visit. I wonder if she ever cared. I wonder if she ever thinks of me. Shall I accept that incident as a happy augury? Well, I am here to find out and find out I will. Aha! there goes the church bell."

Laughing a little at his eagerness he brushed his coat, put on his cap and went down stairs. The settlers with their families were going into the meeting house. As Alfred started up the steps he met Lydia Boggs.

"Why, Mr. Clarke, I heard you had returned," she said, smiling pleasantly and extending her hand. "Welcome to the fort. I am very glad to see you."

While they were chatting her father and Col. Zane came up and both greeted the young man warmly.

"Well, well, back on the frontier," said the Colonel, in his hearty way. "Glad to see you at the fort again. I tell you, Clarke, I have taken a fancy to that black horse you left me last fall. I did not know what to think when Jonathan brought back my horse. To tell you the truth I always looked for you to come back. What have you been doing all winter?"

"I have been at home. My mother was ill all winter and she died in April."

"My lad, that's bad news. I am sorry," said Col. Zane putting his hand kindly on the young man's shoulder. "I was wondering what gave you that older and graver look. It's hard, lad, but it's the way of life."

"I have come back to get my old place with you, Col. Zane, if you will give it to me."

"I will, and can promise you more in the future. I am going to open a road through to Maysville, Kentucky, and start several new settlements along the river. I will need young men, and am more than glad you have returned."

"Thank you, Col. Zane. That is more than I could have hoped for."

Alfred caught sight of a trim figure in a gray linsey gown coming down the road. There were several young people approaching, but he saw only Betty. By some evil chance Betty walked with Ralfe Miller, and for some mysterious reason, which women always keep to themselves, she smiled and looked up into his face at a time of all times she should not have done so. Alfred's heart turned to lead.

When the young people reached the steps the eyes of the rivals met for one brief second, but that was long enough for them to understand each other. They did not speak. Lydia hesitated and looked toward Betty.

"Betty, here is—" began Col. Zane, but Betty passed them with flaming cheeks and with not so much as a glance at Alfred. It was an awkward moment for him.

"Let us go in," he said composedly, and they filed into the church.

As long as he lived Alfred Clarke never forgot that hour. His pride kept him chained in his seat. Outwardly he maintained his composure, but inwardly his brain seemed throbbing, whirling, bursting. What an idiot he had been! He understood now why his letter had never been answered. Betty loved Miller, a man who hated him, a man who would leave no stone unturned to destroy even a little liking which she might have felt for him. Once again Miller had crossed his path and worsted him. With a sudden sickening sense of despair he realized that all his fond hopes had been but dreams, a fool's dreams. The dream of that moment when he would give her his mother's jewels, the dream of that charming face uplifted to his, the dream of the little cottage to which he would hurry after his day's work and find her waiting at the gate,—these dreams must be dispelled forever. He could barely wait until the end of the service. He wanted to be alone; to fight it out with himself; to crush out of his heart that fair image. At length the hour ended and he got out before the congregation and hurried to his room.

Betty had company all that afternoon and it was late in the day when Col. Zane ascended the stairs and entered her room to find her alone.

"Betty, I wish to know why you ignored Mr. Clarke this morning?" said Col. Zane, looking down on his sister. There was a gleam in his eye and an expression about his mouth seldom seen in the Colonel's features.

"I do not know that it concerns any one but myself," answered Betty quickly, as her head went higher and her eyes flashed with a gleam not unlike that in her brother's.

"I beg your pardon. I do not agree with you," replied Col. Zane. "It does concern others. You cannot do things like that in this little place where every one knows all about you and expect it to pass unnoticed. Martin's wife saw you cut Clarke and you know what a gossip she is. Already every one is talking about you and Clarke."

"To that I am indifferent."

"But I care. I won't have people talking about you," replied the Colonel, who began to lose patience. Usually he had the best temper imaginable. "Last fall you allowed Clarke to pay you a good deal of attention and apparently you were on good terms when he went away. Now that he has returned you won't even speak to him. You let this fellow Miller run after you. In my estimation Miller is not to be compared to Clarke, and judging from the warm greetings I saw Clarke receive this morning, there are a number of folk who agree with me. Not that I am praising Clarke. I simply say this because to Bessie, to Jack, to everyone, your act is incomprehensible. People are calling you a flirt and saying that they would prefer some country manners."

"I have not allowed Mr. Miller to run after me, as you are pleased to term it," retorted Betty with indignation. "I do not like him. I never see him any more unless you or Bessie or some one else is present. You know that. I cannot prevent him from walking to church with me."

"No, I suppose not, but are you entirely innocent of those sweet glances which you gave him this morning?"

"I did not," cried Betty with an angry blush. "I won't be called a flirt by you or by anyone else. The moment I am civil to some man all these old maids and old women say I am flirting. It is outrageous."

"Now, Betty, don't get excited. We are getting from the question. Why are you not civil to Clarke?" asked Col. Zane. She did not answer and after a moment he continued. "If there is anything about Clarke that I do not know and that I should know I want you to tell me. Personally I like the fellow. I am not saying that to make you think you ought to like him because I do. You might not care for him at all, but that would be no good reason for your actions. Betty, in these frontier settlements a man is soon known for his real worth. Every one at the Fort liked Clarke. The youngsters adored him. Jessie liked him very much. You know he and Isaac became good friends. I think he acted like a man to-day. I saw the look Miller gave him. I don't like this fellow Miller, anyway. Now, I am taking the trouble to tell you my side of the argument. It is not a question of your liking Clarke—that is none of my affair. It is simply that either he is not the man we all think him or you are acting in a way unbecoming a Zane. I do not purpose to have this state of affairs continue. Now, enough of this beating about the bush."

Betty had seen the Colonel angry more than once, but never with her. It was quite certain she had angered him and she forgot her own resentment. Her heart had warmed with her brother's praise of Clarke. Then as she remembered the past she felt a scorn for her weakness and such a revulsion of feeling that she cried out passionately:

"He is a trifler. He never cared for me. He insulted me."

Col. Zane reached for his hat, got up without saying another word and went down stairs.

Betty had not intended to say quite what she had and instantly regretted her hasty words. She called to the Colonel, but he did not answer her, nor return.

"Betty, what in the world could you have said to my husband?" said Mrs. Zane as she entered the room. She was breathless from running up the stairs and her comely face wore a look of concern. "He was as white as that sheet and he stalked off toward the Fort without a word to me."

"I simply told him Mr. Clarke had insulted me," answered Betty calmly.

"Great Heavens! Betty, what have you done?" exclaimed Mrs. Zane. "You don't know Eb when he is angry. He is a big fool over you, anyway. He is liable to kill Clarke."

Betty's blood was up now and she said that would not be a matter of much importance.

"When did he insult you?" asked the elder woman, yielding to her natural curiosity.

"It was last October."

"Pooh! It took you a long time to tell it. I don't believe it amounted to much. Mr. Clarke did not appear to be the sort of a man to insult anyone. All the girls were crazy about him last year. If he was not all right they would not have been."

"I do not care if they were. The girls can have him and welcome. I don't want him. I never did. I am tired of hearing everyone eulogize him. I hate him. Do you hear? I hate him! And I wish you would go away and leave me alone."

"Well, Betty, all I will say is that you are a remarkable young woman," answered Mrs. Zane, who saw plainly that Betty's violent outburst was a prelude to a storm of weeping. "I don't believe a word you have said. I don't believe you hate him. There!"

Col. Zane walked straight to the Fort, entered the block-house and knocked on the door of Clarke's room. A voice bade him come in. He shoved open the door and went into the room. Clarke had evidently just returned from a tramp in the hills, for his garments were covered with burrs and his boots were dusty. He looked tired, but his face was calm.

"Why, Col. Zane! Have a seat. What can I do for you?"

"I have come to ask you to explain a remark of my sister's."

"Very well, I am at your service," answered Alfred slowly lighting his pipe, after which he looked straight into Col. Zane's face.

"My sister informs me that you insulted her last fall before you left the Fort. I am sure you are neither a liar nor a coward, and I expect you to answer as a man."

"Col. Zane, I am not a liar, and I hope I am not a coward," said Alfred coolly. He took a long pull on his pipe and blew a puff of white smoke toward the ceiling.

"I believe you, but I must have an explanation. There is something wrong somewhere. I saw Betty pass you without speaking this morning. I did not like it and I took her to task about it. She then said you had insulted her. Betty is prone to exaggerate, especially when angry, but she never told me a lie in her life. Ever since you pulled Isaac out of the river I have taken an interest in you. That's why I'd like to avoid any trouble. But this thing has gone far enough. Now be sensible, swallow your pride and let me hear your side of the story."

Alfred had turned pale at his visitor's first words. There was no mistaking Col. Zane's manner. Alfred well knew that the Colonel, if he found Betty had really been insulted, would call him out and kill him. Col. Zane spoke quietly, ever kindly, but there was an undercurrent of intense feeling in his voice, a certain deadly intent which boded ill to anyone who might cross him at that moment. Alfred's first impulse was a reckless desire to tell Col. Zane he had nothing to explain and that he stood ready to give any satisfaction in his power. But he wisely thought better of this. It struck him that this would not be fair, for no matter what the girl had done the Colonel had always been his friend. So Alfred pulled himself together and resolved to make a clean breast of the whole affair.

"Col. Zane, I do not feel that I owe your sister anything, and what I am going to tell you is simply because you have always been my friend, and I do not want you to have any wrong ideas about me. I'll tell you the truth and you can be the judge as to whether or not I insulted your sister. I fell in love with her, almost at first sight. The night after the Indians recaptured your brother, Betty and I stood out in the moonlight and she looked so bewitching and I felt so sorry for her and so carried away by my love for her that I yielded to a momentary impulse and kissed her. I simply could not help it. There is no excuse for me. She struck me across the face and ran into the house. I had intended that night to tell her of my love and place my fate in her hands, but, of course, the unfortunate occurrence made that impossible. As I was to leave at dawn next day, I remained up all night, thinking what I ought to do. Finally I decided to write. I wrote her a letter, telling her all and begging her to become my wife. I gave the letter to your slave, Sam, and told him it was a matter of life and death, and not to lose the letter nor fail to give it to Betty. I have had no answer to that letter. Today she coldly ignored me. That is my story, Col. Zane."

"Well, I don't believe she got the letter," said Col. Zane. "She has not acted like a young lady who has had the privilege of saying 'yes' or 'no' to you. And Sam never had any use for you. He disliked you from the first, and never failed to say something against you."

"I'll kill that d—n nigger if he did not deliver that letter," said Clarke, jumping up in his excitement. "I never thought of that. Good Heaven! What could she have thought of me? She would think I had gone away without a word. If she knew I really loved her she could not think so terribly of me."

"There is more to be explained, but I am satisfied with your side of it," said Col. Zane. "Now I'll go to Sam and see what has become of that letter. I am glad I am justified in thinking of you as I have. I imagine this thing has hurt you and I don't wonder at it. Maybe we can untangle the problem yet. My advice would be—but never mind that now. Anyway, I'm your friend in this matter. I'll let you know the result of my talk with Sam."

"I thought that young fellow was a gentleman," mused Col. Zane as he crossed the green square and started up the hill toward the cabins. He found the old negro seated on his doorstep.

"Sam, what did you do with a letter Mr. Clarke gave you last October and instructed you to deliver to Betty?"

"I dun recollec' no lettah, sah," replied Sam.

"Now, Sam, don't lie about it. Clarke has just told me that he gave you the letter. What did you do with it?"

"Masse Zane, I ain dun seen no lettah," answered the old darkey, taking a dingy pipe from his mouth and rolling his eyes at his master.

"If you lie again I will punish you," said Col. Zane sternly. "You are getting old, Sam, and I would not like to whip you, but I will if you do not find that letter."

Sam grumbled, and shuffled inside the cabin. Col. Zane heard him rummaging around. Presently he came back to the door and handed a very badly soiled paper to the Colonel.

"What possessed you to do this, Sam? You have always been honest. Your act has caused great misunderstanding and it might have led to worse."

"He's one of dem no good Southern white trash; he's good fer nuttin'," said Sam. "I saw yo' sistah, Mis' Betty, wit him, and I seen she was gittin' fond of him, and I says I ain't gwinter have Mis' Betty runnin' off wif him. And I'se never gibbin de lettah to her."

That was all the explanation Sam would vouchsafe, and Col. Zane, knowing it would be useless to say more to the well-meaning but ignorant and superstitious old negro, turned and wended his way back to the house. He looked at the paper and saw that it was addressed to Elizabeth Zane, and that the ink was faded until the letters were scarcely visible.

"What have you there?" asked his wife, who had watched him go up the hill to the negro's cabin. She breathed a sigh of relief when she saw that her husband's face had recovered its usual placid expression.

"It is a little letter for that young fire-brand up stairs, and, I believe it will clear up the mystery. Clarke gave it to Sam last fall and Sam never gave it to Betty."

"I hope with all my heart it may settle Betty. She worries me to death with her love affairs."

Col. Zane went up stairs and found the young lady exactly as he had left her. She gave an impatient toss of her head as he entered.

"Well, Madam, I have here something that may excite even your interest." he said cheerily.

"What?" asked Betty with a start. She flushed crimson when she saw the letter and at first refused to take it from her brother. She was at a loss to understand his cheerful demeanor. He had been anything but pleasant a few moments since.

"Here, take it. It is a letter from Mr. Clarke which you should have received last fall. That last morning he gave this letter to Sam to deliver to you, and the crazy old nigger kept it. However, it is too late to talk of that, only it does seem a great pity. I feel sorry for both of you. Clarke never will forgive you, even if you want him to, which I am sure you do not. I don't know exactly what is in this letter, but I know it will make you ashamed to think you did not trust him."

With this parting reproof the Colonel walked out, leaving Betty completely bewildered. The words "too late," "never forgive," and "a great pity" rang through her head. What did he mean? She tore the letter open with trembling hands and holding it up to the now fast-waning light, she read

"Dear Betty:

"If you had waited only a moment longer I know you would not have been so angry with me. The words I wanted so much to say choked me and I could not speak them. I love you. I have loved you from the very first moment, that blessed moment when I looked up over your pony's head to see the sweetest face the sun ever shone on. I'll be the happiest man on earth if you will say you care a little for me and promise to be my wife.

"It was wrong to kiss you and I beg your forgiveness. Could you but see your face as I saw it last night in the moonlight, I would not need to plead:

you would know that the impulse which swayed me was irresistible. In that kiss I gave you my hope, my love, my life, my all. Let it plead for me.

"I expect to return from Ft. Pitt in about six or eight weeks, but I cannot wait until then for your answer.

"With hope I sign myself,

"Yours until death,

"Alfred."

Betty read the letter through. The page blurred before her eyes; a sensation of oppression and giddiness made her reach out helplessly with both hands. Then she slipped forward and fell on the floor. For the first time in all her young life Betty had fainted. Col. Zane found her lying pale and quiet under the window.

CHAPTER IX.

Yantwaia, or, as he was more commonly called, Cornplanter, was originally a Seneca chief, but when the five war tribes consolidated, forming the historical "Five Nations," he became their leader. An old historian said of this renowned chieftain: "Tradition says that the blood of a famous white man coursed through the veins of Cornplanter. The tribe he led was originally ruled by an Indian queen of singular power and beauty. She was born to govern her people by the force of her character. Many a great chief importuned her to become his wife, but she preferred to cling to her power and dignity. When this white man, then a very young man, came to the Ohio valley the queen fell in love with him, and Cornplanter was their son."

Cornplanter lived to a great age. He was a wise counsellor, a great leader, and he died when he was one hundred years old, having had more conceded to him by the white men than any other chieftain. General Washington wrote of him: "The merits of Cornplanter and his friendship for the United States are well known and shall not be forgotten."

But Cornplanter had not always been a friend to the palefaces. During Dunmore's war and for years after, he was one of the most vindictive of the savage leaders against the invading pioneers.

It was during this period of Cornplanter's activity against the whites that Isaac Zane had the misfortune to fall into the great chief's power.

We remember Isaac last when, lost in the woods, weak from hunger and exposure, he had crawled into a thicket and had gone to sleep. He was awakened by a dog licking his face. He heard Indian voices. He got up and ran as fast as he could, but exhausted as he was he proved no match for his pursuers. They came up with him and seeing that he was unable to defend himself they grasped him by the arms and led him down a well-worn bridle-path.

"D—n poor run. No good legs," said one of his captors, and at this the other two Indians laughed. Then they whooped and yelled, at which signal other Indians joined them. Isaac saw that they were leading him into a large encampment. He asked the big savage who led him what camp it was, and learned that he had fallen into the hands of Cornplanter.

While being marched through the large Indian village Isaac saw unmistakable indications of war. There was a busy hum on all sides; the squaws were preparing large quantities of buffalo meat, cutting it in long, thin strips, and were parching corn in stone vessels. The braves were cleaning rifles, sharpening tomahawks, and mixing war paints. All these things Isaac knew to be preparations for long marches and for battle. That night he heard speech after speech in the lodge next to the one in which he lay, but they were in an unknown tongue. Later he heard the yelling of the Indians and the dull thud of their feet as they stamped on the ground. He heard the ring of the tomahawks as they were struck into hard wood. The Indians were dancing the war-dance round the war-post. This continued with some little intermission all the four days that Isaac lay in the lodge rapidly recovering his strength. The fifth day a man came into the lodge. He was tall and powerful, his hair fell over his shoulders and he wore the scanty buckskin dress of the Indian. But Isaac knew at once he was a white man, perhaps one of the many French traders who passed through the Indian village.

"Your name is Zane," said the man in English, looking sharply at Isaac.

"That is my name. Who are you?" asked Isaac in great surprise.

"I am Girty. I've never seen you, but I knew Col. Zane and Jonathan well. I've seen your sister; you all favor one another."

"Are you Simon Girty?"

"Yes."

"I have heard of your influence with the Indians. Can you do anything to get me out of this?"

"How did you happen to git over here? You are not many miles from Wingenund's Camp," said Girty, giving Isaac another sharp look from his small black eyes.

"Girty, I assure you I am not a spy. I escaped from the Wyandot village on Mad River and after traveling three days I lost my way. I went to sleep in a thicket and when I awoke an Indian dog had found me. I heard voices and saw three Indians. I got up and ran, but they easily caught me."

"I know about you. Old Tarhe has a daughter who kept you from bein' ransomed."

"Yes, and I wish I were back there. I don't like the look of things."

"You are right, Zane. You got ketched at a bad time. The Indians are mad. I suppose you don't know that Col. Crawford massacred a lot of Indians a few days ago. It'll go hard with any white man that gits captured. I'm afraid I can't do nothin' for you."

A few words concerning Simon Girty, the White Savage. He had two brothers, James and George, who had been desperadoes before they were adopted by the Delawares, and who eventually became fierce and relentless savages. Simon had been captured at the same time as his brothers, but he did not at once fall under the influence of the unsettled, free-and-easy life of the Indians. It is probable that while in captivity he acquired the power of commanding the Indians' interest and learned the secret of ruling them— two capabilities few white men ever possessed. It is certain that he, like the noted French-Canadian Joucaire, delighted to sit round the camp fires and to go into the council-lodge and talk to the assembled Indians.

At the outbreak of the revolution Girty was a commissioned officer of militia at Ft. Pitt. He deserted from the Fort, taking with him the Tories McKee and Elliott, and twelve soldiers, and these traitors spread as much terror among the Delaware Indians as they did among the whites. The Delawares had been one of the few peacefully disposed tribes. In order to get them to join their forces with Governor Hamilton, the British commander, Girty declared that Gen. Washington had been killed, that Congress had been dispersed, and that the British were winning all the battles.

Girty spoke most of the Indian languages, and Hamilton employed him to go among the different Indian tribes and incite them to greater hatred of the pioneers. This proved to be just the life that suited him. He soon rose to have a great and bad influence on all the tribes. He became noted for his assisting the Indians in marauds, for his midnight forays, for his scalpings, and his efforts to capture white women, and for his devilish cunning and cruelty.

For many years Girty was the Deathshead of the frontier. The mention of his name alone created terror in any household; in every pioneer's cabin it made the children cry out in fear and paled the cheeks of the stoutest-hearted wife.

It is difficult to conceive of a white man's being such a fiend in human guise. The only explanation that can be given is that renegades rage against the cause of their own blood with the fury of insanity rather than with the malignity of a naturally ferocious temper. In justice to Simon Girty it must be said that facts not known until his death showed he was not so cruel and base as believed; that some deeds of kindness were attributed to him; that he risked his life to save Kenton from the stake, and that many of the terrible crimes laid at his door were really committed by his savage brothers.

Isaac Zane suffered no annoyance at the hands of Cornplanter's braves until the seventh day of his imprisonment. He saw no one except the squaw who brought him corn and meat. On that day two savages came for him and led him into the immense council-lodge of the Five Nations. Cornplanter sat between his right-hand chiefs, Big Tree and Half Town, and surrounded by the other chiefs of the tribes. An aged Indian stood in the center of the lodge and addressed the others. The listening savages sat immovable, their faces as cold and stern as stone masks. Apparently they did not heed the entrance of the prisoner.

"Zane, they're havin' a council," whispered a voice in Isaac's ear. Isaac turned and recognized Girty. "I want to prepare you for the worst."

"Is there, then, no hope for me?" asked Isaac.

"I'm afraid not," continued the renegade, speaking in a low whisper. "They wouldn't let me speak at the council. I told Cornplanter that killin' you might bring the Hurons down on him, but he wouldn't listen. Yesterday, in the camp of the Delawares, I saw Col. Crawford burnt at the stake. He was a friend of mine at Pitt, and I didn't dare to say one word to the frenzied Indians. I had to watch the torture. Pipe and Wingenund, both old friends of Crawford, stood by and watched him walk round the stake on the red-hot coals five hours."

Isaac shuddered at the words of the renegade, but did not answer. He had felt from the first that his case was hopeless, and that no opportunity for escape could possibly present itself in such a large encampment. He set his teeth hard and resolved to show the red devils how a white man could die.

Several speeches were made by different chiefs and then an impressive oration by Big Tree. At the conclusion of the speeches, which were in an unknown tongue to Isaac, Cornplanter handed a war-club to Half Town. This chief got up, walked to the end of the circle, and there brought the club down on the ground with a resounding thud. Then he passed the club to Big Tree. In a solemn and dignified manner every chief duplicated Half Town's performance with the club.

Isaac watched the ceremony as if fascinated. He had seen a war-club used in the councils of the Hurons and knew that striking it on the ground signified war and death.

"White man, you are a killer of Indians," said Cornplanter in good English. "When the sun shines again you die."

A brave came forward and painted Isaac's face black. This Isaac knew to indicate that death awaited him on the morrow. On his way back to his prison-lodge he saw that a war-dance was in progress.

A hundred braves with tomahawks, knives, and mallets in their hands were circling round a post and keeping time to the low music of a muffled drum. Close together, with heads bowed, they marched. At certain moments, which they led up to with a dancing on rigid legs and a stamping with their feet, they wheeled, and uttering hideous yells, started to march in the other direction. When this had been repeated three times a brave stepped from the line, advanced, and struck his knife or tomahawk into the post. Then with a loud voice he proclaimed his past exploits and great deeds in war. The other Indians greeted this with loud yells of applause and a flourishing of weapons. Then the whole ceremony was gone through again.

That afternoon many of the Indians visited Isaac in his lodge and shook their fists at him and pointed their knives at him. They hissed and groaned at him. Their vindictive faces expressed the malignant joy they felt at the expectation of putting him to the torture.

When night came Isaac's guards laced up the lodge-door and shut him from the sight of the maddened Indians. The darkness that gradually enveloped him was a relief. By and by all was silent except for the occasional yell of a drunken savage. To Isaac it sounded like a long, rolling death-cry echoing throughout the encampment and murdering his sleep. Its horrible meaning made him shiver and his flesh creep. At length even that yell ceased. The watch-dogs quieted down and the perfect stillness which ensued could almost be felt. Through Isaac's mind ran over and over again the same words. His last night to live! His last night to live! He forced himself to think of other things. He lay there in the darkness of his tent, but he was far away in thought, far away in the past with his mother and brothers before they had come to this bloodthirsty country. His thoughts wandered to the days of his boyhood when he used to drive the sows to the pasture on the hillside, and in his dreamy, disordered fancy he was once more letting down the bars of the gate. Then he was wading in the brook and whacking the green frogs with his stick. Old playmates' faces, forgotten for years, were there looking at him from the dark wall of his wigwam. There was Andrew's face; the faces of his other brothers; the laughing face of his sister; the serene face of his mother. As he lay there with the shadow of death over him sweet was the thought that soon he would be reunited with that mother. The images faded slowly away, swallowed up in the gloom. Suddenly a vision appeared to him. A radiant white light illumined the lodge and shone full on the beautiful face of the Indian maiden who had loved him so well. Myeerah's dark eyes were bright with an undying love and her lips smiled hope.

A rude kick dispelled Isaac's dreams. A brawny savage pulled him to his feet and pushed him outside of the lodge.

It was early morning. The sun had just cleared the low hills in the east and its red beams crimsoned the edges of the clouds of fog which hung over the river like a great white curtain. Though the air was warm, Isaac shivered a little as the breeze blew softly against his cheek. He took one long look toward the rising sun, toward that east he had hoped to see, and then resolutely turned his face away forever.

Early though it was the Indians were astir and their whooping rang throughout the valley. Down the main street of the village the guards led the prisoner, followed by a screaming mob of squaws and young braves and children who threw sticks and stones at the hated Long Knife.

Soon the inhabitants of the camp congregated on the green oval in the midst of the lodges. When the prisoner appeared they formed in two long lines facing each other, and several feet apart. Isaac was to run the gauntlet—one of the severest of Indian tortures. With the exception of Cornplanter and several of his chiefs, every Indian in the village was in line. Little Indian boys hardly large enough to sling a stone; maidens and squaws with switches or spears; athletic young braves with flashing tomahawks;

grim, matured warriors swinging knotted war clubs,—all were there in line, yelling and brandishing their weapons in a manner frightful to behold.

The word was given, and stripped to the waist, Isaac bounded forward fleet as a deer. He knew the Indian way of running the gauntlet. The head of that long lane contained the warriors and older braves and it was here that the great danger lay. Between these lines he sped like a flash, dodging this way and that, running close in under the raised weapons, taking what blows he could on his uplifted arms, knocking this warrior over and doubling that one up with a lightning blow in the stomach, never slacking his speed for one stride, so that it was extremely difficult for the Indians to strike him effectually. Once past that formidable array, Isaac's gauntlet was run, for the squaws and children scattered screaming before the sweep of his powerful arms.

The old chiefs grunted their approval. There was a bruise on Isaac's forehead and a few drops of blood mingled with the beads of perspiration. Several lumps and scratches showed on his bare shoulders and arms, but he had escaped any serious injury. This was a feat almost without a parallel in gauntlet running.

When he had been tied with wet buckskin thongs to the post in the center of the oval, the youths, the younger braves, and the squaws began circling round him, yelling like so many demons. The old squaws thrust sharpened sticks, which had been soaked in salt water, into his flesh. The maidens struck him with willows which left red welts on his white shoulders. The braves buried the blades of their tomahawks in the post as near as possible to his head without actually hitting him.

Isaac knew the Indian nature well. To command the respect of the savages was the only way to lessen his torture. He knew that a cry for mercy would only increase his sufferings and not hasten his death,—indeed it would prolong both. He had resolved to die without a moan. He had determined to show absolute indifference to his torture, which was the only way to appeal to the savage nature, and if anything could, make the Indians show mercy. Or, if he could taunt them into killing him at once he would be spared all the terrible agony which they were in the habit of inflicting on their victims.

One handsome young brave twirled a glittering tomahawk which he threw from a distance of ten, fifteen, and twenty feet and every time the sharp blade of the hatchet sank deep into the stake within an inch of Isaac's head. With a proud and disdainful look Isaac gazed straight before him and paid no heed to his tormentor.

"Does the Indian boy think he can frighten a white warrior?" said Isaac scornfully at length. "Let him go and earn his eagle plumes. The pale face laughs at him."

The young brave understood the Huron language, for he gave a frightful yell and cast his tomahawk again, this time shaving a lock of hair from

Isaac's head.

This was what Isaac had prayed for. He hoped that one of these glittering hatchets would be propelled less skillfully than its predecessors and would kill him instantly. But the enraged brave had no other opportunity to cast his weapon, for the Indians jeered at him and pushed him from the line.

Other braves tried their proficiency in the art of throwing knives and tomahawks, but their efforts called forth only words of derision from Isaac. They left the weapons sticking in the post until round Isaac's head and shoulders there was scarcely room for another.

"The White Eagle is tired of boys," cried Isaac to a chief dancing near. "What has he done that he be made the plaything of children? Let him die the death of a chief."

The maidens had long since desisted in their efforts to torment the prisoner. Even the hardened old squaws had withdrawn. The prisoner's proud, handsome face, his upright bearing, his scorn for his enemies, his indifference to the cuts and bruises, and red welts upon his clear white skin had won their hearts.

Not so with the braves. Seeing that the pale face scorned all efforts to make him flinch, the young brave turned to Big Tree. At a command from this chief the Indians stopped their maneuvering round the post and formed a large circle. In another moment a tall warrior appeared carrying an armful of fagots.

In spite of his iron nerve Isaac shuddered with horror. He had anticipated running the gauntlet, having his nails pulled out, powder and salt shot into his flesh, being scalped alive and a host of other Indian tortures, but as he had killed no members of this tribe he had not thought of being burned alive. God, it was too horrible!

The Indians were now quiet. Their songs and dances would break out soon enough. They piled fagot after fagot round Isaac's feet. The Indian warrior knelt on the ground the steel clicked on the flint; a little shower of sparks dropped on the pieces of punk and then—a tiny flame shot up, and slender little column of blue smoke floated on the air.

Isaac shut his teeth hard and prayed with all his soul for a speedy death.

Simon Girty came hurriedly through the lines of waiting, watching Indians. He had obtained permission to speak to the man of his own color.

"Zane, you made a brave stand. Any other time but this it might have saved you. If you want I'll get word to your people." And then bending and placing his mouth close to Isaac's ear, he whispered, "I did all I could for you, but it must have been too late."

"Try and tell them at Ft. Henry," Isaac said simply.

There was a little cracking of dried wood and then a narrow tongue of red flame darted up from the pile of fagots and licked at the buckskin fringe on the prisoner's legging. At this supreme moment when the attention of all centered on that motionless figure lashed to the stake, and when only the low chanting of the death-song broke the stillness, a long, piercing yell rang out on the quiet morning air. So strong, so sudden, so startling was the break in that almost perfect calm that for a moment afterward there was a silence as of death. All eyes turned to the ridge of rising ground whence that sound had come. Now came the unmistakable thunder of horses' hoofs pounding furiously on the rocky ground. A moment of paralyzed inaction ensued. The Indians stood bewildered, petrified. Then on that ridge of rising ground stood, silhouetted against the blue sky, a great black horse with arching neck and flying mane. Astride him sat a plumed warrior, who waved his rifle high in the air. Again that shrill screeching yell came floating to the ears of the astonished Indians.

The prisoner had seen that horse and rider before; he had heard that long yell; his heart bounded with hope. The Indians knew that yell; it was the terrible war-cry of the Hurons.

A horse followed closely after the leader, and then another appeared on the crest of the hill. Then came two abreast, and then four abreast, and now the hill was black with plunging horses. They galloped swiftly down the slope and into the narrow street of the village. When the black horse entered the oval the train of racing horses extended to the top of the ridge. The plumes of the riders streamed gracefully on the breeze; their feathers shone; their weapons glittered in the bright sunlight.

Never was there more complete surprise. In the earlier morning the Hurons had crept up to within a rifle shot of the encampment, and at an opportune moment when all the scouts and runners were round the torture-stake, they had reached the hillside from which they rode into the village before the inhabitants knew what had happened. Not an Indian raised a weapon. There were screams from the women and children, a shouted command from Big Tree, and then all stood still and waited.

Thundercloud, the war chief of the Wyandots, pulled his black stallion back on his haunches not twenty feet from the prisoner at the stake. His band of painted devils closed in behind him. Full two hundred strong were they and all picked warriors tried and true. They were naked to the waist. Across their brawny chests ran a broad bar of flaming red paint; hideous designs in black and white covered their faces. Every head had been clean-shaven except where the scalp lock bristled like a porcupine's quills. Each warrior carried a plumed spear, a tomahawk, and a rifle. The shining heads, with the little tufts of hair tied tightly close to the scalp, were enough to show that these Indians were on the war-path.

From the back of one of the foremost horses a slender figure dropped and darted toward the prisoner at the stake. Surely that wildly flying hair proved this was not a warrior. Swift as a flash of light this figure reached the stake, the blazing fagots scattered right and left; a naked blade gleamed; the thongs fell from the prisoner's wrists; and the front ranks of the Hurons opened and closed on the freed man. The deliverer turned to the gaping

Indians, disclosing to their gaze the pale and beautiful face of Myeerah, the Wyandot Princes.

"Summon your chief," she commanded.

The tall form of the Seneca chief moved from among the warriors and with slow and measured tread approached the maiden. His bearing fitted the leader of five nations of Indians. It was of one who knew that he was the wisest of chiefs, the hero of a hundred battles. Who dared beard him in his den? Who dared defy the greatest power in all Indian tribes? When he stood before the maiden he folded his arms and waited for her to speak.

"Myeerah claims the White Eagle," she said.

Cornplanter did not answer at once. He had never seek Myeerah, though he had heard many stories of her loveliness. Now he was face to face with the Indian Princess whose fame had been the theme of many an Indian romance, and whose beauty had been sung of in many an Indian song. The beautiful girl stood erect and fearless. Her disordered garments, torn and bedraggled and stained from the long ride, ill-concealed the grace of her form. Her hair rippled from the uncovered head and fell in dusky splendor over her shoulders; her dark eyes shone with a stern and steady fire: her bosom swelled with each deep breath. She was the daughter of great chiefs; she looked the embodiment of savage love.

"The Huron squaw is brave," said Cornplanter. "By what right does she come to free my captive?"

"He is an adopted Wyandot."

"Why does the paleface hide like a fox near the camp of Cornplanter?"

"He ran away. He lost the trail to the Fort on the river."

"Cornplanter takes prisoners to kill; not to free."

"If you will not give him up Myeerah will take him," she answered, pointing to the long line of mounted warriors. "And should harm befall Tarhe's daughter it will be avenged."

Cornplanter looked at Thundercloud. Well he knew that chief's prowess in the field. He ran his eyes over the silent, watching Hurons, and then back to the sombre face of their leader. Thundercloud sat rigid upon his stallion; his head held high; every muscle tense and strong for instant action. He was ready and eager for the fray. He, and every one of his warriors, would fight like a thousand tigers for their Princess—the pride of the proud race of Wyandots. Cornplanter saw this and he felt that on the eve of important marches he dared not sacrifice one of his braves for any reason, much less a worthless pale face; and yet to let the prisoner go galled the haughty spirit of the Seneca chief.

"The Long Knife is not worth the life of one of my dogs," he said, with scorn in his deep voice. "If Cornplanter willed he could drive the Hurons before him like leaves before the storm. Let Myeerah take the pale face back to her wigwam and there feed him and make a squaw of him. When he stings like a snake in the grass remember the chief's words. Cornplanter turns on his heel from the Huron maiden who forgets her blood."

* * * * * * * * * * * * * * *

When the sun reached its zenith it shone down upon a long line of mounted Indians riding single file along the narrow trail and like a huge serpent winding through the forest and over the plain.

They were Wyandot Indians, and Isaac Zane rode among them. Freed from the terrible fate which had menaced him, and knowing that he was once more on his way to the Huron encampment, he had accepted his destiny and quarreled no more with fate. He was thankful beyond all words for his rescue from the stake.

Coming to a clear, rapid stream, the warriors dismounted and rested while their horses drank thirstily of the cool water. An Indian touched Isaac on the arm and silently pointed toward the huge maple tree under which Thundercloud and Myeerah were sitting. Isaac turned his horse and rode the short distance intervening. When he got near he saw that Myeerah stood with one arm over her pony's neck. She raised eyes that were weary and sad, which yet held a lofty and noble resolve.

"White Eagle, this stream leads straight to the Fort on the river," she said briefly, almost coldly. "Follow it, and when the sun reaches the top of yonder hill you will be with your people. Go, you are free."

She turned her face away. Isaac's head whirled in his amazement. He could not believe his ears. He looked closely at her and saw that though her face was calm her throat swelled, and the hand which lay over the neck of her pony clenched the bridle in a fierce grasp. Isaac glanced at Thundercloud and the other Indians near by. They sat unconcerned with the invariable unreadable expression.

"Myeerah, what do you mean?" asked Isaac.

"The words of Cornplanter cut deep into the heart of Myeerah," she answered bitterly. "They were true. The Eagle does not care for Myeerah. She shall no longer keep him in a cage. He is free to fly away."

"The Eagle does not want his freedom. I love you, Myeerah. You have saved me and I am yours. If you will go home with me and marry me there as my people are married I will go back to the Wyandot village."

Myeerah's eyes softened with unutterable love. With a quick cry she was in his arms. After a few moments of forgetfulness Myeerah spoke to Thundercloud and waved her hand toward the west. The chief swung himself over his horse, shouted a single command, and rode down the bank into the water. His warriors followed him, wading their horses into the shallow creek, with never backward look. When the last rider had disappeared in the willows the lovers turned their horses eastward.

CHAPTER X.

It was near the close of a day in early summer. A small group of persons surrounded Col. Zane where he sat on his doorstep. From time to time he took the long Indian pipe from his mouth and blew great clouds of smoke over his head. Major McColloch and Capt. Boggs were there. Silas Zane half reclined on the grass. The Colonel's wife stood in the door-way, and Betty sat on the lower step with her head leaning against her brother's knee. They all had grave faces. Jonathan Zane had returned that day after an absence of three weeks, and was now answering the many questions with which he was plied.

"Don't ask me any more and I'll tell you the whole thing," he had just said, while wiping the perspiration from his brow. His face was worn; his beard ragged and unkempt; his appearance suggestive of extreme fatigue. "It was this way: Colonel Crawford had four hundred and eighty men under him, with Slover and me acting as guides. This was a large force of men and comprised soldiers from Pitt and the other forts and settlers from all along the river. You see, Crawford wanted to crush the Shawnees at one blow. When we reached the Sandusky River, which we did after an arduous march, not one Indian did we see. You know Crawford expected to surprise the Shawnee camp, and when he found it deserted he didn't know what to do. Slover and I both advised an immediate retreat. Crawford would not listen to us. I tried to explain to him that ever since the Guadenhutten massacre keen-eyed Indian scouts had been watching the border. The news of the present expedition had been carried by fleet runners to the different Indian tribes and they were working like hives of angry bees. The deserted Shawnee village meant to me that the alarm had been sounded in the towns of the Shawnees and the Delawares; perhaps also in the Wyandot towns to the north. Colonel Crawford was obdurate and insisted on resuming the march into the Indian country. The next day we met the Indians coming directly toward us. It was the combined force of the Delaware chiefs, Pipe and Wingenund. The battle had hardly commenced when the redskins were reinforced by four hundred warriors under Shanshota, the Huron chief. The enemy skulked behind trees and rocks, hid in ravines, and crawled through the long grass. They could be picked off only by Indian hunters, of whom Crawford had but few—probably fifty all told. All that day we managed to keep our position, though we lost sixty men. That night we lay down to rest by great fires which we built, to prevent night surprises.

"Early next morning we resumed the fight. I saw Simon Girty on his white horse. He was urging and cheering the Indians on to desperate fighting. Their fire became so deadly that we were forced to retreat. In the afternoon Slover, who had been out scouting, returned with the information that a mounted force was approaching, and that he believed they were the reinforcements which Col. Crawford expected. The reinforcements came up and proved to be Butler's British rangers from Detroit. This stunned Crawford's soldiers. The fire of the enemy became hotter and hotter. Our men were falling like leaves around us. They threw aside their rifles and ran, many of them right into the hands of the savages. I believe some of the experienced bordermen escaped but most of Crawford's force met death on the field. I hid in a hollow log. Next day when I felt that it could be done safely I crawled out. I saw scalped and mutilated bodies everywhere, but did not find Col. Crawford's body. The Indians had taken all the clothing, weapons, blankets and everything of value. The Wyandots took a northwest trail and the Delawares and the Shawnees traveled east. I followed the latter because their trail led toward home. Three days later I stood on the high bluff above Wingenund's camp. From there I saw Col. Crawford tied to a stake and a fire started at his feet. I was not five hundred yards from the camp. I saw the war chiefs, Pipe and Wingenund; I saw Simon Girty and a British officer in uniform. The chiefs and Girty were once Crawford's friends. They stood calmly by and watched the poor victim slowly burn to death. The Indians yelled and danced round the stake; they devised every kind of hellish torture. When at last an Indian ran in and tore off the scalp of the still living man I could bear to see no more, and I turned and ran. I have been in some tough places, but this last was the worst."

"My God! it is awful—and to think that man Girty was once a white man," cried Col. Zane.

"He came very near being a dead man," said Jonathan, with grim humor. "I got a long shot at him and killed his big white horse."

"It's a pity you missed him," said Silas Zane.

"Here comes Wetzel. What will he say about the massacre?" remarked Major McColloch.

Wetzel joined the group at that moment and shook hands with Jonathan. When interrogated about the failure of Col. Crawford's expedition Wetzel said that Slover had just made his appearance at the cabin of Hugh Bennet, and that he was without clothing and almost dead from exposure.

"I'm glad Slover got out alive. He was against the march all along. If

Crawford had listened to us he would have averted this terrible affair and saved his own life. Lew, did Slover know how many men got out?" asked Jonathan.

"He said not many. The redskins killed all the prisoners exceptin' Crawford and Knight."

"I saw Col. Crawford burned at the stake. I did not see Dr. Knight. Maybe they murdered him before I reached the camp of the Delawares," said Jonathan.

"Wetzel, in your judgment, what effect will this massacre and Crawford's death have on the border?" inquired Col. Zane.

"It means another bloody year like 1777," answered Wetzel.

"We are liable to have trouble with the Indians any day. You mean that."

"There'll be war all along the river. Hamilton is hatchin' some new devil's trick with Girty. Col. Zane, I calkilate that Girty has a spy in the river settlements and knows as much about the forts and defense as you do."

"You can't mean a white spy."

"Yes, just that."

"That is a strong assertion, Lewis, but coming from you it means something. Step aside here and explain yourself," said Col. Zane, getting up and walking out to the fence.

"I don't like the looks of things," said the hunter. "A month ago I ketched this man Miller pokin' his nose round the block-house where he hadn't ought to be. And I kep' watchin' him. If my suspicions is correct he's playin' some deep game. I ain't got any proof, but things looks bad."

"That's strange, Lewis," said Col. Zane soberly. "Now that you mention it I remember Jonathan said he met Miller near the Kanawha three weeks ago. That was when Crawford's expedition was on the way to the Shawnee villages. The Colonel tried to enlist Miller, but Miller said he was in a hurry to get back to the Fort. And he hasn't come back yet."

"I ain't surprised. Now, Col. Zane, you are in command here. I'm not a soldier and for that reason I'm all the better to watch Miller. He won't suspect me. You give me authority and I'll round up his little game."

"By all means, Lewis. Go about it your own way, and report anything to me. Remember you may be mistaken and give Miller the benefit of the doubt. I don't like the fellow. He has a way of appearing and disappearing, and for no apparent reason, that makes me distrust him. But for Heaven's sake, Lew, how would he profit by betraying us?"

"I don't know. All I know is he'll bear watchin'."

"My gracious, Lew Wetzel!" exclaimed Betty as her brother and the hunter rejoined the others. "Have you come all the way over here without a gun? And you have on a new suit of buckskin."

Lewis stood a moment by Betty, gazing down at her with his slight smile. He looked exceedingly well. His face was not yet bronzed by summer suns. His long black hair, of which he was as proud as a woman could have been, and of which he took as much care as he did of his rifle, waved over his shoulders.

"Betty, this is my birthday, but that ain't the reason I've got my fine feathers on. I'm goin' to try and make an impression on you," replied Lewis, smiling.

"I declare, this is very sudden. But you have succeeded. Who made the suit? And where did you get all that pretty fringe and those beautiful beads?"

"That stuff I picked up round an Injun camp. The suit I made myself."

"I think, Lewis, I must get you to help me make my new gown," said Betty, roguishly.

"Well, I must be getting' back," said Wetzel, rising.

"Oh, don't go yet. You have not talked to me at all," said Betty petulantly. She walked to the gate with him.

"What can an Injun hunter say to amuse the belle of the border?"

"I don't want to be amused exactly. I mean I'm not used to being unnoticed, especially by you." And then in a lower tone she continued: "What did you mean about Mr. Miller? I heard his name and Eb looked worried. What did you tell him?"

"Never mind now, Betty. Maybe I'll tell you some day. It's enough for you to know the Colonel don't like Miller and that I think he is a bad man. You don't care nothin' for Miller, do you Betty?"

"Not in the least."

"Don't see him any more, Betty. Good-night, now, I must be goin' to supper."

"Lew, stop! or I shall run after you."

"And what good would your runnin' do?" said Lewis "You'd never ketch me. Why, I could give you twenty paces start and beat you to yon tree."

"You can't. Come, try it," retorted Betty, catching hold of her skirt. She could never have allowed a challenge like that to pass.

"Ha! ha! We are in for a race, Betty. if you beat him, start or no start, you will have accomplished something never done before," said Col. Zane.

"Come, Silas, step off twenty paces and make them long ones," said Betty, who was in earnest.

"We'll make it forty paces," said Silas, as he commenced taking immense strides.

"What is Lewis looking at?" remarked Col. Zane's wife.

Wetzel, in taking his position for the race, had faced the river. Mrs. Zane had seen him start suddenly, straighten up and for a moment stand like a statue. Her exclamation drew he attention of the others to the hunter.

"Look!" he cried, waving his hand toward the river.

"I declare, Wetzel, you are always seeing something. Where shall I look? Ah, yes, there is a dark form moving along the bank. By jove! I believe it's an Indian," said Col. Zane.

Jonathan darted into the house. When he reappeared second later he had three rifles.

"I see horses, Lew. What do you make out?" said Jonathan. "It's a bold manoeuvre for Indians unless they have a strong force."

"Hostile Injuns wouldn't show themselves like that. Maybe they ain't redskins at all. We'll go down to the bluff."

"Oh, yes, let us go," cried Betty, walking down the path toward Wetzel.

Col. Zane followed her, and presently the whole party were on their way to the river. When they reached the bluff they saw two horses come down the opposite bank and enter the water. Then they seemed to fade from view. The tall trees cast a dark shadow over the water and the horses had become lost in this obscurity. Col. Zane and Jonathan walked up and down the bank seeking to find a place which afforded a clearer view of the river.

"There they come," shouted Silas.

"Yes, I see them just swimming out of the shadow," said Col. Zane. "Both horses have riders. Lewis, what can you make out?"

"It's Isaac and an Indian girl," answered Wetzel.

This startling announcement created a commotion in the little group. It was followed by a chorus of exclamations.

"Heavens! Wetzel, you have wonderful eyes. I hope to God you are right. There, I see the foremost rider waving his hand," cried Col. Zane.

"Oh, Bessie, Bessie! I believe Lew is right. Look at Tige," said Betty excitedly.

Everybody had forgotten the dog. He had come down the path with Betty and had pressed close to her. First he trembled, then whined, then with a loud bark he ran down the bank and dashed into the water.

"Hel-lo, Betts," came the cry across the water. There was no mistaking that clear voice. It was Isaac's.

Although the sun had long gone down behind the hills daylight lingered. It was bright enough for the watchers to recognize Isaac Zane. He sat high on his horse and in his hand he held the bridle of a pony that was swimming beside him. The pony bore the slender figure of a girl. She was bending forward and her hands were twisted in the pony's mane.

By this time the Colonel and Jonathan were standing in the shallow water waiting to grasp the reins and lead the horses up the steep bank. Attracted by the unusual sight of a wildly gesticulating group on the river bluff, the settlers from the Fort hurried down to the scene of action. Capt. Boggs and Alfred Clarke joined the crowd. Old Sam came running down from the barn. All were intensely excited and Col. Zane and Jonathan reached for the bridles and led the horses up the slippery incline.

"Eb, Jack, Silas, here I am alive and well," cried Isaac as he leaped from his horse. "Betty, you darling, it's Isaac. Don't stand staring as if I were a ghost."

Whereupon Betty ran to him, flung her arms around his neck and clung to him. Isaac kissed her tenderly and disengaged himself from her arms.

"You'll get all wet. Glad to see me? Well, I never had such a happy moment in my life. Betty, I have brought you home one whom you must love. This is Myeerah, your sister. She is wet and cold. Take her home and make her warm and comfortable. You must forget all the past, for Myeerah has saved me from the stake."

Betty had forgotten the other. At her brother's words she turned and saw a slender form. Even the wet, mud-stained and ragged Indian costume failed to hide the grace of that figure. She saw a beautiful face, as white as her own, and dark eyes full of unshed tears.

"The Eagle is free," said the Indian girl in her low, musical voice.

"You have brought him home to us. Come," said Betty taking the hand of the trembling maiden.

The settlers crowded round Isaac and greeted him warmly while they plied him with innumerable questions. Was he free? Who was the Indian girl? Had he run off with her? Were the Indians preparing for war?

On the way to the Colonel's house Isaac told briefly of his escape from the Wyandots, of his capture by Cornplanter, and of his rescue. He also mentioned the preparations for war he had seen in Cornplanter's camp, and Girty's story of Col. Crawford's death.

"How does it come that you have the Indian girl with you?" asked Col. Zane as they left the curious settlers and entered the house.

"I am going to marry Myeerah and I brought her with me for that purpose. When we are married I will go back to the Wyandots and live with them until peace is declared."

"Humph! Will it be declared?"

"Myeerah has promised it, and I believe she can bring it about, especially if I marry her. Peace with the Hurons may help to bring about peace with the Shawnees. I shall never cease to work for that end; but even if peace cannot be secured, my duty still is to Myeerah. She saved me from a most horrible death."

"If your marriage with this Indian girl will secure the friendly offices of that grim old warrior Tarhe, it is far more than fighting will ever do. I do not want you to go back. Would we ever see you again?"

"Oh, yes, often I hope. You see, if I marry Myeerah the Hurons will allow me every liberty."

"Well, that puts a different light on the subject."

"Oh, how I wish you and Jonathan could have seen Thundercloud and his two hundred warriors ride into Cornplanter's camp. It was magnificent! The braves were all crowded near the stake where I was bound. The fire had been lighted. Suddenly the silence was shattered by an awful yell. It was Thundercloud's yell. I knew it because I had heard it before, and anyone who had once heard that yell could never forget it. In what seemed an incredibly short time Thundercloud's warriors were lined up in the middle of the camp. The surprise was so complete that, had it been necessary, they could have ridden Cornplanter's braves down, killed many, routed the others, and burned the village. Cornplanter will not get over that surprise in many a moon."

Betty had always hated the very mention of the Indian girl who had been the cause of her brother's long absence from home. But she was so happy in the knowledge of his return that she felt that it was in her power to forgive much; more over, the white, weary face of the Indian maiden touched Betty's warm heart. With her quick intuition she had divined that this was even a greater trial for Myeerah. Undoubtedly the Indian girl feared the scorn of her lover's people. She showed it in her trembling hands, in her fearful glances.

Finding that Myeerah could speak and understand English, Betty became more interested in her charge every moment. She set about to make Myeerah comfortable, and while she removed the wet and stained garments she talked all the time. She told her how happy she was that Isaac was alive and well. She said Myeerah's heroism in saving him should atone for all the past, and that Isaac's family would welcome her in his home.

Gradually Myeerah's agitation subsided under Betty's sweet graciousness, and by the time Betty had dressed her in a white gown, had brushed the dark hair and added a bright ribbon to the simple toilet, Myeerah had so far forgotten her fears as to take a shy pleasure in the picture of herself in the mirror. As for Betty, she gave vent to a little cry of delight. "Oh, you are perfectly lovely," cried Betty. "In that gown no one would know you as a Wyandot princess."

"Myeerah's mother was a white woman."

"I have heard your story, Myeerah, and it is wonderful. You must tell me all about your life with the Indians. You speak my language almost as well as I do. Who taught you?"

"Myeerah learned to talk with the White Eagle. She can speak French with the Coureurs-des-bois."

"That's more than I can do, Myeerah. And I had French teacher," said Betty, laughing.

"Hello, up there," came Isaac's voice from below.

"Come up, Isaac," called Betty.

"Is this my Indian sweetheart?" exclaimed Isaac, stopping at the door. "Betty, isn't she—"

"Yes," answered Betty, "she is simply beautiful."

"Come, Myeerah, we must go down to supper," said Isaac, taking her in his arms and kissing her. "Now you must not be afraid, nor mind being looked at."

"Everyone will be kind to you," said Betty, taking her hand. Myeerah had slipped from Isaac's arm and hesitated and hung back. "Come," continued Betty, "I will stay with you, and you need not talk if you do not wish."

Thus reassured Myeerah allowed Betty to lead her down stairs. Isaac had gone ahead and was waiting at the door.

The big room was brilliantly lighted with pine knots. Mrs. Zane was arranging the dishes on the table. Old Sam and Annie were hurrying to and fro from the kitchen. Col. Zane had just come up the cellar stairs carrying a mouldy looking cask. From its appearance it might have been a powder keg, but the merry twinkle in the Colonel's eyes showed that the cask contained something as precious, perhaps, as powder, but not quite so dangerous. It was a cask of wine over thirty years old. With Col. Zane's other effects it had stood the test of the long wagon-train journey over the Virginia mountains, and of the raft-ride down the Ohio. Col. Zane thought the feast he had arranged for Isaac would be a fitting occasion for the breaking of the cask.

Major McCullough, Capt. Boggs and Hugh Bennet had been invited. Wetzel had been persuaded to come. Betty's friends Lydia and Alice were there.

As Isaac, with an air of pride, led the two girls into the room Old Sam saw them and he exclaimed, "For de Lawd's sakes, Marsh Zane, dar's two pippins, sure can't tell 'em from one anudder."

Betty and Myeerah did resemble each other. They were of about the same size, tall and slender. Betty was rosy, bright-eyed and smiling; Myeerah was pale one moment and red the next.

"Friends, this is Myeerah, the daughter of Tarhe," said Isaac simply. "We are to be married to-morrow."

"Oh, why did you not tell me?" asked Betty in great surprise. "She said nothing about it."

"You see Myeerah has that most excellent trait in a woman—knowing when to keep silent," answered Isaac with a smile.

The door opened at this moment, admitting Will Martin and Alfred Clarke.

"Everybody is here now, Bessie, and I guess we may as well sit down to supper," said Col. Zane. "And, good friends, let me say that this is an occasion for rejoicing. It is not so much a marriage that I mean. That we might have any day if Lydia or Betty would show some of the alacrity which got a good husband for Alice. Isaac is a free man and we expect his marriage will bring about peace with a powerful tribe of Indians. To us, and particularly to you, young people, that is a matter of great importance. The friendship of the Hurons cannot but exert an influence on other tribes. I, myself, may live to see the day that my dream shall be realized—peaceful and friendly relations with the Indians, the freedom of the soil, well-tilled farms and growing settlements, and at last, the opening of this glorious country to the world. Therefore, let us rejoice; let every one be happy; let your gayest laugh ring out, and tell your best story."

Betty had blushed painfully at the entrance of Alfred and again at the Colonel's remark. To add to her embarrassment she found herself seated opposite Alfred at the table. This was the first time he had been near her since the Sunday at the meeting-house, and the incident had a singular effect on Betty. She found herself possessed, all at once, of an unaccountable shyness, and she could not lift her eyes from her plate. But at length she managed to steal a glance at Alfred. She failed to see any signs in his beaming face of the broken spirit of which her brother had hinted. He looked very well indeed. He was eating his dinner like any other healthy man, and talking and laughing with Lydia. This developed another unaccountable feeling in Betty, but this time it was resentment. Who ever heard of a man, who was as much in love as his letter said, looking well and enjoying himself with any other than the object of his affections? He had got over it, that was all. Just then Alfred turned and gazed full into Betty's eyes. She lowered them instantly, but not so quickly that she failed to see in his a reproach.

"You are going to stay with us a while, are you not?" asked Betty of Isaac.

"No, Betts, not more than a day or so. Now, do not look so distressed. I do not go back as a prisoner. Myeerah and I can often come and visit you. But just now I want to get back and try to prevent the Delawares from urging Tarhe to war."

"Isaac, I believe you are doing the wisest thing possible," said Capt. Boggs. "And when I look at your bride-to-be I confess I do not see how you remained single so long."

"That's so, Captain," answered Isaac. "But you see, I have never been satisfied or contented in captivity, I wanted nothing but to be free."

"In other words, you were blind," remarked Alfred, smiling at Isaac.

"Yes, Alfred, was. And I imagine had you been in my place you would have discovered the beauty and virtue of my Princess long before I did. Nevertheless, please do not favor Myeerah with so many admiring glances. She is not used to it. And that reminds me that I must expect trouble tomorrow. All you fellows will want to kiss her."

"And Betty is going to be maid of honor. She, too, will have her troubles," remarked Col. Zane.

"Think of that, Alfred," said Isaac "A chance to kiss the two prettiest girls on the border—a chance of a lifetime."

"It is customary, is it not?" said Alfred coolly.

"Yes, it's a custom, if you can catch the girl," answered Col. Zane.

Betty's face flushed at Alfred's cool assumption. How dared he? In spite of her will she could not resist the power that compelled her to look at him. As plainly as if it were written there, she saw in his steady blue eyes the light of a memory—the memory of a kiss. And Betty dropped her head, her face burning, her heart on fire with shame, and love, and regret.

"It'll be a good chance for me, too," said Wetzel. His remark instantly turned attention to himself.

"The idea is absurd," said Isaac. "Why, Lew Wetzel, you could not be made to kiss any girl."

"I would not be backward about it," said Col. Zane.

"You have forgotten the fuss you made when the boys were kissing me," said Mrs. Zane with a fine scorn.

"My dear," said Col. Zane, in an aggrieved tone, "I did not make so much of a fuss, as you call it, until they had kissed you a great many times more than was reasonable."

"Isaac, tell us one thing more," said Capt. Boggs. "How did Myeerah learn of your capture by Cornplanter? Surely she could not have trailed you?"

"Will you tell us?" said Isaac to Myeerah.

"A bird sang it to me," answered Myeerah.

"She will never tell, that is certain," said Isaac. "And for that reason I believe Simon Girty got word to her that I was in the hands of Cornplanter. At the last moment when the Indians were lashing me to the stake Girty came to me and said he must have been too late."

"Yes, Girty might have done that," said Col. Zane. "I suppose, though he dared not interfere in behalf of poor Crawford."

"Isaac, Can you get Myeerah to talk? I love to hear her speak," said Betty, in an aside.

"Myeerah, will you sing a Huron love-song?" said Isaac "Or, if you do not wish to sing, tell a story. I want them to know how well you can speak our language."

"What shall Myeerah say?" she said, shyly.

"Tell them the legend of the Standing Stone."

"A beautiful Indian girl once dwelt in the pine forests," began Myeerah, with her eyes cast down and her hand seeking Isaac's. "Her voice was like rippling waters, her beauty like the rising sun. From near and from far came warriors to see the fair face of this maiden. She smiled on them all and they called her Smiling Moon. Now there lived on the Great Lake a Wyandot chief. He was young and bold. No warrior was as great as Tarhe. Smiling Moon cast a spell on his heart. He came many times to woo her and make her his wife. But Smiling Moon said: 'Go, do great deeds, an come again.'

"Tarhe searched the east and the west. He brought her strange gifts from strange lands. She said: 'Go and slay my enemies.' Tarhe went forth in his war paint and killed the braves who named her Smiling Moon. He came again to her and she said: 'Run swifter than the deer, be more cunning than the beaver, dive deeper than the loon.'

"Tarhe passed once more to the island where dwelt Smiling Moon. The ice was thick, the snow was deep. Smiling Moon turned not from her warm fire as she said: 'The chief is a great warrior, but Smiling Moon is not easily won. It is cold. Change winter into summer and then Smiling Moon will love him.'

"Tarhe cried in a loud voice to the Great Spirit: 'Make me a master.'

"A voice out of the forest answered: 'Tarhe, great warrior, wise chief, waste not thy time, go back to thy wigwam.'

"Tarhe unheeding cried 'Tarhe wins or dies. Make him a master so that he may drive the ice northward.'

"Stormed the wild tempest; thundered the rivers of ice; chill blew the north wind, the cold northwest wind, against the mild south wind; snow-spirits and hail-spirits fled before the warm raindrops; the white mountains melted, and lo! it was summer.

"On the mountain top Tarhe waited for his bride. Never wearying, ever faithful he watched many years. There he turned to stone. There he stands to-day, the Standing Stone of ages. And Smiling Moon, changed by the Great Spirit into the Night Wind, forever wails her lament at dusk through the forest trees, and moans over the mountain tops."

Myeerah's story elicited cheers and praises from all. She was entreated to tell another, but smilingly shook her head. Now that her shyness had worn off to some extent she took great interest in the jest and the general conversation.

Col. Zane's fine old wine flowed like water. The custom was to fill a guest's cup as soon as it was empty. Drinking much was rather encouraged than otherwise. But Col. Zane never allowed this custom to go too far in his house.

"Friends, the hour grows late," he said. "To-morrow, after the great event, we shall have games, shooting matches, running races, and contests of all kinds. Capt. Boggs and I have arranged to give prizes, and I expect the girls can give something to lend a zest to the competition."

"Will the girls have a chance in these races?" asked Isaac. "If so, I should like to see Betty and Myeerah run."

"Betty can outrun any woman, red or white, on the border," said Wetzel. "And she could make some of the men run their level best."

"Well, perhaps we shall give her one opportunity to-morrow," observed the Colonel. "She used to be good at running but it seems to me that of late she has taken to books and—"

"Oh, Eb! that is untrue," interrupted Betty.

Col. Zane laughed and patted his sister's cheek. "Never mind, Betty," and then, rising, he continued, "Now let us drink to the bride and groom-to-be. Capt. Boggs, I call on you."

"We drink to the bride's fair beauty; we drink to the groom's good luck," said Capt. Boggs, raising his cup.

"Do not forget the maid-of-honor," said Isaac.

"Yes, and the maid-of-honor. Mr. Clarke, will you say something appropriate?" asked Col. Zane.

Rising, Clarke said: "I would be glad to speak fittingly on this occasion, but I do not think I can do it justice. I believe as Col. Zane does, that this

Indian Princess is the first link in that chain of peace which will some day unite the red men and the white men. Instead of the White Crane she should be called the White Dove. Gentlemen, rise and drink to her long life and happiness."

The toast was drunk. Then Clarke refilled his cup and holding it high over his head he looked at Betty.

"Gentlemen, to the maid-of-honor. Miss Zane, your health, your happiness, in this good old wine."

"I thank you," murmured Betty with downcast eyes. "I bid you all good-night. Come, Myeerah."

Once more alone with Betty, the Indian girl turned to her with eyes like twin stars.

"My sister has made me very happy," whispered Myeerah in her soft, low voice. "Myeerah's heart is full."

"I believe you are happy, for I know you love Isaac dearly."

"Myeerah has always loved him. She will love his sister."

"And I will love you," said Betty. "I will love you because you have saved him. Ah! Myeerah, yours has been wonderful, wonderful love."

"My sister is loved," whispered Myeerah. "Myeerah saw the look in the eyes of the great hunter. It was the sad light of the moon on the water. He loves you. And the other looked at my sister with eyes like the blue of northern skies. He, too, loves you."

"Hush!" whispered Betty, trembling and hiding her face. "Hush! Myeerah, do not speak of him."

CHAPTER XI.

THe following afternoon the sun shone fair and warm; the sweet smell of the tan-bark pervaded the air and the birds sang their gladsome songs. The scene before the grim battle-scarred old fort was not without its picturesqueness. The low vine-covered cabins on the hill side looked more like picture houses than like real habitations of men; the mill with its burned-out roof—a reminder of the Indians—and its great wheel, now silent and still, might have been from its lonely and dilapidated appearance a hundred years old.

On a little knoll carpeted with velvety grass sat Isaac and his Indian bride. He had selected this vantage point because it afforded a fine view of the green square where the races and the matches were to take place. Admiring women stood around him and gazed at his wife. They gossiped in whispers about her white skin, her little hands, her beauty. The girls stared with wide open and wondering eyes. The youngsters ran round and round the little group; they pushed each other over, and rolled in the long grass, and screamed with delight.

It was to be a gala occasion and every man, woman and child in the settlement had assembled on the green. Col. Zane and Sam were planting a post in the center of the square. It was to be used in the shooting matches. Capt. Boggs and Major McColloch were arranging the contestants in order. Jonathan Zane, Will Martin, Alfred Clarke—all the young men were carefully charging and priming their rifles. Betty was sitting on the black stallion which Col. Zane had generously offered as first prize. She was in the gayest of moods and had just coaxed Isaac to lift her on the tall horse, from which height she purposed watching the sports. Wetzel alone did not seem infected by the spirit of gladsomeness which pervaded. He stood apart leaning on his long rifle and taking no interest in the proceedings behind him. He was absorbed in contemplating the forest on the opposite shore of the river.

"Well, boys, I guess we are ready for the fun," called Col. Zane, cheerily.

"Only one shot apiece, mind you, except in case of a tie. Now, everybody shoot his best."

The first contest was a shooting match known as "driving the nail." It was as the name indicated, nothing less than shooting at the head of a nail. In the absence of a nail—for nails were scarce—one was usually fashioned from a knife blade, or an old file, or even a piece of silver. The nail was driven lightly into the stake, the contestants shot at it from a distance as great as the eyesight permitted. To drive the nail hard and fast into the wood at one hundred yards was a feat seldom accomplished. By many hunters it was deemed more difficult than "snuffing the candle," another border pastime, which consisted of placing in the dark at any distance a lighted candle, and then putting out the flame with a single rifle ball. Many settlers, particularly those who handled the plow more than the rifle, sighted from a rest, and placed a piece of moss under the rife-barrel to prevent its spring at the discharge.

The match began. Of the first six shooters Jonathan Zane and Alfred Clarke scored the best shots. Each placed a bullet in the half-inch circle round the nail.

"Alfred, very good, indeed," said Col. Zane. "You have made a decided improvement since the last shooting-match."

Six other settlers took their turns. All were unsuccessful in getting a shot inside the little circle. Thus a tie between Alfred and Jonathan had to be decided.

"Shoot close, Alfred," yelled Isaac. "I hope you beat him. He always won from me and then crowed over it."

Alfred's second shot went wide of the mark, and as Jonathan placed another bullet in the circle, this time nearer the center, Alfred had to acknowledge defeat.

"Here comes Miller," said Silas Zane. "Perhaps he will want a try."

Col. Zane looked round. Miller had joined the party. He carried his rifle and accoutrements, and evidently had just returned to the settlement. He nodded pleasantly to all.

"Miller, will you take a shot for the first prize, which I was about to award to Jonathan?" said Col. Zane.

"No. I am a little late, and not entitled to a shot. I will take a try for the others," answered Miller.

At the arrival of Miller on the scene Wetzel had changed his position to one nearer the crowd. The dog, Tige, trotted closely at his heels. No one heard Tige's low growl or Wetzel's stern word to silence him. Throwing his arm over Betty's pony, Wetzel apparently watched the shooters. In reality he studied intently Miller's every movement.

"I expect some good shooting for this prize," said Col. Zane, waving a beautifully embroidered buckskin bullet pouch, which was one of Betty's donations.

Jonathan having won his prize was out of the lists and could compete no more. This entitled Alfred to the first shot for second prize. He felt he would give anything he possessed to win the dainty trifle which the Colonel had waved aloft. Twice he raised his rifle in his exceeding earnestness to score a good shot and each time lowered the barrel. When finally he did shoot the bullet embedded itself in the second circle. It was a good shot, but he knew it would never win that prize.

"A little nervous, eh?" remarked Miller, with a half sneer on his swarthy face.

Several young settlers followed in succession, but their aims were poor. Then little Harry Bennet took his stand. Harry had won many prizes in former matches, and many of the pioneers considered him one of the best shots in the country.

"Only a few more after you, Harry," said Col. Zane. "You have a good chance."

"All right, Colonel. That's Betty's prize and somebody'll have to do some mighty tall shootin' to beat me," said the lad, his blue eyes flashing as he toed the mark.

Shouts and cheers of approval greeted his attempt. The bullet had passed into the wood so close to the nail that a knife blade could not have been inserted between.

Miller's turn came next. He was a fine marksman and he knew it. With the confidence born of long experience and knowledge of his weapon, he took a careful though quick aim and fired. He turned away satisfied that he would carry off the coveted prize. He had nicked the nail.

But Miller reckoned without his host. Betty had seen the result of his shot and the self-satisfied smile on his face. She watched several of the settlers make poor attempts at the nail, and then, convinced that not one of the other contestants could do so well as Miller, she slipped off the horse and ran around to where Wetzel was standing by her pony.

"Lew, I believe Miller will win my prize," she whispered, placing her hand on the hunter's arm. "He has scratched the nail, and I am sure no one except you can do better. I do not want Miller to have anything of mine."

"And, little girl, you want me to shoot fer you," said Lewis.

"Yes, Lew, please come and shoot for me."

It was said of Wetzel that he never wasted powder. He never entered into the races and shooting-matches of the settlers, yet it was well known that he was the fleetest runner and the most unerring shot on the frontier. Therefore, it was with surprise and pleasure that Col. Zane heard the hunter say he guessed he would like one shot anyway.

Miller looked on with a grim smile. He knew that, Wetzel or no Wetzel, it would take a remarkably clever shot to beat his.

"This shot's for Betty," said Wetzel as he stepped to the mark. He fastened his keen eyes on the stake. At that distance the head of the nail looked like a tiny black speck. Wetzel took one of the locks of hair that waved over his broad shoulders and held it up in front of his eyes a moment. He thus ascertained that there was not any perceptible breeze. The long black barrel started slowly to rise—it seemed to the interested onlookers that it would never reach a level and when, at last, it became rigid, there was a single second in which man and rifle appeared as if carved out of stone. Then followed a burst of red flame, a puff of white smoke, a clear ringing report.

Many thought the hunter had missed altogether. It seemed that the nail had not changed its position; there was no bullet hole in the white lime wash that had been smeared round the nail. But on close inspection the nail was found to have been driven to its head in the wood.

"A wonderful shot!" exclaimed Col. Zane. "Lewis, I don't remember having seen the like more than once or twice in my life."

Wetzel made no answer. He moved away to his former position and commenced to reload his rifle. Betty came running up to him, holding in her hand the prize bullet pouch.

"Oh, Lew, if I dared I would kiss you. It pleases me more for you to have won my prize than if any one else had won it. And it was the finest, straightest shot ever made."

"Betty, it's a little fancy for redskins, but it'll be a keepsake," answered Lewis, his eyes reflecting the bright smile on her face.

Friendly rivalry in feats that called for strength, speed and daring was the diversion of the youth of that period, and the pioneers conducted this good-natured but spirited sport strictly on its merits. Each contestant strove his utmost to outdo his opponent. It was hardly to be expected that Alfred would carry off any of the laurels. Used as he had been to comparative idleness he was no match for the hardy lads who had been brought up and trained to a life of action, wherein a ten mile walk behind a plow, or a cord of wood chopped in a day, were trifles. Alfred lost in the foot-race and the sackrace, but by dint of exerting himself to the limit of his strength, he did manage to take one fall out of the best wrestler. He was content to stop here, and, throwing himself on the grass, endeavored to recover his breath. He felt happier today than for some time past. Twice during the afternoon he had met Betty's eyes and the look he encountered there made his heart stir with a strange feeling of fear and hope. While he was ruminating on what had happened between Betty and himself he allowed his eyes to wander from one person to another. When his gaze alighted on Wetzel it became riveted there. The hunter's attitude struck him as singular. Wetzel had his face half turned toward the boys romping near him and he leaned carelessly against a white oak tree. But a close observer would have seen, as Alfred did, that there was a certain alertness in that rigid and motionless figure. Wetzel's eyes were fixed on the western end of the island. Almost involuntarily Alfred's eyes sought the same direction. The western end of the island ran out into a long low point covered with briars, rushes and sawgrass. As Alfred directed his gaze along the water line of this point he distinctly saw a dark form flit from one bush to another. He was positive he had not been mistaken. He got up slowly and unconcernedly, and strolled over to Wetzel.

"Wetzel, I saw an object just now," he said in a low tone. "It was moving behind those bushes at the head of the island. I am not sure whether it was an animal or an Indian."

"Injuns. Go back and be natur'l like. Don't say nothin' and watch Miller," whispered Wetzel.

Much perturbed by the developments of the last few moments, and wondering what was going to happen, Alfred turned away. He had scarcely reached the others when he heard Betty's voice raised in indignant protest.

"I tell you I did swim my pony across the river," cried Betty. "It was just even with that point and the river was higher than it is now."

"You probably overestimated your feat," said Miller, with his disagreeable, doubtful smile. "I have seen the river so low that it could be waded, and then it would be a very easy matter to cross. But now your pony could not swim half the distance."

"I'll show you," answered Betty, her black eyes flashing. She put her foot in the stirrup and leaped on Madcap.

"Now, Betty, don't try that foolish ride again," implored Mrs. Zane. "What do you care whether strangers believe or not? Eb, make her come back."

Col. Bane only laughed and made no attempt to detain Betty. He rather indulged her caprices.

"Stop her!" cried Clarke.

"Betty, where are you goin'?" said Wetzel, grabbing at Madcap's bridle. But Betty was too quick for him. She avoided the hunter, and with a saucy laugh she wheeled the fiery little pony and urged her over the bank. Almost before any one could divine her purpose she had Madcap in the water up to her knees.

"Betty, stop!" cried Wetzel.

She paid no attention to his call. In another moment the pony would be off the shoal and swimming.

"Stop! Turn back, Betty, or I'll shoot the pony," shouted Wetzel, and this time there was a ring of deadly earnestness in his voice. With the words he had cocked and thrown forward the long rifle.

Betty heard, and in alarm she turned her pony. She looked up with great surprise and concern, for she knew Wetzel was not one to trifle.

"For God's sake!" exclaimed Colonel Zane, looking in amazement at the hunter's face, which was now white and stern.

"Why, Lew, you do not mean you would shoot Madcap?" said Betty, reproachfully, as she reached the shore.

All present in that watching crowd were silent, awaiting the hunter's answer. They felt that mysterious power which portends the revelation of strange events. Col. Zane and Jonathan knew the instant they saw Wetzel that something extraordinary was coming. His face had grown cold and gray; his lips were tightly compressed; his eyes dilated and shone with a peculiar lustre.

"Where were you headin' your pony?" asked Wetzel.

"I wanted to reach that point where the water is shallow," answered Betty.

"That's what I thought. Well, Betty, hostile Injuns are hidin' and waitin' fer you in them high rushes right where you were makin' fer," said Wetzel. Then he shouldered his rifle and walked rapidly away.

"Oh, he cannot be serious!" cried Betty. "Oh, how foolish am I."

"Get back up from the river, everybody," commanded Col. Zane.

"Col. Zane," said Clarke, walking beside the Colonel up the bank, "I saw Wetzel watching the island in a manner that I thought odd, under the circumstances, and I watched too. Presently I saw a dark form dart behind a bush. I went over and told Wetzel, and he said there were Indians on the island."

"This is most d—n strange," said Col. Zane, frowning heavily. "Wetzel's suspicions, Miller turns up, teases Betty attempting that foolhardy trick, and then—Indians! It may be a coincidence, but it looks bad."

"Col. Zane, don't you think Wetzel may be mistaken?" said Miller, coming up. "I came over from the other side this morning and I did not see any Indian sign. Probably Wetzel has caused needless excitement."

"It does not follow that because you came from over the river there are no Indians there," answered Col. Zane, sharply. "Do you presume to criticise Wetzel's judgment?"

"I saw an Indian!" cried Clarke, facing Miller with blazing eyes. "And if you say I did not, you lie! What is more, I believe you know more than any one else about it. I watched you. I saw you were uneasy and that you looked across the river from time to time. Perhaps you had better explain to Col. Zane the reason you taunted his sister into attempting that ride."

With a snarl more like that of a tiger than of a human being, Miller sprang at Clarke. His face was dark with malignant hatred, as he reached for and drew an ugly knife. There were cries of fright from the children and screams from the women. Alfred stepped aside with the wonderful quickness of the trained boxer and shot out his right arm. His fist caught Miller a hard blow on the head, knocking him down and sending the knife flying in the air.

It had all happened so quickly that everyone was as if paralyzed. The settlers stood still and watched Miller rise slowly to his feet.

"Give me my knife!" he cried hoarsely. The knife had fallen at the feet of Major McColloch, who had concealed it with his foot.

"Let this end right here," ordered Col. Zane. "Clarke, you have made a very strong statement. Have you anything to substantiate your words?"

"I think I have," said Clarke. He was standing erect, his face white and his eyes like blue steel. "I knew him at Ft. Pitt. He was a liar and a drunkard there. He was a friend of the Indians and of the British. What he was there he must be here. It was Wetzel who told me to watch him. Wetzel and I both think he knew the Indians were on the island."

"Col. Zane, it is false," said Miller, huskily. "He is trying to put you against me. He hates me because your sister—"

"You cur!" cried Clarke, striking at Miller. Col. Zane struck up the infuriated young man's arm.

"Give us knives, or anything," panted Clarke.

"Yes, let us fight it out now," said Miller.

"Capt. Boggs, take Clarke to the block-house. Make him stay there if you have to lock him up," commanded Col. Zane. "Miller, as for you, I cannot condemn you without proof. If I knew positively that there were Indians on the island and that you were aware of it, you would be a dead man in less time than it takes to say it. I will give you the benefit of the doubt and twenty-four hours to leave the Fort."

The villagers dispersed and went to their homes. They were inclined to take Clarke's side. Miller had become disliked. His drinking habits and his arrogant and bold manner had slowly undermined the friendships he had made during the early part of his stay at Ft. Henry; while Clarke's good humor and willingness to help any one, his gentleness with the children, and his several acts of heroism had strengthened their regard.

"Jonathan, this looks like some of Girty's work. I wish I knew the truth," said Col. Zane, as he, his brothers and Betty and Myeerah entered the house. "Confound it! We can't have even one afternoon of enjoyment. I must see Lewis. I cannot be sure of Clarke. He is evidently bitter against Miller. That would have been a terrible fight. Those fellows have had trouble before, and I am afraid we have not seen the last of their quarrel."

"If they meet again—but how can you keep them apart?" said Silas. "If Miller leaves the Fort without killing Clarke he'll hide around in the woods and wait for a chance to shoot him."

"Not with Wetzel here," answered Col. Zane. "Betty, do you see what your—" he began, turning to his sister, but when he saw her white and miserable face he said no more.

"Don't mind, Betts. It wasn't any fault of yours," said Isaac, putting his arm tenderly round the trembling girl. "I for another believe Clarke was right when he said Miller knew there were Indians over the river. It looks like a plot to abduct you. Have no fear for Alfred. He can take care of himself. He showed that pretty well."

An hour later Clarke had finished his supper and was sitting by his window smoking his pipe. His anger had cooled somewhat and his reflections were not of the pleasantest kind. He regretted that he lowered himself so far as to fight with a man little better than an outlaw. Still there was a grim satisfaction in the thought of the blow he had given Miller. He remembered he had asked for a knife and that his enemy and he be permitted to fight to the death. After all to have ended, then and there, the feud between them would have been the better course; for he well knew Miller's desperate character, that he had killed more than one white man, and that now a fair fight might not be possible. Well, he thought, what did it matter? He was not going to worry himself. He did not care much, one way or another. He had no home; he could not make one without the woman he loved. He was a Soldier of Fortune; he was at the mercy of Fate, and he would drift along and let what came be welcome. A soft footfall on the stairs and a knock on the door interrupted his thoughts.

"Come in," he said.

The door opened and Wetzel strode into the room.

"I come over to say somethin' to you," said the hunter taking the chair by the window and placing his rifle over his knee.

"I will be pleased to listen or talk, as you desire," said Alfred.

"I don't mind tellin' you that the punch you give Miller was what he deserved. If he and Girty didn't hatch up that trick to ketch Betty, I don't know nothin'. But we can't prove nothin' on him yet. Mebbe he knew about the redskins; mebbe he didn't. Personally, I think he did. But I can't kill a white man because I think somethin'. I'd have to know fer sure. What I want to say is to put you on your guard against the baddest man on the river."

"I am aware of that," answered Alfred. "I knew his record at Ft. Pitt. What would you have me do?"

"Keep close till he's gone."

"That would be cowardly."

"No, it wouldn't. He'd shoot you from behind some tree or cabin."

"Well, I'm much obliged to you for your kind advice, but for all that I won't stay in the house," said Alfred, beginning to wonder at the hunter's earnest manner.

"You're in love with Betty, ain't you?"

The question came with Wetzel's usual bluntness and it staggered Alfred. He could not be angry, and he did not know what to say. The hunter went on:

"You needn't say so, because I know it. And I know she loves you and that's why I want you to look out fer Miller."

"My God! man, you're crazy," said Alfred, laughing scornfully. "She cares nothing for me."

"That's your great failin', young feller. You fly off'en the handle too easy. And so does Betty. You both care fer each other and are unhappy about it. Now, you don't know Betty, and she keeps misunderstandin' you."

"For Heaven's sake! Wetzel, if you know anything tell me. Love her?

Why, the words are weak! I love her so well that an hour ago I would have welcomed death at Miller's hands only to fall and die at her feet defending her. Your words set me on fire. What right have you to say that? How do you know?"

The hunter leaned forward and put his hand on Alfred's shoulder. On his pale face was that sublime light which comes to great souls when they give up a life long secret, or when they sacrifice what is best beloved. His broad chest heaved: his deep voice trembled.

"Listen. I'm not a man fer words, and it's hard to tell. Betty loves you. I've carried her in my arms when she was a baby. I've made her toys and played with her when she was a little girl. I know all her moods. I can read her like I do the moss, and the leaves, and the bark of the forest. I've loved her all my life. That's why I know she loves you. I can feel it. Her happiness is the only dear thing left on earth fer me. And that's why I'm your friend."

In the silence that followed his words the door opened and closed and he was gone.

* * * * * * * * * * * * * *

Betty awoke with a start. She was wide awake in a second. The moonbeams came through the leaves of the maple tree near her window and cast fantastic shadows on the wall of her room. Betty lay quiet, watching the fairy-like figures on the wall and listening intently. What had awakened her? The night was still; the crow of a cock in the distance proclaimed that the hour of dawn was near at hand. She waited for Tige's bark under her window, or Sam's voice, or the kicking and trampling of horses in the barn—sounds that usually broke her slumbers in the morning. But no such noises were forthcoming. Suddenly she heard a light, quick tap, tap, and then a rattling in the corner. It was like no sound but that made by a pebble striking the floor, bounding and rolling across the room. There it was again. Some one was tossing stones in at her window. She slipped out of bed, ran, and leaned on the window-sill and looked out. The moon was going down behind the hill, but there was light enough for her to distinguish objects. She saw a dark figure crouching by the fence.

"Who is it?" said Betty, a little frightened, but more curious.

"Sh-h-h, it's Miller," came the answer, spoken in low voice.

The bent form straightened and stood erect. It stepped forward under Betty's window. The light was dim, but Betty recognized the dark face of Miller. He carried a rifle in his hand and a pack on his shoulder.

"Go away, or I'll call my brother. I will not listen to you," said Betty, making a move to leave the window.

"Sh-h-h, not so loud," said Miller, in a quick, hoarse whisper. "You'd better listen. I am going across the border to join Girty. He is going to bring the Indians and the British here to burn the settlement. If you will go away with me I'll save the lives of your brothers and their families. I have aided Girty and I have influence with him. If you won't go you'll be taken captive and you'll see all your friends and relatives scalped and burned. Quick, your answer."

"Never, traitor! Monster! I'd be burned at the stake before I'd go a step with you!" cried Betty.

"Then remember that you've crossed a desperate man. If you escape the massacre you will beg on your knees to me. This settlement is doomed. Now, go to your white-faced lover. You'll find him cold. Ha! Ha! Ha!" and with a taunting laugh he leaped the fence and disappeared in the gloom.

Betty sank to the floor stunned, horrified. She shuddered at the malignity expressed in Miller's words. How had she ever been deceived in him? He was in league with Girty. At heart he was a savage, a renegade. Betty went over his words, one by one.

"Your white-faced lover. You will find him cold," whispered Betty. "What did he mean?"

Then came the thought. Miller had murdered Clarke. Betty gave one agonized quiver, as if a knife had been thrust into her side, and then her paralyzed limbs recovered the power of action. She flew out into the passage-way and pounded on her brother's door.

"Eb! Eb! Get up! Quickly, for God's sake!" she cried. A smothered exclamation, a woman's quick voice, the heavy thud of feet striking the floor followed Betty's alarm. Then the door opened.

"Hello, Betts, what's up?" said Col. Zane, in his rapid voice.

At the same moment the door at the end of the hall opened and Isaac came out.

"Eb, Betty, I heard voices out doors and in the house. What's the row?"

"Oh, Isaac! Oh, Eb! Something terrible has happened!" cried Betty, breathlessly.

"Then it is no time to get excited," said the Colonel, calmly. He placed his arm round Betty and drew her into the room. "Isaac, get down the rifles. Now, Betty, time is precious. Tell me quickly, briefly."

"I was awakened by a stone rolling on the floor. I ran to the window and saw a man by the fence. He came under my window and I saw it was Miller. He said he was going to join Girty. He said if I would go with him he would save the lives of all my relatives. If I would not they would all be killed, massacred, burned alive, and I would be taken away as his captive. I told him I'd rather die before I'd go with him. Then he said we were all doomed, and that my white-faced lover was already cold. With that he gave a laugh which made my flesh creep and ran on toward the river. Oh! he has murdered Mr. Clarke."

"Hell! What a fiend!" cried Col. Zane, hurriedly getting into his clothes. "Betts, you had a gun in there. Why didn't you shoot him? Why didn't I pay more attention to Wetzel's advice?"

"You should have allowed Clarke to kill him yesterday," said Isaac. "Like as not he'll have Girty here with a lot of howling devils.

What's to be done?"

"I'll send Wetzel after him and that'll soon wind up his ball of yarn," answered Col. Zane.

"Please—go—and find—if Mr. Clarke—"

"Yes, Betty, I'll go at once. You must not lose courage, Betty. It's quite probable that Miller has killed Alfred and that there's worse to follow."

"I'll come, Eb, as soon as I have told Myeerah. She is scared half to death," said Isaac, starting for the door.

"All right, only hurry," said Col. Zane, grabbing his rifle. Without wasting more words, and lacing up his hunting shirt as he went he ran out of the room.

The first rays of dawn came streaking in at the window. The chill gray light brought no cheer with its herald of the birth of another day. For what might the morning sun disclose? It might shine on a long line of painted Indians. The fresh breeze from over the river might bring the long war whoop of the savage.

No wonder Noah and his brother, awakened by the voice of their father, sat up in their little bed and looked about with frightened eyes. No wonder Mrs. Zane's face blanched. How many times she had seen her husband grasp his rifle and run out to meet danger!

"Bessie," said Betty. "If it's true I will not be able to bear it. It's all my fault."

"Nonsense! You heard Eb say Miller and Clarke had quarreled before. They hated each other before they ever saw you."

A door banged, quick footsteps sounded on the stairs, and Isaac came rushing into the room. Betty, deathly pale, stood with her hands pressed to her bosom, and looked at Isaac with a question in her eyes that her tongue could not speak.

"Betty, Alfred's badly hurt, but he's alive. I can tell you no more now," said Isaac. "Bessie, bring your needle, silk linen, liniment—everything you need for a bad knife wound, and come quickly."

Betty's haggard face changed as if some warm light had been reflected on it; her lips moved, and with a sob of thankfulness she fled to her room.

Two hours later, while Annie was serving breakfast to Betty and Myeerah, Col. Zane strode into the room.

"Well, one has to eat whatever happens," he said, his clouded face brightening somewhat. "Betty, there's been bad work, bad work. When I got to Clarke's room I found him lying on the bed with a knife sticking in him. As it is we are doubtful about pulling him through."

"May I see him?" whispered Betty, with pale lips.

"If the worst comes to the worst I'll take you over. But it would do no good now and would surely unnerve you. He still has a fighting chance."

"Did they fight, or was Mr. Clarke stabbed in his sleep?"

"Miller climbed into Clarke's window and knifed him in the dark. As I came over I met Wetzel and told him I wanted him to trail Miller and find if there is any truth in his threat about Girty and the Indians. Sam just now found Tige tied fast in the fence corner back of the barn. That explains the mystery of Miller's getting so near the house. You know he always took pains to make friends with Tige. The poor dog was helpless; his legs were tied and his jaws bound fast. Oh, Miller is as cunning as an Indian! He has had this all planned out, and he has had more than one arrow to his bow. But, if I mistake not he has shot his last one."

"Miller must be safe from pursuit by this time," said Betty.

"Safe for the present, yes," answered Col. Zane, "but while Jonathan and Wetzel live I would not give a snap of my fingers for Miller's chances. Hello, I hear some one talking. I sent for Jack and the Major."

The Colonel threw open the door. Wetzel, Major McColloch, Jonathan and Silas Zane were approaching. They were all heavily armed. Wetzel was equipped for a long chase. Double leggins were laced round his legs. A buckskin knapsack was strapped to his shoulders.

"Major, I want you and Jonathan to watch the river," said Col. Zane. "Silas, you are to go to the mouth of Yellow Creek and reconnoiter. We are in for a siege. It may be twenty-four hours and it may be ten days. In the meantime I will get the Fort in shape to meet the attack. Lewis, you have your orders. Have you anything to suggest?"

"I'll take the dog," answered Wetzel. "He'll save time for me. I'll stick to Miller's trail and find Girty's forces. I've believed all along that Miller was helpin' Girty, and I'm thinkin' that where Miller goes there I'll find Girty and his redskins. If it's night when I get back I'll give the call of the hoot-owl three times, quick, so Jack and the Major will know I want to get back across the river."

"All right, Lewis, we'll be expecting you any time," said Col. Zane.

"Betty, I'm goin' now and I want to tell you somethin'," said Wetzel, as Betty appeared. "Come as far as the end of the path with me."

"I'm sorry you must go. But Tige seems delighted," said Betty, walking beside Wetzel, while the dog ran on before.

"Betty, I wanted to tell you to stay close like to the house, fer this feller Miller has been layin' traps fer you, and the Injuns is on the war-path. Don't ride your pony, and stay home now."

"Indeed, I shall never again do anything as foolish as I did yesterday. I have learned my lesson. And Oh! Lew, I am so grateful to you for saving me. When will you return to the Fort?"

"Mebbe never, Betty."

"Oh, no. Don't say that. I know all this Indian talk will blow over, as it always does, and you will come back and everything will be all right again."

"I hope it'll be as you say, Betty, but there's no tellin', there's no tellin'."

"You are going to see if the Indians are making preparations to besiege the Fort?"

"Yes, I am goin' fer that. And if I happen to find Miller on my way I'll give him Betty's regards."

Betty shivered at his covert meaning. Long ago in a moment of playfulness, Betty had scratched her name on the hunter's rifle. Ever after that Wetzel called his fatal weapon by her name.

"If you were going simply to avenge I would not let you go. That wretch will get his just due some day, never fear for that."

"Betty, 'taint likely he'll get away from me, and if he does there's Jonathan. This mornin' when we trailed Miller down to the river bank Jonathan points across the river and says: 'You or me,' and I says: 'Me,' so it's all settled."

"Will Mr. Clarke live?" said Betty, in an altered tone, asking the question which was uppermost in her mind.

"I think so, I hope so. He's a husky young chap and the cut wasn't bad. He lost so much blood. That's why he's so weak. If he gets well he'll have somethin' to tell you."

"Lew, what do you mean?" demanded Betty, quickly.

"Me and him had a long talk last night and—"

"You did not go to him and talk of me, did you?" said Betty, reproachfully.

They had now reached the end of the path. Wetzel stopped and dropped the butt of his rifle on the ground. Tige looked on and wagged his tail. Presently the hunter spoke.

"Yes, we talked about you."

"Oh! Lewis. What did—could you have said?" faltered Betty.

"You think I hadn't ought to speak to him of you?"

"I do not see why you should. Of course you are my good friend, but he—it is not like you to speak of me."

"Fer once I don't agree with you. I knew how it was with him so I told him. I knew how it was with you so I told him, and I know how it is with me, so I told him that too."

"With you?" whispered Betty.

"Yes, with me. That kind of gives me a right, don't it, considerin' it's all fer your happiness?"

"With you?" echoed Betty in a low tone. She was beginning to realize that she had not known this man. She looked up at him. His eyes were misty with an unutterable sadness.

"Oh, no! No! Lew. Say it is not true," she cried, piteously. All in a moment Betty's burdens became too heavy for her. She wrung her little hands. Her brother's kindly advice, Bessie's warnings, and old Grandmother Watkins' words came back to her. For the first time she believed what they said—that Wetzel loved her. All at once the scales fell from her eyes and she saw this man as he really was. All the thousand and one things he had done for her, his simple teaching, his thoughtfulness, his faithfulness, and his watchful protection—all came crowding on her as debts that she could never pay. For now what could she give this man to whom she owed more than her life? Nothing. It was too late. Her love could have reclaimed him, could have put an end to that solitary wandering, and have made him a good, happy man.

"Yes, Betty, it's time to tell it. I've loved you always," he said softly.

She covered her face and sobbed. Wetzel put his arm round her and drew her to him until the dark head rested on his shoulder. Thus they stood a moment.

"Don't cry, little one," he said, tenderly. "Don't grieve fer me. My love fer you has been the only good in my life. It's been happiness to love you. Don't think of me. I can see you and Alfred in a happy home, surrounded by bright-eyed children. There'll be a brave lad named fer me, and when I come, if I ever do, I'll tell him stories, and learn him the secrets of the woods, and how to shoot, and things I know so well."

"I am so wretched—so miserable. To think I have been so—so blind, and I have teased you—and—it might have been—only now it's too late," said Betty, between her sobs.

"Yes, I know, and it's better so. This man you love rings true. He has learnin' and edication. I have nothin' but muscle and a quick eye. And that'll serve you and Alfred when you are in danger. I'm goin' now. Stand here till I'm out of sight."

"Kiss me goodbye," whispered Betty.

The hunter bent his head and kissed her on the brow. Then he turned and with a rapid step went along the bluff toward the west. When he reached the laurel bushes which fringed the edge of the forest he looked back. He saw the slender gray clad figure standing motionless in the narrow path. He waved his hand and then turned and plunged into the forest. The dog looked back, raised his head and gave a long, mournful howl. Then, he too disappeared.

A mile west of the settlement Wetzel abandoned the forest and picked his way down the steep bluff to the river. Here he prepared to swim to the western shore. He took off his buckskin garments, spread them out on the ground, placed his knapsack in the middle, and rolling all into a small bundle tied it round his rifle. Grasping the rifle just above the hammer he waded into the water up to his waist and then, turning easily on his back he held the rifle straight up, allowing the butt to rest on his breast. This left his right arm unhampered. With a powerful back-arm stroke he rapidly swam the river, which was deep and narrow at this point. In a quarter of an hour he was once more in his dry suit.

He was now two miles below the island, where yesterday the Indians had been concealed, and where this morning Miller had crossed. Wetzel knew Miller expected to be trailed, and that he would use every art and cunning of woodcraft to elude his pursuers, or to lead them into a death-trap. Wetzel believed Miller had joined the Indians, who had undoubtedly been waiting for him, or for a signal from him, and that he would use them to ambush the trail.

Therefore Wetzel decided he would try to strike Miller's tracks far west of the river. He risked a great deal in attempting this because it was possible he might fail to find any trace of the spy. But Wetzel wasted not one second. His course was chosen. With all possible speed, which meant with him walking only when he could not run, he traveled northwest. If Miller had taken the direction Wetzel suspected, the trails of the two men would cross about ten miles from the Ohio. But the hunter had not traversed more than a mile of the forest when the dog put his nose high in the air and growled. Wetzel slowed down into a walk and moved cautiously onward, peering through the green aisles of the woods. A few rods farther on Tige uttered another growl and put his nose to the ground. He found a trail. On examination Wetzel discovered in the moss two moccasin tracks. Two Indians had passed that point that morning. They were going northwest directly toward the camp of Wingenund. Wetzel stuck close to the trail all that day and an hour before dusk he heard the sharp crack of a rifle. A moment afterward a doe came crashing through the thicket to Wetzel's right and bounding across a little brook she disappeared.

A tree with a bushy, leafy top had been uprooted by a storm and had fallen across the stream at this point. Wetzel crawled among the branches. The dog followed and lay down beside him. Before darkness set in Wetzel saw that the clear water of the brook had been roiled; therefore, he concluded that somewhere upstream Indians had waded into the brook. Probably they had killed a deer and were getting their evening meal.

Hours passed. Twilight deepened into darkness. One by one the stars appeared; then the crescent moon rose over the wooded hill in the west, and the hunter never moved. With his head leaning against the log he sat quiet and patient. At midnight he whispered to the dog, and crawling from his hiding place glided stealthily up the stream. Far ahead from the dark depths of the forest peeped the flickering light of a camp-fire. Wetzel consumed a half hour in approaching within one hundred feet of this light. Then he got down on his hands and knees and crawled behind a tree on top of the little ridge which had obstructed a view of the camp scene.

From this vantage point Wetzel saw a clear space surrounded by pines and hemlocks. In the center of this glade a fire burned briskly. Two Indians lay wrapped in their blankets, sound asleep. Wetzel pressed the dog close to the ground, laid aside his rifle, drew his tomahawk, and lying flat on his breast commenced to work his way, inch by inch, toward the sleeping savages. The tall ferns trembled as the hunter wormed his way among them, but there was no sound, not a snapping of a twig nor a rustling of a leaf. The nightwind sighed softly through the pines; it blew the bright sparks from the burning logs, and fanned the embers into a red glow; it swept caressingly over the sleeping savages, but it could not warn them that another wind, the Wind-of-Death, was near at hand.

A quarter of an hour elapsed. Nearer and nearer; slowly but surely drew the hunter. With what wonderful patience and self-control did this cold-blooded Nemesis approach his victims! Probably any other Indian slayer would have fired his rifle and then rushed to combat with a knife or a tomahawk. Not so Wetzel. He scorned to use powder. He crept forward like a snake gliding upon its prey. He slid one hand in front of him and pressed it down on the moss, at first gently, then firmly, and when he had secured a good hold he slowly dragged his body forward the length of his arm. At last his dark form rose and stood over the unconscious Indians, like a minister of Doom. The tomahawk flashed once, twice in the firelight, and the Indians, without a moan, and with a convulsive quivering and straightening of their bodies, passed from the tired sleep of nature to the eternal sleep of death.

Foregoing his usual custom of taking the scalps, Wetzel hurriedly left the glade. He had found that the Indians were Shawnees and he had expected they were Delawares. He knew Miller's red comrades belonged to the latter tribe. The presence of Shawnees so near the settlement confirmed his belief that a concerted movement was to be made on the whites in the near future. He would not have been surprised to find the woods full of redskins. He spent the remainder of that night close under the side of a log with the dog curled up beside him.

Next morning Wetzel ran across the trail of a white man and six Indians. He tracked them all that day and half of the night before he again rested. By noon of the following day he came in sight of the cliff from which Jonathan Zane had watched the sufferings of Col. Crawford. Wetzel now made his favorite move, a wide detour, and came up on the other side of the encampment.

From the top of the bluff he saw down into the village of the Delawares. The valley was alive with Indians; they were working like beavers; some with weapons, some painting themselves, and others dancing war-dances. Packs were being strapped on the backs of ponies. Everywhere was the hurry and bustle of the preparation for war. The dancing and the singing were kept up half the night.

At daybreak Wetzel was at his post. A little after sunrise he heard a long yell which he believed announced the arrival of an important party. And so it turned out. Amid thrill yelling and whooping, the like of which Wetzel had never before heard, Simon Girty rode into Wingenund's camp at the head of one hundred Shawnee warriors and two hundred British Rangers from Detroit. Wetzel recoiled when he saw the red uniforms of the Britishers and their bayonets. Including Pipe's and Wingenund's braves the total force which was going to march against the Fort exceeded six hundred. An impotent frenzy possessed Wetzel as he watched the orderly marching of the

Rangers and the proud bearing of the Indian warriors. Miller had spoken the truth. Ft. Henry vas doomed.

"Tige, there's one of them struttin' turkey cocks as won't see the Ohio," said Wetzel to the dog.

Hurriedly slipping from round his neck the bullet-pouch that Betty had given him, he shook out a bullet and with the point of his knife he scratched deep in the soft lead the letter W. Then he cut the bullet half through. This done he detached the pouch from the cord and running the cord through the cut in the bullet he bit the lead. He tied the string round the neck of the dog and pointing eastward he said: "Home."

The intelligent animal understood perfectly. His duty was to get that warning home. His clear brown eyes as much as said: "I will not fail." He wagged his tail, licked the hunter's hand, bounded away and disappeared in the forest.

Wetzel rested easier in mind. He knew the dog would stop for nothing, and that he stood a far better chance of reaching the Fort in safety than did he himself.

With a lurid light in his eyes Wetzel now turned to the Indians. He would never leave that spot without sending a leaden messenger into the heart of someone in that camp. Glancing on all sides he at length selected a place where it was possible he might approach near enough to the camp to get a shot. He carefully studied the lay of the ground, the trees, rocks, bushes, grass,—everything that could help screen him from the keen eye of savage scouts. When he had marked his course he commenced his perilous descent. In an hour he had reached the bottom of the cliff. Dropping flat on the ground, he once more started his snail-like crawl. A stretch of swampy ground, luxuriant with rushes and saw-grass, made a part of the way easy for him, though it led through mud, and slime, and stagnant water. Frogs and turtles warming their backs in the sunshine scampered in alarm from their logs. Lizards blinked at him. Moccasin snakes darted wicked forked tongues at him and then glided out of reach of his tomahawk. The frogs had stopped their deep bass notes. A swamp-blackbird rose in fright from her nest in the saw-grass, and twittering plaintively fluttered round and round over the pond. The flight of the bird worried Wetzel. Such little things as these might attract the attention of some Indian scout. But he hoped that in the excitement of the war preparations these unusual disturbances would escape notice. At last he gained the other side of the swamp. At the end of the cornfield before him was the clump of laurel which he had marked from the cliff as his objective point. The Indian corn was now about five feet high. Wetzel passed through this field unseen. He reached the laurel bushes, where he dropped to the ground and lay quiet a few minutes. In the dash which he would soon make to the forest he needed all his breath and all his fleetness. He looked to the right to see how far the woods was from where he lay. Not more than one hundred feet. He was safe. Once in the dark shade of those trees, and with his foes behind him, he could defy the whole race of Delawares. He looked to his rifle, freshened the powder in the pan, carefully adjusted the flint, and then rose quietly to his feet.

Wetzel's keen gaze, as he swept it from left to right, took in every detail of the camp. He was almost in the village. A tepee stood not twenty feet from his hiding-place. He could have tossed a stone in the midst of squaws, and braves, and chiefs. The main body of Indians was in the center of the camp. The British were lined up further on. Both Indians and soldiers were resting on their arms and waiting. Suddenly Wetzel started and his heart leaped. Under a maple tree not one hundred and fifty yards distant stood four men in earnest consultation. One was an Indian. Wetzel recognized the fierce, stern face, the haughty, erect figure. He knew that long, trailing war-bonnet. It could have adorned the head of but one chief—Wingenund, the sachem of the Delawares. A British officer, girdled and epauletted, stood next to Wingenund. Simon Girty, the renegade, and Miller, the traitor, completed the group.

Wetzel sank to his knees. The perspiration poured from his face. The mighty hunter trembled, but it was from eagerness. Was not Girty, the white savage, the bane of the poor settlers, within range of a weapon that never failed? Was not the murderous chieftain, who had once whipped and tortured him, who had burned Crawford alive, there in plain sight? Wetzel revelled a moment in fiendish glee. He passed his hands tenderly over the long barrel of his rifle. In that moment as never before he gloried in his power—a power which enabled him to put a bullet in the eye of a squirrel at the distance these men were from him. But only for an instant did the hunter yield to this feeling. He knew too well the value of time and opportunity.

He rose again to his feet and peered out from under the shading laurel branches. As he did so the dark face of Miller turned full toward him. A tremor, like the intense thrill of a tiger when he is about to spring, ran over Wetzel's frame. In his mad gladness at being within rifle-shot of his great Indian foe, Wetzel had forgotten the man he had trailed for two days. He had forgotten Miller. He had only one shot—and Betty was to be avenged. He gritted his teeth. The Delaware chief was as safe as though he were a thousand miles away. This opportunity for which Wetzel had waited so many years, and the successful issue of which would have gone so far toward the fulfillment of a life's purpose, was worse than useless. A great temptation assailed the hunter.

Wetzel's face was white when he raised the rifle; his dark eye, gleaming vengefully, ran along the barrel. The little bead on the front sight first covered the British officer, and then the broad breast of Girty. It moved reluctantly and searched out the heart of Wingenund, where it lingered for a fleeting instant. At last it rested upon the swarthy face of Miller.

"Fer Betty," muttered the hunter, between his clenched teeth as he pressed the trigger.

The spiteful report awoke a thousand echoes. When the shot broke the stillness Miller was talking and gesticulating. His hand dropped inertly; he stood upright for a second, his head slowly bowing and his body swaying perceptibly. Then he plunged forward like a log, his face striking the sand. He never moved again. He was dead even before he struck the ground.

Blank silence followed this tragic denouement. Wingenund, a cruel and relentless Indian, but never a traitor, pointed to the small bloody hole in the middle of Miller's forehead, and then nodded his head solemnly. The wondering Indians stood aghast. Then with loud yells the braves ran to the cornfield; they searched the laurel bushes. But they only discovered several moccasin prints in the sand, and a puff of white smoke wafting away upon the summer breeze.

CHAPTER XII.

Alfred Clarke lay between life and death. Miller's knife-thrust, although it had made a deep and dangerous wound, had not pierced any vital part; the amount of blood lost made Alfred's condition precarious. Indeed, he would not have lived through that first day but for a wonderful vitality. Col. Zane's wife, to whom had been consigned the delicate task of dressing the wound, shook her head when she first saw the direction of the cut. She found on a closer examination that the knife-blade had been deflected by a rib, and had just missed the lungs. The wound was bathed, sewed up, and bandaged, and the greatest precaution taken to prevent the sufferer from loosening the linen. Every day when Mrs. Zane returned from the bedside of the young man she would be met at the door by Betty, who, in that time of suspense, had lost her bloom, and whose pale face showed the effects of sleepless nights.

"Betty, would you mind going over to the Fort and relieving Mrs. Martin an hour or two?" said Mrs. Zane one day as she came home, looking worn and weary. "We are both tired to death, and Nell Metzar was unable to come. Clarke is unconscious, and will not know you, besides he is sleeping now."

Betty hurried over to Capt. Boggs' cabin, next the blockhouse, where Alfred lay, and with a palpitating heart and a trepidation wholly out of keeping with the brave front she managed to assume, she knocked gently on the door.

"Ah, Betty, 'tis you, bless your heart," said a matronly little woman who opened the door. "Come right in. He is sleeping now, poor fellow, and it's the first real sleep he has had. He has been raving crazy forty-eight hours."

"Mrs. Martin, what shall I do?" whispered Betty.

"Oh, just watch him, my dear," answered the elder woman.

"If you need me send one of the lads up to the house for me. I shall return as soon as I can. Keep the flies away—they are bothersome—and bathe his head every little while. If he wakes and tries to sit up, as he does sometimes, hold him back. He is as weak as a cat. If he raves, soothe him by talking to him. I must go now, dearie."

Betty was left alone in the little room. Though she had taken a seat near the bed where Alfred lay, she had not dared to look at him. Presently conquering her emotion, Betty turned her gaze on the bed. Alfred was lying easily on his back, and notwithstanding the warmth of the day he was covered with a quilt. The light from the window shone on his face. How deathly white it was! There was not a vestige of color in it; the brow looked like chiseled marble; dark shadows underlined the eyes, and the whole face was expressive of weariness and pain.

There are times when a woman's love is all motherliness. All at once this man seemed to Betty like a helpless child. She felt her heart go out to the poor sufferer with a feeling before unknown. She forgot her pride and her fears and her disappointments. She remembered only that this strong man lay there at death's door because he had resented an insult to her. The past with all its bitterness rolled away and was lost, and in its place welled up a tide of forgiveness strong and sweet and hopeful. Her love, like a fire that had been choked and smothered, smouldering but never extinct, and which blazes up with the first breeze, warmed and quickened to life with the touch of her hand on his forehead.

An hour passed. Betty was now at her ease and happier than she had been for months. Her patient continued to sleep peacefully and dreamlessly. With a feeling of womanly curiosity Betty looked around the room. Over the rude mantelpiece were hung a sword, a brace of pistols, and two pictures. These last interested Betty very much. They were portraits; one of them was a likeness of a sweet-faced woman who Betty instinctively knew was his mother. Her eyes lingered tenderly on that face, so like the one lying on the pillow. The other portrait was of a beautiful girl whose dark, magnetic eyes challenged Betty. Was this his sister or—someone else? She could not restrain a jealous twinge, and she felt annoyed to find herself comparing that face with her own. She looked no longer at that portrait, but recommenced her survey of the room. Upon the door hung a broad-brimmed hat with eagle plumes stuck in the band. A pair of hightopped riding-boots, a saddle, and a bridle lay on the floor in the corner. The table was covered with Indian pipes, tobacco pouches, spurs, silk stocks, and other articles.

Suddenly Betty felt that some one was watching her. She turned timidly toward the bed and became much frightened when she encountered the intense gaze from a pair of steel-blue eyes. She almost fell from the chair; but presently she recollected that Alfred had been unconscious for days, and that he would not know who was watching by his bedside.

"Mother, is that you?" asked Alfred, in a weak, low voice.

"Yes, I am here," answered Betty, remembering the old woman's words about soothing the sufferer.

"But I thought you were ill."

"I was, but I am better now, and it is you who are ill."

"My head hurts so."

"Let me bathe it for you."

"How long have I been home?"

Betty bathed and cooled his heated brow. He caught and held her hands, looking wonderingly at her the while.

"Mother, somehow I thought you had died. I must have dreamed it. I am very happy; but tell me, did a message come for me to-day?"

Betty shook her head, for she could not speak. She saw he was living in the past, and he was praying for the letter which she would gladly have written had she but known.

"No message, and it is now so long."

"It will come to-morrow," whispered Betty.

"Now, mother, that is what you always say," said the invalid, as he began to toss his head wearily to and fro. "Will she never tell me? It is not like her to keep me in suspense. She was the sweetest, truest, loveliest girl in all the world. When I get well, mother, I ant going to find out if she loves me."

"I am sure she does. I know she loves you," answered Betty.

"It is very good of you to say that," he went on in his rambling talk. "Some day I'll bring her to you and we'll make her a queen here in the old home. I'll be a better son now and not run away from home again. I've given the dear old mother many a heartache, but that's all past now. The wanderer has come home. Kiss me good-night, mother."

Betty looked down with tear-blurred eyes on the haggard face. Unconsciously she had been running her fingers through the fair hair that lay so damp over his brow. Her pity and tenderness had carried her far beyond herself, and at the last words she bent her head and kissed him on the lips.

"Who are you? You are not my mother. She is dead," he cried, starting up wildly, and looking at her with brilliant eyes.

Betty dropped the fan and rose quickly to her feet. What had she done? A terrible thought had flashed into her mind. Suppose he were not delirious, and had been deceiving her. Oh! for a hiding-place, or that the floor would swallow her. Oh! if some one would only come.

Footsteps sounded on the stairs and Betty ran to the door. To her great relief Mrs. Martin was coming up.

"You can run home now, there's a dear," said the old lady. "We have several watchers for to-night. It will not be long now when he will commence to mend, or else he will die. Poor boy, please God that he gets well. Has he been good? Did he call for any particular young lady? Never fear, Betty, I'll keep the secret. He'll never know you were here unless you tell him yourself."

Meanwhile the days had been busy ones for Col. Zane. In anticipation of an attack from the Indians, the settlers had been fortifying their refuge and making the block-house as nearly impregnable as possible. Everything that was movable and was of value they put inside the stockade fence, out of reach of the destructive redskins. All the horses and cattle were driven into the inclosure. Wagon-loads of hay, grain and food were stored away in the block-house.

Never before had there been such excitement on the frontier. Runners from Ft. Pitt, Short Creek, and other settlements confirmed the rumor that all the towns along the Ohio were preparing for war. Not since the outbreak of the Revolution had there been so much confusion and alarm among the pioneers. To be sure, those on the very verge of the frontier, as at Ft. Henry, had heretofore little to fear from the British. During most of this time there had been comparative peace on the western border, excepting those occasional murders, raids, and massacres perpetrated by the different Indian tribes, and instigated no doubt by Girty and the British at Detroit. Now all kinds of rumors were afloat: Washington was defeated; a close alliance between England and the confederated western tribes had been formed; Girty had British power and wealth back of him. These and many more alarming reports travelled from settlement to settlement.

The death of Col. Crawford had been a terrible shock to the whole country. On the border spread an universal gloom, and the low, sullen mutterings of revengeful wrath. Crawford had been so prominent a man, so popular, and, except in his last and fatal expedition, such an efficient leader that his sudden taking off was almost a national calamity. In fact no one felt it more keenly than did Washington himself, for Crawford was his esteemed friend.

Col. Zane believed Ft. Henry had been marked by the British and the Indians. The last runner from Ft. Pitt had informed him that the description of Miller tallied with that of one of the ten men who had deserted from Ft. Pitt in 1778 with the tories Girth, McKee, and Elliott. Col. Zane was now satisfied that Miller was an agent of Girty and therefore of the British. So since all the weaknesses of the Fort, the number of the garrison, and the favorable conditions for a siege were known to Girty, there was nothing left for Col. Zane and his men but to make a brave stand.

Jonathan Zane and Major McColloch watched the river. Wetzel had disappeared as if the earth had swallowed him. Some pioneers said he would never return. But Col. Zane believed Wetzel would walk into the Fort, as he had done many times in the last ten years, with full information concerning the doings of the Indians. However, the days passed and nothing happened. Their work completed, the settlers waited for the first sign of an enemy. But as none came, gradually their fears were dispelled and they began to think the alarm had been a false one.

All this time Alfred Clarke was recovering his health and strength. The day came when he was able to leave his bed and sit by the window. How glad it made him feel to look out on the green woods and the broad, winding river; how sweet to his ears were the songs of the birds; how soothing was the drowsy hum of the bees in the fragrant honeysuckle by his window. His hold on life had been slight and life was good. He smiled in pitying derision as he remembered his recklessness. He had not been in love with life. In his gloomy moods he had often thought life was hardly worth the living. What sickly sentiment! He had been on the brink of the grave, but he had been snatched back from the dark river of Death. It needed but this to show him the joy of breathing, the glory of loving, the sweetness of living. He resolved that for him there would be no more drifting, no more purposelessness. If what Wetzel had told him was true, if he really had not loved in vain, then his cup of happiness was overflowing. Like a far-off and almost forgotten strain of music some memory struggled to take definite shape in his mind; but it was so hazy, so vague, so impalpable, that he could remember nothing clearly.

Isaac Zane and his Indian bride called on Alfred that afternoon.

"Alfred, I can't tell you how glad I am to see you up again," said Isaac, earnestly, as he wrung Alfred's hand. "Say, but it was a tight squeeze! It has been a bad time for you."

Nothing could have been more pleasing than Myeerah's shy yet eloquent greeting. She gave Alfred her little hand and said in her figurative style of speaking, "Myeerah is happy for you and for others. You are strong like the West Wind that never dies."

"Myeerah and I are going this afternoon, and we came over to say good-bye to you. We intend riding down the river fifteen miles and then crossing, to avoid running into any band of Indians."

"And how does Myeerah like the settlement by this time?"

"Oh, she is getting on famously. Betty and she have fallen in love with each other. It is amusing to hear Betty try to talk in the Wyandot tongue, and to see Myeerah's consternation when Betty gives her a lesson in deportment."

"I rather fancy it would be interesting, too. Are you not going back to the Wyandots at a dangerous time?"

"As to that I can't say. I believe, though, it is better that I get back to Tarhe's camp before we have any trouble with the Indians. I am anxious to get there before Girty or some of his agents."

"Well, if you must go, good luck to you, and may we meet again."

"It will not be long, I am sure. And, old man," he continued, with a bright smile, "when Myeerah and I come again to Ft. Henry we expect to find all well with you. Cheer up, and good-bye."

All the preparations had been made for the departure of Isaac and Myeerah to their far-off Indian home. They were to ride the Indian ponies on which they had arrived at the Fort. Col. Zane had given Isaac one of his pack horses. This animal carried blankets, clothing, and food which insured comparative comfort in the long ride through the wilderness.

"We will follow the old trail until we reach the hickory swale," Isaac was saying to the Colonel, "and then we will turn off and make for the river. Once across the Ohio we can make the trip in two days."

"I think you'll make it all right," said Col. Zane.

"Even if I do meet Indians I shall have no fear, for I have a protector here," answered Isaac as he led Myeerah's pony to the step.

"Good-bye, Myeerah; he is yours, but do not forget he is dear to us," said Betty, embracing and kissing the Indian girl.

"My sister does not know Myeerah. The White Eagle will return."

"Good-bye, Betts, don't cry. I shall come home again. And when I do I hope I shall be in time to celebrate another event, this time with you as the heroine. Good-bye. Goodbye."

The ponies cantered down the road. At the bend Isaac and Myeerah turned and waved their hands until the foliage of the trees hid them from view.

"Well, these things happen naturally enough. I suppose they must be. But I should much have preferred Isaac staying here. Hello! What the deuce is that? By Lord! It's Tige!"

The exclamation following Col. Zane's remarks had been called forth by Betty's dog. He came limping painfully up the road from the direction of the river. When he saw Col. Zane he whined and crawled to the Colonel's feet. The dog was wet and covered with burrs, and his beautiful glossy coat, which had been Betty's pride, was dripping with blood.

"Silas, Jonathan, come here," cried Col. Zane. "Here's Tige, back without Wetzel, and the poor dog has been shot almost to pieces. What does it mean?"

"Indians," said Jonathan, coming out of the house with Silas, and Mrs. Zane and Betty, who had heard the Colonel's call.

"He has come a long way. Look at his feet. They are torn and bruised," continued Jonathan. "And he has been near Wingenund's camp. You see that red clay on his paws. There is no red clay that I know of round here, and there are miles of it this side of the Delaware camp."

"What is the matter with Tige?" asked Betty.

"He is done for. Shot through, poor fellow. How did he ever reach home?" said Silas.

"Oh, I hope not! Dear old Tige," said Betty as she knelt and tenderly placed the head of the dog in her lap. "Why, what is this? I never put that there. Eb, Jack, look here. There is a string around his neck," and Betty pointed excitedly to a thin cord which was almost concealed in the thick curly hair.

"Good gracious! Eb, look! It is the string off the prize bullet pouch I made, and that Wetzel won on Isaac's wedding day. It is a message from Lew," said Betty.

"Well, by Heavens! This is strange. So it is. I remember that string. Cut it off, Jack," said Col. Zane.

When Jonathan had cut the string and held it up they all saw the lead bullet. Col. Zane examined it and showed them what had been rudely scratched on it.

"A letter W. Does that mean Wetzel?" asked the Colonel.

"It means war. It's a warning from Wetzel—not the slightest doubt of that," said Jonathan. "Wetzel sends this because he knows we are to be attacked, and because there must have been great doubt of his getting back to tell us. And Tige has been shot on his way home."

This called the attention to the dog, which had been momentarily forgotten. His head rolled from Betty's knee; a quiver shook his frame; he struggled to rise to his feet, but his strength was too far spent; he crawled close to Betty's feet; his eyes looked up at her with almost human affection; then they closed, and he lay still. Tige was dead.

"It is all over, Betty. Tige will romp no more. He will never be forgotten, for he was faithful to the end. Jonathan, tell the Major of Wetzel's warning, and both of you go back to your posts on the river. Silas, send Capt. Boggs to me."

An hour after the death of Tige the settlers were waiting for the ring of the meeting-house bell to summon them to the Fort.

Supper at Col. Zane's that night was not the occasion of good-humored jest and pleasant conversation. Mrs. Zane's face wore a distressed and troubled look; Betty was pale and quiet; even the Colonel was gloomy; and the children, missing the usual cheerfulness of the evening meal, shrank close to their mother.

Darkness slowly settled down; and with it came a feeling of relief, at least for the night, for the Indians rarely attacked the settlements after dark. Capt. Boggs came over and he and Col. Zane conversed in low tones.

"The first thing in the morning I want you to ride over to Short Creek for reinforcements. I'll send the Major also and by a different route. I expect to hear tonight from Wetzel. Twelve times has he crossed that threshold with the information which made an Indian surprise impossible. And I feel sure he will come again."

"What was that?" said Betty, who was sitting on the doorstep.

"Sh-h!" whispered Col. Zane, holding up his finger.

The night was warm and still. In the perfect quiet which followed the Colonel's whispered exclamation the listeners heard the beating of their hearts. Then from the river bank came the cry of an owl; low but clear it came floating to their ears, its single melancholy note thrilling them. Faint and far off in the direction of the island sounded the answer.

"I knew it. I told you. We shall know all presently," said Col. Zane. "The first call was Jonathan's, and it was answered."

The moments dragged away. The children had fallen asleep on the bearskin rug. Mrs. Zane and Betty had heard the Colonel's voice, and sat with white faces, waiting, waiting for they knew not what.

A familiar, light-moccasined tread sounded on the path, a tall figure loomed up from the darkness; it came up the path, passed up the steps, and crossed the threshold.

"Wetzel!" exclaimed Col. Zane and Capt. Boggs. It was indeed the hunter. How startling was his appearance! The buckskin hunting coat and leggins were wet, torn and bespattered with mud; the water ran and dripped from him to form little muddy pools on the floor; only his rifle and powder horn were dry. His face was ghastly white except where a bullet wound appeared on his temple, from which the blood had oozed down over his cheek. An unearthly light gleamed from his eyes. In that moment Wetzel was an appalling sight.

"Col. Zane, I'd been here days before, but I run into some Shawnees, and they gave me a hard chase. I have to report that Girty, with four hundred Injuns and two hundred Britishers, are on the way to Ft. Henry."

"My God!" exclaimed Col. Zane. Strong man as he was the hunter's words had unnerved him.

The loud and clear tone of the church-bell rang out on the still night air. Only once it sounded, but it reverberated among the hills, and its single deep-toned ring was like a knell. The listeners almost expected to hear it followed by the fearful war-cry, that cry which betokened for many desolation and death.

CHAPTER XIII.

Morning found the settlers, with the exception of Col. Zane, his brother Jonathan, the negro Sam, and Martin Wetzel, all within the Fort. Col. Zane had determined, long before, that in the event of another siege, he would use his house as an outpost. Twice it had been destroyed by fire at the hands of the Indians. Therefore, surrounding himself by these men, who were all expert marksmen, Col. Zane resolved to protect his property and at the same time render valuable aid to the Fort.

Early that morning a pirogue loaded with cannon balls, from Ft. Pitt and bound for Louisville, had arrived and Captain Sullivan, with his crew of three men, had demanded admittance. In the absence of Capt. Boggs and Major McColloch, both of whom had been dispatched for reinforcements, Col. Zane had placed his brother Silas in command of the Fort. Sullivan informed Silas that he and his men had been fired on by Indians and that they sought the protection of the Fort. The services of himself and men, which he volunteered, were gratefully accepted.

All told, the little force in the block-house did not exceed forty-two, and that counting the boys and the women who could handle rifles. The few preparations had been completed and now the settlers were awaiting the appearance of the enemy. Few words were spoken. The children were secured where they would be out of the way of flying bullets. They were huddled together silent and frightened; pale-faced but resolute women passed up and down the length of the block-house; some carried buckets of water and baskets of food; others were tearing bandages; grim-faced men peered from the portholes; all were listening for the war-cry.

They had not long to wait. Before noon the well-known whoop came from the wooded shore of the river, and it was soon followed by the appearance of hundreds of Indians. The river, which was low, at once became a scene of great animation. From a placid, smoothly flowing stream it was turned into a muddy, splashing, turbulent torrent. The mounted warriors urged their steeds down the bank and into the water; the unmounted improvised rafts and placed their weapons and ammunition upon them; then they swam and pushed, kicked and yelled their way across; other Indians swam, holding the bridles of the pack-horses. A detachment of British soldiers followed the Indians. In an hour the entire army appeared on the river bluff not three hundred yards from the Fort. They were in no hurry to begin the attack. Especially did the Indians seem to enjoy the lull before the storm, and as they stalked to and fro in plain sight of the garrison, or stood in groups watching the Fort, they were seen in all their hideous war-paint and formidable battle-array. They were exultant. Their plumes and eagle feathers waved proudly in the morning breeze. Now and then the long, peculiarly broken yell of the Shawnees rang out clear and strong. The soldiers were drawn off to one side and well out of range of the settlers' guns. Their red coats and flashing bayonets were new to most of the little band of men in the block-house.

"Ho, the Fort!"

It was a strong, authoritative voice and came from a man mounted on a black horse.

"Well, Girty, what is it?" shouted Silas Zane.

"We demand unconditional surrender," was the answer.

"You will never get it," replied Silas.

"Take more time to think it over. You see we have a force here large enough to take the Fort in an hour."

"That remains to be seen," shouted some one through porthole.

An hour passed. The soldiers and the Indians lounged around on the grass and walked to and fro on the bluff. At intervals a taunting Indian yell, horrible in its suggestiveness came floating on the air. When the hour was up three mounted men rode out in advance of the waiting Indians. One was clad in buckskin, another in the uniform of a British officer, and the third was an Indian chief whose powerful form was naked except for his buckskin belt and legging.

"Will you surrender?" came in the harsh and arrogant voice of the renegade.

"Never! Go back to your squaws!" yelled Sullivan.

"I am Capt. Pratt of the Queen's Rangers. If you surrender I will give you the best protection King George affords," shouted the officer.

"To hell with lying George! Go back to your hair-buying Hamilton and tell him the whole British army could not make us surrender," roared Hugh Bennet.

"If you do not give up, the Fort will be attacked and burned. Your men will be massacred and your women given to the Indians," said Girty.

"You will never take a man, woman or child alive," yelled Silas. "We remember Crawford, you white traitor, and we are not going to give up to be butchered. Come on with your red-jackets and your red-devils. We are ready."

"We have captured and killed the messenger you sent out, and now all hope of succor must be abandoned. Your doom is sealed."

"What kind of a man was he?" shouted Sullivan.

"A fine, active young fellow," answered the outlaw.

"That's a lie," snapped Sullivan, "he was an old, gray haired man."

As the officer and the outlaw chief turned, apparently to consult their companion, a small puff of white smoke shot forth from one of the portholes of the block-house. It was followed by the ringing report of a rifle. The Indian chief clutched wildly at his breast, fell forward on his horse, and after vainly trying to keep his seat, slipped to the ground. He raised himself once, then fell backward and lay still. Full two hundred yards was not proof against Wetzel's deadly smallbore, and Red Fox, the foremost war chieftain of the Shawnees, lay dead, a victim to the hunter's vengeance. It was characteristic of Wetzel that he picked the chief, for he could have shot either the British officer or the renegade. They retreated out of range, leaving the body of the chief where it had fallen, while the horse, giving a frightened snort, galloped toward the woods. Wetzel's yell coming quickly after his shot, excited the Indians to a very frenzy, and they started on a run for the Fort, discharging their rifles and screeching like so many demons.

In the cloud of smoke which at once enveloped the scene the Indians spread out and surrounded the Fort. A tremendous rush by a large party of Indians was made for the gate of the Fort. They attacked it fiercely with their tomahawks, and a log which they used as a battering-ram. But the stout gate withstood their united efforts, and the galling fire from the portholes soon forced them to fall back and seek cover behind the trees and the rocks. From these points of vantage they kept up an uninterrupted fire.

The soldiers had made a dash at the stockade-fence, yelling derision at the small French cannon which was mounted on top of the block-house. They thought it a "dummy" because they had learned that in the 1777 siege the garrison had no real cannon, but had tried to utilize a wooden one. They yelled and hooted and mocked at this piece and dared the garrison to fire it. Sullivan, who was in charge of the cannon, bided his time. When the soldiers were massed closely together and making another rush for the stockade-fence Sullivan turned loose the little "bulldog," spreading consternation and destruction in the British ranks.

"Stand back! Stand back!" Capt. Pratt was heard to yell. "By God! there's no wood about that gun."

After this the besiegers withdrew for a breathing spell. At this early stage of the siege the Indians were seen to board Sullivan's pirogue, and it was soon discovered they were carrying the cannon balls from the boat to the top of the bluff. In their simple minds they had conceived a happy thought. They procured a white-oak log probably a foot in diameter, split it through the middle and hollowed out the inside with their tomahawks. Then with iron chains and bars, which they took from Reihart's blacksmith shop, they bound and securely fastened the sides together. They dragged the improvised cannon nearer to the Fort, placed it on two logs and weighted it down with stones. A heavy charge of powder and ball was then rammed into the wooden gun. The soldiers, though much interested in the manoeuvre, moved back to a safe distance, while many of the Indians crowded round the new weapon. The torch was applied; there was a red flash—boom! The hillside was shaken by the tremendous explosion, and when the smoke lifted from the scene the naked forms of the Indians could be seen writhing in agony on the ground. Not a vestige of the wooden gun remained. The iron chains had proved terrible death-dealing missiles to the Indians near the gun. The Indians now took to their natural methods of warfare. They hid in the long grass, in the deserted cabins, behind the trees and up in the branches. Not an Indian was visible, but the rain of bullets pattered steadily against the block-house. Every bush and every tree spouted little puffs of white smoke, and the leaden messengers of Death whistled through the air.

After another unsuccessful effort to destroy a section of the stockade-fence the soldiers had retired. Their red jackets made them a conspicuous mark for the sharp-eyed settlers. Capt. Pratt had been shot through the thigh. He suffered great pain, and was deeply chagrined by the surprising and formidable defense of the garrison which he had been led to believe would fall an easy prey to the King's soldiers. He had lost one-third of his men. Those who were left refused to run straight in the face of certain death. They had not been drilled to fight an unseen enemy. Capt. Pratt was compelled to order a retreat to the river bluff, where he conferred with Girty.

Inside the block-house was great activity, but no confusion. That little band of fighters might have been drilled for a king's bodyguard. Kneeling before each porthole on the river side of the Fort was a man who would fight while there was breath left in him. He did not discharge his weapon aimlessly as the Indians did, but waited until he saw the outline of an Indian form, or a red coat, or a puff of white smoke; then he would thrust the rifle-barrel forward, take a quick aim and fire. By the side of every man stood a heroic woman whose face was blanched, but who spoke never a word as she put the muzzle of the hot rifle into a bucket of water, cooled the barrel, wiped it dry and passed it back to the man beside her.

Silas Zane had been wounded at the first fire. A glancing ball had struck him on the head, inflicting a painful scalp wound. It was now being dressed by Col. Zane's wife, whose skilled fingers were already tired with the washing and the bandaging of the injuries received by the defenders. In all that horrible din of battle, the shrill yells of the savages, the hoarse shouts of the settlers, the boom of the cannon overhead, the cracking of rifles and the whistling of bullets; in all that din of appalling noise, and amid the stifling smoke, the smell of burned powder, the sickening sight of the desperately wounded and the already dead, the Colonel's brave wife had never faltered.

She was here and there; binding the wounds, helping Lydia and Betty mould bullets, encouraging the men, and by her example, enabling those women to whom border war was new to bear up under the awful strain.

Sullivan, who had been on top of the block-house, came down the ladder almost without touching it. Blood was running down his bare arm and dripping from the ends of his fingers.

"Zane, Martin has been shot," he said hoarsely. "The same Indian who shot away these fingers did it. The bullets seem to come from some elevation. Send some scout up there and find out where that damned Indian is hiding."

"Martin shot? God, his poor wife! Is he dead?" said Silas.

"Not yet. Bennet is bringing him down. Here, I want this hand tied up, so that my gun won't be so slippery."

Wetzel was seen stalking from one porthole to another. His fearful yell sounded above all the others. He seemed to bear a charmed life, for not a bullet had so much as scratched him. Silas communicated to him what Sullivan had said. The hunter mounted the ladder and went up on the roof. Soon he reappeared, descended into the room and ran into the west end of the block-house. He kneeled before a porthole through which he pushed the long black barrel of his rifle. Silas and Sullivan followed him and looked in the direction indicated by his weapon. It pointed toward the bushy top of a tall poplar tree which stood on the hill west of the Fort. Presently a little cloud of white smoke issued from the leafy branches, and it was no sooner seen than Wetzel's rifle was discharged. There was a great commotion among the leaves, the branches swayed and thrashed, and then a dark body plunged downward to strike on the rocky slope of the bluff and roll swiftly out of sight. The hunter's unnatural yell pealed out.

"Great God! The man's crazy," cried Sullivan, staring at Wetzel's demon-like face.

"No, no. It's his way," answered Silas.

At that moment the huge frame of Bennet filled up the opening in the roof and started down the ladder. In one arm he carried the limp body of a young man. When he reached the floor he laid the body down and beckoned to Mrs. Zane. Those watching saw that the young man was Will Martin, and that he was still alive. But it was evident that he had not long to live. His face had a leaden hue and his eyes were bright and glassy. Alice, his wife, flung herself on her knees beside him and tenderly raised the drooping head. No words could express the agony in her face as she raised it to Mrs. Zane. In it was a mute appeal, an unutterable prayer for hope. Mrs. Zane turned sorrowfully to her task. There was no need of her skill here. Alfred Clarke, who had been ordered to take Martin's place on top of the block-house, paused a moment in silent sympathy. When he saw that little hole in the bared chest, from which the blood welled up in an awful stream, he shuddered and passed on. Betty looked up from her work and then turned away sick and faint. Her mute lips moved as if in prayer.

Alice was left alone with her dying husband. She tenderly supported his head on her bosom, leaned her face against his and kissed the cold, numb lips. She murmured into his already deaf ear the old tender names. He knew her, for he made a feeble effort to pass his arm round her neck. A smile illumined his face. Then death claimed him. With wild, distended eyes and with hands pressed tightly to her temples Alice rose slowly to her feet.

"Oh, God! Oh, God!" she cried.

Her prayer was answered. In a momentary lull in the battle was heard the deadly hiss of a bullet as it sped through one of the portholes. It ended with a slight sickening spat as the lead struck the flesh. Then Alice, without a cry, fell on the husband's breast. Silas Zane found her lying dead with the body of her husband clasped closely in her arms. He threw a blanket over them and went on his wearying round of the bastions.

* * * * * * * * * * * * * *

The besiegers had been greatly harassed and hampered by the continual fire from Col. Zane's house. It was exceedingly difficult for the Indians, and impossible for the British, to approach near enough to the Colonel's house to get an effective shot. Col. Zane and his men had the advantage of being on higher ground. Also they had four rifles to a man, and they used every spare moment for reloading. Thus they were enabled to pour a deadly fire into the ranks of the enemy, and to give the impression of being much stronger in force than they really were.

About dusk the firing ceased and the Indians repaired to the river bluff. Shortly afterward their camp-fires were extinguished and all became dark and quiet. Two hours passed. Fortunately the clouds, which had at first obscured the moon, cleared away somewhat and enough light was shed on the scene to enable the watchers to discern objects near by.

Col. Zane had just called together his men for a conference. He suspected some cunning deviltry on part of the Indians.

"Sam, take what stuff to eat you can lay your hands on and go up to the loft. Keep a sharp lookout and report anything to Jonathan or me," said the Colonel.

All afternoon Jonathan Zane had loaded and fired his rifles in sullen and dogged determination. He had burst one rifle and disabled another. The other men were fine marksmen, but it was undoubtedly Jonathan's unerring aim that made the house so unapproachable. He used an extremely heavy, large bore rifle. In the hands of a man strong enough to stand its fierce recoil it was a veritable cannon. The Indians had soon learned to respect the range of that rifle, and they gave the cabin a wide berth.

But now that darkness had enveloped the valley the advantage lay with the savages. Col. Zane glanced apprehensively at the blackened face of his brother.

"Do you think the Fort can hold out?" he asked in a husky voice. He was a bold man, but he thought now of his wife and children.

"I don't know," answered Jonathan. "I saw that big Shawnee chief today. His name is Fire. He is well named. He is a fiend. Girty has a picked band."

"The Fort has held out surprisingly well against such combined and fierce attacks. The Indians are desperate. You can easily see that in the way in which they almost threw their lives away. The green square is covered with dead Indians."

"If help does not come in twenty-four hours not one man will escape alive. Even Wetzel could not break through that line of Indians. But if we can hold the Indians off a day longer they will get tired and discouraged. Girty will not be able to hold them much longer. The British don't count. It's not their kind of war. They can't shoot, and so far as I can see they haven't done much damage."

"To your posts, men, and every man think of the women and children in the block-house."

For a long time, which seemed hours to the waiting and watching settlers, not a sound could be heard, nor any sign of the enemy seen. Thin clouds had again drifted over the moon, allowing only a pale, wan light to shine down on the valley. Time dragged on and the clouds grew thicker and denser until the moon and the stars were totally obscured. Still no sign or sound of the savages.

"What was that?" suddenly whispered Col. Zane.

"It was a low whistle from Sam. We'd better go up," said Jonathan.

They went up the stairs to the second floor from which they ascended to the loft by means of a ladder. The loft was as black as pitch. In that Egyptian darkness it was no use to look for anything, so they crawled on their hands and knees over the piles of hides and leather which lay on the floor. When they reached the small window they made out the form of the negro.

"What is it, Sam?" whispered Jonathan.

"Look, see thar, Massa Zane," came the answer in a hoarse whisper from the negro and at the same time he pointed down toward the ground.

Col. Zane put his head alongside Jonathan's and all three men peered out into the darkness.

"Jack, can you see anything?" said Col. Zane.

"No, but wait a minute until the moon throws a light."

A breeze had sprung up. The clouds were passing rapidly over the moon, and at long intervals a rift between the clouds let enough light through to brighten the square for an instant.

"Now, Massa Zane, thar!" exclaimed the slave.

"I can't see a thing. Can you, Jack?"

"I am not sure yet. I can see something, but whether it is a log or not I don't know."

Just then there was a faint light like the brightening of a firefly, or like the blowing of a tiny spark from a stick of burning wood. Jonathan uttered a low curse.

"D—n 'em! At their old tricks with fire. I thought all this quiet meant something. The grass out there is full of Indians, and they are carrying lighted arrows under them so as to cover the light. But we'll fool the red devils this time"

"I can see 'em, Massa Zane."

"Sh-h-h! no more talk," whispered Col. Zane.

The men waited with cocked rifles. Another spark rose seemingly out of the earth. This time it was nearer the house. No sooner had its feeble light disappeared than the report of the negro's rifle awoke the sleeping echoes. It was succeeded by a yell which seemed to come from under the window. Several dark forms rose so suddenly that they appeared to spring out of the ground. Then came the peculiar twang of Indian bows. There were showers of sparks and little streaks of fire with long tails like comets winged their parabolic flight toward the cabin. Falling short they hissed and sputtered in the grass. Jonathan's rifle spoke and one of the fleeing forms tumbled to the earth. A series of long yells from all around the Fort greeted this last shot, but not an Indian fired a rifle.

Fire-tipped arrows were now shot at the block-house, but not one took effect, although a few struck the stockade-fence. Col. Zane had taken the precaution to have the high grass and the clusters of goldenrod cut down all round the Fort. The wisdom of this course now became evident, for the wily savages could not crawl near enough to send their fiery arrows on the roof of the block-house. This attempt failing, the Indians drew back to hatch up some other plot to burn the Fort.

"Look!" suddenly exclaimed Jonathan.

Far down the road, perhaps five hundred yards from the Fort, a point of light had appeared. At first it was still, and then it took an odd jerky motion, to this side and to that, up and down like a jack-o-lantern.

"What the hell?" muttered Col. Zane, sorely puzzled. "Jack, by all that's strange it's getting bigger."

Sure enough the spark of fire, or whatever it was, grew larger and larger. Col. Zane thought it might be a light carried by a man on horseback. But if this were true where was the clatter of the horse's hoofs? On that rocky blur no horse could run noiselessly. It could not be a horse. Fascinated and troubled by this new mystery which seemed to presage evil to them the watchers waited with that patience known only to those accustomed to danger. They knew that whatever it was, it was some satanic stratagem of the savages, and that it would come all too soon.

The light was now zigzagging back and forth across the road, and approaching the Fort with marvelous rapidity. Now its motion was like the wide swinging of a lighted lantern on a dark night. A moment more of breathless suspense and the lithe form of an Indian brave could be seen behind the light. He was running with almost incredible swiftness down the road in the direction of the Fort. Passing at full speed within seventy-five yards of the stockade-fence the Indian shot his arrow. Like a fiery serpent flying through the air the missile sped onward in its graceful flight, going clear over the block-house, and striking with a spiteful thud the roof of one of the cabins beyond. Unhurt by the volley that was fired at him, the daring brave passed swiftly out of sight.

Deeds like this were dear to the hearts of the savages. They were deeds which made a warrior of a brave, and for which honor any Indian would risk his life over and over again. The exultant yells which greeted this performance proclaimed its success.

The breeze had already fanned the smouldering arrow into a blaze and the dry roof of the cabin had caught fire and was burning fiercely.

"That infernal redskin is going to do that again," ejaculated Jonathan.

It was indeed true. That same small bright light could be seen coming down the road gathering headway with every second. No doubt the same Indian, emboldened by his success, and maddened with that thirst for glory so often fatal to his kind, was again making the effort to fire the block-house.

The eyes of Col. Zane and his companions were fastened on the light as it came nearer and nearer with its changing motion. The burning cabin brightened the square before the Fort. The slender, shadowy figure of the Indian could be plainly seen emerging from the gloom. So swiftly did he run that he seemed to have wings. Now he was in the full glare of the light. What a magnificent nerve, what a terrible assurance there was in his action! It seemed to paralyze all. The red arrow emitted a shower of sparks as it was discharged. This time it winged its way straight and true and imbedded itself in the roof of the block-house.

Almost at the same instant a solitary rifle shot rang out and the daring warrior plunged headlong, sliding face downward in the dust of the road, while from the Fort came that demoniac yell now grown so familiar.

"Wetzel's compliments," muttered Jonathan. "But the mischief is done. Look at that damned burning arrow. If it doesn't blow out the Fort will go."

The arrow was visible, but it seemed a mere spark. It alternately paled and glowed. One moment it almost went out, and the next it gleamed brightly. To the men, compelled to look on and powerless to prevent the burning of the now apparently doomed block-house, that spark was like the eye of Hell.

"Ho, the Fort," yelled Col. Zane with all the power of his strong lungs. "Ho, Silas, the roof is on fire!"

Pandemonium had now broken out among the Indians. They could be plainly seen in the red glare thrown by the burning cabin. It had been a very dry season, the rough shingles were like tinder, and the inflammable material burst quickly into great flames, lighting up the valley as far as the edge of the forest. It was an awe-inspiring and a horrible spectacle. Columns of yellow and black smoke rolled heavenward; every object seemed dyed a deep crimson; the trees assumed fantastic shapes; the river veiled itself under a red glow. Above the roaring and crackling of the flames rose the inhuman yelling of the savages. Like demons of the inferno they ran to and fro, their naked painted bodies shining in the glare. One group of savages formed a circle and danced hands-around a stump as gayly as a band of school-girls at a May party. They wrestled with and hugged one another; they hopped, skipped and jumped, and in every possible way manifested their fiendish joy.

The British took no part in this revelry. To their credit it must be said they kept in the background as though ashamed of this horrible fire-war on people of their own blood.

"Why don't they fire the cannon?" impatiently said Col. Zane. "Why don't they do something?"

"Perhaps it is disabled, or maybe they are short of ammunition," suggested Jonathan.

"The block-house will burn down before our eyes. Look! The hellhounds have set fire to the fence. I see men running and throwing water."

"I see something on the roof of the block-house," cried Jonathan. "There, down towards the east end of the roof and in the shadow of the chimney. And as I'm a living sinner it's a man crawling towards that blazing arrow. The Indians have not discovered him yet. He is still in the shadow. But they'll see him. God! What a nervy thing to do in the face of all those redskins. It is almost certain death!"

"Yes, and they see him," said the Colonel.

With shrill yells the Indians bounded forward and aimed and fired their rifles at the crouching figure of the man. Some hid behind the logs they had rolled toward the Fort; others boldly faced the steady fire now pouring from the portholes. The savages saw in the movement of that man an attempt to defeat their long-cherished hope of burning the Fort. Seeing he was discovered, the man did not hesitate, nor did he lose a second. Swiftly he jumped and ran toward the end of the roof where the burning arrow, now surrounded by blazing shingles, was sticking in the roof. How he ever ran along that slanting roof and with a pail in his hand was incomprehensible. In moments like that men become superhuman. It all happened in an instant. He reached the arrow, kicked it over the wall, and then dashed the bucket of water on the blazing shingles. In that single instant, wherein his tall form was outlined against the bright light behind him, he presented the fairest kind of a mark for the Indians. Scores of rifles were levelled and discharged at him. The bullets pattered like hail on the roof of the block-house, but apparently none found their mark, for the man ran back and disappeared.

"It was Clarke!" exclaimed Col. Zane. "No one but Clarke has such light hair. Wasn't that a plucky thing?"

"It has saved the block-house for to-night," answered Jonathan. "See, the

Indians are falling back. They can't stand in the face of that shooting. Hurrah! Look at them fall! It could not have happened better. The light from the cabin will prevent any more close attacks for an hour and daylight is   near."

CHAPTER XIV.

The sun rose red. Its ruddy rays peeped over the eastern hills, kissed the tree-tops, glinted along the stony bluffs, and chased away the gloom of night from the valley. Its warm gleams penetrated the portholes of the Fort and cast long bright shadows on the walls; but it brought little cheer to the sleepless and almost exhausted defenders. It brought to many of the settlers the familiar old sailor's maxim: "Redness 'a the morning, sailor's warning." Rising in its crimson glory the sun flooded the valley, dyeing the river, the leaves, the grass, the stones, tingeing everything with that awful color which stained the stairs, the benches, the floor, even the portholes of the block-house.

Historians call this the time that tried men's souls. If it tried the men think what it must have been to those grand, heroic women. Though they had helped the men load and fire nearly forty-eight hours; though they had worked without a moment's rest and were now ready to succumb to exhaustion; though the long room was full of stifling smoke and the sickening odor of burned wood and powder, and though the row of silent, covered bodies had steadily lengthened, the thought of giving up never occurred to the women. Death there would be sweet compared to what it would be at the hands of the redmen.

At sunrise Silas Zane, bare-chested, his face dark and fierce, strode into the bastion which was connected with the blockhouse. It was a small shedlike room, and with portholes opening to the river and the forest. This bastion had seen the severest fighting. Five men had been killed here. As Silas entered four haggard and powder-begrimed men, who were kneeling before the portholes, looked up at him. A dead man lay in one corner.

"Smith's dead. That makes fifteen," said Silas. "Fifteen out of forty-two, that leaves twenty-seven. We must hold out. Len, don't expose yourselves recklessly. How goes it at the south bastion?"

"All right. There's been firin' over there all night," answered one of the men. "I guess it's been kinder warm over that way. But I ain't heard any shootin' for some time."

"Young Bennet is over there, and if the men needed anything they would send him for it," answered Silas. "I'll send some food and water. Anything else?"

"Powder. We're nigh out of powder," replied the man addressed. "And we might jes as well make ready fer a high old time. The red devils hadn't been quiet all this last hour fer nothin'."

Silas passed along the narrow hallway which led from the bastion into the main room of the block-house. As he turned the corner at the head of the stairway he encountered a boy who was dragging himself up the steps.

"Hello! Who's this? Why, Harry!" exclaimed Silas, grasping the boy and drawing him into the room. Once in the light Silas saw that the lad was so weak he could hardly stand. He was covered with blood. It dripped from a bandage wound tightly about his arm; it oozed through a hole in his hunting shirt, and it flowed from a wound over his temple. The shadow of death was already stealing over the pallid face, but from the grey eyes shone an indomitable spirit, a spirit which nothing but death could quench.

"Quick!" the lad panted. "Send men to the south wall. The redskins are breakin' in where the water from the spring runs under the fence."

"Where are Metzar and the other men?"

"Dead! Killed last night. I've been there alone all night. I kept on shootin'. Then I gets plugged here under the chin. Knowin' it's all up with me I deserted my post when I heard the Injuns choppin' on the fence where it was on fire last night. But I only—run—because—they're gettin' in."

"Wetzel, Bennet, Clarke!" yelled Silas, as he laid the boy on the bench.

Almost as Silas spoke the tall form of the hunter confronted him. Clarke and the other men were almost as prompt.

"Wetzel, run to the south wall. The Indians are cutting a hole through the fence."

Wetzel turned, grabbed his rifle and an axe and was gone like a flash.

"Sullivan, you handle the men here. Bessie, do what you can for this brave lad. Come, Bennet, Clarke, we must follow Wetzel," commanded Silas.

Mrs. Zane hastened to the side of the fainting lad. She washed away the blood from the wound over his temple. She saw that a bullet had glanced on the bone and that the wound was not deep or dangerous. She unlaced the hunting shirt at the neck and pulled the flaps apart. There on the right breast, on a line with the apex of the lung, was a horrible gaping wound. A murderous British slug had passed through the lad. From the hole at every heart-beat poured the dark, crimson life-tide. Mrs. Zane turned her white face away for a second; then she folded a small piece of linen, pressed it tightly over the wound, and wrapped a towel round the lad's breast.

"Don't waste time on me. It's all over," he whispered. "Will you call Betty here a minute?"

Betty came, white-faced and horror-stricken. For forty hours she had been living in a maze of terror. Her movements had almost become mechanical. She had almost ceased to hear and feel. But the light in the eyes of this dying boy brought her back to the horrible reality of the present.

"Oh, Harry! Harry! Harry!" was all Betty could whisper.

"I'm goin', Betty. And I wanted—you to say a little prayer for me—and say good-bye to me," he panted.

Betty knelt by the bench and tried to pray.

"I hated to run, Betty, but I waited and waited and nobody came, and the Injuns was gettin' in. They'll find dead Injuns in piles out there. I was shootin' fer you, Betty, and every time I aimed I thought of you."

The lad rambled on, his voice growing weaker and weaker and finally ceasing. The hand which had clasped Betty's so closely loosened its hold. His eyes closed. Betty thought he was dead, but no! he still breathed. Suddenly his eyes opened. The shadow of pain was gone. In its place shone a beautiful radiance.

"Betty, I've cared a lot for you—and I'm dyin'—happy because I've fought fer you—and somethin' tells me—you'll—be saved. Good-bye." A smile transformed his face and his gray eyes gazed steadily into hers. Then his head fell back. With a sigh his brave spirit fled.

Hugh Bennet looked once at the pale face of his son, then he ran down the stairs after Silas and Clarke. When the three men emerged from behind Capt. Boggs' cabin, which was adjacent to the block-house, and which hid the south wall from their view, they were two hundred feet from Wetzel. They heard the heavy thump of a log being rammed against the fence; then a splitting and splintering of one of the six-inch oak planks. Another and another smashing blow and the lower half of one of the planks fell inwards, leaving an aperture large enough to admit an Indian. The men dashed forward to the assistance of Wetzel, who stood by the hole with upraised axe. At the same moment a shot rang out. Bennet stumbled and fell headlong. An Indian had shot through the hole in the fence. Silas and Alfred sheered off toward the fence, out of line. When within twenty yards of Wetzel they saw a swarthy-faced and athletic savage squeeze through the narrow crevice. He had not straightened up before the axe, wielded by the giant hunter, descended on his head, cracking his skull as if it were an eggshell. The savage sank to the earth without even a moan. Another savage naked and powerful, slipped in. He had to stoop to get through. He raised himself, and seeing Wetzel, he tried to dodge the lightning sweep of the axe. It missed his head, at which it had been aimed, but struck just over the shoulders, and buried itself in flesh and bone. The Indian uttered an agonizing yell which ended in a choking, gurgling sound as the blood spurted from his throat. Wetzel pulled the weapon from the body of his victim, and with the same motion he swung it around. This time the blunt end met the next Indian's head with a thud like that made by the butcher when he strikes the bullock to the ground. The Indian's rifle dropped, his tomahawk flew into the air, while his body rolled down the little embankment into the spring. Another and another Indian met the same fate. Then two Indians endeavored to get through the aperture. The awful axe swung by those steel arms, dispatched both of than in the twinkling of an eye. Their bodies stuck in the hole.

Silas and Alfred stood riveted to the spot. Just then Wetzel in all his horrible glory was a sight to freeze the marrow of any man. He had cast aside his hunting shirt in that run to the fence and was now stripped to the waist. He was covered with blood. The muscles of his broad back and his brawny arms swelled and rippled under the brown skin. At every swing of the gory axe he let out a yell the like of which had never before been heard by the white men. It was the hunter's mad yell of revenge. In his thirst for vengeance he had forgotten that he was defending the Fort with its women and its children; he was fighting because he loved to kill.

Silas Zane heard the increasing clamor outside and knew that hundreds of Indians were being drawn to the spot. Something must be done at once. He looked around and his eyes fell on a pile of white-oak logs that had been hauled inside the Fort. They had been placed there by Col. Zane, with wise forethought. Silas grabbed Clarke and pulled him toward the pile of logs, at the same time communicating his plan. Together they carried a log to the fence and dropped it in front of the hole. Wetzel immediately stepped on it and took a vicious swing at an Indian who was trying to poke his rifle sideways through the hole. This Indian had discharged his weapon twice. While Wetzel held the Indians at bay, Silas and Clarke piled the logs one upon another, until the hole was closed. This effectually fortified and barricaded the weak place in the stockade fence. The settlers in the bastions were now pouring such a hot fire into the ranks of the savage that they were compelled to retreat out of range.

While Wetzel washed the blood from his arms and his shoulders Silas and Alfred hurried back to where Bennet had fallen. They expected to find him dead, and were overjoyed to see the big settler calmly sitting by the brook binding up a wound in his shoulder.

"It's nothin' much. Jest a scratch, but it tumbled me over," he said. "I was comin' to help you. That was the wust Injun scrap I ever saw. Why didn't you keep on lettin' 'em come in? The red varmints would'a kept on comin' and Wetzel was good fer the whole tribe. All you'd had to do was to drag the dead Injuns aside and give him elbow room."

Wetzel joined them at this moment, and they hurried back to the block-house. The firing had ceased on the bluff. They met Sullivan at the steps of the Fort. He was evidently coming in search of them.

"Zane, the Indians and the Britishers are getting ready for more determined and persistent effort than any that has yet been made," said Sullivan.

"How so?" asked Silas.

"They have got hammers from the blacksmith's shop, and they boarded my boat and found a keg of nails. Now they are making a number of ladders. If they make a rush all at once and place ladders against the fence we'll have the Fort full of Indians in ten minutes. They can't stand in the face of a cannon charge. We *must* use the cannon."

"Clarke, go into Capt. Boggs' cabin and fetch out two kegs of powder," said Silas.

The young man turned in the direction of the cabin, while Silas and the others ascended the stairs.

"The firing seems to be all on the south side," said Silas, "and is not so heavy as it was."

"Yes, as I said, the Indians on the river front are busy with their new plans," answered Sullivan.

"Why does not Clarke return?" said Silas, after waiting a few moments at the door of the long room. "We have no time to lose. I want to divide one keg of that powder among the men."

Clarke appeared at the moment. He was breathing heavily as though he had run up the stairs, or was laboring under a powerful emotion. His face was gray.

"I could not find any powder!" he exclaimed. "I searched every nook and corner in Capt. Boggs' house. There is no powder there."

A brief silence ensued. Everyone in the block-house heard the young man's voice. No one moved. They all seemed waiting for someone to speak. Finally Silas Zane burst out:

"Not find it? You surely could not have looked well. Capt. Boggs himself told me there were three kegs of powder in the storeroom. I will go and find it myself."

Alfred did not answer, but sat down on a bench with an odd numb feeling round his heart. He knew what was coming. He had been in the Captain's house and had seen those kegs of powder. He knew exactly where they had been. Now they were not on the accustomed shelf, nor at any other place in the storeroom. While he sat there waiting for the awful truth to dawn on the garrison, his eyes roved from one end of the room to the other. At last they found what they were seeking. A young woman knelt before a charcoal fire which she was blowing with a bellows. It was Betty. Her face was pale and weary, her hair dishevelled, her shapely arms blackened with charcoal, but notwithstanding she looked calm, resolute, self-contained. Lydia was kneeling by her side holding a bullet-mould on a block of wood. Betty lifted the ladle from the red coals and poured the hot metal with a steady hand and an admirable precision. Too much or too little lead would make an imperfect ball. The little missile had to be just so for those soft-metal, smooth-bore rifles. Then Lydia dipped the mould in a bucket of water, removed it and knocked it on the floor. A small, shiny lead bullet rolled out. She rubbed it with a greasy rag and then dropped it in a jar. For nearly forty hours, without sleep or rest, almost without food, those brave girls had been at their post.

Silas Zane came running into the room. His face was ghastly, even his lips were white and drawn.

"Sullivan, in God's name, what can we do? The powder is gone!" he cried in a strident voice.

"Gone?" repeated several voices.

"Gone?" echoed Sullivan. "Where?"

"God knows. I found where the kegs stood a few days ago. There were marks in the dust. They have been moved."

"Perhaps Boggs put them here somewhere," said Sullivan. "We will look."

"No use. No use. We were always careful to keep the powder out of here on account of fire. The kegs are gone, gone."

"Miller stole them," said Wetzel in his calm voice.

"What difference does that make now?" burst out Silas, turning passionately on the hunter, whose quiet voice in that moment seemed so unfeeling. "They're gone!"

In the silence which ensued after these words the men looked at each other with slowly whitening faces. There was no need of words. Their eyes told one another what was coming. The fate which had overtaken so many border forts was to be theirs. They were lost! And every man thought not of himself, cared not for himself, but for those innocent children, those brave young girls and heroic women.

A man can die. He is glorious when he calmly accepts death; but when he fights like a tiger, when he stands at bay his back to the wall, a broken weapon in his hand, bloody, defiant, game to the end, then he is sublime. Then he wrings respect from the souls of even his bitterest foes. Then he is avenged even in his death.

But what can women do in times of war? They help, they cheer, they inspire, and if their cause is lost they must accept death or worse. Few women have the courage for self-destruction. "To the victor belong the spoils," and women have ever been the spoils of war.

No wonder Silas Zane and his men weakened in that moment. With only a few charges for their rifles and none for the cannon how could they hope to hold out against the savages? Alone they could have drawn their tomahawks and have made a dash through the lines of Indians, but with the women and the children that was impossible.

"Wetzel, what can we do? For God's sake, advise us!" said Silas hoarsely. "We cannot hold the Fort without powder. We cannot leave the women here. We had better tomahawk every woman in the block-house than let her fall into the hands of Girty."

"Send someone fer powder," answered Wetzel.

"Do you think it possible," said Silas quickly, a ray of hope lighting up his haggard features. "There's plenty of powder in Eb's cabin. Whom shall we send? Who will volunteer?"

Three men stepped forward, and others made a movement.

"They'd plug a man full of lead afore he'd get ten foot from the gate," said Wetzel. "I'd go myself, but it wouldn't do no good. Send a boy, and one as can run like a streak."

"There are no lads big enough to carry a keg of powder. Harry Bennett might go," said Silas. "How is he, Bessie?"

"He is dead," answered Mrs. Zane.

Wetzel made a motion with his hands and turned away. A short, intense silence followed this indication of hopelessness from him. The women understood, for some of them covered their faces, while others sobbed.

"I will go."

It was Betty's voice, and it rang clear and vibrant throughout the room. The miserable women raised their drooping heads, thrilled by that fresh young voice. The men looked stupefied. Clarke seemed turned to stone. Wetzel came quickly toward her.

"Impossible!" said Sullivan.

Silas Zane shook his head as if the idea were absurd.

"Let me go, brother, let me go?" pleaded Betty as she placed her little hands softly, caressingly on her brother's bare arm. "I know it is only a forlorn chance, but still it is a chance. Let me take it. I would rather die that way than remain here and wait for death."

"Silas, it ain't a bad plan," broke in Wetzel. "Betty can run like a deer. And bein' a woman they may let her get to the cabin without shootin'."

Silas stood with arms folded across his broad chest. As he gazed at his sister great tears coursed down his dark cheeks and splashed on the hands which so tenderly clasped his own. Betty stood before him transformed; all signs of weariness had vanished; her eyes shone with a fateful resolve; her white and eager face was surpassingly beautiful with its light of hope, of prayer, of heroism.

"Let me go, brother. You know I can run, and oh! I will fly today. Every moment is precious. Who knows? Perhaps Capt. Boggs is already near at hand with help. You cannot spare a man. Let me go."

"Betty, Heaven bless and save you, you shall go," said Silas.

"No! No! Do not let her go!" cried Clarke, throwing himself before them. He was trembling, his eyes were wild, and he had the appearance of a man suddenly gone mad.

"She shall not go," he cried.

"What authority have you here?" demanded Silas Zane, sternly. "What right have you to speak?"

"None, unless it is that I love her and I will go for her," answered Alfred desperately.

"Stand back!" cried Wetzel, placing his powerful hard on Clarke's breast and pushing him backward. "If you love her you don't want to have her wait here for them red devils," and he waved his hand toward the river. "If she gets back she'll save the Fort. If she fails she'll at least escape Girty."

Betty gazed into the hunter's eyes and then into Alfred's. She understood both men. One was sending her out to her death because he knew it would be a thousand times more merciful than the fate which awaited her at the hands of the Indians. The other had not the strength to watch her go to her death. He had offered himself rather than see her take such fearful chances.

"I know. If it were possible you would both save me," said Betty, simply. "Now you can do nothing but pray that God may spare my life long enough to reach the gate. Silas, I am ready."

Downstairs a little group of white-faced men were standing before the gateway. Silas Zane had withdrawn the iron bar. Sullivan stood ready to swing in the ponderous gate. Wetzel was speaking with a clearness and a rapidity which were wonderful under the circumstances.

"When we let you out you'll have a clear path. Run, but not very fast. Save your speed. Tell the Colonel to empty a keg of powder in a table cloth. Throw it over your shoulder and start back. Run like you was racin' with me, and keep on comin' if you do get hit. Now go!"

The huge gate creaked and swung in. Betty ran out, looking straight before her. She had covered half the distance between the Fort and the Colonel's house when long taunting yells filled the air.

"Squaw! Waugh! Squaw! Waugh!" yelled the Indians in contempt.

Not a shot did they fire. The yells ran all along the river front, showing that hundreds of Indians had seen the slight figure running up the gentle slope toward the cabin.

Betty obeyed Wetzel's instructions to the letter. She ran easily and not at all hurriedly, and was as cool as if there had not been an Indian within miles.

Col. Zane had seen the gate open and Betty come forth. When she bounded up the steps he flung open that door and she ran into his arms.

"Betts, for God's sake! What's this?" he cried.

"We are out of powder. Empty a keg of powder into a table cloth. Quick! I've not a second to lose," she answered, at the same time slipping off her outer skirt. She wanted nothing to hinder that run for the block-house.

Jonathan Zane heard Betty's first words and disappeared into the magazine-room. He came out with a keg in his arms. With one blow of an axe he smashed in the top of the keg. In a twinkling a long black stream of the precious stuff was piling up in a little hill in the center of the table. Then the corners of the table cloth were caught up, turned and twisted, and the bag of powder was thrown over Betty's shoulder.

"Brave girl, so help me God, you are going to do it!" cried Col. Zane, throwing open the door. "I know you can. Run as you never ran in all your life."

Like an arrow sprung from a bow Betty flashed past the Colonel and out on the green. Scarcely ten of the long hundred yards had been covered by her flying feet when a roar of angry shouts and yells warned Betty that the keen-eyed savages saw the bag of powder and now knew they had been deceived by a girl. The cracking of rifles began at a point on the bluff nearest Col. Zane's house, and extended in a half circle to the eastern end of the clearing. The leaden messengers of Death whistled past Betty. They sped before her and behind her, scattering pebbles in her path, striking up the dust, and ploughing little furrows in the ground. A quarter of the distance covered! Betty had passed the top of the knoll now and she was going down the gentle slope like the wind. None but a fine marksman could have hit that small, flitting figure. The yelling and screeching had become deafening. The reports of the rifles blended in a roar. Yet above it all Betty heard Wetzel's stentorian yell. It lent wings to her feet. Half the distance covered! A hot, stinging pain shot through Betty's arm, but she heeded it not. The bullets were raining about her. They sang over her head; hissed close to her ears, and cut the grass in front of her; they pattered like hail on the stockade-fence, but still untouched, unharmed, the slender brown figure sped toward the gate. Three-fourths of the distance covered! A tug at the flying hair, and a long, black tress cut off by a bullet, floated away on the breeze. Betty saw the big gate swing; she saw the tall figure of the hunter; she saw her brother. Only a few more yards! On! On! On! A blinding red mist obscured her sight. She lost the opening in the fence, but unheeding she rushed on. Another second and she stumbled; she felt herself grasped by eager arms; she heard the gate slam and the iron bar shoot into place; then she felt and heard no more.

Silas Zane bounded up the stairs with a doubly precious burden in his arms. A mighty cheer greeted his entrance. It aroused Alfred Clarke, who had bowed his head on the bench and had lost all sense of time and place. What were the women sobbing and crying over? To whom belonged that white face? Of course, it was the face of the girl he loved. The face of the girl who had gone to her death. And he writhed in his agony.

Then something wonderful happened. A warm, living flush swept over that pale face. The eyelids fluttered; they opened, and the dark eyes, radiant, beautiful, gazed straight into Alfred's.

Still Alfred could not believe his eyes. That pale face and the wonderful eyes belonged to the ghost of his sweetheart. They had come back to haunt him. Then he heard a voice.

"O-h! but that brown place burns!"

Alfred saw a bare and shapely arm. Its beauty was marred by a cruel red welt. He heard that same sweet voice laugh and cry together. Then he came back to life and hope. With one bound he sprang to a porthole.

"God, what a woman!" he said between his teeth, as he thrust the rifle forward.

It was indeed not a time for inaction. The Indians, realizing they had been tricked and had lost a golden opportunity, rushed at the Fort with renewed energy. They attacked from all sides and with the persistent fury of savages long disappointed in their hopes. They were received with a scathing, deadly fire. Bang! roared the cannon, and the detachment of savages dropped their ladders and fled. The little "bull dog" was turned on its swivel and directed at another rush of Indians. Bang! and the bullets, chainlinks, and bits of iron ploughed through the ranks of the enemy. The Indians never lived who could stand in the face of well-aimed cannon-shot. They fell back. The settlers, inspired, carried beyond themselves by the heroism of a girl, fought as they had never fought before. Every shot went to a redskin's heart, impelled by the powder for which a brave girl had offered her life, guided by hands and arms of iron, and aimed by eyes as fixed and stern as Fate, every bullet shed the life-blood of a warrior.

Slowly and sullenly the red men gave way before that fire. Foot by foot they retired. Girty was seen no more. Fire, the Shawnee chief, lay dead in the road almost in the same spot where two days before his brother chief, Red Fox, had bit the dust. The British had long since retreated.

When night came the exhausted and almost famished besiegers sought rest and food.

The moon came out clear and beautiful, as if ashamed at her traitor's part of the night before, and brightened up the valley, bathing the Fort, the river, and the forest in her silver light.

Shortly after daybreak the next morning the Indians, despairing of success, held a pow-wow. While they were grouped in plain view of the garrison, and probably conferring over the question of raising the siege, the long, peculiar whoop of an Indian spy, who had been sent out to watch for the approach of a relief party, rang out. This seemed a signal for retreat. Scarcely had the shrill cry ceased to echo in the hills when the Indians and the British, abandoning their dead, moved rapidly across the river.

After a short interval a mounted force was seen galloping up the creek road. It proved to be Capt. Boggs, Swearengen, and Williamson with seventy men. Great was the rejoicing. Capt. Boggs had expected to find only the ashes of the Fort. And the gallant little garrison, although saddened by the loss of half its original number, rejoiced that it had repulsed the united forces of braves and British.

CHAPTER XV.

Peace and quiet reigned ones more at Ft. Henry. Before the glorious autumn days had waned, the settlers had repaired the damage done to their cabins, and many of them were now occupied with the fall plowing. Never had the Fort experienced such busy days. Many new faces were seen in the little meeting-house. Pioneers from Virginia, from Ft. Pitt, and eastward had learned that Fort Henry had repulsed the biggest force of Indians and soldiers that Governor Hamilton and his minions could muster. Settlers from all points along the river were flocking to Col. Zane's settlement. New cabins dotted the hillside; cabins and barns in all stages of construction could be seen. The sounds of hammers, the ringing stroke of the axe, and the crashing down of mighty pines or poplars were heard all day long.

Col. Zane sat oftener and longer than ever before in his favorite seat on his doorstep. On this evening he had just returned from a hard day in the fields, and sat down to rest a moment before going to supper. A few days previous Isaac Zane and Myeerah had come to the settlement. Myeerah brought a treaty of peace signed by Tarhe and the other Wyandot chieftains. The once implacable Huron was now ready to be friendly with the white people. Col. Zane and his brothers signed the treaty, and Betty, by dint of much persuasion, prevailed on Wetzel to bury the hatchet with the Hurons. So Myeerah's love, like the love of many other women, accomplished more than years of war and bloodshed.

The genial and happy smile never left Col. Zane's face, and as he saw the well-laden rafts coming down the river, and the air of liveliness and animation about the growing settlement, his smile broadened into one of pride and satisfaction. The prophecy that he had made twelve years before was fulfilled. His dream was realized. The wild, beautiful spot where he had once built a bark shack and camped half a year without seeing a white man was now the scene of a bustling settlement; and he believed he would live to see that settlement grow into a prosperous city. He did not think of the thousands of acres which would one day make him a wealthy man. He was a pioneer at heart; he had opened up that rich new country; he had conquered all obstacles, and that was enough to make him content.

"Papa, when shall I be big enough to fight bars and bufflers and Injuns?" asked Noah, stopping in his play and straddling his father's knee.

"My boy, did you not have Indians enough a short time ago?"

"But, papa, I did not get to see any. I heard the shooting and yelling. Sammy was afraid, but I wasn't. I wanted to look out of the little holes, but they locked us up in the dark room."

"If that boy ever grows up to be like Jonathan or Wetzel it will be the death of me," said the Colonel's wife, who had heard the lad's chatter.

"Don't worry, Bessie. When Noah grows to be a man the Indians will be gone."

Col. Zane heard the galloping of a horse and looking up saw Clarke coming down the road on his black thoroughbred. The Colonel rose and walked out to the hitching-block, where Clarke had reined in his fiery steed.

"Ah, Alfred. Been out for a ride?"

"Yes, I have been giving Roger a little exercise."

"That's a magnificent animal. I never get tired watching him move. He's the best bit of horseflesh on the river. By the way, we have not seen much of you since the siege. Of course you have been busy. Getting ready to put on the harness, eh? Well, that's what we want the young men to do. Come over and see us."

"I have been trying to come. You know how it is with me—about Betty, I mean. Col. Zane, I—I love her. That's all."

"Yes, I know, Alfred, and I don't wonder at your fears. But I have always liked you, and now I guess it's about time for me to put a spoke in your wheel of fortune. If Betty cares for you—and I have a sneaking idea she does—I will give her to you."

"I have nothing. I gave up everything when I left home."

"My lad, never mind about that," said the Colonel, laying his hand on Clarke's knee. "We don't need riches. I have so often said that we need nothing out here on the border but honest hearts and strong, willing hands. These you have. That is enough for me and for my people, and as for land, why, I have enough for an army of young men. I got my land cheap. That whole island there I bought from Cornplanter. You can have that island or any tract of land along the river. Some day I shall put you at the head of my men. It will take you years to cut that road through to Maysville. Oh, I have plenty of work for you."

"Col. Zane, I cannot thank you," answered Alfred, with emotion. "I shall try to merit your friendship and esteem. Will you please tell your sister I shall come over in the morning and beg to see her alone."

"That I will, Alfred. Goodnight."

Col. Zane strode across his threshold with a happy smile on his face. He loved to joke and tease, and never lost an opportunity.

"Things seem to be working out all right. Now for some fun with Her Highness," he said to himself.

As the Colonel surveyed the pleasant home scene he felt he had nothing more to wish for. The youngsters were playing with a shaggy little pup which had already taken Tige's place in their fickle affections. His wife was crooning a lullaby as she gently rocked the cradle to and fro. A wonderful mite of humanity peacefully slumbered in that old cradle. Annie was beginning to set the table for the evening meal. Isaac lay with a contented smile on his face, fast asleep on the couch, where, only a short time before, he had been laid bleeding and almost dead. Betty was reading to Myeerah, whose eyes were rapturously bright as she leaned her head against her sister and listened to the low voice.

"Well, Betty, what do you think?" said Col. Zane, stopping before the girls.

"What do I think?" retorted Betty. "Why, I think you are very rude to interrupt me. I am reading to Myeerah her first novel."

"I have a very important message for you."

"For me? What! From whom?"

"Guess."

Betty ran through a list of most of her acquaintances, but after each name her brother shook his head.

"Oh, well, I don't care," she finally said. The color in her cheeks had heightened noticeably.

"Very well. If you do not care, I will say nothing more," said Col. Zane.

At this juncture Annie called them to supper. Later, when Col. Zane sat on the doorstep smoking, Betty came and sat beside him with her head resting against his shoulder. The Colonel smoked on in silence. Presently the dusky head moved restlessly.

"Eb, tell me the message," whispered Betty.

"Message? What message?" asked Col. Zone. "What are you talking about?"

"Do not tease—not now. Tell me." There was an undercurrent of wistfulness in Betty's voice which touched the kindhearted brother.

"Well, to-day a certain young man asked me if he could relieve me of the responsibility of looking after a certain young lady."

"Oh——"

"Wait a moment. I told him I would be delighted."

"Eb, that was unkind."

"Then he asked me to tell her he was coming over to-morrow morning to fix it up with her."

"Oh, horrible!" cried Betty. "Were those the words he used?"

"Betts, to tell the honest truth, he did not say much of anything. He just said: 'I love her,' and his eyes blazed."

192

Betty uttered a half articulate cry and ran to her room. Her heart was throbbing. What could she do? She felt that if she looked once into her lover's eyes she would have no strength. How dared she allow herself to be so weak! Yet she knew this was the end. She could deceive him no longer. For she felt a stir in her heart, stronger than all, beyond all resistance, an exquisite agony, the sweet, blind, tumultuous exultation of the woman who loves and is loved.

* * * * * * * * * * * * * * *

"Bess, what do you think?" said Col. Zane, going into the kitchen next morning, after he had returned from the pasture. "Clarke just came over and asked for Betty. I called her. She came down looking as sweet and cool as one of the lilies out by the spring. She said: 'Why, Mr. Clarke, you are almost a stranger. I am pleased to see you. Indeed, we are all very glad to know you have recovered from your severe burns.' She went on talking like that for all the world like a girl who didn't care a snap for him. And she knows as well as I do. Not only that, she has been actually breaking her heart over him all these months. How did she do it? Oh, you women beat me all hollow!"

"Would you expect Betty to fall into his arms?" asked the Colonel's worthy spouse, indignantly.

"Not exactly. But she was too cool, too friendly. Poor Alfred looked as if he hadn't slept. He was nervous and scared to death. When Betty ran up stairs I put a bug in Alfred's ear. He'll be all right now, if he follows my advice."

"Humph! What did Colonel Ebenezer Zane tell him?" asked Bessie, in disgust.

"Oh, not much. I simply told him not to lose his nerve; that a woman never meant 'no'; that she often says it only to be made say 'yes.' And I ended up with telling him if she got a little skittish, as thoroughbreds do sometimes, to try a strong arm. That was my way."

"Col. Zane, if my memory does not fail me, you were as humble and beseeching as the proudest girl could desire."

"I beseeching? Never!"

"I hope Alfred's wooing may go well. I like him very much. But I'm afraid. Betty has such a spirit that it is quite likely she will refuse him for no other reason than that he built his cabin before he asked her."

"Nonsense. He asked her long ago. Never fear, Bess, my sister will come back as meek as a lamb."

Meanwhile Betty and Alfred were strolling down the familiar path toward the river. The October air was fresh with a suspicion of frost. The clear notes of a hunter's horn came floating down from the hills. A flock of wild geese had alighted on the marshy ground at the end of the island where they kept up a continual honk! honk! The brown hills, the red forest, and the yellow fields were now at the height of their autumnal beauty. Soon the November north wind would thrash the trees bare, and bow the proud heads of the daisies and the goldenrod; but just now they flashed in the sun, and swayed back and forth in all their glory.

"I see you limp. Are you not entirely well?" Betty was saying.

"Oh, I am getting along famously, thank you," said Alfred. "This one foot was quite severely burned and is still tender."

"You have had your share of injuries. I heard my brother say you had been wounded three times within a year."

"Four times."

"Jonathan told of the axe wound; then the wound Miller gave you, and finally the burns. These make three, do they not?"

"Yes, but you see, all three could not be compared to the one you forgot to mention."

"Let us hurry past here," said Betty, hastening to change the subject. "This is where you had the dreadful fight with Miller."

"As Miller did go to meet Girty, and as he did not return to the Fort with the renegade, we must believe he is dead. Of course, we do not know this to be actually a fact. But something makes me think so. Jonathan and Wetzel have not said anything; I can't get any satisfaction on that score from either; but I am sure neither of them would rest until Miller was dead."

"I think you are right. But we may never know. All I can tell you is that Wetzel and Jack trailed Miller to the river, and then they both came back. I was the last to see Lewis that night before he left on Miller's trail. It isn't likely I shall forget what Lewis said and how he looked. Miller was a wicked man; yes, a traitor."

"He was a bad man, and he nearly succeeded in every one of his plans. I have not the slightest doubt that had he refrained from taking part in the shooting match he would have succeeded in abducting you, in killing me, and in leading Girty here long before he was expected."

"There are many things that may never be explained, but one thing Miller did always mystify us. How did he succeed in binding Tige?"

"To my way of thinking that was not so difficult as climbing into my room and almost killing me, or stealing the powder from Capt. Boggs' room."

"The last, at least, gave me a chance to help," said Betty, with a touch of her odd roguishness.

"That was the grandest thing a woman ever did," said Alfred, in a low tone.

"Oh, no, I only ran fast."

"I would have given the world to have seen you, but I was lying on the bench wishing I were dead. I did not have strength to look out of a porthole. Oh! that horrible time! I can never forget it. I lie awake at night and hear the yelling and shooting. Then I dream of running over the burning roofs and it all comes back so vividly I can almost feel the flames and smell the burnt wood. Then I wake up and think of that awful moment when you were carried into the blockhouse white, and, as I thought, dead."

"But I wasn't. And I think it best for us to forget that horrible siege. It is past. It is a miracle that any one was spared. Ebenezer says we should not grieve for those who are gone; they were heroic; they saved the Fort. He says too, that we shall never again be troubled by Indians. Therefore let us forget and be happy. I have forgotten Miller. You can afford to do the same."

"Yes, I forgive him." Then, after a long silence, Alfred continued, "Will you go down to the old sycamore?"

Down the winding path they went. Coming to a steep place in the rocky bank Alfred jumped down and then turned to help Betty. But she avoided his gaze, pretended to not see his outstretched hands, and leaped lightly down beside him. He looked at her with perplexity and anxiety in his eyes. Before he could speak she ran on ahead of him and climbed down the bank to the pool. He followed slowly, thoughtfully. The supreme moment had come. He knew it, and somehow he did not feel the confidence the Colonel had inspired in him. It had been easy for him to think of subduing this imperious young lady; but when the time came to assert his will he found he could not remember what he had intended to say, and his feelings were divided between his love for her and the horrible fear that he should lose her.

When he reached the sycamore tree he found her sitting behind it with a cluster of yellow daisies in her lap. Alfred gazed at her, conscious that all his hopes of happiness were dependent on the next few words that would issue from her smiling lips. The little brown hands, which were now rather nervously arranging the flowers, held more than his life.

"Are they not sweet?" asked Betty, giving him a fleeting glance. "We call them 'black-eyed Susans.' Could anything be lovelier than that soft, dark brown?"

"Yes," answered Alfred, looking into her eyes.

"But—but you are not looking at my daisies at all," said Betty, lowering her eyes.

"No, I am not," said Alfred. Then suddenly: "A year ago this very day we were here."

"Here? Oh, yes, I believe I do remember. It was the day we came in my canoe and had such fine fishing."

"Is that all you remember?"

"I can recollect nothing in particular. It was so long ago."

"I suppose you will say you had no idea why I wanted you to come to this spot in particular."

"I supposed you simply wanted to take a walk, and it is very pleasant here."

"Then Col. Zane did not tell you?" demanded Alfred. Receiving no reply he went on.

"Did you read my letter?"

"What letter?"

"The letter old Sam should have given you last fall. Did you read it?"

"Yes," answered Betty, faintly.

"Did your brother tell you I wanted to see you this morning?"

"Yes, he told me, and it made me very angry," said Betty, raising her head. There was a bright red spot in each cheek. "You—you seemed to think you—that I—well—I did not like it."

"I think I understand; but you are entirely wrong. I have never thought you cared for me. My wildest dreams never left me any confidence. Col. Zane and Wetzel both had some deluded notion that you cared—"

"But they had no right to say that or to think it," said Betty, passionately. She sprang to her feet, scattering the daisies over the grass. "For them to presume that I cared for you is absurd. I never gave them any reason to think so, for—for I—I don't."

"Very well, then, there is nothing more to be said," answered Alfred, in a voice that was calm and slightly cold. "I'm sorry if you have been annoyed. I have been mad, of course, but I promise you that you need fear no further annoyance from me. Come, I think we should return to the house."

And he turned and walked slowly up the path. He had taken perhaps a dozen steps when she called him.

"Mr. Clarke, come back."

Alfred retraced his steps and stood before her again. Then he saw a different Betty. The haughty poise had disappeared. Her head was bowed. Her little hands were tightly pressed over a throbbing bosom.

"Well," said Alfred, after a moment.

"Why—why are you in such a hurry to go?"

"I have learned what I wanted to know. And after that I do not imagine I would be very agreeable. I am going back. Are you coming?"

"I did not mean quite what I said," whispered Betty.

"Then what did you mean?" asked Alfred, in a stern voice.

"I don't know. Please don't speak so."

"Betty, forgive my harshness. Can you expect a man to feel as I do and remain calm? You know I love you. You must not trifle any longer. You must not fight any longer."

"But I can't help fighting."

"Look at me," said Alfred, taking her hands. "Let me see your eyes. I believe you care a little for me, or else you wouldn't have called me back. I love you. Can you understand that?"

"Yes, I can; and I think you should love me a great deal to make up for what you made me suffer."

"Betty, look at me."

Slowly she raised her head and lifted the downcast eyes. Those telltale traitors no longer hid her secret. With a glad cry Alfred caught her in his arms. She tried to hide her face, but he got his hand under her chin and held it firmly so that the sweet crimson lips were very near his own. Then he slowly bent his head.

Betty saw his intention, closed her eyes and whispered.

"Alfred, please don't—it's not fair—I beg of you—Oh!"

That kiss was Betty's undoing. She uttered a strange little cry. Then her dark head found a hiding place over his heart, and her slender form, which a moment before had resisted so fiercely, sank yielding into his embrace.

"Betty, do you dare tell me now that you do not care for me?" Alfred whispered into the dusky hair which rippled over his breast.

Betty was brave even in her surrender. Her hands moved slowly upward along his arms, slipped over his shoulders, and clasped round his neck. Then she lifted a flushed and tearstained face with tremulous lips and wonderful shining eyes.

"Alfred, I do love you—with my whole heart I love you. I never knew until now."

The hours flew apace. The prolonged ringing of the dinner bell brought the lovers back to earth, and to the realization that the world held others than themselves. Slowly they climbed the familiar path, but this time as never before. They walked hand in hand. From the blur they looked back. They wanted to make sure they were not dreaming. The water rushed over the fall more musically than ever before; the white patches of foam floated round and round the shady pool; the leaves of the sycamore rustled cheerily in the breeze. On a dead branch a wood-pecker hammered industriously.

"Before we get out of sight of that dear old tree I want to make a confession," said Betty, as she stood before Alfred. She was pulling at the fringe on his hunting-coat.

"You need not make confessions to me."

"But this was dreadful; it preys on my conscience."

"Very well, I will be your judge. Your punishment shall be slight."

"One day when you were lying unconscious from your wound, Bessie sent me to watch you. I nursed you for hours; and—and—do not think badly of me—I—I kissed you."

"My darling," cried the enraptured young man.

When they at last reached the house they found Col. Zane on the doorstep.

"Where on earth have you been?" he said. "Wetzel was here. He said he would not wait to see you. There he goes up the hill. He is behind that laurel."

They looked and presently saw the tall figure of the hunter emerge from the bushes. He stopped and leaned on his rifle. For a minute he remained motionless. Then he waved his hand and plunged into the thicket. Betty sighed and Alfred said:

"Poor Wetzel! ever restless, ever roaming."

"Hello, there!" exclaimed a gay voice. The lovers turned to see the smiling face of Isaac, and over his shoulder Myeerah's happy face beaming on them. "Alfred, you are a lucky dog. You can thank Myeerah and me for this; because if I had not taken to the river and nearly drowned myself to give you that opportunity you would not wear that happy face to-day. Blush away, Betts, it becomes you mightily."

"Bessie, here they are!" cried Col. Zane, in his hearty voice. "She is tamed at last. No excuses, Alfred, in to dinner you go."

Col. Zane pushed the young people up the steps before him, and stopping on the threshold while he knocked the ashes from his pipe, he smiled contentedly.

AFTERWORD.

Betty lived all her after life on the scene of her famous exploit. She became a happy wife and mother. When she grew to be an old lady, with her grandchildren about her knee, she delighted to tell them that when a girl she had run the gauntlet of the Indians.

Col. Zane became the friend of all redmen. He maintained a trading-post for many years, and his dealings were ever kind and honorable. After the country got settled he received from time to time various marks of distinction from the State, Colonial, and National governments. His most noted achievement was completed about 1796. President Washington, desiring to open a National road from Fort Henry to Maysville, Kentucky, paid a great tribute to Col. Zane's ability by employing him to undertake the arduous task. His brother Jonathan and the Indian guide, Tomepomehala, rendered valuable aid in blazing out the path through the wilderness. This road, famous for many years as Zane's Trace, opened the beautiful Ohio valley to the ambitious pioneer. For this service Congress granted Col. Zane the privilege of locating military warrants upon three sections of land, each a square mile in extent, which property the government eventually presented to him. Col. Zane was the founder of Wheeling, Zanesville, Martin's Ferry, and Bridgeport. He died in 1811.

Isaac Zane received from the government a patent of ten thousand acres of land on Mad river. He established his home in the center of this tract, where he lived with the Wyandot until his death. A white settlement sprang up, prospered, and grew, and today it is the thriving city of Zanesfield.

Jonathan Zane settled down after peace was declared with the Indians, found himself a wife, and eventually became an influential citizen. However, he never lost his love for the wild woods. At times he would take down the old rifle and disappear for two or three days. He always returned cheerful and happy from these lonely hunts.

Wetzel alone did not take kindly to the march of civilization; but then he was a hunter, not a pioneer. He kept his word of peace with his old enemies, the Hurons, though he never abandoned his wandering and vengeful quests after the Delawares.

As the years passed Wetzel grew more silent and taciturn. From time to time he visited Ft. Henry, and on these visits he spent hours playing with Betty's children. But he was restless in the settlement, and his sojourns grew briefer and more infrequent as time rolled on. True to his conviction that no wife existed on earth for him, he never married. His home was the trackless wilds, where he was true to his calling—a foe to the redman.

Wonderful to relate his long, black hair never adorned the walls of an Indian's lodge, where a warrior might point with grim pride and say: "No more does the Deathwind blow over the hills and vales." We could tell of how his keen eye once again saw Wingenund over the sights of his fatal rifle, and how he was once again a prisoner in the camp of that lifelong foe, but that's another story, which, perhaps, we may tell some day.

To-day the beautiful city of Wheeling rises on the banks of the Ohio, where the yells of the Indians once blanched the cheeks of the pioneers. The broad, winding river rolls on as of yore; it alone remains unchanged. What were Indians and pioneers, forts and cities to it? Eons of time before human beings lived it flowed slowly toward the sea, and ages after men and their works are dust, it will roll on placidly with its eternal scheme of nature.

Upon the island still stand noble beeches, oaks, and chestnuts—trees that long ago have covered up their bullet-scars, but they could tell, had they the power to speak, many a wild thrilling tale. Beautiful parks and stately mansions grace the island; and polished equipages roll over the ground that once knew naught save the soft tread of the deer and the moccasin.

McColloch's Rock still juts boldly out over the river as deep and rugged as when the brave Major leaped to everlasting fame. Wetzel's Cave, so named to this day, remains on the side of the bluff overlooking the creek. The grapevines and wild rose-bushes still cluster round the cavern-entrance, where, long ago, the wily savage was wont to lie in wait for the settler, lured there by the false turkey-call. The boys visit the cave on Saturday afternoons and play "Injuns."

Not long since the writer spent a quiet afternoon there, listening to the musical flow of the brook, and dreaming of those who had lived and loved, fought and died by that stream one hundred and twenty years ago. The city with its long blocks of buildings, its spires and bridges, faded away, leaving the scene as it was in the days of Fort Henry—unobscured by smoke, the river undotted by pulling boats, and everywhere the green and verdant forest.

Nothing was wanting in that dream picture: Betty tearing along on her pony; the pioneer plowing in the field; the stealthy approach of the savage; Wetzel and Jonathan watching the river; the deer browsing with the cows in the pasture, and the old fort, grim and menacing on the bluff—all were there as natural as in those times which tried men's souls.

And as the writer awoke to the realities of life, that his dreams were of long ago, he was saddened by the thought that the labor of the pioneer is ended; his faithful, heroic wife's work is done. That beautiful country, which their sacrifices made ours, will ever be a monument to them.

Sad, too, is the thought that the poor Indian is unmourned. He is almost forgotten; he is in the shadow; his songs are sung; no more will he sing to his dusky bride: his deeds are done; no more will he boast of his all-conquering arm or of his speed like the Northwind; no more will his heart bound at the whistle of the stag, for he sleeps in the shade of the oaks, under the moss and the ferns.

The Spirit of the Border

A Romance of the Early Settlers in the Ohio Valley

To my brother

With many fond recollections of days spent in the solitude of the forests where only can be satisfied that wild fever of freedom of which this book tells; where to hear the whirr of a wild duck in his rapid flight is joy; where the quiet of an autumn afternoon swells the heart, and where one may watch the fragrant wood-smoke curl from the campfire, and see the stars peep over dark, wooded hills as twilight deepens, and know a happiness that dwells in the wilderness alone.

Introduction

The author does not intend to apologize for what many readers may call the "brutality" of the story; but rather to explain that its wild spirit is true to the life of the Western border as it was known only a little more than one hundred years ago.

The writer is the fortunate possessor of historical material of undoubted truth and interest. It is the long-lost journal of Colonel Ebenezer Zane, one of the most prominent of the hunter-pioneer, who labored in the settlement of the Western country.

The story of that tragic period deserves a higher place in historical literature than it has thus far been given, and this unquestionably because of a lack of authentic data regarding the conquering of the wilderness. Considering how many years the pioneers struggled on the border of this country, the history of their efforts is meager and obscure.

If the years at the close of the eighteenth and the beginning of the nineteenth century were full of stirring adventure on the part of the colonists along the Atlantic coast, how crowded must they have been for the almost forgotten pioneers who daringly invaded the trackless wilds! None there was to chronicle the fight of these sturdy, travelers toward the setting sun. The story of their stormy lives, of their heroism, and of their sacrifice for the benefit of future generations is too little known.

It is to a better understanding of those days that the author has labored to draw from his ancestor's notes a new and striking portrayal of the frontier; one which shall paint the fever of freedom, that powerful impulse which lured so many to unmarked graves; one which shall show his work, his love, the effect of the causes which rendered his life so hard, and surely one which does not forget the wronged Indian.

The frontier in 1777 produced white men so savage as to be men in name only. These outcasts and renegades lived among the savages, and during thirty years harassed the border, perpetrating all manner of fiendish cruelties upon the settlers. They were no less cruel to the redmen whom they ruled, and at the height of their bloody careers made futile the Moravian missionaries' long labors, and destroyed the beautiful hamlet of the Christian Indians, called Gnaddenhutten, or Village of Peace.

And while the border produced such outlaws so did it produce hunters

Eke Boone, the Zanes, the McCollochs, and Wetzel, that strange, silent man whose deeds are still whispered in the country where he once roamed in his insatiate pursuit of savages and renegades, and who was purely a product of the times. Civilization could not have brought forth a man like Wetzel. Great revolutions, great crises, great moments come, and produce the men to deal with them.

The border needed Wetzel. The settlers would have needed many more years in which to make permanent homes had it not been for him. He was never a pioneer; but always a hunter after Indians. When not on the track of the savage foe, he was in the settlement, with his keen eye and ear ever alert for signs of the enemy. To the superstitious Indians he was a shadow; a spirit of the border, which breathed menace from the dark forests. To the settlers he was the right arm of defense, a fitting leader for those few implacable and unerring frontiersmen who made the settlement of the West a possibility.

And if this story of one of his relentless pursuits shows the man as he truly was, loved by pioneers, respected and feared by redmen, and hated by renegades; if it softens a little the ruthless name history accords him, the writer will have been well repaid.

Z. G.

CHAPTER I.

"Nell, I'm growing powerful fond of you."

"So you must be, Master Joe, if often telling makes it true."

The girl spoke simply, and with an absence of that roguishness which was characteristic of her. Playful words, arch smiles, and a touch of coquetry had seemed natural to Nell; but now her grave tone and her almost wistful glance disconcerted Joe.

During all the long journey over the mountains she had been gay and bright, while now, when they were about to part, perhaps never to meet again, she showed him the deeper and more earnest side of her character. It checked his boldness as nothing else had done. Suddenly there came to him the real meaning of a woman's love when she bestows it without reservation. Silenced by the thought that he had not understood her at all, and the knowledge that he had been half in sport, he gazed out over the wild country before them.

The scene impressed its quietness upon the young couple and brought more forcibly to their minds the fact that they were at the gateway of the unknown West; that somewhere beyond this rude frontier settlement, out there in those unbroken forests stretching dark and silent before them, was to be their future home.

From the high bank where they stood the land sloped and narrowed gradually until it ended in a sharp point which marked the last bit of land between the Allegheny and Monongahela rivers. Here these swift streams merged and formed the broad Ohio. The new-born river, even here at its beginning proud and swelling as if already certain of its far-away grandeur, swept majestically round a wide curve and apparently lost itself in the forest foliage.

On the narrow point of land commanding a view of the rivers stood a long, low structure enclosed by a stockade fence, on the four corners of which were little box-shaped houses that bulged out as if trying to see what was going on beneath. The massive timbers used in the construction of this fort, the square, compact form, and the small, dark holes cut into the walls, gave the structure a threatening, impregnable aspect.

Below Nell and Joe, on the bank, were many log cabins. The yellow clay which filled the chinks between the logs gave these a peculiar striped appearance. There was life and bustle in the vicinity of these dwellings, in sharp contrast with the still grandeur of the neighboring forests. There were canvas-covered wagons around which curly-headed youngsters were playing. Several horses were grazing on the short grass, and six red and white oxen munched at the hay that had been thrown to them. The smoke of many fires curled upward, and near the blaze hovered ruddy-faced women who stirred the contents of steaming kettles. One man swung an axe with a vigorous sweep, and the clean, sharp strokes rang on the air; another hammered stakes into the ground on which to hang a kettle. Before a large cabin a fur-trader was exhibiting his wares to three Indians. A second redskin was carrying a pack of pelts from a canoe drawn up on the river bank. A small group of persons stood near; some were indifferent, and others gazed curiously at the savages. Two children peeped from behind their mother's skirts as if half-curious, half-frightened.

From this scene, the significance of which had just dawned on him, Joe turned his eyes again to his companion. It was a sweet face he saw; one that was sedate, but had a promise of innumerable smiles. The blue eyes could not long hide flashes of merriment. The girl turned, and the two young people looked at each other. Her eyes softened with a woman's gentleness as they rested upon him, for, broad of shoulder, and lithe and strong as a deer stalker, he was good to look at.

"Listen," she said. "We have known each other only three weeks. Since you joined our wagon-train, and have been so kind to me and so helpful to make that long, rough ride endurable, you have won my regard. I—I cannot say more, even if I would. You told me you ran away from your Virginian home to seek adventure on the frontier, and that you knew no one in all this wild country. You even said you could not, or would not, work at farming. Perhaps my sister and I are as unfitted as you for this life; but we must cling to our uncle because he is the only relative we have. He has come out here to join the Moravians, and to preach the gospel to these Indians. We shall share his life, and help him all we can. You have been telling me you—you cared for me, and now that we are about to part I—I don't know what to say to you—unless it is: Give up this intention of yours to seek adventure, and come with us. It seems to me you need not hunt for excitement here; it will come unsought."

"I wish I were Jim," said he, suddenly.

"Who is Jim?"

"My brother."

"Tell me of him."

"There's nothing much to tell. He and I are all that are left of our people, as are you and Kate of yours. Jim's a preacher, and the best fellow—oh! I cared a lot for Jim."

"Then, why did you leave him?"

"I was tired of Williamsburg—I quarreled with a fellow, and hurt him. Besides, I wanted to see the West; I'd like to hunt deer and bear and fight Indians. Oh, I'm not much good."

"Was Jim the only one you cared for?" asked Nell, smiling. She was surprised to find him grave.

"Yes, except my horse and dog, and I had to leave them behind," answered Joe, bowing his head a little.

"You'd like to be Jim because he's a preacher, and could help uncle convert the Indians?"

"Yes, partly that, but mostly because—somehow—something you've said or done has made me care for you in a different way, and I'd like to be worthy of you."

"I don't think I can believe it, when you say you are 'no good,'" she replied.

"Nell," he cried, and suddenly grasped her hand.

She wrenched herself free, and leaped away from him. Her face was bright now, and the promise of smiles was made good.

"Behave yourself, sir." She tossed her head with a familiar backward motion to throw the chestnut hair from her face, and looked at him with eyes veiled slightly under their lashes. "You will go with Kate and me?"

Before he could answer, a cry from some one on the plain below attracted their attention. They turned and saw another wagon-train pulling into the settlement. The children were shooting and running alongside the weary oxen; men and women went forward expectantly.

"That must be the train uncle expected. Let us go down," said Nell.

Joe did not answer; but followed her down the path. When they gained a clump of willows near the cabins he bent forward and took her hand. She saw the reckless gleam in his eyes.

"Don't. They'll see," she whispered.

"If that's the only reason you have, I reckon I don't care," said Joe.

"What do you mean? I didn't say—I didn't tell—oh! let me go!" implored Nell.

She tried to release the hand Joe had grasped in his broad palm, but in vain; the more she struggled the firmer was his hold. A frown wrinkled her brow and her eyes sparkled with spirit. She saw the fur-trader's wife looking out of the window, and remembered laughing and telling the good woman she did not like this young man; it was, perhaps, because she feared those sharp eyes that she resented his audacity. She opened her mouth to rebuke him; but no words came. Joe had bent his head and softly closed her lips with his own.

For the single instant during which Nell stood transfixed, as if with surprise, and looking up at Joe, she was dumb. Usually the girl was ready with sharp or saucy words and impulsive in her movements; but now the bewilderment of being kissed, particularly within view of the trader's wife, confused her. Then she heard voices, and as Joe turned away with a smile on his face, the unusual warmth in her heart was followed by an angry throbbing.

Joe's tall figure stood out distinctly as he leisurely strolled toward the incoming wagon-train without looking backward. Flashing after him a glance that boded wordy trouble in the future, she ran into the cabin.

As she entered the door it seemed certain the grizzled frontiersman sitting on the bench outside had grinned knowingly at her, and winked as if to say he would keep her secret. Mrs. Wentz, the fur-trader's wife, was seated by the open window which faced the fort; she was a large woman, strong of feature, and with that calm placidity of expression common to people who have lived long in sparsely populated districts. Nell glanced furtively at her and thought she detected the shadow of a smile in the gray eyes.

"I saw you and your sweetheart makin' love behind the willow," Mrs. Wentz said in a matter-of-fact voice. "I don't see why you need hide to do it. We folks out here like to see the young people sparkin'. Your young man is a fine-appearin' chap. I felt certain you was sweethearts, for all you allowed you'd known him only a few days. Lize Davis said she saw he was sweet on you. I like his face. Jake, my man, says as how he'll make a good husband for you, and he'll take to the frontier like a duck does to water. I'm sorry you'll not tarry here awhile. We don't see many lasses, especially any as pretty as you, and you'll find it more quiet and lonesome the farther West you get. Jake knows all about Fort Henry, and Jeff Lynn, the hunter outside, he knows Eb and Jack Zane, and Wetzel, and all those Fort Henry men. You'll be gettin' married out there, won't you?"

"You are—quite wrong," said Nell, who all the while Mrs. Wentz was speaking grew rosier and rosier. "We're not anything——"

Then Nell hesitated and finally ceased speaking. She saw that denials or explanations were futile; the simple woman had seen the kiss, and formed her own conclusions. During the few days Nell had spent at Fort Pitt, she had come to understand that the dwellers on the frontier took everything as a matter of course. She had seen them manifest a certain pleasure; but neither surprise, concern, nor any of the quick impulses so common among other people. And this was another lesson Nell took to heart. She realized that she was entering upon a life absolutely different from her former one, and the thought caused her to shrink from the ordeal. Yet all the suggestions regarding her future home; the stories told about Indians, renegades, and of the wild border-life, fascinated her. These people who had settled in this wild region were simple, honest and brave; they accepted what came as facts not to be questioned, and believed what looked true. Evidently the fur-trader's wife and her female neighbors had settled in their minds the relation in which the girl stood to Joe.

This latter reflection heightened Nell's resentment toward her lover. She stood with her face turned away from Mrs. Wentz; the little frown deepened, and she nervously tapped her foot on the floor.

"Where is my sister?" she presently asked.

"She went to see the wagon-train come in. Everybody's out there."

Nell deliberated a moment and then went into the open air. She saw a number of canvas-covered wagons drawn up in front of the cabins; the vehicles were dusty and the wheels encrusted with yellow mud. The grizzled frontiersman who had smiled at Nell stood leaning on his gun, talking to three men, whose travel-stained and worn homespun clothes suggested a long and toilsome journey. There was the bustle of excitement incident to the arrival of strangers; to the quick exchange of greetings, the unloading of wagons and unharnessing of horses and oxen.

Nell looked here and there for her sister. Finally she saw her standing near her uncle while he conversed with one of the teamsters. The girl did not approach them; but glanced quickly around in search of some one else. At length she saw Joe unloading goods from one of the wagons; his back was turned toward her, but she at once recognized the challenge conveyed by the broad shoulders. She saw no other person; gave heed to nothing save what was to her, righteous indignation.

Hearing her footsteps, the young man turned, glancing at her admiringly, said:

"Good evening, Miss."

Nell had not expected such a matter-of-fact greeting from Joe. There was not the slightest trace of repentance in his calm face, and he placidly continued his labor.

"Aren't you sorry you—you treated me so?" burst out Nell.

His coolness was exasperating. Instead of the contrition and apology she had expected, and which was her due, he evidently intended to tease her, as he had done so often.

The young man dropped a blanket and stared.

"I don't understand," he said, gravely. "I never saw you before."

This was too much for quick-tempered Nell. She had had some vague idea of forgiving him, after he had sued sufficiently for pardon; but now, forgetting her good intentions in the belief that he was making sport of her when he should have pleaded for forgiveness, she swiftly raised her hand and slapped him smartly.

The red blood flamed to the young man's face; as he staggered backward with his hand to his cheek, she heard a smothered exclamation behind her, and then the quick, joyous barking of a dog.

When Nell turned she was amazed to see Joe standing beside the wagon, while a big white dog was leaping upon him. Suddenly she felt faint.

Bewildered, she looked from Joe to the man she had just struck; but could not say which was the man who professed to love her.

"Jim! So you followed me!" cried Joe, starting forward and flinging his arms around the other.

"Yes, Joe, and right glad I am to find you," answered the young man, while a peculiar expression of pleasure came over his face.

"It's good to see you again! And here's my old dog Mose! But how on earth did you know? Where did you strike my trail? What are you going to do out here on the frontier? Tell me all. What happened after I left——"

Then Joe saw Nell standing nearby, pale and distressed, and he felt something was amiss. He glanced quickly from her to his brother; she seemed to be dazed, and Jim looked grave.

"What the deuce——? Nell, this is my brother Jim, the one I told you about. Jim, this is my friend, Miss Wells."

"I am happy to meet Miss Wells," said Jim, with a smile, "even though she did slap my face for nothing."

"Slapped you? What for?" Then the truth dawned on Joe, and he laughed until the tears came into his eyes. "She took you for me! Ha, ha, ha! Oh, this is great!"

Nell's face was now rosy red and moisture glistened in her eyes; but she tried bravely to stand her ground. Humiliation had taken the place of anger.

"I—I—am sorry, Mr. Downs. I did take you for him. He—he has insulted me." Then she turned and ran into the cabin.

CHAPTER II.

Joe and Jim were singularly alike. They were nearly the same size, very tall, but so heavily built as to appear of medium height, while their grey eyes and, indeed, every feature of their clean-cut faces corresponded so exactly as to proclaim them brothers.

"Already up to your old tricks?" asked Jim, with his hand on Joe's shoulder, as they both watched Nell's flight.

"I'm really fond of her, Jim, and didn't mean to hurt her feelings. But tell me about yourself; what made you come West?"

"To teach the Indians, and I was, no doubt, strongly influenced by your being here."

"You're going to do as you ever have—make some sacrifice. You are always devoting yourself; if not to me, to some other. Now it's your life you're giving up. To try to convert the redskins and influence me for good is in both cases impossible. How often have I said there wasn't any good in me! My desire is to kill Indians, not preach to them, Jim. I'm glad to see you; but I wish you hadn't come. This wild frontier is no place for a preacher."

"I think it is," said Jim, quietly.

"What of Rose—the girl you were to marry?"

Joe glanced quickly at his brother. Jim's face paled slightly as he turned away.

"I'll speak once more of her, and then, never again," he answered. "You knew Rose better than I did. Once you tried to tell me she was too fond of admiration, and I rebuked you; but now I see that your wider experience of women had taught you things I could not then understand. She was untrue. When you left Williamsburg, apparently because you had gambled with Jewett and afterward fought him, I was not misled. You made the game of cards a pretense; you sought it simply as an opportunity to wreak your vengeance on him for his villainy toward me. Well, it's all over now. Though you cruelly beat and left him disfigured for life, he will live, and you are saved from murder, thank God! When I learned of your departure I yearned to follow. Then I met a preacher who spoke of having intended to go West with a Mr. Wells, of the Moravian Mission. I immediately said I would go in his place, and here I am. I'm fortunate in that I have found both him and you."

"I'm sorry I didn't kill Jewett; I certainly meant to. Anyway, there's some comfort in knowing I left my mark on him. He was a sneaking, cold-blooded fellow, with his white hair and pale face, and always fawning round the girls. I hated him, and gave it to him good." Joe spoke musingly and complacently as though it was a trivial thing to compass the killing of a man.

"Well, Jim, you're here now, and there's no help for it. We'll go along with this Moravian preacher and his nieces. If you haven't any great regrets for the past, why, all may be well yet. I can see that the border is the place for me. But now, Jim, for once your life take a word of advice from me. We're out on the frontier, where every man looks after himself. Your being a minister won't protect you here where every man wears a knife and a tomahawk, and where most of them are desperadoes. Cut out that soft voice and most of your gentle ways, and be a little more like your brother. Be as kind as you like, and preach all you want to; but when some of these buckskin-legged frontiermen try to walk all over you, as they will, take your own part in a way you have never taken it before. I had my lesson the first few days out with that wagon-train. It was a case of four fights; but I'm all right now."

"Joe, I won't run, if that's what you mean," answered Jim, with a laugh. "Yes, I understand that a new life begins here, and I am content. If I can find my work in it, and remain with you, I shall be happy."

"Ah! old Mose! I'm glad to see you," Joe cried to the big dog who came nosing round him. "You've brought this old fellow; did you bring the horses?"

"Look behind the wagon."

With the dog bounding before him, Joe did as he was directed, and there found two horses tethered side by side. Little wonder that his eyes gleamed with delight. One was jet-black; the other iron-gray and in every line the clean-limbed animals showed the thoroughbred. The black threw up his slim head and whinnied, with affection clearly shining in his soft, dark eyes as he recognized his master.

"Lance, old fellow, how did I ever leave you!" murmured Joe, as he threw his arm over the arched neck. Mose stood by looking up, and wagging his tail in token of happiness at the reunion of the three old friends. There were tears in Joe's eyes when, with a last affectionate caress, he turned away from his pet.

"Come, Jim, I'll take you to Mr. Wells."

They stated across the little square, while Mose went back under the wagon; but at a word from Joe he bounded after them, trotting contentedly at their heels. Half way to the cabins a big, raw-boned teamster, singing in a drunken voice, came staggering toward them. Evidently he had just left the group of people who had gathered near the Indians.

"I didn't expect to see drunkenness out here," said Jim, in a low tone.

"There's lots of it. I saw that fellow yesterday when he couldn't walk. Wentz told me he was a bad customer."

The teamster, his red face bathed in perspiration, and his sleeves rolled up, showing brown, knotty arms, lurched toward them. As they met he aimed a kick at the dog; but Mose leaped nimbly aside, avoiding the heavy boot. He did not growl, nor show his teeth; but the great white head sank forward a little, and the lithe body crouched for a spring.

"Don't touch that dog; he'll tear your leg off!" Joe cried sharply.

"Say, pard, cum an' hev' a drink," replied the teamster, with a friendly leer.

"I don't drink," answered Joe, curtly, and moved on.

The teamster growled something of which only the word "parson" was intelligible to the brothers. Joe stopped and looked back. His gray eyes seemed to contract; they did not flash, but shaded and lost their warmth. Jim saw the change, and, knowing what it signified, took Joe's arm as he gently urged him away. The teamster's shrill voice could be heard until they entered the fur-trader's cabin.

An old man with long, white hair flowing from beneath his wide-brimmed hat, sat near the door holding one of Mrs. Wentz's children on his knee. His face was deep-lined and serious; but kindness shone from his mild blue eyes.

"Mr. Wells, this is my brother James. He is a preacher, and has come in place of the man you expected from Williamsburg."

The old minister arose, and extended his hand, gazing earnestly at the new-comer meanwhile. Evidently he approved of what he saw in his quick scrutiny of the other's face, for his lips were wreathed with a smile of welcome.

"Mr. Downs, I am glad to meet you, and to know you will go with me. I thank God I shall take into the wilderness one who is young enough to carry on the work when my days are done."

"I will make it my duty to help you in whatsoever way lies in my power," answered Jim, earnestly.

"We have a great work before us. I have heard many scoffers who claim that it is worse than folly to try to teach these fierce savages Christianity; but I know it can be done, and my heart is in the work. I have no fear; yet I would not conceal from you, young man, that the danger of going among these hostile Indians must be great."

"I will not hesitate because of that. My sympathy is with the redman. I have had an opportunity of studying Indian nature and believe the race inherently noble. He has been driven to make war, and I want to help him into other paths."

Joe left the two ministers talking earnestly and turned toward Mrs. Wentz. The fur-trader's wife was glowing with pleasure. She held in her hand several rude trinkets, and was explaining to her listener, a young woman, that the toys were for the children, having been brought all the way from Williamsburg.

"Kate, where's Nell?" Joe asked of the girl.

"She went on an errand for Mrs. Wentz."

Kate Wells was the opposite of her sister. Her motions were slow, easy and consistent with her large, full, form. Her brown eyes and hair contrasted sharply with Nell's. The greatest difference in the sisters lay in that Nell's face was sparkling and full of the fire of her eager young life, while Kate's was calm, like the unruffled surface of a deep lake.

"That's Jim, my brother. We're going with you," said Joe.

"Are you? I'm glad," answered the girl, looking at the handsome earnest face of the young minister.

"Your brother's like you for all the world," whispered Mrs. Wentz.

"He does look like you," said Kate, with her slow smile.

"Which means you think, or hope, that that is all," retorted Joe laughingly. "Well, Kate, there the resemblance ends, thank God for Jim!"

He spoke in a sad, bitter tone which caused both women to look at him wonderingly. Joe had to them ever been full of surprises; never until then had they seen evidences of sadness in his face. A moment's silence ensued. Mrs. Wentz gazed lovingly at the children who were playing with the trinkets; while Kate mused over the young man's remark, and began studying his, half-averted face. She felt warmly drawn to him by the strange expression in the glance he had given his brother. The tenderness in his eyes did not harmonize with much of this wild and reckless boy's behavior. To Kate he had always seemed so bold, so cold, so different from other men, and yet here was proof that Master Joe loved his brother.

The murmured conversation of the two ministers was interrupted by a low cry from outside the cabin. A loud, coarse laugh followed, and then a husky voice:

"Hol' on, my purty lass.'"

Joe took two long strides, and was on the door-step. He saw Nell struggling violently in the grasp of the half-drunken teamster.

"I'll jes' hev' to kiss this lassie fer luck," he said in a tone of good humor.

At the same instant Joe saw three loungers laughing, and a fourth, the grizzled frontiersman, starting forward with a yell.

"Let me go!" cried Nell.

Just when the teamster had pulled her close to him, and was bending his red, moist face to hers, two brown, sinewy hands grasped his neck with an angry clutch. Deprived thus of breath, his mouth opened, his tongue protruded; his eyes seemed starting from their sockets, and his arms beat the air. Then he was lifted and flung with a crash against the cabin wall. Falling, he lay in a heap on the grass, while the blood flowed from a cut on his temple.

"What's this?" cried a man, authoritatively. He had come swiftly up, and arrived at the scene where stood the grizzled frontiersman.

"It was purty handy, Wentz. I couldn't hev' did better myself, and I was comin' for that purpose," said the frontiersman. "Leffler was tryin' to kiss the lass. He's been drunk fer two days. That little girl's sweetheart kin handle himself some, now you take my word on it."

"I'll agree Leff's bad when he's drinkin'," answered the fur-trader, and to Joe he added, "He's liable to look you up when he comes around."

"Tell him if I am here when he gets sober, I'll kill him," Joe cried in a sharp voice. His gaze rested once more on the fallen teamster, and again an odd contraction of his eyes was noticeable. The glance was cutting, as if with the flash of cold gray steel. "Nell, I'm sorry I wasn't round sooner," he said, apologetically, as if it was owing to his neglect the affair had happened.

As they entered the cabin Nell stole a glance at him. This was the third time he had injured a man because of her. She had on several occasions seen that cold, steely glare in his eyes, and it had always frightened her. It was gone, however, before they were inside the building. He said something which she did not hear distinctly, and his calm voice allayed her excitement. She had been angry with him; but now she realized that her resentment had disappeared. He had spoken so kindly after the outburst. Had he not shown that he considered himself her protector and lover? A strange emotion, sweet and subtle as the taste of wine, thrilled her, while a sense of fear because of his strength was mingled with her pride in it. Any other girl would have been only too glad to have such a champion; she would, too, hereafter, for he was a man of whom to be proud.

"Look here, Nell, you haven't spoken to me," Joe cried suddenly, seeming to understand that she had not even heard what he said, so engrossed had she been with her reflections. "Are you mad with me yet?" he continued. "Why, Nell, I'm in—I love you!"

Evidently Joe thought such fact a sufficient reason for any act on his part. His tender tone conquered Nell, and she turned to him with flushed cheeks and glad eyes.

"I wasn't angry at all," she whispered, and then, eluding the arm he extended, she ran into the other room.

CHAPTER III.

Joe lounged in the doorway of the cabin, thoughtfully contemplating two quiet figures that were lying in the shade of a maple tree. One he recognized as the Indian with whom Jim had spent an earnest hour that morning; the red son of the woods was wrapped in slumber. He had placed under his head a many-hued homespun shirt which the young preacher had given him; but while asleep his head had rolled off this improvised pillow, and the bright garment lay free, attracting the eye. Certainly it had led to the train of thought which had found lodgment in Joe's fertile brain.

The other sleeper was a short, stout man whom Joe had seen several times before. This last fellow did not appear to be well-balanced in his mind, and was the butt of the settlers' jokes, while the children called him "Loorey." He, like the Indian, was sleeping off the effects of the previous night's dissipation.

During a few moments Joe regarded the recumbent figures with an expression on his face which told that he thought in them were great possibilities for sport. With one quick glance around he disappeared within the cabin, and when he showed himself at the door, surveying the village square with mirthful eyes, he held in his hand a small basket of Indian design. It was made of twisted grass, and simply contained several bits of soft, chalky stone such as the Indians used for painting, which collection Joe had discovered among the fur-trader's wares.

He glanced around once more, and saw that all those in sight were busy with their work. He gave the short man a push, and chuckled when there was no response other than a lazy grunt. Joe took the Indians' gaudy shirt, and, lifting Loorey, slipped it around him, shoved the latter's arms through the sleeves, and buttoned it in front. He streaked the round face with red and white paint, and then, dexterously extracting the eagle plume from the Indian's head-dress, stuck it in Loorey's thick shock of hair. It was all done in a moment, after which Joe replaced the basket, and went down to the river.

Several times that morning he had visited the rude wharf where Jeff Lynn, the grizzled old frontiersman, busied himself with preparations for the raft-journey down the Ohio. Lynn had been employed to guide the missionary's party to Fort Henry, and, as the brothers had acquainted him with their intention of accompanying the travelers, he had constructed a raft for them and their horses.

Joe laughed when he saw the dozen two-foot logs fastened together, upon which a rude shack had been erected for shelter. This slight protection from sun and storm was all the brothers would have on their long journey.

Joe noted, however, that the larger raft had been prepared with some thought for the comfort of the girls. The floor of the little hut was raised so that the waves which broke over the logs could not reach it. Taking a peep into the structure, Joe was pleased to see that Nell and Kate would be comfortable, even during a storm. A buffalo robe and two red blankets gave to the interior a cozy, warm look. He observed that some of the girls' luggage was already on board.

"When'll we be off?" he inquired.

"Sun-up," answered Lynn, briefly.

"I'm glad of that. I like to be on the go in the early morning," said Joe, cheerfully.

"Most folks from over Eastways ain't in a hurry to tackle the river," replied Lynn, eyeing Joe sharply.

"It's a beautiful river, and I'd like to sail on it from here to where it ends, and then come back to go again," Joe replied, warmly.

"In a hurry to be a-goin'? I'll allow you'll see some slim red devils, with feathers in their hair, slipping among the trees along the bank, and mebbe you'll hear the ping which's made when whistlin' lead hits. Perhaps you'll want to be back here by termorrer sundown."

"Not I," said Joe, with his short, cool laugh.

The old frontiersman slowly finished his task of coiling up a rope of wet cowhide, and then, producing a dirty pipe, he took a live ember from the fire and placed it on the bowl. He sucked slowly at the pipe-stem, and soon puffed out a great cloud of smoke. Sitting on a log, he deliberately surveyed the robust shoulders and long, heavy limbs of the young man, with a keen appreciation of their symmetry and strength. Agility, endurance and courage were more to a borderman than all else; a new-comer on the frontier was always "sized-up" with reference to these "points," and respected in proportion to the measure in which he possessed them.

Old Jeff Lynn, riverman, hunter, frontiersman, puffed slowly at his pipe while he mused thus to himself: "Mebbe I'm wrong in takin' a likin' to this youngster so sudden. Mebbe it's because I'm fond of his sunny-haired lass, an' ag'in mebbe it's because I'm gettin' old an' likes young folks better'n I onct did. Anyway, I'm kinder thinkin, if this young feller gits worked out, say fer about twenty pounds less, he'll lick a whole raft-load of wild-cats."

Joe walked to and fro on the logs, ascertained how the raft was put together, and took a pull on the long, clumsy steering-oar. At length he seated himself beside Lynn. He was eager to ask questions; to know about the rafts, the river, the forest, the Indians—everything in connection with this wild life; but already he had learned that questioning these frontiersmen is a sure means of closing their lips.

"Ever handle the long rifle?" asked Lynn, after a silence.

"Yes," answered Joe, simply.

"Ever shoot anythin'?" the frontiersman questioned, when he had taken four or five puffs at his pipe.

"Squirrels."

"Good practice, shootin' squirrels," observed Jeff, after another silence, long enough to allow Joe to talk if he was so inclined. "Kin ye hit one—say, a hundred yards?"

"Yes, but not every time in the head," returned Joe. There was an apologetic tone in his answer.

Another interval followed in which neither spoke. Jeff was slowly pursuing his line of thought. After Joe's last remark he returned his pipe to his pocket and brought out a tobacco-pouch. He tore off a large portion of the weed and thrust it into his mouth. Then he held out the little buckskin sack to Joe.

"Hev' a chaw," he said.

To offer tobacco to anyone was absolutely a borderman's guarantee of friendliness toward that person.

Jeff expectorated half a dozen times, each time coming a little nearer the stone he was aiming at, some five yards distant. Possibly this was the borderman's way of oiling up his conversational machinery. At all events, he commenced to talk.

"Yer brother's goin' to preach out here, ain't he? Preachin' is all right, I'll allow; but I'm kinder doubtful about preachin' to redskins. Howsumever, I've knowed Injuns who are good fellows, and there's no tellin'. What are ye goin' in fer—farmin'?"

"No, I wouldn't make a good farmer."

"Jest cum out kinder wild like, eh?" rejoined Jeff, knowingly.

"I wanted to come West because I was tired of tame life. I love the forest; I want to fish and hunt; and I think I'd like to—to see Indians."

"I kinder thought so," said the old frontiersman, nodding his head as though he perfectly understood Joe's case. "Well, lad, where you're goin' seein' Injuns ain't a matter of choice. You has to see 'em, and fight 'em, too. We've had bad times for years out here on the border, and I'm thinkin' wuss is comin'. Did ye ever hear the name Girty?"

"Yes; he's a renegade."

"He's a traitor, and Jim and George Girty, his brothers, are p'isin rattlesnake Injuns. Simon Girty's bad enough; but Jim's the wust. He's now wusser'n a full-blooded Delaware. He's all the time on the lookout to capture white wimen to take to his Injun teepee. Simon Girty and his pals, McKee and Elliott, deserted from that thar fort right afore yer eyes. They're now livin' among the redskins down Fort Henry way, raisin' as much hell fer the settlers as they kin."

"Is Fort Henry near the Indian towns?" asked Joe.

"There's Delawares, Shawnees and Hurons all along the Ohio below Fort Henry."

"Where is the Moravian Mission located?"

"Why, lad, the Village of Peace, as the Injuns call it, is right in the midst of that Injun country. I 'spect it's a matter of a hundred miles below and cross-country a little from Fort Henry."

"The fort must be an important point, is it not?"

"Wal, I guess so. It's the last place on the river," answered Lynn, with a grim smile. "There's only a stockade there, an' a handful of men. The Injuns hev swarmed down on it time and ag'in, but they hev never burned it. Only such men as Colonel Zane, his brother Jack, and Wetzel could hev kept that fort standin' all these bloody years. Eb Zane's got but a few men, yet he kin handle 'em some, an' with such scouts as Jack Zane and Wetzel, he allus knows what's goin' on among the Injuns."

"I've heard of Colonel Zane. He was an officer under Lord Dunmore. The hunters here speak often of Jack Zane and Wetzel. What are they?"

"Jack Zane is a hunter an' guide. I knowed him well a few years back. He's a quiet, mild chap; but a streak of chain-lightnin' when he's riled. Wetzel is an Injun-killer. Some people say as how he's crazy over scalp-huntin'; but I reckon that's not so. I've seen him a few times. He don't hang round the settlement 'cept when the Injuns are up, an' nobody sees him much. At home he sets round silent-like, an' then mebbe next mornin' he'll be gone, an' won't show up fer days or weeks. But all the frontier knows of his deeds. Fer instance, I've hearn of settlers gettin' up in the mornin' an' findin' a couple of dead and scalped Injuns right in front of their cabins. No one knowed who killed 'em, but everybody says 'Wetzel.' He's allus warnin' the settlers when they need to flee to the fort, and sure he's right every time, because when these men go back to their cabins they find nothin' but ashes. There couldn't be any farmin' done out there but fer Wetzel."

"What does he look like?" questioned Joe, much interested.

"Wetzel stands straight as the oak over thar. He'd hev' to go sideways to git his shoulders in that door, but he's as light of foot an' fast as a deer. An' his eyes—why, lad, ye kin hardly look into 'em. If you ever see Wetzel you'll know him to onct."

"I want to see him," Joe spoke quickly, his eyes lighting with an eager flash. "He must be a great fighter."

"Is he? Lew Wetzel is the heftiest of 'em all, an' we hev some as kin fight out here. I was down the river a few years ago and joined a party to go out an' hunt up some redskins as had been reported. Wetzel was with us. We soon struck Injun sign, and then come on to a lot of the pesky varmints. We was all fer goin' home, because we had a small force. When we started to go we finds Wetzel sittin' calm-like on a log. We said: 'Ain't ye goin' home?' and he replied, 'I cum out to find redskins, an' now as we've found 'em, I'm not goin' to run away.' An' we left him settin' thar. Oh, Wetzel is a fighter!"

"I hope I shall see him," said Joe once more, the warm light, which made him look so boyish, still glowing in his face.

"Mebbe ye'll git to; and sure ye'll see redskins, an' not tame ones, nuther."

At this moment the sound of excited voices near the cabins broke in on the conversation. Joe saw several persons run toward the large cabin and disappear behind it. He smiled as he thought perhaps the commotion had been caused by the awakening of the Indian brave.

Rising to his feet, Joe went toward the cabin, and soon saw the cause of the excitement. A small crowd of men and women, all laughing and talking, surrounded the Indian brave and the little stout fellow. Joe heard some one groan, and then a deep, guttural voice:

"Paleface—big steal—ugh! Injun mad—heap mad—kill paleface."

After elbowing his way into the group, Joe saw the Indian holding Loorey with one hand, while he poked him on the ribs with the other. The captive's face was the picture of dismay; even the streaks of paint did not hide his look of fear and bewilderment. The poor half-witted fellow was so badly frightened that he could only groan.

"Silvertip scalp paleface. Ugh!" growled the savage, giving Loorey another blow on the side. This time he bent over in pain. The bystanders were divided in feeling; the men laughed, while the women murmured sympathetically.

"This's not a bit funny," muttered Joe, as he pushed his way nearly to the middle of the crowd. Then he stretched out a long arm that, bare and brawny, looked as though it might have been a blacksmith's, and grasped the Indian's sinewy wrist with a force that made him loosen his hold on Loorey instantly.

"I stole the shirt—fun—joke," said Joe. "Scalp me if you want to scalp anyone."

The Indian looked quickly at the powerful form before him. With a twist he slipped his arm from Joe's grasp.

"Big paleface heap fun—all squaw play," he said, scornfully. There was a menace in his somber eyes as he turned abruptly and left the group.

"I'm afraid you've made an enemy," said Jake Wentz to Joe. "An Indian never forgets an insult, and that's how he regarded your joke. Silvertip has been friendly here because he sells us his pelts. He's a Shawnee chief. There he goes through the willows!"

By this time Jim and Mr. Wells, Mrs. Wentz and the girls had joined the group. They all watched Silvertip get into his canoe and paddle away.

"A bad sign," said Wentz, and then, turning to Jeff Lynn, who joined the party at that moment, he briefly explained the circumstances.

"Never did like Silver. He's a crafty redskin, an' not to be trusted," replied Jeff.

"He has turned round and is looking back," Nell said quickly.

"So he has," observed the fur-trader.

The Indian was now several hundred yards down the swift river, and for an instant had ceased paddling. The sun shone brightly on his eagle plumes. He remained motionless for a moment, and even at such a distance the dark, changeless face could be discerned. He lifted his hand and shook it menacingly.

"If ye don't hear from that redskin ag'in Jeff Lynn don't know nothin'," calmly said the old frontiersman.

CHAPTER IV.

As the rafts drifted with the current the voyagers saw the settlers on the landing-place diminish until they had faded from indistinct figures to mere black specks against the green background. Then came the last wave of a white scarf, faintly in the distance, and at length the dark outline of the fort was all that remained to their regretful gaze. Quickly that, too, disappeared behind the green hill, which, with its bold front, forces the river to take a wide turn.

The Ohio, winding in its course between high, wooded bluffs, rolled on and on into the wilderness.

Beautiful as was the ever-changing scenery, rugged gray-faced cliffs on one side contrasting with green-clad hills on the other, there hovered over land and water something more striking than beauty. Above all hung a still atmosphere of calmness—of loneliness.

And this penetrating solitude marred somewhat the pleasure which might have been found in the picturesque scenery, and caused the voyagers, to whom this country was new, to take less interest in the gaily-feathered birds and stealthy animals that were to be seen on the way. By the forms of wild life along the banks of the river, this strange intruder on their peace was regarded with attention. The birds and beasts evinced little fear of the floating rafts. The sandhill crane, stalking along the shore, lifted his long neck as the unfamiliar thing came floating by, and then stood still and silent as a statue until the rafts disappeared from view. Blue-herons feeding along the bars, saw the unusual spectacle, and, uttering surprised "booms," they spread wide wings and lumbered away along the shore. The crows circled above the voyagers, cawing in not unfriendly excitement. Smaller birds alighted on the raised poles, and several—a robin, a catbird and a little brown wren—ventured with hesitating boldness to peck at the crumbs the girls threw to them. Deer waded knee-deep in the shallow water, and, lifting their heads, instantly became motionless and absorbed. Occasionally a buffalo appeared on a level stretch of bank, and, tossing his huge head, seemed inclined to resent the coming of this stranger into his domain.

All day the rafts drifted steadily and swiftly down the river, presenting to the little party ever-varying pictures of densely wooded hills, of jutting, broken cliffs with scant evergreen growth; of long reaches of sandy bar that glistened golden in the sunlight, and over all the flight and call of wildfowl, the flitting of woodland songsters, and now and then the whistle and bellow of the horned watchers in the forest.

The intense blue of the vault above began to pale, and low down in the west a few fleecy clouds, gorgeously golden for a fleeting instant, then crimson-crowned for another, shaded and darkened as the setting sun sank behind the hills. Presently the red rays disappeared, a pink glow suffused the heavens, and at last, as gray twilight stole down over the hill-tops, the crescent moon peeped above the wooded fringe of the western bluffs.

"Hard an' fast she is," sang out Jeff Lynn, as he fastened the rope to a tree at the head of a small island. "All off now, and' we'll hev' supper. Thar's a fine spring under yon curly birch, an' I fetched along a leg of deer-meat. Hungry, little 'un?"

He had worked hard all day steering the rafts, yet Nell had seen him smiling at her many times during the journey, and he had found time before the early start to arrange for her a comfortable seat. There was now a solicitude in the frontiersman's voice that touched her.

"I am famished," she replied, with her bright smile. "I am afraid I could eat a whole deer."

They all climbed the sandy slope, and found themselves on the summit of an oval island, with a pretty glade in the middle surrounded by birches. Bill, the second raftsman, a stolid, silent man, at once swung his axe upon a log of driftwood. Mr. Wells and Jim walked to and fro under the birches, and Kate and Nell sat on the grass watching with great interest the old helmsman as he came up from the river, his brown hands and face shining from the scrubbing he had given them. Soon he had a fire cheerfully blazing, and after laying out the few utensils, he addressed himself to Joe:

"I'll tell ye right here, lad, good venison kin be spoiled by bad cuttin' and cookin'. You're slicin' it too thick. See—thar! Now salt good, an' keep outen the flame; on the red coals is best."

With a sharpened stick Jeff held the thin slices over the fire for a few moments. Then he laid them aside on some clean white-oak chips Bill's axe had provided. The simple meal of meat, bread, and afterward a drink of the cold spring water, was keenly relished by the hungry voyagers. When it had been eaten, Jeff threw a log on the fire and remarked:

"Seein' as how we won't be in redskin territory fer awhile yit, we kin hev a fire. I'll allow ye'll all be chilly and damp from river-mist afore long, so toast yerselves good."

"How far have we come to-day?" inquired Mr. Wells, his mind always intent on reaching the scene of his cherished undertaking.

"'Bout thirty-odd mile, I reckon. Not much on a trip, thet's sartin, but we'll pick up termorrer. We've some quicker water, an' the rafts hev to go separate."

"How quiet!" exclaimed Kate, suddenly breaking the silence that followed the frontiersman's answer.

"Beautiful!" impetuously said Nell, looking up at Joe. A quick flash from his gray eyes answered her; he did not speak; indeed he had said little to her since the start, but his glance showed her how glad he was that she felt the sweetness and content of this wild land.

"I was never in a wilderness before," broke in the earnest voice of the young minister. "I feel an almost overpowering sense of loneliness. I want to get near to you all; I feel lost. Yet it is grand, sublime!"

"Here is the promised land—the fruitful life—Nature as it was created by God," replied the old minister, impressively.

"Tell us a story," said Nell to the old frontiersman, as he once more joined the circle round the fire.

"So, little 'un, ye want a story?" queried Jeff, taking up a live coal and placing it in the bowl of his pipe. He took off his coon-skin cap and carefully laid it aside. His weather-beaten face beamed in answer to the girl's request. He drew a long and audible pull at his black pipe, and send forth slowly a cloud of white smoke. Deliberately poking the fire with a stick, as if stirring into life dead embers of the past, he sucked again at his pipe, and emitted a great puff of smoke that completely enveloped the grizzled head. From out that white cloud came his drawling voice.

"Ye've seen thet big curly birch over thar—thet 'un as bends kind of sorrowful like. Wal, it used to stand straight an' proud. I've knowed thet tree all the years I've navigated this river, an' it seems natural like to me thet it now droops dyin', fer it shades the grave of as young, an' sweet, an' purty a lass as yerself, Miss Nell. Rivermen called this island George's Island, 'cause Washington onct camped here; but of late years the name's got changed, an' the men say suthin' like this: 'We'll try an' make Milly's birch afore sundown,' jest as Bill and me hev done to-day. Some years agone I was comin' up from Fort Henry, an' had on board my slow old scow a lass named Milly—we never learned her other name. She come to me at the fort, an' tells as how her folks hed been killed by Injuns, an' she wanted to git back to Pitt to meet her sweetheart. I was ag'in her comin' all along, an' fust off I said 'No.' But when I seen tears in her blue eyes, an' she puts her little hand on mine, I jest wilted, an' says to Jim Blair, 'She goes.' Wal, jest as might hev been expected—an' fact is I looked fer it—we wus tackled by redskins. Somehow, Jim Girty got wind of us hevin' a lass aboard, an' he ketched up with us jest below here. It's a bad place, called Shawnee Rock, an' I'll show it to ye termorrer. The renegade, with his red devils, attacked us thar, an' we had a time gittin' away. Milly wus shot. She lived fer awhile, a couple of days, an' all the time wus so patient, an' sweet, an' brave with thet renegade's bullet in her—fer he shot her when he seen he couldn't capture her—thet thar wusn't a blame man of us who wouldn't hev died to grant her prayer, which wus that she could live to onct more see her lover."

There was a long silence, during which the old frontiersman sat gazing into the fire with sad eyes.

"We couldn't do nuthin', an' we buried her thar under thet birch, where she smiled her last sad, sweet smile, an' died. Ever since then the river has been eatn' away at this island. It's only half as big as it wus onct, an' another flood will take away this sand-bar, these few birches—an' Milly's grave."

The old frontiersman's story affected all his listeners. The elder minister bowed his head and prayed that no such fate might overtake his nieces. The young minister looked again, as he had many times that day, at Nell's winsome face. The girls cast grave glances at the drooping birch, and their bright tears glistened in the fire-glow. Once more Joe's eyes glinted with that steely flash, and as he gazed out over the wide, darkening expanse of water his face grew cold and rigid.

"I'll allow I might hev told a more cheerful story, an' I'll do so next time; but I wanted ye all, particular the lasses, to know somethin' of the kind of country ye're goin' into. The frontier needs women; but jist yit it deals hard with them. An' Jim Girty, with more of his kind, ain't dead yit."

"Why don't some one kill him?" was Joe's sharp question.

"Easier said than done, lad. Jim Girty is a white traitor, but he's a cunnin' an' fierce redskin in his ways an' life. He knows the woods as a crow does, an' keeps outer sight 'cept when he's least expected. Then ag'in, he's got Simon Girty, his brother, an' almost the whole redskin tribe behind him. Injuns stick close to a white man that has turned ag'inst his own people, an' Jim Girty hain't ever been ketched. Howsumever, I heard last trip thet he'd been tryin' some of his tricks round Fort Henry, an' thet Wetzel is on his trail. Wal, if it's so thet Lew Wetzel is arter him, I wouldn't give a pinch o' powder fer the white-redskin's chances of a long life."

No one spoke, and Jeff, after knocking the ashes from his pipe, went down to the raft, returning shortly afterward with his blanket. This he laid down and rolled himself in it. Presently from under his coon-skin cap came the words:

"Wal, I've turned in, an' I advise ye all to do the same."

All save Joe and Nell acted on Jeff's suggestion. For a long time the young couple sat close together on the bank, gazing at the moonlight on the river.

The night was perfect. A cool wind fanned the dying embers of the fire and softly stirred the leaves. Earlier in the evening a single frog had voiced his protest against the loneliness; but now his dismal croak was no longer heard. A snipe, belated in his feeding, ran along the sandy shore uttering his tweet-tweet, and his little cry, breaking in so softly on the silence, seemed only to make more deeply felt the great vast stillness of the night.

Joe's arm was around Nell. She had demurred at first, but he gave no heed to her slight resistance, and finally her head rested against his shoulder. There was no need of words.

Joe had a pleasurable sense of her nearness, and there was a delight in the fragrance of her hair as it waved against his cheek; but just then love was not uppermost in his mind. All day he had been silent under the force of an emotion which he could not analyze. Some power, some feeling in which the thought of Nell had no share, was drawing him with irresistible strength. Nell had just begun to surrender to him in the sweetness of her passion; and yet even with that knowledge knocking reproachfully at his heart, he could not help being absorbed in the shimmering water, in the dark reflection of the trees, the gloom and shadow of the forest.

Presently he felt her form relax in his arms; then her soft regular breathing told him she had fallen asleep and he laughed low to himself. How she would pout on the morrow when he teased her about it! Then, realizing that she was tired with her long day's journey, he reproached himself for keeping her from the needed rest, and instantly decided to carry her to the raft. Yet such was the novelty of the situation that he yielded to its charm, and did not go at once. The moonlight found bright threads in her wavy hair; it shone caressingly on her quiet face, and tried to steal under the downcast lashes.

Joe made a movement to rise with her, when she muttered indistinctly as if speaking to some one. He remembered then she had once told him that she talked in her sleep, and how greatly it annoyed her. He might hear something more with which to tease her; so he listened.

"Yes—uncle—I will go—Kate, we must—go. . ."

Another interval of silence, then more murmurings. He distinguished his own name, and presently she called clearly, as if answering some inward questioner.

"I—love him—yes—I love Joe—he has mastered me. Yet I wish he were—like Jim—Jim who looked at me—so—with his deep eyes—and I. . . ."

Joe lifted her as if she were a baby, and carrying her down to the raft, gently laid her by her sleeping sister.

The innocent words which he should not have heard were like a blow. What she would never have acknowledged in her waking hours had been revealed in her dreams. He recalled the glance of Jim's eyes as it had rested on Nell many times that day, and now these things were most significant.

He found at the end of the island a great, mossy stone. On this he climbed, and sat where the moonlight streamed upon him. Gradually that cold bitterness died out from his face, as it passed from his heart, and once more he became engrossed in the silver sheen on the water, the lapping of the waves on the pebbly beach, and in that speaking, mysterious silence of the woods.

* * *

When the first faint rays of red streaked over the eastern hill-tops, and the river mist arose from the water in a vapory cloud, Jeff Lynn rolled out of his blanket, stretched his long limbs, and gave a hearty call to the morning. His cheerful welcome awakened all the voyagers except Joe, who had spent the night in watching and the early morning in fishing.

"Wal, I'll be darned," ejaculated Jeff as he saw Joe. "Up afore me, an' ketched a string of fish."

"What are they?" asked Joe, holding up several bronze-backed fish.

"Bass—black bass, an' thet big feller is a lammin' hefty 'un. How'd ye ketch 'em?"

"I fished for them."

"Wal, so it 'pears," growled Jeff, once more reluctantly yielding to his admiration for the lad. "How'd ye wake up so early?"

"I stayed up all night. I saw three deer swim from the mainland, but nothing else came around."

"Try yer hand at cleanin' 'em fer breakfast," continued Jeff, beginning to busy himself with preparations for that meal. "Wal, wal, if he ain't surprisin'! He'll do somethin' out here on the frontier, sure as I'm a born sinner," he muttered to himself, wagging his head in his quaint manner.

Breakfast over, Jeff transferred the horses to the smaller raft, which he had cut loose from his own, and, giving a few directions to Bill, started down-stream with Mr. Wells and the girls.

The rafts remained close together for a while, but as the current quickened and was more skillfully taken advantage of by Jeff, the larger raft gained considerable headway, gradually widening the gap between the two.

All day they drifted. From time to time Joe and Jim waved their hands to the girls; but the greater portion of their attention was given to quieting the horses. Mose, Joe's big white dog, retired in disgust to the hut, where he watched and dozed by turns. He did not fancy this kind of voyaging. Bill strained his sturdy arms all day on the steering-oar.

About the middle of the afternoon Joe observed that the hills grew more rugged and precipitous, and the river ran faster. He kept a constant lookout for the wall of rock which marked the point of danger. When the sun had disappeared behind the hills, he saw ahead a gray rock protruding from the green foliage. It was ponderous, overhanging, and seemed to frown down on the river. This was Shawnee Rock. Joe looked long at the cliff, and wondered if there was now an Indian scout hidden behind the pines that skirted the edge. Prominent on the top of the bluff a large, dead tree projected its hoary, twisted branches.

Bill evidently saw the landmark, for he stopped in his monotonous walk to and fro across the raft, and pushing his oar amidships he looked ahead for the other raft. The figure of the tall frontiersman could be plainly seen as he labored at the helm.

The raft disappeared round a bend, and as it did so Joe saw a white scarf waved by Nell.

Bill worked the clumsy craft over toward the right shore where the current was more rapid. He pushed with all his strength, and when the oar had reached its widest sweep, he lifted it and ran back across the raft for another push. Joe scanned the river ahead. He saw no rapids; only rougher water whirling over some rocks. They were where the channel narrowed and ran close to the right-hand bank. Under a willow-flanked ledge was a sandbar. To Joe there seemed nothing hazardous in drifting through this pass.

"Bad place ahead," said Bill, observing Joe's survey of the river.

"It doesn't look so," replied Joe.

"A raft ain't a boat. We could pole a boat. You has to hev water to float logs, an' the river's run out considerable. I'm only afeerd fer the horses. If we hit or drag, they might plunge around a bit."

When the raft passed into the head of the bend it struck the rocks several times, but finally gained the channel safely, and everything seemed propitious for an easy passage.

But, greatly to Bill's surprise, the wide craft was caught directly in the channel, and swung round so that the steering-oar pointed toward the opposite shore. The water roared a foot deep over the logs.

"Hold hard on the horses!" yelled Bill. "Somethin's wrong. I never seen a snag here."

The straining mass of logs, insecurely fastened together, rolled and then pitched loose again, but the short delay had been fatal to the steering apparatus.

Joe would have found keen enjoyment in the situation, had it not been for his horse, Lance. The thoroughbred was difficult to hold. As Bill was making strenuous efforts to get in a lucky stroke of the oar, he failed to see a long length of grapevine floating like a brown snake of the water below. In the excitement they heeded not the barking of Mose. Nor did they see the grapevine straighten and become taut just as they drifted upon it; but they felt the raft strike and hold on some submerged object. It creaked and groaned and the foamy water surged, gurgling, between the logs.

Jim's mare snorted with terror, and rearing high, pulled her halter loose and plunged into the river. But Jim still held her, at risk of being drawn overboard.

"Let go! She'll drag you in!" yelled Joe, grasping him with his free hand. Lance trembled violently and strained at the rope, which his master held with a strong grip.

CRACK!

The stinging report of a rifle rang out above the splashing of the water.

Without a cry, Bill's grasp on the oar loosened; he fell over it limply, his head striking the almost submerged log. A dark-red fluid colored the water; then his body slipped over the oar and into the river, where it sank.

"My God! Shot!" cried Jim, in horrified tones.

He saw a puff of white smoke rising above the willows. Then the branches parted, revealing the dark forms of several Indian warriors. From the rifle in the foremost savage's hand a slight veil of smoke rose. With the leap of a panther the redskin sprang from the strip of sand to the raft.

"Hold, Jim! Drop that ax! We're caught!" cried Joe.

"It's that Indian from the fort!" gasped Jim.

The stalwart warrior was indeed Silvertip. But how changed! Stripped of the blanket he had worn at the settlement, now standing naked but for his buckskin breech-cloth, with his perfectly proportioned form disclosed in all its sinewy beauty, and on his swarthy, evil face an expression of savage scorn, he surely looked a warrior and a chief.

He drew his tomahawk and flashed a dark glance at Joe. For a moment he steadily regarded the young man; but if he expected to see fear in the latter's face he was mistaken, for the look was returned coolly.

"Paleface steal shirt," he said in his deep voice. "Fool paleface play—Silvertip no forget."

CHAPTER V.

Silvertip turned to his braves, and giving a brief command, sprang from the raft. The warriors closed in around the brothers; two grasping each by the arms, and the remaining Indian taking care of the horse. The captives were then led ashore, where Silvertip awaited them.

When the horse was clear of the raft, which task necessitated considerable labor on the part of the Indians, the chief seized the grapevine, that was now plainly in sight, and severed it with one blow of his tomahawk. The raft dashed forward with a lurch and drifted downstream.

In the clear water Joe could see the cunning trap which had caused the death of Bill, and insured the captivity of himself and his brother. The crafty savages had trimmed a six-inch sapling and anchored it under the water. They weighted the heavy end, leaving the other pointing upstream. To this last had been tied the grapevine. When the drifting raft reached the sapling, the Indians concealed in the willows pulled hard on the improvised rope; the end of the sapling stuck up like a hook, and the aft was caught and held. The killing of the helmsman showed the Indians' foresight; even had the raft drifted on downstream the brothers would have been helpless on a craft they could not manage. After all, Joe thought, he had not been so far wrong when he half fancied that an Indian lay behind Shawnee Rock, and he marveled at this clever trick which had so easily effected their capture.

But he had little time to look around at the scene of action. There was a moment only in which to study the river to learn if the unfortunate raftsman's body had appeared. It was not to be seen. The river ran swiftly and hid all evidence of the tragedy under its smooth surface. When the brave who had gone back to the raft for the goods joined his companion the two hurried Joe up the bank after the others.

Once upon level ground Joe saw before him an open forest. On the border of this the Indians stopped long enough to bind the prisoners' wrists with thongs of deerhide. While two of the braves performed this office, Silvertip leaned against a tree and took no notice of the brothers. When they were thus securely tied one of their captors addressed the chief, who at once led the way westward through the forest. The savages followed in single file, with Joe and Jim in the middle of the line. The last Indian tried to mount Lance; but the thoroughbred would have none of him, and after several efforts the savage was compelled to desist. Mose trotted reluctantly along behind the horse.

Although the chief preserved a dignified mien, his braves were disposed to be gay. They were in high glee over their feat of capturing the palefaces, and kept up an incessant jabbering. One Indian, who walked directly behind Joe, continually prodded him with the stock of a rifle; and whenever Joe turned, the brawny redskin grinned as he grunted, "Ugh!" Joe observed that this huge savage had a broad face of rather a lighter shade of red than his companions. Perhaps he intended those rifle-prods in friendliness, for although they certainly amused him, he would allow no one else to touch Joe; but it would have been more pleasing had he shown his friendship in a gentle manner. This Indian carried Joe's pack, much to his own delight, especially as his companions evinced an envious curiosity. The big fellow would not, however, allow them to touch it.

"He's a cheerful brute," remarked Joe to Jim.

"Ugh!" grunted the big Indian, jamming Joe with his rifle-stock.

Joe took heed to the warning and spoke no more. He gave all his attention to the course over which he was being taken. Here was his first opportunity to learn something of Indians and their woodcraft. It occurred to him that his captors would not have been so gay and careless had they not believed themselves safe from pursuit, and he concluded they were leisurely conducting him to one of the Indian towns. He watched the supple figure before him, wondering at the quick step, light as the fall of a leaf, and tried to walk as softly. He found, however, that where the Indian readily avoided the sticks and brush, he was unable to move without snapping twigs. Now and then he would look up and study the lay of the land ahead; and as he came nearer to certain rocks and trees he scrutinized them closely, in order to remember their shape and general appearance. He believed he was blazing out in his mind this woodland trail, so that should fortune favor him and he contrive to escape, he would be able to find his way back to the river. Also, he was enjoying the wild scenery.

This forest would have appeared beautiful, even to one indifferent to such charms, and Joe was far from that. Every moment he felt steal stronger over him a subtle influence which he could not define. Half unconsciously he tried to analyze it, but it baffled him. He could no more explain what fascinated him than he could understand what caused the melancholy quiet which hung over the glades and hollows. He had pictured a real forest so differently from this. Here was a long lane paved with springy moss and fenced by bright-green sassafras; there a secluded dale, dotted with pale-blue blossoms, over which the giant cottonwoods leaned their heads, jealously guarding the delicate flowers from the sun. Beech trees, growing close in clanny groups, spread their straight limbs gracefully; the white birches gleamed like silver wherever a stray sunbeam stole through the foliage, and the oaks, monarchs of the forest, rose over all, dark, rugged, and kingly.

Joe soon understood why the party traveled through such open forest. The chief, seeming hardly to deviate from his direct course, kept clear of broken ground, matted thickets and tangled windfalls. Joe got a glimpse of dark ravines and heard the music of tumbling waters; he saw gray cliffs grown over with vines, and full of holes and crevices; steep ridges, covered with dense patches of briar and hazel, rising in the way. Yet the Shawnee always found an easy path.

The sun went down behind the foliage in the west, and shadows appeared low in the glens; then the trees faded into an indistinct mass; a purple shade settled down over the forest, and night brought the party to a halt.

The Indians selected a sheltered spot under the lee of a knoll, at the base of which ran a little brook. Here in this inclosed space were the remains of a camp-fire. Evidently the Indians had halted there that same day, for the logs still smouldered. While one brave fanned the embers, another took from a neighboring branch a haunch of deer meat. A blaze was soon coaxed from the dull coals, more fuel was added, and presently a cheerful fire shone on the circle of dusky forms.

It was a picture which Joe had seen in many a boyish dream; now that he was a part of it he did not dwell on the hopelessness of the situation, nor of the hostile chief whose enmity he had incurred. Almost, it seemed, he was glad of this chance to watch the Indians and listen to them. He had been kept apart from Jim, and it appeared to Joe that their captors treated his brother with a contempt which they did not show him. Silvertip had, no doubt, informed them that Jim had been on his way to teach the Indians of the white man's God.

Jim sat with drooping head; his face was sad, and evidently he took the most disheartening view of his capture. When he had eaten the slice of venison given him he lay down with his back to the fire.

Silvertip, in these surroundings, showed his real character. He had appeared friendly in the settlement; but now he was the relentless savage, a son of the wilds, free as an eagle. His dignity as a chief kept him aloof from his braves. He had taken no notice of the prisoners since the capture. He remained silent, steadily regarding the fire with his somber eyes. At length, glancing at the big Indian, he motioned toward the prisoners and with a single word stretched himself on the leaves.

Joe noted the same changelessness of expression in the other dark faces as he had seen in Silvertip's. It struck him forcibly. When they spoke in their soft, guttural tones, or burst into a low, not unmusical laughter, or sat gazing stolidly into the fire, their faces seemed always the same, inscrutable, like the depths of the forest now hidden in night. One thing Joe felt rather than saw—these savages were fierce and untamable. He was sorry for Jim, because, as he believed, it would be as easy to teach the panther gentleness toward his prey as to instill into one of these wild creatures a belief in Christ.

The braves manifested keen pleasure in anticipation as to what they would get out of the pack, which the Indian now opened. Time and again the big brave placed his broad hand on the shoulder of a comrade Indian and pushed him backward.

Finally the pack was opened. It contained a few articles of wearing apparel, a pair of boots, and a pipe and pouch of tobacco. The big Indian kept the latter articles, grunting with satisfaction, and threw the boots and clothes to the others. Immediately there was a scramble. One brave, after a struggle with another, got possession of both boots. He at once slipped off his moccasins and drew on the white man's foot-coverings. He strutted around in them a few moments, but his proud manner soon changed to disgust.

Cowhide had none of the soft, yielding qualities of buckskin, and hurt the Indian's feet. Sitting down, he pulled one off, not without difficulty, for the boots were wet; but he could not remove the other. He hesitated a moment, being aware of the subdued merriment of his comrades, and then held up his foot to the nearest one. This chanced to be the big Indian, who evidently had a keen sense of humor. Taking hold of the boot with both hands, he dragged the luckless brave entirely around the camp-fire. The fun, however, was not to be all one-sided. The big Indian gave a more strenuous pull, and the boot came off suddenly. Unprepared for this, he lost his balance and fell down the bank almost into the creek. He held on to the boot, nevertheless, and getting up, threw it into the fire.

The braves quieted down after that, and soon lapsed into slumber, leaving the big fellow, to whom the chief had addressed his brief command, acting, as guard. Observing Joe watching him as he puffed on his new pipe, he grinned, and spoke in broken English that was intelligible, and much of a surprise to the young man.

"Paleface—tobac'—heap good."

Then, seeing that Joe made no effort to follow his brother's initiative, for Jim was fast asleep, he pointed to the recumbent figures and spoke again.

"Ugh! Paleface sleep—Injun wigwams—near setting sun."

On the following morning Joe was awakened by the pain in his legs, which had been bound all night. He was glad when the bonds were cut and the party took up its westward march.

The Indians, though somewhat quieter, displayed the same carelessness: they did not hurry, nor use particular caution, but selected the most open paths through the forest. They even halted while one of their number crept up on a herd of browsing deer. About noon the leader stopped to drink from a spring; his braves followed suit and permitted the white prisoners to quench their thirst.

When they were about to start again the single note of a bird far away in the woods sounded clearly on the quiet air. Joe would not have given heed to it had he been less attentive. He instantly associated this peculiar bird-note with the sudden stiffening of Silvertip's body and his attitude of intense listening. Low exclamations came from the braves as they bent to catch the lightest sound. Presently, above the murmur of the gentle fall of water over the stones, rose that musical note once more. It was made by a bird, Joe thought, and yet, judged by the actions of the Indians, how potent with meaning beyond that of the simple melody of the woodland songster! He turned, half expecting to see somewhere in the tree-tops the bird which had wrought so sudden a change in his captors. As he did so from close at hand came the same call, now louder, but identical with the one that had deceived him. It was an answering signal, and had been given by Silvertip.

It flashed into Joe's mind that other savages were in the forest; they had run across the Shawnees' trail, and were thus communicating with them. Soon dark figures could be discerned against the patches of green thicket; they came nearer and nearer, and now entered the open glade where Silvertip stood with his warriors.

Joe counted twelve, and noted that they differed from his captors. He had only time to see that this difference consisted in the head-dress, and in the color and quantity of paint on their bodies, when his gaze was attracted and riveted to the foremost figures.

The first was that of a very tall and stately chief, toward whom Silvertip now advanced with every show of respect. In this Indian's commanding stature, in his reddish-bronze face, stern and powerful, there were readable the characteristics of a king. In his deep-set eyes, gleaming from under a ponderous brow; in his mastiff-like jaw; in every feature of his haughty face were visible all the high intelligence, the consciousness of past valor, and the power and authority that denote a great chieftain.

The second figure was equally striking for the remarkable contrast it afforded to the chief's. Despite the gaudy garments, the paint, the fringed and beaded buckskin leggins—all the Indian accouterments and garments which bedecked this person, he would have been known anywhere as a white man. His skin was burned to a dark bronze, but it had not the red tinge which characterizes the Indian. This white man had, indeed, a strange physiognomy. The forehead was narrow and sloped backward from the brow, denoting animal instincts. The eyes were close together, yellowish-brown in color, and had a peculiar vibrating movement, as though they were hung on a pivot, like a compass-needle. The nose was long and hooked, and the mouth set in a thin, cruel line. There was in the man's aspect an extraordinary combination of ignorance, vanity, cunning and ferocity.

While the two chiefs held a short consultation, this savage-appearing white man addressed the brothers.

"Who're you, an' where you goin'?" he asked gruffly, confronting Jim.

"My name is Downs. I am a preacher, and was on my way to the Moravian Mission to preach to the Indians. You are a white man; will you help us?"

If Jim expected the information would please his interrogator, he was mistaken.

"So you're one of 'em? Yes, I'll do suthin' fer you when I git back from this hunt. I'll cut your heart out, chop it up, an' feed it to the buzzards," he said fiercely, concluding his threat by striking Jim a cruel blow on the head.

Joe paled deathly white at this cowardly action, and his eyes, as they met the gaze of the ruffian, contracted with their characteristic steely glow, as if some powerful force within the depths of his being were at white heat and only this pale flash came to the surface.

"You ain't a preacher?" questioned the man, meeting something in Joe's glance that had been absent from Jim's.

Joe made no answer, and regarded questioner steadily.

"Ever see me afore? Ever hear of Jim Girty?" he asked boastfully.

"Before you spoke I knew you were Girty," answered Joe quietly.

"How d'you know? Ain't you afeared?"

"Of what?"

"Me—me?"

Joe laughed in the renegades face.

"How'd you knew me?" growled Girty. "I'll see thet you hev cause to remember me after this."

"I figured there was only one so-called white man in these woods who is coward enough to strike a man whose hands are tied."

"Boy, ye're too free with your tongue. I'll shet off your wind." Girty's hand was raised, but it never reached Joe's neck.

The big Indian had an hour or more previous cut Joe's bonds, but he still retained the thong which was left attached to Joe's left wrist. This allowed the young man free use of his right arm, which, badly swollen or not, he brought into quick action.

When the renegade reached toward him Joe knocked up the hand, and, instead of striking, he grasped the hooked nose with all the powerful grip of his fingers. Girty uttered a frightful curse; he writhed with pain, but could not free himself from the vise-like clutch. He drew his tomahawk and with a scream aimed a vicious blow at Joe. He missed his aim, however, for Silvertip had intervened and turned the course of the keen hatchet. But the weapon struck Joe a glancing blow, inflicting a painful, though not dangerous wound.

The renegade's nose was skinned and bleeding profusely. He was frantic with fury, and tried to get at Joe; but Silvertip remained in front of his captive until some of the braves led Girty into the forest, where the tall chief had already disappeared.

The nose-pulling incident added to the gayety of the Shawnees, who evidently were pleased with Girty's discomfiture. They jabbered among themselves and nodded approvingly at Joe, until a few words spoken by Silvertip produced a sudden change.

What the words were Joe could not understand, but to him they sounded like French. He smiled at the absurdity of imagining he had heard a savage speak a foreign language. At any rate, whatever had been said was trenchant with meaning. The Indians changed from gay to grave; they picked up their weapons and looked keenly on every side; the big Indian at once retied Joe, and then all crowded round the chief.

"Did you hear what Silvertip said, and did you notice the effect it had?" whispered Jim, taking advantage of the moment.

"It sounded like French, but of course it wasn't," replied Joe.

"It was French. 'Le Vent de la Mort.'"

"By Jove, that's it. What does it mean?" asked Joe, who was not a scholar.

"The Wind of Death."

"That's English, but I can't apply it here. Can you?"

"No doubt it is some Indian omen."

The hurried consultation over, Silvertip tied Joe's horse and dog to the trees, and once more led the way; this time he avoided the open forest and kept on low ground. For a long time he traveled in the bed of the brook, wading when the water was shallow, and always stepping where there was the least possibility of leaving a footprint. Not a word was spoken. If either of the brothers made the lightest splash in the water, or tumbled a stone into the brook, the Indian behind rapped him on the head with a tomahawk handle.

At certain places, indicated by the care which Silvertip exercised in walking, the Indian in front of the captives turned and pointed where they were to step. They were hiding the trail. Silvertip hurried them over the stony places; went more slowly through the water, and picked his way carefully over the soft ground it became necessary to cross. At times he stopped, remaining motionless many seconds.

This vigilance continued all the afternoon. The sun sank; twilight spread its gray mantle, and soon black night enveloped the forest. The Indians halted, but made no fire; they sat close together on a stony ridge, silent and watchful.

Joe pondered deeply over this behavior. Did the Shawnees fear pursuit? What had that Indian chief told Silvertip? To Joe it seemed that they acted as if believing foes were on all sides. Though they hid their tracks, it was, apparently, not the fear of pursuit alone which made them cautious.

Joe reviewed the afternoon's march and dwelt upon the possible meaning of the cat-like steps, the careful brushing aside of branches, the roving eyes, suspicious and gloomy, the eager watchfulness of the advance as well as to the rear, and always the strained effort to listen, all of which gave him the impression of some grave, unseen danger.

And now as he lay on the hard ground, nearly exhausted by the long march and suffering from the throbbing wound, his courage lessened somewhat, and he shivered with dread. The quiet and gloom of the forest; these fierce, wild creatures, free in the heart of their own wilderness yet menaced by a foe, and that strange French phrase which kept recurring in his mind—all had the effect of conjuring up giant shadows in Joe's fanciful mind. During all his life, until this moment, he had never feared anything; now he was afraid of the darkness. The spectral trees spread long arms overhead, and phantom forms stalked abroad; somewhere out in that dense gloom stirred this mysterious foe—the "Wind of Death."

Nevertheless, he finally slept. In the dull-gray light of early morning the Indians once more took up the line of march toward the west. They marched all that day, and at dark halted to eat and rest. Silvertip and another Indian stood watch.

Some time before morning Joe suddenly awoke. The night was dark, yet it was lighter than when he had fallen asleep. A pale, crescent moon shown dimly through the murky clouds. There was neither movement of the air nor the chirp of an insect. Absolute silence prevailed.

Joe saw the Indian guard leaning against a tree, asleep. Silvertip was gone. The captive raised his head and looked around for the chief. There were only four Indians left, three on the ground and one against the tree.

He saw something shining near him. He looked more closely, and made out the object to be an eagle plume Silvertip had worn, in his head-dress. It lay on the ground near the tree. Joe made some slight noise which awakened the guard. The Indian never moved a muscle; but his eyes roved everywhere. He, too, noticed the absence of the chief.

At this moment from out of the depths of the woods came a swelling sigh, like the moan of the night wind. It rose and died away, leaving the silence apparently all the deeper.

A shudder ran over Joe's frame. Fascinated, he watched the guard. The Indian uttered a low gasp; his eyes started and glared wildly; he rose very slowly to his full height and stood waiting, listening. The dark hand which held the tomahawk trembled so that little glints of moonlight glanced from the bright steel.

From far back in the forest-deeps came that same low moaning: "Um-m-mm-woo-o-o-o!"

It rose from a faint murmur and swelled to a deep moan, soft but clear, and ended in a wail like that of a lost soul.

The break it made in that dead silence was awful. Joe's blood seemed to have curdled and frozen; a cold sweat oozed from his skin, and it was as if a clammy hand clutched at his heart. He tried to persuade himself that the fear displayed by the savage was only superstition, and that that moan was but the sigh of the night wind.

The Indian sentinel stood as if paralyzed an instant after that weird cry, and then, swift as a flash, and as noiseless, he was gone into the gloomy forest. He had fled without awakening his companions.

Once more the moaning cry arose and swelled mournfully on the still night air. It was close at hand!

"The Wind of Death," whispered Joe.

He was shaken and unnerved by the events of the past two days, and dazed from his wound. His strength deserted him, and he lost consciousness.

CHAPTER VI.

One evening, several day previous to the capture of the brothers, a solitary hunter stopped before a deserted log cabin which stood on the bank of a stream fifty miles or more inland from the Ohio River. It was rapidly growing dark; a fine, drizzling rain had set in, and a rising wind gave promise of a stormy night.

Although the hunter seemed familiar with his surroundings, he moved cautiously, and hesitated as if debating whether he should seek the protection of this lonely hut, or remain all night under dripping trees. Feeling of his hunting frock, he found that it was damp and slippery. This fact evidently decided him in favor of the cabin, for he stooped his tall figure and went in. It was pitch dark inside; but having been there before, the absence of a light did not trouble him. He readily found the ladder leading to the loft, ascended it, and lay down to sleep.

During the night a noise awakened him. For a moment he heard nothing except the fall of the rain. Then came the hum of voices, followed by the soft tread of moccasined feet. He knew there was an Indian town ten miles across the country, and believed some warriors, belated on a hunting trip, had sought the cabin for shelter.

The hunter lay perfectly quiet, awaiting developments. If the Indians had flint and steel, and struck a light, he was almost certain to be discovered. He listened to their low conversation, and understood from the language that they were Delawares.

A moment later he heard the rustling of leaves and twigs, accompanied by the metallic click of steel against some hard substance. The noise was repeated, and then followed by a hissing sound, which he knew to be the burning of a powder on a piece of dry wood, after which rays of light filtered through cracks of the unstable floor of the loft.

The man placed his eye to one of these crevices, and counted eleven Indians, all young braves, with the exception of the chief. The Indians had been hunting; they had haunches of deer and buffalo tongues, together with several packs of hides. Some of them busied themselves drying their weapons; others sat down listlessly, plainly showing their weariness, and two worked over the smouldering fire. The damp leaves and twigs burned faintly, yet there was enough to cause the hunter fear that he might be discovered. He believed he had not much to worry about from the young braves, but the hawk-eyed chief was dangerous.

And he was right. Presently the stalwart chief heard, or saw, a drop of water fall from the loft. It came from the hunter's wet coat. Almost any one save an Indian scout would have fancied this came from the roof. As the chief's gaze roamed everywhere over the interior of the cabin his expression was plainly distrustful. His eye searched the wet clay floor, but hardly could have discovered anything there, because the hunter's moccasined tracks had been obliterated by the footprints of the Indians. The chief's suspicions seemed to be allayed.

But in truth this chief, with the wonderful sagacity natural to Indians, had observed matters which totally escaped the young braves, and, like a wily old fox, he waited to see which cub would prove the keenest. Not one of them, however, noted anything unusual. They sat around the fire, ate their meat and parched corn, and chatted volubly.

The chief arose and, walking to the ladder, ran his hand along one of the rungs.

"Ugh!" he exclaimed.

Instantly he was surrounded by ten eager, bright-eyed braves. He extended his open palm; it was smeared with wet clay like that under his feet. Simultaneously with their muttered exclamations the braves grasped their weapons. They knew there was a foe above them. It was a paleface, for an Indian would have revealed himself.

The hunter, seeing he was discovered, acted with the unerring judgment and lightning-like rapidity of one long accustomed to perilous situations. Drawing his tomahawk and noiselessly stepping to the hole in the loft, he leaped into the midst of the astounded Indians.

Rising from the floor like the rebound of a rubber ball, his long arm with the glittering hatchet made a wide sweep, and the young braves scattered like frightened sheep.

He made a dash for the door and, incredible as it may seem, his movements were so quick he would have escaped from their very midst without a scratch but for one unforeseen circumstance. The clay floor was wet and slippery; his feet were hardly in motion before they slipped from under him and he fell headlong.

With loud yells of triumph the band jumped upon him. There was a convulsive, heaving motion of the struggling mass, one frightful cry of agony, and then hoarse commands. Three of the braves ran to their packs, from which they took cords of buckskin. So exceedingly powerful was the hunter that six Indians were required to hold him while the others tied his hands and feet. Then, with grunts and chuckles of satisfaction, they threw him into a corner of the cabin.

Two of the braves had been hurt in the brief struggle, one having a badly wrenched shoulder and the other a broken arm. So much for the hunter's power in that single moment of action.

The loft was searched, and found to be empty. Then the excitement died away, and the braves settled themselves down for the night. The injured ones bore their hurts with characteristic stoicism; if they did not sleep, both remained quiet and not a sigh escaped them.

The wind changed during the night, the storm abated, and when daylight came the sky was cloudless. The first rays of the sun shone in the open door, lighting up the interior of the cabin.

A sleepy Indian who had acted as guard stretched his limbs and yawned. He looked for the prisoner, and saw him sitting up in the corner. One arm was free, and the other nearly so. He had almost untied the thongs which bound him; a few moments more and he would have been free.

"Ugh!" exclaimed the young brave, awakening his chief and pointing to the hunter.

The chief glanced at his prisoner; then looked more closely, and with one spring was on his feet, a drawn tomahawk in his hand. A short, shrill yell issued from his lips. Roused by that clarion call, the young braves jumped up, trembling in eager excitement. The chief's summons had been the sharp war-cry of the Delawares.

He manifested as intense emotion as could possibly have been betrayed by a matured, experienced chieftain, and pointing to the hunter, he spoke a single word.

* * *

At noonday the Indians entered the fields of corn which marked the outskirts of the Delaware encampment.

"Kol-loo—kol-loo—kol-loo."

The long signal, heralding the return of the party with important news, pealed throughout the quiet valley; and scarcely had the echoes died away when from the village came answering shouts.

Once beyond the aisles of waving corn the hunter saw over the shoulders of his captors the home of the redmen. A grassy plain, sloping gradually from the woody hill to a winding stream, was brightly beautiful with chestnut trees and long, well-formed lines of lodges. Many-hued blankets hung fluttering in the sun, and rising lazily were curling columns of blue smoke. The scene was picturesque and reposeful; the vivid hues suggesting the Indians love of color and ornament; the absence of life and stir, his languorous habit of sleeping away the hot noonday hours.

The loud whoops, however, changed the quiet encampment into a scene of animation. Children ran from the wigwams, maidens and braves dashed here and there, squaws awakened from their slumber, and many a doughty warrior rose from his rest in the shade. French fur traders came curiously from their lodges, and renegades hurriedly left their blankets, roused to instant action by the well-known summons.

The hunter, led down the lane toward the approaching crowd, presented a calm and fearless demeanor. When the Indians surrounded him one prolonged, furious yell rent the air, and then followed an extraordinary demonstration of fierce delight. The young brave's staccato yell, the maiden's scream, the old squaw's screech, and the deep war-cry of the warriors intermingled in a fearful discordance.

Often had this hunter heard the name which the Indian called him; he had been there before, a prisoner; he had run the gauntlet down the lane; he had been bound to a stake in front of the lodge where his captors were now leading him. He knew the chief, Wingenund, sachem of the Delawares. Since that time, now five years ago, when Wingenund had tortured him, they had been bitterest foes.

If the hunter heard the hoarse cries, or the words hissed into his ears; if he saw the fiery glances of hatred, and sudden giving way to ungovernable rage, unusual to the Indian nature; if he felt in their fierce exultation the hopelessness of succor or mercy, he gave not the slightest sign.

"Atelang! Atelang! Atelang!" rang out the strange Indian name.

The French traders, like real savages, ran along with the procession, their feathers waving, their paint shining, their faces expressive of as much excitement as the Indians' as they cried aloud in their native tongue:

"Le Vent de la Mort! Le Vent de la Mort! La Vent de la Mort!"

The hunter, while yet some paces distant, saw the lofty figure of the chieftain standing in front of his principal men. Well he knew them all. There were the crafty Pipe, and his savage comrade, the Half King; there was Shingiss, who wore on his forehead a scar—the mark of the hunter's bullet; there were Kotoxen, the Lynx, and Misseppa, the Source, and Winstonah, the War-cloud, chiefs of sagacity and renown. Three renegades completed the circle; and these three traitors represented a power which had for ten years left an awful, bloody trail over the country. Simon Girty, the so-called White Indian, with his keen, authoritative face turned expectantly; Elliott, the Tory deserter, from Fort Pitt, a wiry, spider-like little man; and last, the gaunt and gaudily arrayed form of the demon of the frontier—Jim Girty.

The procession halted before this group, and two brawny braves pushed the hunter forward. Simon Girty's face betrayed satisfaction; Elliott's shifty eyes snapped, and the dark, repulsive face of the other Girty exhibited an exultant joy. These desperadoes had feared this hunter.

Wingenund, with a majestic wave of his arm, silenced the yelling horde of frenzied savages and stepped before the captive.

The deadly foes were once again face to face. The chieftain's lofty figure and dark, sleek head, now bare of plumes, towered over the other Indians, but he was not obliged to lower his gaze in order to look straight into the hunter's eyes.

Verily this hunter merited the respect which shone in the great chieftain's glance. Like a mountain-ash he stood, straight and strong, his magnificent frame tapering wedge-like from his broad shoulders. The bulging line of his thick neck, the deep chest, the knotty contour of his bared forearm, and the full curves of his legs—all denoted a wonderful muscular development.

The power expressed in this man's body seemed intensified in his features. His face was white and cold, his jaw square and set; his coal-black eyes glittered with almost a superhuman fire. And his hair, darker than the wing of a crow, fell far below his shoulders; matted and tangled as it was, still it hung to his waist, and had it been combed out, must have reached his knees.

One long moment Wingenund stood facing his foe, and then over the multitude and through the valley rolled his sonorous voice:

"Deathwind dies at dawn!"

The hunter was tied to a tree and left in view of the Indian populace. The children ran fearfully by; the braves gazed long at the great foe of their race; the warriors passed in gloomy silence. The savages' tricks of torture, all their diabolical ingenuity of inflicting pain was suppressed, awaiting the hour of sunrise when this hated Long Knife was to die.

Only one person offered an insult to the prisoner; he was a man of his own color. Jim Girty stopped before him, his yellowish eyes lighted by a tigerish glare, his lips curled in a snarl, and from between them issuing the odor of the fir traders' vile rum.

"You'll soon be feed fer the buzzards," he croaked, in his hoarse voice. He had so often strewed the plains with human flesh for the carrion birds that the thought had a deep fascination for him. "D'ye hear, scalp-hunter? Feed for buzzards!" He deliberately spat in the hunter's face. "D'ye hear?" he repeated.

There was no answer save that which glittered in the hunter's eye. But the renegade could not read it because he did not meet that flaming glance. Wild horses could not have dragged him to face this man had he been free. Even now a chill crept over Girty. For a moment he was enthralled by a mysterious fear, half paralyzed by a foreshadowing of what would be this hunter's vengeance. Then he shook off his craven fear. He was free; the hunter's doom was sure. His sharp face was again wreathed in a savage leer, and he spat once more on the prisoner.

His fierce impetuosity took him a step too far. The hunter's arms and waist were fastened, but his feet were free. His powerful leg was raised suddenly; his foot struck Girty in the pit of the stomach. The renegade dropped limp and gasping. The braves carried him away, his gaudy feathers trailing, his long arms hanging inertly, and his face distorted with agony.

The maidens of the tribe, however, showed for the prisoner an interest that had in it something of veiled sympathy. Indian girls were always fascinated by white men. Many records of Indian maidens' kindness, of love, of heroism for white prisoners brighten the dark pages of frontier history. These girls walked past the hunter, averting their eyes when within his range of vision, but stealing many a sidelong glance at his impressive face and noble proportions. One of them, particularly, attracted the hunter's eye.

This was because, as she came by with her companions, while they all turned away, she looked at him with her soft, dark eyes. She was a young girl, whose delicate beauty bloomed fresh and sweet as that of a wild rose. Her costume, fringed, beaded, and exquisitely wrought with fanciful design, betrayed her rank, she was Wingenund's daughter. The hunter had seen her when she was a child, and he recognized her now. He knew that the beauty of Aola, of Whispering Winds Among the Leaves, had been sung from the Ohio to the Great Lakes.

Often she passed him that afternoon. At sunset, as the braves untied him and led him away, he once more caught the full, intense gaze of her lovely eyes.

That night as he lay securely bound in the corner of a lodge, and the long hours wore slowly away, he strained at his stout bonds, and in his mind revolved different plans of escape. It was not in this man's nature to despair; while he had life he would fight. From time to time he expanded his muscles, striving to loosen the wet buckskin thongs.

The dark hours slowly passed, no sound coming to him save the distant bark of a dog and the monotonous tread of his guard; a dim grayness pervaded the lodge. Dawn was close at hand—his hour was nearly come.

Suddenly his hearing, trained to a most acute sensibility, caught a faint sound, almost inaudible. It came from without on the other side of the lodge. There it was again, a slight tearing sound, such as is caused by a knife when it cuts through soft material.

Some one was slitting the wall of the lodge.

The hunter rolled noiselessly over and over until he lay against the skins. In the dim grayness he saw a bright blade moving carefully upward through the deer-hide. Then a long knife was pushed into the opening; a small, brown hand grasped the hilt. Another little hand followed and felt of the wall and floor, reaching out with groping fingers.

The, hunter rolled again so that his back was against the wall and his wrists in front of the opening. He felt the little hand on his arm; then it slipped down to his wrists. The contact of cold steel set a tremor of joy through his heart. The pressure of his bonds relaxed, ceased; his arms were free. He turned to find the long-bladed knife on the ground. The little hands were gone.

In a tinkling he rose unbound, armed, desperate. In another second an Indian warrior lay upon the ground in his death-throes, while a fleeing form vanished in the gray morning mist.

CHAPTER VII.

Joe felt the heavy lethargy rise from him like the removal of a blanket; his eyes became clear, and he saw the trees and the forest gloom; slowly he realized his actual position.

He was a prisoner, lying helpless among his sleeping captors. Silvertip and the guard had fled into the woods, frightened by the appalling moan which they believed sounded their death-knell. And Joe believed he might have fled himself had he been free. What could have caused that sound? He fought off the numbing chill that once again began to creep over him. He was wide-awake now; his head was clear, and he resolved to retain his senses. He told himself there could be nothing supernatural in that wind, or wail, or whatever it was, which had risen murmuring from out the forest-depths.

Yet, despite his reasoning, Joe could not allay his fears. That thrilling cry haunted him. The frantic flight of an Indian brave—nay, of a cunning, experienced chief—was not to be lightly considered. The savages were at home in these untracked wilds. Trained from infancy to scent danger and to fight when they had an equal chance they surely would not run without good cause.

Joe knew that something moved under those dark trees. He had no idea what. It might be the fretting night wind, or a stealthy, prowling, soft-footed beast, or a savage alien to these wild Indians, and wilder than they by far. The chirp of a bird awoke the stillness. Night had given way to morning. Welcoming the light that was chasing away the gloom, Joe raised his head with a deep sigh of relief. As he did so he saw a bush move; then a shadow seemed to sink into the ground. He had seen an object lighter than the trees, darker than the gray background. Again, that strange sense of the nearness of something thrilled him.

Moments, passed—to him long as hours. He saw a tall fern waver and tremble. A rabbit, or perhaps a snake, had brushed it. Other ferns moved, their tops agitated, perhaps, by a faint breeze. No; that wavering line came

245

straight toward him; it could not be the wind; it marked the course of a creeping, noiseless thing. It must be a panther crawling nearer and nearer.

Joe opened his lips to awaken his captors, but could not speak; it was as if his heart had stopped beating. Twenty feet away the ferns were parted to disclose a white, gleaming face, with eyes that seemingly glittered. Brawny shoulders were upraised, and then a tall, powerful man stood revealed. Lightly he stepped over the leaves into the little glade. He bent over the sleeping Indians. Once, twice, three times a long blade swung high. One brave shuddered another gave a sobbing gasp, and the third moved two fingers—thus they passed from life to death.

"Wetzel!" cried Joe.

"I reckon so," said the deliverer, his deep, calm voice contrasting strangely with what might have been expected from his aspect. Then, seeing Joe's head covered with blood, he continued: "Able to get up?"

"I'm not hurt," answered Joe, rising when his bonds had been cut.

"Brothers, I reckon?" Wetzel said, bending over Jim.

"Yes, we're brothers. Wake up, Jim, wake up! We're saved!"

"What? Who's that?" cried Jim, sitting up and staring at Wetzel.

"This man has saved our lives! See, Jim, the Indians are dead! And, Jim, it's Wetzel, the hunter. You remember, Jeff Lynn said I'd know him if I ever saw him and——"

"What happened to Jeff?" inquired Wetzel, interrupting. He had turned from Jim's grateful face.

"Jeff was on the first raft, and for all we know he is now safe at Fort Henry. Our steersman was shot, and we were captured."

"Has the Shawnee anythin' ag'inst you boys?"

"Why, yes, I guess so. I played a joke on him—took his shirt and put it on another fellow."

"Might jes' as well kick an' Injun. What has he ag'in you?"

"I don't know. Perhaps he did not like my talk to him," answered Jim. "I am a preacher, and have come west to teach the gospel to the Indians."

"They're good Injuns now," said Wetzel, pointing to the prostrate figures.

"How did you find us?" eagerly asked Joe.

"Run acrost yer trail two days back."

"And you've been following us?"

The hunter nodded.

"Did you see anything of another band of Indians? A tall chief and Jim Girty were among them."

"They've been arter me fer two days. I was followin' you when Silvertip got wind of Girty an' his Delawares. The big chief was Wingenund. I seen you pull Girty's nose. Arter the Delawares went I turned loose yer dog an' horse an' lit out on yer trail."

"Where are the Delawares now?"

"I reckon there nosin' my back trail. We must be gittin'. Silvertip'll soon hev a lot of Injuns here."

Joe intended to ask the hunter about what had frightened the Indians, but despite his eager desire for information, he refrained from doing so.

"Girty nigh did fer you," remarked Wetzel, examining Joe's wound. "He's in a bad humor. He got kicked a few days back, and then hed the skin pulled offen his nose. Somebody'll hev to suffer. Wal, you fellers grab yer rifles, an' we'll be startin' fer the fort."

Joe shuddered as he leaned over one of the dusky forms to detach powder and bullet horn. He had never seen a dead Indian, and the tense face, the sightless, vacant eyes made him shrink. He shuddered again when he saw the hunter scalp his victims. He shuddered the third time when he saw Wetzel pick up Silvertip's beautiful white eagle plume, dabble it in a pool of blood, and stick it in the bark of a tree. Bereft of its graceful beauty, drooping with its gory burden, the long leather was a deadly message. It had been Silvertip's pride; it was now a challenge, a menace to the Shawnee chief.

"Come," said Wetzel, leading the way into the forest.

* * *

Shortly after daylight on the second day following the release of the Downs brothers the hunter brushed through a thicket of alder and said: "Thar's Fort Henry."

The boys were on the summit of a mountain from which the land sloped in a long incline of rolling ridges and gentle valleys like a green, billowy sea, until it rose again abruptly into a peak higher still than the one upon which they stood. The broad Ohio, glistening in the sun, lay at the base of the mountain.

Upon the bluff overlooking the river, and under the brow of the mountain, lay the frontier fort. In the clear atmosphere it stood out in bold relief. A small, low structure surrounded by a high stockade fence was all, and yet it did not seem unworthy of its fame. Those watchful, forbidding loopholes, the blackened walls and timbers, told the history of ten long, bloody years. The whole effect was one of menace, as if the fort sent out a defiance to the wilderness, and meant to protect the few dozen log cabins clustered on the hillside.

"How will we ever get across that big river?" asked Jim, practically.

"Wade—swim," answered the hunter, laconically, and began the descent of the ridge. An hour's rapid walking brought the three to the river. Depositing his rifle in a clump of willows, and directing the boys to do the same with their guns, the hunter splashed into the water. His companions followed him into the shallow water, and waded a hundred yards, which brought them near the island that they now perceived hid the fort. The hunter swam the remaining distance, and, climbing the bank, looked back for the boys. They were close behind him. Then he strode across the island, perhaps a quarter of a mile wide.

"We've a long swim here," said Wetzel, waving his hand toward the main channel of the river. "Good fer it?" he inquired of Joe, since Jim had not received any injuries during the short captivity and consequently showed more endurance.

"Good for anything," answered Joe, with that coolness Wetzel had been quick to observe in him.

The hunter cast a sharp glance at the lad's haggard face, his bruised temple, and his hair matted with blood. In that look he read Joe thoroughly. Had the young man known the result of that scrutiny, he would have been pleased as well as puzzled, for the hunter had said to himself: "A brave lad, an' the border fever's on him."

"Swim close to me," said Wetzel, and he plunged into the river. The task was accomplished without accident.

"See the big cabin, thar, on the hillside? Thar's Colonel Zane in the door," said Wetzel.

As they neared the building several men joined the one who had been pointed out as the colonel. It was evident the boys were the subject of their conversation. Presently Zane left the group and came toward them. The brothers saw a handsome, stalwart man, in the prime of life.

"Well, Lew, what luck?" he said to Wetzel.

"Not much. I treed five Injuns, an' two got away," answered the hunter as he walked toward the fort.

"Lads, welcome to Fort Henry," said Colonel Zane, a smile lighting his dark face. "The others of your party arrived safely. They certainly will be overjoyed to see you."

"Colonel Zane, I had a letter from my uncle to you," replied Jim; "but the Indians took that and everything else we had with us."

"Never mind the letter. I knew your uncle, and your father, too. Come into the house and change those wet clothes. And you, my lad, have got an ugly knock on the head. Who gave you that?"

"Jim Girty."

"What?" exclaimed the colonel.

"Jim Girty did that. He was with a party of Delawares who ran across us. They were searching for Wetzel."

"Girty with the Delawares! The devil's to pay now. And you say hunting Wetzel? I must learn more about this. It looks bad. But tell me, how did Girty come to strike you?"

"I pulled his nose."

"You did? Good! Good!" cried Colonel Zane, heartily. "By George, that's great! Tell me—but wait until you are more comfortable. Your packs came safely on Jeff's raft, and you will find them inside."

As Joe followed the colonel he heard one of the other men say:

"Like as two peas in a pod."

Farther on he saw an Indian standing a little apart from the others.

Hearing Joe's slight exclamation of surprise, he turned, disclosing a fine, manly countenance, characterized by calm dignity. The Indian read the boy's thought.

"Ugh! Me friend," he said in English.

"That's my Shawnee guide, Tomepomehala. He's a good fellow, although Jonathan and Wetzel declare the only good Indian is a dead one. Come right in here. There are your packs, and you'll find water outside the door."

Thus saying, Colonel Zane led the brothers into a small room, brought out their packs, and left them. He came back presently with a couple of soft towels.

"Now you lads fix up a bit; then come out and meet my family and tell us all about your adventure. By that time dinner will be ready."

"Geminy! Don't that towel remind you of home?" said Joe, when the colonel had gone. "From the looks of things, Colonel Zane means to have comfort here in the wilderness. He struck me as being a fine man."

The boys were indeed glad to change the few articles of clothing the Indians had left them, and when they were shaved and dressed they presented an entirely different appearance. Once more they were twin brothers, in costume and feature. Joe contrived, by brushing his hair down on his forehead, to conceal the discolored bump.

"I think I saw a charming girl," observed Joe.

"Suppose you did—what then?" asked Jim, severely.

"Why—nothing—see here, mayn't I admire a pretty girl if I want?"

"No, you may not. Joe, will nothing ever cure you? I should think the thought of Miss Wells——"

"Look here, Jim; she don't care—at least, it's very little she cares. And I'm—I'm not worthy of her."

"Turn around here and face me," said the young minister sharply.

Joe turned and looked in his brother's eyes.

"Have you trifled with her, as you have with so many others? Tell me. I know you don't lie."

"No."

"Then what do you mean?"

"Nothing much, Jim, except I'm really not worthy of her. I'm no good, you know, and she ought to get a fellow like—like you."

"Absurd! You ought to be ashamed of yourself."

"Never mind me. See here; don't you admire her?"

"Why—why, yes," stammered Jim, flushing a dark, guilty red at the direct question. "Who could help admiring her?"

"That's what I thought. And I know she admires you for qualities which I lack. Nell's like a tender vine just beginning to creep around and cling to something strong. She cares for me; but her love is like the vine. It may hurt her a little to tear that love away, but it won't kill her; and in the end it will be best for her. You need a good wife. What could I do with a woman? Go in and win her, Jim."

"Joe, you're sacrificing yourself again for me," cried Jim, white to the lips. "It's wrong to yourself and wrong to her. I tell you——"

"Enough!" Joe's voice cut in cold and sharp. "Usually you influence me; but sometimes you can't; I say this: Nell will drift into your arms as surely as the leaf falls. It will not hurt her—will be best for her. Remember, she is yours for the winning."

"You do not say whether that will hurt you," whispered Jim.

"Come—we'll find Colonel Zane," said Joe, opening the door.

They went out in the hallway which opened into the yard as well as the larger room through which the colonel had first conducted them. As Jim, who was in advance, passed into this apartment a trim figure entered from the yard. It was Nell, and she ran directly against him. Her face was flushed, her eyes were beaming with gladness, and she seemed the incarnation of girlish joy.

"Oh, Joe," was all she whispered. But the happiness and welcome in that whisper could never have been better expressed in longer speech. Then slightly, ever so slightly, she tilted her sweet face up to his.

It all happened with the quickness of thought. In a single instant Jim saw the radiant face, the outstretched hands, and heard the glad whisper. He knew that she had a again mistaken him for Joe; but for his life he could not draw back his head. He had kissed her, and even as his lips thrilled with her tremulous caress he flushed with the shame of his deceit.

"You're mistaken again—I'm Jim," he whispered.

For a moment they stood staring into each other's eyes, slowly awakening to what had really happened, slowly conscious of a sweet, alluring power. Then Colonel Zane's cheery voice rang in their ears.

"Ah, here's Nellie and your brother! Now, lads, tell me which is which?'

"That's Jim, and I'm Joe," answered the latter. He appeared not to notice his brother, and his greeting to Nell was natural and hearty. For the moment she drew the attention of the others from them.

Joe found himself listening to the congratulations of a number of people. Among the many names he remembered were those of Mrs. Zane, Silas Zane, and Major McColloch. Then he found himself gazing at the most beautiful girl he had ever seen in his life.

"My only sister, Mrs. Alfred Clarke—once Betty Zane, and the heroine of Fort Henry," said Colonel Zane proudly, with his arm around the slender, dark-eyed girl.

"I would brave the Indians and the wilderness again for this pleasure," replied Joe gallantly, as he bowed low over the little hand she cordially extended.

"Bess, is dinner ready?" inquired Colonel Zane of his comely wife. She nodded her head, and the colonel led the way into the adjoining room. "I know you boys must be hungry as bears."

During the meal Colonel Zane questioned his guests about their journey, and as to the treatment they had received at the hands of the Indians. He smiled at the young minister's earnestness in regard to the conversion of the redmen, and he laughed outright when Joe said "he guessed he came to the frontier because it was too slow at home."

"I am sure your desire for excitement will soon be satisfied, if indeed it be not so already," remarked the colonel. "But as to the realization of your brother's hopes I am not so sanguine. Undoubtedly the Moravian missionaries have accomplished wonders with the Indians. Not long ago I visited the Village of Peace—the Indian name for the mission—and was struck by the friendliness and industry which prevailed there. Truly it was a village of peace. Yet it is almost to early to be certain of permanent success of this work. The Indian's nature is one hard to understand. He is naturally roving and restless, which, however, may be owing to his habit of moving from place to place in search of good hunting grounds. I believe—though I must confess I haven't seen any pioneers who share my belief—that the savage has a beautiful side to his character. I know of many noble deeds done by them, and I believe, if they are honestly dealt with, they will return good for good. There are bad ones, of course; but the French traders, and men like the Girtys, have caused most of this long war. Jonathan and Wetzel tell me the Shawnees and Chippewas have taken the warpath again. Then the fact that the Girtys are with the Delawares is reason for alarm. We have been comparatively quiet here of late. Did you boys learn to what tribe your captors belong? Did Wetzel say?"

"He did not; he spoke little, but I will say he was exceedingly active," answered Joe, with a smile.

"To have seen Wetzel fight Indians is something you are not likely to forget," said Colonel Zane grimly. "Now, tell me, how did those Indians wear their scalp-lock?"

"Their heads were shaved closely, with the exception of a little place on top. The remaining hair was twisted into a tuft, tied tightly, and into this had been thrust a couple of painted pins. When Wetzel scalped the Indians the pins fell out. I picked one up, and found it to be bone."

"You will make a woodsman, that's certain," replied Colonel Zane. "The Indians were Shawnee on the warpath. Well, we will not borrow trouble, for when it comes in the shape of redskins it usually comes quickly. Mr. Wells seemed anxious to resume the journey down the river; but I shall try to persuade him to remain with us awhile. Indeed, I am sorry I cannot keep you all here at Fort Henry, and more especially the girls. On the border we need young people, and, while I do not want to frighten the women, I fear there will be more than Indians fighting for them."

"I hope not; but we have come prepared for anything," said Kate, with a quiet smile. "Our home was with uncle, and when he announced his intention of going west we decided our duty was to go with him."

"You were right, and I hope you will find a happy home," rejoined Colonel Zane. "If life among the Indians, proves to be too hard, we shall welcome you here. Betty, show the girls your pets and Indian trinkets. I am going to take the boys to Silas' cabin to see Mr. Wells, and then show them over the fort."

As they went out Joe saw the Indian guide standing in exactly the same position as when they entered the building.

"Can't that Indian move?" he asked curiously.

"He can cover one hundred miles in a day, when he wants to," replied Colonel Zane. "He is resting now. An Indian will often stand or sit in one position for many hours."

"He's a fine-looking chap," remarked Joe, and then to himself: "but I don't like him. I guess I'm prejudiced."

"You'll learn to like Tome, as we call him."

"Colonel Zane, I want a light for my pipe. I haven't had a smoke since the day we were captured. That blamed redskin took my tobacco. It's lucky I had some in my other pack. I'd like to meet him again; also Silvertip and that brute Girty."

"My lad, don't make such wishes," said Colonel Zane, earnestly. "You were indeed fortunate to escape, and I can well understand your feelings. There is nothing I should like better than to see Girty over the sights of my rifle; but I never hunt after danger, and to look for Girty is to court death."

"But Wetzel—"

"Ah, my lad, I know Wetzel goes alone in the woods; but then, he is different from other men. Before you leave I will tell you all about him."

Colonel Zane went around the corner of the cabin and returned with a live coal on a chip of wood, which Joe placed in the bowl of his pipe, and because of the strong breeze stepped close to the cabin wall. Being a keen observer, he noticed many small, round holes in the logs. They were so near together that the timbers had an odd, speckled appearance, and there was hardly a place where he could have put his thumb without covering a hole. At first he thought they were made by a worm or bird peculiar to that region; but finally lie concluded that they were bullet-holes. He thrust his knife blade into one, and out rolled a leaden ball.

"I'd like to have been here when these were made," he said.

"Well, at the time I wished I was back on the Potomac," replied Colonel Zane.

They found the old missionary on the doorstep of the adjacent cabin. He appeared discouraged when Colonel Zane interrogated him, and said that he was impatient because of the delay.

"Mr. Wells, is it not possible that you underrate the danger of your enterprise?"

"I fear naught but the Lord," answered the old man.

"Do you not fear for those with you?" went on the colonel earnestly. "I am heart and soul with you in your work, but want to impress upon you that the time is not propitious. It is a long journey to the village, and the way is beset with dangers of which you have no idea. Will you not remain here with me for a few weeks, or, at least, until my scouts report?"

"I thank you; but go I will."

"Then let me entreat you to remain here a few days, so that I may send my brother Jonathan and Wetzel with you. If any can guide you safely to the Village of Peace it will be they."

At this moment Joe saw two men approaching from the fort, and recognized one of them as Wetzel. He doubted not that the other was Lord Dunmore's famous guide and hunter, Jonathan Zane. In features he resembled the colonel, and was as tall as Wetzel, although not so muscular or wide of chest.

Joe felt the same thrill he had experienced while watching the frontiersmen at Fort Pitt. Wetzel and Jonathan spoke a word to Colonel Zane and then stepped aside. The hunters stood lithe and erect, with the easy, graceful poise of Indians.

"We'll take two canoes, day after to-morrow," said Jonathan, decisively, to Colonel Zane. "Have you a rifle for Wetzel? The Delawares got his."

Colonel Zane pondered over the question; rifles were not scarce at the fort, but a weapon that Wetzel would use was hard to find.

"The hunter may have my rifle," said the old missionary. "I have no use for a weapon with which to destroy God's creatures. My brother was a frontiersman; he left this rifle to me. I remember hearing him say once that if a man knew exactly the weight of lead and powder needed, it would shoot absolutely true."

He went into the cabin, and presently came out with a long object wrapped in linsey cloths. Unwinding the coverings, he brought to view a rifle, the proportions of which caused Jonathan's eyes to glisten, and brought an exclamation from Colonel Zane. Wetzel balanced the gun in his hands. It was fully six feet long; the barrel was large, and the dark steel finely polished; the stock was black walnut, ornamented with silver trimmings. Using Jonathan's powder-flask and bullet-pouch, Wetzel proceeded to load the weapon. He poured out a quantity of powder into the palm of his hand, performing the action quickly and dexterously, but was so slow while measuring it that Joe wondered if he were counting the grains. Next he selected a bullet out of a dozen which Jonathan held toward him. He examined it carefully and tried it in the muzzle of the rifle. Evidently it did not please him, for he took another. Finally he scraped a bullet with his knife, and placing it in the center of a small linsey rag, deftly forced it down. He adjusted the flint, dropped a few grains of powder in the pan, and then looked around for a mark at which to shoot.

Joe observed that the hunters and Colonel Zane were as serious regarding the work as if at that moment some important issue depended upon the accuracy of the rifle.

"There, Lew; there's a good shot. It's pretty far, even for you, when you don't know the gun," said Colonel Zane, pointing toward the river.

Joe saw the end of a log, about the size of a man's head, sticking out of the water, perhaps an hundred and fifty yards distant. He thought to hit it would be a fine shot; but was amazed when he heard Colonel Zane say to several men who had joined the group that Wetzel intended to shoot at a turtle on the log. By straining his eyes Joe succeeded in distinguishing a small lump, which he concluded was the turtle.

Wetzel took a step forward; the long, black rifle was raised with a stately sweep. The instant it reached a level a thread of flame burst forth, followed by a peculiarly clear, ringing report.

"Did he hit?" asked Colonel Zane, eagerly as a boy.

"I allow he did," answered Jonathan.

"I'll go and see," said Joe. He ran down the bank, along the beach, and stepped on the log. He saw a turtle about the size of an ordinary saucer. Picking it up, he saw a bullet-hole in the shell near the middle. The bullet had gone through the turtle, and it was quite dead. Joe carried it to the waiting group.

"I allowed so," declared Jonathan.

Wetzel examined the turtle, and turning to the old missionary, said:

"Your brother spoke the truth, an' I thank you fer the rifle."

CHAPTER VIII.

"So you want to know all about Wetzel?" inquired Colonel Zane of Joe, when, having left Jim and Mr. Wells, they returned to the cabin.

"I am immensely interested in him," replied Joe.

"Well, I don't think there's anything singular in that. I know Wetzel better, perhaps, than any man living; but have seldom talked about him. He doesn't like it. He is by birth a Virginian; I should say, forty years old. We were boys together, and and I am a little beyond that age. He was like any of the lads, except that he excelled us all in strength and agility. When he was nearly eighteen years old a band if Indians—Delawares, I think—crossed the border on a marauding expedition far into Virginia. They burned the old Wetzel homestead and murdered the father, mother, two sisters, and a baby brother. The terrible shock nearly killed Lewis, who for a time was very ill. When he recovered he went in search of his brothers, Martin and John Wetzel, who were hunting, and brought them back to their desolated home. Over the ashes of the home and the graves of the loved ones the brothers swore sleepless and eternal vengeance. The elder brothers have been devoted all these twenty years and more to the killing of Indians; but Lewis has been the great foe of the redman. You have already seen an example of his deeds, and will hear of more. His name is a household word on the border. Scores of times he has saved, actually saved, this fort and settlement. His knowledge of savage ways surpasses by far Boone's, Major McColloch's, Jonathan's, or any of the hunters'."

"Then hunting Indians is his sole occupation?"

"He lives for that purpose alone. He is very seldom in the settlement. Sometimes he stays here a few days, especially if he is needed; but usually he roams the forests."

"What did Jeff Lynn mean when he said that some people think Wetzel is crazy?"

"There are many who think the man mad; but I do not. When the passion for Indian hunting comes upon him he is fierce, almost frenzied, yet

255

perfectly sane. While here he is quiet, seldom speaks except when spoken to, and is taciturn with strangers. He often comes to my cabin and sits beside the fire for hours. I think he finds pleasure in the conversation and laughter of friends. He is fond of the children, and would do anything for my sister Betty."

"His life must be lonely and sad," remarked Joe.

"The life of any borderman is that; but Wetzel's is particularly so."

"What is he called by the Indians?"

"They call him Atelang, or, in English, Deathwind."

"By George! That's what Silvertip said in French—'Le Vent de la Mort.'"

"Yes; you have it right. A French fur trader gave Wetzel that name years ago, and it has clung to him. The Indians say the Deathwind blows through the forest whenever Wetzel stalks on their trail."

"Colonel Zane, don't you think me superstitious," whispered Joe, leaning toward the colonel, "but I heard that wind blow through the forest."

"What!" ejaculated Colonel Zane. He saw that Joe was in earnest, for the remembrance of the moan had more than once paled his cheek and caused beads of perspiration to collect on his brow.

Joe related the circumstances of that night, and at the end of his narrative Colonel Zane sat silent and thoughtful.

"You don't really think it was Wetzel who moaned?" he asked, at length.

"No, I don't," replied Joe quickly; "but, Colonel Zane, I heard that moan as plainly as I can hear your voice. I heard it twice. Now, what was it?"

"Jonathan said the same thing to me once. He had been out hunting with Wetzel; they separated, and during the night Jonathan heard the wind. The next day he ran across a dead Indian. He believes Wetzel makes the noise, and so do the hunters; but I think it is simply the moan of the night wind through the trees. I have heard it at times, when my very blood seemingly ran cold."

"I tried to think it was the wind soughing through the pines, but am afraid I didn't succeed very well. Anyhow, I knew Wetzel instantly, just as Jeff Lynn said I would. He killed those Indians in an instant, and he must have an iron arm."

"Wetzel excels in strength and speed any man, red or white, on the frontier. He can run away from Jonathan, who is as swift as an Indian. He's stronger than any of the other men. I remember one day old Hugh Bennet's wagon wheels stuck in a bog down by the creek. Hugh tried, as several others did, to move the wheels; but they couldn't be made to budge. Along came Wetzel, pushed away the men, and lifted the wagon unaided. It would take hours to tell you about him. In brief, among all the border scouts and hunters Wetzel stands alone. No wonder the Indians fear him. He is as swift as an eagle, strong as mountain-ash, keen as a fox, and absolutely tireless and implacable."

"How long have you been here, Colonel Zane?"

"More than twelve years, and it has been one long fight."

"I'm afraid I'm too late for the fun," said Joe, with his quiet laugh.

"Not by about twelve more years," answered Colonel Zane, studying the expression on Joe's face. "When I came out here years ago I had the same adventurous spirit which I see in you. It has been considerably quelled, however. I have seen many a daring young fellow get the border fever, and with it his death. Let me advise you to learn the ways of the hunters; to watch some one skilled in woodcraft. Perhaps Wetzel himself will take you in hand. I don't mind saying that he spoke of you to me in a tone I never heard Lew use before."

"He did?" questioned Joe, eagerly, flushing with pleasure. "Do you think he'd take me out? Dare I ask him?"

"Don't be impatient. Perhaps I can arrange it. Come over here now to Metzar's place. I want to make you acquainted with him. These boys have all been cutting timber; they've just come in for dinner. Be easy and quiet with them; then you'll get on."

Colonel Zane introduced Joe to five sturdy boys and left him in their company. Joe sat down on a log outside a cabin and leisurely surveyed the young men. They all looked about the same: strong without being heavy, light-haired and bronze-faced. In their turn they carefully judged Joe. A newcomer from the East was always regarded with some doubt. If they expected to hear Joe talk much they were mistaken. He appeared good-natured, but not too friendly.

"Fine weather we're havin'," said Dick Metzar.

"Fine," agreed Joe, laconically.

"Like frontier life?"

"Sure."

A silence ensued after this breaking of the ice. The boys were awaiting their turn at a little wooden bench upon which stood a bucket of water and a basin.

"Hear ye got ketched by some Shawnees?" remarked another youth, as he rolled up his shirt-sleeves. They all looked at Joe now. It was not improbably their estimate of him would be greatly influenced by the way he answered this question.

"Yes; was captive for three days."

"Did ye knock any redskins over?" This question was artfully put to draw Joe out. Above all things, the bordermen detested boastfulness; tried on Joe the ruse failed signally.

"I was scared speechless most of the time," answered Joe, with his pleasant smile.

"By gosh, I don't blame ye!" burst out Will Metzar. "I hed that experience onct, an' onct's enough."

The boys laughed and looked in a more friendly manner at Joe. Though he said he had been frightened, his cool and careless manner belied his words. In Joe's low voice and clear, gray eye there was something potent and magnetic, which subtly influenced those with whom he came in contact.

While his new friends were at dinner Joe strolled over to where Colonel Zane sat on the doorstep of his home.

"How did you get on with the boys?" inquired the colonel.

"All right, I hope. Say, Colonel Zane, I'd like to talk to your Indian guide."

Colonel Zane spoke a few words in the Indian language to the guide, who left his post and came over to them. The colonel then had a short conversation with him, at the conclusion of which he pointed toward Joe.

"How do—shake," said Tome, extending his hand.

Joe smiled, and returned the friendly hand-pressure.

"Shawnee—ketch'um?" asked the Indian, in his fairly intelligible English.

Joe nodded his head, while Colonel Zane spoke once more in Shawnee, explaining the cause of Silvertip's emnity.

"Shawnee—chief—one—bad—Injun," replied Tome, seriously. "Silvertip—mad—thunder-mad. Ketch'um paleface—scalp'um sure."

After giving this warning the chief returned to his former position near the corner of the cabin.

"He can talk in English fairly well, much better than the Shawnee brave who talked with me the other day," observed Joe.

"Some of the Indians speak the language almost fluently," said Colonel Zane. "You could hardly have distinguished Logan's speech from a white man's. Corn-planter uses good English, as also does my brother's wife, a Wyandot girl."

"Did your brother marry an Indian?" and Joe plainly showed his surprise.

"Indeed he did, and a most beautiful girl she is. I'll tell you Isaac's story some time. He was a captive among the Wyandots for ten years. The chief's daughter, Myeerah, loved him, kept him from being tortured, and finally saved him from the stake."

"Well, that floors me," said Joe; "yet I don't see why it should. I'm just surprised. Where is your brother now?"

"He lives with the tribe. He and Myeerah are working hard for peace. We are now on more friendly terms with the great Wyandots, or Hurons, as we call them, than ever before."

"Who is this big man coming from the the fort?" asked Joe, suddenly observing a stalwart frontiersman approaching.

"Major Sam McColloch. You have met him. He's the man who jumped his horse from yonder bluff."

"Jonathan and he have the same look, the same swing," observed Joe, as he ran his eye over the major. His faded buckskin costume, beaded, fringed, and laced, was similar to that of the colonel's brother. Powder-flask and bullet-pouch were made from cow-horns and slung around his neck on deerhide strings. The hunting coat was unlaced, exposing, under the long, fringed borders, a tunic of the same well-tanned, but finer and softer, material. As he walked, the flaps of his coat fell back, showing a belt containing two knives, sheathed in heavy buckskin, and a bright tomahawk. He carried a long rifle in the hollow of his arm.

"These hunters have the same kind of buckskin suits," continued Joe; "still, it doesn't seem to me the clothes make the resemblance to each other. The way these men stand, walk and act is what strikes me particularly, as in the case of Wetzel."

"I know what you mean. The flashing eye, the erect poise of expectation, and the springy step—those, my lad, come from a life spent in the woods. Well, it's a grand way to live."

"Colonel, my horse is laid up," said Major McColloch, coming to the steps. He bowed pleasantly to Joe.

"So you are going to Short Creek? You can have one of my horses; but first come inside and we'll talk over you expedition."

The afternoon passed uneventfully for Joe. His brother and Mr. Wells were absorbed in plans for their future work, and Nell and Kate were resting; therefore he was forced to find such amusement or occupation as was possible in or near the stockade.

CHAPTER IX.

Joe went to bed that night with a promise to himself to rise early next morning, for he had been invited to take part in a "raising," which term meant that a new cabin was to be erected, and such task was ever an event in the lives of the settlers.

The following morning Joe rose early, dressing himself in a complete buckskin suit, for which he had exchanged his good garments of cloth. Never before had he felt so comfortable. He wanted to hop, skip and jump. The soft, undressed buckskin was as warm and smooth as silk-plush; the weight so light, the moccasins so well-fitting and springy, that he had to put himself under considerable restraint to keep from capering about like a frolicsome colt.

The possession of this buckskin outfit, and the rifle and accouterments which went with the bargain, marked the last stage in Joe's surrender to the border fever. The silent, shaded glens, the mystery of the woods, the breath of this wild, free life claimed him from this moment entirely and forever.

He met the others, however, with a serene face, showing no trace of the emotion which welled up strongly from his heart. Nell glanced shyly at him; Kate playfully voiced her admiration; Jim met him with a brotherly ridicule which bespoke his affection as well as his amusement; but Colonel Zane, having once yielded to the same burning, riotous craving for freedom which now stirred in the boy's heart, understood, and felt warmly drawn toward the lad. He said nothing, though as he watched Joe his eyes were grave and kind. In his long frontier life, where many a day measured the life and fire of ordinary years, he had seen lad after lad go down before this forest fever. It was well, he thought, because the freedom of the soil depended on these wild, light-footed boys; yet it always made him sad. How many youths, his brother among them, lay under the fragrant pine-needle carpet of the forest, in their last earthly sleep!

The "raising" brought out all the settlement—the women to look on and gossip, while the children played; the men to bend their backs in the moving of the heavy timbers. They celebrated the erection of a new cabin as a noteworthy event. As a social function it had a prominent place in the settlers' short list of pleasures.

Joe watched the proceeding with the same pleasure and surprise he had felt in everything pertaining to border life.

To him this log-raising appeared the hardest kind of labor. Yet it was plain these hardy men, these low-voiced women, and merry children regarded the work as something far more significant than the mere building of a cabin. After a while he understood the meaning of the scene. A kindred spirit, the spirit of the pioneer, drew them all into one large family. This was another cabin; another home; another advance toward the conquering of the wilderness, for which these brave men and women were giving their lives. In the bright-eyed children's glee, when they clapped their little hands at the mounting logs, Joe saw the progress, the march of civilization.

"Well, I'm sorry you're to leave us to-night," remarked Colonel Zane to Joe, as the young man came over to where he, his wife, and sister watched the work. "Jonathan said all was ready for your departure at sundown."

"Do we travel by night?"

"Indeed, yes, my lad. There are Indians everywhere on the river. I think, however, with Jack and Lew handling the paddles, you will slip by safely. The plan is to keep along the south shore all night; then cross over at a place called Girty's Point, where you are to remain in hiding during daylight. From there you paddle up Yellow Creek; then portage across country to the head of the Tuscarwawas. Another night's journey will then bring you to the Village of Peace."

Jim and Mr. Wells, with his nieces, joined the party now, and all stood watching as the last logs were put in place.

"Colonel Zane, my first log-raising is an education to me," said the young minister, in his earnest manner. "This scene is so full of life. I never saw such goodwill among laboring men. Look at that brawny-armed giant standing on the topmost log. How he whistles as he swings his ax! Mr. Wells, does it not impress you?"

"The pioneers must be brothers because of their isolation and peril; to be brothers means to love one another; to love one another is to love God. What you see in this fraternity is God. And I want to see this same beautiful feeling among the Indians."

"I have seen it," said Colonel Zane, to the old missionary. "When I came out here alone twelve years ago the Indians were peaceable. If the pioneers had paid for land, as I paid Cornplanter, there would never have been a border war. But no; the settlers must grasp every acre they could. Then the Indians rebelled; then the Girtys and their allies spread discontent, and now the border is a bloody warpath."

"Have the Jesuit missionaries accomplished anything with these war tribes?" inquired Jim.

"No; their work has been chiefly among the Indians near Detroit and northward. The Hurons, Delawares, Shawnees and other western tribes have been demoralized by the French traders' rum, and incited to fierce hatred by Girty and his renegades. Your work at Gnaddenhutten must be among these hostile tribes, and it is surely a hazardous undertaking."

"My life is God's," murmured the old minister. No fear could assail his steadfast faith.

"Jim, it strikes me you'd be more likely to impress these Indians Colonel Zane spoke of if you'd get a suit like mine and wear a knife and tomahawk," interposed Joe, cheerfully. "Then, if you couldn't convert, you could scalp them."

"Well, well, let us hope for the best," said Colonel Zane, when the laughter had subsided. "We'll go over to dinner now. Come, all of you. Jonathan, bring Wetzel. Betty, make him come, if you can."

As the party slowly wended its way toward the colonel's cabin Jim and Nell found themselves side by side. They had not exchanged a word since the evening previous, when Jim had kissed her. Unable to look at each other now, and finding speech difficult, they walked in embarrassed silence.

"Doesn't Joe look splendid in his hunting suit?" asked Jim, presently.

"I hadn't noticed. Yes; he looks well," replied Nell, carelessly. She was too indifferent to be natural.

"Are you angry with him?"

"Certainly not."

Jim was always simple and frank in his relations with women. He had none of his brother's fluency of speech, with neither confidence, boldness nor understanding of the intricate mazes of a woman's moods.

"But—you are angry with—me?" he whispered.

Nell flushed to her temples, yet she did not raise her eyes nor reply.

"It was a terrible thing for me to do," went on Jim, hesitatingly. "I don't know why I took advantage—of—of your mistaking me for Joe. If you only hadn't held up your mouth. No—I don't mean that—of course you didn't. But—well, I couldn't help it. I'm guilty. I have thought of little else. Some wonderful feeling has possessed me ever since—since—"

"What has Joe been saying about me?" demanded Nell, her eyes burning like opals.

"Why, hardly anything," answered Jim, haltingly. "I took him to task about—about what I considered might be wrong to you. Joe has never been very careful of young ladies' feelings, and I thought—well, it was none of my business. He said he honestly cared for you, that you had taught him how unworthy he was of a good woman. But he's wrong there. Joe is wild and reckless, yet his heart is a well of gold. He is a diamond in the rough. Just now he is possessed by wild notions of hunting Indians and roaming through the forests; but he'll come round all right. I wish I could tell you how much he has done for me, how much I love him, how I know him! He can be made worthy of any woman. He will outgrow this fiery, daring spirit, and then—won't you help him?"

"I will, if he will let me," softly whispered Nell, irresistibly drawn by the strong, earnest love thrilling in his voice.

CHAPTER X.

Once more out under the blue-black vault of heaven, with its myriads of twinkling stars, the voyagers resumed their westward journey. Whispered farewells of new but sincere friends lingered in their ears. Now the great looming bulk of the fort above them faded into the obscure darkness, leaving a feeling as if a protector had gone—perhaps forever. Admonished to absolute silence by the stern guides, who seemed indeed to have embarked upon a dark and deadly mission, the voyagers lay back in the canoes and thought and listened. The water eddied with soft gurgles in the wake of the racing canoes; but that musical sound was all they heard. The paddles might have been shadows, for all the splash they made; they cut the water swiftly and noiselessly. Onward the frail barks glided into black space, side by side, close under the overhanging willows. Long moments passed into long hours, as the guides paddled tirelessly as if their sinews were cords of steel.

With gray dawn came the careful landing of the canoes, a cold breakfast eaten under cover of a willow thicket, and the beginning of a long day while they were lying hidden from the keen eyes of Indian scouts, waiting for the friendly mantle of night.

The hours dragged until once more the canoes were launched, this time not on the broad Ohio, but on a stream that mirrored no shining stars as it flowed still and somber under the dense foliage.

The voyagers spoke not, nor whispered, nor scarcely moved, so menacing had become the slow, listening caution of Wetzel and Zane. Snapping of twigs somewhere in the inscrutable darkness delayed them for long moments. Any movement the air might resound with the horrible Indian war-whoop. Every second was heavy with fear. How marvelous that these scouts, penetrating the wilderness of gloom, glided on surely, silently, safely! Instinct, or the eyes of the lynx, guide their course. But another dark night wore on to the tardy dawn, and each of its fearful hours numbered miles past and gone.

The sun was rising in ruddy glory when Wetzel ran his canoe into the bank just ahead of a sharp bend in the stream.

"Do we get out here?" asked Jim, seeing Jonathan turn his canoe toward Wetzel's.

"The village lies yonder, around the bend," answered the guide. "Wetzel cannot go there, so I'll take you all in my canoe."

"There's no room; I'll wait," replied Joe, quietly. Jim noted his look—a strange, steady glance it was—and then saw him fix his eyes upon Nell, watching her until the canoe passed around the green-bordered bend in the stream.

Unmistakable signs of an Indian town were now evident. Dozens of graceful birchen canoes lay upon the well-cleared banks; a log bridge spanned the stream; above the slight ridge of rising ground could be seen the poles of Indian teepees.

As the canoe grated upon the sandy beach a little Indian boy, who was playing in the shallow water, raised his head and smiled.

"That's an Indian boy," whispered Kate.

"The dear little fellow!" exclaimed Nell.

The boy came running up to them, when they were landed, with pleasure and confidence shining in his dusky eyes. Save for tiny buckskin breeches, he was naked, and his shiny skin gleamed gold-bronze in the sunlight. He was a singularly handsome child.

"Me—Benny," he lisped in English, holding up his little hand to Nell.

The action was as loving and trusting as any that could have been manifested by a white child. Jonathan Zane stared with a curious light in his dark eyes; Mr. Wells and Jim looked as though they doubted the evidence of their own sight. Here, even in an Indian boy, was incontestable proof that the savage nature could be tamed and civilized.

With a tender exclamation Nell bent over the child and kissed him.

Jonathan Zane swung his canoe up-stream for the purpose of bringing Joe. The trim little bark slipped out of sight round the bend. Presently its gray, curved nose peeped from behind the willows; then the canoe swept into view again. There was only one person in it, and that the guide.

"Where is my brother?" asked Jim, in amazement.

"Gone," answered Zane, quietly.

"Gone! What do you mean? Gone? Perhaps you have missed the spot where you left him."

"They're both gone."

Nell and Jim gazed at each other with slowly whitening faces.

"Come, I'll take you up to the village," said Zane, getting out of his canoe. All noticed that he was careful to take his weapons with him.

"Can't you tell us what it means—this disappearance?" asked Jim, his voice low and anxious.

"They're gone, canoe and all. I knew Wetzel was going, but I didn't calkilate on the lad. Mebbe he followed Wetzel, mebbe he didn't," answered the taciturn guide, and he spoke no more.

In his keen expectation and wonder as to what the village would be like, Jim momentarily forgot his brother's disappearance, and when he arrived at the top of the bank he surveyed the scene with eagerness. What he saw was more imposing than the Village of Peace which he had conjured up in his imagination. Confronting him was a level plain, in the center of which stood a wide, low structure surrounded by log cabins, and these in turn encircled by Indian teepees. A number of large trees, mostly full-foliaged maples, shaded the clearing. The settlement swarmed with Indians. A few shrill halloes uttered by the first observers of the newcomers brought braves, maidens and children trooping toward the party with friendly curiosity.

Jonathan Zane stepped before a cabin adjoining the large structure, and called in at the open door. A short, stoop-shouldered white man, clad in faded linsey, appeared on the threshold. His serious, lined face had the unmistakable benevolent aspect peculiar to most teachers of the gospel.

"Mr. Zeisberger, I've fetched a party from Fort Henry," said Zane, indicating those he had guided. Then, without another word, never turning his dark face to the right or left, he hurried down the lane through the throng of Indians.

Jim remembered, as he saw the guide vanish over the bank of the creek, that he had heard Colonel Zane say that Jonathan, as well as Wetzel, hated the sight of an Indian. No doubt long years of war and bloodshed had rendered these two great hunters callous. To them there could be no discrimination—an Indian was an Indian.

"Mr. Wells, welcome to the Village of Peace!" exclaimed Mr. Zeisberger, wringing the old missionary's hand. "The years have not been so long but that I remember you."

"Happy, indeed, am I to get here, after all these dark, dangerous journeys," returned Mr. Wells. "I have brought my nieces, Nell and Kate, who were children when you left Williamsburg, and this young man, James Downs, a minister of God, and earnest in his hope for our work."

"A glorious work it is! Welcome, young ladies, to our peaceful village. And, young man, I greet you with heartfelt thankfulness. We need young men. Come in, all of your, and share my cabin. I'll have your luggage brought up. I have lived in this hut alone. With some little labor, and the magic touch women bring to the making of a home, we can be most comfortable here."

Mr. Zeisberger gave his own room to the girls, assuring them with a smile that it was the most luxurious in the village. The apartment contained a chair, a table, and a bed of Indian blankets and buffalo robes. A few pegs driven in the chinks between the logs completed the furnishings. Sparse as were the comforts, they appealed warmly to the girls, who, weary from their voyage, lay down to rest.

"I am not fatigued," said Mr. Wells, to his old friend. "I want to hear all about your work, what you have done, and what you hope to do."

"We have met with wonderful success, far beyond our wildest dreams," responded Mr. Zeisberger. "Certainly we have been blessed of God."

Then the missionary began a long, detailed account of the Moravian Mission's efforts among the western tribes. The work lay chiefly among the Delawares, a noble nation of redmen, intelligent, and wonderfully susceptible to the teaching of the gospel. Among the eastern Delawares, living on the other side of the Allegheny Mountains, the missionaries had succeeded in converting many; and it was chiefly through the western explorations of Frederick Post that his Church decided the Indians of the west could as well be taught to lead Christian lives. The first attempt to convert the western redmen took place upon the upper Allegheny, where many Indians, including Allemewi, a blind Delaware chief, accepted the faith. The mission decided, however, it would be best to move farther west, where the Delawares had migrated and were more numerous.

In April, 1770, more than ten years before, sixteen canoes, filled with converted Indians and missionaries, drifted down the Allegheny to Fort Pitt; thence down the Ohio to the Big Beaver; up that stream and far into the Ohio wilderness.

Upon a tributary of the Muskingong, called the Tuscarwawas, a settlement was founded. Near and far the news was circulated. Redmen from all tribes came flocking to the new colony. Chiefs and warriors, squaws and maidens, were attracted by the new doctrine of the converted Indians. They were astonished at the missionaries' teachings. Many doubted, some were converted, all listened. Great excitement prevailed when old Glickhican, one of the wisest chiefs of the Turtle tribe of the Delawares, became a convert to the palefaces' religion.

The interest widened, and in a few years a beautiful, prosperous town arose, which was called Village of Peace. The Indians of the warlike tribes bestowed the appropriate name. The vast forests were rich in every variety of game; the deep, swift streams were teeming with fish. Meat and grain in abundance, buckskin for clothing, and soft furs for winter garments were to be had for little labor. At first only a few wigwams were erected. Soon a large log structure was thrown up and used as a church. Then followed a school, a mill, and a workshop. The verdant fields were cultivated and surrounded by rail fences. Horses and cattle grazed with the timid deer on the grassy plains.

The Village of Peace blossomed as a rose. The reports of the love and happiness existing in this converted community spread from mouth to mouth, from town to town, with the result that inquisitive savages journeyed from all points to see this haven. Peaceful and hostile Indians were alike amazed at the change in their brethren. The good-fellowship and industry of the converts had a widespread and wonderful influence. More, perhaps, than any other thing, the great fields of waving corn, the hills covered with horses and cattle, those evidences of abundance, impressed the visitors with the well-being of the Christians. Bands of traveling Indians, whether friendly or otherwise, were treated with hospitality, and never sent away empty-handed. They were asked to partake of the abundance and solicited to come again.

A feature by no means insignificant in the popularity of the village was the church bell. The Indians loved music, and this bell charmed them. On still nights the savages in distant towns could hear at dusk the deep-toned, mellow notes of the bell summoning the worshipers to the evening service. Its ringing clang, so strange, so sweet, so solemn, breaking the vast dead wilderness quiet, haunted the savage ear as though it were a call from a woodland god.

"You have arrived most opportunely," continued Mr. Zeisberger. "Mr. Edwards and Mr. Young are working to establish other missionary posts. Heckewelder is here now in the interest of this branching out."

"How long will it take me to learn the Delaware language?" inquired Jim.

"Not long. You do not, however, need to speak the Indian tongue, for we have excellent interpreters."

"We heard much at Fort Pitt and Fort Henry about the danger, as well as uselessness, of our venture," Jim continued. "The frontiersmen declared that every rod of the way was beset with savage foes, and that, even in the unlikely event of our arriving safely at the Village of Peace, we would then be hemmed in by fierce, vengeful tribes."

"Hostile savages abound here, of course; but we do not fear them. We invite them. Our work is to convert the wicked, to teach them to lead good, useful lives. We will succeed."

Jim could not help warming to the minister for his unswervable faith, his earnest belief that the work of God could not fail; nevertheless, while he felt no fear and intended to put all his heart in the work, he remembered with disquietude Colonel Zane's warnings. He thought of the wonderful precaution and eternal vigilance of Jonathan and Wetzel—men of all men who most understood Indian craft and cunning. It might well be possible that these good missionaries, wrapped up in saving the souls of these children of the forest, so full of God's teachings as to have little mind for aught else, had no knowledge of the Indian nature beyond what the narrow scope of their work invited. If what these frontiersmen asserted was true, then the ministers' zeal had struck them blind.

Jim had a growing idea of the way in which the savages could be best taught. He resolved to go slowly; to study the redmen's natures; not to preach one word of the gospel to them until he had mastered their language and could convey to their simple minds the real truth. He would make Christianity as clear to them as were the deer-trails on the moss and leaves of the forest.

"Ah, here you are. I hope you have rested well," said Mr. Zeisberger, when at the conclusion of this long recital Nell and Kate came into the room.

"Thank you, we feel much better," answered Kate. The girls certainly looked refreshed. The substitution of clean gowns for their former travel-stained garments made a change that called forth the minister's surprise and admiration.

"My! My! Won't Edwards and Young beg me to keep them here now!" he exclaimed, his pleased eyes resting on Nell's piquant beauty and Kate's noble proportions and rich coloring. "Come; I will show you over the Village of Peace."

"Are all these Indians Christians?" asked Jim.

"No, indeed. These Indians you see here, and out yonder under the shade, though they are friendly, are not Christians. Our converts employ themselves in the fields or shops. Come; take a peep in here. This is where we preach in the evenings and during inclement weather. On pleasant days we use the maple grove yonder."

Jim and the others looked in at the door of the large log structure. They saw an immense room, the floor covered with benches, and a raised platform at one end. A few windows let in the light. Spacious and barn-like was this apartment; but undoubtedly, seen through the beaming eyes of the missionary, it was a grand amphitheater for worship. The hard-packed clay floor was velvet carpet; the rude seats soft as eiderdown; the platform with its white-oak cross, an altar of marble and gold.

"This is one of our shops," said Mr. Zeisberger, leading them to a cabin. "Here we make brooms, harness for the horses, farming implements—everything useful that we can. We have a forge here. Behold an Indian blacksmith!"

The interior of the large cabin presented a scene of bustling activity. Twenty or more Indians bent their backs in earnest employment. In one corner a savage stood holding a piece of red-hot iron on an anvil, while a brawny brave wielded a sledge-hammer. The sparks flew; the anvil rang. In another corner a circle of braves sat around a pile of dried grass and flags. They were twisting and fashioning these materials into baskets. At a bench three Indian carpenters were pounding and sawing. Young braves ran back and forth, carrying pails, rough-hewn boards and blocks of wood.

Instantly struck by two things, Jim voiced his curiosity:

"Why do these Indians all wear long hair, smooth and shiny, without adornment?"

"They are Christians. They wear neither headdress, war-bonnet, nor scalp-lock," replied Mr. Zeisberger, with unconscious pride.

"I did not expect to see a blacksmith's anvil out here in the wilderness. Where did you procure these tools?"

"We have been years getting them here. Some came by way of the Ohio River; others overland from Detroit. That anvil has a history. It was lost once, and lay for years in the woods, until some Indians found it again. It is called the Ringing Stone, and Indians come from miles around to see and hear it."

The missionary pointed out wide fields of corn, now growing yellow, and hillsides doted with browsing cattle, droves of sturdy-limbed horses, and pens of fat, grunting pigs—all of which attested to the growing prosperity of the Village of Peace.

On the way back to the cabin, while the others listened to and questioned Mr. Zeisberger, Jim was silent and thoughtful, for his thoughts reverted to his brother.

Later, as he walked with Nell by the golden-fringed stream, he spoke of Joe.

"Joe wanted so much to hunt with Wetzel. He will come back; surely he will return to us when he has satisfied his wild craving for adventure. Do you not think so?"

There was an eagerness that was almost pleading in Jim's voice. What he so much hoped for—that no harm had befallen Joe, and that he would return—he doubted. He needed the encouragement of his hope.

"Never," answered Nell, solemnly.

"Oh, why—why do you say that?"

"I saw him look at you—a strange, intent glance. He gazed long at me as we separated. Oh! I can feel his eyes. No; he will never come back."

"Nell, Nell, you do not mean he went away deliberately—because, oh! I cannot say it."

"For no reason, except that the wilderness called him more than love for you or—me."

"No, no," returned Jim, his face white. "You do not understand. He really loved you—I know it. He loved me, too. Ah, how well! He has gone because—I can't tell you."

"Oh, Jim, I hope—he loved—me," sobbed Nell, bursting into tears. "His coldness—his neglect those—last few days—hurt me—so. If he cared—as you say—I won't be—so—miserable."

"We are both right—you when you say he will never return, and I when I say he loved us both," said Jim sadly, as the bitter certainty forced itself into his mind.

As she sobbed softly, and he gazed with set, stern face into the darkening forest, the deep, mellow notes of the church bell pealed out. So thrilled, so startled were they by this melody wondrously breaking the twilight stillness, that they gazed mutely at each other. Then they remembered. It was the missionary's bell summoning the Christian Indians to the evening service.

CHAPTER XI.

The, sultry, drowsy, summer days passed with no untoward event to mar their slumbering tranquillity. Life for the newcomers to the Village of Peace brought a content, the like of which they had never dreamed of. Mr. Wells at once began active work among the Indians, preaching to them through an interpreter; Nell and Kate, in hours apart from household duties, busied themselves brightening their new abode, and Jim entered upon the task of acquainting himself with the modes and habits of the redmen. Truly, the young people might have found perfect happiness in this new and novel life, if only Joe had returned. His disappearance and subsequent absence furnished a theme for many talks and many a quiet hour of dreamy sadness. The fascination of his personality had been so impelling that long after it was withdrawn a charm lingered around everything which reminded them of him; a subtle and sweet memory, with perverse and half bitter persistence, returned hauntingly. No trace of Joe had been seen by any of the friendly Indian runners. He was gone into the mazes of deep-shadowed forests, where to hunt for him would be like striving to trail the flight of a swallow. Two of those he had left behind always remembered him, and in their thoughts followed him in his wanderings.

Jim settled down to his study of Indians with single-heartedness of purpose. He spent part of every morning with the interpreters, with whose assistance he rapidly acquired the Delaware language. He went freely among the Indians, endeavoring to win their good-will. There were always fifty to an hundred visiting Indians at the village; sometimes, when the missionaries had advertised a special meeting, there were assembled in the shady maple grove as many as five hundred savages. Jim had, therefore, opportunities to practice his offices of friendliness.

Fortunately for him, he at once succeeded in establishing himself in the good graces of Glickhican, the converted Delaware chief. The wise old Indian was of inestimable value to Jim. Early in their acquaintance he evinced an earnest regard for the young minister, and talked with him for

271

hours.

From Glickhican Jim learned the real nature of the redmen. The Indian's love of freedom and honor, his hatred of subjection and deceit, as explained by the good old man, recalled to Jim Colonel Zane's estimate of the savage character. Surely, as the colonel had said, the Indians had reason for their hatred of the pioneers. Truly, they were a blighted race.

Seldom had the rights of the redmen been thought of. The settler pushed onward, plodding, as it were, behind his plow with a rifle. He regarded the Indian as little better than a beast; he was easier to kill than to tame. How little the settler knew the proud independence, the wisdom, the stainless chastity of honor, which belonged so truly to many Indian chiefs!

The redmen were driven like hounded deer into the untrodden wilds. From freemen of the forests, from owners of the great boundless plains, they passed to stern, enduring fugitives on their own lands. Small wonder that they became cruel where once they had been gentle! Stratagem and cunning, the night assault, the daylight ambush took the place of their one-time open warfare. Their chivalrous courage, that sublime inheritance from ancestors who had never known the paleface foe, degenerated into a savage ferocity.

Interesting as was this history to Jim, he cared more for Glickhican's rich portrayal of the redmen's domestic life, for the beautiful poetry of his tradition and legends. He heard with delight the exquisite fanciful Indian lore. From these romantic legends, beautiful poems, and marvelous myths he hoped to get ideas of the Indian's religion. Sweet and simple as childless dreams were these quaint tales—tales of how the woodland fairies dwelt in fern-carpeted dells; how at sunrise they came out to kiss open the flowers; how the forest walks were spirit-haunted paths; how the leaves whispered poetry to the winds; how the rocks harbored Indian gods and masters who watched over their chosen ones.

Glickhican wound up his long discourses by declaring he had never lied in the whole course of his seventy years, had never stolen, never betrayed, never murdered, never killed, save in self-defence. Gazing at the chief's fine features, now calm, yet showing traces of past storms, Jim believed he spoke the truth.

When the young minister came, however, to study the hostile Indians that flocked to the village, any conclusive delineation of character, or any satisfactory analysis of their mental state in regard to the paleface religion, eluded him. Their passive, silent, sphinx-like secretiveness was baffling. Glickhican had taught him how to propitiate the friendly braves, and with these he was successful. Little he learned, however, from the unfriendly ones. When making gifts to these redmen he could never be certain that his offerings were appreciated. The jewels and gold he had brought west with him went to the French traders, who in exchange gave him trinkets, baubles, bracelets and weapons. Jim made hundreds of presents. Boldly going up to befeathered and befringed chieftains, he offered them knives, hatchets, or strings of silvery beads. Sometimes his kindly offerings were repelled with a haughty stare; at other times they would be accepted coldly, suspiciously, as if the gifts brought some unknown obligation.

For a white man it was a never-to-be-forgotten experience to see eight or ten of these grim, slowly stepping forest kings, arrayed in all the rich splendor of their costume, stalking among the teepees of the Village of Peace. Somehow, such a procession always made Jim shiver. The singing, praying and preaching they heard unmoved. No emotion was visible on their bronzed faces; nothing changed their unalterable mien. Had they not moved, or gazed with burning eyes, they would have been statues. When these chieftains looked at the converted Indians, some of whom were braves of their nations, the contempt in their glances betrayed that they now regarded these Christian Indians as belonging to an alien race.

Among the chiefs Glickhican pointed out to Jim were Wingenund, the Delaware; Tellane, the Half-King; Shingiss and Kotoxen—all of the Wolf tribe of the Delawares.

Glickhican was careful to explain that the Delaware nation had been divided into the Wolf and Turtle tribes, the former warlike people, and the latter peaceable. Few of the Wolf tribe had gone over to the new faith, and those who had were scorned. Wingenund, the great power of the Delawares—indeed, the greatest of all the western tribes—maintained a neutral attitude toward the Village of Peace. But it was well known that his right-hand war-chiefs, Pipe and Wishtonah, remained coldly opposed.

Jim turned all he had learned over and over in his mind, trying to construct part of it to fit into a sermon that would be different from any the Indians had ever heard. He did not want to preach far over their heads. If possible, he desired to keep to their ideals—for he deemed them more beautiful than his own—and to conduct his teaching along the simple lines of their belief, so that when he stimulated and developed their minds he could pass from what they knew to the unknown Christianity of the white man.

His first address to the Indians was made one day during the indisposition of Mr. Wells—who had been over-working himself—and the absence of the other missionaries. He did not consider himself at all ready for preaching, and confined his efforts to simple, earnest talk, a recital of the thoughts he had assimilated while living here among the Indians.

Amazement would not have described the state of his feelings when he learned that he had made a powerful impression. The converts were loud in his praise; the unbelievers silent and thoughtful. In spite of himself, long before he had been prepared, he was launched on his teaching. Every day he was called upon to speak; every day one savage, at least, was convinced; every day the throng of interested Indians was augmented. The elder missionaries were quite overcome with joy; they pressed him day after day to speak, until at length he alone preached during the afternoon service.

The news flew apace; the Village of Peace entertained more redmen than ever before. Day by day the faith gained a stronger foothold. A kind of religious trance affected some of the converted Indians, and this greatly influenced the doubting ones. Many of them half believed the Great Manitou had come.

Heckewelder, the acknowledged leader of the western Moravian Mission, visited the village at this time, and, struck by the young missionary's success, arranged a three days' religious festival. Indian runners were employed to carry invitations to all the tribes. The Wyandots in the west, the Shawnees in the south, and the Delawares in the north were especially requested to come. No deception was practiced to lure the distant savages to the Village of Peace. They were asked to come, partake of the feasts, and listen to the white man's teaching.

CHAPTER XII.

"The Groves Were God's First Temples."

From dawn until noon on Sunday bands of Indians arrived at the Village of Peace. Hundreds of canoes glided down the swift stream and bumped their prows into the pebbly beach. Groups of mounted warriors rode out of the forests into the clearing; squaws with papooses, maidens carrying wicker baskets, and children playing with rude toys, came trooping along the bridle-paths.

Gifts were presented during the morning, after which the visitors were feasted. In the afternoon all assembled in the grove to hear the preaching.

The maple grove wherein the service was to be conducted might have been intended by Nature for just such a purpose as it now fulfilled. These trees were large, spreading, and situated far apart. Mossy stones and the thick carpet of grass afforded seats for the congregation.

Heckewelder—a tall, spare, and kindly appearing man—directed the arranging of the congregation. He placed the converted Indians just behind the knoll upon which the presiding minister was to stand. In a half circle facing the knoll he seated the chieftains and important personages of the various tribes. He then made a short address in the Indian language, speaking of the work of the mission, what wonders it had accomplished, what more good work it hoped to do, and concluded by introducing the young missionary.

While Heckewelder spoke, Jim, who stood just behind, employed the few moments in running his eye over the multitude. The sight which met his gaze was one he thought he would never forget. An involuntary word escaped him.

"Magnificent!" he exclaimed.

The shady glade had been transformed into a theater, from which gazed a thousand dark, still faces. A thousand eagle plumes waved, and ten thousand bright-hued feathers quivered in the soft breeze. The fantastically dressed scalps presented a contrast to the smooth, unadorned heads of the

275

converted redmen. These proud plumes and defiant feathers told the difference between savage and Christian.

In front of the knoll sat fifty chiefs, attentive and dignified. Representatives of every tribe as far west as the Scioto River were numbered in that circle. There were chiefs renowned for war, for cunning, for valor, for wisdom. Their stately presence gave the meeting tenfold importance. Could these chiefs be interested, moved, the whole western world of Indians might be civilized.

Hepote, a Maumee chief, of whom it was said he had never listened to words of the paleface, had the central position in this circle. On his right and left, respectively, sat Shaushoto and Pipe, implacable foes of all white men. The latter's aspect did not belie his reputation. His copper-colored, repulsive visage compelled fear; it breathed vindictiveness and malignity. A singular action of his was that he always, in what must have been his arrogant vanity, turned his profile to those who watched him, and it was a remarkable one; it sloped in an oblique line from the top of his forehead to his protruding chin, resembling somewhat the carved bowl of his pipe, which was of flint and a famed inheritance from his ancestors. From it he took his name. One solitary eagle plume, its tip stained vermilion, stuck from his scalp-lock. It slated backward on a line with his profile.

Among all these chiefs, striking as they were, the figure of Wingenund, the Delaware, stood out alone.

His position was at the extreme left of the circle, where he leaned against a maple. A long, black mantle, trimmed with spotless white, enveloped him. One bronzed arm, circled by a heavy bracelet of gold, held the mantle close about his lofty form. His headdress, which trailed to the ground, was exceedingly beautiful. The eagle plumes were of uniform length and pure white, except the black-pointed tips.

At his feet sat his daughter, Whispering Winds. Her maidens were gathered round her. She raised her soft, black eyes, shining with a wondrous light of surprise and expectation, to the young missionary's face.

Beyond the circle the Indians were massed together, even beyond the limits of the glade. Under the trees on every side sat warriors astride their steeds; some lounged on the green turf; many reclined in the branches of low-spreading maples.

As Jim looked out over the sea of faces he started in surprise. The sudden glance of fiery eyes had impelled his gaze. He recognized Silvertip, the Shawnee chief. The Indian sat motionless on a powerful black horse. Jim started again, for the horse was Joe's thoroughbred, Lance. But Jim had no further time to think of Joe's enemy, for Heckewelder stepped back.

Jim took the vacated seat, and, with a far-reaching, resonant voice began his discourse to the Indians.

"Chieftains, warriors, maidens, children of the forest, listen, and your ears shall hear no lie. I am come from where the sun rises to tell you of the Great

Spirit of the white man.

"Many, many moons ago, as many as blades of grass grow on yonder plain, the Great Spirit of whom I shall speak created the world. He made the sparkling lakes and swift rivers, the boundless plains and tangled forests, over which He caused the sun to shine and the rain to fall. He gave life to the kingly elk, the graceful deer, the rolling bison, the bear, the fox—all the beasts and birds and fishes. But He was not content; for nothing He made was perfect in His sight. He created the white man in His own image, and from this first man's rib He created his mate—a woman. He turned them free in a beautiful forest.

"Life was fair in the beautiful forest. The sun shone always, the birds sang, the waters flowed with music, the flowers cast sweet fragrance on the air. In this forest, where fruit bloomed always, was one tree, the Tree of Life, the apple of which they must not eat. In all this beautiful forest of abundance this apple alone was forbidden them.

"Now evil was born with woman. A serpent tempted her to eat of the apple of Life, and she tempted the man to eat. For their sin the Great Spirit commanded the serpent to crawl forever on his belly, and He drove them from the beautiful forest. The punishment for their sin was to be visited on their children's children, always, until the end of time. The two went afar into the dark forest, to learn to live as best they might. From them all tribes descended. The world is wide. A warrior might run all his days and not reach the setting sun, where tribes of yellow-skins live. He might travel half his days toward the south-wind, where tribes of black-skins abound. People of all colors inhabited the world. They lived in hatred toward one another. They shed each other's blood; they stole each other's lands, gold, and women. They sinned.

"Many moons ago the Great Spirit sorrowed to see His chosen tribe, the palefaces, living in ignorance and sin. He sent His only Son to redeem them, and said if they would listen and believe, and teach the other tribes, He would forgive their sin and welcome them to the beautiful forest.

"That was moons and moons ago, when the paleface killed his brother for gold and lands, and beat his women slaves to make them plant his corn. The Son of the Great Spirit lifted the cloud from the palefaces' eyes, and they saw and learned. So pleased was the Great Spirit that He made the palefaces wiser and wiser, and master of the world. He bid them go afar to teach the ignorant tribes.

"To teach you is why the young paleface journeyed from the rising sun. He wants no lands or power. He has given all that he had. He walks among you without gun or knife. He can gain nothing but the happiness of opening the redmen's eyes.

"The Great Spirit of whom I teach and the Great Manitou, your idol, are the same; the happy hunting ground of the Indian and the beautiful forest of the paleface are the same; the paleface and the redman are the same. There is but one Great Spirit, that is God; but one eternal home, that is heaven; but one human being, that is man.

"The Indian knows the habits of the beaver; he can follow the paths of the forests; he can guide his canoe through the foaming rapids; he is honest, he is brave, he is great; but he is not wise. His wisdom is clouded with the original sin. He lives in idleness; he paints his face; he makes his squaw labor for him, instead of laboring for her; he kills his brothers. He worships the trees and rocks. If he were wise he would not make gods of the swift arrow and bounding canoe; of the flowering ash and the flaming flint. For these things have not life. In his dreams he sees his arrow speed to the reeling deer; in his dreams he sees his canoe shoot over the crest of shining waves; and in his mind he gives them life. When his eyes are opened he will see they have no spirit. The spirit is in his own heart. It guides the arrow to the running deer, and steers the canoe over the swirling current. The spirit makes him find the untrodden paths, and do brave deeds, and love his children and his honor. It makes him meet his foe face to face, and if he is to die it gives him strength to die—a man. The spirit is what makes him different from the arrow, the canoe, the mountain, and all the birds and beasts. For it is born of the Great Spirit, the creator of all. Him you must worship.

"Redmen, this worship is understanding your spirit and teaching it to do good deeds. It is called Christianity. Christianity is love. If you will love the Great Spirit you will love your wives, your children, your brothers, your friends, your foes—you will love the palefaces. No more will you idle in winter and wage wars in summer. You will wear your knife and tomahawk only when you hunt for meat. You will be kind, gentle, loving, virtuous— you will have grown wise. When your days are done you will meet all your loved ones in the beautiful forest. There, where the flowers bloom, the fruits ripen always, where the pleasant water glides and the summer winds whisper sweetly, there peace will dwell forever.

"Comrades, be wise, think earnestly. Forget the wicked paleface; for there are many wicked palefaces. They sell the serpent firewater; they lie and steal and kill. These palefaces' eyes are still clouded. If they do not open they will never see the beautiful forest. You have much to forgive, but those who forgive please the Great Spirit; you must give yourselves to love, but those who love are loved; you must work, but those who work are happy.

"Behold the Village of Peace! Once it contained few; now there are many. Where once the dark forest shaded the land, see the cabins, the farms, the horses, the cattle! Field on field of waving, golden grain shine there under your eyes. The earth has blossomed abundance. Idling and fighting made not these rich harvests. Belief made love; love made wise eyes; wise eyes saw, and lo! there came plenty.

"The proof of love is happiness. These Christian Indians are happy. They are at peace with the redman and the paleface. They till the fields and work in the shops. In days to come cabins and farms and fields of corn will be theirs. They will bring up their children, not to hide in the forest to slay, but to walk hand in hand with the palefaces as equals.

"Oh, open your ears! God speaks to you; peace awaits you! Cast the bitterness from your hearts; it is the serpent-poison. While you hate, God shuts His eyes. You are great on the trail, in the council, in war; now be great in forgiveness. Forgive the palefaces who have robbed you of your lands. Then will come peace. If you do not forgive, the war will go on; you will lose lands and homes, to find unmarked graves under the forest leaves. Revenge is sweet; but it is not wise. The price of revenge is blood and life. Root it out of your hearts. Love these Christian Indians; love the missionaries as they love you; love all living creatures. Your days are but few; therefore, cease the the strife. Let us say, 'Brothers, that is God's word, His law; that is love; that is Christianity!' If you will say from your heart, brother, you are a Christian.

"Brothers, the paleface teacher beseeches you. Think not of this long, bloody war, of your dishonored dead, of your silenced wigwams, of your nameless graves, of your homeless children. Think of the future. One word from you will make peace over all this broad land. The paleface must honor a Christian. He can steal no Christian's land. All the palefaces, as many as the stars of the great white path, dare not invade the Village of Peace. For God smiles here. Listen to His words: 'Come unto me all that are weary and heavy laden, and I will give you rest.'"

Over the multitude brooded an impressive, solemn silence. Then an aged Delaware chief rose, with a mien of profound thought, and slowly paced before the circle of chiefs. Presently he stopped, turned to the awaiting Indians, and spoke:

"Netawatwees is almost persuaded to be a Christian." He resumed his seat.

Another interval of penetrating quiet ensued. At length a venerable-looking chieftain got up:

"White Eyes hears the rumbling thunder in his ears. The smoke blows from his eyes. White Eyes is the oldest chief of the Lenni-Lenape. His days are many; they are full; they draw near the evening of his life; he rejoices that wisdom is come before his sun is set.

"White Eyes believes the young White Father. The ways of the Great Spirit are many as the fluttering leaves; they are strange and secret as the flight of a loon; White Eyes believes the redman's happy hunting grounds need not be forgotten to love the palefaces' God. As a young brave pants and puzzles over his first trail, so the grown warrior feels in his understanding of his God. He gropes blindly through dark ravines.

"White Eyes speaks few words to-day, for he is learning wisdom; he bids his people hearken to the voice of the White Father. War is wrong; peace is best. Love is the way to peace. The paleface advances one step nearer his God. He labors for his home; he keeps the peace; he asks but little; he frees his women. That is well. White Eyes has spoken."

The old chief slowly advanced toward the Christian Indians. He laid aside his knife and tomahawk, and then his eagle plumes and war-bonnet. Bareheaded, he seated himself among the converted redmen. They began chanting in low, murmuring tones.

Amid the breathless silence that followed this act of such great significance, Wingenund advanced toward the knoll with slow, stately step. His dark eye swept the glade with lightning scorn; his glance alone revealed the passion that swayed him.

"Wingenund's ears are keen; they have heard a feather fall in the storm; now they hear a soft-voiced thrush. Wingenund thunders to his people, to his friends, to the chiefs of other tribes: 'Do not bury the hatchet!' The young White Father's tongue runs smooth like the gliding brook; it sings as the thrush calls its mate. Listen; but wait, wait! Let time prove his beautiful tale; let the moons go by over the Village of Peace.

"Wingenund does not flaunt his wisdom. He has grown old among his warriors; he loves them; he fears for them. The dream of the palefaces' beautiful forest glimmers as the rainbow glows over the laughing falls of the river. The dream of the paleface is too beautiful to come true. In the days of long ago, when Wingenund's forefathers heard not the paleface's ax, they lived in love and happiness such as the young White Father dreams may come again. They waged no wars. A white dove sat in every wigwam. The lands were theirs and they were rich. The paleface came with his leaden death, his burning firewater, his ringing ax, and the glory of the redmen faded forever.

"Wingenund seeks not to inflame his braves to anger. He is sick of blood-spilling—not from fear; for Wingenund cannot feel fear. But he asks his people to wait. Remember, the gifts of the paleface ever contained a poisoned arrow. Wingenund's heart is sore. The day of the redman is gone. His sun is setting. Wingenund feels already the gray shades of evening."

He stopped one long moment as if to gather breath for his final charge to his listeners. Then with a magnificent gesture he thundered:

"Is the Delaware a fool? When Wingenund can cross unarmed to the Big Water he shall change his mind. When Deathwind ceases to blow his bloody trail over the fallen leaves Wingenund will believe."

CHAPTER XIII.

As the summer waned, each succeeding day, with its melancholy calm, its changing lights and shades, its cool, damp evening winds, growing more and more suggestive of autumn, the little colony of white people in the Village of Peace led busy, eventful lives.

Upwards of fifty Indians, several of them important chiefs, had become converted since the young missionary began preaching. Heckewelder declared that this was a wonderful showing, and if it could be kept up would result in gaining a hold on the Indian tribes which might not be shaken. Heckewelder had succeeded in interesting the savages west of the Village of Peace to the extent of permitting him to establish missionary posts in two other localities—one near Goshhocking, a Delaware town; and one on the Muskingong, the principal river running through central Ohio. He had, with his helpers, Young and Edwards, journeyed from time to time to these points, preaching, making gifts, and soliciting help from chiefs.

The most interesting feature, perhaps, of the varied life of the missionary party was a rivalry between Young and Edwards for the elder Miss Wells. Usually Nell's attractiveness appealed more to men than Kate's; however, in this instance, although the sober teachers of the gospel admired Nell's winsome beauty, they fell in love with Kate. The missionaries were both under forty, and good, honest men, devoted to the work which had engrossed them for years. Although they were ardent lovers, certainly they were not picturesque. Two homelier men could hardly have been found. Moreover, the sacrifice of their lives to missionary work had taken them far from the companionship of women of their own race, so that they lacked the ease of manner which women like to see in men. Young and Edwards were awkward, almost uncouth. Embarrassment would not have done justice to their state of feeling while basking in the shine of Kate's quiet smile. They were happy, foolish, and speechless.

If Kate shared in the merriment of the others—Heckewelder could not conceal his, and Nell did not try very hard to hide hers—she never allowed a suspicion of it to escape. She kept the easy, even tenor of her life, always kind and gracious in her quaint way, and precisely the same to both her lovers. No doubt she well knew that each possessed, under all his rough exterior, a heart of gold.

One day the genial Heckewelder lost, or pretended to lose, his patience.

"Say, you worthy gentlemen are becoming ornamental instead of useful. All this changing of coats, trimming of mustaches, and eloquent sighing doesn't seem to have affected the young lady. I've a notion to send you both to Maumee town, one hundred miles away. This young lady is charming, I admit, but if she is to keep on seriously hindering the work of the Moravian Mission I must object. As for that matter, I might try conclusions myself. I'm as young as either of you, and, I flatter myself, much handsomer. You'll have a dangerous rival presently. Settle it! You can't both have her; settle it!"

This outburst from their usually kind leader placed the earnest but awkward gentlemen in a terrible plight.

On the afternoon following the crisis Heckewelder took Mr. Wells to one of the Indian shops, and Jim and Nell went canoeing. Young and Edwards, after conferring for one long, trying hour, determined on settling the question.

Young was a pale, slight man, very homely except when he smiled. His smile not only broke up the plainness of his face, but seemed to chase away a serious shadow, allowing his kindly, gentle spirit to shine through. He was nervous, and had a timid manner. Edwards was his opposite, being a man of robust frame, with a heavy face, and a manner that would have suggested self-confidence in another man.

They were true and tried friends.

"Dave, I couldn't ask her," said Young, trembling at the very thought. "Besides, there's no hope for me. I know it. That's why I'm afraid, why I don't want to ask her. What'd such a glorious creature see in a poor, puny little thing like me?"

"George, you're not over-handsome," admitted Dave, shaking his head. "But you can never tell about women. Sometimes they like even little, insignificant fellows. Don't be too scared about asking her. Besides, it will make it easier for me. You might tell her about me—you know, sort of feel her out, so I'd——"

Dave's voice failed him here; but he had said enough, and that was most discouraging to poor George. Dave was so busy screwing up his courage that he forgot all about his friend.

"No; I couldn't," gasped George, falling into a chair. He was ghastly pale. "I couldn't ask her to accept me, let alone do another man's wooing. She thinks more of you. She'll accept you."

"You really think so?" whispered Dave, nervously.

"I know she will. You're such a fine, big figure of a man. She'll take you, and I'll be glad. This fever and fretting has about finished me. When she's yours I'll not be so bad. I'll be happy in your happiness. But, Dave, you'll let me see her occasionally, won't you? Go! Hurry—get it over!"

"Yes; we must have it over," replied Dave, getting up with a brave, effort. Truly, if he carried that determined front to his lady-love he would look like a masterful lover. But when he got to the door he did not at all resemble a conqueror.

"You're sure she—cares for me?" asked Dave, for the hundredth time. This time, as always, his friend was faithful and convincing.

"I know she does. Go—hurry. I tell you I can't stand this any longer," cried George, pushing Dave out of the door.

"You won't go—first?" whispered Dave, clinging to the door.

"I won't go at all. I couldn't ask her—I don't want her—go! Get out!"

Dave started reluctantly toward the adjoining cabin, from the open window of which came the song of the young woman who was responsible for all this trouble. George flung himself on his bed. What a relief to feel it was all over! He lay there with eyes shut for hours, as it seemed. After a time Dave came in. George leaped to his feet and saw his friend stumbling over a chair. Somehow, Dave did not look as usual. He seemed changed, or shrunken, and his face wore a discomfited, miserable expression.

"Well?" cried George, sharply. Even to his highly excited imagination this did not seem the proper condition for a victorious lover.

"She refused—refused me," faltered Dave. "She was very sweet and kind; said something about being my sister—I don't remember just what—but she wouldn't have me."

"What did you say to her?" whispered George, a paralyzing hope almost rendering him speechless.

"I—I told her everything I could think of," replied Dave, despondently; "even what you said."

"What I said? Dave, what did you tell her I said?"

"Why, you know—about she cared for me—that you were sure of it, and that you didn't want her—"

"Jackass!" roared George, rising out of his meekness like a lion roused from slumber.

"Didn't you—say so?" inquired Dave, weakly.

"No! No! No! Idiot!"

As one possessed, George rushed out of the cabin, and a moment later stood disheveled and frantic before Kate.

"Did that fool say I didn't love you?" he demanded.

Kate looked up, startled; but as an understanding of George's wild aspect and wilder words dawned upon her, she resumed her usual calm demeanor. Looking again to see if this passionate young man was indeed George, she turned her face as she said:

"If you mean Mr. Edwards, yes; I believe he did say as much. Indeed, from his manner, he seemed to have monopolized all the love near the Village of Peace."

"But it's not true. I do love you. I love you to distraction. I have loved you ever since I first saw you. I told Dave that. Heckewelder knows it; even the Indians know it," cried George, protesting vehemently against the disparaging allusion to his affections. He did not realize he was making a most impassioned declaration of love. When he was quite out of breath he sat down and wiped his moist brow.

A pink bloom tinged Kate's cheeks, and her eyes glowed with a happy light; but George never saw these womanly evidences of pleasure.

"Of course I know you don't care for me——"

"Did Mr. Edwards tell you so?" asked Kate, glancing up quickly.

"Why, yes, he has often said he thought that. Indeed, he always seemed to regard himself as the fortunate object of your affections. I always believed he was."

"But it wasn't true."

"What?"

"It's not true."

"What's not true?"

"Oh—about my—not caring."

"Kate!" cried George, quite overcome with rapture. He fell over two chairs getting to her; but he succeeded, and fell on his knees to kiss her hand.

"Foolish boy! It has been you all the time," whispered Kate, with her quiet smile.

* * *

"Look here, Downs; come to the door. See there," said Heckewelder to Jim.

Somewhat surprised at Heckewelder's grave tone, Jim got up from the supper-table and looked out of the door. He saw two tall Indians pacing to and fro under the maples. It was still early twilight and light enough to see clearly. One Indian was almost naked; the lithe, graceful symmetry of his dark figure standing out in sharp contrast to the gaunt, gaudily-costumed form of the other.

"Silvertip! Girty!" exclaimed Jim, in a low voice.

"Girty I knew, of course; but I was not sure the other was the Shawnee who captured you and your brother," replied Heckewelder, drawing Jim into another room.

"What do they mean by loitering around the village? Inquired Jim, apprehensively. Whenever he heard Girty's name mentioned, or even thought of him, he remembered with a shudder the renegade's allusion to the buzzards. Jim never saw one of these carrion birds soaring overhead but his thoughts instantly reverted to the frontier ruffian and his horrible craving.

"I don't know," answered Heckewelder. "Girty has been here several times of late. I saw him conferring with Pipe at Goshhocking. I hope there's no deviltry afoot. Pipe is a relentless enemy of all Christians, and Girty is a fiend, a hyena. I think, perhaps, it will be well for you and the girls to stay indoors while Girty and Silvertip are in the village."

That evening the entire missionary party were gathered in Mr. Wells' room. Heckewelder told stories of Indian life; Nell sang several songs, and Kate told many amusing things said and done by the little Indian boys in her class at the school. Thus the evening passed pleasantly for all.

"So next Wednesday I am to perform the great ceremony," remarked Heckewelder, laying his hand kindly on Young's knee. "We'll celebrate the first white wedding in the Village of Peace."

Young looked shyly down at his boots; Edwards crossed one leg over the other, and coughed loudly to hide his embarrassment. Kate wore, as usual, her pensive smile; Nell's eyes twinkled, and she was about to speak, when Heckewelder's quizzical glance in her direction made her lips mute.

"I hope I'll have another wedding on my hands soon," he said placidly.

This ordinary remark had an extraordinary effect. Nell turned with burning cheeks and looked out of the window. Jim frowned fiercely and bit his lips. Edwards began to laugh, and even Mr. Wells' serious face lapsed into a smile.

"I mean I've picked out a nice little Delaware squaw for Dave," said Heckewelder, seeing his badinage had somehow gone amiss.

"Oh-h!" suddenly cried Nell, in shuddering tones.

They all gazed at her in amazement. Every vestige of color had receded from her face, leaving it marblelike. Her eyes were fixed in startled horror. Suddenly she relaxed her grasp on the windowsill and fell back limp and senseless.

Heckewelder ran to the door to look out, while the others bent over the unconscious girl, endeavoring to revive her. Presently a fluttering breath and a quivering of her dark lashes noted a return of suspended life. Then her beautiful eyes opened wide to gaze with wonder and fear into the grave faces bent so anxiously over her.

"Nell, dearest, you are safe. What was it? What frightened you so?" said Kate, tenderly.

"Oh, it was fearful!" gasped Nell, sitting up. She clung to her sister with one hand, while the other grasped Jim's sleeve.

"I was looking out into the dark, when suddenly I beheld a face, a terrible face!" cried Nell. Those who watched her marveled at the shrinking, awful fear in her eyes. "It was right by the window. I could have touched it. Such a greedy, wolfish face, with a long, hooked nose! The eyes, oh! the eyes! I'll never forget them. They made me sick; they paralyzed me. It wasn't an Indian's face. It belonged to that white man, that awful white man! I never saw him before; but I knew him."

"Girty!" said Heckewelder, who had come in with his quiet step. "He looked in at the window. Calm yourself, Nellie. The renegade has gone."

The incident worried them all at the time, and made Nell nervous for several days; but as Girty had disappeared, and nothing more was heard of him, gradually they forgot. Kate's wedding day dawned with all the little party well and happy. Early in the afternoon Jim and Nell, accompanied by Kate and her lover, started out into the woods just beyond the clearing for the purpose of gathering wild flowers to decorate the cabin.

"We are both thinking of—him," Jim said, after he and Nell had walked some little way in silence.

"Yes," answered Nell, simply.

"I hope—I pray Joe comes back, but if he doesn't—Nell—won't you care a little for me?"

He received no answer. But Nell turned her face away.

"We both loved him. If he's gone forever our very love for him should bring us together. I know—I know he would have wished that."

"Jim, don't speak of love to me now," she whispered. Then she turned to the others. "Come quickly; here are great clusters of wild clematis and goldenrod. How lovely! Let us gather a quantity."

The young men had almost buried the girls under huge masses of the beautiful flowers, when the soft tread of moccasined feet caused them all to turn in surprise. Six savages stood waist-deep in the bushes, where they had lain concealed. Fierce, painted visages scowled from behind leveled rifles.

"Don't yell!" cried a hoarse voice in English. Following the voice came a snapping of twigs, and then two other figures came into view. They were Girty and Silvertip.

"Don't yell, er I'll leave you layin' here fer the buzzards," said the renegade. He stepped forward and grasped Young, at the same time speaking in the Indian language and pointing to a nearby tree. Strange to relate, the renegade apparently wanted no bloodshed. While one of the savages began to tie Young to the tree, Girty turned his gaze on the girls. His little, yellow eyes glinted; he stroked his chin with a bony hand, and his dark, repulsive face was wreathed in a terrible, meaning smile.

"I've been layin' fer you," he croaked, eyeing Nell. "Ye're the purtiest lass, 'ceptin' mebbe Bet Zane, I ever seed on the border. I got cheated outen her, but I've got you; arter I feed yer Injun preacher to ther buzzards mebbe ye'll larn to love me."

Nell gazed one instant into the monster's face. Her terror-stricken eyes were piteous to behold. She tried to speak; but her voice failed. Then, like stricken bird, she fell on the grass.

CHAPTER XIV.

Not many miles from the Village of Peace rose an irregular chain of hills, the first faint indications of the grand Appalachian Mountain system. These ridges were thickly wooded with white oak, poplar and hickory, among which a sentinel pine reared here and there its evergreen head. There were clefts in the hills, passes lined by gray-stoned cliffs, below which ran clear brooks, tumbling over rocks in a hurry to meet their majestic father, the Ohio.

One of these valleys, so narrow that the sun seldom brightened the merry brook, made a deep cut in the rocks. The head of this valley tapered until the walls nearly met; it seemed to lose itself in the shade of fern-faced cliffs, shadowed as they were by fir trees leaning over the brink, as though to search for secrets of the ravine. So deep and dark and cool was this sequestered nook that here late summer had not dislodged early spring. Everywhere was a soft, fresh, bright green. The old gray cliffs were festooned with ferns, lichens and moss. Under a great, shelving rock, damp and stained by the copper-colored water dripping down its side, was a dewy dell into which the sunshine had never peeped. Here the swift brook tarried lovingly, making a wide turn under the cliff, as though loth to leave this quiet nook, and then leaped once more to enthusiasm in its murmuring flight.

Life abounded in this wild, beautiful, almost inaccessible spot. Little brown and yellow birds flitted among the trees; thrushes ran along the leaf-strewn ground; orioles sang their melancholy notes; robins and flickers darted beneath the spreading branches. Squirrels scurried over the leaves like little whirlwinds, and leaped daringly from the swinging branches or barked noisily from woody perches. Rabbits hopped inquisitively here and there while nibbling at the tender shoots of sassafras and laurel.

Along this flower-skirted stream a tall young man, carrying a rifle cautiously stepped, peering into the branches overhead. A gray flash shot along a limb of a white oak; then the bushy tail of a squirrel flitted into a well-protected notch, from whence, no doubt, a keen little eye watched the

287

hunter's every movement.

The rifle was raised; then lowered. The hunter walked around the tree. Presently up in the tree top, snug under a knotty limb, he spied a little ball of gray fur. Grasping a branch of underbush, he shook it vigorously. The thrashing sound worried the gray squirrel, for he slipped from his retreat and stuck his nose over the limb. CRACK! With a scratching and tearing of bark the squirrel loosened his hold and then fell; alighting with a thump. As the hunter picked up his quarry a streak of sunshine glinting through the tree top brightened his face.

The hunter was Joe.

He was satisfied now, for after stowing the squirrel in the pocket of his hunting coat he shouldered his rifle and went back up the ravine. Presently a dull roar sounded above the babble of the brook. It grew louder as he threaded his way carefully over the stones. Spots of white foam flecked the brook. Passing under the gray, stained cliff, Joe turned around a rocky corner, and came to an abrupt end of the ravine. A waterfall marked the spot where the brook entered. The water was brown as it took the leap, light green when it thinned out; and below, as it dashed on the stones, it became a beautiful, sheeny white.

Upon a flat rock, so near the cascade that spray flew over him, sat another hunter. The roaring falls drowned all other sounds, yet the man roused from his dreamy contemplation of the waterfall when Joe rounded the corner.

"I heerd four shots," he said, as Joe came up.

"Yes; I got a squirrel for every shot."

Wetzel led the way along a narrow foot trail which gradually wound toward the top of the ravine. This path emerged presently, some distance above the falls, on the brink of a bluff. It ran along the edge of the precipice a few yards, then took a course back into densely wooded thickets. Just before stepping out on the open cliff Wetzel paused and peered keenly on all sides. There was no living thing to be seen; the silence was the deep, unbroken calm of the wilderness.

Wetzel stepped to the bluff and looked over. The stony wall opposite was only thirty feet away, and somewhat lower. From Wetzel's action it appeared as if he intended to leap the fissure. In truth, many a band of Indians pursuing the hunter into this rocky fastness had come out on the bluff, and, marveling at what they thought Wetzel's prowess, believed he had made a wonderful leap, thus eluding them. But he had never attempted that leap, first, because he knew it was well-nigh impossible, and secondly, there had never been any necessity for such risk.

Any one leaning over this cliff would have observed, perhaps ten feet below, a narrow ledge projecting from the face of the rock. He would have imagined if he were to drop on that ledge there would be no way to get off and he would be in a worse predicament.

Without a moment's hesitation Wetzel swung himself over the ledge. Joe followed suit. At one end of this lower ledge grew a hardy shrub of the ironwood species, and above it a scrub pine leaned horizontally out over the ravine. Laying his rifle down, Wetzel grasped a strong root and cautiously slid over the side. When all of his body had disappeared, with the exception of his sinewy fingers, they loosened their hold on the root, grasped the rifle, and dragged it down out of sight. Quietly, with similar caution, Joe took hold of the same root, let himself down, and when at full length swung himself in under the ledge. His feet found a pocket in the cliff. Letting go of the root, he took his rifle, and in another second was safe.

Of all Wetzel's retreats—for he had many—he considered this one the safest. The cavern under the ledge he had discovered by accident. One day, being hotly pursued by Shawnees, he had been headed off on this cliff, and had let himself down on the ledge, intending to drop from it to the tops of the trees below. Taking advantage of every little aid, he hung over by means of the shrub, and was in the act of leaping when he saw that the cliff shelved under the ledge, while within reach of his feet was the entrance to a cavern. He found the cave to be small with an opening at the back into a split in the rock. Evidently the place had been entered from the rear by bears, who used the hole for winter sleeping quarters. By crawling on his hands and knees, Wetzel found the rear opening. Thus he had established a hiding place where it was almost impossible to locate him. He provisioned his retreat, which he always entered by the cliff and left by the rear.

An evidence of Wetzel's strange nature, and of his love for this wild home, manifested itself when he bound Joe to secrecy. It was unlikely, even if the young man ever did get safely out of the wilderness, that any stories he might relate would reveal the hunter's favorite rendezvous. But Wetzel seriously demanded this secrecy, as earnestly as if the forest were full of Indians and white men, all prowling in search of his burrow.

Joe was in the seventh heaven of delight, and took to the free life as a wild gosling takes to the water. No place had ever appealed to him as did this dark, silent hole far up on the side of a steep cliff. His interest in Wetzel soon passed into a great admiration, and from that deepened to love.

This afternoon, when they were satisfied that all was well within their refuge, Joe laid aside his rifle, and, whistling softly, began to prepare supper. The back part of the cave permitted him to stand erect, and was large enough for comparative comfort. There was a neat, little stone fireplace, and several cooking utensils and gourds. From time to time Wetzel had brought these things. A pile of wood and a bundle of pine cones lay in one corner. Haunches of dried beef, bear and buffalo meat hung from pegs; a bag of parched corn, another of dried apples lay on a rocky shelf. Nearby hung a powder-horn filled with salt and pepper. In the cleft back of the cave was a spring of clear, cold water.

The wants of woodsmen are few and simple. Joe and Wetzel, with appetites whetted by their stirring outdoor life, relished the frugal fare as they could never have enjoyed a feast. As the shadows of evening entered the cave, they lighted their pipes to partake of the hunter's sweetest solace, a quiet smoke.

Strange as it may appear, this lonely, stern Indian-hunter and the reckless, impulsive boy were admirably suited for companionship. Wetzel had taken a liking to the young man when he led the brothers to Fort Henry. Subsequent events strengthened his liking, and now, many days after, Joe having followed him into the forest, a strong attachment had been insensibly forged between them.

Wetzel understood Joe's burning desire to roam the forests; but he half expected the lad would soon grow tired of this roving life, but exactly the opposite symptoms were displayed. The hunter had intended to take his comrade on a hunting trip, and to return with him, after that was over, to Fort Henry. They had now been in the woods for weeks and every day in some way had Joe showed his mettle. Wetzel finally admitted him into the secrets of his most cherished hiding place. He did not want to hurt the lad's feelings by taking him back to the settlement; he could not send him back. So the days wore on swiftly; full of heart-satisfying incident and life, with man and boy growing closer in an intimacy that was as warm as it was unusual.

Two reasons might account for this: First, there is no sane human being who is not better off for companionship. An exile would find something of happiness in one who shared his misery. And, secondly, Joe was a most acceptable comrade, even for a slayer of Indians. Wedded as Wetzel was to the forest trails, to his lonely life, to the Nemesis-pursuit he had followed for eighteen long years, he was still a white man, kind and gentle in his quiet hours, and because of this, though he knew it not, still capable of affection. He had never known youth; his manhood had been one pitiless warfare against his sworn foes; but once in all those years had his sore, cold heart warmed; and that was toward a woman who was not for him. His life had held only one purpose—a bloody one. Yet the man had a heart, and he could not prevent it from responding to another. In his simple ignorance he rebelled against this affection for anything other than his forest homes. Man is weak against hate; what can he avail against love? The dark caverns of Wetzel's great heart opened, admitting to their gloomy depths this stranger. So now a new love was born in that cheerless heart, where for so long a lonely inmate, the ghost of old love, had dwelt in chill seclusion.

The feeling of comradeship which Wetzel had for Joe was something altogether new in the hunter's life. True he had hunted with Jonathan Zane, and accompanied expeditions where he was forced to sleep with another scout; but a companion, not to say friend, he had never known. Joe was a boy, wilder than an eagle, yet he was a man. He was happy and enthusiastic, still his good spirits never jarred on the hunter; they were restrained. He never asked questions, as would seem the case in any eager lad; he waited until he was spoken to. He was apt; he never forgot anything; he had the eye of a born woodsman, and lastly, perhaps what went far with Wetzel, he was as strong and supple as a young lynx, and absolutely fearless.

On this evening Wetzel and Joe followed their usual custom; they smoked a while before lying down to sleep. Tonight the hunter was even more silent than usual, and the lad, tired out with his day's tramp, lay down on a bed of fragrant boughs.

Wetzel sat there in the gathering gloom while he pulled slowly on his pipe. The evening was very quiet; the birds had ceased their twittering; the wind had died away; it was too early for the bay of a wolf, the wail of a panther, or hoot of an owl; there was simply perfect silence.

The lad's deep, even breathing caught Wetzel's ear, and he found himself meditating, as he had often of late, on this new something that had crept into his life. For Joe loved him; he could not fail to see that. The lad had preferred to roam with the lonely Indian-hunter through the forests, to encounter the perils and hardships of a wild life, rather than accept the smile of fortune and of love. Wetzel knew that Colonel Zane had taken a liking to the boy, and had offered him work and a home; and, also, the hunter remembered the warm light he had seen in Nell's hazel eyes. Musing thus, the man felt stir in his heart an emotion so long absent that it was unfamiliar. The Avenger forgot, for a moment his brooding plans. He felt strangely softened. When he laid his head on the rude pillow it was with some sense of gladness that, although he had always desired a lonely life, and wanted to pass it in the fulfillment of his vow, his loneliness was now shared by a lad who loved him.

Joe was awakened by the merry chirp of a chipmunk that every morning ran along the seamy side of the opposite wall of the gorge. Getting up, he went to the back of the cave, where he found Wetzel combing out his long hair. The lad thrust his hands into the cold pool, and bathed his face. The water was icy cold, and sent an invigorating thrill through him. Then he laughed as he took a rude comb Wetzel handed to him.

"My scalp is nothing to make an Indian very covetous, is it?" said he, eyeing in admiration the magnificent black hair that fell over the hunter's shoulders.

"It'll grow," answered Wetzel.

Joe did not wonder at the care Wetzel took of his hair, nor did he misunderstand the hunter's simple pride. Wetzel was very careful of his rifle, he was neat and clean about his person, he brushed his buckskin costume, he polished his knife and tomahawk; but his hair received more attention than all else. It required much care. When combed out it reached fully to his knees. Joe had seen him, after he returned from a long hunt, work patiently for an hour with his wooden comb, and not stop until every little burr was gone, or tangle smoothed out. Then he would comb it again in the morning—this, of course, when time permitted—and twist and tie it up so as to offer small resistance to his slipping through the underbush. Joe knew the hunter's simplicity was such, that if he cut off his hair it would seem he feared the Indians—for that streaming black hair the Indians had long coveted and sworn to take. It would make any brave a famous chief, and was the theme of many a savage war tale.

After breakfast Wetzel said to Joe:

"You stay here, an' I'll look round some; mebbe I'll come back soon, and we'll go out an' kill a buffalo. Injuns sometimes foller up a buffalo trail, an' I want to be sure none of the varlets are chasin' that herd we saw to-day."

Wetzel left the cave by the rear. It took him fifteen minutes to crawl to the head of the tortuous, stony passage. Lifting the stone which closed up the aperture, he looked out and listened. Then, rising, he replaced the stone, and passed down the wooded hillside.

It was a beautiful morning; the dew glistened on the green leaves, the sun shone bright and warm, the birds warbled in the trees. The hunter's moccasins pressed so gently on the moss and leaves that they made no more sound than the soft foot of a panther. His trained ear was alert to catch any unfamiliar noise; his keen eyes sought first the remoter open glades and glens, then bent their gaze on the mossy bluff beneath his feet. Fox squirrels dashed from before him into bushy retreats; grouse whirred away into the thickets; startled deer whistled, and loped off with their white-flags upraised. Wetzel knew from the action of these denizens of the woods that he was the only creature, not native to these haunts, who had disturbed them this morning. Otherwise the deer would not have been grazing, but lying low in some close thicket; fox squirrels seldom or never were disturbed by a hunter twice in one day, for after being frightened these little animals, wilder and shyer than gray squirrels, remained hidden for hours, and grouse that have been flushed a little while before, always get up unusually quick, and fly very far before alighting.

Wetzel circled back over the hill, took a long survey from a rocky eminence, and then reconnoitered the lowland for several miles. He located the herd of buffalo, and satisfying himself there were no Indians near—for the bison were grazing quietly—he returned to the cave. A soft whistle into the back door of the rocky home told Joe that the hunter was waiting.

"Coast clear?" whispered the lad, thrusting his head out of the entrance. His gray eyes gleamed brightly, showing his eager spirit.

The hunter nodded, and, throwing his rifle in the hollow of his arm, proceeded down the hill. Joe followed closely, endeavoring, as Wetzel had trained him, to make each step precisely in the hunter's footprints. The lad had soon learned to step nimbly and softly as a cat. When half way down the bill Wetzel paused.

"See anythin'?" he whispered.

Joe glanced on all sides. Many mistakes had taught him to be cautious.

He had learned from experience that for every woodland creature he saw, there were ten watching his every move. Just now he could not see even a little red squirrel. Everywhere were sturdy hickory and oak trees, thickets and hazelnuts, slender ash saplings, and, in the open glades, patches of sumach. Rotting trees lay on the ground, while ferns nodded long, slender heads over the fallen monarchs. Joe could make out nothing but the colors of the woods, the gray of the tree trunks, and, in the openings through the forest-green, the dead purple haze of forests farther on. He smiled, and, shaking his head at the hunter, by his action admitted failure.

"Try again. Dead ahead," whispered Wetzel.

Joe bent a direct gaze on the clump of sassafras one hundred feet ahead. He searched the open places, the shadows—even the branches. Then he turned his eyes slowly to the right. Whatever was discernible to human vision he studied intently. Suddenly his eye became fixed on a small object protruding from behind a beech tree. It was pointed, and in color darker than the gray bark of the beech. It had been a very easy matter to pass over this little thing; but now that the lad saw it, he knew to what it belonged.

"That's a buck's ear," he replied.

Hardly had he finished speaking when Wetzel intentionally snapped a twig. There was a crash and commotion in the thicket; branches moved and small saplings waved; then out into the open glade bounded a large buck with a whistle of alarm. Throwing his rifle to a level, Joe was trying to cover the bounding deer, when the hunter struck up his piece.

"Lad, don't kill fer the sake of killin'," he said, quietly. "We have plenty of venison. We'll go arter a buffalo. I hev a hankerin' fer a good rump steak."

Half an hour later, the hunters emerged from the forest into a wide plain of waving grass. It was a kind of oval valley, encircled by hills, and had been at one time, perhaps, covered with water. Joe saw a herd of large animals browsing, like cattle, in a meadow. His heart beat high, for until that moment the only buffalo he had seen were the few which stood on the river banks as the raft passed down the Ohio. He would surely get a shot at one of these huge fellows.

Wetzel bade Joe do exactly as he did, whereupon he dropped on his hands and knees and began to crawl through the long grass. This was easy for the hunter, but very bard for the lad to accomplish. Still, he managed to keep his comrade in sight, which was a matter for congratulation, because the man crawled as fast as he walked. At length, after what to Joe seemed a very long time, the hunter paused.

"Are we near enough?" whispered Joe, breathlessly.

"Nope. We're just circlin' on 'em. The wind's not right, an' I'm afeered they'll get our scent."

Wetzel rose carefully and peeped over the top of the grass; then, dropping on all fours, he resumed the advance.

He paused again, presently and waited for Joe to come up.

"See here, young fellar, remember, never hurry unless the bizness calls fer speed, an' then act like lightnin'."

Thus admonishing the eager lad, Wetzel continued to crawl. It was easy for him. Joe wondered how those wide shoulders got between the weeds and grasses without breaking, or, at least, shaking them. But so it was.

"Flat now," whispered Wetzel, putting his broad hand on Joe's back and pressing him down. "Now's yer time fer good practice. Trail yer rifle over yer back—if yer careful it won't slide off—an' reach out far with one arm an' dig yer fingers in deep. Then pull yerself forrard."

Wetzel slipped through the grass like a huge buckskin snake. His long, lithe body wormed its way among the reeds. But for Joe, even with the advantage of having the hunter's trail to follow, it was difficult work. The dry reeds broke under him, and the stalks of saw-grass shook. He worked persistently at it, learning all the while, and improving with every rod. He was surprised to hear a swish, followed by a dull blow on the ground. Raising his head, he looked forward. He saw the hunter wipe his tomahawk on the grass.

"Snake," whispered Wetzel.

Joe saw a huge blacksnake squirming in the grass. Its head had been severed. He caught glimpses of other snakes gliding away, and glossy round moles darting into their holes. A gray rabbit started off with a leap.

"We're near enough," whispered Wetzel, stopping behind a bush. He rose and surveyed the plain; then motioned Joe to look.

Joe raised himself on his knees. As his gaze reached the level of the grassy plain his heart leaped. Not fifty yards away was a great, shaggy, black buffalo. He was the king of the herd; but ill at ease, for he pawed the grass and shook his huge head. Near him were several cows and a half-grown calf. Beyond was the main herd, extending as far as Joe could see—a great sea of black humps! The lad breathed hard as he took in the grand sight.

"Pick out the little fellar—the reddish-brown one—an' plug him behind the shoulder. Shoot close now, fer if we miss, mebbe I can't hit one, because I'm not used to shootin' at sich small marks."

Wetzel's rare smile lighted up his dark face. Probably he could have shot a fly off the horn of the bull, if one of the big flies or bees, plainly visible as they swirled around the huge head, had alighted there.

Joe slowly raised his rifle. He had covered the calf, and was about to pull the trigger, when, with a sagacity far beyond his experience as hunter, he whispered to Wetzel:

"If I fire they may run toward us."

"Nope; they'll run away," answered Wetzel, thinking the lad was as keen as an Indian.

Joe quickly covered the calf again, and pulled the trigger. Bellowing loud the big bull dashed off. The herd swung around toward the west, and soon were galloping off with a lumbering roar. The shaggy humps bobbed up and down like hot, angry waves on a storm-blackened sea.

Upon going forward, Wetzel and Joe found the calf lying dead in the grass.

"You might hev did better'n that," remarked the hunter, as he saw where the bullet had struck. "You went a little too fer back, but mebbe thet was 'cause the calf stepped as you shot."

CHAPTER XV.

So the days passed swiftly, dreamily, each one bringing Joe a keener delight. In a single month he was as good a woodsman as many pioneers who had passed years on the border, for he had the advantage of a teacher whose woodcraft was incomparable. Besides, he was naturally quick in learning, and with all his interest centered upon forest lore, it was no wonder he assimilated much of Wetzel's knowledge. He was ever willing to undertake anything whereby he might learn. Often when they were miles away in the dense forest, far from their cave, he asked Wetzel to let him try to lead the way back to camp. And he never failed once, though many times he got off a straight course, thereby missing the easy travelling.

Joe did wonderfully well, but he lacked, as nearly all white men do, the subtler, intuitive forest-instinct, which makes the Indian as much at home in the woods as in his teepee. Wetzel had this developed to a high degree. It was born in him. Years of training, years of passionate, unrelenting search for Indians, had given him a knowledge of the wilds that was incomprehensible to white men, and appalling to his red foes.

Joe saw how Wetzel used this ability, but what it really was baffled him. He realized that words were not adequate to explain fully this great art. Its possession required a marvelously keen vision, an eye perfectly familiar with every creature, tree, rock, shrub and thing belonging in the forest; an eye so quick in flight as to detect instantly the slightest change in nature, or anything unnatural to that environment. The hearing must be delicate, like that of a deer, and the finer it is, the keener will be the woodsman. Lastly, there is the feeling that prompts the old hunter to say: "No game to-day." It is something in him that speaks when, as he sees a night-hawk circling low near the ground, he says: "A storm to-morrow." It is what makes an Indian at home in any wilderness. The clouds may hide the guiding star; the northing may be lost; there may be no moss on the trees, or difference in their bark; the ridges may be flat or lost altogether, and there may be no water-courses; yet the Indian brave always goes for his teepee, straight as a crow flies. It was this voice which rightly bade Wetzel, when he was baffled by an Indian's trail fading among the rocks, to cross, or circle, or advance in the direction taken by his wily foe.

Joe had practiced trailing deer and other hoofed game, until he was true as a hound. Then he began to perfect himself in the art of following a human being through the forest. Except a few old Indian trails, which the rain had half obliterated, he had no tracks to discover save Wetzel's, and these were as hard to find as the airy course of a grosbeak. On soft ground or marshy grass, which Wetzel avoided where he could, he left a faint trail, but on a hard surface, for all the traces he left, he might as well not have gone over the ground at all.

Joe's persistence stood him in good stead; he hung on, and the more he failed, the harder he tried. Often he would slip out of the cave after Wetzel had gone, and try to find which way he had taken. In brief, the lad became a fine marksman, a good hunter, and a close, persevering student of the wilderness. He loved the woods, and all they contained. He learned the habits of the wild creatures. Each deer, each squirrel, each grouse that he killed, taught him some lesson.

He was always up with the lark to watch the sun rise red and grand over the eastern hills, and chase away the white mist from the valleys. Even if he was not hunting, or roaming the woods, if it was necessary for him to lie low in camp awaiting Wetzel's return, he was always content. Many hours he idled away lying on his back, with the west wind blowing softly over him, his eye on the distant hills, where the cloud shadows swept across with slow, majestic movement, like huge ships at sea.

If Wetzel and Joe were far distant from the cave, as was often the case, they made camp in the open woods, and it was here that Joe's contentment was fullest. Twilight shades stealing down over the camp-fire; the cheery glow of red embers; the crackling of dry stocks; the sweet smell of wood smoke, all had for the lad a subtle, potent charm.

The hunter would broil a venison steak, or a partridge, on the coals. Then they would light their pipes and smoke while twilight deepened. The oppressive stillness of the early evening hour always brought to the younger man a sensation of awe. At first he attributed this to the fact that he was new to this life; however, as the days passed and the emotion remained, nay, grew stronger, he concluded it was imparted by this close communion with nature. Deep solemn, tranquil, the gloaming hour brought him no ordinary fullness of joy and clearness of perception.

"Do you ever feel this stillness?" he asked Wetzel one evening, as they sat near their flickering fire.

The hunter puffed his pipe, and, like an Indian, seemed to let the question take deep root.

"I've scalped redskins every hour in the day, 'ceptin' twilight," he replied.

Joe wondered no longer whether the hunter was too hardened to feel this beautiful tranquillity. That hour which wooed Wetzel from his implacable pursuit was indeed a bewitching one.

There was never a time, when Joe lay alone in camp waiting for Wetzel, that he did not hope the hunter would return with information of Indians. The man never talked about the savages, and if he spoke at all it was to tell of some incident of his day's travel. One evening he came back with a large black fox that he had killed.

"What beautiful, glossy fur!" said Joe. "I never saw a black fox before."

"I've been layin' fer this fellar some time," replied Wetzel, as he began his first evening task, that of combing his hair. "Jest back here in a clump of cottonwoods there's a holler log full of leaves. Happenin' to see a blacksnake sneakin' round, I thought mebbe he was up to somethin', so I investigated, an' found a nest full of young rabbits. I killed the snake, an' arter that took an interest in 'em. Every time I passed I'd look in at the bunnies, an' each time I seen signs that some tarnal varmint had been prowlin' round. One day I missed a bunny, an' next day another; so on until only one was left, a peart white and gray little scamp. Somethin' was stealin' of 'em, an' it made me mad. So yistidday an' to-day I watched, an' finally I plugged this black thief. Yes, he's got a glossy coat; but he's a bad un fer all his fine looks. These black foxes are bigger, stronger an' cunniner than red ones. In every litter you'll find a dark one, the black sheep of the family. Because he grows so much faster, an' steals all the food from the others, the mother jest takes him by the nape of the neck an' chucks him out in the world to shift fer hisself. An' it's a good thing."

The next day Wetzel told Joe they would go across country to seek new game fields. Accordingly the two set out, and tramped industriously until evening. They came upon a country no less beautiful than the one they had left, though the picturesque cliffs and rugged hills had given way to a rolling land, the luxuriance of which was explained by the abundant springs and streams. Forests and fields were thickly interspersed with bubbling springs, narrow and deep streams, and here and there a small lake with a running outlet.

Wetzel had said little concerning this region, but that little was enough to rouse all Joe's eagerness, for it was to the effect that they were now in a country much traversed by Indians, especially runners and hunting parties travelling from north to south. The hunter explained that through the center of this tract ran a buffalo road; that the buffalo always picked out the straightest, lowest and dryest path from one range to another, and the Indians followed these first pathfinders.

Joe and Wetzel made camp on the bank of a stream that night, and as the lad watched the hunter build a hidden camp-fire, he peered furtively around half expecting to see dark forms scurrying through the forest. Wetzel was extremely cautious. He stripped pieces of bark from fallen trees and built a little hut over his firewood. He rubbed some powder on a piece of punk, and then with flint and steel dropped two or three sparks on the inflammable substance. Soon he had a blaze. He arranged the covering so that not a ray of light escaped. When the flames had subsided, and the wood had burned down to a glowing bed of red, he threw aside the bark, and broiled the strips of venison they had brought with them.

They rested on a bed of boughs which they had cut and arranged alongside a huge log. For hours Joe lay awake, he could not sleep. He listened to the breeze rustling the leaves, and shivered at the thought of the sighing wind he had once heard moan through the forest. Presently he turned over. The slight noise instantly awakened Wetzel who lifted his dark face while he listened intently. He spoke one word: "Sleep," and lay back again on the leaves. Joe forced himself to be quiet, relaxed all his muscles and soon slumbered.

On the morrow Wetzel went out to look over the hunting prospects. About noon he returned. Joe was surprised to find some slight change in the hunter. He could not tell what it was.

"I seen Injun sign," said Wetzel. "There's no tellin' how soon we may run agin the sneaks. We can't hunt here. Like as not there's Hurons and Delawares skulkin' round. I think I'd better take you back to the village."

"It's all on my account you say that," said Joe.

"Sure," Wetzel replied.

"If you were alone what would you do?"

"I calkilate I'd hunt fer some red-skinned game."

The supreme moment had come. Joe's heart beat hard. He could not miss this opportunity; he must stay with the hunter. He looked closely at Wetzel.

"I won't go back to the village," he said.

The hunter stood in his favorite position, leaning on his long rifle, and made no response.

"I won't go," continued Joe, earnestly. "Let me stay with you. If at any time I hamper you, or can not keep the pace, then leave me to shift for myself; but don't make me go until I weaken. Let me stay."

Fire and fearlessness spoke in Joe's every word, and his gray eyes contracted with their peculiar steely flash. Plain it was that, while he might fail to keep pace with Wetzel, he did not fear this dangerous country, and, if it must be, would face it alone.

Wetzel extended his broad hand and gave his comrade's a viselike squeeze. To allow the lad to remain with him was more than he would have done for any other person in the world. Far better to keep the lad under his protection while it was possible, for Joe was taking that war-trail which had for every hunter, somewhere along its bloody course, a bullet, a knife, or a tomahawk. Wetzel knew that Joe was conscious of this inevitable conclusion, for it showed in his white face, and in the resolve in his big, gray eyes.

So there, in the shade of a towering oak, the Indian-killer admitted the boy into his friendship, and into a life which would no longer be play, but eventful, stirring, hazardous.

"Wal, lad, stay," he said, with that rare smile which brightened his dark face like a ray of stray sunshine. "We'll hang round these diggins a few days. First off, we'll take in the lay of the land. You go down stream a ways an' scout round some, while I go up, an' then circle down. Move slow, now, an' don't miss nothin'."

Joe followed the stream a mile or more. He kept close in the shade of willows, and never walked across an open glade without first waiting and watching. He listened to all sounds; but none were unfamiliar. He closely examined the sand along the stream, and the moss and leaves under the trees. When he had been separated from Wetzel several hours, and concluded he would slowly return to camp, he ran across a well-beaten path winding through the forest. This was, perhaps, one of the bridle-trails Wetzel had referred to. He bent over the worn grass with keen scrutiny.

CRACK!

The loud report of a heavily charged rifle rang out. Joe felt the zip of a bullet as it fanned his cheek. With an agile leap he gained the shelter of a tree, from behind which he peeped to see who had shot at him. He was just in time to detect the dark form of an Indian dart behind the foliage an hundred yards down the path. Joe expected to see other Indians, and to hear more shots, but he was mistaken. Evidently the savage was alone, for the tree Joe had taken refuge behind was scarcely large enough to screen his body, which disadvantage the other Indians would have been quick to note.

Joe closely watched the place where his assailant had disappeared, and presently saw a dark hand, then a naked elbow, and finally the ramrod of a rifle. The savage was reloading. Soon a rifle-barrel protruded from behind the tree. With his heart beating like a trip-hammer, and the skin tightening on his face, Joe screened his body as best he might. The tree was small, but it served as a partial protection. Rapidly he revolved in his mind plans to outwit the enemy. The Indian was behind a large oak with a low limb over which he could fire without exposing his own person to danger.

"Bang!" The Indian's rifle bellowed; the bullet crumbled the bark close to Joe's face. The lad yelled loudly, staggered to his knees, and then fell into the path, where he lay quiet.

The redskin gave an exultant shout. Seeing that the fallen figure remained quite motionless he stepped forward, drawing his knife as he came. He was a young brave, quick and eager in his movements, and came nimbly up the path to gain his coveted trophy, the paleface's scalp.

Suddenly Joe sat up, raised his rifle quickly as thought, and fired point-blank at the Indian.

But he missed.

The redskin stopped aghast when he saw the lad thus seemingly come back to life. Then, realizing that Joe's aim had been futile, he bounded forward, brandishing his knife, and uttering infuriated yells.

Joe rose to his feet with rifle swung high above his head.

When the savage was within twenty feet, so near that his dark face, swollen with fierce passion, could be plainly discerned, a peculiar whistling noise sounded over Joe's shoulder. It was accompanied, rather than followed, by a clear, ringing rifleshot.

The Indian stopped as if he had encountered a heavy shock from a tree or stone barring his way. Clutching at his breast, he uttered a weird cry, and sank slowly on the grass.

Joe ran forward to bend over the prostrate figure. The Indian, a slender, handsome young brave, had been shot through the breast. He held his hand tightly over the wound, while bright red blood trickled between his fingers, flowed down his side, and stained the grass.

The brave looked steadily up at Joe. Shot as he was, dying as he knew himself to be, there was no yielding in the dark eye—only an unquenchable hatred. Then the eyes glazed; the fingers ceased twitching.

Joe was bending over a dead Indian.

It flashed into his mind, of course, that Wetzel had come up in time to save his life, but he did not dwell on the thought; he shrank from this violent death of a human being. But it was from the aspect of the dead, not from remorse for the deed. His heart beat fast, his fingers trembled, yet he felt only a strange coldness in all his being. The savage had tried to kill him, perhaps, even now, had it not been for the hunter's unerring aim, would have been gloating over a bloody scalp.

Joe felt, rather than heard, the approach of some one, and he turned to see Wetzel coming down the path.

"He's a lone Shawnee runner," said the hunter, gazing down at the dead Indian. "He was tryin' to win his eagle plumes. I seen you both from the hillside."

"You did!" exclaimed Joe. Then he laughed. "It was lucky for me. I tried the dodge you taught me, but in my eagerness I missed."

"Wal, you hadn't no call fer hurry. You worked the trick clever, but you missed him when there was plenty of time. I had to shoot over your shoulder, or I'd hev plugged him sooner."

"Where were you?" asked Joe.

"Up there by that bit of sumach!" and Wetzel pointed to an open ridge on a hillside not less than one hundred and fifty yards distant.

Joe wondered which of the two bullets, the death-seeking one fired by the savage, or the life-saving missile from Wetzel's fatal weapon, had passed nearest to him.

"Come," said the hunter, after he had scalped the Indian.

"What's to be done with this savage?" inquired Joe, as Wetzel started up the path.

"Let him lay."

They returned to camp without further incident. While the hunter busied himself reinforcing their temporary shelter—for the clouds looked threatening—Joe cut up some buffalo meat, and then went down to the brook for a gourd of water. He came hurriedly back to where Wetzel was working, and spoke in a voice which he vainly endeavors to hold steady:

"Come quickly. I have seen something which may mean a good deal."

He led the way down to the brookside.

"Look!" Joe said, pointing at the water.

Here the steam was about two feet deep, perhaps twenty wide, and had just a noticeable current. Shortly before, it had been as clear as a bright summer sky; it was now tinged with yellow clouds that slowly floated downstream, each one enlarging and becoming fainter as the clear water permeated and stained. Grains of sand glided along with the current, little pieces of bark floated on the surface, and minnows darted to and fro nibbling at these drifting particles.

"Deer wouldn't roil the water like that. What does it mean?" asked Joe.

"Injuns, an' not fer away."

Wetzel returned to the shelter and tore it down. Then he bent the branch of a beech tree low over the place. He pulled down another branch over the remains of the camp-fire. These precautions made the spot less striking. Wetzel knew that an Indian scout never glances casually; his roving eyes survey the forest, perhaps quickly, but thoroughly. An unnatural position of bush or log always leads to an examination.

This done, the hunter grasped Joe's hand and led him up the knoll. Making his way behind a well-screened tree, which had been uprooted, he selected a position where, hidden themselves, they could see the creek.

Hardly had Wetzel, admonished Joe to lie perfectly still, when from a short distance up the stream came the sound of splashing water; but nothing could be seen above the open glade, as in that direction willows lined the creek in dense thickets. The noise grew more audible.

Suddenly Joe felt a muscular contraction pass over the powerful frame lying close beside him. It was a convulsive thrill such as passes through a tiger when he is about to spring upon his quarry. So subtle and strong was its meaning, so clearly did it convey to the lad what was coming, that he felt it himself; save that in his case it was a cold, chill shudder.

Breathless suspense followed. Then into the open space along the creek glided a tall Indian warrior. He was knee-deep in the water, where he waded with low, cautious steps. His garish, befrilled costume seemed familiar to Joe. He carried a rifle at a low trail, and passed slowly ahead with evident distrust. The lad believed he recognized that head, with its tangled black hair, and when he saw the swarthy, villainous countenance turned full toward him, he exclaimed:

"Girty! by——"

Wetzel's powerful arm forced him so hard against the log that he could not complete the exclamation; but he could still see. Girty had not heard that stifled cry, for he continued his slow wading, and presently his tall, gaudily decorated form passed out of sight.

Another savage appeared in the open space, and then another. Close between them walked a white man, with hands bound behind him. The prisoner and guards disappeared down stream among the willows.

The splashing continued—grew even louder than before. A warrior came into view, then another, and another. They walked close together. Two more followed. They were wading by the side of a raft made of several logs, upon which were two prostrate figures that closely resembled human beings.

Joe was so intent upon the lithe forms of the Indians that he barely got a glimpse of their floating prize, whatever it might have been. Bringing up the rear was an athletic warrior, whose broad shoulders, sinewy arms, and shaved, polished head Joe remembered well. It was the Shawnee chief, Silvertip.

When he, too, passed out of sight in the curve of willows, Joe found himself trembling. He turned eagerly to Wetzel; but instantly recoiled.

Terrible, indeed, had been the hunter's transformation. All calmness of facial expression was gone; he was now stern, somber. An intense emotion was visible in his white face; his eyes seemed reduced to two dark shining points, and they emitted so fierce, so piercing a flash, so deadly a light, that Joe could not bear their glittering gaze.

"Three white captives, two of 'em women," uttered the hunter, as if weighing in his mind the importance of this fact.

"Were those women on the raft?" questioned Joe, and as Wetzel only nodded, he continued, "A white man and two women, six warriors, Silvertip, and that renegade, Jim Girty!"

Wetzel deigned not to answer Joe's passionate outburst, but maintained silence and his rigid posture. Joe glanced once more at the stern face.

"Considering we'd go after Girty and his redskins if they were alone, we're pretty likely to go quicker now that they've got white women prisoners, eh?" and Joe laughed fiercely between his teeth.

The lad's heart expanded, while along every nerve tingled an exquisite thrill of excitement. He had yearned for wild, border life. Here he was in it, with the hunter whose name alone was to the savages a symbol for all that was terrible.

Wetzel evidently decided quickly on what was to be done, for in few words he directed Joe to cut up so much of the buffalo meat as they could stow in their pockets. Then, bidding the lad to follow, he turned into the woods, walking rapidly, and stopping now and then for a brief instant. Soon they emerged from the forest into more open country. They faced a wide plain skirted on the right by a long, winding strip of bright green willows which marked the course of the stream. On the edge of this plain Wetzel broke into a run. He kept this pace for a distance of an hundred yards, then stopped to listen intently as he glanced sharply on all sides, after which he was off again.

Half way across this plain Joe's wind began to fail, and his breathing became labored; but he kept close to the hunter's heels. Once he looked back to see a great wide expanse of waving grass. They had covered perhaps four miles at a rapid pace, and were nearing the other side of the plain. The lad felt as if his head was about to burst; a sharp pain seized upon his side; a blood-red film obscured his sight. He kept doggedly on, and when utterly exhausted fell to the ground.

When, a few minutes later, having recovered his breath, he got up, they had crossed the plain and were in a grove of beeches. Directly in front of him ran a swift stream, which was divided at the rocky head of what appeared to be a wooded island. There was only a slight ripple and fall of the water, and, after a second glance, it was evident that the point of land was not an island, but a portion of the mainland which divided the stream. The branches took almost opposite courses.

Joe wondered if they had headed off the Indians. Certainly they had run fast enough. He was wet with perspiration. He glanced at Wetzel, who was standing near. The man's broad breast rose and fell a little faster; that was the only evidence of exertion. The lad had a painful feeling that he could never keep pace with the hunter, if this five-mile run was a sample of the speed he would be forced to maintain.

"They've got ahead of us, but which crick did they take?" queried Wetzel, as though debating the question with himself.

"How do you know they've passed?"

"We circled," answered Wetzel, as he shook his head and pointed into the bushes. Joe stepped over and looked into the thicket. He found a quantity of dead leaves, sticks, and litter thrown aside, exposing to light a long, hollowed place on the ground. It was what would be seen after rolling over a log that had lain for a long time. Little furrows in the ground, holes, mounds, and curious winding passages showed where grubs and crickets had made their homes. The frightened insects were now running round wildly.

"What was here? A log?"

"A twenty-foot canoe was hid under thet stuff. The Injuns has taken one of these streams."

"How can we tell which one?"

"Mebbe we can't; but we'll try. Grab up a few of them bugs, go below thet rocky point, an' crawl close to the bank so you can jest peep over. Be keerful not to show the tip of your head, an' don't knock nothin' off'en the bank into the water. Watch fer trout. Look everywheres, an' drop in a bug now and then. I'll do the same fer the other stream. Then we'll come back here an' talk over what the fish has to say about the Injuns."

Joe walked down stream a few paces, and, dropping on his knees, crawled carefully to the edge of the bank. He slightly parted the grass so he could peep through, and found himself directly over a pool with a narrow shoal running out from the opposite bank. The water was so clear he could see the pebbly bottom in all parts, except a dark hole near a bend in the shore close by. He did not see a living thing in the water, not a crawfish, turtle, nor even a frog. He peered round closely, then flipped in one of the bugs he had brought along. A shiny yellow fish flared up from the depths of the deep hole and disappeared with the cricket; but it was a bass or a pike, not a trout. Wetzel had said there were a few trout living near the cool springs of these streams. The lad tried again to coax one to the surface. This time the more fortunate cricket swam and hopped across the stream to safety.

When Joe's eyes were thoroughly accustomed to the clear water, with its deceiving lights and shades, he saw a fish lying snug under the side of a stone. The lad thought he recognized the snub-nose, the hooked, wolfish jaw, but he could not get sufficient of a view to classify him. He crawled to a more advantageous position farther down stream, and then he peered again through the woods. Yes, sure enough, he had espied a trout. He well knew those spotted silver sides, that broad, square tail. Such a monster! In his admiration for the fellow, and his wish for a hook and line to try conclusions with him, Joe momentarily forgot his object. Remembering, he tossed out a big, fat cricket, which alighted on the water just above the fish. The trout never moved, nor even blinked. The lad tried again, with no better success. The fish would not rise. Thereupon Joe returned to the point where he had left Wetzel.

"I couldn't see nothin' over there," said the hunter, who was waiting. "Did you see any?'

"One, and a big fellow."

"Did he see you?"

"No."

"Did he rise to a bug?"

"No, he didn't; but then maybe he wasn't hungry" answered Joe, who could not understand what Wetzel was driving at.

"Tell me exactly what he did."

"That's just the trouble; he didn't do anything," replied Joe, thoughtfully. "He just lay low, stifflike, under a stone. He never batted an eye. But his side-fins quivered like an aspen leaf."

"Them side-fins tell us the story. Girty, an' his redskins hev took this branch," said Wetzel, positively. "The other leads to the Huron towns. Girty's got a place near the Delaware camp somewheres. I've tried to find it a good many times. He's took more'n one white lass there, an' nobody ever seen her agin."

"Fiend! To think of a white woman, maybe a girl like Nell Wells, at the mercy of those red devils!"

"Young fellar, don't go wrong. I'll allow Injuns is bad enough; but I never hearn tell of one abusin' a white woman, as mayhap you mean. Injuns marry white women sometimes; kill an' scalp 'em often, but that's all. It's men of our own color, renegades like this Girty, as do worse'n murder."

Here was the amazing circumstance of Lewis Wetzel, the acknowledged unsatiable foe of all redmen, speaking a good word for his enemies. Joe was so astonished he did not attempt to answer.

"Here's where they got in the canoe. One more look, an' then we're off," said Wetzel. He strode up and down the sandy beach; examined the willows, and scrutinized the sand. Suddenly he bent over and picked up an object from the water. His sharp eyes had caught the glint of something white, which, upon being examined, proved to be a small ivory or bone buckle with a piece broken out. He showed it to Joe.

"By heavens! Wetzel, that's a buckle off Nell Well's shoe. I've seen it too many times to mistake it."

"I was afeared Girty hed your friends, the sisters, an' mebbe your brother, too. Jack Zane said the renegade was hangin' round the village, an' that couldn't be fer no good."

"Come on. Let's kill the fiend!" cried Joe, white to the lips.

"I calkilate they're about a mile down stream, makin' camp fer the night. I know the place. There's a fine spring, an, look! D'ye see them crows flyin' round thet big oak with the bleached top? Hear them cawin'? You might think they was chasin' a hawk, or king-birds were arter 'em, but thet fuss they're makin' is because they see Injuns."

"Well?" asked Joe, impatiently.

"It'll be moonlight a while arter midnight. We'll lay low an' wait, an' then—"

The sharp click of his teeth, like the snap of a steel trap, completed the sentence. Joe said no more, but followed the hunter into the woods. Stopping near a fallen tree, Wetzel raked up a bundle of leaves and spread them on the ground. Then he cut a few spreading branches from a beech, and leaned them against a log. Bidding the lad crawl in before he took one last look around and then made his way under the shelter.

It was yet daylight, which seemed a strange time to creep into this little nook; but, Joe thought, it was not to sleep, only to wait, wait, wait for the long hours to pass. He was amazed once more, because, by the time twilight had given place to darkness, Wetzel was asleep. The lad said then to himself that he would never again be surprised at the hunter. He assumed once and for all that Wetzel was capable of anything. Yet how could he lose himself in slumber? Feeling, as he must, over the capture of the girls; eager to draw a bead on the black-hearted renegade; hating Indians with all his soul and strength, and lying there but a few hours before what he knew would be a bloody battle, Wetzel calmly went to sleep. Knowing the hunter to be as bloodthirsty as a tiger, Joe had expected he would rush to a combat with his foes; but, no, this man, with his keen sagacity, knew when to creep upon his enemy; he bided that time, and, while he waited, slept.

Joe could not close his eyes in slumber. Through the interstices in the branches he saw the stars come out one by one, the darkness deepened, and the dim outline of tall trees over the dark hill came out sharply. The moments dragged, each one an hour. He heard a whippoorwill call, lonely and dismal; then an owl hoot monotonously. A stealthy footed animal ran along the log, sniffed at the boughs, and then scurried away over the dry leaves. By and by the dead silence of night fell over all. Still Joe lay there wide awake, listening—his heart on fire. He was about to rescue Nell; to kill that hawk-nosed renegade; to fight Silvertip to the death.

The hours passed, but not Joe's passionate eagerness. When at last he saw the crescent moon gleam silver-white over the black hilltop he knew the time was nigh, and over him ran thrill on thrill.

CHAPTER XVI.

When the waning moon rose high enough to shed a pale light over forest and field, two dark figures, moving silently from the shade of the trees, crossed the moonlit patches of ground, out to the open plain where low on the grass hung silver mists.

A timber wolf, gray and gaunt, came loping along with lowered nose. A new scent brought the animal to a standstill. His nose went up, his fiery eyes scanned the plain. Two men had invaded his domain, and, with a short, dismal bark, he dashed away.

Like spectres, gliding swiftly with noiseless tread, the two vanished. The long grass had swallowed them.

Deserted once again seemed the plain. It became unutterably lonely. No stir, no sound, no life; nothing but a wide expanse bathed in sad, gray light.

The moon shone steadily; the silver radiance mellowed; the stars paled before this brighter glory.

Slowly the night hours wore away.

On the other side of the plain, near where the adjoining forest loomed darkling, the tall grass parted to disclose a black form. Was it only a deceiving shade cast by a leafy branch—only a shadow? Slowly it sank, and was lost. Once more the gray, unwavering line of silver-crested grass tufts was unbroken.

Only the night breeze, wandering caressingly over the grass, might have told of two dark forms gliding, gliding, gliding so softly, so surely, so surely toward the forest. Only the moon and the pale stars had eyes to see these creeping figures.

Like avengers they moved, on a mission to slay and to save!

On over the dark line where plain merged into forest they crawled. No whispering, no hesitating; but a silent, slow, certain progress showed their purpose. In single file they slipped over the moss, the leader clearing the path. Inch by inch they advanced. Tedious was this slow movement, difficult and painful this journey which must end in lightninglike speed. They rustled no leaf, nor snapped a twig, nor shook a fern, but passed onward slowly, like the approach of Death. The seconds passed as minutes; minutes as hours; an entire hour was spent in advancing twenty feet!

At last the top of the knoll was reached. The Avenger placed his hand on his follower's shoulder. The strong pressure was meant to remind, to warn, to reassure. Then, like a huge snake, the first glided away.

He who was left behind raised his head to look into the open place called the glade of the Beautiful Spring. An oval space lay before him, exceedingly lovely in the moonlight; a spring, as if a pearl, gemmed the center. An Indian guard stood statuelike against a stone. Other savages lay in a row, their polished heads shining. One slumbering form was bedecked with feathers and frills. Near him lay an Indian blanket, from the border of which peered two faces, gleaming white and sad in the pitying moonlight.

The watcher quivered at the sight of those pale faces; but he must wait while long moments passed. He must wait for the Avenger to creep up, silently kill the guard, and release the prisoners without awakening the savages. If that plan failed, he was to rush into the glade, and in the excitement make off with one of the captives.

He lay there waiting, listening, wrought up to the intensest pitch of fierce passion. Every nerve was alert, every tendon strung, and every muscle strained ready for the leap.

Only the faint rustling of leaves, the low swish of swaying branches, the soft murmur of falling water, and over all the sigh of the night wind, proved to him that this picture was not an evil dream. His gaze sought the quiet figures, lingered hopefully on the captives, menacingly on the sleeping savages, and glowered over the gaudily arrayed form. His glance sought the upright guard, as he stood a dark blot against the gray stone. He saw the Indian's plume, a single feather waving silver-white. Then it became riveted on the bubbling, refulgent spring. The pool was round, perhaps five feet across, and shone like a burnished shield. It mirrored the moon, the twinkling stars, the spectre trees.

An unaccountable horror suddenly swept over the watching man. His hair stood straight up; a sensation as of cold stole chillingly over him. Whether it was the climax of this long night's excitement, or anticipation of the bloody struggle soon to come, he knew not. Did this boiling spring, shimmering in the sliver moon-rays, hold in its murky depths a secret? Did these lonesome, shadowing trees, with their sad drooping branches, harbor a mystery? If a future tragedy was to be enacted here in this quiet glade, could the murmuring water or leaves whisper its portent? No; they were only silent, only unintelligible with nature's mystery.

The waiting man cursed himself for a craven coward; he fought back the benumbing sense; he steeled his heart. Was this his vaunted willingness to share the Avenger's danger? His strong spirit rose up in arms; once more he was brave and fierce.

He fastened a piercing gaze on the plumed guard. The Indian's lounging posture against the rock was the same as it had been before, yet now it seemed to have a kind of strained attention. The savage's head was poised, like that of a listening deer. The wary Indian scented danger.

A faint moan breathed low above the sound of gently splashing water somewhere beyond the glade.

"Woo-o-oo."

The guard's figure stiffened, and became rigidly erect; his blanket slowly slid to his feet.

"Ah-oo-o," sighed the soft breeze in the tree tops.

Louder then, with a deep wail, a moan arose out of the dark gray shadows, swelled thrilling on the still air, and died away mournfully.

"Um-m-mmwoo-o-o-o!"

The sentinel's form melted into the shade. He was gone like a phantom.

Another Indian rose quickly, and glanced furtively around the glade. He bent over a comrade and shook him. Instantly the second Indian was on his feet. Scarcely had he gained a standing posture when an object, bounding like a dark ball, shot out of the thicket and hurled both warriors to the earth. A moonbeam glinted upon something bright. It flashed again on a swift, sweeping circle. A short, choking yell aroused the other savages. Up they sprang, alarmed, confused.

The shadow-form darted among them. It moved with inconceivable rapidity; it became a monster. Terrible was the convulsive conflict. Dull blows, the click of steel, angry shouts, agonized yells, and thrashing, wrestling sounds mingled together and half drowned by an awful roar like that of a mad bull. The strife ceased as suddenly as it had begun. Warriors lay still on the grass; others writhed in agony. For an instant a fleeting shadow crossed the open lane leading out of the glade; then it vanished.

Three savages had sprung toward their rifles. A blinding flash, a loud report burst from the thicket overhead. The foremost savage sank lifelessly. The others were intercepted by a giant shadow with brandished rifle. The watcher on the knoll had entered the glade. He stood before the stacked rifles and swung his heavy gun. Crash! An Indian went down before that sweep, but rose again. The savages backed away from this threatening figure, and circled around it.

The noise of the other conflict ceased. More savages joined the three who glided to and fro before their desperate foe. They closed in upon him, only to be beaten back. One savage threw a glittering knife, another hurled a stone, a third flung his tomahawk, which struck fire from the swinging rifle.

He held them at bay. While they had no firearms he was master of the situation. With every sweep of his arms he brought the long rifle down and knocked a flint from the firelock of an enemy's weapon. Soon the Indians' guns were useless. Slowly then he began to edge away from the stone, toward the opening where he had seen the fleeting form vanish.

His intention was to make a dash for life, for he had heard a noise behind the rock, and remembered the guard. He saw the savages glance behind him, and anticipated danger from that direction, but he must not turn. A second there might be fatal. He backed defiantly along the rock until he gained its outer edge. But too late! The Indians glided before him, now behind him; he was surrounded. He turned around and around, with the ever-circling rifle whirling in the faces of the baffled foe.

Once opposite the lane leading from the glade he changed his tactics, and plunged with fierce impetuosity into the midst of the painted throng. Then began a fearful conflict. The Indians fell before the sweep of his powerful arms; but grappled with him from the ground. He literally plowed his way through the struggling mass, warding off an hundred vicious blows. Savage after savage he flung off, until at last he had a clear path before him. Freedom lay beyond that shiny path. Into it he bounded.

As he left the glade the plumed guard stepped from behind a tree near the entrance of the path, and cast his tomahawk.

A white, glittering flash, it flew after the fleeing runner; its aim was true.

Suddenly the moonlight path darkened in the runner's sight; he saw a million flashing stars; a terrible pain assailed him; he sank slowly, slowly down; then all was darkness.

CHAPTER XVII.

Joe awoke as from a fearsome nightmare. Returning consciousness brought a vague idea that he had been dreaming of clashing weapons, of yelling savages, of a conflict in which he had been clutched by sinewy fingers. An acute pain pulsed through his temples; a bloody mist glazed his eyes; a sore pressure cramped his arms and legs. Surely he dreamed this distress, as well as the fight. The red film cleared from his eyes. His wandering gaze showed the stern reality.

The bright sun, making the dewdrops glisten on the leaves, lighted up a tragedy. Near him lay an Indian whose vacant, sightless eyes were fixed in death. Beyond lay four more savages, the peculiar, inert position of whose limbs, the formlessness, as it were, as if they had been thrown from a great height and never moved again, attested that here, too, life had been extinguished. Joe took in only one detail—the cloven skull of the nearest—when he turned away sickened. He remembered it all now. The advance, the rush, the fight—all returned. He saw again Wetzel's shadowy form darting like a demon into the whirl of conflict; he heard again that hoarse, booming roar with which the Avenger accompanied his blows. Joe's gaze swept the glade, but found no trace of the hunter.

He saw Silvertip and another Indian bathing a wound on Girty's head. The renegade groaned and writhed in pain. Near him lay Kate, with white face and closed eyes. She was unconscious, or dead. Jim sat crouched under a tree to which he was tied.

"Joe, are you badly hurt?" asked the latter, in deep solicitude.

"No, I guess not; I don't know," answered Joe. "Is poor Kate dead?"

"No, she has fainted."

"Where's Nell?"

"Gone," replied Jim, lowering his voice, and glancing at the Indians. They were too busy trying to bandage Girty's head to pay any attention to their prisoners. "That whirlwind was Wetzel, wasn't it?"

"Yes; how'd you know?"

"I was awake last night. I had an oppressive feeling, perhaps a presentiment. Anyway, I couldn't sleep. I heard that wind blow through the forest, and thought my blood would freeze. The moan is the same as the night wind, the same soft sigh, only louder and somehow pregnant with superhuman power. To speak of it in broad daylight one seems superstitious, but to hear it in the darkness of this lonely forest, it is fearful! I hope I am not a coward; I certainly know I was deathly frightened. No wonder I was scared! Look at these dead Indians, all killed in a moment. I heard the moan; I saw Silvertip disappear, and the other two savages rise. Then something huge dropped from the rock; a bright object seemed to circle round the savages; they uttered one short yell, and sank to rise no more. Somehow at once I suspected that this shadowy form, with its lightninglike movements, its glittering hatchet, was Wetzel. When he plunged into the midst of the other savages I distinctly recognized him, and saw that he had a bundle, possibly his coat, wrapped round his left arm, and his right hand held the glittering tomahawk. I saw him strike that big Indian there, the one lying with split skull. His wonderful daring and quickness seemed to make the savages turn at random. He broke through the circle, swung Nell under his arm, slashed at my bonds as he passed by, and then was gone as he had come. Not until after you were struck, and Silvertip came up to me, was I aware my bonds were cut. Wetzel's hatchet had severed them; it even cut my side, which was bleeding. I was free to help, to fight, and I did not know it. Fool that I am!"

"I made an awful mess of my part of the rescue," groaned Joe. "I wonder if the savages know it was Wetzel."

"Do they? Well, I rather think so. Did you not hear them scream that French name? As far as I am able to judge, only two Indians were killed instantly. The others died during the night. I had to sit here, tied and helpless, listening as they groaned and called the name of their slayer, even in their death-throes. Deathwind! They have named him well."

"I guess he nearly killed Girty."

"Evidently, but surely the evil one protects the renegade."

"Jim Girty's doomed," whispered Joe, earnestly. "He's as good as dead already. I've lived with Wetzel, and know him. He told me Girty had murdered a settler, a feeble old man, who lived near Fort Henry with his son. The hunter has sworn to kill the renegade; but, mind you, he did not tell me that. I saw it in his eyes. It wouldn't surprise me to see him jump out of these bushes at any moment. I'm looking for it. If he knows there are only three left, he'll be after them like a hound on a trail. Girty must hurry. Where's he taking you?"

"To the Delaware town."

"I don't suppose the chiefs will let any harm befall you; but Kate and I would be better off dead. If we can only delay the march, Wetzel will surely return."

"Hush! Girty's up."

The renegade staggered to an upright position, and leaned on the Shawnee's arm. Evidently he had not been seriously injured, only stunned. Covered with blood from a swollen, gashed lump on his temple, he certainly presented a savage appearance.

"Where's the yellow-haired lass?" he demanded, pushing away Silvertip's friendly arm. He glared around the glade. The Shawnee addressed him briefly, whereupon he raged to and fro under the tree, cursing with foam-flecked lips, and actually howling with baffled rage. His fury was so great that he became suddenly weak, and was compelled to sit down.

"She's safe, you villainous renegade!" cried Joe.

"Hush, Joe! Do not anger him. It can do no good," interposed Jim.

"Why not? We couldn't be worse off," answered Joe.

"I'll git her, I'll git her agin," panted Girty. "I'll keep her, an' she'll love me."

The spectacle of this perverted wretch speaking as if he had been cheated out of love was so remarkable, so pitiful, so monstrous, that for a moment Joe was dumbfounded.

"Bah! You white-livered murderer!" Joe hissed. He well knew it was not wise to give way to his passion; but he could not help it. This beast in human guise, whining for love, maddened him. "Any white woman on earth would die a thousand deaths and burn for a million years afterward rather than love you!"

"I'll see you killed at the stake, beggin' fer mercy, an' be feed fer buzzards," croaked the renegade.

"Then kill me now, or you may slip up on one of your cherished buzzard-feasts," cried Joe, with glinting eye and taunting voice. "Then go sneaking back to your hole like a hyena, and stay there. Wetzel is on your trail! He missed you last night; but it was because of the girl. He's after you, Girty; he'll get you one of these days, and when he does—My God!—-"

Nothing could be more revolting than that swarthy, evil face turned pale with fear. Girty's visage was a ghastly, livid white. So earnest, so intense was Joe's voice, that it seemed to all as if Wetzel was about to dart into the glade, with his avenging tomahawk uplifted to wreak an awful vengeance on the abductor. The renegade's white, craven heart contained no such thing as courage. If he ever fought it was like a wolf, backed by numbers. The resemblance ceased here, for even a cornered wolf will show his teeth, and Girty, driven to bay, would have cringed and cowered. Even now at the mention of Wetzel's enmity he trembled.

"I'll shet yer wind," he cried, catching up his tomahawk and making for Joe.

Silvertip intervened, and prevented the assault. He led Girty back to his seat and spoke low, evidently trying to soothe the renegade's feelings.

"Silvertip, give me a tomahawk, and let me fight him," implored Joe.

"Paleface brave—like Injun chief. Paleface Shawnee's prisoner—no speak more," answered Silvertip, with respect in his voice.

"Oh, where's Nellie?"

A grief-stricken whisper caught Jim's ear. He turned to see Kate's wide, questioning eyes fixed upon him.

"Nell was rescued."

"Thank God!" murmured the girl.

"Come along," shouted Girty, in his harsh voice, as, grasping Kate's arm, he pulled the girl violently to her feet. Then, picking up his rifle, he led her into the forest. Silvertip followed with Joe, while the remaining Indian guarded Jim.

* * *

The great council-lodge of the Delawares rang with savage and fiery eloquence. Wingenund paced slowly before the orators. Wise as he was, he wanted advice before deciding what was to be done with the missionary. The brothers had been taken to the chief, who immediately called a council. The Indians sat in a half circle around the lodge. The prisoners, with hands bound, guarded by two brawny braves, stood in one corner gazing with curiosity and apprehension at this formidable array. Jim knew some of the braves, but the majority of those who spoke bitterly against the palefaces had never frequented the Village of Peace. Nearly all were of the Wolf tribe of Delawares. Jim whispered to Joe, interpreting that part of the speeches bearing upon the disposal to be made of them. Two white men, dressed in Indian garb, held prominent positions before Wingenund. The boys saw a resemblance between one of these men and Jim Girty, and accordingly concluded he was the famous renegade, or so-called white Indian, Simon Girty. The other man was probably Elliott, the Tory, with whom Girty had deserted from Fort Pitt. Jim Girty was not present. Upon nearing the encampment he had taken his captive and disappeared in a ravine.

Shingiss, seldom in favor of drastic measures with prisoners, eloquently urged initiating the brothers into the tribe. Several other chiefs were favorably inclined, though not so positive as Shingiss. Kotoxen was for the death penalty; the implacable Pipe for nothing less than burning at the stake. Not one was for returning the missionary to his Christian Indians. Girty and Elliott, though requested to speak, maintained an ominous silence.

Wingenund strode with thoughtful mien before his council. He had heard all his wise chiefs and his fiery warriors. Supreme was his power. Freedom or death for the captives awaited the wave of his hand. His impassive face gave not the slightest inkling of what to expect. Therefore the prisoners were forced to stand there with throbbing hearts while the chieftain waited the customary dignified interval before addressing the council.

"Wingenund has heard the Delaware wise men and warriors. The white Indian opens not his lips; his silence broods evil for the palefaces. Pipe wants the blood of the white men; the Shawnee chief demands the stake. Wingenund says free the white father who harms no Indian. Wingenund hears no evil in the music of his voice. The white father's brother should die. Kill the companion of Deathwind!"

A plaintive murmur, remarkable when coming from an assembly of stern-browed chiefs, ran round the circle at the mention of the dread appellation.

"The white father is free," continued Wingenund. "Let one of my runners conduct him to the Village of Peace."

A brave entered and touched Jim on the shoulder.

Jim shook his head and pointed to Joe. The runner touched Joe.

"No, no. I am not the missionary," cried Joe, staring aghast at his brother. "Jim, have you lost your senses?"

Jim sadly shook his head, and turning to Wingenund made known in a broken Indian dialect that his brother was the missionary, and would sacrifice himself, taking this opportunity to practice the Christianity he had taught.

"The white father is brave, but he is known," broke in Wingenund's deep voice, while he pointed to the door of the lodge. "Let him go back to his Christian Indians."

The Indian runner cut Joe's bonds, and once more attempted to lead him from the lodge. Rage and misery shown in the lad's face. He pushed the runner aside. He exhausted himself trying to explain, to think of Indian words enough to show he was not the missionary. He even implored Girty to speak for him. When the renegade sat there stolidly silent Joe's rage burst out.

"Curse you all for a lot of ignorant redskins. I am not a missionary. I am Deathwind's friend. I killed a Delaware. I was the companion of Le Vent de la Mort!"

Joe's passionate vehemence, and the truth that spoke from his flashing eyes compelled the respect, if not the absolute belief of the Indians. The savages slowly shook their heads. They beheld the spectacle of two brothers, one a friend, the other an enemy of all Indians, each willing to go to the stake, to suffer an awful agony, for love of the other. Chivalrous deeds always stir an Indian's heart. It was like a redman to die for his brother. The indifference, the contempt for death, won their admiration.

"Let the white father stand forth," sternly called Wingenund.

A hundred somber eyes turned on the prisoners. Except that one wore a buckskin coat, the other a linsey one, there was no difference. The strong figures were the same, the white faces alike, the stern resolve in the gray eyes identical—they were twin brothers.

Wingenund once more paced before his silent chiefs. To deal rightly with this situation perplexed him. To kill both palefaces did not suit him. Suddenly he thought of a way to decide.

"Let Wingenund's daughter come," he ordered.

A slight, girlish figure entered. It was Whispering Winds. Her beautiful face glowed while she listened to her father.

"Wingenund's daughter has her mother's eyes, that were beautiful as a doe's, keen as a hawk's, far-seeing as an eagle's. Let the Delaware maiden show her blood. Let her point out the white father."

Shyly but unhesitatingly Whispering Winds laid her hand Jim's arm.

"Missionary, begone!" came the chieftain's command. "Thank Wingenund's daughter for your life, not the God of your Christians!"

He waved his hand to the runner. The brave grasped Jim's arm.

"Good-by, Joe," brokenly said Jim.

"Old fellow, good-by," came the answer.

They took one last, long look into each others' eyes. Jim's glance betrayed his fear—he would never see his brother again. The light in Joe's eyes was the old steely flash, the indomitable spirit—while there was life there was hope.

"Let the Shawnee chief paint his prisoner black," commanded Wingenund.

When the missionary left the lodge with the runner, Whispering Winds had smiled, for she had saved him whom she loved to hear speak; but the dread command that followed paled her cheek. Black paint meant hideous death. She saw this man so like the white father. Her piteous gaze tried to turn from that white face; but the cold, steely eyes fascinated her.

She had saved one only to be the other's doom!

She had always been drawn toward white men. Many prisoners had she rescued. She had even befriended her nation's bitter foe, Deathwind. She had listened to the young missionary with rapture; she had been his savior. And now when she looked into the eyes of this young giant, whose fate had rested on her all unwitting words, she resolved to save him.

She had been a shy, shrinking creature, fearing to lift her eyes to a paleface's, but now they were raised clear and steadfast.

As she stepped toward the captive and took his hand, her whole person radiated with conscious pride in her power. It was the knowledge that she could save. When she kissed his hand, and knelt before him, she expressed a tender humility.

She had claimed questionable right of an Indian maiden; she asked what no Indian dared refuse a chief's daughter; she took the paleface for her husband.

Her action was followed by an impressive silence. She remained kneeling. Wingenund resumed his slow march to and fro. Silvertip retired to his corner with gloomy face. The others bowed their heads as if the maiden's decree was irrevocable.

Once more the chieftain's sonorous command rang out. An old Indian, wrinkled and worn, weird of aspect, fanciful of attire, entered the lodge and waved his wampum wand. He mumbled strange words, and departed chanting a long song.

Whispering Winds arose, a soft, radiant smile playing over her face, and, still holding Joe's hand, she led him out of the lodge, through long rows of silent Indians, down a land bordered by teepees, he following like one in a dream.

He expected to awaken at any minute to see the stars shining through the leaves. Yet he felt the warm, soft pressure of a little hand. Surely this slender, graceful figure was real.

She bade him enter a lodge of imposing proportions. Still silent, in amazement and gratitude, he obeyed.

The maiden turned to Joe. Though traces of pride still lingered, all her fire had vanished. Her bosom rose with each quick-panting breath; her lips quivered, she trembled like a trapped doe.

But at last the fluttering lashes rose. Joe saw two velvety eyes dark with timid fear, yet veiling in their lustrous depths an unuttered hope and love.

"Whispering Winds—save—paleface," she said, in a voice low and tremulous. "Fear—father. Fear—tell—Wingenund—she—Christian."

* * *

Indian summer, that enchanted time, unfolded its golden, dreamy haze over the Delaware village. The forests blazed with autumn fire, the meadows boomed in rich luxuriance. All day low down in the valleys hung a purple smoke which changed, as the cool evening shades crept out of the woodland, into a cloud of white mist. All day the asters along the brooks lifted golden-brown faces to the sun as if to catch the warning warmth of his smile. All day the plains and forests lay in melancholy repose. The sad swish of the west wind over the tall grass told that he was slowly dying away before his enemy, the north wind. The sound of dropping nuts was heard under the motionless trees.

For Joe the days were days of enchantment. His wild heart had found its mate. A willing captive he was now. All his fancy for other women, all his memories faded into love for his Indian bride.

Whispering Winds charmed the eye, mind, and heart. Every day her beauty seemed renewed. She was as apt to learn as she was quick to turn her black-crowned head, but her supreme beauty was her loving, innocent soul. Untainted as the clearest spring, it mirrored the purity and simplicity of her life. Indian she might be, one of a race whose morals and manners were alien to the man she loved, yet she would have added honor to the proudest name.

When Whispering Winds raised her dark eyes they showed radiant as a lone star; when she spoke low her voice made music.

"Beloved," she whispered one day to him, "teach the Indian maiden more love for you, and truth, and God. Whispering Winds yearns to go to the Christians, but she fears her stern father. Wingenund would burn the

318

Village of Peace. The Indian tribes tremble before the thunder of his wrath. Be patient, my chief. Time changes the leaves, so it will the anger of the warriors. Whispering Winds will set you free, and be free herself to go far with you toward the rising sun, where dwell your people. She will love, and be constant, as the northern star. Her love will be an eternal spring where blossoms bloom ever anew, and fresh, and sweet. She will love your people, and raise Christian children, and sit ever in the door of your home praying for the west wind to blow. Or, if my chief wills, we shall live the Indian life, free as two eagles on their lonely crag."

Although Joe gave himself up completely to his love for his bride, he did not forget that Kate was in the power of the renegade, and that he must rescue her. Knowing Girty had the unfortunate girls somewhere near the Delaware encampment, he resolved to find the place. Plans of all kinds he resolved in his mind. The best one he believed lay through Whispering Winds. First to find the whereabouts of Girty; kill him if possible, or at least free Kate, and then get away with her and his Indian bride. Sanguine as he invariably was, he could not but realize the peril of this undertaking. If Whispering Winds betrayed her people, it meant death to her as well as to him. He would far rather spend the remaining days of his life in the Indian village, than doom the maiden whose love had saved him. Yet he thought he might succeed in getting away with her, and planned to that end. His natural spirit, daring, reckless, had gained while he was associated with Wetzel.

Meanwhile he mingled freely with the Indians, and here, as elsewhere, his winning personality, combined with his athletic prowess, soon made him well liked. He was even on friendly terms with Pipe. The swarthy war chief liked Joe because, despite the animosity he had aroused in some former lovers of Whispering Winds, he actually played jokes on them. In fact, Joe's pranks raised many a storm; but the young braves who had been suitors for Wingenund's lovely daughter, feared the muscular paleface, and the tribe's ridicule more; so he continued his trickery unmolested. Joe's idea was to lead the savages to believe he was thoroughly happy in his new life, and so he was, but it suited him better to be free. He succeeded in misleading the savages. At first he was closely watched, the the vigilance relaxed, and finally ceased.

This last circumstance was owing, no doubt, to a ferment of excitement that had suddenly possessed the Delawares. Council after council was held in the big lodge. The encampment was visited by runner after runner. Some important crisis was pending.

Joe could not learn what it all meant, and the fact that Whispering Winds suddenly lost her gladsome spirit and became sad caused him further anxiety. When he asked her the reason for her unhappiness, she was silent. Moreover, he was surprised to learn, when he questioned her upon the subject of their fleeing together, that she was eager to go immediately. While all this mystery puzzled Joe, it did not make any difference to him or in his plans. It rather favored the latter. He understood that the presence of Simon Girty and Elliott, with several other renegades unknown to him, was significant of unrest among the Indians. These presagers of evil were accustomed to go from village to village, exciting the savages to acts of war. Peace meant the downfall and death of these men. They were busy all day and far into the night. Often Joe heard Girty's hoarse voice lifted in the council lodge. Pipe thundered incessantly for war. But Joe could not learn against whom. Elliott's suave, oily oratory exhorted the Indians to vengeance. But Joe could not guess upon whom. He was, however, destined to learn.

The third day of the councils a horseman stopped before Whispering Winds' lodge, and called out. Stepping to the door, Joe saw a white man, whose dark, keen, handsome face seemed familiar. Yet Joe knew he had never seen this stalwart man.

"A word with you," said the stranger. His tone was curt, authoritative, as that of a man used to power.

"As many as you like. Who are you?"

"I am Isaac Zane. Are you Wetzel's companion, or the renegade Deering?"

"I am not a renegade any more than you are. I was rescued by the Indian girl, who took me as her husband," said Joe coldly. He was surprised, and did not know what to make of Zane's manner.

"Good! I'm glad to meet you," instantly replied Zane, his tone and expression changing. He extended his hand to Joe. "I wanted to be sure. I never saw the renegade Deering. He is here now. I am on my way to the Wyandot town. I have been to Fort Henry, where my brother told me of you and the missionaries. When I arrived here I heard your story from Simon Girty. If you can, you must get away from here. If I dared I'd take you to the Huron village, but it's impossible. Go, while you have a chance."

"Zane, I thank you. I've suspected something was wrong. What is it?"

"Couldn't be worse," whispered Zane, glancing round to see if they were overheard. "Girty and Elliott, backed by this Deering, are growing jealous of the influence of Christianity on the Indians. They are plotting against the Village of Peace. Tarhe, the Huron chief, has been approached, and asked to join in a concerted movement against religion. Seemingly it is not so much the missionaries as the converted Indians, that the renegades are fuming over. They know if the Christian savages are killed, the strength of the missionaries' hold will be forever broken. Pipe is wild for blood. These renegades are slowly poisoning the minds of the few chiefs who are favorably disposed. The outlook is bad! bad!"

"What can I do?"

"Cut out for yourself. Get away, if you can, with a gun. Take the creek below, follow the current down to the Ohio, and then make east for Fort Henry.

"But I want to rescue the white girl Jim Girty has concealed here somewhere."

"Impossible! Don't attempt it unless you want to throw your life away. Buzzard Jim, as we call Girty, is a butcher; he has probably murdered the girl."

"I won't leave without trying. And there's my wife, the Indian girl who saved me. Zane, she's a Christian. She wants to go with me. I can't leave her."

"I am warning you, that's all. If I were you I'd never leave without a try to find the white girl, and I'd never forsake my Indian bride. I've been through the same thing. You must be a good woodsman, or Wetzel wouldn't have let you stay with him. Pick out a favorable time and make the attempt. I suggest you make your Indian girl show you where Girty is. She knows, but is afraid to tell you, for she fears Girty. Get your dog and horse from the Shawnee. That's a fine horse. He can carry you both to safety. Take him away from Silvertip."

"How?"

"Go right up and demand your horse and dog. Most of these Delawares are honest, for all their blood-shedding and cruelty. With them might is right. The Delawares won't try to get your horse for you; but they'll stick to you when you assert your rights. They don't like the Shawnee, anyhow. If Silvertip refuses to give you the horse, grab him before he can draw a weapon, and beat him good. You're big enough to do it. The Delawares will be tickled to see you pound him. He's thick with Girty; that's why he lays round here. Take my word, it's the best way. Do it openly, and no one will interfere."

"By Heavens, Zane, I'll give him a drubbing. I owe him one, and am itching to get hold of him."

"I must go now. I shall send a Wyandot runner to your brother at the village. They shall be warned. Good-by. Good luck. May we meet again."

Joe watched Zane ride swiftly down the land and disappear in the shrubbery. Whispering Winds came to the door of the lodge. She looked anxiously at him. He went within, drawing her along with him, and quickly informed her that he had learned the cause of the council, that he had resolved to get away, and she must find out Girty's hiding place. Whispering Winds threw herself into his arms, declaring with an energy and passion unusual to her, that she would risk anything for him. She informed Joe that she knew the direction from which Girty always returned to the village. No doubt she could find his retreat. With a cunning that showed her Indian nature, she suggested a plan which Joe at once saw was excellent. After Joe got his horse, she would ride around the village, then off into the woods, where she could leave the horse and return to say he had run away from her. As was their custom during afternoons, they would walk leisurely along the brook, and, trusting to the excitement created by the councils, get away unobserved. Find the horse, if possible rescue the prisoner, and then travel east with all speed.

Joe left the lodge at once to begin the working out of the plan. Luck favored him at the outset, for he met Silvertip before the council lodge. The Shawnee was leading Lance, and the dog followed at his heels. The spirit of Mose had been broken. Poor dog, Joe thought, he had been beaten until he was afraid to wag his tail at his old master. Joe's resentment blazed into fury, but he kept cool outwardly.

Right before a crowd of Indians waiting for the council to begin, Joe planted himself in front of the Shawnee, barring his way.

"Silvertip has the paleface's horse and dog," said Joe, in a loud voice.

The chief stared haughtily while the other Indians sauntered nearer. They all knew how the Shawnee had got the animals, and now awaited the outcome of the white man's challenge.

"Paleface—heap—liar," growled the Indian. His dark eyes glowed craftily, while his hand dropped, apparently in careless habit, to the haft of his tomahawk.

Joe swung his long arm; his big fist caught the Shawnee on the jaw, sending him to the ground. Uttering a frightful yell, Silvertip drew his weapon and attempted to rise, but the moment's delay in seizing the hatchet, was fatal to his design. Joe was upon him with tigerlike suddenness. One kick sent the tomahawk spinning, another landed the Shawnee again on the ground. Blind with rage, Silvertip leaped up, and without a weapon rushed at his antagonist; but the Indian was not a boxer, and he failed to get his hands on Joe. Shifty and elusive, the lad dodged around the struggling savage. One, two, three hard blows staggered Silvertip, and a fourth, delivered with the force of Joe's powerful arm, caught the Indian when he was off his balance, and felled him, battered and bloody, on the grass. The surrounding Indians looked down at the vanquished Shawnee, expressing their approval in characteristic grunts.

With Lance prancing proudly, and Mose leaping lovingly beside him, Joe walked back to his lodge. Whispering Winds sprang to meet him with joyful face. She had feared the outcome of trouble with the Shawnee, but no queen ever bestowed upon returning victorious lord a loftier look of pride, a sweeter glance of love, than the Indian maiden bent upon her lover.

Whispering Winds informed Joe that an important council was to be held that afternoon. It would be wise for them to make the attempt to get away immediately after the convening of the chiefs. Accordingly she got upon Lance and rode him up and down the village lane, much to the pleasure of the watching Indians. She scattered the idle crowds on the grass plots, she dashed through the side streets, and let every one in the encampment see her clinging to the black stallion. Then she rode him out along the creek. Accustomed to her imperious will, the Indians thought nothing unusual. When she returned an hour later, with flying hair and disheveled costume, no one paid particular attention to her.

That afternoon Joe and his bride were the favored of fortune. With Mose running before them, they got clear of the encampment and into the woods. Once in the forest Whispering Winds rapidly led the way east. When they climbed to the top of a rocky ridge she pointed down into a thicket before her, saying that somewhere in this dense hollow was Girty's hut. Joe hesitated about taking Mose. He wanted the dog, but in case he had to run it was necessary Whispering Winds should find his trail, and for this he left the dog with her.

He started down the ridge, and had not gone a hundred paces when over some gray boulders he saw the thatched roof of a hut. So wild and secluded was the spot, that he would never have discovered the cabin from any other point than this, which he had been so fortunate as to find.

His study and practice under Wetzel now stood him in good stead. He picked out the best path over the rough stones and through the brambles, always keeping under cover. He stepped as carefully as if the hunter was behind him. Soon he reached level ground. A dense laurel thicket hid the cabin, but he knew the direction in which it lay. Throwing himself flat on the ground, he wormed his way through the thicket, carefully, yet swiftly, because he knew there was no time to lose. Finally the rear of the cabin stood in front of him.

It was made of logs, rudely hewn, and as rudely thrown together. In several places clay had fallen from chinks between the timbers, leaving small holes. Like a snake Joe slipped close to the hut. Raising his head he looked through one of the cracks.

Instantly he shrank back into the grass, shivering with horror. He almost choked in his attempt to prevent an outcry.

CHAPTER XVIII.

The sight which Joe had seen horrified him, for several moments, into helpless inaction. He lay breathing heavily, impotent, in an awful rage. As he remained there stunned by the shock, he gazed up through the open space in the leaves, trying to still his fury, to realize the situation, to make no hasty move. The soft blue of the sky, the fleecy clouds drifting eastward, the fluttering leaves and the twittering birds—all assured him he was wide awake. He had found Girty's den where so many white women had been hidden, to see friends and home no more. He had seen the renegade sleeping, calmly sleeping like any other man. How could the wretch sleep! He had seen Kate. It had been the sight of her that had paralyzed him. To make a certainty of his fears, he again raised himself to peep into the hole. As he did so a faint cry came from within.

Girty lay on a buffalo robe near a barred door. Beyond him sat Kate, huddled in one corner of the cabin. A long buckskin thong was knotted round her waist, and tied to a log. Her hair was matted and tangled, and on her face and arms were many discolored bruises. Worse still, in her plaintive moaning, in the meaningless movement of her head, in her vacant expression, was proof that her mind had gone. She was mad. Even as an agonizing pity came over Joe, to be followed by the surging fire of rage, blazing up in his breast, he could not but thank God that she was mad! It was merciful that Kate was no longer conscious of her suffering.

Like leaves in a storm wavered Joe's hands as he clenched them until the nails brought blood. "Be calm, be cool," whispered his monitor, Wetzel, ever with him in spirit. But God! Could he be cool? Bounding with lion-spring he hurled his heavy frame against the door.

Crash! The door was burst from its fastenings.

Girty leaped up with startled yell, drawing his knife as he rose. It had not time to descend before Joe's second spring, more fierce even than the other, carried him directly on top of the renegade. As the two went down Joe caught the villain's wrist with a grip that literally cracked the bones. The knife fell and rolled away from the struggling men. For an instant they tumbled about on the floor, clasped in a crushing embrace. The renegade was strong, supple, slippery as an eel. Twice he wriggled from his foe. Gnashing his teeth, he fought like a hyena. He was fighting for life—life, which is never so dear as to a coward and a murderer. Doom glared from Joe's big eyes, and scream after scream issued from the renegade's white lips.

Terrible was this struggle, but brief. Joe seemingly had the strength of ten men. Twice he pulled Girty down as a wolf drags a deer. He dashed him against the wall, throwing him nearing and nearer the knife. Once within reach of the blade Joe struck the renegade a severe blow on the temple and the villain's wrestling became weaker. Planting his heavy knee on Girty's breast, Joe reached for the knife, and swung it high. Exultantly he cried, mad with lust for the brute's blood.

But the slight delay saved Girty's life.

The knife was knocked from Joe's hand and he leaped erect to find himself confronted by Silvertip. The chief held a tomahawk with which he had struck the weapon from the young man's grasp, and, to judge from his burning eyes and malignant smile, he meant to brain the now defenseless paleface.

In a single fleeting instant Joe saw that Girty was helpless for the moment, that Silvertip was confident of his revenge, and that the situation called for Wetzel's characteristic advice, "act like lightnin'."

Swifter than the thought was the leap he made past Silvertip. It carried him to a wooden bar which lay on the floor. Escape was easy, for the door was before him and the Shawnee behind, but Joe did not flee! He seized the bar and rushed at the Indian. Then began a duel in which the savage's quickness and cunning matched the white man's strength and fury. Silvertip dodged the vicious swings Joe aimed at him; he parried many blows, any one of which would have crushed his skull. Nimble as a cat, he avoided every rush, while his dark eyes watched for an opening. He fought wholly on the defensive, craftily reserving his strength until his opponent should tire.

At last, catching the bar on his hatchet, he broke the force of the blow, and then, with agile movement, dropped to the ground and grappled Joe's legs. Long before this he had drawn his knife, and now he used it, plunging the blade into the young man's side.

Cunning and successful as was the savage's ruse, it failed signally, for to get hold of the Shawnee was all Joe wanted. Feeling the sharp pain as they fell together, he reached his hand behind him and caught Silvertip's wrist. Exerting all his power, he wrenched the Indian's arm so that it was not only dislocated, but the bones cracked.

Silvertip saw his fatal mistake, but he uttered no sound. Crippled, though he was, he yet made a supreme effort, but it was as if he had been in the hands of a giant. The lad handled him with remorseless and resistless fury. Suddenly he grasped the knife, which Silvertip had been unable to hold with his crippled hand, and thrust it deeply into the Indian's side.

All Silvertip's muscles relaxed as if a strong tension had been removed. Slowly his legs straightened, his arms dropped, and from his side gushed a dark flood. A shadow crept over his face, not dark nor white, but just a shadow. His eyes lost their hate; they no longer saw the foe, they looked beyond with gloomy question, and then were fixed cold in death. Silvertip died as he had lived—a chief.

Joe glared round for Girty. He was gone, having slipped away during the fight. The lad turned to release the poor prisoner, when he started back with a cry of fear. Kate lay bathed in a pool of blood—dead. The renegade, fearing she might be rescued, had murdered her, and then fled from the cabin.

Almost blinded by horror, and staggering with weakness, Joe turned to leave the cabin. Realizing that he was seriously, perhaps dangerously, wounded he wisely thought he must not leave the place without weapons. He had marked the pegs where the renegade's rifle hung, and had been careful to keep between that and his enemies. He took down the gun and horns, which were attached to it, and, with one last shuddering glance at poor Kate, left the place.

He was conscious of a queer lightness in his head, but he suffered no pain. His garments were dripping with blood. He did not know how much of it was his, or the Indian's. Instinct rather than sight was his guide. He grew weaker and weaker; his head began to whirl, yet he kept on, knowing that life and freedom were his if he found Whispering Winds. He gained the top of the ridge; his eyes were blurred, his strength gone. He called aloud, and then plunged forward on his face. He heard dimly, as though the sound were afar off, the whine of a dog. He felt something soft and wet on his face. Then consciousness left him.

When he regained his senses he was lying on a bed of ferns under a projecting rock. He heard the gurgle of running water mingling with the song of birds. Near him lay Mose, and beyond rose a wall of green thicket. Neither Whispering Winds nor his horse was visible.

He felt a dreamy lassitude. He was tired, but had no pain. Finding he could move without difficulty, he concluded his weakness was more from loss of blood than a dangerous wound. He put his hand on the place where he had been stabbed, and felt a soft, warm compress such as might have been made by a bunch of wet leaves. Some one had unlaced his hunting-shirt—for he saw the strings were not as he usually tied them—and had dressed the wound. Joe decided, after some deliberation, that Whispering Winds had found him, made him as comfortable as possible, and, leaving Mose on guard, had gone out to hunt for food, or perhaps back to the Indian encampment. The rifle and horns he had taken from Girty's hut, together with Silvertip's knife, lay beside him.

As Joe lay there hoping for Whispering Winds' return, his reflections were not pleasant. Fortunate, indeed, he was to be alive; but he had no hope he could continue to be favored by fortune. Odds were now against his escape. Girty would have the Delawares on his trail like a pack of hungry wolves. He could not understand the absence of Whispering Winds. She would have died sooner than desert him. Girty had, perhaps, captured her, and was now scouring the woods for him.

"I'll get him next time, or he'll get me," muttered Joe, in bitter wrath. He could never forgive himself for his failure to kill the renegade.

The recollection of how nearly he had forever ended Girty's brutal career brought before Joe's mind the scene of the fight. He saw again Buzzard Jim's face, revolting, unlike anything human. There stretched Silvertip's dark figure, lying still and stark, and there was Kate's white form in its winding, crimson wreath of blood. Hauntingly her face returned, sad, stern in its cold rigidity.

"Poor girl, better for her to be dead," he murmured. "Not long will she be unavenged!"

His thoughts drifted to the future. He had no fear of starvation, for Mose could catch a rabbit or woodchuck at any time. When the strips of meat he had hidden in his coat were gone, he could start a fire and roast more. What concerned him most was pursuit. His trail from the cabin had been a bloody one, which would render it easily followed. He dared not risk exertion until he had given his wound time to heal. Then, if he did escape from Girty and the Delawares, his future was not bright. His experiences of the last few days had not only sobered, but brought home to him this real border life. With all his fire and daring he new he was no fool. He had eagerly embraced a career which, at the present stage of his training, was beyond his scope—not that he did not know how to act in sudden crises, but because he had not had the necessary practice to quickly and surely use his knowledge.

Bitter, indeed, was his self-scorn when he recalled that of the several critical positions he had been in since his acquaintance with Wetzel, he had failed in all but one. The exception was the killing of Silvertip. Here his fury had made him fight as Wetzel fought with only his every day incentive. He realized that the border was no place for any save the boldest and most experienced hunters—men who had become inured to hardship, callous as to death, keen as Indians. Fear was not in Joe nor lack of confidence; but he had good sense, and realized he would have done a wiser thing had he stayed at Fort Henry. Colonel Zane was right. The Indians were tigers, the renegades vultures, the vast untrammeled forests and plains their covert. Ten years of war had rendered this wilderness a place where those few white men who had survived were hardened to the spilling of blood, stern even in those few quiet hours which peril allowed them, strong in their sacrifice of all for future generations.

A low growl from Mose broke into Joe's reflections. The dog had raised his nose from his paws and sniffed suspiciously at the air. The lad heard a slight rustling outside, and in another moment was overjoyed at seeing Whispering Winds. She came swiftly, with a lithe, graceful motion, and flying to him like a rush of wind, knelt beside him. She kissed him and murmured words of endearment.

"Winds, where have you been?" he asked her, in the mixed English and Indian dialect in which they conversed.

She told him the dog had led her to him two evenings before. He was insensible. She had bathed and bandaged his wound, and remained with him all that night. The next day, finding he was ill and delirious, she decided to risk returning to the village. If any questions arose, she could say he had left her. Then she would find a way to get back to him, bringing healing herbs for his wound and a soothing drink. As it turned out Girty had returned to the camp. He was battered and bruised, and in a white heat of passion. Going at once to Wingenund, the renegade openly accused Whispering Winds of aiding her paleface lover to escape. Wingenund called his daughter before him, and questioned her. She confessed all to her father.

"Why is the daughter of Wingenund a traitor to her race?" demanded the chief.

"Whispering Winds is a Christian."

Wingenund received this intelligence as a blow. He dismissed Girty and sent his braves from his lodge, facing his daughter alone. Gloomy and stern, he paced before her.

"Wingenund's blood might change, but would never betray. Wingenund is the Delaware chief," he said. "Go. Darken no more the door of Wingenund's wigwam. Let the flower of the Delawares fade in alien pastures. Go. Whispering Winds is free!"

Tears shone brightly in the Indian girl's eyes while she told Joe her story. She loved her father, and she would see him no more.

"Winds is free," she whispered. "When strength returns to her master she can follow him to the white villages. Winds will live her life for him."

"Then we have no one to fear?" asked Joe.

"No redman, now that the Shawnee chief is dead."

"Will Girty follow us? He is a coward; he will fear to come alone."

"The white savage is a snake in the grass."

Two long days followed, during which the lovers lay quietly in hiding. On the morning of the third day Joe felt that he might risk the start for the Village of Peace. Whispering Winds led the horse below a stone upon which the invalid stood, thus enabling him to mount. Then she got on behind him.

The sun was just gilding the horizon when they rode out of the woods into a wide plain. No living thing could be seen. Along the edge of the forest the ground was level, and the horse traveled easily. Several times during the morning Joe dismounted beside a pile of stones or a fallen tree. The miles were traversed without serious inconvenience to the invalid, except that he grew tired. Toward the middle of the afternoon, when they had ridden perhaps twenty-five miles, they crossed a swift, narrow brook. The water was a beautiful clear brown. Joe made note of this, as it was an unusual circumstance. Nearly all the streams, when not flooded, were green in color. He remembered that during his wanderings with Wetzel they had found one stream of this brown, copper-colored water. The lad knew he must take a roundabout way to the village so that he might avoid Indian runners or scouts, and he hoped this stream would prove to be the one he had once camped upon.

As they were riding toward a gentle swell or knoll covered with trees and shrubbery, Whispering Winds felt something warm on her hand, and, looking, was horrified to find it covered with blood. Joe's wound had opened. She told him they must dismount here, and remain until he was stronger. The invalid himself thought this conclusion was wise. They would be practically safe now, since they must be out of the Indian path, and many miles from the encampment. Accordingly he got off the horse, and sat down on a log, while Whispering Winds searched for a suitable place in which to erect a temporary shelter.

Joe's wandering gaze was arrested by a tree with a huge knotty formation near the ground. It was like many trees, but this peculiarity was not what struck Joe. He had seen it before. He never forgot anything in the woods that once attracted his attention. He looked around on all sides. Just behind him was an opening in the clump of trees. Within this was a perpendicular stone covered with moss and lichens; above it a beech tree spread long, graceful branches. He thrilled with the remembrance these familiar marks brought. This was Beautiful Spring, the place where Wetzel rescued Nell, where he had killed the Indians in that night attack he would never forget.

CHAPTER XIX.

One evening a week or more after the disappearance of Jim and the girls, George Young and David Edwards, the missionaries, sat on the cabin steps, gazing disconsolately upon the forest scenery. Hard as had been the ten years of their labor among the Indians, nothing had shaken them as the loss of their young friends.

"Dave, I tell you your theory about seeing them again is absurd," asserted George. "I'll never forget that wretch, Girty, as he spoke to Nell. Why, she just wilted like a flower blasted by fire. I can't understand why he let me go, and kept Jim, unless the Shawnee had something to do with it. I never wished until now that I was a hunter. I'd go after Girty. You've heard as well as I of his many atrocities. I'd rather have seen Kate and Nell dead than have them fall into his power. I'd rather have killed them myself!"

Young had aged perceptibly in these last few days. The blue veins showed at his temples; his face had become thinner and paler, his eyes had a look of pain. The former expression of patience, which had sat so well on him, was gone.

"George, I can't account for my fancies or feelings, else, perhaps, I'd be easier in mind," answered Dave. His face, too, showed the ravages of grief. "I've had queer thoughts lately, and dreams such as I never had before. Perhaps it's this trouble which has made me so nervous. I don't seem able to pull myself together. I can neither preach nor work."

"Neither can I! This trouble has hit you as hard as it has me. But, Dave, we've still our duty. To endure, to endure—that is our life. Because a beam of sunshine brightened, for a brief time, the gray of our lives, and then faded away, we must not shirk nor grow sour and discontented."

"But how cruel is this border life!"

"Nature itself is brutal."

"Yes, I know, and we have elected to spend our lives here in the midst of this ceaseless strife, to fare poorly, to have no pleasure, never to feel the comfort of a woman's smiles, nor the joy of a child's caress, all because out in the woods are ten or twenty or a hundred savages we may convert."

"That is why, and it is enough. It is hard to give up the women you love to a black-souled renegade, but that is not for my thought. What kills me is the horror for her—for her."

"I, too, suffer with that thought; more than that, I am morbid and depressed. I feel as if some calamity awaited us here. I have never been superstitious, nor have I had presentiments, but of late there are strange fears in my mind."

At this juncture Mr. Wells and Heckewelder came out of the adjoining cabin.

"I had word from a trustworthy runner to-day. Girty and his captives have not been seen in the Delaware towns," said Heckewelder.

"It is most unlikely that he will take them to the towns," replied Edwards. "What do you make of his capturing Jim?"

"For Pipe, perhaps. The Delaware Wolf is snapping his teeth. Pipe is particularly opposed to Christianity, and—what's that?"

A low whistle from the bushes near the creek bank attracted the attention of all. The younger men got up to investigate, but Heckewelder detained them.

"Wait," he added. "There is no telling what that signal may mean."

They waited with breathless interest. Presently the whistle was repeated, and an instant later the tall figure of a man stepped from behind a thicket. He was a white man, but not recognizable at that distance, even if a friend. The stranger waved his hand as if asking them to be cautious, and come to him.

They went toward the thicket, and when within a few paces of the man Mr. Wells exclaimed:

"It's the man who guided my party to the village. It is Wetzel!"

The other missionaries had never seen the hunter though, of course, they were familiar with his name, and looked at him with great curiosity. The hunter's buckskin garments were wet, torn, and covered with burrs. Dark spots, evidently blood stains, showed on his hunting-shirt.

"Wetzel?" interrogated Heckewelder.

The hunter nodded, and took a step behind the bush. Bending over he lifted something from the ground. It was a girl. It was Nell! She was very white—but alive. A faint, glad smile lighted up her features.

Not a word was spoken. With an expression of tender compassion Mr. Wells received her into his arms. The four missionaries turned fearful, questioning eyes upon the hunter, but they could not speak.

"She's well, an' unharmed," said Wetzel, reading their thoughts, "only worn out. I've carried her these ten miles."

"God bless you, Wetzel!" exclaimed the old missionary. "Nellie, Nellie, can you speak?"

"Uncle dear—I'm—all right," came the faint answer.

"Kate? What—of her?" whispered George Young with lips as dry as corn husks.

"I did my best," said the hunter with a simple dignity. Nothing but the agonized appeal in the young man's eyes could have made Wetzel speak of his achievement.

"Tell us," broke in Heckewelder, seeing that fear had stricken George dumb.

"We trailed 'em an' got away with the golden-haired lass. The last I saw of Joe he was braced up agin a rock fightin' like a wildcat. I tried to cut Jim loose as I was goin' by. I s'pect the wust fer the brothers an' the other lass."

"Can we do nothing?" asked Mr. Wells.

"Nothin'!"

"Wetzel, has the capturing of James Downs any significance to you?" inquired Heckewelder.

"I reckon so."

"What?"

"Pipe an' his white-redskin allies are agin Christianity."

"Do you think we are in danger?"

"I reckon so."

"What do you advise?"

"Pack up a few of your traps, take the lass, an' come with me. I'll see you back in Fort Henry."

Heckewelder nervously walked up to the tree and back again. Young and Edwards looked blankly at one another. They both remembered Edward's presentiment. Mr. Wells uttered an angry exclamation.

"You ask us to fail in our duty? No, never! To go back to the white settlements and acknowledge we were afraid to continue teaching the Gospel to the Indians! You can not understand Christianity if you advise that. You have no religion. You are a killer of Indians."

A shadow that might have been one of pain flitted over the hunter's face.

"No, I ain't a Christian, an' I am a killer of Injuns," said Wetzel, and his deep voice had a strange tremor. "I don't know nothin' much 'cept the woods an' fields, an' if there's a God fer me He's out thar under the trees an' grass. Mr. Wells, you're the first man as ever called me a coward, an' I overlook it because of your callin'. I advise you to go back to Fort Henry, because if you don't go now the chances are agin your ever goin'. Christianity or no Christianity, such men as you hev no bisness in these woods."

"I thank you for your advice, and bless you for your rescue of this child; but I can not leave my work, nor can I understand why all this good work we have done should be called useless. We have converted Indians, saved their souls. Is that not being of some use, of some good here?"

"It's accordin' to how you look at it. Now I know the bark of an oak is different accordin' to the side we see from. I'll allow, hatin' Injuns as I do, is no reason you oughtn't to try an' convert 'em. But you're bringin' on a war. These Injuns won't allow this Village of Peace here with its big fields of corn, an' shops an' workin' redskins. It's agin their nature. You're only sacrificin' your Christian Injuns."

"What do you mean?" asked Mr. Wells, startled by Wetzel's words.

"Enough. I'm ready to guide you to Fort Henry."

"I'll never go."

Wetzel looked at the other men. No one would have doubted him. No one could have failed to see he knew that some terrible anger hovered over the Village of Peace.

"I believe you, Wetzel, but I can not go," said Heckewelder, with white face.

"I will stay," said George, steadily.

"And I," said Dave.

Wetzel nodded, and turned to depart when George grasped his arm. The young missionary's face was drawn and haggard; he fixed an intense gaze upon the hunter.

"Wetzel, listen;" his voice was low and shaken with deep feeling. "I am a teacher of God's word, and I am as earnest in that purpose as you are in your life-work. I shall die here; I shall fill an unmarked grave; but I shall have done the best I could. This is the life destiny has marked out for me, and I will live it as best I may; but in this moment, preacher as I am, I would give all I have or hope to have, all the little good I may have done, all my life, to be such a man as you. For I would avenge the woman I loved. To torture, to kill Girty! I am only a poor, weak fellow who would be lost a mile from this village, and if not, would fall before the youngest brave. But you with your glorious strength, your incomparable woodcraft, you are the man to kill Girty. Rid the frontier of this fiend. Kill him! Wetzel, kill him! I beseech you for the sake of some sweet girl who even now may be on her way to this terrible country, and who may fall into Girty's power—for her sake, Wetzel, kill him. Trail him like a bloodhound, and when you find him remember my broken heart, remember Nell, remember, oh, God! remember poor Kate!"

Young's voice broke into dry sobs. He had completely exhausted himself, so that he was forced to lean against the tree for support.

Wetzel spoke never a word. He stretched out his long, brawny arm and gripped the young missionary's shoulder. His fingers clasped hard. Simple, without words as the action was, it could not have been more potent. And then, as he stood, the softer look faded slowly from his face. A ripple seemed to run over his features, which froze, as it subsided, into a cold, stone rigidity.

His arm dropped; he stepped past the tree, and, bounding lightly as a deer, cleared the creek and disappeared in the bushes.

Mr. Wells carried Nell to his cabin where she lay for hours with wan face and listless languor. She swallowed the nourishing drink an old Indian nurse forced between her teeth; she even smiled weakly when the missionaries spoke to her; but she said nothing nor seemed to rally from her terrible shock. A dark shadow lay always before her, conscious of nothing present, living over again her frightful experience. Again she seemed sunk in dull apathy.

"Dave, we're going to loose Nell. She's fading slowly," said George, one evening, several days after the girl's return. "Wetzel said she was unharmed, yet she seems to have received a hurt more fatal than a physical one. It's her mind—her mind. If we cannot brighten her up to make her forget, she'll die."

"We've done all within our power. If she could only be brought out of this trance! She lies there all day long with those staring eyes. I can't look into them. They are the eyes of a child who has seen murder."

"We must try in some way to get her out of this stupor, and I have an idea. Have you noticed that Mr. Wells has failed very much in the last few weeks?"

"Indeed I have, and I'm afraid he's breaking down. He has grown so thin, eats very little, and doesn't sleep. He is old, you know, and, despite his zeal, this border life is telling on him."

"Dave, I believe he knows it. Poor, earnest old man! He never says a word about himself, yet he must know he is going down hill. Well, we all begin, sooner or later, that descent which ends in the grave. I believe we might stir Nellie by telling her Mr. Wells' health is breaking."

"Let us try."

A hurried knock on the door interrupted their conversation.

"Come in," said Edwards.

The door opened to admit a man, who entered eagerly.

"Jim! Jim!" exclaimed both missionaries, throwing themselves upon the newcomer.

It was, indeed, Jim, but no answering smile lighted his worn, distressed face while he wrung his friends' hands.

"You're not hurt?" asked Dave.

"No, I'm uninjured."

"Tell us all. Did you escape? Did you see your brother? Did you know Wetzel rescued Nell?"

"Wingenund set me free in spite of many demands for my death. He kept Joe a prisoner, and intends to kill him, for the lad was Wetzel's companion. I saw the hunter come into the glade where we camped, break through the line of fighting Indians and carry Nell off."

"Kate?" faltered Young, with ashen face.

"George, I wish to God I could tell you she is dead," answered Jim, nervously pacing the room. "But she was well when I last saw her. She endured the hard journey better than either Nell or I. Girty did not carry her into the encampment, as Silvertip did Joe and me, but the renegade left us on the outskirts of the Delaware town. There was a rocky ravine with dense undergrowth where he disappeared with his captive. I suppose he has his den somewhere in that ravine."

George sank down and buried his face in his arms; neither movement nor sound betokened consciousness.

"Has Wetzel come in with Nell? Joe said he had a cave where he might have taken her in case of illness or accident."

"Yes, he brought her back," answered Edwards, slowly.

"I want to see her," said Jim, his haggard face expressing a keen anxiety. "She's not wounded? hurt? ill?"

"No, nothing like that. It's a shock which she can't get over, can't forget."

"I must see her," cried Jim, moving toward the door.

"Don't go," replied Dave, detaining him. "Wait. We must see what's best to be done. Wait till Heckewelder comes. He'll be here soon. Nell thinks you're dead, and the surprise might be bad for her."

Heckewelder came in at that moment, and shook hands warmly with Jim.

"The Delaware runner told me you were here. I am overjoyed that Wingenund freed you," said the missionary. "It is a most favorable sign. I have heard rumors from Goshocking and Sandusky that have worried me. This good news more than offsets the bad. I am sorry about your brother. Are you well?"

"Well, but miserable. I want to see Nell. Dave tells me she is not exactly ill, but something is wrong with her. Perhaps I ought not to see her just yet."

"It'll be exactly the tonic for her," replied Heckewelder. "She'll be surprised out of herself. She is morbid, apathetic, and, try as we may, we can't interest her. Come at once."

Heckewelder had taken Jim's arm and started for the door when he caught sight of Young, sitting bowed and motionless. Turning to Jim he whispered:

"Kate?"

"Girty did not take her into the encampment," answered Jim, in a low voice. "I hoped he would, because the Indians are kind, but he didn't. He took her to his den."

Just then Young raised his face. The despair in it would have melted a heart of stone. It had become the face of an old man.

"If only you'd told me she had died," he said to Jim, "I'd have been man enough to stand it, but—this—this kills me—I can't breathe!"

He staggered into the adjoining room, where he flung himself upon a bed.

"It's hard, and he won't be able to stand up under it, for he's not strong," whispered Jim.

Heckewelder was a mild, pious man, in whom no one would ever expect strong passion; but now depths were stirred within his heart that had ever been tranquil. He became livid, and his face was distorted with rage.

"It's bad enough to have these renegades plotting and working against our religion; to have them sow discontent, spread lies, make the Indians think we have axes to grind, to plant the only obstacle in our path—all this is bad; but to doom an innocent white woman to worse than death! What can I call it!"

"What can we do?" asked Jim.

"Do? That's the worst of it. We can do nothing, nothing. We dare not move."

"Is there no hope of getting Kate back?"

"Hope? None. That villain is surrounded by his savages. He'll lie low now for a while. I've heard of such deeds many a time, but it never before came so close home. Kate Wells was a pure, loving Christian woman. She'll live an hour, a day, a week, perhaps, in that snake's clutches, and then she'll die. Thank God!"

"Wetzel has gone on Girty's trail. I know that from his manner when he left us," said Edwards.

"Wetzel may avenge her, but he can never save her. It's too late. Hello—"

The exclamation was called forth by the appearance of Young, who entered with a rifle in his hands.

"George, where are you going with that gun?" asked Edwards, grasping his friend by the arm.

"I'm going after her," answered George wildly. He tottered as he spoke, but wrenched himself free from Dave.

"Come, George, listen, listen to reason," interposed Heckewelder, laying hold of Young. "You are frantic with grief now. So are all of us. But calm yourself. Why, man, you're a preacher, not a hunter. You'd be lost, you'd starve in the woods before getting half way to the Indian town. This is terrible enough; don't make it worse by throwing your life away. Think of us, your friends; think of your Indian pupils who rely so much on you. Think of the Village of Peace. We can pray, but we can't prevent these border crimes. With civilization, with the spread of Christianity, they will pass away. Bear up under this blow for the sake of your work. Remember we alone can check such barbarity. But we must not fight. We must sacrifice all that men hold dear, for the sake of the future."

He took the rifle away from George, and led him back into the little, dark room. Closing the door he turned to Jim and Dave.

"He is in a bad way, and we must carefully watch him for a few days."

"Think of George starting out to kill Girty!" exclaimed Dave. "I never fired a gun, but yet I'd go too."

"So would we all, if we did as our hearts dictate," retorted Heckewelder, turning fiercely upon Dave as if stung. "Man! we have a village full of Christians to look after. What would become of them? I tell you we've all we can do here to outwit these border ruffians. Simon Girty is plotting our ruin.

I heard it to-day from the Delaware runner who is my friend. He is jealous of our influence, when all we desire is to save these poor Indians. And, Jim, Girty has killed our happiness. Can we ever recover from the misery brought upon us by poor Kate's fate?"

The missionary raised his hand as if to exhort some power above.

"Curse the Girty's!" he exclaimed in a sudden burst of uncontrollable passion. "Having conquered all other obstacles, must we fail because of wicked men of our own race? Oh, curse them!"

"Come," he said, presently, in a voice which trembled with the effort he made to be calm. "We'll go in to Nellie."

The three men entered Mr. Wells' cabin. The old missionary, with bowed head and hands clasped behind his back, was pacing to and fro. He greeted Jim with glad surprise.

"We want Nellie to see him," whispered Heckewelder. "We think the surprise will do her good."

"I trust it may," said Mr. Wells.

"Leave it to me."

They followed Heckewelder into an adjoining room. A torch flickered over the rude mantle-shelf, lighting up the room with fitful flare. It was a warm night, and the soft breeze coming in the window alternately paled and brightened the flame.

Jim saw Nell lying on the bed. Her eyes were closed, and her long, dark lashes seemed black against the marble paleness of her skin.

"Stand behind me," whispered Heckewelder to Jim.

"Nellie," he called softly, but only a faint flickering of her lashes answered him.

"Nellie, Nellie," repeated Heckewelder, his deep, strong voice thrilling.

Her eyes opened. They gazed at Mr. Wells on one side, at Edwards standing at the foot of the bed, at Heckewelder leaning over her, but there was no recognition or interest in her look.

"Nellie, can you understand me?" asked Heckewelder, putting into his voice all the power and intensity of feeling of which he was capable.

An almost imperceptible shadow of understanding shone in her eyes.

"Listen. You have had a terrible shock, and it has affected your mind. You are mistaken in what you think, what you dream of all the time. Do you understand? You are wrong!"

Nell's eyes quickened with a puzzled, questioning doubt. The minister's magnetic, penetrating voice had pierced her dulled brain.

"See, I have brought you Jim!"

Heckewelder stepped aside as Jim fell on his knees by the bed. He took her cold hands in his and bent over her. For the moment his voice failed.

The doubt in Nell's eyes changed to a wondrous gladness. It was like the rekindling of a smoldering fire.

"Jim?" she whispered.

"Yes, Nellie, it's Jim alive and well. It's Jim come back to you."

A soft flush stained her white face. She slipped her arm tenderly around his neck, and held her cheek close to his.

"Jim," she murmured.

"Nellie, don't you know me?" asked Mr. Wells, trembling, excited. This was the first word she had spoken in four days.

"Uncle!" she exclaimed, suddenly loosening her hold on Jim, and sitting up in bed, then she gazed wildly at the others.

"Was it all a horrible dream?"

Mr. Wells took her hand soothingly, but he did not attempt to answer her question. He looked helplessly at Heckewelder, but that missionary was intently studying the expression on Nell's face.

"Part of it was a dream," he answered, impressively.

"Then that horrible man did take us away?"

"Yes."

"Oh-h! but we're free now? This is my room. Oh, tell me?"

"Yes, Nellie, you're safe at home now."

"Tell—tell me," she cried, shudderingly, as she leaned close to Jim and raised a white, imploring face to his. "Where is Kate?—Oh! Jim—say, say she wasn't left with Girty?"

"Kate is dead," answered Jim, quickly. He could not endure the horror in her eyes. He deliberately intended to lie, as had Heckewelder.

It was as if the tension of Nell's nerves was suddenly relaxed. The relief from her worst fear was so great that her mind took in only the one impression. Then, presently, a choking cry escaped her, to be followed by a paroxysm of sobs.

CHAPTER XX.

Early on the following day Heckewelder, astride his horse, appeared at the door of Edwards' cabin.

"How is George?" he inquired of Dave, when the latter had opened the door.

"He had a bad night, but is sleeping now. I think he'll be all right after a time," answered Dave.

"That's well. Nevertheless keep a watch on him for a few days."

"I'll do so."

"Dave, I leave matters here to your good judgment. I'm off to Goshocking to join Zeisberger. Affairs there demand our immediate attention, and we must make haste."

"How long do you intend to be absent?"

"A few days; possibly a week. In case of any unusual disturbance among the Indians, the appearance of Pipe and his tribe, or any of the opposing factions, send a fleet runner at once to warn me. Most of my fears have been allayed by Wingenund's attitude toward us. His freeing Jim in face of the opposition of his chiefs is a sure sign of friendliness. More than once I have suspected that he was interested in Christianity. His daughter, Whispering Winds, exhibited the same intense fervor in religion as has been manifested by all our converts. It may be that we have not appealed in vain to Wingenund and his daughter; but their high position in the Delaware tribe makes it impolitic for them to reveal a change of heart. If we could win over those two we'd have every chance to convert the whole tribe. Well, as it is we must be thankful for Wingenund's friendship. We have two powerful allies now. Tarhe, the Wyandot chieftain, remains neutral, to be sure, but that's almost as helpful as his friendship."

"I, too, take a hopeful view of the situation," replied Edwards.

"We'll trust in Providence, and do our best," said Heckewelder, as he turned his horse. "Good-by."

"Godspeed!" called Edwards, as his chief rode away.

The missionary resumed his work of getting breakfast. He remained in doors all that day, except for the few moments when he ran over to Mr. Wells' cabin to inquire regarding Nell's condition. He was relieved to learn she was so much better that she had declared her intention of moving about the house. Dave kept a close watch on Young. He, himself, was suffering from the same blow which had prostrated his friend, but his physical strength and fortitude were such that he did not weaken. He was overjoyed to see that George rallied, and showed no further indications of breaking down.

True it was, perhaps, that Heckewelder's earnest prayer on behalf of the converted Indians had sunk deeply into George's heart and thus kept it from breaking. No stronger plea could have been made than the allusion to those gentle, dependent Christians. No one but a missionary could realize the sweetness, the simplicity, the faith, the eager hope for a good, true life which had been implanted in the hearts of these Indians. To bear it in mind, to think of what he, as a missionary and teacher, was to them, relieved him of half his burden, and for strength to bear the remainder he went to God. For all worry there is a sovereign cure, for all suffering there is a healing balm; it is religious faith. Happiness had suddenly flashed with a meteor-like radiance into Young's life only to be snuffed out like a candle in a windy gloom, but his work, his duty remained. So in his trial he learned the necessity of resignation. He chaffed no more at the mysterious, seemingly brutal methods of nature; he questioned no more. He wondered no more at the apparent indifference of Providence. He had one hope, which was to be true to his faith, and teach it to the end.

Nell mastered her grief by an astonishing reserve of strength. Undoubtedly it was that marvelously merciful power which enables a person, for the love of others, to bear up under a cross, or even to fight death himself. As Young had his bright-eyed Indian boys and girls, who had learned Christianity from him, and whose future depended on him, so Nell had her aged and weakening uncle to care for and cherish.

Jim's attentions to her before the deep affliction had not been slight, but now they were so marked as to be unmistakable. In some way Jim seemed changed since he had returned from the Delaware encampment. Although he went back to the work with his old aggressiveness, he was not nearly so successful as he had been before. Whether or not this was his fault, he took his failure deeply to heart. There was that in his tenderness which caused Nell to regard him, in one sense, as she did her uncle. Jim, too, leaned upon her, and she accepted his devotion where once she had repelled it. She had unconsciously betrayed a great deal when she had turned so tenderly to him in the first moments after her recognition, and he remembered it. He did not speak of love to her; he let a thousand little acts of kindness, a constant thoughtfulness of her plead his cause.

The days succeeding Heckewelder's departure were remarkable for several reasons. Although the weather was enticing, the number of visiting Indians gradually decreased. Not a runner from any tribe came into the village, and finally the day dawned when not a single Indian from the outlying towns was present to hear the preaching.

Jim spoke, as usual. After several days had passed and none but converted Indians made up the congregation, the young man began to be uneasy in mind.

Young and Edwards were unable to account for the unusual absence from worship, yet they did not see in it anything to cause especial concern. Often there had been days without visitation to the Village of Peace.

Finally Jim went to consult Glickhican. He found the Delaware at work in the potato patch. The old Indian dropped his hoe and bowed to the missionary. A reverential and stately courtesy always characterized the attitude of the Indians toward the young white father.

"Glickhican, can you tell me why no Indians have come here lately?"

The old chief shook his head.

"Does their absence signify ill to the Village of Peace?"

"Glickhican saw a blackbird flitting in the shadow of the moon. The bird hovered above the Village of Peace, but sang no song."

The old Delaware vouchsafed no other than this strange reply.

Jim returned to his cabin decidedly worried. He did not at all like Glickhican's answer. The purport of it seemed to be that a cloud was rising on the bright horizon of the Christian village. He confided his fears to Young and Edwards. After discussing the situation, the three missionaries decided to send for Heckewelder. He was the leader of the Mission; he knew more of Indian craft than any of them, and how to meet it. If this calm in the heretofore busy life of the Mission was the lull before a storm, Heckewelder should be there with his experience and influence.

"For nearly ten years Heckewelder has anticipated trouble from hostile savages," said Edwards, "but so far he has always averted it. As you know, he has confined himself mostly to propitiating the Indians, and persuading them to be friendly, and listen to us. We'll send for him."

Accordingly they dispatched a runner to Goshocking. In due time the Indian returned with the startling news that Heckewelder had left the Indian village days before, as had, in fact, all the savages except the few converted ones. The same held true in the case of Sandusky, the adjoining town. Moreover, it had been impossible to obtain any news in regard to Zeisberger.

The missionaries were now thoroughly alarmed, and knew not what to do. They concealed the real state of affairs from Nell and her uncle, desiring to keep them from anxiety as long as possible. That night the three teachers went to bed with heavy hearts.

The following morning at daybreak, Jim was awakened from a sound sleep by some one calling at his window. He got up to learn who it was, and, in the gray light, saw Edwards standing outside.

"What's the matter?" questioned Jim, hurriedly.

"Matter enough. Hurry. Get into your clothes," replied Edwards. "As soon as you are dressed, quietly awaken Mr. Wells and Nellie, but do not frighten them."

"But what's the trouble?" queried Jim, as he began to dress.

"The Indians are pouring into the village as thickly as flying leaves in autumn."

Edwards' exaggerated assertion proved to be almost literally true. No sooner had the rising sun dispelled the mist, than it shone on long lines of marching braves, mounted warriors, hundreds of packhorses approaching from the forests. The orderly procession was proof of a concerted plan on the part of the invaders.

From their windows the missionaries watched with bated breath; with wonder and fear they saw the long lines of dusky forms. When they were in the clearing the savages busied themselves with their packs. Long rows of teepees sprung up as if by magic. The savages had come to stay! The number of incoming visitors did not lessen until noon, when a few straggling groups marked the end of the invading host. Most significant of all was the fact that neither child, maiden, nor squaw accompanied this army.

Jim appraised the number at six or seven hundred, more than had ever before visited the village at one time. They were mostly Delawares, with many Shawnees, and a few Hurons among them. It was soon evident, however, that for the present, at least, the Indians did not intend any hostile demonstration. They were quiet in manner, and busy about their teepees and camp-fires, but there was an absence of the curiosity that had characterized the former sojourns of Indians at the peaceful village.

After a brief consultation with his brother missionaries, who all were opposed to his preaching that afternoon, Jim decided he would not deviate from his usual custom. He held the afternoon service, and spoke to the largest congregation that had ever sat before him. He was surprised to find that the sermon, which heretofore so strongly impressed the savages, did not now arouse the slightest enthusiasm. It was followed by a brooding silence of a boding, ominous import.

Four white men, dressed in Indian garb, had been the most attentive listeners to Jim's sermon. He recognized three as Simon Girty, Elliott and Deering, the renegades, and he learned from Edwards that the other was the notorious McKee. These men went through the village, stalking into the shops and cabins, and acting as do men who are on a tour of inspection.

So intrusive was their curiosity that Jim hurried back to Mr. Well's cabin and remained there in seclusion. Of course, by this time Nell and her uncle knew of the presence of the hostile savages. They were frightened, and barely regained their composure when the young man assured them he was certain they had no real cause for fear.

Jim was sitting at the doorstep with Mr. Wells and Edwards when Girty, with his comrades, came toward them. The renegade leader was a tall, athletic man, with a dark, strong face. There was in it none of the brutality and ferocity which marked his brother's visage. Simon Girty appeared keen, forceful, authoritative, as, indeed, he must have been to have attained the power he held in the confederated tribes. His companions presented wide contrasts. Elliott was a small, spare man of cunning, vindictive aspect; McKee looked, as might have been supposed from his reputation, and Deering was a fit mate for the absent Girty. Simon appeared to be a man of some intelligence, who had used all his power to make that position a great one. The other renegades were desperadoes.

"Where's Heckewelder?" asked Girty, curtly, as he stopped before the missionaries.

"He started out for the Indian towns on the Muskingong," answered Edwards. "But we have had no word from either him or Zeisberger."

"When d'ye expect him?"

"I can't say. Perhaps to-morrow, and then, again, maybe not for a week."

"He is in authority here, ain't he?"

"Yes; but he left me in charge of the Mission. Can I serve you in any way?"

"I reckon not," said the renegade, turning to his companions. They conversed in low tones for a moment. Presently McKee, Elliott and Deering went toward the newly erected teepees.

"Girty, do you mean us any ill will?" earnestly asked Edwards. He had met the man on more than one occasion, and had no hesitation about questioning him.

"I can't say as I do," answered the renegade, and those who heard him believed him. "But I'm agin this redskin preachin', an' hev been all along. The injuns are mad clear through, an' I ain't sayin' I've tried to quiet 'em any. This missionary work has got to be stopped, one way or another. Now what I waited here to say is this: I ain't quite forgot I was white once, an' believe you fellars are honest. I'm willin' to go outer my way to help you git away from here."

"Go away?" echoed Edwards.

"That's it," answered Girty, shouldering his rifle.

"But why? We are perfectly harmless; we are only doing good and hurt no one. Why should we go?"

"'Cause there's liable to be trouble," said the renegade, significantly.

Edwards turned slowly to Mr. Wells and Jim. The old missionary was trembling visibly. Jim was pale; but more with anger than fear.

"Thank you, Girty, but we'll stay," and Jim's voice rang clear.

CHAPTER XXI.

"Jim, come out here," called Edwards at the window of Mr. Wells' cabin.

The young man arose from the breakfast table, and when outside found Edwards standing by the door with an Indian brave. He was a Wyandot lightly built, lithe and wiry, easily recognizable as an Indian runner. When Jim appeared the man handed him a small packet. He unwound a few folds of some oily skin to find a square piece of birch bark, upon which were scratched the following words:

"Rev. J. Downs. Greeting.

"Your brother is alive and safe. Whispering Winds rescued him by taking him as her husband. Leave the Village of Peace. Pipe and Half King have been influenced by Girty.

"Zane."

"Now, what do you think of that?" exclaimed Jim, handing the message to Edwards. "Thank Heaven, Joe was saved!"

"Zane? That must be the Zane who married Tarhe's daughter," answered Edwards, when he had read the note. "I'm rejoiced to hear of your brother."

"Joe married to that beautiful Indian maiden! Well, of all wonderful things," mused Jim. "What will Nell say?"

"We're getting warnings enough. Do you appreciate that?" asked Edwards. "'Pipe and Half King have been influenced by Girty.' Evidently the writer deemed that brief sentence of sufficient meaning."

"Edwards, we're preachers. We can't understand such things. I am learning, at least something every day. Colonel Zane advised us not to come here. Wetzel said, 'Go back to Fort Henry.' Girty warned us, and now comes this peremptory order from Isaac Zane."

"Well?"

"It means that these border men see what we will not admit. We ministers have such hope and trust in God that we can not realize the dangers of this life. I fear that our work has been in vain."

"Never. We have already saved many souls. Do not be discouraged."

All this time the runner had stood near at hand straight as an arrow. Presently Edwards suggested that the Wyandot was waiting to be questioned, and accordingly he asked the Indian if he had anything further to communicate.

"Huron—go by—paleface." Here he held up both hands and shut his fists several times, evidently enumerating how many white men he had seen. "Here—when—high—sun."

With that he bounded lightly past them, and loped off with an even, swinging stride.

"What did he mean?" asked Jim, almost sure he had not heard the runner aright.

"He meant that a party of white men are approaching, and will be here by noon. I never knew an Indian runner to carry unreliable information. We have joyful news, both in regard to your brother, and the Village of Peace. Let us go in to tell the others."

The Huron runner's report proved to be correct. Shortly before noon signals from Indian scouts proclaimed the approach of a band of white men. Evidently Girty's forces had knowledge beforehand of the proximity of this band, for the signals created no excitement. The Indians expressed only a lazy curiosity. Soon several Delaware scouts appeared, escorting a large party of frontiersmen.

These men turned out to be Captain Williamson's force, which had been out on an expedition after a marauding tribe of Chippewas. This last named tribe had recently harried the remote settlers, and committed depredations on the outskirts of the white settlements eastward. The company was composed of men who had served in the garrison at Fort Pitt, and hunters and backwoodsmen from Yellow Creek and Fort Henry. The captain himself was a typical borderman, rough and bluff, hardened by long years of border life, and, like most pioneers, having no more use for an Indian than for a snake. He had led his party after the marauders, and surprised and slaughtered nearly all of them. Returning eastward he had passed through Goshocking, where he learned of the muttering storm rising over the Village of Peace, and had come more out of curiosity than hope to avert misfortune.

The advent of so many frontiersmen seemed a godsend to the perplexed and worried missionaries. They welcomed the newcomers most heartily. Beds were made in several of the newly erected cabins; the village was given over for the comfort of the frontiersmen. Edwards conducted Captain Williamson through the shops and schools, and the old borderman's weather-beaten face expressed a comical surprise.

"Wal, I'll be durned if I ever expected to see a redskin work," was his only comment on the industries.

"We are greatly alarmed by the presence of Girty and his followers," said Edwards. "We have been warned to leave, but have not been actually threatened. What do you infer from the appearance here of these hostile savages?"

"It hardly 'pears to me they'll bother you preachers. They're agin the Christian redskins, that's plain."

"Why have we been warned to go?"

"That's natural, seein' they're agin the preachin'."

"What will they do with the converted Indians?"

"Mighty onsartin. They might let them go back to the tribes, but 'pears to me these good Injuns won't go. Another thing, Girty is afeered of the spread of Christianity."

"Then you think our Christians will be made prisoners?"

"'Pears likely."

"And you, also, think we'd do well to leave here."

"I do, sartin. We're startin' for Fort Henry soon. You'd better come along with us."

"Captain Williamson, we're going to stick it out, Girty or no Girty."

"You can't do no good stayin' here. Pipe and Half King won't stand for the singin', prayin' redskins, especially when they've got all these cattle and fields of grain."

"Wetzel said the same."

"Hev you seen Wetzel?"

"Yes; he rescued a girl from Jim Girty, and returned her to us."

"That so? I met Wetzel and Jack Zane back a few miles in the woods. They're layin' for somebody, because when I asked them to come along they refused, sayin' they had work as must be done. They looked like it, too. I never hern tell of Wetzel advisin' any one before; but I'll say if he told me to do a thing, by Gosh! I'd do it."

"As men, we might very well take the advice given us, but as preachers we must stay here to do all we can for these Christian Indians. One thing more: will you help us?"

"I reckon I'll stay here to see the thing out," answered Williamson. Edwards made a mental note of the frontiersman's evasive answer.

Jim had, meanwhile, made the acquaintance of a young minister, John Christy by name, who had lost his sweetheart in one of the Chippewa raids, and had accompanied the Williamson expedition in the hope he might rescue her.

"How long have you been out?" asked Jim.

"About four weeks now," answered Christy. "My betrothed was captured five weeks ago yesterday. I joined Williamson's band, which made up at Short Creek to take the trail of the flying Chippewas, in the hope I might find her. But not a trace! The expedition fell upon a band of redskins over on the Walhonding, and killed nearly all of them. I learned from a wounded Indian that a renegade had made off with a white girl about a week previous. Perhaps it was poor Lucy."

Jim related the circumstances of his own capture by Jim Girty, the rescue of Nell, and Kate's sad fate.

"Could Jim Girty have gotten your girl?" inquired Jim, in conclusion.

"It's fairly probable. The description doesn't tally with Girty's. This renegade was short and heavy, and noted especially for his strength. Of course, an Indian would first speak of some such distinguishing feature. There are, however, ten or twelve renegades on the border, and, excepting Jim Girty, one's as bad as another."

"Then it's a common occurrence, this abducting girls from the settlements?"

"Yes, and the strange thing is that one never hears of such doings until he gets out on the frontier."

"For that matter, you don't hear much of anything, except of the wonderful richness and promise of the western country."

"You're right. Rumors of fat, fertile lands induce the colonist to become a pioneer. He comes west with his family; two out of every ten lose their scalps, and in some places the average is much greater. The wives, daughters and children are carried off into captivity. I have been on the border two years, and know that the rescue of any captive, as Wetzel rescued your friend, is a remarkable exception."

"If you have so little hope of recovering your sweetheart, what then is your motive for accompanying this band of hunters?"

"Revenge!"

"And you are a preacher?" Jim's voice did not disguise his astonishment.

"I was a preacher, and now I am thirsting for vengeance," answered Christy, his face clouding darkly. "Wait until you learn what frontier life means. You are young here yet; you are flushed with the success of your teaching; you have lived a short time in this quiet village, where, until the last few days, all has been serene. You know nothing of the strife, of the necessity of fighting, of the cruelty which makes up this border existence. Only two years have hardened me so that I actually pant for the blood of the renegade who has robbed me. A frontiersman must take his choice of succumbing or cutting his way through flesh and bone. Blood will be spilled; if not yours, then your foe's. The pioneers run from the plow to the fight; they halt in the cutting of corn to defend themselves, and in winter must battle against cold and hardship, which would be less cruel if there was time in summer to prepare for winter, for the savages leave them hardly an opportunity to plant crops. How many pioneers have given up, and gone back east? Find me any who would not return home to-morrow, if they could. All that brings them out here is the chance for a home, and all that keeps them out here is the poor hope of finally attaining their object. Always there is a possibility of future prosperity. But this generation, if it survives, will never see prosperity and happiness. What does this border life engender in a pioneer who holds his own in it? Of all things, not Christianity. He becomes a fighter, keen as the redskin who steals through the coverts."

* * *

The serene days of the Village of Peace had passed into history. Soon that depraved vagabond, the French trader, with cheap trinkets and vile whisky, made his appearance. This was all that was needed to inflame the visitors. Where they had been only bold and impudent, they became insulting and abusive. They execrated the Christian indians for their neutrality; scorned them for worshiping this unknown God, and denounced a religion which made women of strong men.

The slaughtering of cattle commenced; the despoiling of maize fields, and robbing of corn-cribs began with the drunkenness.

All this time it was seen that Girty and Elliott consulted often with Pipe and Half King. The latter was the only Huron chief opposed to neutrality toward the Village of Peace, and he was, if possible, more fierce in his hatred than Pipe. The future of the Christian settlement rested with these two chiefs. Girty and Elliott, evidently, were the designing schemers, and they worked diligently on the passions of these simple-minded, but fierce, warlike chiefs.

Greatly to the relief of the distracted missionaries, Heckewelder returned to the village. Jaded and haggard, he presented a travel-worn appearance. He made the astonishing assertions that he had been thrice waylaid and assaulted on his way to Goshocking; then detained by a roving band of Chippewas, and soon after his arrival at their camping ground a renegade had run off with a white woman captive, while the Indians west of the village were in an uproar. Zeisberger, however, was safe in the Moravian town of Salem, some miles west of Goshocking. Heckewelder had expected to find the same condition of affairs as existed in the Village of Peace; but he was bewildered by the great array of hostile Indians. Chiefs who had once extended friendly hands to him, now drew back coldly, as they said:

"Washington is dead. The American armies are cut to pieces. The few thousands who had escaped the British are collecting at Fort Pitt to steal the Indian's land."

Heckewelder vigorously denied all these assertions, knowing they had been invented by Girty and Elliott. He exhausted all his skill and patience in the vain endeavor to show Pipe where he was wrong. Half King had been so well coached by the renegades that he refused to listen. The other chiefs maintained a cold reserve that was baffling and exasperating. Wingenund took no active part in the councils; but his presence apparently denoted that he had sided with the others. The outlook was altogether discouraging.

"I'm completely fagged out," declared Heckewelder, that night when he returned to Edwards' cabin. He dropped into a chair as one whose strength is entirely spent, whose indomitable spirit has at last been broken.

"Lie down to rest," said Edwards.

"Oh, I can't. Matters look so black."

"You're tired out and discouraged. You'll feel better to-morrow. The situation is not, perhaps, so hopeless. The presence of these frontiersmen should encourage us."

"What will they do? What can they do?" cried Heckewelder, bitterly. "I tell you never before have I encountered such gloomy, stony Indians. It seems to me that they are in no vacillating state. They act like men whose course is already decided upon, and who are only waiting."

"For what?" asked Jim, after a long silence.

"God only knows! Perhaps for a time; possibly for a final decision, and, it may be, for a reason, the very thought of which makes me faint."

"Tell us," said Edwards, speaking quietly, for he had ever been the calmest of the missionaries.

"Never mind. Perhaps it's only my nerves. I'm all unstrung, and could suspect anything to-night."

"Heckewelder, tell us?" Jim asked, earnestly.

"My friends, I pray I am wrong. God help us if my fears are correct. I believe the Indians are waiting for Jim Girty."

CHAPTER XXII.

Simon Girty lolled on a blanket in Half King's teepee. He was alone, awaiting his allies. Rings of white smoke curled lazily from his lips as he puffed on a long Indian pipe, and gazed out over the clearing that contained the Village of Peace.

Still water has something in its placid surface significant of deep channels, of hidden depths; the dim outline of the forest is dark with meaning, suggestive of its wild internal character. So Simon Girty's hard, bronzed face betrayed the man. His degenerate brother's features were revolting; but his own were striking, and fell short of being handsome only because of their craggy hardness. Years of revolt, of bitterness, of consciousness of wasted life, had graven their stern lines on that copper, masklike face. Yet despite the cruelty there, the forbidding shade on it, as if a reflection from a dark soul, it was not wholly a bad countenance. Traces still lingered, faintly, of a man in whom kindlier feelings had once predominated.

In a moment of pique Girty had deserted his military post at Fort Pitt, and become an outlaw of his own volition. Previous to that time he had been an able soldier, and a good fellow. When he realized that his step was irrevocable, that even his best friends condemned him, he plunged, with anger and despair in his heart, into a war upon his own race. Both of his brothers had long been border ruffians, whose only protection from the outraged pioneers lay in the faraway camps of hostile tribes. George Girty had so sunk his individuality into the savage's that he was no longer a white man. Jim Girty stalked over the borderland with a bloody tomahawk, his long arm outstretched to clutch some unfortunate white woman, and with his hideous smile of death. Both of these men were far lower than the worst savages, and it was almost wholly to their deeds of darkness that Simon Girty owed his infamous name.

To-day White Chief, as Girty was called, awaited his men. A slight tremor of the ground caused him to turn his gaze. The Huron chief, Half King, resplendent in his magnificent array, had entered the teepee. He squatted in a corner, rested the bowl of his great pipe on his knee, and smoked in silence. The habitual frown of his black brow, like a shaded, overhanging cliff; the fire flashing from his eyes, as a shining light is reflected from a dark pool; his closely-shut, bulging jaw, all bespoke a nature, lofty in its Indian pride and arrogance, but more cruel than death.

Another chief stalked into the teepee and seated himself. It was Pipe. His countenance denoted none of the intelligence that made Wingenund's face so noble; it was even coarser than Half King's, and his eyes, resembling live coals in the dark; the long, cruel lines of his jaw; the thin, tightly-closed lips, which looked as if they could relax only to utter a savage command, expressed fierce cunning and brutality.

"White Chief is idle to-day," said Half King, speaking in the Indian tongue.

"King, I am waiting. Girty is slow, but sure," answered the renegade.

"The eagle sails slowly round and round, up and up," replied Half King, with majestic gestures, "until his eye sees all, until he knows his time; then he folds his wings and swoops down from the blue sky like the forked fire. So does White Chief. But Half King is impatient."

"To-day decides the fate of the Village of Peace," answered Girty, imperturbably.

"Ugh!" grunted Pipe.

Half King vented his approval in the same meaning exclamation.

An hour passed; the renegade smoked in silence; the chiefs did likewise.

A horseman rode up to the door of the teepee, dismounted, and came in. It was Elliott. He had been absent twenty hours. His buckskin suit showed the effect of hard riding through the thickets.

"Hullo, Bill, any sign of Jim?" was Girty's greeting to his lieutenant.

"Nary. He's not been seen near the Delaware camp. He's after that chap who married Winds."

"I thought so. Jim's roundin' up a tenderfoot who will be a bad man to handle if he has half a chance. I saw as much the day he took his horse away from Silver. He finally did fer the Shawnee, an' almost put Jim out. My brother oughtn't to give rein to personal revenge at a time like this." Girty's face did not change, but his tone was one of annoyance.

"Jim said he'd be here to-day, didn't he?"

"To-day is as long as we allowed to wait."

"He'll come. Where's Jake and Mac?"

"They're here somewhere, drinkin' like fish, an' raisin' hell."

Two more renegades appeared at the door, and, entering the teepee, squatted down in Indian fashion. The little wiry man with the wizened face was McKee; the other was the latest acquisition to the renegade force, Jake Deering, deserter, thief, murderer—everything that is bad. In appearance he was of medium height, but very heavily, compactly built, and evidently as strong as an ox. He had a tangled shock of red hair, a broad, bloated face;

big, dull eyes, like the openings of empty furnaces, and an expression of beastliness.

Deering and McKee were intoxicated.

"Bad time fer drinkin'," said Girty, with disapproval in his glance.

"What's that ter you?" growled Deering. "I'm here ter do your work, an' I reckon it'll be done better if I'm drunk."

"Don't git careless," replied Girty, with that cool tone and dark look such as dangerous men use. "I'm only sayin' it's a bad time fer you, because if this bunch of frontiersmen happen to git onto you bein' the renegade that was with the Chippewas an' got thet young feller's girl, there's liable to be trouble."

"They ain't agoin' ter find out."

"Where is she?"

"Back there in the woods."

"Mebbe it's as well. Now, don't git so drunk you'll blab all you know. We've lots of work to do without havin' to clean up Williamson's bunch," rejoined Girty. "Bill, tie up the tent flaps an' we'll git to council."

Elliott arose to carry out the order, and had pulled in the deer-hide flaps, when one of them was jerked outward to disclose the befrilled person of Jim Girty. Except for a discoloration over his eye, he appeared as usual.

"Ugh!" grunted Pipe, who was glad to see his renegade friend.

Half King evinced the same feeling.

"Hullo," was Simon Girty's greeting.

"'Pears I'm on time fer the picnic," said Jim Girty, with his ghastly leer.

Bill Elliott closed the flaps, after giving orders to the guard to prevent any Indians from loitering near the teepee.

"Listen," said Simon Girty, speaking low in the Delaware language. "The time is ripe. We have come here to break forever the influence of the white man's religion. Our councils have been held; we shall drive away the missionaries, and burn the Village of Peace."

He paused, leaning forward in his exceeding earnestness, with his bronzed face lined by swelling veins, his whole person made rigid by the murderous thought. Then he hissed between his teeth: "What shall we do with these Christian Indians?"

Pipe raised his war-club, struck it upon the ground; then handed it to Half King.

Half King took the club and repeated the action.

Both chiefs favored the death penalty.

"Feed 'em to ther buzzards," croaked Jim Girty.

Simon Girty knitted his brow in thought. The question of what to do with the converted Indians had long perplexed him.

"No," said he; "let us drive away the missionaries, burn the village, and take the Indians back to camp. We'll keep them there; they'll soon forget."

"Pipe does not want them," declared the Delaware.

"Christian Indians shall never sit round Half King's fire," cried the Huron.

Simon Girty knew the crisis had come; that but few moments were left him to decide as to the disposition of the Christians; and he thought seriously. Certainly he did not want the Christians murdered. However cruel his life, and great his misdeeds, he was still a man. If possible, he desired to burn the village and ruin the religious influence, but without shedding blood. Yet, with all his power, he was handicapped, and that by the very chiefs most nearly under his control. He could not subdue this growing Christian influence without the help of Pipe and Half King. To these savages a thing was either right or wrong. He had sown the seed of unrest and jealousy in the savage breasts, and the fruit was the decree of death. As far as these Indians were concerned, this decision was unalterable.

On the other hand, if he did not spread ruin over the Village of Peace, the missionaries would soon get such a grasp on the tribes that their hold would never be broken. He could not allow that, even if he was forced to sacrifice the missionaries along with their converts, for he saw in the growth of this religion his own downfall. The border must be hostile to the whites, or it could no longer be his home. To be sure, he had aided the British in the Revolution, and could find a refuge among them; but this did not suit him.

He became an outcast because of failure to win the military promotion which he had so much coveted. He had failed among his own people. He had won a great position in an alien race, and he loved his power. To sway men—Indians, if not others—to his will; to avenge himself for the fancied wrong done him; to be great, had been his unrelenting purpose.

He knew he must sacrifice the Christians, or eventually lose his own power. He had no false ideas about the converted Indians. He knew they were innocent; that they were a thousand times better off than the pagan Indians; that they had never harmed him, nor would they ever do so; but if he allowed them to spread their religion there was an end of Simon Girty.

His decision was characteristic of the man. He would sacrifice any one, or all, to retain his supremacy. He knew the fulfillment of the decree as laid down by Pipe and Half King would be known as his work. His name, infamous now, would have an additional horror, and ever be remembered by posterity in unspeakable loathing, in unsoftening wrath. He knew this, and deep down in his heart awoke a numbed chord of humanity that twinged with strange pain. What awful work he must sanction to keep his vaunted power! More bitter than all was the knowledge that to retain this hold over the indians he must commit a deed which, so far as the whites were concerned, would take away his great name, and brand him a coward.

He briefly reviewed his stirring life. Singularly fitted for a leader, in a few years he had risen to the most powerful position on the border. He wielded more influence than any chief. He had been opposed to the invasion of the pioneers, and this alone, without his sagacity or his generalship, would have given him control of many tribes. But hatred for his own people, coupled with unerring judgment, a remarkable ability to lead expeditions, and his invariable success, had raised him higher and higher until he stood alone. He was the most powerful man west of the Alleghenies. His fame was such that the British had importuned him to help them, and had actually, in more than one instance, given him command over British subjects.

All of which meant that he had a great, even though an infamous name. No matter what he was blamed for; no matter how many dastardly deeds had been committed by his depraved brothers and laid to his door, he knew he had never done a cowardly act. That which he had committed while he was drunk he considered as having been done by the liquor, and not by the man. He loved his power, and he loved his name.

In all Girty's eventful, ignoble life, neither the alienation from his people, the horror they ascribed to his power, nor the sacrifice of his life to stand high among the savage races, nor any of the cruel deeds committed while at war, hurt him a tithe as much as did this sanctioning the massacre of the Christians.

Although he was a vengeful, unscrupulous, evil man, he had never acted the coward.

Half King waited long for Girty to speak; since he remained silent, the wily Huron suggested they take a vote on the question.

"Let us burn the Village of Peace, drive away the missionaries, and take the Christians back to the Delaware towns—all without spilling blood," said Girty, determined to carry his point, if possible.

"I say the same," added Elliott, refusing the war-club held out to him by Half King.

"Me, too," voted McKee, not so drunk but that he understood the lightninglike glance Girty shot at him.

"Kill 'em all; kill everybody," cried Deering in drunken glee. He took the club and pounded with it on the ground.

Pipe repeated his former performance, as also did Half King, after which he handed the black, knotted symbol of death to Jim Girty.

Three had declared for saving the Christians, and three for the death penalty.

Six pairs of burning eyes were fastened on the Deaths-head.

Pipe and Half King were coldly relentless; Deering awoke to a brutal earnestness; McKee and Elliott watched with bated breath. These men had formed themselves into a tribunal to decide on the life or death of many, and the situation, if not the greatest in their lives, certainly was one of vital importance.

Simon Girty cursed all the fates. He dared not openly oppose the voting, and he could not, before those cruel but just chiefs, try to influence his brother's vote.

As Jim Girty took the war-club, Simon read in his brother's face the doom of the converted Indians and he muttered to himself:

"Now tremble an' shrink, all you Christians!"

Jim was not in a hurry. Slowly he poised the war-club. He was playing as a cat plays with a mouse; he was glorying in his power. The silence was that of death. It signified the silence of death. The war-club descended with violence.

"Feed the Christians to ther buzzards!"

CHAPTER XXIII.

"I have been here before," said Joe to Whispering Winds. "I remember that vine-covered stone. We crawled over it to get at Girty and Silvertip. There's the little knoll; here's the very spot where I was hit by a flying tomahawk. Yes, and there's the spring. Let me see, what did Wetzel call this spot?"

"Beautiful Spring," answered the Indian girl.

"That's it, and it's well named. What a lovely place!"

Nature had been lavish in the beautifying of this inclosed dell. It was about fifty yards wide, and nestled among little, wooded knolls and walls of gray, lichen-covered stone. Though the sun shone brightly into the opening, and the rain had free access to the mossy ground, no stormy winds ever entered this well protected glade.

Joe reveled in the beauty of the scene, even while he was too weak to stand erect. He suffered no pain from his wound, although he had gradually grown dizzy, and felt as if the ground was rising before him. He was glad to lie upon the mossy ground in the little cavern under the cliff.

Upon examination his wound was found to have opened, and was bleeding. His hunting coat was saturated with blood. Whispering Winds washed the cut, and dressed it with cooling leaves. Then she rebandaged it tightly with Joe's linsey handkerchiefs, and while he rested comfortable she gathered bundles of ferns, carrying them to the little cavern. When she had a large quantity of these she sat down near Joe, and began to weave the long stems into a kind of screen. The fern stalks were four feet long and half a foot wide; these she deftly laced together, making broad screens which would serve to ward off the night dews. This done, she next built a fireplace with flat stones. She found wild apples, plums and turnips on the knoll above the glade. Then she cooked strips of meat which had been brought with them. Lance grazed on the long grass just without the glade, and Mose caught two rabbits. When darkness settled down Whispering Winds called the dog within the cavern, and hung the screens before the opening.

Several days passed. Joe rested quietly, and began to recover strength. Besides the work of preparing their meals, Whispering Winds had nothing to do save sit near the invalid and amuse or interest him so that he would not fret or grow impatient, while his wound was healing.

They talked about their future prospects. After visiting the Village of Peace, they would go to Fort Henry, where Joe could find employment. They dwelt upon the cabin they would build, and passed many happy moments planning a new home. Joe's love of the wilderness had in no wise diminished; but a blow on his head from a heavy tomahawk, and a vicious stab in the back, had lessened his zeal so far that he understood it was not wise to sacrifice life for the pleasures of the pathless woods. He could have the last without the danger of being shot at from behind every tree. He reasoned that it would be best for him to take his wife to Fort Henry, there find employment, and devote his leisure time to roaming in the forest.

"Will the palefaces be kind to an Indian who has learned to love them?" Whispering Winds asked wistfully of Joe.

"Indeed they will," answered Joe, and he told her the story of Isaac Zane; how he took his Indian bride home; how her beauty and sweetness soon won all the white people's love. "It will be so with you, my wife."

"Whispering Winds knows so little," she murmured.

"Why, you are learning every day, and even if such was not the case, you know enough for me."

"Whispering Winds will be afraid; she fears a little to go."

"I'll be glad when we can be on the move," said Joe, with his old impatient desire for action. "How soon, Winds, can we set off?"

"As many days," answered the Indian girl, holding up five fingers.

"So long? I want to leave this place."

"Leave Beautiful Spring?"

"Yes, even this sweet place. It has a horror for me. I'll never forget the night I first saw that spring shining in the moonlight. It was right above the rock that I looked into the glade. The moon was reflected in the dark pool, and as I gazed into the shadowy depths of the dark water I suddenly felt an unaccountable terror; but I oughtn't to have the same feeling now. We are safe, are we not?"

"We are safe," murmured Whispering Winds.

"Yet I have the same chill of fear whenever I look at the beautiful spring, and at night as I awake to hear the soft babble of running water, I freeze until my heart feels like cold lead. Winds, I'm not a coward; but I can't help this feeling. Perhaps, it's only the memory of that awful night with Wetzel."

"An Indian feels so when he passes to his unmarked grave," answered Winds, gazing solemnly at him. "Whispering Winds does not like this fancy of yours. Let us leave Beautiful Spring. You are almost well. Ah! if Whispering Winds should lose you! I love you!"

"And I love you, my beautiful wild flower," answered Joe, stroking the dark head so near his own.

A tender smile shone on his face. He heard a slight noise without the cave, and, looking up, saw that which caused the smile to fade quickly.

"Mose!" he called, sharply. The dog was away chasing rabbits.

Whispering Winds glanced over her shoulder with a startled cry, which ended in a scream.

Not two yards behind her stood Jim Girty.

Hideous was his face in its triumphant ferocity. He held a long knife in his hand, and, snarling like a mad wolf, he made a forward lunge.

Joe raised himself quickly; but almost before he could lift his hand in defense, the long blade was sheathed in his breast.

Slowly he sank back, his gray eyes contracting with the old steely flash. The will to do was there, but the power was gone forever.

"Remember, Girty, murderer! I am Wetzel's friend," he cried, gazing at his slayer with unutterable scorn.

Then the gray eyes softened, and sought the blanched face of the stricken maiden.

"Winds," he whispered faintly.

She was as one frozen with horror.

The gray eyes gazed into hers with lingering tenderness; then the film of death came upon them.

The renegade raised his bloody knife, and bent over the prostrate form.

Whispering Winds threw herself upon Girty with the blind fury of a maddened lioness. Cursing fiercely, he stabbed her once, twice, three times. She fell across the body of her lover, and clasped it convulsively.

Girty gave one glance at his victims; deliberately wiped the gory knife on Wind's leggins, and, with another glance, hurried and fearful, around the glade, he plunged into the thicket.

An hour passed. A dark stream crept from the quiet figures toward the spring. It dyed the moss and the green violet leaves. Slowly it wound its way to the clear water, dripping between the pale blue flowers. The little fall below the spring was no longer snowy white; blood had tinged it red.

A dog came bounding into the glade. He leaped the brook, hesitated on the bank, and lowered his nose to sniff at the water. He bounded up the bank to the cavern.

A long, mournful howl broke the wilderness's quiet.

Another hour passed. The birds were silent; the insects still. The sun sank behind the trees, and the shades of evening gathered.

The ferns on the other side of the glade trembled. A slight rustle of dead leaves disturbed the stillness. The dog whined, then barked. The tall form of a hunter rose out of the thicket, and stepped into the glade with his eyes bent upon moccasin tracks in the soft moss.

The trail he had been following led him to this bloody spring.

"I might hev knowed it," he muttered.

Wetzel, for it was he, leaned upon his long rifle while his keen eyes took in the details of the tragedy. The whining dog, the bloody water, the motionless figures lying in a last embrace, told the sad story.

"Joe an' Winds," he muttered.

Only a moment did he remain lost in sad reflection. A familiar moccasin-print in the sand on the bank pointed westward. He examined it carefully.

"Two hours gone," he muttered. "I might overtake him."

Then his motions became swift. With two blows of his tomahawk he secured a long piece of grapevine. He took a heavy stone from the bed of the brook. He carried Joe to the spring, and, returning for Winds, placed her beside her lover. This done, he tied one end of the grapevine around the stone, and wound the other about the dead bodies.

He pushed them off the bank into the spring. As the lovers sank into the deep pool they turned, exposing first Winds' sad face, and then Joe's. Then they sank out of sight. Little waves splashed on the shore of the pool; the ripple disappeared, and the surface of the spring became tranquil.

Wetzel stood one moment over the watery grave of the maiden who had saved him, and the boy who had loved him. In the gathering gloom his stalwart form assumed gigantic proportions, and when he raised his long arm and shook his clenched fist toward the west, he resembled a magnificent statue of dark menace.

With a single bound he cleared the pool, and then sped out of the glade. He urged the dog on Girty's trail, and followed the eager beast toward the west. As he disappeared, a long, low sound like the sigh of the night wind swelled and moaned through the gloom.

CHAPTER XXIV.

When the first ruddy rays of the rising sun crimsoned the eastern sky, Wetzel slowly wound his way down a rugged hill far west of Beautiful Spring. A white dog, weary and footsore, limped by his side. Both man and beast showed evidence of severe exertion.

The hunter stopped in a little cave under a projecting stone, and, laying aside his rifle, began to gather twigs and sticks. He was particular about selecting the wood, and threw aside many pieces which would have burned well; but when he did kindle a flame it blazed hotly, yet made no smoke.

He sharpened a green stick, and, taking some strips of meat from his pocket, roasted them over the hot flame. He fed the dog first. Mose had crouched close on the ground with his head on his paws, and his brown eyes fastened upon the hunter.

"He had too big a start fer us," said Wetzel, speaking as if the dog were human. It seemed that Wetzel's words were a protest against the meaning in those large, sad eyes.

Then the hunter put out the fire, and, searching for a more secluded spot, finally found one on top of the ledge, where he commanded a good view of his surroundings. The weary dog was asleep. Wetzel settled himself to rest, and was soon wrapped in slumber.

About noon he awoke. He arose, stretched his limbs, and then took an easy position on the front of the ledge, where he could look below. Evidently the hunter was waiting for something. The dog slept on. It was the noonday hour, when the stillness of the forest almost matched that of midnight. The birds were more quiet than at any other time during daylight.

Wetzel reclined there with his head against the stone, and his rifle resting across his knees.

He listened now to the sounds of the forest. The soft breeze fluttering among the leaves, the rain-call of the tree frog, the caw of crows from distant hilltops, the sweet songs of the thrush and oriole, were blended together naturally, harmoniously.

But suddenly the hunter raised his head. A note, deeper than the others, a little too strong, came from far down the shaded hollow. To Wetzel's trained ear it was a discord. He manifested no more than this attention, for the birdcall was the signal he had been awaiting. He whistled a note in answer that was as deep and clear as the one which had roused him.

Moments passed. There was no repetition of the sound. The songs of the other birds had ceased. Besides Wetzel there was another intruder in the woods.

Mose lifted his shaggy head and growled. The hunter patted the dog. In a few minutes the figure of a tall man appeared among the laurels down the slope. He stopped while gazing up at the ledge. Then, with noiseless step, he ascended the ridge, climbed the rocky ledge, and turned the corner of the stone to face Wetzel. The newcomer was Jonathan Zane.

"Jack, I expected you afore this," was Wetzel's greeting.

"I couldn't make it sooner," answered Zane. "After we left Williamson and separated, I got turned around by a band of several hundred redskins makin' for the Village of Peace. I went back again, but couldn't find any sign of the trail we're huntin'. Then I makes for this meetin' place. I've been goin' for some ten hours, and am hungry."

"I've got some bar ready cooked," said Wetzel, handing Zane several strips of meat.

"What luck did you have?"

"I found Girty's trail, an old one, over here some eighteen or twenty miles, an' follered it until I went almost into the Delaware town. It led to a hut in a deep ravine. I ain't often surprised, but I wus then. I found the dead body of that girl, Kate Wells, we fetched over from Fort Henry. Thet's sad, but it ain't the surprisin' part. I also found Silvertip, the Shawnee I've been lookin' fer. He was all knocked an' cut up, deader'n a stone. There'd been somethin' of a scrap in the hut. I calkilate Girty murdered Kate, but I couldn't think then who did fer Silver, though I allowed the renegade might hev done thet, too. I watched round an' seen Girty come back to the hut. He had ten Injuns with him, an' presently they all made fer the west. I trailed them, but didn't calkilate it'd be wise to tackle the bunch single-handed, so laid back. A mile or so from the hut I came across hoss tracks minglin' with the moccasin-prints. About fifteen mile or from the Delaware town, Girty left his buckskins, an' they went west, while he stuck to the hoss tracks. I was onto his game in a minute. I cut across country fer Beautiful Spring, but I got there too late. I found the warm bodies of Joe and thet Injun girl, Winds. The snake hed murdered them."

"I allow Joe won over Winds, got away from the Delaware town with her, tried to rescue Kate, and killed Silver in the fight. Girty probably was surprised, an' run after he had knifed the girl."

"'Pears so to me. Joe had two knife cuts, an' one was an old wound."

"You say it was a bad fight?"

"Must hev been. The hut was all knocked in, an' stuff scattered about. Wal, Joe could go some if he onct got started."

"I'll bet he could. He was the likeliest lad I've seen for many a day."

"If he'd lasted, he'd been somethin' of a hunter an' fighter."

"Too bad. But Lord! you couldn't keep him down, no more than you can lots of these wild young chaps that drift out here."

"I'll allow he had the fever bad."

"Did you hev time to bury them?"

"I hedn't time fer much. I sunk them in the spring."

"It's a pretty deep hole," said Zane, reflectively. "Then, you and the dog took Girty's trail, but couldn't catch up with him. He's now with the renegade cutthroats and hundreds of riled Indians over there in the Village of Peace."

"I reckon you're right."

A long silence ensued. Jonathan finished his simple repast, drank from the little spring that trickled under the stone, and, sitting down by the dog, smoothed out his long silken hair.

"Lew, we're pretty good friends, ain't we?" he asked, thoughtfully.

"Jack, you an' the colonel are all the friends I ever hed, 'ceptin' that boy lyin' quiet back there in the woods."

"I know you pretty well, and ain't sayin' a word about your runnin' off from me on many a hunt, but I want to speak plain about this fellow Girty."

"Wal?" said Wetzel, as Zane hesitated.

"Twice in the last few years you and I have had it in for the same men, both white-livered traitors. You remember? First it was Miller, who tried to ruin my sister Betty, and next it was Jim Girty, who murdered our old friend, as good an old man as ever wore moccasins. Wal, after Miller ran off from the fort, we trailed him down to the river, and I points across and says, 'You or me?' and you says, 'Me.' You was Betty's friend, and I knew she'd be avenged. Miller is lyin' quiet in the woods, and violets have blossomed twice over his grave, though you never said a word; but I know it's true because I know you."

Zane looked eagerly into the dark face of his friend, hoping perhaps to get some verbal assurance there that his belief was true. But Wetzel did not speak, and he continued:

"Another day not so long ago we both looked down at an old friend, and saw his white hair matted with blood. He'd been murdered for nothin'. Again you and me trailed a coward and found him to be Jim Girty. I knew you'd been huntin' him for years, and so I says, 'Lew, you or me?' and you says, 'Me.' I give in to you, for I knew you're a better man than me, and because I wanted you to have the satisfaction. Wal, the months have gone by, and Jim Girty's still livin' and carryin' on. Now he's over there after them poor preachers. I ain't sayin', Lew, that you haven't more agin him than me, but I do say, let me in on it with you. He always has a gang of redskins with him; he's afraid to travel alone, else you'd had him long ago. Two of us'll have more chance to get him. Let me go with you. When it comes to a finish, I'll stand aside while you give it to him. I'd enjoy seein' you cut him from shoulder to hip. After he leaves the Village of Peace we'll hit his trail, camp on it, and stick to it until it ends in his grave."

The earnest voice of the backwoodsman ceased. Both men rose and stood facing each other. Zane's bronzed face was hard and tense, expressive of an indomitable will; Wetzel's was coldly dark, with fateful resolve, as if his decree of vengeance, once given, was as immutable as destiny. The big, horny hands gripped in a viselike clasp born of fierce passion, but no word was spoken.

Far to the west somewhere, a befrilled and bedizened renegade pursued the wild tenor of his ways; perhaps, even now steeping his soul in more crime, or staining his hands a deeper red, but sleeping or waking, he dreamed not of this deadly compact that meant his doom.

The two hunters turned their stern faces toward the west, and passed silently down the ridge into the depths of the forest. Darkness found them within rifle-shot of the Village of Peace. With the dog creeping between them, they crawled to a position which would, in daylight, command a view of the clearing. Then, while one stood guard, the other slept.

When morning dawned they shifted their position to the top of a low, fern-covered cliff, from which they could see every movement in the village. All the morning they watched with that wonderful patience of men who knew how to wait. The visiting savages were quiet, the missionaries moved about in and out of the shops and cabins; the Christian indians worked industriously in the fields, while the renegades lolled before a prominent teepee.

"This quiet looks bad," whispered Jonathan to Wetzel. No shouts were heard; not a hostile Indian was seen to move.

"They've come to a decision," whispered Jonathan, and Wetzel answered him:

"If they hev, the Christians don't know it."

An hour later the deep pealing of the church bell broke the silence. The entire band of Christian Indians gathered near the large log structure, and then marched in orderly form toward the maple grove where the service was always held in pleasant weather. This movement brought the Indians within several hundred yards of the cliff where Zane and Wetzel lay concealed.

"There's Heckewelder walking with old man Wells," whispered Jonathan. "There's Young and Edwards, and, yes, there's the young missionary, brother of Joe. 'Pears to me they're foolish to hold service in the face of all those riled Injuns."

"Wuss'n foolish," answered Wetzel.

"Look! By gum! As I'm a livin' sinner there comes the whole crowd of hostile redskins. They've got their guns, and—by Gum! they're painted.

Looks bad, bad! Not much friendliness about that bunch!"

"They ain't intendin' to be peaceable."

"By gum! You're right. There ain't one of them settin' down. 'Pears to me I know some of them redskins. There's Pipe, sure enough, and Kotoxen. By gum! If there ain't Shingiss; he was friendly once."

"None of them's friendly."

"Look! Lew, look! Right behind Pipe. See that long war-bonnet. As I'm a born sinner, that's your old friend, Wingenund. 'Pears to me we've rounded up all our acquaintances."

The two bordermen lay close under the tall ferns and watched the proceedings with sharp eyes. They saw the converted Indians seat themselves before the platform. The crowd of hostile Indians surrounded the glade on all sides, except on, which, singularly enough, was next to the woods.

"Look thar!" exclaimed Wetzel, under his breath. He pointed off to the right of the maple glade. Jonathan gazed in the direction indicated, and saw two savages stealthily slipping through the bushes, and behind trees. Presently these suspicious acting spies, or scouts, stopped on a little knoll perhaps an hundred yards from the glade.

Wetzel groaned.

"This ain't comfortable," growled Zane, in a low whisper. "Them red devils are up to somethin' bad. They'd better not move round over here."

The hunters, satisfied that the two isolated savages meant mischief, turned their gaze once more toward the maple grove.

"Ah! Simon you white traitor! See him, Lew, comin' with his precious gang," said Jonathan. "He's got the whole thing fixed, you can plainly see that. Bill Elliott, McKee; and who's that renegade with Jim Girty? I'll allow he must be the fellar we heard was with the Chippewas. Tough lookin' customer; a good mate fer Jim Girty! A fine lot of border-hawks!"

"Somethin' comin' off," whispered Wetzel, as Zane's low growl grew unintelligible.

Jonathan felt, rather than saw, Wetzel tremble.

"The missionaries are consultin'. Ah! there comes one! Which? I guess it's Edwards. By gum! who's that Injun stalkin' over from the hostile bunch. Big chief, whoever he is. Blest if it ain't Half King!"

The watchers saw the chief wave his arm and speak with evident arrogance to Edwards, who, however, advanced to the platform and raised his hand to address the Christians.

"Crack!"

A shot rang out from the thicket. Clutching wildly at his breast, the missionary reeled back, staggered, and fell.

"One of those skulkin' redskins has killed Edwards," said Zane. "But, no; he's not dead! He's gettin' up. Mebbe he ain't hurt bad. By gum! there's Young comin' forward. Of all the fools!"

It was indeed true that Young had faced the Indians. Half King addressed him as he had the other; but Young raised his hand and began speaking.

"Crack!"

Another shot rang out. Young threw up his hands and fell heavily. The missionaries rushed toward him. Mr. Wells ran round the group, wringing his hands as if distracted.

"He's hard hit," hissed Zane, between his teeth. "You can tell that by the way he fell."

Wetzel did not answer. He lay silent and motionless, his long body rigid, and his face like marble.

"There comes the other young fellar—Joe's brother. He'll get plugged, too," continued Zane, whispering rather to himself than to his companion. "Oh, I hoped they'd show some sense! It's noble for them to die for Christianity, but it won't do no good. By gum! Heckewelder has pulled him back. Now, that's good judgment!"

Half King stepped before the Christians and addressed them. He held in his hand a black war-club, which he wielded as he spoke.

Jonathan's attention was now directed from the maple grove to the hunter beside him. He had heard a slight metallic click, as Wetzel cocked his rifle. Then he saw the black barrel slowly rise.

"Listen, Lew. Mebbe it ain't good sense. We're after Girty, you remember; and it's a long shot from here—full three hundred yards."

"You're right, Jack, you're right," answered Wetzel, breathing hard.

"Let's wait, and see what comes off."

"Jack, I can't do it. It'll make our job harder; but I can't help it. I can put a bullet just over the Huron's left eye, an' I'm goin' to do it."

"You can't do it, Lew; you can't! It's too far for any gun. Wait! Wait!" whispered Jonathan, laying his hand on Wetzel's shoulder.

"Wait? Man, can't you see what the unnamable villain is doin'?"

"What?" asked Zane, turning his eyes again to the glade.

The converted Indians sat with bowed heads. Half King raised his war-club, and threw it on the ground in front of them.

"He's announcin' the death decree!" hissed Wetzel.

"Well! if he ain't!"

Jonathan looked at Wetzel's face. Then he rose to his knees, as had Wetzel, and tightened his belt. He knew that in another instant they would be speeding away through the forest.

"Lew, my rifle's no good fer that distance. But mebbe yours is. You ought to know. It's not sense, because there's Simon Girty, and there's Jim, the men we're after. If you can hit one, you can another. But go ahead, Lew. Plug that cowardly redskin!"

Wetzel knelt on one knee, and thrust the black rifle forward through the fern leaves. Slowly the fatal barrel rose to a level, and became as motionless as the immovable stones.

Jonathan fixed his keen gaze on the haughty countenance of Half King as he stood with folded arms and scornful mien in front of the Christians he had just condemned.

Even as the short, stinging crack of Wetzel's rifle broke the silence, Jonathan saw the fierce expression of Half King's dark face change to one of vacant wildness. His arms never relaxed from their folded position. He fell, as falls a monarch of the forest trees, a dead weight.

CHAPTER XXV.

"Please do not preach to-day," said Nell, raising her eyes imploringly to Jim's face.

"Nellie, I must conduct the services as usual. I can not shirk my duty, nor let these renegades see I fear to face them."

"I have such a queer feeling. I am afraid. I don't want to be left alone. Please do not leave me."

Jim strode nervously up and down the length of the room. Nell's worn face, her beseeching eyes and trembling hands touched his heart. Rather than almost anything else, he desired to please her, to strengthen her; yet how could he shirk his duty?

"Nellie, what is it you fear?" he asked, holding her hands tightly.

"Oh, I don't know what—everything. Uncle is growing weaker every day. Look at Mr. Young; he is only a shadow of his former self, and this anxiety is wearing Mr. Heckewelder out. He is more concerned than he dares admit. You needn't shake your head, for I know it. Then those Indians who are waiting, waiting—for God only knows what! Worse than all to me, I saw that renegade, that fearful beast who made way with poor dear Kate!"

Nell burst into tears, and leaned sobbing on Jim's shoulder.

"Nell, I've kept my courage only because of you," replied Jim, his voice trembling slightly.

She looked up quickly. Something in the pale face which was bent over her told that now, if ever, was the time for a woman to forget herself, and to cheer, to inspire those around her.

"I am a silly baby, and selfish!" she cried, freeing herself from his hold. "Always thinking of myself." She turned away and wiped the tears from her eyes. "Go, Jim, do you duty; I'll stand by and help you all a woman can."

* * *

The missionaries were consulting in Heckewelder's cabin. Zeisberger had returned that morning, and his aggressive, dominating spirit was just what they needed in an hour like this. He raised the downcast spirits of the ministers.

"Hold the service? I should say we will," he declared, waving his hands. "What have we to be afraid of?"

"I do not know," answered Heckewelder, shaking his head doubtfully. "I do not know what to fear. Girty himself told me he bore us no ill will; but I hardly believe him. All this silence, this ominous waiting perplexes, bewilders me."

"Gentlemen, our duty at least is plain," said Jim, impressively. "The faith of these Christian Indians in us is so absolute that they have no fear. They believe in God, and in us. These threatening savages have failed signally to impress our Christians. If we do not hold the service they will think we fear Girty, and that might have a bad influence."

"I am in favor of postponing the preaching for a few days. I tell you I am afraid of Girty's Indians, not for myself, but for these Christians whom we love so well. I am afraid." Heckewelder's face bore testimony to his anxious dread.

"You are our leader; we have but to obey," said Edwards. "Yet I think we owe it to our converts to stick to our work until we are forced by violence to desist."

"Ah! What form will that violence take?" cried Heckewelder, his face white. "You cannot tell what these savages mean. I fear! I fear!"

"Listen, Heckewelder, you must remember we had this to go through once before," put in Zeisberger earnestly. "In '78 Girty came down on us like a wolf on the fold. He had not so many Indians at his beck and call as now; but he harangued for days, trying to scare us and our handful of Christians. He set his drunken fiends to frighten us, and he failed. We stuck it out and won. He's trying the same game. Let us stand against him, and hold our services as usual. We should trust in God!"

"Never give up!" cried Jim.

"Gentlemen, you are right; you shame me, even though I feel that I understand the situation and its dread possibilities better than any one of you. Whatever befalls we'll stick to our post. I thank you for reviving the spirit in my cowardly heart. We will hold the service to-day as usual and to make it more impressive, each shall address the congregation in turn."

"And, if need be, we will give our lives for our Christians," said Young, raising his pale face.

* * *

The deep mellow peals of the church bell awoke the slumbering echoes. Scarcely had its melody died away in the forest when a line of Indians issued from the church and marched toward the maple grove. Men, women, youths, maidens and children.

Glickhican, the old Delaware chief, headed the line. His step was firm, his head erect, his face calm in its noble austerity. His followers likewise expressed in their countenances the steadfastness of their belief. The maidens' heads were bowed, but with shyness, not fear. The children were happy, their bright faces expressive of the joy they felt in the anticipation of listening to their beloved teachers.

This procession passed between rows of painted savages, standing immovable, with folded arms, and somber eyes.

No sooner had the Christians reached the maple grove, when from all over the clearing appeared hostile Indians, who took positions near the knoll where the missionaries stood.

Heckewelder's faithful little band awaited him on the platform. The converted Indians seated themselves as usual at the foot of the knoll. The other savages crowded closely on both sides. They carried their weapons, and maintained the same silence that had so singularly marked their mood of the last twenty-four hours. No human skill could have divined their intention. This coldness might be only habitual reserve, and it might be anything else.

Heckewelder approached at the same time that Simon Girty and his band of renegades appeared. With the renegades were Pipe and Half King. These two came slowly across the clearing, passed through the opening in the crowd, and stopped close to the platform.

Heckewelder went hurriedly up to his missionaries. He seemed beside himself with excitement, and spoke with difficulty.

"Do not preach to-day. I have been warned again," he said, in a low voice.

"Do you forbid it?" inquired Edwards.

"No, no. I have not that authority, but I implore it. Wait, wait until the Indians are in a better mood."

Edwards left the group, and, stepping upon the platform, faced the Christians.

At the same moment Half King stalked majestically from before his party. He carried no weapon save a black, knotted war-club. A surging forward of the crowd of savages behind him showed the intense interest which his action had aroused. He walked forward until he stood half way between the platform and the converts. He ran his evil glance slowly over the Christians, and then rested it upon Edwards.

"Half King's orders are to be obeyed. Let the paleface keep his mouth closed," he cried in the Indian tongue. The imperious command came as a thunderbolt from a clear sky. The missionaries behind Edwards stood bewildered, awaiting the outcome.

But Edwards, without a moment's hesitation, calmly lifted his hand and spoke.

"Beloved Christians, we meet to-day as we have met before, as we hope to meet in——"

"Spang!"

The whistling of a bullet over the heads of the Christians accompanied the loud report of a rifle. All presently plainly heard the leaden missile strike. Edwards wheeled, clutching his side, breathed hard, and then fell heavily without uttering a cry. He had been shot by an Indian concealed in the thicket.

For a moment no one moved, nor spoke. The missionaries were stricken with horror; the converts seemed turned to stone, and the hostile throng waited silently, as they had for hours.

"He's shot! He's shot! Oh, I feared this!" cried Heckewelder, running forward. The missionaries followed him. Edwards was lying on his back, with a bloody hand pressed to his side.

"Dave, Dave, how is it with you?" asked Heckewelder, in a voice low with fear.

"Not bad. It's too far out to be bad, but it knocked me over," answered Edwards, weakly. "Give me—water."

They carried him from the platform, and laid him on the grass under a tree.

Young pressed Edwards' hand; he murmured something that sounded like a prayer, and then walked straight upon the platform, as he raised his face, which was sublime with a white light.

"Paleface! Back!" roared Half King, as he waved his war-club.

"You Indian dog! Be silent!"

Young's clear voice rolled out on the quiet air so imperiously, so powerful in its wonderful scorn and passion, that the hostile savages were overcome by awe, and the Christians thrilled anew with reverential love.

Young spoke again in a voice which had lost its passion, and was singularly sweet in its richness.

"Beloved Christians, if it is God's will that we must die to prove our faith, then as we have taught you how to live, so we can show you how to die——"

"Spang!"

Again a whistling sound came with the bellow of an overcharged rifle; again the sickening thud of a bullet striking flesh.

Young fell backwards from the platform.

The missionaries laid him beside Edwards, and then stood in shuddering silence. A smile shone on Young's pale face; a stream of dark blood welled from his breast. His lips moved; he whispered:

"I ask no more—God's will."

Jim looked down once at his brother missionaries; then with blanched face, but resolute and stern, he marched toward the platform.

Heckewelder ran after him, and dragged him back.

"No! no! no! My God! Would you be killed? Oh! I tried to prevent this!" cried Heckewelder, wringing his hands.

One long, fierce, exultant yell pealed throughout the grove. It came from those silent breasts in which was pent up hatred; it greeted this action which proclaimed victory over the missionaries.

All eyes turned on Half King. With measured stride he paced to and fro before the Christian Indians.

Neither cowering nor shrinking marked their manner; to a man, to a child, they rose with proud mien, heads erect and eyes flashing. This mighty chief with his blood-thirsty crew could burn the Village of Peace, could annihilate the Christians, but he could never change their hope and trust in God.

"Blinded fools!" cried Half King. "The Huron is wise; he tells no lies. Many moons ago he told the Christians they were sitting half way between two angry gods, who stood with mouths open wide and looking ferociously at each other. If they did not move back out of the road they would be ground to powder by the teeth of one or the other, or both. Half King urged them to leave the peaceful village, to forget the paleface God; to take their horses, and flocks, and return to their homes. The Christians scorned the Huron King's counsel. The sun has set for the Village of Peace. The time has come. Pipe and the Huron are powerful. They will not listen to the paleface God. They will burn the Village of Peace. Death to the Christians!"

Half King threw the black war-club with a passionate energy on the grass before the Indians.

They heard this decree of death with unflinching front. Even the children were quiet. Not a face paled, not an eye was lowered.

Half King cast their doom in their teeth. The Christians eyed him with unspoken scorn.

"My God! My God! It is worse than I thought!" moaned Heckewelder. "Utter ruin! Murder! Murder!"

In the momentary silence which followed his outburst, a tiny cloud of blue-white smoke came from the ferns overhanging a cliff.

Crack!

All heard the shot of a rifle; all noticed the difference between its clear, ringing intonation and the loud reports of the other two. All distinctly heard the zip of a bullet as it whistled over their heads.

All? No, not all. One did not hear that speeding bullet. He who was the central figure in this tragic scene, he who had doomed the Christians might have seen that tiny puff of smoke which heralded his own doom, but before the ringing report could reach his ears a small blue hole appeared, as if by magic, over his left eye, and pulse, and sense, and life had fled forever.

Half King, great, cruel chieftain, stood still for an instant as if he had been an image of stone; his haughty head lost its erect poise, the fierceness seemed to fade from his dark face, his proud plume waved gracefully as he swayed to and fro, and then fell before the Christians, inert and lifeless.

No one moved; it was as if no one breathed. The superstitious savages awaited fearfully another rifle shot; another lightning stroke, another visitation from the paleface's God.

But Jim Girty, with a cunning born of his terrible fear, had recognized the ring of that rifle. He had felt the zip of a bullet which could just as readily have found his brain as Half King's. He had stood there as fair a mark as the cruel Huron, yet the Avenger had not chosen him. Was he reserved for a different fate? Was not such a death too merciful for the frontier Deathshead? He yelled in his craven fear:

"Le vent de la Mort!"

The well known, dreaded appellation aroused the savages from a fearful stupor into a fierce manifestation of hatred. A tremendous yell rent the air. Instantly the scene changed.

CHAPTER XXVI.

In the confusion the missionaries carried Young and Edwards into Mr. Wells' cabin. Nell's calm, white face showed that she had expected some such catastrophe as this, but she of all was the least excited. Heckewelder left them at the cabin and hurried away to consult Captain Williamson. While Zeisberger, who was skilled in surgery, attended to the wounded men, Jim barred the heavy door, shut the rude, swinging windows, and made the cabin temporarily a refuge from prowling savages.

Outside the clamor increased. Shrill yells rent the air, long, rolling war-cries sounded above all the din. The measured stamp of moccasined feet, the rush of Indians past the cabin, the dull thud of hatchets struck hard into the trees—all attested to the excitement of the savages, and the imminence of terrible danger.

In the front room of Mr. Wells' cabin Edwards lay on a bed, his face turned to the wall, and his side exposed. There was a bloody hole in his white skin. Zeisberger was probing for the bullet. He had no instruments, save those of his own manufacture, and they were darning needles with bent points, and a long knife-blade ground thin.

"There, I have it," said Zeisberger. "Hold still, Dave. There!" As Edwards moaned Zeisberger drew forth the bloody bullet. "Jim, wash and dress this wound. It isn't bad. Dave will be all right in a couple of days. Now I'll look at George."

Zeisberger hurried into the other room. Young lay with quiet face and closed eyes, breathing faintly. Zeisberger opened the wounded man's shirt and exposed the wound, which was on the right side, rather high up. Nell, who had followed Zeisberger that she might be of some assistance if needed, saw him look at the wound and then turn a pale face away for a second. That hurried, shuddering movement of the sober, practical missionary was most significant. Then he bent over Young and inserted on of the probes into the wound. He pushed the steel an inch, two, three, four inches into Young's breast, but the latter neither moved nor moaned. Zeisberger shook his head, and finally removed the instrument. He raised the sufferer's shoulder to find the bed saturated with blood. The bullet wound extended completely through the missionary's body, and was bleeding from the back. Zeisberger folded strips of linsey cloth into small pads and bound them tightly over both apertures of the wound.

"How is he?" asked Jim, when the amateur surgeon returned to the other room, and proceeded to wash the blood from his hands.

Zeisberger shook his head gloomily.

"How is George?" whispered Edwards, who had heard Jim's question.

"Shot through the right lung. Human skill can not aid him! Only God can save."

"Didn't I hear a third shot?" whispered Dave, gazing round with sad, questioning eyes. "Heckewelder?"

"Is safe. He has gone to see Williamson. You did hear a third shot. Half King fell dead with a bullet over his left eye. He had just folded his arms in a grand pose after his death decree to the Christians."

"A judgment of God!"

"It does seem so, but it came in the form of leaden death from Wetzel's unerring rifle. Do you hear all that yelling? Half King's death has set the Indians wild."

There was a gentle knock at the door, and then the word, "Open," in Heckewelder's voice.

Jim unbarred the door. Heckewelder came in carrying over his shoulder what apparently was a sack of meal. He was accompanied by young Christy. Heckewelder put the bag down, opened it, and lifted out a little Indian boy. The child gazed round with fearful eyes.

"Save Benny! Save Benny!" he cried, running to Nell, and she clasped him closely in her arms.

Heckewelder's face was like marble as he asked concerning Edwards' condition.

"I'm not badly off," said the missionary with a smile.

"How's George?" whispered Heckewelder.

No one answered him. Zeisberger raised his hands. All followed Heckewelder into the other room, where Young lay in the same position as when first brought in. Heckewelder stood gazing down into the wan face with its terribly significant smile.

"I brought him out here. I persuaded him to come!" whispered Heckewelder. "Oh, Almighty God!" he cried. His voice broke, and his prayer ended with the mute eloquence of clasped hands and uplifted, appealing face.

"Come out," said Zeisberger, leading him into the larger room. The others followed, and Jim closed the door.

"What's to be done?" said Zeisberger, with his practical common sense.

"What did Williamson say? Tell us what you learned?"

"Wait—directly," answered Heckewelder, sitting down and covering his face with his hands. There was a long silence. At length he raised his white face and spoke calmly:

"Gentlemen, the Village of Peace is doomed. I entreated Captain Williamson to help us, but he refused. Said he dared not interfere. I prayed that he would speak at least a word to Girty, but he denied my request."

"Where are the converts?"

"Imprisoned in the church, every one of them except Benny. Mr. Christy and I hid the child in the meal sack and were thus able to get him here. We must save him."

"Save him?" asked Nell, looking from Heckewelder to the trembling Indian boy.

"Nellie, the savages have driven all our Christians into the church, and shut them up there, until Girty and his men shall give the word to complete their fiendish design. The converts asked but one favor—an hour in which to pray. It was granted. The savages intend to murder them all."

"Oh! Horrible! Monstrous!" cried Nell. "How can they be so inhuman?" She lifted Benny up in her arms. "They'll never get you, my boy. We'll save you—I'll save you!" The child moaned and clung to her neck.

"They are scouring the clearing now for Christians, and will search all the cabins. I'm positive."

"Will they come here?" asked Nell, turning her blazing eyes on Heckewelder.

"Undoubtedly. We must try to hide Benny. Let me think; where would be a good place? We'll try a dark corner of the loft."

"No, no," cried Nell.

"Put Benny in Young's bed," suggested Jim.

"No, no," cried Nell.

"Put him in a bucket and let him down in the well," whispered Edwards, who had listened intently to the conversation.

"That's a capital place," said Heckewelder. "But might he not fall out and drown?"

"Tie him in the bucket," said Jim.

"No, no, no," cried Nell.

"But Nellie, we must decide upon a hiding place, and in a hurry."

"I'll save Benny."

"You? Will you stay here to face those men? Jim Girty and Deering are searching the cabins. Could you bear it to see them? You couldn't."

"Oh! No, I believe it would kill me! That man! that beast! will he come here?" Nell grew ghastly pale, and looked as if about to faint. She shrunk in horror at the thought of again facing Girty. "For God's sake, Heckewelder, don't let him see me! Don't let him come in! Don't!"

Even as the imploring voice ceased a heavy thump sounded on the door.

"Who's there?" demanded Heckewelder.

Thump! Thump!

The heavy blows shook the cabin. The pans rattled on the shelves. No answer came from without.

"Quick! Hide Benny! It's as much as our lives are worth to have him found here," cried Heckewelder in a fierce whisper, as he darted toward the door.

"All right, all right, in a moment," he called out, fumbling over the bar.

He opened the door a moment later and when Jim Girty and Deering entered he turned to his friends with a dread uncertainty in his haggard face.

Edwards lay on the bed with wide-open eyes staring at the intruders. Mr. Wells sat with bowed head. Zeisberger calmly whittled a stick, and Jim stood bolt upright, with a hard light in his eyes.

Nell leaned against the side of a heavy table. Wonderful was the change that had transformed her from a timid, appealing, fear-agonized girl to a woman whose only evidence of unusual excitement were the flame in her eyes and the peculiar whiteness of her face.

Benny was gone!

Heckewelder's glance returned to the visitors. He thought he had never seen such brutal, hideous men.

"Wal, I reckon a preacher ain't agoin' to lie. Hev you seen any Injun Christians round here?" asked Girty, waving a heavy sledge-hammer.

"Girty, we have hidden no Indians here," answered Heckewelder, calmly.

"Wal, we'll hev a look, anyway," answered the renegade.

Girty surveyed the room with wolfish eyes. Deering was so drunk that he staggered. Both men, in fact, reeked with the vile fumes of rum. Without another word they proceeded to examine the room, by looking into every box, behind a stone oven, and in the cupboard. They drew the bedclothes from the bed, and with a kick demolished a pile of stove wood. Then the ruffians passed into the other apartments, where they could be heard making thorough search. At length both returned to the large room, when Girty directed Deering to climb a ladder leading to the loft, but because Deering was too much under the influence of liquor to do so, he had to go himself. He rummaged around up there for a few minutes, and then came down.

"Wal, I reckon you wasn't lyin' about it," said Girty, with his ghastly leer.

He and his companion started to go out. Deering had stood with bloodshot eyes fixed on Nell while Girty searched the loft, and as they passed the girl on their way to the open air, the renegade looked at Girty as he motioned with his head toward her. His besotted face expressed some terrible meaning.

Girty had looked at Nell when he first entered, but had not glanced twice at her. As he turned now, before going out of the door, he fixed on her his baleful glance. His aspect was more full of meaning than could have been any words. A horrible power, of which he was boastfully conscious, shone from his little, pointed eyes. His mere presence was deadly. Plainly as if he had spoken was the significance of his long gaze. Any one could have translated that look.

Once before Nell had faced it, and fainted when its dread meaning grew clear to her. But now she returned his gaze with one in which flashed lightning scorn, and repulsion, in which glowed a wonderful defiance.

The cruel face of this man, the boastful barbarity of his manner, the long, dark, bloody history which his presence recalled, was, indeed, terrifying without the added horror of his intent toward her, but now the self-forgetfulness of a true woman sustained her.

Girty and Deering backed out of the door. Heckewelder closed it, and dropped the bar in place.

Nell fell over the table with a long, low gasp. Then with one hand she lifted her skirt. Benny walked from under it. His big eyes were bright. The young woman clasped him again in her arms. Then she released him, and, laboring under intense excitement, ran to the window.

"There he goes! Oh, the horrible beast! If I only had a gun and could shoot! Oh, if only I were a man! I'd kill him. To think of poor Kate! Ah! he intends the same for me!"

Suddenly she fell upon the floor in a faint. Mr. Wells and Jim lifted her on the bed beside Edwards, where they endeavored to revive her. It was some moments before she opened her eyes.

Jim sat holding Nell's hand. Mr. Wells again bowed his head. Zeisberger continued to whittle a stick, and Heckewelder paced the floor. Christy stood by with every evidence of sympathy for this distracted group. Outside the clamor increased.

"Just listen!" cried Heckewelder. "Did you ever hear the like? All drunk, crazy, fiendish! They drank every drop of liquor the French traders had. Curses on the vagabond dealers! Rum has made these renegades and savages wild. Oh! my poor, innocent Christians!"

Heckewelder leaned his head against the mantle-shelf. He had broken down at last. Racking sobs shook his frame.

"Are you all right again?" asked Jim of Nell.

"Yes."

"I am going out, first to see Williamson, and then the Christians," he said, rising very pale, but calm.

"Don't go!" cried Heckewelder. "I have tried everything. It was all of no use."

"I will go," answered Jim.

"Yes, Jim, go," whispered Nell, looking up into his eyes. It was an earnest gaze in which a faint hope shone.

Jim unbarred the door and went out.

"Wait, I'll go along," cried Zeisberger, suddenly dropping his knife and stick.

As the two men went out a fearful spectacle met their eyes. The clearing was alive with Indians. But such Indians! They were painted demons, maddened by rum. Yesterday they had been silent; if they moved at all it had been with deliberation and dignity. To-day they were a yelling, running, blood-seeking mob.

"Awful! Did you ever see human beings like these?" asked Zeisberger.

"No, no!"

"I saw such a frenzy once before, but, of course, only in a small band of savages. Many times have I seen Indians preparing for the war-path, in search of both white men and redskins. They were fierce then, but nothing like this. Every one of these frenzied fiends is honest. Think of that! Every man feels it his duty to murder these Christians. Girty has led up to this by cunning, and now the time is come to let them loose."

"It means death for all."

"I have given up any thought of escaping," said Zeisberger, with the calmness that had characterized his manner since he returned to the village. "I shall try to get into the church."

"I'll join you there as soon as I see Williamson."

Jim walked rapidly across the clearing to the cabin where Captain Williamson had quarters. The frontiersmen stood in groups, watching the savages with an interest which showed little or no concern.

"I want to see Captain Williamson," said Jim to a frontiersman on guard at the cabin door.

"Wal, he's inside," drawled the man.

Jim thought the voice familiar, and he turned sharply to see the sun-burnt features of Jeff Lynn, the old riverman who had taken Mr. Wells' party to Fort Henry.

"Why, Lynn! I'm glad to see you," exclaimed Jim.

"Purty fair to middlin'," answered Jeff, extending his big hand.

"Say, how's the other one, your brother as wus called Joe?"

"I don't know. He ran off with Wetzel, was captured by Indians, and when I last heard of him he had married Wingenund's daughter."

"Wal, I'll be dog-goned!" Jeff shook his grizzled head and slapped his leg. "I jest knowed he'd raise somethin'."

"I'm in a hurry. Do you think Captain Williamson will stand still and let all this go on?"

"I'm afeerd so."

Evidently the captain heard the conversation, for he appeared at the cabin door, smoking a long pipe.

"Captain Williamson, I have come to entreat you to save the Christians from this impending massacre."

"I can't do nuthin'," answered Williamson, removing his pipe to puff forth a great cloud of smoke.

"You have eighty men here!"

"If we interfered Pipe would eat us alive in three minutes. You preacher fellows don't understand this thing. You've got Pipe and Girty to deal with. If you don't know them, you'll be better acquainted by sundown."

"I don't care who they are. Drunken ruffians and savages! That's enough. Will you help us? We are men of your own race, and we come to you for help. Can you withhold it?"

"I won't hev nuthin' to do with this bizness. The chiefs hev condemned the village, an' it'll hev to go. If you fellars hed been careful, no white blood would hev been spilled. I advise you all to lay low till it's over."

"Will you let me speak to your men, to try and get them to follow me?"

"Heckewelder asked that same thing. He was persistent, and I took a vote fer him just to show how my men stood. Eighteen of them said they'd follow him; the rest wouldn't interfere."

"Eighteen! My God!" cried Jim, voicing the passion which consumed him. "You are white men, yet you will stand by and see these innocent people murdered! Man, where's your humanity? Your manhood? These converted Indians are savages no longer, they are Christians. Their children are as good, pure, innocent as your own. Can you remain idle and see these little ones murdered?"

Williamson made no answer, the men who had crowded round were equally silent. Not one lowered his head. Many looked at the impassioned missionary; others gazed at the savages who were circling around the trees brandishing their weapons. If any pitied the unfortunate Christians, none showed it. They were indifferent, with the indifference of men hardened to cruel scenes.

Jim understood, at last, as he turned from face to face to find everywhere that same imperturbability. These bordermen were like Wetzel and Jonathan Zane. The only good Indian was a dead Indian. Years of war and bloodshed, of merciless cruelty at the hands of redmen, of the hard, border life had rendered these frontiersmen incapable of compassion for any savage.

Jim no longer restrained himself.

"Bordermen you may be, but from my standpoint, from any man's, from God's, you are a lot of coldly indifferent cowards!" exclaimed Jim, with white, quivering lips. "I understand now. Few of you will risk anything for Indians. You will not believe a savage can be a Christian. You don't care if they are all murdered. Any man among you—any man, I say—would step out before those howling fiends and boldly demand that there be no bloodshed. A courageous leader with a band of determined followers could avert this tragedy. You might readily intimidate yonder horde of drunken demons. Captain Williamson, I am only a minister, far removed from a man of war and leader, as you claim to be, but, sir, I curse you as a miserable coward. If I ever get back to civilization I'll brand this inhuman coldness of yours, as the most infamous and dastardly cowardice that ever disgraced a white man. You are worse than Girty!"

Williamson turned a sickly yellow; he fumbled a second with the handle of his tomahawk, but made no answer. The other bordermen maintained the same careless composure. What to them was the raving of a mad preacher?

Jim saw it and turned baffled, fiercely angry, and hopeless. As he walked away Jeff Lynn took his arm, and after they were clear of the crowd of frontiersmen he said:

"Young feller, you give him pepper, an' no mistake. An' mebbe you're right from your side the fence. But you can't see the Injuns from our side. We hunters hevn't much humanity—I reckon that's what you called it—but we've lost so many friends an' relatives, an' hearn of so many murders by the reddys that we look on all of 'em as wild varmints that should be killed on sight. Now, mebbe it'll interest you to know I was the feller who took the vote Williamson told you about, an' I did it 'cause I had an interest in you. I wus watchin' you when Edwards and the other missionary got shot. I like grit in a man, an' I seen you had it clear through. So when Heckewelder comes over I talked to the fellers, an' all I could git interested was eighteen, but they wanted to fight simply fer fightin' sake. Now, ole Jeff Lynn is your friend. You just lay low until this is over."

Jim thanked the old riverman and left him. He hardly knew which way to turn. He would make one more effort. He crossed the clearing to where the renegades' teepee stood. McKee and Elliott were sitting on a log. Simon Girty stood beside them, his hard, keen, roving eyes on the scene. The missionary was impressed by the white leader. There was a difference in his aspect, a wilder look than the others wore, as if the man had suddenly awakened to the fury of his Indians. Nevertheless the young man went straight toward him.

"Girty, I come—"

"Git out! You meddlin' preacher!" yelled the renegade, shaking his fist at Jim.

Simon Girty was drunk.

Jim turned from the white fiends. He knew his life to them was not worth a pinch of powder.

"Lost! Lost! All lost!" he exclaimed in despair.

As he went toward the church he saw hundreds of savages bounding over the grass, brandishing weapons and whooping fiendishly. They were concentrating around Girty's teepee, where already a great throng had congregated. Of all the Indians to be seen not one walked. They leaped by Jim, and ran over the grass nimble as deer.

He saw the eager, fire in their dusky eyes, and the cruelly clenched teeth like those of wolves when they snarl. He felt the hissing breath of many savages as they raced by him. More than one whirled a tomahawk close to Jim's head, and uttered horrible yells in his ear. They were like tigers lusting for blood.

Jim hurried to the church. Not an Indian was visible near the log structure. Even the savage guards had gone. He entered the open door to be instantly struck with reverence and awe.

The Christians were singing.

Miserable and full of sickening dread though Jim was, he could not but realize that the scene before him was one of extraordinary beauty and pathos. The doomed Indians lifted up their voices in song. Never had they sung so feelingly, so harmoniously.

When the song ended Zeisberger, who stood upon a platform, opened his Bible and read:

"In a little wrath I hid my face from thee for a moment, but with everlasting kindness will I have mercy on thee, saith the Lord, thy Redeemer."

In a voice low and tremulous the venerable missionary began his sermon.

The shadow of death hovered over these Christian martyrs; it was reflected in their somber eyes, yet not one was sullen or sad. The children who were too young to understand, but instinctively feeling the tragedy soon to be enacted there, cowered close to their mothers.

Zeisberger preached a touching and impressive, though short, sermon. At its conclusion the whole congregation rose and surrounded the missionary. The men shook his hands, the women kissed them, the children clung to his legs. It was a wonderful manifestation of affection.

Suddenly Glickhican, the old Delaware chief, stepped on the platform, raised his hand and shouted one Indian word.

A long, low wail went up from the children and youths; the women slowly, meekly bowed their heads. The men, due to the stoicism of their nature and the Christianity they had learned, stood proudly erect awaiting the death that had been decreed.

Glickhican pulled the bell rope.

A deep, mellow tone pealed out.

The sound transfixed all the Christians. No one moved.

Glickhican had given the signal which told the murderers the Christians were ready.

"Come, man, my God! We can't stay here!" cried Jim to Zeisberger.

As they went out both men turned to look their last on the martyrs. The death knell which had rung in the ears of the Christians, was to them the voice of God. Stern, dark visages of men and the sweet, submissive faces of women were uplifted with rapt attention. A light seemed to shine from these faces as if the contemplation of God had illumined them.

As Zeisberger and Jim left the church and hurried toward the cabins, they saw the crowd of savages in a black mass round Girty's teepee. The yelling and leaping had ceased.

Heckewelder opened the door. Evidently he had watched for them.

"Jim! Jim!" cried Nell, when he entered the cabin. "Oh-h! I was afraid. Oh! I am glad you're back safe. See, this noble Indian has come to help us."

Wingenund stood calm and erect by the door.

"Chief, what will you do?"

"Wingenund will show you the way to the big river," answered the chieftain, in his deep bass.

"Run away? No, never! That would be cowardly. Heckewelder, you would not go? Nor you, Zeisberger? We may yet be of use, we may yet save some of the Christians."

"Save the yellow-hair," sternly said Wingenund.

"Oh, Jim, you don't understand. The chief has come to warn me of Girty. He intends to take me as he has others, as he did poor Kate. did you not see the meaning in his eyes to-day? How they scorched me! Ho! Jim, take me away! Save me! Do not leave me here to that horrible fate? Oh! Jim, take me away!"

"Nell, I will take you," cried Jim, grasping her hands.

"Hurry! There's a blanket full of things I packed for you," said Heckewelder. "Lose no time. Ah! hear that! My Heavens! what a yell!" Heckewelder rushed to the door and looked out. "There they go, a black mob of imps; a pack of hungry wolves! Jim Girty is in the lead. How he leaps! How he waves his sledge! He leads the savages toward the church. Oh! it's the end!"

"Benny? Where's Benny?" cried Jim, hurriedly lacing the hunting coat he had flung about him.

"Benny's safe. I've hidden him. I'll get him away from here," answered young Christy. "Go! Now's your time. Godspeed you!"

"I'm ready," declared Mr. Wells. "I—have—finished!"

"There goes Wingenund! He's running. Follow him, quick! Good-by! Good-by! God be with you!" cried Heckewelder.

"Good-by! Good-by!"

Jim hurried Nell toward the bushes where Wingenund's tall form could dimly be seen. Mr. Wells followed them. On the edge of the clearing Jim and Nell turned to look back.

They saw a black mass of yelling, struggling, fighting savages crowding around the church.

"Oh! Jim, look back! Look back!" cried Nell, holding hard to his hand. "Look back! See if Girty is coming!"

CHAPTER XXVII.

At last the fugitives breathed free under the gold and red cover of the woods. Never speaking, never looking back, the guide hurried eastward with long strides. His followers were almost forced to run in order to keep him in sight. He had waited at the edge of the clearing for them, and, relieving Jim of the heavy pack, which he swung slightly over his shoulder, he set a pace that was most difficult to maintain. The young missionary half led, half carried Nell over the stones and rough places. Mr. Wells labored in the rear.

"Oh! Jim! Look back! Look back! See if we are pursued!" cried Nell frequently, with many a earful glance into the dense thickets.

The Indian took a straight course through the woods. He leaped the brooks, climbed the rough ridges, and swiftly trod the glades that were free of windfalls. His hurry and utter disregard for the plain trail left behind, proved his belief in the necessity of placing many miles between the fugitives and the Village of Peace. Evidently they would be followed, and it would be a waste of valuable time to try to conceal their trail. Gradually the ground began to rise, the way become more difficult, but Wingenund never slackened his pace. Nell was strong, supple, and light of foot. She held her own with Jim, but time and time again they were obliged to wait for her uncle. Once he was far behind. Wingenund halted for them at the height of a ridge where the forest was open.

"Ugh!" exclaimed the chieftain, as they finished the ascent. He stretched a long arm toward the sun; his falcon eye gleamed.

Far in the west a great black and yellow cloud of smoke rolled heavenward. It seemed to rise from out the forest, and to hang low over the trees; then it soared aloft and grew thinner until it lost its distinct line far in the clouds. The setting sun stood yet an hour high over a distant hill, and burned dark red through the great pall of smoke.

"Is it a forest fire?" asked Nell, fearfully.

"Fire, of course, but——" Jim did not voice his fear; he looked closely at Wingenund.

The chieftain stood silent a moment as was his wont when addressed. The dull glow of the sun was reflected in the dark eyes that gazed far away over forest and field.

"Fire," said Wingenund, and it seemed that as he spoke a sterner shadow flitted across his bronzed face. "The sun sets to-night over the ashes of the Village of Peace."

He resumed his rapid march eastward. With never a backward glance the saddened party followed. Nell kept close beside Jim, and the old man tramped after them with bowed head. The sun set, but Wingenund never slackened his stride. Twilight deepened, yet he kept on.

"Indian, we can go no further to-night, we must rest," cried Jim, as Nell stumbled against him, and Mr. Wells panted wearily in the rear.

"Rest soon," replied the chief, and kept on.

Darkness had settled down when Wingenund at last halted. The fugitives could see little in the gloom, but they heard the music of running water, and felt soft moss beneath their feet.

They sank wearily down upon a projecting stone. The moss was restful to their tired limbs. Opening the pack they found food with which to satisfy the demands of hunger. Then, close under the stone, the fugitives sank into slumber while the watchful Indian stood silent and motionless.

Jim thought he had but just closed his eyes when he felt a gentle pressure on his arm.

"Day is here," said the Indian.

Jim opened his eyes to see the bright red sun crimsoning the eastern hills, and streaming gloriously over the colored forests. He raised himself on his elbow to look around. Nell was still asleep. The blanket was tucked close to her chin. Her chestnut hair was tumbled like a schoolgirl's; she looked as fresh and sweet as the morning.

"Nell, Nell, wake up," said Jim, thinking the while how he would love to kiss those white eyelids.

Nell's eyes opened wide; a smile lay deep in their hazel shadows.

"Where a I? Oh, I remember," she cried, sitting up. "Oh, Jim, I had such a sweet dream. I was at home with mother and Kate. Oh, to wake and find it all a dream! I am fleeing for life. But, Jim, we are safe, are we not?"

"Another day, and we'll be safe."

"Let us fly," she cried, leaping up and shaking out her crumpled skirt. "Uncle, come!"

Mr. Wells lay quietly with his mild blue eyes smiling up at her. He neither moved nor spoke.

"Eat, drink," said the chief, opening the pack.

"What a beautiful place," exclaimed Nell, taking the bread and meat handed to her. "This is a lovely little glade. Look at those golden flowers, the red and purple leaves, the brown shining moss, and those lichen-covered stones. Why! Some one has camped here. See the little cave, the screens of

384

plaited ferns, and the stone fireplace."

"It seems to me this dark spring and those gracefully spreading branches are familiar," said Jim.

"Beautiful Spring," interposed Wingenund.

"Yes, I know this place," cried Nell excitedly. "I remember this glade though it was moonlight when I saw it. Here Wetzel rescued me from Girty."

"Nell, you're right," replied Jim. "How strange we should run across this place again."

Strange fate, indeed, which had brought them again to Beautiful Spring! It was destined that the great scenes of their lives were to be enacted in this mossy glade.

"Come, uncle, you are lazy," cried Nell, a touch of her old roguishness making playful her voice.

Mr. Wells lay still, and smiled up at them.

"You are not ill?" cried Nell, seeing for the first time how pallid was his face.

"Dear Nellie, I am not ill. I do not suffer, but I am dying," he answered, again with that strange, sweet smile.

"Oh-h-h!" breathed Nell, falling on her knees.

"No, no, Mr. Wells, you are only weak; you will be all right again soon," cried Jim.

"Jim, Nellie, I have known all night. I have lain here wakeful. My heart never was strong. It gave out yesterday, and now it is slowly growing weaker. Put your hand on my breast. Feel. Ah! you see! My life is flickering. God's will be done. I am content. My work is finished. My only regret is that I brought you out to this terrible borderland. But I did not know. If only I could see you safe from the peril of this wilderness, at home, happy, married."

Nell bent over him blinded by her tears, unable to see or speak, crushed by this last overwhelming blow. Jim sat on the other side of the old missionary, holding his hand. For many moments neither spoke. They glanced at the pale face, watching with eager, wistful eyes for a smile, or listening for a word.

"Come," said the Indian.

Nell silently pointed toward her uncle.

"He is dying," whispered Jim to the Indian.

"Go, leave me," murmured Mr. Wells. "You are still in danger."

"We'll not leave you," cried Jim.

"No, no, no," sobbed Nell, bending over to kiss him.

"Nellie, may I marry you to Jim?" whispered Mr. Wells into her ear. "He has told me how it is with him. He loves you, Nellie. I'd die happier knowing I'd left you with him."

Even at that moment, with her heart almost breaking, Nell's fair face flushed.

"Nell, will you marry me?" asked Jim, softly. Low though it was, he had heard Mr. Wells' whisper.

Nell stretched a little trembling hand over her uncle to Jim, who inclosed it in his own. Her eyes met his. Through her tears shone faintly a light, which, but for the agony that made it dim, would have beamed radiant.

"Find the place," said Mr. Wells, handing Jim a Bible. It was the one he always carried in his pocket.

With trembling hand Jim turned the leaves. At last he found the lines, and handed the book back to the old man.

Simple, sweet and sad was that marriage service. Nell and Jim knelt with hands clasped over Mr. Wells. The old missionary's voice was faint; Nell's responses were low, and Jim answered with deep and tender feeling. Beside them stood Wingenund, a dark, magnificent figure.

"There! May God bless you!" murmured Mr. Wells, with a happy smile, closing the Bible.

"Nell, my wife!" whispered Jim, kissing her hand.

"Come!" broke in Wingenund's voice, deep, strong, like that of a bell.

Not one of them had observed the chief as he stood erect, motionless, poised like a stag scenting the air. His dark eyes seemed to pierce the purple-golden forest, his keen ear seemed to drink in the singing of the birds and the gentle rustling of leaves. Native to these haunts as were the wild creatures, they were no quicker than the Indian to feel the approach of foes. The breeze had borne faint, suspicious sounds.

"Keep—the—Bible," said Mr. Wells, "remember—its—word." His hand closely clasped Nell's, and then suddenly loosened. His pallid face was lighted by a meaning, tender smile which slowly faded—faded, and was gone. The venerable head fell back. The old missionary was dead.

Nell kissed the pale, cold brow, and then rose, half dazed and shuddering. Jim was vainly trying to close the dead man's eyes. She could no longer look. On rising she found herself near the Indian chief. He took her fingers in his great hand, and held them with a strong, warm pressure. Strangely thrilled, she looked up at Wingenund. His somber eyes, fixed piercingly on the forest, and his dark stern face, were, as always, inscrutable. No compassion shone there; no emotion unbefitting a chieftain would ever find expression in that cold face, but Nell felt a certain tenderness in this Indian, a response in his great heart. Felt it so surely, so powerfully that she leaned her head against him. She knew he was her friend.

"Come," said the chief once more. He gently put Nell aside before Jim arose from his sad task.

"We can not leave him unburied," expostulated Jim.

Wingenund dragged aside a large stone which formed one wall of the cavern. Then he grasped a log which was half covered by dirt, and, exerting his great strength, pulled it from its place. There was a crash, a rumble, the jar of a heavy weight striking the earth, then the rattling of gravel, and, before Nell and Jim realized what had happened, the great rock forming the roof of the cavern slipped down the bank followed by a small avalanche. The cavern was completely covered. Mr. Wells was buried. A mossy stone marked the old missionary's grave.

Nell and Jim were lost in wonder and awe.

"Ugh!" cried the chief, looking toward the opening in the glade.

Fearfully Nell and Jim turned, to be appalled by four naked, painted savages standing with leveled rifles. Behind them stood Deering and Jim Girty.

"Oh, God! We are lost! Lost! Lost!" exclaimed Jim, unable to command himself. Hope died in his heart.

No cry issued from Nell's white lips. She was dazed by this final blow. Having endured so much, this last misfortune, apparently the ruin of her life, brought no added suffering, only a strange, numb feeling.

"Ah-huh! Thought you'd give me the slip, eh?" croaked Girty, striding forward, and as he looked at Wingenund his little, yellow eyes flared like flint. "Does a wolf befriend Girty's captives? Chief you hev led me a hard chase."

Wingenund deigned no reply. He stood as he did so often, still and silent, with folded arms, and a look that was haughty, unresponsive.

The Indians came forward into the glade, and one of them quickly bound Jim's hands behind his back. The savages wore a wild, brutish look. A feverish ferocity, very near akin to insanity, possessed them. They were not quiet a moment, but ran here and there, for no apparent reason, except, possibly, to keep in action with the raging fire in their hearts. The cleanliness which characterized the normal Indian was absent in them; their scant buckskin dress was bedraggled and stained. They were still drunk with rum and the lust for blood. Murder gleamed from the glance of their eyes.

"Jake, come over here," said Girty to his renegade friend. "Ain't she a prize?"

Girty and Deering stood before the poor, stricken girl, and gloated over her fair beauty. She stood as when first transfixed by the horror from which she had been fleeing. Her pale face was lowered, her hands clenched tightly in the folds of her skirt.

Never before had two such coarse, cruel fiends as Deering and Girty encumbered the earth. Even on the border, where the best men were bad, they were the worst. Deering was yet drunk, but Girty had recovered somewhat from the effects of the rum he had absorbed. The former rolled his big eyes and nodded his shaggy head. He was passing judgment, from his point of view, on the fine points of the girl.

"She cer'aintly is," he declared with a grin. "She's a little beauty. Beats any I ever seen!"

Jim Girty stroked his sharp chin with dirty fingers. His yellow eyes, his burnt saffron skin, his hooked nose, his thin lips—all his evil face seemed to shine with an evil triumph. To look at him was painful. To have him gaze at her was enough to drive any woman mad.

Dark stains spotted the bright frills of his gaudy dress, his buckskin coat and leggins, and dotted his white eagle plumes. Dark stains, horribly suggestive, covered him from head to foot. Blood stains! The innocent blood of Christians crimsoned his renegade's body, and every dark red blotch cried murder.

"Girl, I burned the Village of Peace to git you," growled Girty.

"Come here!"

With a rude grasp that tore open her dress, exposing her beautiful white shoulder and bosom, the ruffian pulled her toward him. His face was transfixed with a fierce joy, a brutal passion.

Deering looked on with a drunken grin, while his renegade friend hugged the almost dying girl. The Indians paced the glade with short strides like leashed tigers. The young missionary lay on the moss with closed eyes. He could not endure the sight of Nell in Girty's arms.

No one noticed Wingenund. He stood back a little, half screened by drooping branches. Once again the chief's dark eyes gleamed, his head turned a trifle aside, and, standing in the statuesque position habitual with him when resting, he listened, as one who hears mysterious sounds. Suddenly his keen glance was riveted on the ferns above the low cliff. He had seen their graceful heads quivering. Then two blinding sheets of flame burst from the ferns.

Spang! Spang!

The two rifle reports thundered through the glade. Two Indians staggered and fell in their tracks—dead without a cry.

A huge yellow body, spread out like a panther in his spring, descended with a crash upon Deering and Girty. The girl fell away from the renegade as he went down with a shrill screech, dragging Deering with him. Instantly began a terrific, whirling, wrestling struggle.

A few feet farther down the cliff another yellow body came crashing down to alight with a thud, to bound erect, to rush forward swift as a leaping deer. The two remaining Indians had only time to draw their weapons before this lithe, threatening form whirled upon them. Shrill cries, hoarse yells, the clash of steel and dull blows mingled together. One savage went down, twisted over, writhed and lay still. The other staggered, warded off lightninglike blows until one passed under his guard, and crashed dully on his head. Then he reeled, rose again, but only to have his skull cloven by a bloody tomahawk.

The victor darted toward the whirling mass.

"Lew, shake him loose! Let him go!" yelled Jonathan Zane, swinging his bloody weapon.

High above Zane's cry, Deering's shouts and curses, Girty's shrieks of fear and fury, above the noise of wrestling bodies and dull blows, rose a deep booming roar.

It was Wetzel's awful cry of vengeance.

"Shake him loose," yelled Jonathan.

Baffled, he ran wildly around the wrestlers. Time and time again his gory tomahawk was raised only to be lowered. He found no opportunity to strike. Girty's ghastly countenance gleamed at him from the whirl of legs, and arms and bodies. Then Wetzel's dark face, lighted by merciless eyes, took its place, and that gave way to Deering's broad features. The men being clad alike in buckskin, and their motions so rapid, prevented Zane from lending a helping hand.

Suddenly Deering was propelled from the mass as if by a catapult. His body straightened as it came down with a heavy thud. Zane pounced upon it with catlike quickness. Once more he swung aloft the bloody hatchet; then once more he lowered it, for there was no need to strike. The renegade's side was torn open from shoulder to hip. A deluge of blood poured out upon the moss. Deering choked, a bloody froth formed on his lips. His fingers clutched at nothing. His eyes rolled violently and then were fixed in an awful stare.

The girl lying so quiet in the woods near the old hut was avenged!

Jonathan turned again to Wetzel and Girty, not with any intention to aid the hunter, but simply to witness the end of the struggle.

Without the help of the powerful Deering, how pitifully weak was the Deathshead of the frontier in the hands of the Avenger!

Jim Girty's tomahawk was thrown in one direction and his knife in another. He struggled vainly in the iron grip that held him.

Wetzel rose to his feet clutching the renegade. With his left arm, which had been bared in the fight, he held Girty by the front of his buckskin shirt, and dragged him to that tree which stood alone in the glade. He pushed him against it, and held him there.

The white dog leaped and snarled around the prisoner.

Girty's hands pulled and tore at the powerful arm which forced him hard against the beech. It was a brown arm, and huge with its bulging, knotted, rigid muscles. A mighty arm, strong as the justice which ruled it.

"Girty, thy race is run!" Wetzel's voice cut the silence like a steel whip.

The terrible, ruthless smile, the glittering eyes of doom seemed literally to petrify the renegade.

The hunter's right arm rose slowly. The knife in his hand quivered as if with eagerness. The long blade, dripping with Deering's blood, pointed toward the hilltop.

"Look thar! See 'em! Thar's yer friends!" cried Wetzel.

On the dead branches of trees standing far above the hilltop, were many great, dark birds. They sat motionless as if waiting.

"Buzzards! Buzzards!" hissed Wetzel.

Girty's ghastly face became an awful thing to look upon. No living countenance ever before expressed such fear, such horror, such agony. He foamed at the mouth, he struggled, he writhed. With a terrible fascination he watched that quivering, dripping blade, now poised high.

Wetzel's arm swung with the speed of a shooting star. He drove the blade into Girty's groin, through flesh and bone, hard and fast into the tree. He nailed the renegade to the beech, there to await his lingering doom.

"Ah-h! Ah-h! Ah-h!" shrieked Girty, in cries of agony. He fumbled and pulled at the haft of the knife, but could not loosen it. He beat his breast, he tore his hair. His screams were echoed from the hilltop as if in mockery.

The white dog stood near, his hair bristling, his teeth snapping.

The dark birds sat on the dead branches above the hilltop, as if waiting for their feast.

CHAPTER XXVIII.

Zane turned and cut the young missionary's bonds. Jim ran to where Nell was lying on the ground, and tenderly raised her head, calling to her that they were saved. Zane bathed the girl's pale face.

Presently she sighed and opened her eyes.

Then Zane looked from the statuelike form of Wingenund to the motionless figure of Wetzel. The chief stood erect with his eyes on the distant hills. Wetzel remained with folded arms, his cold eyes fixed upon the writhing, moaning renegade.

"Lew, look here," said Zane, unhesitatingly, and pointed toward the chief.

Wetzel quivered as if sharply stung; the cold glitter in his eyes changed to lurid fire. With upraised tomahawk he bounded across the brook.

"Lew, wait a minute!" yelled Zane.

"Wetzel! wait, wait!" cried Jim, grasping the hunter's arm; but the latter flung him off, as the wind tosses a straw.

"Wetzel, wait, for God's sake, wait!" screamed Nell. She had risen at Zane's call, and now saw the deadly resolve in the hunter's eyes. Fearlessly she flung herself in front of him; bravely she risked her life before his mad rush; frantically she threw her arms around him and clung to his hands desperately.

Wetzel halted; frenzied as he was at the sight of his foe, he could not hurt a woman.

"Girl, let go!" he panted, and his broad breast heaved.

"No, no, no! Listen, Wetzel, you must not kill the chief. He is a friend."

"He is my great foe!"

"Listen, oh! please listen!" pleaded Nell. "He warned me to flee from Girty; he offered to guide us to Fort Henry. He has saved my life. For my sake, Wetzel, do not kill him! Don't let me be the cause of his murder! Wetzel, Wetzel, lower your arm, drop your hatchet. For pity's sake do not spill more blood. Wingenund is a Christian!"

Wetzel stepped back breathing heavily. His white face resembled chiseled marble. With those little hands at his breast he hesitated in front of the chief he had hunted for so many long years.

"Would you kill a Christian?" pleaded Nell, her voice sweet and earnest.

"I reckon not, but this Injun ain't one," replied Wetzel slowly.

"Put away your hatchet. Let me have it. Listen, and I will tell you, after thanking you for this rescue. Do you know of my marriage? Come, please listen! Forget for a moment your enmity. Oh! you must be merciful! Brave men are always merciful!"

"Injun, are you a Christian?" hissed Wetzel.

"Oh! I know he is! I know he is!" cried Nell, still standing between Wetzel and the chief.

Wingenund spoke no word. He did not move. His falcon eyes gazed tranquilly at his white foe. Christian or pagan, he would not speak one word to save his life.

"Oh! tell him you are a Christian," cried Nell, running to the chief.

"Yellow-hair, the Delaware is true to his race."

As he spoke gently to Nell a noble dignity shone upon his dark face.

"Injun, my back bears the scars of your braves' whips," hissed Wetzel, once more advancing.

"Deathwind, your scars are deep, but the Delaware's are deeper," came the calm reply. "Wingenund's heart bears two scars. His son lies under the moss and ferns; Deathwind killed him; Deathwind alone knows his grave. Wingenund's daughter, the delight of his waning years, freed the Delaware's great foe, and betrayed her father. Can the Christian God tell Wingenund of his child?"

Wetzel shook like a tree in a storm. Justice cried out in the Indian's deep voice. Wetzel fought for mastery of himself.

"Delaware, your daughter lays there, with her lover," said Wetzel firmly, and pointed into the spring.

"Ugh!" exclaimed the Indian, bending over the dark pool. He looked long into its murky depths. Then he thrust his arm down into the brown water.

"Deathwind tells no lie," said the chief, calmly, and pointed toward Girty. The renegade had ceased struggling, his head was bowed upon his breast. "The white serpent has stung the Delaware."

"What does it mean?" cried Jim.

"Your brother Joe and Whispering Winds lie in the spring," answered Jonathan Zane. "Girty murdered them, and Wetzel buried the two there."

"Oh, is it true?" cried Nell.

"True, lass," whispered Jim, brokenly, holding out his arms to her. Indeed, he needed her strength as much as she needed his. The girl gave one shuddering glance at the spring, and then hid her face on her husband's shoulder.

"Delaware, we are sworn foes," cried Wetzel.

"Wingenund asks no mercy."

"Are you a Christian?"

"Wingenund is true to his race."

"Delaware, begone! Take these weapons an' go. When your shadow falls shortest on the ground, Deathwind starts on your trail."

"Deathwind is the great white chief; he is the great Indian foe; he is as sure as the panther in his leap; as swift as the wild goose in his northern flight. Wingenund never felt fear." The chieftain's sonorous reply rolled through the quiet glade. "If Deathwind thirsts for Wingenund's blood, let him spill it now, for when the Delaware goes into the forest his trail will fade."

"Begone!" roared Wetzel. The fever for blood was once more rising within him.

The chief picked up some weapons of the dead Indians, and with haughty stride stalked from the glade.

"Oh, Wetzel, thank you, I knew——" Nell's voice broke as she faced the hunter. She recoiled from this changed man.

"Come, we'll go," said Jonathan Zane. "I'll guide you to Fort Henry." He lifted the pack, and led Nell and Jim out of the glade.

They looked back once to picture forever in their minds the lovely spot with its ghastly quiet bodies, the dark, haunting spring, the renegade nailed to the tree, and the tall figure of Wetzel as he watched his shadow on the ground.

* * *

When Wetzel also had gone, only two living creatures remained in the glade—the doomed renegade, and the white dog. The gaunt beast watched the man with hungry, mad eyes.

A long moan wailed through the forest. It swelled mournfully on the air, and died away. The doomed man heard it. He raised his ghastly face; his dulled senses seemed to revive. He gazed at the stiffening bodies of the Indians, at the gory corpse of Deering, at the savage eyes of the dog.

Suddenly life seemed to surge strong within him.

"Hell's fire! I'm not done fer yet," he gasped. "This damned knife can't kill me; I'll pull it out."

He worked at the heavy knife hilt. Awful curses passed his lips, but the blade did not move. Retribution had spoken his doom.

Suddenly he saw a dark shadow moving along the sunlit ground. It swept past him. He looked up to see a great bird with wide wings sailing far above. He saw another still higher, and then a third. He looked at the hilltop. The quiet, black birds had taken wing. They were floating slowly, majestically upward. He watched their graceful flight. How easily they swooped in wide circles. He remembered that they had fascinated him when a boy, long, long ago, when he had a home. Where was that home? He had one once. Ah! the long, cruel years have rolled back. A youth blotted out by evil returned. He saw a little cottage, he saw the old Virginia homestead, he saw his brothers and his mother.

"Ah-h!" A cruel agony tore his heart. He leaned hard against the knife. With the pain the present returned, but the past remained. All his youth, all his manhood flashed before him. The long, bloody, merciless years faced him, and his crimes crushed upon him with awful might.

Suddenly a rushing sound startled him. He saw a great bird swoop down and graze the tree tops. Another followed, and another, and then a flock of them. He saw their gray, spotted breasts and hooked beaks.

"Buzzards," he muttered, darkly eyeing the dead savages. The carrion birds were swooping to their feast.

"By God! He's nailed me fast for buzzards!" he screamed in sudden, awful frenzy. "Nailed fast! Ah-h! Ah-h! Ah-h! Eaten alive by buzzards! Ah-h! Ah-h! Ah-h!"

He shrieked until his voice failed, and then he gasped.

Again the buzzards swooped overhead, this time brushing the leaves. One, a great grizzled bird, settled upon a limb of the giant oak, and stretched its long neck. Another alighted beside him. Others sailed round and round the dead tree top.

The leader arched his wings, and with a dive swooped into the glade. He alighted near Deering's dead body. He was a dark, uncanny bird, with long, scraggy, bare neck, a wreath of white, grizzled feathers, a cruel, hooked beak, and cold eyes.

The carrion bird looked around the glade, and put a great claw on the dead man's breast.

"Ah-h! Ah-h!" shrieked Girty. His agonized yell of terror and horror echoed mockingly from the wooded bluff.

The huge buzzard flapped his wings and flew away, but soon returned to his gruesome feast. His followers, made bold by their leader, floated down into the glade. Their black feathers shone in the sun. They hopped over the moss; they stretched their grizzled necks, and turned their heads sideways.

Girty was sweating blood. It trickled from his ghastly face. All the suffering and horror he had caused in all his long career was as nothing to that which then rended him. He, the renegade, the white Indian, the Deathshead of the frontier, panted and prayed for a merciful breath. He was exquisitely alive. He was human.

Presently the huge buzzard, the leader, raised his hoary head. He saw the man nailed to the tree. The bird bent his head wisely to one side, and then lightly lifted himself into the air. He sailed round the glade, over the fighting buzzards, over the spring, and over the doomed renegade. He flew out of the glade, and in again. He swooped close to Girty. His broad wings scarcely moved as he sailed along.

Girty tried to strike the buzzard as he sailed close by, but his arm fell useless. He tried to scream, but his voice failed.

Slowly the buzzard king sailed by and returned. Every time he swooped a little nearer, and bent his long, scraggy neck.

Suddenly he swooped down, light and swift as a hawk; his wide wings fanned the air; he poised under the tree, and then fastened sharp talons in the doomed man's breast.

CHAPTER XXIX.

The fleeting human instinct of Wetzel had given way to the habit of years. His merciless quest for many days had been to kill the frontier fiend. Now that it had been accomplished, he turned his vengeance into its accustomed channel, and once more became the ruthless Indian-slayer.

A fierce, tingling joy surged through him as he struck the Delaware's trail. Wingenund had made little or no effort to conceal his tracks; he had gone northwest, straight as a crow flies, toward the Indian encampment. He had a start of sixty minutes, and it would require six hours of rapid traveling to gain the Delaware town.

"Reckon he'll make fer home," muttered Wetzel, following the trail with all possible speed.

The hunter's method of trailing an Indian was singular. Intuition played as great a part as sight. He seemed always to divine his victim's intention. Once on the trail he was as hard to shake off as a bloodhound. Yet he did not, by any means, always stick to the Indian's footsteps. With Wetzel the direction was of the greatest importance.

For half a mile he closely followed the Delaware's plainly marked trail. Then he stopped to take a quick survey of the forest before him. He abruptly left the trail, and, breaking into a run, went through the woods as fleetly and noiselessly as a deer, running for a quarter of a mile, when he stopped to listen. All seemed well, for he lowered his head, and walked slowly along, examining the moss and leaves. Presently he came upon a little open space where the soil was a sandy loam. He bent over, then rose quickly. He had come upon the Indian's trail. Cautiously he moved forward, stopping every moment to listen. In all the close pursuits of his maturer years he had never been a victim of that most cunning of Indian tricks, an ambush. He relied solely on his ear to learn if foes were close by. The wild creatures of the forest were his informants. As soon as he heard any change in their twittering, humming or playing—whichever way they manifested their joy or fear of life—he became as hard to see, as difficult to hear as a creeping snake.

The Delaware's trail led to a rocky ridge and there disappeared. Wetzel made no effort to find the chief's footprints on the flinty ground, but halted a moment and studied the ridge, the lay of the land around, a ravine on one side, and a dark impenetrable forest on the other. He was calculating his chances of finding the Delaware's trail far on the other side. Indian woodcraft, subtle, wonderful as it may be, is limited to each Indian's ability. Savages, as well as other men, were born unequal. One might leave a faint trail through the forest, while another could be readily traced, and a third, more cunning and skillful than his fellows, have flown under the shady trees, for all the trail he left. But redmen followed the same methods of woodcraft from tradition, as Wetzel had learned after long years of study and experience.

And now, satisfied that he had divined the Delaware's intention, he slipped down the bank of the ravine, and once more broke into a run. He leaped lightly, sure-footed as a goat, from stone to stone, over fallen logs, and the brawling brook. At every turn of the ravine, at every open place, he stopped to listen.

Arriving on the other side of the ridge, he left the ravine and passed along the edge of the rising ground. He listened to the birds, and searched the grass and leaves. He found not the slightest indication of a trail where he had expected to find one. He retraced his steps patiently, carefully, scrutinizing every inch of the ground. But it was all in vain. Wingenund had begun to show his savage cunning. In his warrior days for long years no chief could rival him. His boast had always been that, when Wingenund sought to elude his pursuers, his trail faded among the moss and the ferns.

Wetzel, calm, patient, resourceful, deliberated a moment. The Delaware had not crossed this rocky ridge. He had been cunning enough to make his pursuer think such was his intention. The hunter hurried to the eastern end of the ridge for no other reason than apparently that course was the one the savage had the least reason to take. He advanced hurriedly because every moment was precious. Not a crushed blade of grass, a brushed leaf, an overturned pebble nor a snapped twig did he find. He saw that he was getting near to the side of the ridge where the Delaware's trail had abruptly ended. Ah! what was there? A twisted bit of fern, with the drops of dew brushed off. Bending beside the fern, Wetzel examined the grass; it was not crushed. A small plant with triangular leaves of dark green, lay under the fern. Breaking off one of these leaves, he exposed its lower side to the light. The fine, silvery hair of fuzz that grew upon the leaf had been crushed. Wetzel knew that an Indian could tread so softly as not to break the springy grass blades, but the under side of one of these leaves, if a man steps on it, always betrays his passage through the woods. To keen eyes this leaf showed that it had been bruised by a soft moccasin. Wetzel had located the trail, but was still ignorant of its direction. Slowly he traced the shaken ferns and bruised leaves down over the side of the ridge, and at last, near a stone, he found a moccasin-print in the moss. It pointed east. The Delaware was traveling in exactly the opposite direction to that which he should be going. He was, moreover, exercising wonderful sagacity in hiding his trail. This, however, did not trouble Wetzel, for if it took him a long time to find the trail, certainly the Delaware had expended as much, or more, in choosing hard ground, logs or rocks on which to tread.

Wetzel soon realized that his own cunning was matched. He trusted no more to his intuitive knowledge, but stuck close to the trail, as a hungry wolf holds to the scent of his quarry.

The Delaware trail led over logs, stones and hard-baked ground, up stony ravines and over cliffs. The wily chief used all of his old skill; he walked backward over moss and sand where his footprints showed plainly; he leaped wide fissures in stony ravines, and then jumped back again; he let himself down over ledges by branches; he crossed creeks and gorges by swinging himself into trees and climbing from one to another; he waded brooks where he found hard bottom, and avoided swampy, soft ground.

With dogged persistence and tenacity of purpose Wetzel stuck to this gradually fading trail. Every additional rod he was forced to go more slowly, and take more time in order to find any sign of his enemy's passage through the forests. One thing struck him forcibly. Wingenund was gradually circling to the southwest, a course that took him farther and farther from the Delaware encampment.

Slowly it dawned upon Wetzel that the chief could hardly have any reason for taking this circling course save that of pride and savage joy in misleading, in fooling the foe of the Delawares, in deliberately showing Deathwind that there was one Indian who could laugh at and loose him in the forests. To Wetzel this was bitter as gall. To be led a wild goose chase! His fierce heart boiled with fury. His dark, keen eyes sought the grass and moss with terrible earnestness. Yet in spite of the anger that increased to the white heat of passion, he became aware of some strange sensation creeping upon him. He remembered that the Delawares had offered his life. Slowly, like a shadow, Wetzel passed up and down the ridges, through the brown and yellow aisles of the forest, over the babbling brooks, out upon the golden-flecked fields—always close on the trail.

At last in an open part of the forest, where a fire had once swept away the brush and smaller timber, Wetzel came upon the spot where the Delaware's trail ended.

There in the soft, black ground was a moccasin-print. The forest was not dense; there was plenty of light; no logs, stones or trees were near, and yet over all that glade no further evidence of the Indian's trail was visible.

It faded there as the great chief had boasted it would.

Wetzel searched the burnt ground; he crawled on his hands and knees; again and again he went over the surroundings. The fact that one moccasin-print pointed west and the other east, showed that the Delaware had turned in his tracks, was the most baffling thing that had ever crossed the hunter in all his wild wanderings.

For the first time in many years he had failed. He took his defeat hard, because he had been successful for so long he thought himself almost infallible, and because the failure lost him the opportunity to kill his great foe. In his passion he cursed himself for being so weak as to let the prayer of a woman turn him from his life's purpose.

With bowed head and slow, dragging steps he made his way westward. The land was strange to him, but he knew he was going toward familiar ground. For a time he walked quietly, all the time the fierce fever in his veins slowly abating. Calm he always was, except when that unnatural lust for Indians' blood overcame him.

On the summit of a high ridge he looked around to ascertain his bearings. He was surprised to find he had traveled in a circle. A mile or so below him arose the great oak tree which he recognized as the landmark of Beautiful Spring. He found himself standing on the hill, under the very dead tree to which he had directed Girty's attention a few hours previous.

With the idea that he would return to the spring to scalp the dead Indians, he went directly toward the big oak tree. Once out of the forest a wide plain lay between him and the wooded knoll which marked the glade of Beautiful Spring. He crossed this stretch of verdant meadow-land, and entered the copse.

Suddenly he halted. His keen sense of the usual harmony of the forest, with its innumerable quiet sounds, had received a severe shock. He sank into the tall weeds and listened. Then he crawled a little farther. Doubt became certainty. A single note of an oriole warned him, and it needed not the quick notes of a catbird to tell him that near at hand, somewhere, was human life.

Once more Wetzel became a tiger. The hot blood leaped from his heart, firing all his veins and nerves. But calmly noiseless, certain, cold, deadly as a snake he began the familiar crawling method of stalking his game.

On, on under the briars and thickets, across the hollows full of yellow leaves, up over stony patches of ground to the fern-covered cliff overhanging the glade he glided—lithe, sinuous, a tiger in movement and in heart.

He parted the long, graceful ferns and gazed with glittering eyes down into the beautiful glade.

He saw not the shining spring nor the purple moss, nor the ghastly white bones—all that the buzzards had left of the dead—nor anything, save a solitary Indian standing erect in the glade.

There, within range of his rifle, was his great Indian foe, Wingenund.

Wetzel sank back into the ferns to still the furious exultations which almost consumed him during the moment when he marked his victim. He lay there breathing hard, gripping tightly his rifle, slowly mastering the passion that alone of all things might render his aim futile.

For him it was the third great moment of his life, the last of three moments in which the Indian's life had belonged to him. Once before he had seen that dark, powerful face over the sights of his rifle, and he could not shoot because his one shot must be for another. Again had that lofty, haughty figure stood before him, calm, disdainful, arrogant, and he yielded to a woman's prayer.

The Delaware's life was his to take, and he swore he would have it! He trembled in the ecstasy of his triumphant passion; his great muscles rippled and quivered, for the moment was entirely beyond his control. Then his passion calmed. Such power for vengeance had he that he could almost still the very beats of his heart to make sure and deadly his fatal aim. Slowly he raised himself; his eyes of cold fire glittered; slowly he raised the black rifle.

Wingenund stood erect in his old, grand pose, with folded arms, but his eyes, instead of being fixed on the distant hills, were lowered to the ground.

An Indian girl, cold as marble, lay at his feet. Her garments were wet, and clung to her slender form. Her sad face was frozen into an eternal rigidity.

By her side was a newly dug grave.

The bead on the front sight of the rifle had hardly covered the chief's dark face when Wetzel's eye took in these other details. He had been so absorbed in his purpose that he did not dream of the Delaware's reason for returning to the Beautiful Spring.

Slowly Wetzel's forefinger stiffened; slowly he lowered the black rifle.

Wingenund had returned to bury Whispering Winds.

Wetzel's teeth clenched, an awful struggle tore his heart. Slowly the rifle rose, wavered and fell. It rose again, wavered and fell. Something terrible was wrong with him; something awful was awakening in his soul.

Wingenund had not made a fool of him. The Delaware had led him a long chase, had given him the slip in the forest, not to boast of it, but to hurry back to give his daughter Christian burial.

Wingenund was a Christian!

Had he not been, once having cast his daughter from him, he would never have looked upon her face again.

Wingenund was true to his race, but he was a Christian.

Suddenly Wetzel's terrible temptation, his heart-racking struggle ceased. He lowered the long, black rifle. He took one last look at the chieftain's dark, powerful face.

Then the Avenger fled like a shadow through the forest.

CHAPTER XXX.

It was late afternoon at Fort Henry. The ruddy sun had already sunk behind the wooded hill, and the long shadows of the trees lengthened on the green square in front of the fort.

Colonel Zane stood in his doorway watching the river with eager eyes. A few minutes before a man had appeared on the bank of the island and hailed. The colonel had sent his brother Jonathan to learn what was wanted. The latter had already reached the other shore in his flatboat, and presently the little boat put out again with the stranger seated at the stern.

"I thought, perhaps, it might be Wetzel," mused the colonel, "though I never knew of Lew's wanting a boat."

Jonathan brought the man across the river, and up the winding path to where Colonel Zane was waiting.

"Hello! It's young Christy!" exclaimed the colonel, jumping off the steps, and cordially extending his hand. "Glad to see you! Where's Williamson. How did you happen over here?"

"Captain Williamson and his men will make the river eight or ten miles above," answered Christy. "I came across to inquire about the young people who left the Village of Peace. Was glad to learn from Jonathan they got out all right."

"Yes, indeed, we're all glad. Come and sit down. Of course you'll stay over night. You look tired and worn. Well, no wonder, when you saw that Moravian massacre. You must tell me about it. I saw Sam Brady yesterday, and he spoke of seeing you over there. Sam told me a good deal. Ah! here's Jim now."

The young missionary came out of the open door, and the two young men greeted each other warmly.

"How is she?" asked Christy, when the first greetings had been exchanged.

"Nell's just beginning to get over the shock. She'll be glad to see you."

"Jonathan tells me you got married just before Girty came up with you at

Beautiful Spring."

"Yes; it is true. In fact, the whole wonderful story is true, yet I cannot believe as yet. You look thin and haggard. When we last met you were well."

"That awful time pulled me down. I was an unwilling spectator of all that horrible massacre, and shall never get over it. I can still see the fiendish savages running about with the reeking scalps of their own people. I actually counted the bodies of forty-nine grown Christians and twenty-seven children. An hour after you left us the church was in ashes, and the next day I saw the burned bodies. Oh! the sickening horror of the scene! It haunts me! That monster Jim Girty killed fourteen Christians with his sledge-hammer."

"Did you hear of his death?" asked Colonel Zane.

"Yes, and a fitting end it was to the frontier 'Skull and Cross-bones'."

"It was like Wetzel to think of such a vengeance."

"Has Wetzel come in since?"

"No. Jonathan says he went after Wingenund, and there's no telling when he'll return."

"I hoped he would spare the Delaware."

"Wetzel spare an Indian!"

"But the chief was a friend. He surely saved the girl."

"I am sorry, too, because Wingenund was a fine Indian. But Wetzel is implacable."

"Here's Nell, and Mrs. Clarke too. Come out, both of you," cried Jim.

Nell appeared in the doorway with Colonel Zane's sister. The two girls came down the steps and greeted the young man. The bride's sweet face was white and thin, and there was a shadow in her eyes.

"I am so glad you got safely away from—from there," said Christy, earnestly.

"Tell me of Benny?" asked Nell, speaking softly.

"Oh, yes, I forgot. Why, Benny is safe and well. He was the only Christian Indian to escape the Christian massacre. Heckewelder hid him until it was all over. He is going to have the lad educated."

"Thank Heaven!" murmured Nell.

"And the missionaries?" inquired Jim, earnestly.

"Were all well when I left, except, of course, Young. He was dying. The others will remain out there, and try to get another hold, but I fear it's impossible."

"It is impossible, not because the Indian does not want Christianity, but because such white men as the Girty's rule. The beautiful Village of Peace owes its ruin to the renegades," said Colonel Zane impressively.

"Captain Williamson could have prevented the massacre," remarked

Jim.

"Possibly. It was a bad place for him, and I think he was wrong not to try," declared the colonel.

"Hullo!" cried Jonathan Zane, getting up from the steps where he sat listening to the conversation.

A familiar soft-moccasined footfall sounded on the path. All turned to see Wetzel come slowly toward them. His buckskin hunting costume was ragged and worn. He looked tired and weary, but the dark eyes were calm.

It was the Wetzel whom they all loved.

They greeted him warmly. Nell gave him her hands, and smiled up at him.

"I'm so glad you've come home safe," she said.

"Safe an' sound, lass, an' glad to find you well," answered the hunter, as he leaned on his long rifle, looking from Nell to Colonel Zane's sister. "Betty, I allus gave you first place among border lasses, but here's one as could run you most any kind of a race," he said, with the rare smile which so warmly lighted his dark, stern face.

"Lew Wetzel making compliments! Well, of all things!" exclaimed the colonel's sister.

Jonathan Zane stood closely scanning Wetzel's features. Colonel Zane, observing his brother's close scrutiny of the hunter, guessed the cause, and said:

"Lew, tell us, did you see Wingenund over the sights of your rifle?"

"Yes," answered the hunter simply.

A chill seemed to strike the hearts of the listeners. That simple answer, coming from Wetzel, meant so much. Nell bowed her head sadly. Jim turned away biting his lip. Christy looked across the valley. Colonel Zane bent over and picked up some pebbles which he threw hard at the cabin wall. Jonathan Zane abruptly left the group, and went into the house.

But the colonel's sister fixed her large, black eyes on Wetzel's face.

"Well?" she asked, and her voice rang.

Wetzel was silent for a moment. He met her eyes with that old, inscrutable smile in his own. A slight shade flitted across his face.

"Betty, I missed him," he said, calmly, and, shouldering his long rifle, he strode away.

* * *

Nell and Jim walked along the bluff above the river. Twilight was deepening. The red glow in the west was slowly darkening behind the boldly defined hills.

"So it's all settled, Jim, that we stay here," said Nell.

"Yes, dear. Colonel Zane has offered me work, and a church besides. We are very fortunate, and should be contented. I am happy because you're my wife, and yet I am sad when I think of—him. Poor Joe!"

"Don't you ever think we—we wronged him?" whispered Nell.

"No, he wished it. I think he knew how he would end. No, we did not wrong him; we loved him."

"Yes, I loved him—I loved you both," said Nell softly.

"Then let us always think of him as he would have wished."

"Think of him? Think of Joe? I shall never forget. In winter, spring and summer I shall remember him, but always most in autumn. For I shall see that beautiful glade with its gorgeous color and the dark, shaded spring where he lies asleep."

* * *

The years rolled by with their changing seasons; every autumn the golden flowers bloomed richly, and the colored leaves fell softly upon the amber moss in the glade of Beautiful Spring.

The Indians camped there no more; they shunned the glade and called it the Haunted Spring. They said the spirit of a white dog ran there at night, and the Wind-of-Death mourned over the lonely spot.

At long intervals an Indian chief of lofty frame and dark, powerful face stalked into the glade to stand for many moments silent and motionless.

And sometimes at twilight when the red glow of the sun had faded to gray, a stalwart hunter slipped like a shadow out of the thicket, and leaned upon a long, black rifle while he gazed sadly into the dark spring, and listened to the sad murmur of the waterfall. The twilight deepened while he stood motionless. The leaves fell into the water with a soft splash, a whippoorwill caroled his melancholy song.

From the gloom of the forest came a low sigh which swelled thrillingly upon the quiet air, and then died away like the wailing of the night wind.

Quiet reigned once more over the dark, murky grave of the boy who gave his love and his life to the wilderness.

The Last Trail

CHAPTER I.

Twilight of a certain summer day, many years ago, shaded softly down over the wild Ohio valley bringing keen anxiety to a traveler on the lonely river trail. He had expected to reach Fort Henry with his party on this night, thus putting a welcome end to the long, rough, hazardous journey through the wilderness; but the swift, on-coming dusk made it imperative to halt. The narrow, forest-skirted trail, difficult to follow in broad daylight, apparently led into gloomy aisles in the woods. His guide had abandoned him that morning, making excuse that his services were no longer needed; his teamster was new to the frontier, and, altogether, the situation caused him much uneasiness.

"I wouldn't so much mind another night in camp, if the guide had not left us," he said in a low tone to the teamster.

That worthy shook his shaggy head, and growled while he began unhitching the horses.

"Uncle," said a young man, who had clambered out from the wagon, "we must be within a few miles of Fort Henry."

"How d'ye know we're near the fort?" interrupted the teamster, "or safe, either, fer thet matter? I don't know this country."

"The guide assured me we could easily make Fort Henry by sundown."

"Thet guide! I tell ye, Mr. Sheppard——"

"Not so loud. Do not alarm my daughter," cautioned the man who had been called Sheppard.

"Did ye notice anythin' queer about thet guide?" asked the teamster, lowering his voice. "Did ye see how oneasy he was last night? Did it strike ye he left us in a hurry, kind of excited like, in spite of his offhand manner?"

"Yes, he acted odd, or so it seemed to me," replied Sheppard. "How about you, Will?"

"Now that I think of it, I believe he was queer. He behaved like a man who expected somebody, or feared something might happen. I fancied, however, that it was simply the manner of a woodsman."

"Wal, I hev my opinion," said the teamster, in a gruff whisper. "Ye was in a hurry to be a-goin', an' wouldn't take no advice. The fur-trader at Fort Pitt didn't give this guide Jenks no good send off. Said he wasn't well-known round Pitt, 'cept he could handle a knife some."

"What is your opinion?" asked Sheppard, as the teamster paused.

"Wal, the valley below Pitt is full of renegades, outlaws an' hoss-thieves. The redskins ain't so bad as they used to be, but these white fellers are wusser'n ever. This guide Jenks might be in with them, that's all. Mebbe I'm wrong. I hope so. The way he left us looks bad."

"We won't borrow trouble. If we have come all this way without seeing either Indian or outlaw—in fact, without incident—I feel certain we can perform the remainder of the journey in safety." Then Mr. Sheppard raised his voice. "Here, Helen, you lazy girl, come out of that wagon. We want some supper. Will, you gather some firewood, and we'll soon give this gloomy little glen a more cheerful aspect."

As Mr. Sheppard turned toward the canvas-covered wagon a girl leaped lightly down beside him. She was nearly as tall as he.

"Is this Fort Henry?" she asked, cheerily, beginning to dance around him. "Where's the inn? I'm *so* hungry. How glad I am to get out of that wagon! I'd like to run. Isn't this a lonesome, lovely spot?"

A camp-fire soon crackled with hiss and sputter, and fragrant wood-smoke filled the air. Steaming kettle, and savory steaks of venison cheered the hungry travelers, making them forget for the time the desertion of their guide and the fact that they might be lost. The last glow faded entirely out of the western sky. Night enveloped the forest, and the little glade was a bright spot in the gloom.

The flickering light showed Mr. Sheppard to be a well-preserved old man with gray hair and ruddy, kindly face. The nephew had a boyish, frank expression. The girl was a splendid specimen of womanhood. Her large, laughing eyes were as dark as the shadows beneath the trees.

Suddenly a quick start on Helen's part interrupted the merry flow of conversation. She sat bolt upright with half-averted face.

"Cousin, what is the matter?" asked Will, quickly.

Helen remained motionless.

"My dear," said Mr. Sheppard sharply.

"I heard a footstep," she whispered, pointing with trembling finger toward the impenetrable blackness beyond the camp-fire.

All could hear a soft patter on the leaves. Then distinct footfalls broke the silence.

The tired teamster raised his shaggy head and glanced fearfully around the glade. Mr. Sheppard and Will gazed doubtfully toward the foliage; but Helen did not change her position. The travelers appeared stricken by the silence and solitude of the place. The faint hum of insects, and the low moan of the night wind, seemed accentuated by the almost painful stillness.

"A panther, most likely," suggested Sheppard, in a voice which he intended should be reassuring. "I saw one to-day slinking along the trail."

"I'd better get my gun from the wagon," said Will.

"How dark and wild it is here!" exclaimed Helen nervously. "I believe I was frightened. Perhaps I fancied it—there! Again—listen. Ah!"

Two tall figures emerged from the darkness into the circle of light, and with swift, supple steps gained the camp-fire before any of the travelers had time to move. They were Indians, and the brandishing of their tomahawks proclaimed that they were hostile.

"Ugh!" grunted the taller savage, as he looked down upon the defenseless, frightened group.

As the menacing figures stood in the glare of the fire gazing at the party with shifty eyes, they presented a frightful appearance. Fierce lineaments, all the more so because of bars of paint, the hideous, shaven heads adorned with tufts of hair holding a single feather, sinewy, copper-colored limbs suggestive of action and endurance, the general aspect of untamed ferocity, appalled the travelers and chilled their blood.

Grunts and chuckles manifested the satisfaction with which the Indians fell upon the half-finished supper. They caused it to vanish with astonishing celerity, and resembled wolves rather than human beings in their greediness.

Helen looked timidly around as if hoping to see those who would aid, and the savages regarded her with ill humor. A movement on the part of any member of the group caused muscular hands to steal toward the tomahawks.

Suddenly the larger savage clutched his companion's knee. Then lifting his hatchet, shook it with a significant gesture in Sheppard's face, at the same time putting a finger on his lips to enjoin silence. Both Indians became statuesque in their immobility. They crouched in an attitude of listening, with heads bent on one side, nostrils dilated, and mouths open.

One, two, three moments passed. The silence of the forest appeared to be unbroken; but ears as keen as those of a deer had detected some sound. The larger savage dropped noiselessly to the ground, where he lay stretched out with his ear to the ground. The other remained immovable; only his beady eyes gave signs of life, and these covered every point.

Finally the big savage rose silently, pointed down the dark trail, and strode out of the circle of light. His companion followed close at his heels. The two disappeared in the black shadows like specters, as silently as they had come.

"Well!" breathed Helen.

"I am immensely relieved!" exclaimed Will.

"What do you make of such strange behavior?" Sheppard asked of the teamster.

"I'spect they got wind of somebody; most likely thet guide, an'll be back again. If they ain't, it's because they got switched off by some signs or tokens, skeered, perhaps, by the scent of the wind."

Hardly had he ceased speaking when again the circle of light was invaded by stalking forms.

"I thought so! Here comes the skulkin' varmints," whispered the teamster.

But he was wrong. A deep, calm voice spoke the single word: "Friends."

Two men in the brown garb of woodsmen approached. One approached the travelers; the other remained in the background, leaning upon a long, black rifle.

Thus exposed to the glare of the flames, the foremost woodsman presented a singularly picturesque figure. His costume was the fringed buckskins of the border. Fully six feet tall, this lithe-limbed young giant had something of the wild, free grace of the Indian in his posture.

He surveyed the wondering travelers with dark, grave eyes.

"Did the reddys do any mischief?" he asked.

"No, they didn't harm us," replied Sheppard. "They ate our supper, and slipped off into the woods without so much as touching one of us. But, indeed, sir, we are mighty glad to see you."

Will echoed this sentiment, and Helen's big eyes were fastened upon the stranger in welcome and wonder.

"We saw your fire blazin' through the twilight, an' came up just in time to see the Injuns make off."

"Might they not hide in the bushes and shoot us?" asked Will, who had listened to many a border story at Fort Pitt. "It seems as if we'd make good targets in this light."

The gravity of the woodsman's face relaxed.

"You will pursue them?" asked Helen.

"They've melted into the night-shadows long ago," he replied. "Who was your guide?"

"I hired him at Fort Pitt. He left us suddenly this morning. A big man, with black beard and bushy eyebrows. A bit of his ear had been shot or cut out," Sheppard replied.

"Jenks, one of Bing Legget's border-hawks."

"You have his name right. And who may Bing Legget be?"

"He's an outlaw. Jenks has been tryin' to lead you into a trap. Likely he expected those Injuns to show up a day or two ago. Somethin' went wrong with the plan, I reckon. Mebbe he was waitin' for five Shawnees, an' mebbe he'll never see three of 'em again."

Something suggestive, cold, and grim, in the last words did not escape the listeners.

"How far are we from Fort Henry?" asked Sheppard.

"Eighteen miles as a crow flies; longer by trail."

"Treachery!" exclaimed the old man. "We were no more than that this morning. It is indeed fortunate that you found us. I take it you are from Fort Henry, and will guide us there? I am an old friend of Colonel Zane's. He will appreciate any kindness you may show us. Of course you know him?"

"I am Jonathan Zane."

Sheppard suddenly realized that he was facing the most celebrated scout on the border. In Revolutionary times Zane's fame had extended even to the far Atlantic Colonies.

"And your companion?" asked Sheppard with keen interest. He guessed what might be told. Border lore coupled Jonathan Zane with a strange and terrible character, a border Nemesis, a mysterious, shadowy, elusive man, whom few pioneers ever saw, but of whom all knew.

"Wetzel," answered Zane.

With one accord the travelers gazed curiously at Zane's silent companion. In the dim background of the glow cast by the fire, he stood a gigantic figure, dark, quiet, and yet with something intangible in his shadowy outline.

Suddenly he appeared to merge into the gloom as if he really were a phantom. A warning, "Hist!" came from the bushes.

With one swift kick Zane scattered the camp-fire.

The travelers waited with bated breaths. They could hear nothing save the beating of their own hearts; they could not even see each other.

"Better go to sleep," came in Zane's calm voice. What a relief it was! "We'll keep watch, an' at daybreak guide you to Fort Henry."

CHAPTER II.

Colonel Zane, a rugged, stalwart pioneer, with a strong, dark face, sat listening to his old friend's dramatic story. At its close a genial smile twinkled in his fine dark eyes.

"Well, well, Sheppard, no doubt it was a thrilling adventure to you," he said. "It might have been a little more interesting, and doubtless would, had I not sent Wetzel and Jonathan to look you up."

"You did? How on earth did you know I was on the border? I counted much on the surprise I should give you."

"My Indian runners leave Fort Pitt ahead of any travelers, and acquaint me with particulars."

"I remembered a fleet-looking Indian who seemed to be asking for information about us, when we arrived at Fort Pitt. I am sorry I did not take the fur-trader's advice in regard to the guide. But I was in such a hurry to come, and didn't feel able to bear the expense of a raft or boat that we might come by river. My nephew brought considerable gold, and I all my earthly possessions."

"All's well that ends well," replied Colonel Zane cheerily. "But we must thank Providence that Wetzel and Jonathan came up in the nick of time."

"Indeed, yes. I'm not likely to forget those fierce savages. How they slipped off into the darkness! I wonder if Wetzel pursued them? He disappeared last night, and we did not see him again. In fact we hardly had a fair look at him. I question if I should recognize him now, unless by his great stature."

"He was ahead of Jonathan on the trail. That is Wetzel's way. In times of danger he is seldom seen, yet is always near. But come, let us go out and look around. I am running up a log cabin which will come in handy for you."

They passed out into the shade of pine and maples. A winding path led down a gentle slope. On the hillside under a spreading tree a throng of bearded pioneers, clad in faded buckskins and wearing white-ringed coonskin caps, were erecting a log cabin.

"Life here on the border is keen, hard, invigorating," said Colonel Zane. "I tell you, George Sheppard, in spite of your gray hair and your pretty daughter, you have come out West because you want to live among men who do things."

"Colonel, I won't gainsay I've still got hot blood," replied Sheppard; "but I came to Fort Henry for land. My old home in Williamsburg has fallen into ruin together with the fortunes of my family. I brought my daughter and my nephew because I wanted them to take root in new soil."

"Well, George, right glad we are to have you. Where are your sons? I remember them, though 'tis sixteen long years since I left old Williamsburg."

"Gone. The Revolution took my sons. Helen is the last of the family."

"Well, well, indeed that's hard. Independence has cost you colonists as big a price as border-freedom has us pioneers. Come, old friend, forget the past. A new life begins for you here, and it will be one which gives you much. See, up goes a cabin; that will soon be your home."

Sheppard's eye marked the sturdy pioneers and a fast diminishing pile of white-oak logs.

"Ho-heave!" cried a brawny foreman.

A dozen stout shoulders sagged beneath a well-trimmed log.

"Ho-heave!" yelled the foreman.

"See, up she goes," cried the colonel, "and to-morrow night she'll shed rain."

They walked down a sandy lane bounded on the right by a wide, green clearing, and on the left by a line of chestnuts and maples, outposts of the thick forests beyond.

"Yours is a fine site for a house," observed Sheppard, taking in the clean-trimmed field that extended up the hillside, a brook that splashed clear and noisy over the stones to tarry in a little grass-bound lake which forced water through half-hollowed logs into a spring house.

"I think so; this is the fourth time I've put up a' cabin on this land," replied the colonel.

"How's that?"

"The redskins are keen to burn things."

Sheppard laughed at the pioneer's reply. "It's not difficult, Colonel Zane, to understand why Fort Henry has stood all these years, with you as its leader. Certainly the location for your cabin is the finest in the settlement. What a view!"

High upon a bluff overhanging the majestic, slow-winding Ohio, the colonel's cabin afforded a commanding position from which to view the picturesque valley. Sheppard's eye first caught the outline of the huge, bold, time-blackened fort which frowned protectingly over surrounding log-cabins; then he saw the wide-sweeping river with its verdant islands, golden, sandy bars, and willow-bordered shores, while beyond, rolling pastures of wavy grass merging into green forests that swept upward with slow swell until lost in the dim purple of distant mountains.

"Sixteen years ago I came out of the thicket upon yonder bluff, and saw this valley. I was deeply impressed by its beauty, but more by its wonderful promise."

"Were you alone?"

"I and my dog. There had been a few white men before me on the river; but I was the first to see this glorious valley from the bluff. Now, George, I'll let you have a hundred acres of well-cleared land. The soil is so rich you can raise two crops in one season. With some stock, and a few good hands, you'll soon be a busy man."

"I didn't expect so much land; I can't well afford to pay for it."

"Talk to me of payment when the farm yields an income. Is this young nephew of yours strong and willing?"

"He is, and has gold enough to buy a big farm."

"Let him keep his money, and make a comfortable home for some good lass. We marry our young people early out here. And your daughter, George, is she fitted for this hard border life?"

"Never fear for Helen."

"The brunt of this pioneer work falls on our women. God bless them, how heroic they've been! The life here is rough for a man, let alone a woman. But it is a man's game. We need girls, girls who will bear strong men. Yet I am always saddened when I see one come out on the border."

"I think I knew what I was bringing Helen to, and she didn't flinch," said Sheppard, somewhat surprised at the tone in which the colonel spoke.

"No one knows until he has lived on the border. Well, well, all this is discouraging to you. Ah! here is Miss Helen with my sister."

The colonel's fine, dark face lost its sternness, and brightened with a smile.

"I hope you rested well after your long ride."

"I am seldom tired, and I have been made most comfortable. I thank you and your sister," replied the girl, giving Colonel Zane her hand, and including both him and his sister in her grateful glance.

The colonel's sister was a slender, handsome young woman, whose dark beauty showed to most effective advantage by the contrast with her companion's fair skin, golden hair, and blue eyes.

Beautiful as was Helen Sheppard, it was her eyes that held Colonel Zane irresistibly. They were unusually large, of a dark purple-blue that changed, shaded, shadowed with her every thought.

"Come, let us walk," Colonel Zane said abruptly, and, with Mr. Sheppard, followed the girls down the path. He escorted them to the fort, showed a long room with little squares cut in the rough-hewn logs, many bullet holes, fire-charred timbers, and dark stains, terribly suggestive of the pain and heroism which the defense of that rude structure had cost.

Under Helen's eager questioning Colonel Zane yielded to his weakness for story-telling, and recited the history of the last siege of Fort Henry; how the renegade Girty swooped down upon the settlement with hundreds of Indians and British soldiers; how for three days of whistling bullets, flaming arrows, screeching demons, fire, smoke, and attack following attack, the brave defenders stood at their posts, there to die before yielding.

"Grand!" breathed Helen, and her eyes glowed. "It was then Betty Zane ran with the powder? Oh! I've heard the story."

"Let my sister tell you of that," said the colonel, smiling.

"You! Was it you?" And Helen's eyes glowed brighter with the light of youth's glory in great deeds.

"My sister has been wedded and widowed since then," said Colonel Zane, reading in Helen's earnest scrutiny of his sister's calm, sad face a wonder if this quiet woman could be the fearless and famed Elizabeth Zane.

Impulsively Helen's hand closed softly over her companion's. Out of the girlish sympathetic action a warm friendship was born.

"I imagine things do happen here," said Mr. Sheppard, hoping to hear more from Colonel Zane.

The colonel smiled grimly.

"Every summer during fifteen years has been a bloody one on the border. The sieges of Fort Henry, and Crawford's defeat, the biggest things we ever knew out here, are matters of history; of course you are familiar with them. But the numberless Indian forays and attacks, the women who have been carried into captivity by renegades, the murdered farmers, in fact, ceaseless war never long directed at any point, but carried on the entire length of the river, are matters known only to the pioneers. Within five miles of Fort Henry I can show you where the laurel bushes grow three feet high over the ashes of two settlements, and many a clearing where some unfortunate pioneer had staked his claim and thrown up a log cabin, only to die fighting for his wife and children. Between here and Fort Pitt there is only one settlement, Yellow Creek, and most of its inhabitants are survivors of abandoned villages farther up the river. Last summer we had the Moravian Massacre, the blackest, most inhuman deed ever committed. Since then Simon Girty and his bloody redskins have lain low."

"You must always have had a big force," said Sheppard.

"We've managed always to be strong enough, though there never were a large number of men here. During the last siege I had only forty in the fort, counting men, women and boys. But I had pioneers and women who could handle a rifle, and the best bordermen on the frontier."

"Do you make a distinction between pioneers and bordermen?" asked Sheppard.

"Indeed, yes. I am a pioneer; a borderman is an Indian hunter, or scout. For years my cabins housed Andrew Zane, Sam and John McCollock, Bill Metzar, and John and Martin Wetzel, all of whom are dead. Not one saved his scalp. Fort Henry is growing; it has pioneers, rivermen, soldiers, but only two bordermen. Wetzel and Jonathan are the only ones we have left of those great men."

"They must be old," mused Helen, with a dreamy glow still in her eyes.

"Well, Miss Helen, not in years, as you mean. Life here is old in experience; few pioneers, and no bordermen, live to a great age. Wetzel is about forty, and my brother Jonathan still a young man; but both are old in border lore."

Earnestly, as a man who loves his subject, Colonel Zane told his listeners of these two most prominent characters of the border. Sixteen years previously, when but boys in years, they had cast in their lot with his, and journeyed over the Virginian Mountains, Wetzel to devote his life to the vengeful calling he had chosen, and Jonathan to give rein to an adventurous spirit and love of the wilds. By some wonderful chance, by cunning, woodcraft, or daring, both men had lived through the years of border warfare which had brought to a close the careers of all their contemporaries.

For many years Wetzel preferred solitude to companionship; he roamed the wilderness in pursuit of Indians, his life-long foes, and seldom appeared at the settlement except to bring news of an intended raid of the savages. Jonathan also spent much time alone in the woods, or scouting along the river. But of late years a friendship had ripened between the two bordermen. Mutual interest had brought them together on the trail of a noted renegade, and when, after many long days of patient watching and persistent tracking, the outlaw paid an awful penalty for his bloody deeds, these lone and silent men were friends.

Powerful in build, fleet as deer, fearless and tireless, Wetzel's peculiar bloodhound sagacity, ferocity, and implacability, balanced by Jonathan's keen intelligence and judgment caused these bordermen to become the bane of redmen and renegades. Their fame increased with each succeeding summer, until now the people of the settlement looked upon wonderful deeds of strength and of woodcraft as a matter of course, rejoicing in the power and skill with which these men were endowed.

By common consent the pioneers attributed any mysterious deed, from the finding of a fat turkey on a cabin doorstep, to the discovery of a savage scalped and pulled from his ambush near a settler's spring, to Wetzel and Jonathan. All the more did they feel sure of this conclusion because the bordermen never spoke of their deeds. Sometimes a pioneer living on the outskirts of the settlement would be awakened in the morning by a single rifle shot, and on peering out would see a dead Indian lying almost across his doorstep, while beyond, in the dim, gray mist, a tall figure stealing away. Often in the twilight on a summer evening, while fondling his children and enjoying his smoke after a hard day's labor in the fields, this same settler would see the tall, dark figure of Jonathan Zane step noiselessly out of a thicket, and learn that he must take his family and flee at once to the fort for safety. When a settler was murdered, his children carried into captivity by

Indians, and the wife given over to the power of some brutal renegade, tragedies wofully frequent on the border, Wetzel and Jonathan took the trail alone. Many a white woman was returned alive and, sometimes, unharmed to her relatives; more than one maiden lived to be captured, rescued, and returned to her lover, while almost numberless were the bones of brutal redmen lying in the deep and gloomy woods, or bleaching on the plains, silent, ghastly reminders of the stern justice meted out by these two heroes.

"Such are my two bordermen, Miss Sheppard. The fort there, and all these cabins, would be only black ashes, save for them, and as for us, our wives and children—God only knows."

"Haven't they wives and children, too?" asked Helen.

"No," answered Colonel Zane, with his genial smile. "Such joys are not for bordermen."

"Why not? Fine men like them deserve happiness," declared Helen.

"It is necessary we have such," said the colonel simply, "and they cannot be bordermen unless free as the air blows. Wetzel and Jonathan have never had sweethearts. I believe Wetzel loved a lass once; but he was an Indian-killer whose hands were red with blood. He silenced his heart, and kept to his chosen, lonely life. Jonathan does not seem to realize that women exist to charm, to please, to be loved and married. Once we twitted him about his brothers doing their duty by the border, whereupon he flashed out: 'My life is the border's: my sweetheart is the North Star!'"

Helen dreamily watched the dancing, dimpling waves that broke on the stones of the river shore. All unconscious of the powerful impression the colonel's recital had made upon her, she was feeling the greatness of the lives of these bordermen, and the glory it would now be for her to share with others the pride in their protection.

"Say, Sheppard, look here," said Colonel Zane, on the return to his cabin, "that girl of yours has a pair of eyes. I can't forget the way they flashed! They'll cause more trouble here among my garrison than would a swarm of redskins."

"No! You don't mean it! Out here in this wilderness?" queried Sheppard doubtfully.

"Well, I do."

"O Lord! What a time I've had with that girl! There was one man especially, back home, who made our lives miserable. He was rich and well born; but Helen would have none of him. He got around me, old fool that I am! Practically stole what was left of my estate, and gambled it away when Helen said she'd die before giving herself to him. It was partly on his account that I brought her away. Then there were a lot of moon-eyed beggars after her all the time, and she's young and full of fire. I hoped I'd marry her to some farmer out here, and end my days in peace."

"Peace? With eyes like those? Never on this green earth," and Colonel Zane laughed as he slapped his friend on the shoulder. "Don't worry, old fellow. You can't help her having those changing dark-blue eyes any more than you can help being proud of them. They have won me, already, susceptible old backwoodsman! I'll help you with this spirited young lady. I've had experience, Sheppard, and don't you forget it. First, my sister, a Zane all through, which is saying enough. Then as sweet and fiery a little Indian princess as ever stepped in a beaded moccasin, and since, more than one beautiful, impulsive creature. Being in authority, I suppose it's natural that all the work, from keeping the garrison ready against an attack, to straightening out love affairs, should fall upon me. I'll take the care off your shoulders; I'll keep these young dare-devils from killing each other over Miss Helen's favors. I certainly—Hello! There are strangers at the gate. Something's up."

Half a dozen rough-looking men had appeared from round the corner of the cabin, and halted at the gate.

"Bill Elsing, and some of his men from Yellow Creek," said Colonel Zane, as he went toward the group.

"Hullo, Kurnel," was the greeting of the foremost, evidently the leader. "We've lost six head of hosses over our way, an' are out lookin' 'em up."

"The deuce you have! Say, this horse-stealing business is getting interesting. What did you come in for?"

"Wal, we meets Jonathan on the ridge about sunup, an' he sent us back lickety-cut. Said he had two of the hosses corralled, an' mebbe Wetzel could git the others."

"That's strange," replied Colonel Zane thoughtfully.

"'Pears to me Jack and Wetzel hev some redskins treed, an' didn't want us to spile the fun. Mebbe there wasn't scalps enough to go round. Anyway, we come in, an' we'll hang up here to-day."

"Bill, who's doing this horse-stealing?"

"Damn if I know. It's a mighty pert piece of work. I've a mind it's some slick white fellar, with Injuns backin' him."

Helen noted, when she was once more indoors, that Colonel Zane's wife appeared worried. Her usual placid expression was gone. She put off the playful overtures of her two bright boys with unusual indifference, and turned to her husband with anxious questioning as to whether the strangers brought news of Indians. Upon being assured that such was not the case, she looked relieved, and explained to Helen that she had seen armed men come so often to consult the colonel regarding dangerous missions and expeditions, that the sight of a stranger caused her unspeakable dread.

"I am accustomed to danger, yet I can never control my fears for my husband and children," said Mrs. Zane. "The older I grow the more of a coward I am. Oh! this border life is sad for women. Only a little while ago my brother Samuel McColloch was shot and scalped right here on the river bank. He was going to the spring for a bucket of water. I lost another brother in almost the same way. Every day during the summer a husband

and a father fall victim to some murderous Indian. My husband will go in the same way some day. The border claims them all."

"Bessie, you must not show your fears to our new friend. And, Miss Helen, don't believe she's the coward she would make out," said the colonel's sister smilingly.

"Betty is right, Bess, don't frighten her," said Colonel Zane. "I'm afraid I talked too much to-day. But, Miss Helen, you were so interested, and are such a good listener, that I couldn't refrain. Once for all let me say that you will no doubt see stirring life here; but there is little danger of its affecting you. To be sure I think you'll have troubles; but not with Indians or outlaws."

He winked at his wife and sister. At first Helen did not understand his sally, but then she blushed red all over her fair face.

Some time after that, while unpacking her belongings, she heard the clatter of horses' hoofs on the rocky road, accompanied by loud voices. Running to the window, she saw a group of men at the gate.

"Miss Sheppard, will you come out?" called Colonel Zane's sister from the door. "My brother Jonathan has returned."

Helen joined Betty at the door, and looked over her shoulder.

"Wal, Jack, ye got two on 'em, anyways," drawled a voice which she recognized as that of Elsing's.

A man, lithe and supple, slipped from the back of one of the horses, and, giving the halter to Elsing with a single word, turned and entered the gate. Colonel Zane met him there.

"Well, Jonathan, what's up?"

"There's hell to pay," was the reply, and the speaker's voice rang clear and sharp.

Colonel Zane laid his hand on his brother's shoulder, and thus they stood for a moment, singularly alike, and yet the sturdy pioneer was, somehow, far different from the dark-haired borderman.

"I thought we'd trouble in store from the look on your face," said the colonel calmly. "I hope you haven't very bad news on the first day, for our old friends from Virginia."

"Jonathan," cried Betty when he did not answer the colonel. At her call he half turned, and his dark eyes, steady, strained like those of a watching deer, sought his sister's face.

"Betty, old Jake Lane was murdered by horse thieves yesterday, and Mabel Lane is gone."

"Oh!" gasped Betty; but she said nothing more.

Colonel Zane cursed inaudibly.

"You know, Eb, I tried to keep Lane in the settlement for Mabel's sake. But he wanted to work that farm. I believe horse-stealing wasn't as much of an object as the girl. Pretty women are bad for the border, or any other place, I guess. Wetzel has taken the trail, and I came in because I've serious suspicions—I'll explain to you alone."

The borderman bowed gravely to Helen, with a natural grace, and yet a manner that sat awkwardly upon him. The girl, slightly flushed, and somewhat confused by this meeting with the man around whom her romantic imagination had already woven a story, stood in the doorway after giving him a fleeting glance, the fairest, sweetest picture of girlish beauty ever seen.

The men went into the house; but their voices came distinctly through the door.

"Eb, if Bing Legget or Girty ever see that big-eyed lass, they'll have her even if Fort Henry has to be burned, an' in case they do get her, Wetzel an' I'll have taken our last trail."

CHAPTER III.

Supper over, Colonel Zane led his guests to a side porch, where they were soon joined by Mrs. Zane and Betty. The host's two boys, Noah and Sammy, who had preceded them, were now astride the porch-rail and, to judge by their antics, were riding wild Indian mustangs.

"It's quite cool," said Colonel Zane; "but I want you to see the sunset in the valley. A good many of your future neighbors may come over to-night for a word of welcome. It's the border custom."

He was about to seat himself by the side of Mr. Sheppard, on a rustic bench, when a Negro maid appeared in the doorway carrying a smiling, black-eyed baby. Colonel Zane took the child and, holding it aloft, said with fatherly pride:

"This is Rebecca Zane, the first girl baby born to the Zanes, and destined to be the belle of the border."

"May I have her?" asked Helen softly, holding out her arms. She took the child, and placed it upon her knee where its look of solemnity soon changed to one of infantile delight.

"Here come Nell and Jim," said Mrs. Zane, pointing toward the fort.

"Yes, and there comes my brother Silas with his wife, too," added Colonel Zane. "The first couple are James Douns, our young minister, and Nell, his wife. They came out here a year or so ago. James had a brother Joe, the finest young fellow who ever caught the border fever. He was killed by one of the Girtys. His was a wonderful story, and some day you shall hear about the parson and his wife."

"What's the border fever?" asked Mr. Sheppard.

"It's what brought you out here," replied Colonel Zane with a hearty laugh.

Helen gazed with interest at the couple now coming into the yard, and when they gained the porch she saw that the man was big and tall, with a frank, manly bearing, while his wife was a slender little woman with bright, sunny hair, and a sweet, smiling face. They greeted Helen and her father

420

cordially.

Next came Silas Zane, a typical bronzed and bearded pioneer, with his buxom wife. Presently a little group of villagers joined the party. They were rugged men, clad in faded buckskins, and sober-faced women who wore dresses of plain gray linsey. They welcomed the newcomers with simple, homely courtesy. Then six young frontiersmen appeared from around a corner of the cabin, advancing hesitatingly. To Helen they all looked alike, tall, awkward, with brown faces and big hands. When Colonel Zane cheerily cried out to them, they stumbled forward with evident embarrassment, each literally crushing Helen's hand in his horny palm. Afterward they leaned on the rail and stole glances at her.

Soon a large number of villagers were on the porch or in the yard. After paying their respects to Helen and her father they took part in a general conversation. Two or three girls, the latest callers, were surrounded by half a dozen young fellows, and their laughter sounded high above the hum of voices.

Helen gazed upon this company with mingled feelings of relief and pleasure. She had been more concerned regarding the young people with whom her lot might be cast, than the dangers of which others had told. She knew that on the border there was no distinction of rank. Though she came of an old family, and, during her girlhood, had been surrounded by refinement, even luxury, she had accepted cheerfully the reverses of fortune, and was determined to curb the pride which had been hers. It was necessary she should have friends. Warm-hearted, impulsive and loving, she needed to have around her those in whom she could confide. Therefore it was with sincere pleasure she understood how groundless were her fears and knew that if she did not find good, true friends the fault would be her own. She saw at a glance that the colonel's widowed sister was her equal, perhaps her superior, in education and breeding, while Nellie Douns was as well-bred and gracious a little lady as she had ever met. Then, the other girls, too, were charming, with frank wholesomeness and freedom.

Concerning the young men, of whom there were about a dozen, Helen had hardly arrived at a conclusion. She liked the ruggedness, the signs of honest worth which clung to them. Despite her youth, she had been much sought after because of her personal attractions, and had thus added experience to the natural keen intuition all women possess. The glances of several of the men, particularly the bold regard of one Roger Brandt, whom Colonel Zane introduced, she had seen before, and learned to dislike. On the whole, however, she was delighted with the prospect of new friends and future prosperity, and she felt even greater pleasure in the certainty that her father shared her gratification.

Suddenly she became aware that the conversation had ceased. She looked up to see the tall, lithe form of Jonathan Zane as he strode across the porch. She could see that a certain constraint had momentarily fallen upon the company. It was an involuntary acknowledgment of the borderman's presence, of a presence that worked on all alike with a subtle, strong magnetism.

"Ah, Jonathan, come out to see the sunset? It's unusually fine to-night," said Colonel Zane.

With hardly more than a perceptible bow to those present, the borderman took a seat near the rail, and, leaning upon it, directed his gaze westward.

Helen sat so near she could have touched him. She was conscious of the same strange feeling, and impelling sense of power, which had come upon her so strongly at first sight of him. More than that, a lively interest had been aroused in her. This borderman was to her a new and novel character. She was amused at learning that here was a young man absolutely indifferent to the charms of the opposite sex, and although hardly admitting such a thing, she believed it would be possible to win him from his indifference. On raising her eyelids, it was with the unconcern which a woman feigns when suspecting she is being regarded with admiring eyes. But Jonathan Zane might not have known of her presence, for all the attention he paid her. Therefore, having a good opportunity to gaze at this borderman of daring deeds, Helen regarded him closely.

He was clad from head to foot in smooth, soft buckskin which fitted well his powerful frame. Beaded moccasins, leggings bound high above the knees, hunting coat laced and fringed, all had the neat, tidy appearance due to good care. He wore no weapons. His hair fell in a raven mass over his shoulders. His profile was regular, with a long, straight nose, strong chin, and eyes black as night. They were now fixed intently on the valley. The whole face gave an impression of serenity, of calmness.

Helen was wondering if the sad, almost stern, tranquility of that face ever changed, when the baby cooed and held out its chubby little hands. Jonathan's smile, which came quickly, accompanied by a warm light in the eyes, relieved Helen of an unaccountable repugnance she had begun to feel toward the borderman. That smile, brief as a flash, showed his gentle kindness and told that he was not a creature who had set himself apart from human life and love.

As he took little Rebecca, one of his hands touched Helen's. If he had taken heed of the contact, as any ordinary man might well have, she would, perhaps, have thought nothing about it, but because he did not appear to realize that her hand had been almost inclosed in his, she could not help again feeling his singular personality. She saw that this man had absolutely no thought of her. At the moment this did not awaken resentment, for with all her fire and pride she was not vain; but amusement gave place to a respect which came involuntarily.

Little Rebecca presently manifested the faithlessness peculiar to her sex, and had no sooner been taken upon Jonathan's knee than she cried out to go back to Helen.

"Girls are uncommon coy critters," said he, with a grave smile in his eyes. He handed back the child, and once more was absorbed in the setting sun.

Helen looked down the valley to behold the most beautiful spectacle she had ever seen. Between the hills far to the west, the sky flamed with a red and gold light. The sun was poised above the river, and the shimmering waters merged into a ruddy horizon. Long rays of crimson fire crossed the smooth waters. A few purple clouds above caught the refulgence, until aided by the delicate rose and blue space beyond, they became many hued ships sailing on a rainbow sea. Each second saw a gorgeous transformation. Slowly the sun dipped into the golden flood; one by one the clouds changed from crimson to gold, from gold to rose, and then to gray; slowly all the tints faded until, as the sun slipped out of sight, the brilliance gave way to the soft afterglow of warm lights. These in turn slowly toned down into gray twilight.

Helen retired to her room soon afterward, and, being unusually thoughtful, sat down by the window. She reviewed the events of this first day of her new life on the border. Her impressions had been so many, so varied, that she wanted to distinguish them. First she felt glad, with a sweet, warm thankfulness, that her father seemed so happy, so encouraged by the outlook. Breaking old ties had been, she knew, no child's play for him. She realized also that it had been done solely because there had been nothing left to offer her in the old home, and in a new one were hope and possibilities. Then she was relieved at getting away from the attentions of a man whose persistence had been most annoying to her. From thoughts of her father, and the old life, she came to her new friends of the present. She was so grateful for their kindness. She certainly would do all in her power to win and keep their esteem.

Somewhat of a surprise was it to her, that she reserved for Jonathan Zane the last and most prominent place in her meditations. She suddenly asked herself how she regarded this fighting borderman. She recalled her unbounded enthusiasm for the man as Colonel Zane had told of him; then her first glimpse, and her surprise and admiration at the lithe-limbed young giant; then incredulity, amusement, and respect followed in swift order, after which an unaccountable coldness that was almost resentment. Helen was forced to admit that she did not know how to regard him, but surely he was a man, throughout every inch of his superb frame, and one who took life seriously, with neither thought nor time for the opposite sex. And this last brought a blush to her cheek, for she distinctly remembered she had expected, if not admiration, more than passing notice from this hero of the border.

Presently she took a little mirror from a table near where she sat. Holding it to catch the fast-fading light, she studied her face seriously.

"Helen Sheppard, I think on the occasion of your arrival in a new country a little plain talk will be wholesome. Somehow or other, perhaps because of a crowd of idle men back there in the colonies, possibly from your own misguided fancy, you imagined you were fair to look at. It is well to be undeceived."

Scorn spoke in Helen's voice. She was angry because of having been interested in a man, and allowed that interest to betray her into a girlish expectation that he would treat her as all other men had. The mirror, even in the dim light, spoke more truly than she, for it caught the golden tints of her luxuriant hair, the thousand beautiful shadows in her great, dark eyes, the white glory of a face fair as a star, and the swelling outline of neck and shoulders.

With a sudden fiery impetuosity she flung the glass to the floor, where it was broken into several pieces.

"How foolish of me! What a temper I have!" she exclaimed repentantly. "I'm glad I have another glass. Wouldn't Mr. Jonathan Zane, borderman, Indian fighter, hero of a hundred battles and never a sweetheart, be flattered? No, most decidedly he wouldn't. He never looked at me. I don't think I expected that; I'm sure I didn't want it; but still he might have—Oh! what am I thinking, and he a stranger?"

Before Helen lost herself in slumber on that eventful evening, she vowed to ignore the borderman; assured herself that she did not want to see him again, and, rather inconsistently, that she would cure him of his indifference.

* * * * *

When Colonel Zane's guests had retired, and the villagers were gone to their homes, he was free to consult with Jonathan.

"Well, Jack," he said, "I'm ready to hear about the horse thieves."

"Wetzel makes it out the man who's runnin' this hoss-stealin' is located right here in Fort Henry," answered the borderman.

The colonel had lived too long on the frontier to show surprise; he hummed a tune while the genial expression faded slowly from his face.

"Last count there were one hundred and ten men at the fort," he replied thoughtfully. "I know over a hundred, and can trust them. There are some new fellows on the boats, and several strangers hanging round Metzar's."

"'Pears to Lew an' me that this fellar is a slick customer, an' one who's been here long enough to know our hosses an' where we keep them."

"I see. Like Miller, who fooled us all, even Betty, when he stole our powder and then sold us to Girty," rejoined Colonel Zane grimly.

"Exactly, only this fellar is slicker an' more desperate than Miller."

"Right you are, Jack, for the man who is trusted and betrays us, must be desperate. Does he realize what he'll get if we ever find out, or is he underrating us?"

"He knows all right, an' is matchin' his cunnin' against our'n."

"Tell me what you and Wetzel learned."

The borderman proceeded to relate the events that had occurred during a recent tramp in the forest with Wetzel. While returning from a hunt in a swamp several miles over the ridge, back of Fort Henry, they ran across the trail of three Indians. They followed this until darkness set in, when both laid down to rest and wait for the early dawn, that time most propitious for taking the savage by surprise. On resuming the trail they found that other Indians had joined the party they were tracking. To the bordermen this was significant of some unusual activity directed toward the settlement. Unable to learn anything definite from the moccasin traces, they hurried up on the trail to find that the Indians had halted.

Wetzel and Jonathan saw from their covert that the savages had a woman prisoner. A singular feature about it all was that the Indians remained in the same place all day, did not light a camp-fire, and kept a sharp lookout. The bordermen crept up as close as safe, and remained on watch during the day and night.

Early next morning, when the air was fading from black to gray, the silence was broken by the snapping of twigs and a tremor of the ground. The bordermen believed another company of Indians was approaching; but they soon saw it was a single white man leading a number of horses. He departed before daybreak. Wetzel and Jonathan could not get a clear view of him owing to the dim light; but they heard his voice, and afterwards found the imprint of his moccasins. They did, however, recognize the six horses as belonging to settlers in Yellow Creek.

While Jonathan and Wetzel were consulting as to what it was best to do, the party of Indians divided, four going directly west, and the others north. Wetzel immediately took the trail of the larger party with the prisoner and four of the horses. Jonathan caught two of the animals which the Indians had turned loose, and tied them in the forest. He then started after the three Indians who had gone northward.

"Well?" Colonel Zane said impatiently, when Jonathan hesitated in his story.

"One got away," he said reluctantly. "I barked him as he was runnin' like a streak through the bushes, an' judged that he was hard hit. I got the hosses, an' turned back on the trail of the white man."

"Where did it end?"

"In that hard-packed path near the blacksmith shop. An' the fellar steps as light as an Injun."

"He's here, then, sure as you're born. We've lost no horses yet, but last week old Sam heard a noise in the barn, and on going there found Betty's mare out of her stall."

"Some one as knows the lay of the land had been after her," suggested Jonathan.

"You can bet on that. We've got to find him before we lose all the fine horse-flesh we own. Where do these stolen animals go? Indians would steal any kind; but this thief takes only the best."

"I'm to meet Wetzel on the ridge soon, an' then we'll know, for he's goin' to find out where the hosses are taken."

"That'll help some. On the way back you found where the white girl had been taken from. Murdered father, burned cabin, the usual deviltry."

"Exactly."

"Poor Mabel! Do you think this white thief had anything to do with carrying her away?"

"No. Wetzel says that's Bing Legget's work. The Shawnees were members of his gang."

"Well, Jack, what'll I do?"

"Keep quiet an' wait," was the borderman's answer.

Colonel Zane, old pioneer and frontiersman though he was, shuddered as he went to his room. His brother's dark look, and his deadly calmness, were significant.

CHAPTER IV.

To those few who saw Jonathan Zane in the village, it seemed as if he was in his usual quiet and dreamy state. The people were accustomed to his silence, and long since learned that what little time he spent in the settlement was not given to sociability. In the morning he sometimes lay with Colonel Zane's dog, Chief, by the side of a spring under an elm tree, and in the afternoon strolled aimlessly along the river bluff, or on the hillside. At night he sat on his brother's porch smoking a long Indian pipe. Since that day, now a week past, when he had returned with the stolen horses, his movements and habits were precisely what would have been expected of an unsuspicious borderman.

In reality, however, Jonathan was not what he seemed. He knew all that was going on in the settlement. Hardly a bird could have entered the clearing unobserved.

At night, after all the villagers were in bed, he stole cautiously about the stockade, silencing with familiar word the bristling watch-hounds, and went from barn to barn, ending his stealthy tramp at the corral where Colonel Zane kept his thoroughbreds.

But all this scouting by night availed nothing. No unusual event occurred, not even the barking of a dog, a suspicious rustling among the thickets, or whistling of a night-hawk had been heard.

Vainly the borderman strained ears to catch some low night-signal given by waiting Indians to the white traitor within the settlement. By day there was even less to attract the sharp-eyed watcher. The clumsy river boats, half raft, half sawn lumber, drifted down the Ohio on their first and last voyage, discharged their cargoes of grain, liquor, or merchandise, and were broken up. Their crews came back on the long overland journey to Fort Pitt, there to man another craft. The garrison at the fort performed their customary duties; the pioneers tilled the fields; the blacksmith scattered sparks, the wheelwright worked industriously at his bench, and the housewives attended to their many cares. No strangers arrived at Fort Henry. The quiet life of the village was uninterrupted.

Near sunset of a long day Jonathan strolled down the sandy, well-trodden path toward Metzar's inn. He did not drink, and consequently seldom visited the rude, dark, ill-smelling bar-room. When occasion demanded his presence there, he was evidently not welcome. The original owner, a sturdy soldier and pioneer, came to Fort Henry when Colonel Zane founded the settlement, and had been killed during Girty's last attack. His successor, another Metzar, was, according to Jonathan's belief, as bad as the whiskey he dispensed. More than one murder had been committed at the inn; countless fatal knife and tomahawk fights had stained red the hard clay floor; and more than one desperate character had been harbored there. Once Colonel Zane sent Wetzel there to invite a thief and outlaw to quit the settlement, with the not unexpected result that it became necessary the robber be carried out.

Jonathan thought of the bad name the place bore all over the frontier, and wondered if Metzar could tell anything about the horse-thieves. When the borderman bent his tall frame to enter the low-studded door he fancied he saw a dark figure disappear into a room just behind the bar. A roughly-clad, heavily-bearded man turned hastily at the same moment.

"Hullo," he said gruffly.

"H' are you, Metzar. I just dropped in to see if I could make a trade for your sorrel mare," replied Jonathan. Being well aware that the innkeeper would not part with his horse, the borderman had made this announcement as his reason for entering the bar-room.

"Nope, I'll allow you can't," replied Metzar.

As he turned to go, Jonathan's eyes roamed around the bar-room. Several strangers of shiftless aspect bleared at him.

"They wouldn't steal a pumpkin," muttered Jonathan to himself as he left the inn. Then he added suspiciously, "Metzar was talkin' to some one, an' 'peared uneasy. I never liked Metzar. He'll bear watchin'."

The borderman passed on down the path thinking of what he had heard against Metzar. The colonel had said that the man was prosperous for an innkeeper who took pelts, grain or meat in exchange for rum. The village gossips disliked him because he was unmarried, taciturn, and did not care for their company. Jonathan reflected also on the fact that Indians were frequently coming to the inn, and this made him distrustful of the proprietor. It was true that Colonel Zane had red-skinned visitors, but there was always good reason for their coming. Jonathan had seen, during the Revolution, more than one trusted man proven to be a traitor, and the conviction settled upon him that some quiet scouting would show up the innkeeper as aiding the horse-thieves if not actually in league with them.

"Good evening, Jonathan Zane."

This greeting in a woman's clear voice brought Jonathan out from his reveries. He glanced up to see Helen Sheppard standing in the doorway of her father's cabin.

"Evenin', miss," he said with a bow, and would have passed on.

"Wait," she cried, and stepped out of the door.

He waited by the gate with a manner which showed that such a summons was novel to him.

Helen, piqued at his curt greeting, had asked him to wait without any idea of what she would say. Coming slowly down the path she felt again a subtle awe of this borderman. Regretting her impulsiveness, she lost confidence.

Gaining the gate she looked up intending to speak; but was unable to do so as she saw how cold and grave was his face, and how piercing were his eyes. She flushed slightly, and then, conscious of an embarrassment new and strange to her, blushed rosy red, making, as it seemed to her, a stupid remark about the sunset. When he took her words literally, and said the sunset was fine, she felt guilty of deceitfulness. Whatever Helen's faults, and they were many, she was honest, and because of not having looked at the sunset, but only wanting him to see her as did other men, the innocent ruse suddenly appeared mean and trifling.

Then, with a woman's quick intuition, she understood that coquetries were lost on this borderman, and, with a smile, got the better of her embarrassment and humiliation by telling the truth.

"I wanted to ask a favor of you, and I'm a little afraid."

She spoke with girlish shyness, which increased as he stared at her.

"Why—why do you look at me so?"

"There's a lake over yonder which the Shawnees say is haunted by a woman they killed," he replied quietly. "You'd do for her spirit, so white an' beautiful in the silver moonlight."

"So my white dress makes me look ghostly," she answered lightly, though deeply conscious of surprise and pleasure at such an unexpected reply from him. This borderman might be full of surprises. "Such a time as I had bringing my dresses out here! I don't know when I can wear them. This is the simplest one."

"An' it's mighty new an' bewilderin' for the border," he replied with a smile in his eyes.

"When these are gone I'll get no more except linsey ones," she said brightly, yet her eyes shone with a wistful uncertainty of the future.

"Will you be happy here?"

"I am happy. I have always wanted to be of some use in the world. I assure you, Master Zane, I am not the butterfly I seem. I have worked hard all day, that is, until your sister Betty came over. All the girls have helped me fix up the cabin until it's more comfortable than I ever dreamed one could be on the frontier. Father is well content here, and that makes me happy. I haven't had time for forebodings. The young men of Fort Henry have been—well, attentive; in fact, they've been here all the time."

She laughed a little at this last remark, and looked demurely at him.

"It's a frontier custom," he said.

"Oh, indeed? Do all the young men call often and stay late?"

"They do."

"You didn't," she retorted. "You're the only one who hasn't been to see me."

"I do not wait on the girls," he replied with a grave smile.

"Oh, you don't? Do you expect them to wait on you?" she asked, feeling, now she had made this silent man talk, once more at her ease.

"I am a borderman," replied Jonathan. There was a certain dignity or sadness in his answer which reminded Helen of Colonel Zane's portrayal of a borderman's life. It struck her keenly. Here was this young giant standing erect and handsome before her, as rugged as one of the ash trees of his beloved forest. Who could tell when his strong life might be ended by an Indian's hatchet?

"For you, then, is there no such thing as friendship?" she asked.

"On the border men are serious."

This recalled his sister's conversation regarding the attentions of the young men, that they would follow her, fight for her, and give her absolutely no peace until one of them had carried her to his cabin a bride.

She could not carry on the usual conventional conversation with this borderman, but remained silent for a time. She realized more keenly than ever before how different he was from other men, and watched closely as he stood gazing out over the river. Perhaps something she had said caused him to think of the many pleasures and joys he missed. But she could not be certain what was in his mind. She was not accustomed to impassive faces and cold eyes with unlit fires in their dark depths. More likely he was thinking of matters nearer to his wild, free life; of his companion Wetzel somewhere out beyond those frowning hills. Then she remembered that the colonel had told her of his brother's love for nature in all its forms; how he watched the shades of evening fall; lost himself in contemplation of the last copper glow flushing the western sky, or became absorbed in the bright stars. Possibly he had forgotten her presence. Darkness was rapidly stealing down upon them. The evening, tranquil and gray, crept over them with all its mystery. He was a part of it. She could not hope to understand him; but saw clearly that his was no common personality. She wanted to speak, to voice a sympathy strong within her; but she did not know what to say to this borderman.

"If what your sister tells me of the border is true, I may soon need a friend," she said, after weighing well her words. She faced him modestly yet bravely, and looked him straight in the eyes. Because he did not reply she spoke again.

"I mean such a friend as you or Wetzel."

"You may count on both," he replied.

"Thank you," she said softly, giving him her hand. "I shall not forget.

One more thing. Will you break a borderman's custom, for my sake?"

"How?"

"Come to see me when you are in the settlement?"

Helen said this in a low voice with just a sob in her breath; but she met his gaze fairly. Her big eyes were all aglow, alight with girlish appeal, and yet proud with a woman's honest demand for fair exchange. Promise was there, too, could he but read it, of wonderful possibilities.

"No," he answered gently.

Helen was not prepared for such a rebuff. She was interested in him, and not ashamed to show it. She feared only that he might misunderstand her; but to refuse her proffered friendship, that was indeed unexpected. Rude she thought it was, while from brow to curving throat her fair skin crimsoned. Then her face grew pale as the moonlight. Hard on her resentment had surged the swell of some new emotion strong and sweet. He refused her friendship because he did not dare accept it; because his life was not his own; because he was a borderman.

While they stood thus, Jonathan looking perplexed and troubled, feeling he had hurt her, but knowing not what to say, and Helen with a warm softness in her eyes, the stalwart figure of a man loomed out of the gathering darkness.

"Ah, Miss Helen! Good evening," he said.

"Is it you, Mr. Brandt?" asked Helen. "Of course you know Mr. Zane."

Brandt acknowledged Jonathan's bow with an awkwardness which had certainly been absent in his greeting to Helen. He started slightly when she spoke the borderman's name.

A brief pause ensued.

"Good night," said Jonathan, and left them.

He had noticed Brandt's gesture of surprise, slight though it was, and was thinking about it as he walked away. Brandt may have been astonished at finding a borderman talking to a girl, and certainly, as far as Jonathan was concerned, the incident was without precedent. But, on the other hand, Brandt may have had another reason, and Jonathan tried to study out what it might be.

He gave but little thought to Helen. That she might like him exceedingly well, did not come into his mind. He remembered his sister Betty's gossip regarding Helen and her admirers, and particularly Roger Brandt; but felt no great concern; he had no curiosity to know more of her. He admired Helen because she was beautiful, yet the feeling was much the same he might have experienced for a graceful deer, a full-foliaged tree, or a dark mossy-stoned bend in a murmuring brook. The girl's face and figure, perfect and alluring as they were, had not awakened him from his indifference.

On arriving at his brother's home, he found the colonel and Betty sitting on the porch.

"Eb, who is this Brandt?" he asked.

"Roger Brandt? He's a French-Canadian; came here from Detroit a year ago. Why do you ask?"

"I want to know more about him."

Colonel Zane reflected a moment, first as to this unusual request from Jonathan, and secondly in regard to what little he really did know of Roger Brandt.

"Well, Jack, I can't tell you much; nothing of him before he showed up here. He says he has been a pioneer, hunter, scout, soldier, trader— everything. When he came to the fort we needed men. It was just after Girty's siege, and all the cabins had been burned. Brandt seemed honest, and was a good fellow. Besides, he had gold. He started the river barges, which came from Fort Pitt. He has surely done the settlement good service, and has prospered. I never talked a dozen times to him, and even then, not for long. He appears to like the young people, which is only natural. That's all I know; Betty might tell you more, for he tried to be attentive to her."

"Did he, Betty?" Jonathan asked.

"He followed me until I showed him I didn't care for company," answered Betty.

"What kind of a man is he?"

"Jack, I know nothing against him, although I never fancied him. He's better educated than the majority of frontiersmen; he's good-natured and agreeable, and the people like him."

"Why don't you?"

Betty looked surprised at his blunt question, and then said with a laugh: "I never tried to reason why; but since you have spoken I believe my dislike was instinctive."

After Betty had retired to her room the brothers remained on the porch smoking.

"Betty's pretty keen, Jack. I never knew her to misjudge a man. Why this sudden interest in Roger Brandt?"

The borderman puffed his pipe in silence.

"Say, Jack," Colonel Zane said suddenly, "do you connect Brandt in any way with this horse-stealing?"

"No more than some, an' less than others," replied Jonathan curtly.

Nothing more was said for a time. To the brothers this hour of early dusk brought the same fullness of peace. From gray twilight to gloomy dusk quiet reigned. The insects of night chirped and chorused with low, incessant hum. From out the darkness came the peeping of frogs.

Suddenly the borderman straightened up, and, removing the pipe from his mouth, turned his ear to the faint breeze, while at the same time one hand closed on the colonel's knee with a warning clutch.

Colonel Zane knew what that clutch signified. Some faint noise, too low for ordinary ears, had roused the borderman. The colonel listened, but heard nothing save the familiar evening sounds.

"Jack, what'd you hear?" he whispered.

"Somethin' back of the barn," replied Jonathan, slipping noiselessly off the steps, lying at full length with his ear close to the ground. "Where's the dog?" he asked.

"Chief must have gone with Sam. The old nigger sometimes goes at this hour to see his daughter."

Jonathan lay on the grass several moments; then suddenly he arose much as a bent sapling springs to place.

"I hear footsteps. Get the rifles," he said in a fierce whisper.

"Damn! There is some one in the barn."

"No; they're outside. Hurry, but softly."

Colonel Zane had but just risen to his feet, when Mrs. Zane came to the door and called him by name.

Instantly from somewhere in the darkness overhanging the road, came a low, warning whistle.

"A signal!" exclaimed Colonel Zane.

"Quick, Eb! Look toward Metzar's light. One, two, three, shadows—Injuns!"

"By the Lord Harry! Now they're gone; but I couldn't mistake those round heads and bristling feathers."

"Shawnees!" said the borderman, and his teeth shut hard like steel on flint.

"Jack, they were after the horses, and some one was on the lookout! By God! right under our noses!"

"Hurry," cried Jonathan, pulling his brother off the porch.

Colonel Zane followed the borderman out of the yard, into the road, and across the grassy square.

"We might find the one who gave the signal," said the colonel. "He was near at hand, and couldn't have passed the house."

Colonel Zane was correct, for whoever had whistled would be forced to take one of two ways of escape; either down the straight road ahead, or over the high stockade fence of the fort.

"There he goes," whispered Jonathan.

"Where? I can't see a blamed thing."

"Go across the square, run around the fort, an' head him off on the road. Don't try to stop him for he'll have weapons, just find out who he is."

"I see him now," replied Colonel Zane, as he hurried off into the darkness.

During a few moments Jonathan kept in view the shadow he had seen first come out of the gloom by the stockade, and thence pass swiftly down the road. He followed swiftly, silently. Presently a light beyond threw a glare across the road. He thought he was approaching a yard where there was a fire, and the flames proved to be from pine cones burning in the yard of Helen Sheppard. He remembered then that she was entertaining some of the young people.

The figure he was pursuing did not pass the glare. Jonathan made certain it disappeared before reaching the light, and he knew his eyesight too well not to trust to it absolutely. Advancing nearer the yard, he heard the murmur of voices in gay conversation, and soon saw figures moving about under the trees.

No doubt was in his mind but that the man who gave the signal to warn the Indians, was one of Helen Sheppard's guests.

Jonathan had walked across the street then down the path, before he saw the colonel coming from the opposite direction. Halting under a maple he waited for his brother to approach.

"I didn't meet any one. Did you lose him?" whispered Colonel Zane breathlessly.

"No; he's in there."

"That's Sheppard's place. Do you mean he's hiding there?"

"No!"

Colonel Zane swore, as was his habit when exasperated. Kind and generous man that he was, it went hard with him to believe in the guilt of any of the young men he had trusted. But Jonathan had said there was a traitor among them, and Colonel Zane did not question this assertion. He knew the borderman. During years full of strife, and war, and blood had he lived beside this silent man who said little, but that little was the truth. Therefore Colonel Zane gave way to anger.

"Well, I'm not so damned surprised! What's to be done?"

"Find out what men are there?"

"That's easy. I'll go to see George and soon have the truth."

"Won't do," said the borderman decisively. "Go back to the barn, an' look after the hosses."

When Colonel Zane had obeyed Jonathan dropped to his hands and knees, and swiftly, with the agile movements of an Indian, gained a corner of the Sheppard yard. He crouched in the shade of a big plum tree. Then, at a favorable opportunity, vaulted the fence and disappeared under a clump of lilac bushes.

The evening wore away no more tediously to the borderman, than to those young frontiersmen who were whispering tender or playful words to their partners. Time and patience were the same to Jonathan Zane. He lay hidden under the fragrant lilacs, his eyes, accustomed to the dark from long practice, losing no movement of the guests. Finally it became evident that the party was at an end. One couple took the initiative, and said good night to their hostess.

"Tom Bennet, I hope it's not you," whispered the borderman to himself, as he recognized the young fellow.

A general movement followed, until the merry party were assembled about Helen near the front gate.

"Jim Morrison, I'll bet it's not you," was Jonathan's comment. "That soldier Williams is doubtful; Hart an' Johnson being strangers, are unknown quantities around here, an' then comes Brandt."

All departed except Brandt, who remained talking to Helen in low, earnest tones. Jonathan lay very quietly, trying to decide what should be his next move in the unraveling of the mystery. He paid little attention to the young couple, but could not help overhearing their conversation.

"Indeed, Mr. Brandt, you frontiersmen are not backward," Helen was saying in her clear voice. "I am surprised to learn that you love me upon such short acquaintance, and am sorry, too, for I hardly know whether I even so much as like you."

"I love you. We men of the border do things rapidly," he replied earnestly.

"So it seems," she said with a soft laugh.

"Won't you care for me?" he pleaded.

"Nothing is surer than that I never know what I am going to do," Helen replied lightly.

"All these fellows are in love with you. They can't help it any more than I. You are the most glorious creature. Please give me hope."

"Mr. Brandt, let go my hand. I'm afraid I don't like such impulsive men."

"Please let me hold your hand."

"Certainly not."

"But I will hold it, and if you look at me like that again I'll do more," he said.

"What, bold sir frontiersman?" she returned, lightly still, but in a voice which rang with a deeper note.

"I'll kiss you," he cried desperately.

"You wouldn't dare."

"Wouldn't I though? You don't know us border fellows yet. You come here with your wonderful beauty, and smile at us with that light in your eyes which makes men mad. Oh, you'll pay for it."

The borderman listened to all this love-making half disgusted, until he began to grow interested. Brandt's back was turned to him, and Helen stood so that the light from the pine cones shone on her face. Her eyes were brilliant, otherwise she seemed a woman perfectly self-possessed. Brandt held her hand despite the repeated efforts she made to free it. But she did not struggle violently, or make an outcry.

Suddenly Brandt grasped her other hand, pulling her toward him.

"These other fellows will kiss you, and I'm going to be the first!" he declared passionately.

Helen drew back, now thoroughly alarmed by the man's fierce energy. She had been warned against this very boldness in frontiersmen; but had felt secure in her own pride and dignity. Her blood boiled at the thought that she must exert strength to escape insult. She struggled violently when Brandt bent his head. Almost sick with fear, she had determined to call for help, when a violent wrench almost toppled her over. At the same instant her wrists were freed; she heard a fierce cry, a resounding blow, and then the sodden thud of a heavy body falling. Recovering her balance, she saw a tall figure beside her, and a man in the act of rising from the ground.

"You?" whispered Helen, recognizing the tall figure as Jonathan's.

The borderman did not answer. He stepped forward, slipping his hand inside his hunting frock. Brandt sprang nimbly to his feet, and with a face which, even in the dim light, could be seen distorted with fury, bent forward to look at the stranger. He, too, had his hand within his coat, as if grasping a weapon; but he did not draw it.

"Zane, a lighter blow would have been easier to forget," he cried, his voice clear and cutting. Then he turned to the girl. "Miss Helen, I got what I deserved. I crave your forgiveness, and ask you to understand a man who was once a gentleman. If I am one no longer, the frontier is to blame. I was mad to treat you as I did."

Thus speaking, he bowed low with the grace of a man sometimes used to the society of ladies, and then went out of the gate.

"Where did you come from?" asked Helen, looking up at Jonathan.

He pointed under the lilac bushes.

"Were you there?" she asked wonderingly. "Did you hear all?"

"I couldn't help hearin'."

"It was fortunate for me; but why—why were you there?"

Helen came a step nearer, and regarded him curiously with her great eyes now black with excitement.

The borderman was silent.

Helen's softened mood changed instantly. There was nothing in his cold face which might have betrayed in him a sentiment similar to that of her admirers.

"Did you spy on me?" she asked quickly, after a moment's thought.

"No," replied Jonathan calmly.

Helen gazed in perplexity at this strange man. She did not know how to explain it; she was irritated, but did her best to conceal it. He had no interest in her, yet had hidden under the lilacs in her yard. She was grateful because he had saved her from annoyance, yet could not fathom his reason for being so near.

"Did you come here to see me?" she asked, forgetting her vexation.

"No."

"What for, then?"

"I reckon I won't say," was the quiet, deliberate refusal.

Helen stamped her foot in exasperation.

"Be careful that I do not put a wrong construction on your strange action," said she coldly. "If you have reasons, you might trust me. If you are only——"

"Sh-s-sh!" he breathed, grasping her wrist, and holding it firmly in his powerful hand. The whole attitude of the man had altered swiftly, subtly. The listlessness was gone. His lithe body became rigid as he leaned forward, his head toward the ground, and turned slightly in a manner that betokened intent listening.

Helen trembled as she felt his powerful frame quiver. Whatever had thus changed him, gave her another glimpse of his complex personality. It seemed to her incredible that with one whispered exclamation this man could change from cold indifference to a fire and force so strong as to dominate her.

Statue-like she remained listening; but hearing no sound, and thrillingly conscious of the hand on her arm.

Far up on the hillside an owl hooted dismally, and an instant later, faint and far away, came an answer so low as to be almost indistinct.

The borderman raised himself erect as he released her.

"It's only an owl," she said in relief.

His eyes gleamed like stars.

"It's Wetzel, an' it means Injuns!"

Then he was gone into the darkness.

CHAPTER VI.

In the misty morning twilight Colonel Zane, fully armed, paced to and fro before his cabin, on guard. All night he had maintained a watch. He had not considered it necessary to send his family into the fort, to which they had often been compelled to flee. On the previous night Jonathan had come swiftly back to the cabin, and, speaking but two words, seized his weapons and vanished into the black night. The words were "Injuns! Wetzel!" and there were none others with more power to affect hearers on the border. The colonel believed that Wetzel had signaled to Jonathan.

On the west a deep gully with precipitous sides separated the settlement from a high, wooded bluff. Wetzel often returned from his journeying by this difficult route. He had no doubt seen Indian signs, and had communicated the intelligence to Jonathan by their system of night-bird calls. The nearness of the mighty hunter reassured Colonel Zane.

When the colonel returned from his chase of the previous night, he went directly to the stable, there to find that the Indians had made off with a thoroughbred, and Betty's pony. Colonel Zane was furious, not on account of the value of the horses, but because Bess was his favorite bay, and Betty loved nothing more than her pony Madcap. To have such a march stolen on him after he had heard and seen the thieves was indeed hard. High time it was that these horse thieves be run to earth. No Indian had planned these marauding expeditions. An intelligent white man was at the bottom of the thieving, and he should pay for his treachery.

The colonel's temper, however, soon cooled. He realized after thinking over the matter, that he was fortunate it passed off without bloodshed. Very likely the intent had been to get all his horses, perhaps his neighbor's as well, and it had been partly frustrated by Jonathan's keen sagacity. These Shawnees, white leader or not, would never again run such risks.

"It's like a skulking Shawnee," muttered Colonel Zane, "to slip down here under cover of early dusk, when no one but an Indian hunter could detect him. I didn't look for trouble, especially so soon after the lesson we gave Girty and his damned English and redskins. It's lucky Jonathan was here. I'll go back to the old plan of stationing scouts at the outposts until

438

snow flies."

While Colonel Zane talked to himself and paced the path he had selected to patrol, the white mists cleared, and a rosy hue followed the brightening in the east. The birds ceased twittering to break into gay songs, and the cock in the barnyard gave one final clarion-voiced salute to the dawn. The rose in the east deepened into rich red, and then the sun peeped over the eastern hilltops to drench the valley with glad golden light.

A blue smoke curling lazily from the stone chimney of his cabin, showed that Sam had made the kitchen fire, and a little later a rich, savory odor gave pleasing evidence that his wife was cooking breakfast.

"Any sign of Jack?" a voice called from the open door, and Betty appeared.

"Nary sign."

"Of the Indians, then?"

"Well, Betts, they left you a token of their regard," and Colonel Zane smiled as he took a broken halter from the fence.

"Madcap?" cried Betty.

"Yes, they've taken Madcap and Bess."

"Oh, the villains! Poor pony," exclaimed Betty indignantly. "Eb, I'll coax Wetzel to fetch the pony home if he has to kill every Shawnee in the valley."

"Now you're talking, Betts," Colonel Zane replied. "If you could get Lew to do that much, you'd be blessed from one end of the border to the other."

He walked up the road; then back, keeping a sharp lookout on all sides, and bestowing a particularly keen glance at the hillside across the ravine, but could see no sign of the bordermen. As it was now broad daylight he felt convinced that further watch was unnecessary, and went in to breakfast. When he came out again the villagers were astir. The sharp strokes of axes rang out on the clear morning air, and a mellow anvil-clang pealed up from the blacksmith shop. Colonel Zane found his brother Silas and Jim Douns near the gate.

"Morning, boys," he cried cheerily.

"Any glimpse of Jack or Lew?" asked Silas.

"No; but I'm expecting one of 'em any moment."

"How about the Indians?" asked Douns. "Silas roused me out last night; but didn't stay long enough to say more than 'Indians.'"

"I don't know much more than Silas. I saw several of the red devils who stole the horses; but how many, where they've gone, or what we're to expect, I can't say. We've got to wait for Jack or Lew. Silas, keep the garrison in readiness at the fort, and don't allow a man, soldier or farmer, to leave the clearing until further orders. Perhaps there were only three of those Shawnees, and then again the woods might have been full of them. I take it something's amiss, or Jack and Lew would be in by now."

"Here come Sheppard and his girl," said Silas, pointing down the lane. "'Pears George is some excited."

Colonel Zane had much the same idea as he saw Sheppard and his daughter. The old man appeared in a hurry, which was sufficient reason to believe him anxious or alarmed, and Helen looked pale.

"Ebenezer, what's this I hear about Indians?" Sheppard asked excitedly. "What with Helen's story about the fort being besieged, and this brother of yours routing honest people from their beds, I haven't had a wink of sleep. What's up? Where are the redskins?"

"Now, George, be easy," said Colonel Zane calmly. "And you, Helen, mustn't be frightened. There's no danger. We did have a visit from Indians last night; but they hurt no one, and got only two horses."

"Oh, I'm so relieved that it's not worse," said Helen.

"It's bad enough, Helen," Betty cried, her black eyes flashing, "my pony Madcap is gone."

"Colonel Zane, come here quick!" cried Douns, who stood near the gate.

With one leap Colonel Zane was at the gate, and, following with his eyes the direction indicated by Douns' trembling finger, he saw two tall, brown figures striding down the lane. One carried two rifles, and the other a long bundle wrapped in a blanket.

"It's Jack and Wetzel," whispered Colonel Zane to Jim. "They've got the girl, and by God! from the way that bundle hangs, I think she's dead. Here," he added, speaking loudly, "you women get into the house."

Mrs. Zane, Betty and Helen stared.

"Go into the house!" he cried authoritatively.

Without a protest the three women obeyed.

At that moment Nellie Douns came across the lane; Sam shuffled out from the backyard, and Sheppard arose from his seat on the steps. They joined Colonel Zane, Silas and Jim at the gate.

"I wondered what kept you so late," Colonel Zane said to Jonathan, as he and his companion came up. "You've fetched Mabel, and she's——". The good man could say no more. If he should live an hundred years on the border amid savage murderers, he would still be tender-hearted. Just now he believed the giant borderman by the side of Jonathan held a dead girl, one whom he had danced, when a child, upon his knee.

"Mabel, an' jest alive," replied Jonathan.

"By God! I'm glad!" exclaimed Colonel Zane. "Here, Lew, give her to me."

Wetzel relinquished his burden to the colonel.

"Lew, any bad Indian sign?" asked Colonel Zane as he turned to go into the house.

The borderman shook his head.

"Wait for me," added the colonel.

He carried the girl to that apartment in the cabin which served the purpose of a sitting-room, and laid her on a couch. He gently removed the folds of the blanket, disclosing to view a fragile, white-faced girl.

"Bess, hurry, hurry!" he screamed to his wife, and as she came running in, followed no less hurriedly by Betty, Helen and Nellie, he continued, "Here's Mabel Lane, alive, poor child; but in sore need of help. First see whether she has any bodily injury. If a bullet must be cut out, or a knife-wound sewed up, it's better she remained unconscious. Betty, run for Bess's instruments, and bring brandy and water. Lively now!" Then he gave vent to an oath and left the room.

Helen, her heart throbbing wildly, went to the side of Mrs. Zane, who was kneeling by the couch. She saw a delicate girl, not over eighteen years old, with a face that would have been beautiful but for the set lips, the closed eyelids, and an expression of intense pain.

"Oh! Oh!" breathed Helen.

"Nell, hand me the scissors," said Mrs. Zane, "and help me take off this dress. Why, it's wet, but, thank goodness! 'tis not with blood. I know that slippery touch too well. There, that's right. Betty, give me a spoonful of brandy. Now heat a blanket, and get one of your linsey gowns for this poor child."

Helen watched Mrs. Zane as if fascinated. The colonel's wife continued to talk while with deft fingers she forced a few drops of brandy between the girl's closed teeth. Then with the adroitness of a skilled surgeon, she made the examination. Helen had heard of this pioneer woman's skill in setting broken bones and treating injuries, and when she looked from the calm face to the steady fingers, she had no doubt as to the truth of what had been told.

"Neither bullet wound, cut, bruise, nor broken bone," said Mrs. Zane. "It's fear, starvation, and the terrible shock."

She rubbed Mabel's hands while gazing at her pale face. Then she forced more brandy between the tightly-closed lips. She was rewarded by ever so faint a color tinging the wan cheeks, to be followed by a fluttering of the eyelids. Then the eyes opened wide. They were large, soft, dark and humid with agony.

Helen could not bear their gaze. She saw the shadow of death, and of worse than death. She looked away, while in her heart rose a storm of passionate fury at the brutes who had made of this tender girl a wreck.

The room was full of women now, sober-faced matrons and grave-eyed girls, yet all wore the same expression, not alone of anger, nor fear, nor pity, but of all combined.

Helen instinctively felt that this was one of the trials of border endurance, and she knew from the sterner faces of the maturer women that such a trial was familiar. Despite all she had been told, the shock and pain were too great, and she went out of the room sobbing.

She almost fell over the broad back of Jonathan Zane who was sitting on the steps. Near him stood Colonel Zane talking with a tall man clad in faded buckskin.

"Lass, you shouldn't have stayed," said Colonel Zane kindly.

"It's—hurt—me—here," said Helen, placing her hand over her heart.

"Yes, I know, I know; of course it has," he replied, taking her hand. "But be brave, Helen, bear up, bear up. Oh! this border is a stern place! Do not think of that poor girl. Come, let me introduce Jonathan's friend, Wetzel!"

Helen looked up and held out her hand. She saw a very tall man with extremely broad shoulders, a mass of raven-black hair, and a white face. He stepped forward, and took her hand in his huge, horny palm, pressing it, he stepped back without speaking. Colonel Zane talked to her in a soothing voice; but she failed to hear what he said. This Wetzel, this Indian-hunter whom she had heard called "Deathwind of the Border," this companion, guide, teacher of Jonathan Zane, this borderman of wonderful deeds, stood before her.

Helen saw a cold face, deathly in its pallor, lighted by eyes sloe-black but like glinting steel. Striking as were these features, they failed to fascinate as did the strange tracings which apparently showed through the white, drawn skin. This first repelled, then drew her with wonderful force. Suffering, of fire, and frost, and iron was written there, and, stronger than all, so potent as to cause fear, could be read the terrible purpose of this man's tragic life.

"You avenged her! Oh! I know you did!" cried Helen, her whole heart leaping with a blaze to her eyes.

She was answered by a smile, but such a smile! Kindly it broke over the stern face, giving a glimpse of a heart still warm beneath that steely cold. Behind it, too, there was something fateful, something deadly.

Helen knew, though the borderman spoke not, that somewhere among the grasses of the broad plains, or on the moss of the wooded hills, lay dead the perpetrators of this outrage, their still faces bearing the ghastly stamp of Deathwind.

CHAPTER VI.

Happier days than she had hoped for, dawned upon Helen after the first touch of border sorrow. Mabel Lane did not die. Helen and Betty nursed the stricken girl tenderly, weeping for very joy when signs of improvement appeared. She had remained silent for several days, always with that haunting fear in her eyes, and then gradually came a change. Tender care and nursing had due effect in banishing the dark shadow. One morning after a long sleep she awakened with a bright smile, and from that time her improvement was rapid.

Helen wanted Mabel to live with her. The girl's position was pitiable. Homeless, fatherless, with not a relative on the border, yet so brave, so patient that she aroused all the sympathy in Helen's breast. Village gossip was in substance, that Mabel had given her love to a young frontiersman, by name Alex Bennet, who had an affection for her, so it was said, but as yet had made no choice between her and the other lasses of the settlement. What effect Mabel's terrible experience might have on this lukewarm lover, Helen could not even guess; but she was not hopeful as to the future. Colonel Zane and Betty approved of Helen's plan to persuade Mabel to live with her, and the latter's faint protestations they silenced by claiming she could be of great assistance in the management of the house, therefore it was settled.

Finally the day came when Mabel was ready to go with Helen. Betty had given her a generous supply of clothing, for all her belongings had been destroyed when the cabin was burned. With Helen's strong young arm around her she voiced her gratitude to Betty and Mrs. Zane and started toward the Sheppard home.

From the green square, where the ground was highest, an unobstructed view could be had of the valley. Mabel gazed down the river to where her home formerly stood. Only a faint, dark spot, like a blur on the green landscape, could be seen. Her soft eyes filled with tears; but she spoke no word.

443

"She's game and that's why she didn't go under," Colonel Zane said to himself as he mused on the strength and spirit of borderwomen. To their heroism, more than any other thing, he attributed the establishing of homes in this wilderness.

In the days that ensued, as Mabel grew stronger, the girls became very fond of each other. Helen would have been happy at any time with such a sweet companion, but just then, when the poor girl's mind was so sorely disturbed she was doubly glad. For several days, after Mabel was out of danger, Helen's thoughts had dwelt on a subject which caused extreme vexation. She had begun to suspect that she encouraged too many admirers for whom she did not care, and thought too much of a man who did not reciprocate. She was gay and moody in turn. During the moody hours she suspected herself, and in her gay ones, scorned the idea that she might ever care for a man who was indifferent. But that thought once admitted, had a trick of returning at odd moments, clouding her cheerful moods.

One sunshiny morning while the May flowers smiled under the hedge, when dew sparkled on the leaves, and the locust-blossoms shone creamy-white amid the soft green of the trees, the girls set about their much-planned flower gardening. Helen was passionately fond of plants, and had brought a jar of seeds of her favorites all the way from her eastern home.

"We'll plant the morning-glories so they'll run up the porch, and the dahlias in this long row and the nasturtiums in this round bed," Helen said.

"You have some trailing arbutus," added Mabel, "and must have clematis, wild honeysuckle and golden-glow, for they are all sweet flowers."

"This arbutus is so fresh, so dewy, so fragrant," said Helen, bending aside a lilac bush to see the pale, creeping flowers. "I never saw anything so beautiful. I grow more and more in love with my new home and friends. I have such a pretty garden to look into, and I never tire of the view beyond."

Helen gazed with pleasure and pride at the garden with its fresh green and lavender-crested lilacs, at the white-blossomed trees, and the vine-covered log cabins with blue smoke curling from their stone chimneys. Beyond, the great bulk of the fort stood guard above the willow-skirted river, and far away over the winding stream the dark hills, defiant, kept their secrets.

"If it weren't for that threatening fort one could imagine this little hamlet, nestling under the great bluff, as quiet and secure as it is beautiful," said Helen. "But that charred stockade fence with its scarred bastions and these lowering port-holes, always keep me alive to the reality."

"It wasn't very quiet when Girty was here," Mabel replied thoughtfully.

"Were you in the fort then?" asked Helen breathlessly.

"Oh, yes, I cooled the rifles for the men," replied Mabel calmly.

"Tell me all about it."

Helen listened again to a story she had heard many times; but told by new lips it always gained in vivid interest. She never tired of hearing how the notorious renegade, Girty, rode around the fort on his white horse, giving the defenders an hour in which to surrender; she learned again of the attack, when the British soldiers remained silent on an adjoining hillside, while the Indians yelled exultantly and ran about in fiendish glee, when Wetzel began the battle by shooting an Indian chieftain who had ventured within range of his ever fatal rifle. And when it came to the heroic deeds of that memorable siege Helen could not contain her enthusiasm. She shed tears over little Harry Bennet's death at the south bastion where, though riddled with bullets, he stuck to his post until relieved. Clark's race, across the roof of the fort to extinguish a burning arrow, she applauded with clapping hands. Her great eyes glowed and burned, but she was silent, when hearing how Wetzel ran alone to a break in the stockade, and there, with an ax, the terrible borderman held at bay the whole infuriated Indian mob until the breach was closed. Lastly Betty Zane's never-to-be-forgotten run with the powder to the relief of the garrison and the saving of the fort was something not to cry over or applaud; but to dream of and to glorify.

"Down that slope from Colonel Zane's cabin is where Betty ran with the powder," said Mabel, pointing.

"Did you see her?" asked Helen.

"Yes, I looked out of a port-hole. The Indians stopped firing at the fort in their eagerness to shoot Betty. Oh, the banging of guns and yelling of savages was one fearful, dreadful roar! Through all that hail of bullets Betty ran swift as the wind."

"I almost wish Girty would come again," said Helen.

"Don't; he might."

"How long has Betty's husband, Mr. Clarke, been dead?" inquired Helen.

"I don't remember exactly. He didn't live long after the siege. Some say he inhaled the flames while fighting fire inside the stockade."

"How sad!"

"Yes, it was. It nearly killed Betty. But we border girls do not give up easily; we must not," replied Mabel, an unquenchable spirit showing through the sadness of her eyes.

Merry voices interrupted them, and they turned to see Betty and Nell entering the gate. With Nell's bright chatter and Betty's wit, the conversation became indeed vivacious, running from gossip to gowns, and then to that old and ever new theme, love. Shortly afterward the colonel entered the gate, with swinging step and genial smile.

"Well, now, if here aren't four handsome lasses," he said with an admiring glance.

"Eb, I believe if you were single any girl might well suspect you of being a flirt," said Betty.

"No girl ever did. I tell you I was a lady-killer in my day," replied Colonel Zane, straightening his fine form. He was indeed handsome, with his stalwart frame, dark, bronzed face and rugged, manly bearing.

"Bess said you were; but that it didn't last long after you saw her," cried Betty, mischief gleaming in her dark eye.

"Well, that's so," replied the colonel, looking a trifle crest-fallen; "but you know every dog has his day." Then advancing to the porch, he looked at Mabel with a more serious gaze as he asked, "How are you to-day?"

"Thank you, Colonel Zane, I am getting quite strong."

"Look up the valley. There's a raft coming down the river," said he softly.

Far up the broad Ohio a square patch showed dark against the green water.

Colonel Zane saw Mabel start, and a dark red flush came over her pale face. For an instant she gazed with an expression of appeal, almost fear. He knew the reason. Alex Bennet was on that raft.

"I came over to ask if I can be of any service?"

"Tell him," she answered simply.

"I say, Betts," Colonel Zane cried, "has Helen's cousin cast any more such sheep eyes at you?"

"Oh, Eb, what nonsense!" exclaimed Betty, blushing furiously.

"Well, if he didn't look sweet at you I'm an old fool."

"You're one anyway, and you're horrid," said Betty, tears of anger glistening in her eyes.

Colonel Zane whistled softly as he walked down the lane. He went into the wheelwright's shop to see about some repairs he was having made on a wagon, and then strolled on down to the river. Two Indians were sitting on the rude log wharf, together with several frontiersmen and rivermen, all waiting for the raft. He conversed with the Indians, who were friendly Chippewas, until the raft was tied up. The first person to leap on shore was a sturdy young fellow with a shock of yellow hair, and a warm, ruddy skin.

"Hello, Alex, did you have a good trip?" asked Colonel Zane of the youth.

"H'are ye, Colonel Zane. Yes, first-rate trip," replied young Bennet. "Say, I've a word for you. Come aside," and drawing Colonel Zane out of earshot of the others, he continued, "I heard this by accident, not that I didn't spy a bit when I got interested, for I did; but the way it came about was all chance. Briefly, there's a man, evidently an Englishman, at Fort Pitt whom I overheard say he was out on the border after a Sheppard girl. I happened to hear from one of Brandt's men, who rode into Pitt just before we left, that you had new friends here by that name. This fellow was a handsome chap, no common sort, but lordly, dissipated and reckless as the devil. He had a servant traveling with him, a sailor, by his gab, who was about the toughest customer I've met in many a day. He cut a fellow in bad shape at Pitt. These two will be on the next boat, due here in a day or so, according to river and weather conditions, an' I thought, considerin' how unusual the thing was, I'd better tell ye."

"Well, well," said Colonel Zane reflectively. He recalled Sheppard's talk about an Englishman. "Alex, you did well to tell me. Was the man drunk when he said he came west after a woman?"

"Sure he was," replied Alex. "But not when he spoke the name. Ye see I got suspicious, an' asked about him. It's this way: Jake Wentz, the trader, told me the fellow asked for the Sheppards when he got off the wagon-train. When I first seen him he was drunk, and I heard Jeff Lynn say as how the border was a bad place to come after a woman. That's what made me prick up my ears. Then the Englishman said: 'It is, eh? By God! I'd go to hell after a woman I wanted.' An' Colonel, he looked it, too."

Colonel Zane remained thoughtful while Alex made up a bundle and forced the haft of an ax under the string; but as the young man started away the colonel suddenly remembered his errand down to the wharf.

"Alex, come back here," he said, and wondered if the lad had good stuff in him. The boatman's face was plain, but not evil, and a close scrutiny of it rather prepossessed the colonel.

"Alex, I've some bad news for you," and then bluntly, with his keen gaze fastened on the young man's face, he told of old Lane's murder, of Mabel's abduction, and of her rescue by Wetzel.

Alex began to curse and swear vengeance.

"Stow all that," said the colonel sharply. "Wetzel followed four Indians who had Mabel and some stolen horses. The redskins quarreled over the girl, and two took the horses, leaving Mabel to the others. Wetzel went after these last, tomahawked them, and brought Mabel home. She was in a bad way, but is now getting over the shock."

"Say, what'd we do here without Wetzel?" Alex said huskily, unmindful of the tears that streamed from his eyes and ran over his brown cheeks. "Poor old Jake! Poor Mabel! Damn me! it's my fault. If I'd 'a done right an' married her as I should, as I wanted to, she wouldn't have had to suffer. But I'll marry her yet, if she'll have me. It was only because I had no farm, no stock, an' only that little cabin as is full now, that I waited."

"Alex, you know me," said Colonel Zane in kindly tones. "Look there, down the clearing half a mile. See that green strip of land along the river, with the big chestnut in the middle and a cabin beyond. There's as fine farming land as can be found on the border, eighty acres, well watered. The day you marry Mabel that farm is yours."

Alex grew red, stammered, and vainly tried to express his gratitude.

"Come along, the sooner you tell Mabel the better," said the colonel with glowing face. He was a good matchmaker. He derived more pleasure from a little charity bestowed upon a deserving person, than from a season's crops.

When they arrived at the Sheppard house the girls were still on the porch. Mabel rose when she saw Alex, standing white and still. He, poor fellow, was embarrassed by the others, who regarded him with steady eyes.

Colonel Zane pushed Alex up on the porch, and said in a low voice: "Mabel, I've just arranged something you're to give Alex. It's a nice little farm, and it'll be a wedding present."

Mabel looked in a bewildered manner from Colonel Zane's happy face to the girls, and then at the red, joyous features of her lover. Only then did she understand, and uttering a strange little cry, put her trembling hands to her bosom as she swayed to and fro.

But she did not fall, for Alex, quick at the last, leaped forward and caught her in his arms.

* * * * *

That evening Helen denied herself to Mr. Brandt and several other callers. She sat on the porch with her father while he smoked his pipe.

"Where's Will?" she asked.

"Gone after snipe, so he said," replied her father.

"Snipe? How funny! Imagine Will hunting! He's surely catching the wild fever Colonel Zane told us about."

"He surely is."

Then came a time of silence. Mr. Sheppard, accustomed to Helen's gladsome spirit and propensity to gay chatter, noted how quiet she was, and wondered.

"Why are you so still?"

"I'm a little homesick," Helen replied reluctantly.

"No? Well, I declare! This is a glorious country; but not for such as you, dear, who love music and gaiety. I often fear you'll not be happy here, and then I long for the old home, which reminds me of your mother."

"Dearest, forget what I said," cried Helen earnestly. "I'm only a little blue to-day; perhaps not at all homesick."

"Indeed, you always seemed happy."

"Father, I am happy. It's only—only a girl's foolish sentiment."

"I've got something to tell you, Helen, and it has bothered me since Colonel Zane spoke of it to-night. Mordaunt is coming to Fort Henry."

"Mordaunt? Oh, impossible! Who said so? How did you learn?"

"I fear 'tis true, my dear. Colonel Zane told me he had heard of an Englishman at Fort Pitt who asked after us. Moreover, the fellow answers the description of Mordaunt. I am afraid it is he, and come after you."

"Suppose he has—who cares? We owe him nothing. He cannot hurt us."

"But, Helen, he's a desperate man. Aren't you afraid of him?"

"Not I," cried Helen, laughing in scorn. "He'd better have a care. He can't run things with a high hand out here on the border. I told him I would have none of him, and that ended it."

"I'm much relieved. I didn't want to tell you; but it seemed necessary. Well, child, good night, I'll go to bed."

Long after Mr. Sheppard had retired Helen sat thinking. Memories of the past, and of the unwelcome suitor, Mordaunt, thronged upon her thick and fast. She could see him now with his pale, handsome face, and distinguished bearing. She had liked him, as she had other men, until he involved her father, with himself, in financial ruin, and had made his attention to her unpleasantly persistent. Then he had followed the fall of fortune with wild dissipation, and became a gambler and a drunkard. But he did not desist in his mad wooing. He became like her shadow, and life grew to be unendurable, until her father planned to emigrate west, when she hailed the news with joy. And now Mordaunt had tracked her to her new home. She was sick with disgust. Then her spirit, always strong, and now freer for this new, wild life of the frontier, rose within her, and she dismissed all thoughts of this man and his passion.

The old life was dead and buried. She was going to be happy here. As for the present, it was enough to think of the little border village, now her home; of her girl friends; of the quiet borderman: and, for the moment, that the twilight was somber and beautiful.

High up on the wooded bluff rising so gloomily over the village, she saw among the trees something silver-bright. She watched it rise slowly from behind the trees, now hidden, now white through rifts in the foliage, until it soared lovely and grand above the black horizon. The ebony shadows of night seemed to lift, as might a sable mantle moved by invisible hands. But dark shadows, safe from the moon-rays, lay under the trees, and a pale, misty vapor hung below the brow of the bluff.

Mysterious as had grown the night before darkness yielded to the moon, this pale, white light flooding the still valley, was even more soft and strange. To one of Helen's temperament no thought was needed; to see was enough. Yet her mind was active. She felt with haunting power the beauty of all before her; in fancy transporting herself far to those silver-tipped clouds, and peopling the dells and shady nooks under the hills with spirits and fairies, maidens and valiant knights. To her the day was as a far-off dream. The great watch stars grew wan before the radiant moon; it reigned alone. The immensity of the world with its glimmering rivers, pensive valleys and deep, gloomy forests lay revealed under the glory of the clear light.

Absorbed in this contemplation Helen remained a long time gazing with dreamy ecstasy at the moonlit valley until a slight chill disturbed her happy thoughts. She knew she was not alone. Trembling, she stood up to see, easily recognizable in the moonlight, the tall buckskin-garbed figure of Jonathan Zane.

"Well, sir," she called, sharply, yet with a tremor in her voice.

The borderman came forward and stood in front of her. Somehow he appeared changed. The long, black rifle, the dull, glinting weapons made her shudder. Wilder and more untamable he looked than ever. The very silence of the forest clung to him; the fragrance of the grassy plains came faintly from his buckskin garments.

"Evenin', lass," he said in his slow, cool manner.

"How did you get here?" asked Helen presently, because he made no effort to explain his presence at such a late hour.

"I was able to walk."

Helen observed, with a vaulting spirit, one ever ready to rise in arms, that Master Zane was disposed to add humor to his penetrating mysteriousness. She flushed hot and then paled. This borderman certainly possessed the power to vex her, and, reluctantly she admitted, to chill her soul and rouse her fear. She strove to keep back sharp words, because she had learned that this singular individual always gave good reason for his odd actions.

"I think in kindness to me," she said, choosing her words carefully, "you might tell me why you appear so suddenly, as if you had sprung out of the ground."

"Are you alone?"

"Yes. Father is in bed; so is Mabel, and Will has not yet come home. Why?"

"Has no one else been here?"

"Mr. Brandt came, as did some others; but wishing to be alone, I did not see them," replied Helen in perplexity.

"Have you seen Brandt since?"

"Since when?"

"The night I watched by the lilac bush."

"Yes, several times," replied Helen. Something in his tone made her ashamed. "I couldn't very well escape when he called. Are you surprised because after he insulted me I'd see him?"

"Yes."

Helen felt more ashamed.

"You don't love him?" he continued.

Helen was so surprised she could only look into the dark face above her. Then she dropped her gaze, abashed by his searching eyes. But, thinking of his question, she subdued the vague stirrings of pleasure in her breast, and answered coldly:

"No, I do not; but for the service you rendered me I should never have answered such a question."

"I'm glad, an' hope you care as little for the other five men who were here that night."

"I declare, Master Zane, you seem exceedingly interested in the affairs of a young woman whom you won't visit, except as you have come to-night."

He looked at her with his piercing eyes.

"You spied upon my guests," she said, in no wise abashed now that her temper was high. "Did you care so very much?"

"Care?" he asked slowly.

"Yes; you were interested to know how many of my admirers were here, what they did, and what they said. You even hint disparagingly of them."

"True, I wanted to know," he replied; "but I don't hint about any man."

"You are so interested you wouldn't call on me when I invited you," said Helen, with poorly veiled sarcasm. It was this that made her bitter; she could never forget that she had asked this man to come to see her, and he had refused.

"I reckon you've mistook me," he said calmly.

"Why did you come? Why do you shadow my friends? This is twice you have done it. Goodness knows how many times you've been here! Tell me."

The borderman remained silent.

"Answer me," commanded Helen, her eyes blazing. She actually stamped her foot. "Borderman or not, you have no right to pry into my affairs. If you are a gentleman, tell me why you came here?"

The eyes Jonathan turned on Helen stilled all the angry throbbing of her blood.

"I come here to learn which of your lovers is the dastard who plotted the abduction of Mabel Lane, an' the thief who stole our hosses. When I find the villain I reckon Wetzel an' I'll swing him to some tree."

The borderman's voice rang sharp and cold, and when he ceased speaking she sank back upon the step, shocked, speechless, to gaze up at him with staring eyes.

"Don't look so, lass; don't be frightened," he said, his voice gentle and kind as it had been hard. He took her hand in his. "You nettled me into replyin'. You have a sharp tongue, lass, and when I spoke I was thinkin' of him. I'm sorry."

"A horse-thief and worse than murderer among my friends!" murmured Helen, shuddering, yet she never thought to doubt his word.

"I followed him here the night of your company."

"Do you know which one?"

"No."

He still held her hand, unconsciously, but Helen knew it well. A sense of his strength came with the warm pressure, and comforted her. She would need that powerful hand, surely, in the evil days which seemed to darken the horizon.

"What shall I do?" she whispered, shuddering again.

"Keep this secret between you an' me."

"How can I? How can I?"

"You must," his voice was deep and low. "If you tell your father, or any one, I might lose the chance to find this man, for, lass, he's desperate cunnin'. Then he'd go free to rob others, an' mebbe help make off with other poor girls. Lass, keep my secret."

"But he might try to carry me away," said Helen in fearful perplexity.

"Most likely he might," replied the borderman with the smile that came so rarely.

"Oh! Knowing all this, how can I meet any of these men again? I'd betray myself."

"No; you've got too much pluck. It so happens you are the one to help me an' Wetzel rid the border of these hell-hounds, an' you won't fail. I know a woman when it comes to that."

"I—I help you and Wetzel?"

"Exactly."

"Gracious!" cried Helen, half-laughing, half-crying. "And poor me with more trouble coming on the next boat."

"Lass, the colonel told me about the Englishman. It'll be bad for him to annoy you."

Helen thrilled with the depth of meaning in the low voice. Fate surely was weaving a bond between her and this borderman. She felt it in his steady, piercing gaze; in her own tingling blood.

Then as her natural courage dispelled all girlish fears, she faced him, white, resolute, with a look in her eyes that matched his own.

"I will do what I can," she said.

CHAPTER VII.

Westward from Fort Henry, far above the eddying river, Jonathan Zane slowly climbed a narrow, hazel-bordered, mountain trail. From time to time he stopped in an open patch among the thickets and breathed deep of the fresh, wood-scented air, while his keen gaze swept over the glades near by, along the wooded hillsides, and above at the timber-strewn woodland.

This June morning in the wild forest was significant of nature's brightness and joy. Broad-leaved poplars, dense foliaged oaks, and vine-covered maples shaded cool, mossy banks, while between the trees the sunshine streamed in bright spots. It shone silver on the glancing silver-leaf, and gold on the colored leaves of the butternut tree. Dewdrops glistened on the ferns; ripples sparkled in the brooks; spider-webs glowed with wondrous rainbow hues, and the flower of the forest, the sweet, pale-faced daisy, rose above the green like a white star.

Yellow birds flitted among the hazel bushes caroling joyously, and cat-birds sang gaily. Robins called; bluejays screeched in the tall, white oaks; wood-peckers hammered in the dead hard-woods, and crows cawed overhead. Squirrels chattered everywhere. Ruffed grouse rose with great bustle and a whirr, flitting like brown flakes through the leaves. From far above came the shrill cry of a hawk, followed by the wilder scream of an eagle.

Wilderness music such as all this fell harmoniously on the borderman's ear. It betokened the gladsome spirit of his wild friends, happy in the warm sunshine above, or in the cool depths beneath the fluttering leaves, and everywhere in those lonely haunts unalarmed and free.

Familiar to Jonathan, almost as the footpath near his home, was this winding trail. On the height above was a safe rendezvous, much frequented by him and Wetzel. Every lichen-covered stone, mossy bank, noisy brook and giant oak on the way up this mountain-side, could have told, had they spoken their secrets, stories of the bordermen. The fragile ferns and slender-bladed grasses peeping from the gray and amber mosses, and the flowers

453

that hung from craggy ledges, had wisdom to impart. A borderman lived under the green tree-tops, and, therefore, all the nodding branches of sassafras and laurel, the grassy slopes and rocky cliffs, the stately ash trees, kingly oaks and dark, mystic pines, together with the creatures that dwelt among them, save his deadly red-skinned foes, he loved. Other affection as close and true as this, he had not known. Hearkening thus with single heart to nature's teachings, he learned her secrets. Certain it was, therefore, that the many hours he passed in the woods apart from savage pursuits, were happy and fruitful.

Slowly he pressed on up the ascent, at length coming into open light upon a small plateau marked by huge, rugged, weather-chipped stones. On the eastern side was a rocky promontory, and close to the edge of this cliff, an hundred feet in sheer descent, rose a gnarled, time and tempest-twisted chestnut tree. Here the borderman laid down his rifle and knapsack, and, half-reclining against the tree, settled himself to rest and wait.

This craggy point was the lonely watch-tower of eagles. Here on the highest headland for miles around where the bordermen were wont to meet, the outlook was far-reaching and grand.

Below the gray, splintered cliffs sheered down to meet the waving tree-tops, and then hill after hill, slope after slope, waved and rolled far, far down to the green river. Open grassy patches, bright little islands in that ocean of dark green, shone on the hillsides. The rounded ridges ran straight, curved, or zigzag, but shaped their graceful lines in the descent to make the valley. Long, purple-hued, shadowy depressions in the wide expanse of foliage marked deep clefts between ridges where dark, cool streams bounded on to meet the river. Lower, where the land was level, in open spaces could be seen a broad trail, yellow in the sunlight, winding along with the curves of the water-course. On a swampy meadow, blue in the distance, a herd of buffalo browsed. Beyond the river, high over the green island, Fort Henry lay peaceful and solitary, the only token of the works of man in all that vast panorama.

Jonathan Zane was as much alone as if one thousand miles, instead of five, intervened between him and the settlement. Loneliness was to him a passion. Other men loved home, the light of woman's eyes, the rattle of dice or the lust of hoarding; but to him this wild, remote promontory, with its limitless view, stretching away to the dim hazy horizon, was more than all the aching joys of civilization.

Hours here, or in the shady valley, recompensed him for the loss of home comforts, the soft touch of woman's hands, the kiss of baby lips, and also for all he suffered in his pitiless pursuits, the hard fare, the steel and blood of a borderman's life.

Soon the sun shone straight overhead, dwarfing the shadow of the chestnut on the rock.

During such a time it was rare that any connected thought came into the borderman's mind. His dark eyes, now strangely luminous, strayed lingeringly over those purple, undulating slopes. This intense watchfulness had no object, neither had his listening. He watched nothing; he hearkened to the silence. Undoubtedly in this state of rapt absorption his perceptions were acutely alert; but without thought, as were those of the savage in the valley below, or the eagle in the sky above.

Yet so perfectly trained were these perceptions that the least unnatural sound or sight brought him wary and watchful from his dreamy trance.

The slight snapping of a twig in the thicket caused him to sit erect, and reach out toward his rifle. His eyes moved among the dark openings in the thicket. In another moment a tall figure pressed the bushes apart. Jonathan let fall his rifle, and sank back against the tree once more. Wetzel stepped over the rocks toward him.

"Come from Blue Pond?" asked Jonathan as the newcomer took a seat beside him.

Wetzel nodded as he carefully laid aside his long, black rifle.

"Any Injun sign?" continued Jonathan, pushing toward his companion the knapsack of eatables he had brought from the settlement.

"Nary Shawnee track west of this divide," answered Wetzel, helping himself to bread and cheese.

"Lew, we must go eastward, over Bing Legget's way, to find the trail of the stolen horses."

"Likely, an' it'll be a long, hard tramp."

"Who's in Legget's gang now beside Old Horse, the Chippewa, an' his Shawnee pard, Wildfire? I don't know Bing; but I've seen some of his Injuns an' they remember me."

"Never seen Legget but onct," replied Wetzel, "an' that time I shot half his face off. I've been told by them as have seen him since, that he's got a nasty scar on his temple an' cheek. He's a big man an' knows the woods. I don't know who all's in his gang, nor does anybody. He works in the dark, an' for cunnin' he's got some on Jim Girty, Deerin', an' several more renegades we know of lyin' quiet back here in the woods. We never tackled as bad a gang as his'n; they're all experienced woodsmen, old fighters, an' desperate, outlawed as they be by Injuns an' whites. It wouldn't surprise me to find that it's him an' his gang who are runnin' this hoss-thievin'; but bad or no, we're goin' after 'em."

Jonathan told of his movements since he had last seen his companion.

"An' the lass Helen is goin' to help us," said Wetzel, much interested. "It's a good move. Women are keen. Betty put Miller's schemin' in my eye long 'afore I noticed it. But girls have chances we men'd never get."

"Yes, an' she's like Betts, quicker'n lightnin'. She'll find out this hoss-thief in Fort Henry; but Lew, when we do get him we won't be much better off. Where do them hosses go? Who's disposin' of 'em for this fellar?"

"Where's Brandt from?" asked Wetzel.

"Detroit; he's a French-Canadian."

Wetzel swung sharply around, his eyes glowing like wakening furnaces.

"Bing Legget's a French-Canadian, an' from Detroit. Metzar was once thick with him down Fort Pitt way 'afore he murdered a man an' became an outlaw. We're on the trail, Jack."

"Brandt an' Metzar, with Legget backin' them, an' the horses go overland to Detroit?"

"I calkilate you've hit the mark."

"What'll we do?" asked Jonathan.

"Wait; that's best. We've no call to hurry. We must know the truth before makin' a move, an' as yet we're only suspicious. This lass'll find out more in a week than we could in a year. But Jack, have a care she don't fall into any snare. Brandt ain't any too honest a lookin' chap, an' them renegades is hell for women. The scars you wear prove that well enough. She's a rare, sweet, bloomin' lass, too. I never seen her equal. I remember how her eyes flashed when she said she knew I'd avenged Mabel. Jack, they're wonderful eyes; an' that girl, however sweet an' good as she must be, is chain-lightnin' wrapped up in a beautiful form. Aren't the boys at the fort runnin' arter her?"

"Like mad; it'd make you laugh to see 'em," replied Jonathan calmly.

"There'll be some fights before she's settled for, an' mebbe arter thet. Have a care for her, Jack, an' see that she don't ketch you."

"No more danger than for you."

"I was ketched onct," replied Wetzel.

Jonathan Zane looked up at his companion. Wetzel's head was bowed; but there was no merriment in the serious face exposed to the borderman's scrutiny.

"Lew, you're jokin'."

"Not me. Some day, when you're ketched good, an' I have to go back to the lonely trail, as I did afore you an' me become friends, mebbe then, when I'm the last borderman, I'll tell you."

"Lew, 'cordin' to the way settlers are comin', in a few more years there won't be any need for a borderman. When the Injuns are all gone where'll be our work?"

"'Tain't likely either of us'll ever see them times," said Wetzel, "an' I don't want to. Wal, Jack, I'm off now, an' I'll meet you here every other day."

Wetzel shouldered his long rifle, and soon passed out of sight down the mountain-side.

Jonathan arose, shook himself as a big dog might have done, and went down into the valley. Only once did he pause in his descent, and that was when a crackling twig warned him some heavy body was moving near. Silently he sank into the bushes bordering the trail. He listened with his ear close to the ground. Presently he heard a noise as of two hard substances striking together. He resumed his walk, having recognized the grating noise of a deer-hoof striking a rock. Farther down he espied a pair grazing. The buck ran into the thicket; but the doe eyed him curiously.

Less than an hour's rapid walking brought him to the river. Here he plunged into a thicket of willows, and emerged on a sandy strip of shore. He carefully surveyed the river bank, and then pulled a small birch-bark canoe from among the foliage. He launched the frail craft, paddled across the river and beached it under a reedy, over-hanging bank.

The distance from this point in a straight line to his destination was only a mile; but a rocky bluff and a ravine necessitated his making a wide detour. While lightly leaping over a brook his keen eye fell on an imprint in the sandy loam. Instantly he was on his knees. The footprint was small, evidently a woman's, and, what was more unusual, instead of the flat, round moccasin-track, it was pointed, with a sharp, square heel. Such shoes were not worn by border girls. True Betty and Nell had them; but they never went into the woods without moccasins.

Jonathan's experienced eye saw that this imprint was not an hour old. He gazed up at the light. The day was growing short. Already shadows lay in the glens. He would not long have light enough to follow the trail; but he hurried on hoping to find the person who made it before darkness came. He had not traveled many paces before learning that the one who made it was lost. The uncertainty in those hasty steps was as plain to the borderman's eyes, as if it had been written in words on the sand. The course led along the brook, avoiding the rough places; and leading into the open glades and glens; but it drew no nearer to the settlement. A quarter of an hour of rapid trailing enabled Jonathan to discern a dark figure moving among the trees. Abandoning the trail, he cut across a ridge to head off the lost woman. Stepping out of a sassafras thicket, he came face to face with Helen Sheppard.

"Oh!" she cried in alarm, and then the expression of terror gave place to one of extreme relief and gladness. "Oh! Thank goodness! You've found me. I'm lost!"

"I reckon," answered Jonathan grimly. "The settlement's only five hundred yards over that hill."

"I was going the wrong way. Oh! suppose you hadn't come!" exclaimed Helen, sinking on a log and looking up at him with warm, glad eyes.

"How did you lose your way?" Jonathan asked. He saw neither the warmth in her eyes nor the gladness.

"I went up the hillside, only a little way, after flowers, keeping the fort in sight all the time. Then I saw some lovely violets down a little hill, and thought I might venture. I found such loads of them I forgot everything else, and I must have walked on a little way. On turning to go back I couldn't find the little hill. I have hunted in vain for the clearing. It seems as if I have been wandering about for hours. I'm so glad you've found me!"

"Weren't you told to stay in the settlement, inside the clearing?" demanded Jonathan.

"Yes," replied Helen, with her head up.

"Why didn't you?"

"Because I didn't choose."

"You ought to have better sense."

"It seems I hadn't," Helen said quietly, but her eyes belied that calm voice.

"You're a headstrong child," Jonathan added curtly.

"Mr. Zane!" cried Helen with pale face.

"I suppose you've always had your own sweet will; but out here on the border you ought to think a little of others, if not of yourself."

Helen maintained a proud silence.

"You might have run right into prowlin' Shawnees."

"That dreadful disaster would not have caused you any sorrow," she flashed out.

"Of course it would. I might have lost my scalp tryin' to get you back home," said Jonathan, beginning to hesitate. Plainly he did not know what to make of this remarkable young woman.

"Such a pity to have lost all your fine hair," she answered with a touch of scorn.

Jonathan flushed, perhaps for the first time in his life. If there was anything he was proud of, it was his long, glossy hair.

"Miss Helen, I'm a poor hand at words," he said, with a pale, grave face. "I was only speakin' for your own good."

"You are exceedingly kind; but need not trouble yourself."

"Say," Jonathan hesitated, looking half-vexed at the lovely, angry face. Then an idea occurred to him. "Well, I won't trouble. Find your way home yourself."

Abruptly he turned and walked slowly away. He had no idea of allowing her to go home alone; but believed it might be well for her to think so. If she did not call him back he would remain near at hand, and when she showed signs of anxiety or fear he could go to her.

Helen determined she would die in the woods, or be captured by Shawnees, before calling him back. But she watched him. Slowly the tall, strong figure, with its graceful, springy stride, went down the glade. He would be lost to view in a moment, and then she would be alone. How dark it had suddenly become! The gray cloak of twilight was spread over the forest, and in the hollows night already had settled down. A breathless silence pervaded the woods. How lonely! thought Helen, with a shiver. Surely it would be dark before she could find the settlement. What hill hid the settlement from view? She did not know, could not remember which he had pointed out. Suddenly she began to tremble. She had been so frightened before he had found her, and so relieved afterward; and now he was going away.

"Mr. Zane," she cried with a great effort. "Come back."

458

Jonathan kept slowly on.

"Come back, Jonathan, please."

The borderman retraced his steps.

"Please take me home," she said, lifting a fair face all flushed, tear-stained, and marked with traces of storm. "I was foolish, and silly to come into the woods, and so glad to see you! But you spoke to me—in—in a way no one ever used before. I'm sure I deserved it. Please take me home. Papa will be worried."

Softer eyes and voice than hers never entreated man.

"Come," he said gently, and, taking her by the hand, he led her up the ridge.

Thus they passed through the darkening forest, hand in hand, like a dusky redman and his bride. He helped her over stones and logs, but still held her hand when there was no need of it. She looked up to see him walking, so dark and calm beside her, his eyes ever roving among the trees. Deepest remorse came upon her because of what she had said. There was no sentiment for him in this walk under the dark canopy of the leaves. He realized the responsibility. Any tree might hide a treacherous foe. She would atone for her sarcasm, she promised herself, while walking, ever conscious of her hand in his, her bosom heaving with the sweet, undeniable emotion which came knocking at her heart.

Soon they were out of the thicket, and on the dusty lane. A few moments of rapid walking brought them within sight of the twinkling lights of the village, and a moment later they were at the lane leading to Helen's home. Releasing her hand, she stopped him with a light touch and said:

"Please don't tell papa or Colonel Zane."

"Child, I ought. Some one should make you stay at home."

"I'll stay. Please don't tell. It will worry papa."

Jonathan Zane looked down into her great, dark, wonderful eyes with an unaccountable feeling. He really did not hear what she asked. Something about that upturned face brought to his mind a rare and perfect flower which grew in far-off rocky fastnesses. The feeling he had was intangible, like no more than a breath of fragrant western wind, faint with tidings of some beautiful field.

"Promise me you won't tell."

"Well, lass, have it your own way," replied Jonathan, wonderingly conscious that it was the first pledge ever asked of him by a woman.

"Thank you. Now we have two secrets, haven't we?" she laughed, with eyes like stars.

"Run home now, lass. Be careful hereafter. I do fear for you with such spirit an' temper. I'd rather be scalped by Shawnees than have Bing Legget so much as set eyes on you."

"You would? Why?" Her voice was like low, soft music.

"Why?" he mused. "It'd seem like a buzzard about to light on a doe."

"Good-night," said Helen abruptly, and, wheeling, she hurried down the lane.

CHAPTER VIII.

"Jack," said Colonel Zane to his brother next morning, "to-day is Saturday and all the men will be in. There was high jinks over at Metzar's place yesterday, and I'm looking for more to-day. The two fellows Alex Bennet told me about, came on day-before-yesterday's boat. Sure enough, one's a lordly Englishman, and the other, the cussedest-looking little chap I ever saw. They started trouble immediately. The Englishman, his name is Mordaunt, hunted up the Sheppards and as near as I can make out from George's story, Helen spoke her mind very plainly. Mordaunt and Case, that's his servant, the little cuss, got drunk and raised hell down at Metzar's where they're staying. Brandt and Williams are drinking hard, too, which is something unusual for Brandt. They got chummy at once with the Englishman, who seems to have plenty of gold and is fond of gambling. This Mordaunt is a gentleman, or I never saw one. I feel sorry for him. He appears to be a ruined man. If he lasts a week out here I'll be surprised. Case looks ugly, as if he were spoiling to cut somebody. I want you to keep your eye peeled. The day may pass off as many other days of drinking bouts have, without anything serious, and on the other hand there's liable to be trouble."

Jonathan's preparations were characteristic of the borderman. He laid aside his rifle, and, removing his short coat, buckled on a second belt containing a heavier tomahawk and knife than those he had been wearing. Then he put on his hunting frock, or shirt, and wore it loose with the belts underneath, instead of on the outside. Unfastened, the frock was rather full, and gave him the appearance of a man unarmed and careless.

Jonathan Zane was not so reckless as to court danger, nor, like many frontiersmen, fond of fighting for its own sake. Colonel Zane was commandant of the fort, and, in a land where there was no law, tried to maintain a semblance of it. For years he had kept thieves, renegades and outlaws away from his little settlement by dealing out stern justice. His word was law, and his bordermen executed it as such. Therefore Jonathan and Wetzel made it their duty to have a keen eye on all that was happening. They

461

kept the colonel posted, and never interfered in any case without orders.

The morning passed quietly. Jonathan strolled here or loitered there; but saw none of the roisterers. He believed they were sleeping off the effects of their orgy on the previous evening. After dinner he smoked his pipe. Betty and Helen passed, and Helen smiled. It struck him suddenly that she had never looked at him in such a way before. There was meaning in that warm, radiant flash. A little sense of vexation, the source of which he did not understand, stirred in him against this girl; but with it came the realization that her white face and big, dark eyes had risen before him often since the night before. He wished, for the first time, that he could understand women better.

"Everything quiet?" asked Colonel Zane, coming out on the steps.

"All quiet," answered Jonathan.

"They'll open up later, I suspect. I'm going over to Sheppard's for a while, and, later, will drop into Metzar's. I'll make him haul in a yard or two. I don't like things I hear about his selling the youngsters rum. I'd like you to be within call."

The borderman strolled down the bluff and along the path which overhung the river. He disliked Metzar more than his brother suspected, and with more weighty reason than that of selling rum to minors. Jonathan threw himself at length on the ground and mused over the situation.

"We never had any peace in this settlement, an' never will in our day. Eb is hopeful an' looks at the bright side, always expectin' to-morrow will be different. What have the past sixteen years been? One long bloody fight, an' the next sixteen won't be any better. I make out that we'll have a mix-up soon. Metzar an' Brandt with their allies, whoever they are, will be in it, an' if Bing Legget's in the gang, we've got, as Wetzel said, a long, hard trail, which may be our last. More'n that, there'll be trouble about this chain-lightnin' girl, as Wetzel predicted. Women make trouble anyways; an' when they're winsome an' pretty they cause more; but if they're beautiful an' fiery, bent on havin' their way, as this new lass is, all hell couldn't hold a candle to them. We don't need the Shawnees an' Girtys, an' hoss thieves round this here settlement to stir up excitin' times, now we've got this dark-eyed lass. An' yet any fool could see she's sweet, an' good, an' true as gold."

Toward the middle of the afternoon Jonathan sauntered in the direction of Metzar's inn. It lay on the front of the bluff, with its main doors looking into the road. A long, one-story log structure with two doors, answered as a bar-room. The inn proper was a building more pretentious, and joined the smaller one at its western end. Several horses were hitched outside, and two great oxen yoked to a cumbersome mud-crusted wagon stood patiently by.

Jonathan bent his tall head as he entered the noisy bar-room. The dingy place reeked with tobacco smoke and the fumes of vile liquor. It was crowded with men. The lawlessness of the time and place was evident. Gaunt, red-faced frontiersmen reeled to and fro across the sawdust floor;

hunters and fur-traders, raftsmen and farmers, swelled the motley crowd; young men, honest-faced, but flushed and wild with drink, hung over the bar; a group of sullen-visaged, serpent-eyed Indians held one corner. The black-bearded proprietor dealt out the rum.

From beyond the bar-room, through a door entering upon the back porch, came the rattling of dice. Jonathan crossed the bar-room apparently oblivious to the keen glance Metzar shot at him, and went out upon the porch. This also was crowded, but there was more room because of greater space. At one table sat some pioneers drinking and laughing; at another were three men playing with dice. Colonel Zane, Silas, and Sheppard were among the lookers-on at the game. Jonathan joined them, and gazed at the gamesters.

Brandt he knew well enough; he had seen that set, wolfish expression in the riverman's face before. He observed, however, that the man had flushed cheeks and trembling hands, indications of hard drinking. The player sitting next to Brandt was Williams, one of the garrison, and a good-natured fellow, but garrulous and wickedly disposed when drunk. The remaining player Jonathan at once saw was the Englishman, Mordaunt. He was a handsome man, with fair skin, and long, silken, blond mustache. Heavy lines, and purple shades under his blue eyes, were the unmistakable stamp of dissipation. Reckless, dissolute, bad as he looked, there yet clung something favorable about the man. Perhaps it was his cool, devil-may-care way as he pushed over gold piece after gold piece from the fast diminishing pile before him. His velvet frock and silken doublet had once been elegant; but were now sadly the worse for border roughing.

Behind the Englishman's chair Jonathan saw a short man with a face resembling that of a jackal. The grizzled, stubbly beard, the protruding, vicious mouth, the broad, flat nose, and deep-set, small, glittering eyes made a bad impression on the observer. This man, Jonathan concluded, was the servant, Case, who was so eager with his knife. The borderman made the reflection, that if knife-play was the little man's pastime, he was not likely to go short of sport in that vicinity.

Colonel Zane attracted Jonathan's attention at this moment. The pioneers had vacated the other table, and Silas and Sheppard now sat by it. The colonel wanted his brother to join them.

"Here, Johnny, bring drinks," he said to the serving boy. "Tell Metzar who they're for." Then turning to Sheppard he continued: "He keeps good whiskey; but few of these poor devils ever see it." At the same time Colonel Zane pressed his foot upon that of Jonathan's.

The borderman understood that the signal was intended to call attention to Brandt. The latter had leaned forward, as Jonathan passed by to take a seat with his brother, and said something in a low tone to Mordaunt and Case. Jonathan knew by the way the Englishman and his man quickly glanced up at him, that he had been the subject of the remark.

Suddenly Williams jumped to his feet with an oath.

"I'm cleaned out," he cried.

"Shall we play alone?" asked Brandt of Mordaunt.

"As you like," replied the Englishman, in a tone which showed he cared not a whit whether he played or not.

"I've got work to do. Let's have some more drinks, and play another time," said Brandt.

The liquor was served and drank. Brandt pocketed his pile of Spanish and English gold, and rose to his feet. He was a trifle unsteady; but not drunk.

"Will you gentlemen have a glass with me?" Mordaunt asked of Colonel Zane's party.

"Thank you, some other time, with pleasure. We have our drink now," Colonel Zane said courteously.

Meantime Brandt had been whispering in Case's ear. The little man laughed at something the riverman said. Then he shuffled from behind the table. He was short, his compact build gave promise of unusual strength and agility.

"What are you going to do now?" asked Mordaunt, rising also. He looked hard at Case.

"Shiver my sides, cap'n, if I don't need another drink," replied the sailor.

"You have had enough. Come upstairs with me," said Mordaunt.

"Easy with your hatch, cap'n," grinned Case. "I want to drink with that ther' Injun killer. I've had drinks with buccaneers, and bad men all over the world, and I'm not going to miss this chance."

"Come on; you will get into trouble. You must not annoy these gentlemen," said Mordaunt.

"Trouble is the name of my ship, and she's a trim, fast craft," replied the man.

His loud voice had put an end to the convention. Men began to crowd in from the bar-room. Metzar himself came to see what had caused the excitement.

The little man threw up his cap, whooped, and addressed himself to Jonathan:

"Injun-killer, bad man of the border, will you drink with a jolly old tar from England?"

Suddenly a silence reigned, like that in the depths of the forest. To those who knew the borderman, and few did not know him, the invitation was nothing less than an insult. But it did not appear to them, as to him, like a pre-arranged plot to provoke a fight.

"Will you drink, redskin-hunter?" bawled the sailor.

"No," said Jonathan in his quiet voice.

"Maybe you mean that against old England?" demanded Case fiercely.

The borderman eyed him steadily, inscrutable as to feeling or intent, and was silent.

"Go out there and I'll see the color of your insides quicker than I'd take a drink," hissed the sailor, with his brick-red face distorted and hideous to look upon. He pointed with a long-bladed knife that no one had seen him draw, to the green sward beyond the porch.

The borderman neither spoke, nor relaxed a muscle.

"Ho! ho! my brave pirate of the plains!" cried Case, and he leered with braggart sneer into the faces of Jonathan and his companions.

It so happened that Sheppard sat nearest to him, and got the full effect of the sailor's hot, rum-soaked breath. He arose with a pale face.

"Colonel, I can't stand this," he said hastily. "Let's get away from that drunken ruffian."

"Who's a drunken ruffian?" yelled Case, more angry than ever. "I'm not drunk; but I'm going to be, and cut some of you white-livered border mates. Here, you old masthead, drink this to my health, damn you!"

The ruffian had seized a tumbler of liquor from the table, and held it toward Sheppard while he brandished his long knife.

White as snow, Sheppard backed against the wall; but did not take the drink.

The sailor had the floor; no one save him spoke a word. The action had been so rapid that there had hardly been time. Colonel Zane and Silas were as quiet and tense as the borderman.

"Drink!" hoarsely cried the sailor, advancing his knife toward Sheppard's body.

When the sharp point all but pressed against the old man, a bright object twinkled through the air. It struck Case's wrist, knocked the knife from his fingers, and, bounding against the wall, fell upon the floor. It was a tomahawk.

The borderman sprang over the table like a huge catamount, and with movement equally quick, knocked Case with a crash against the wall; closed on him before he could move a hand, and flung him like a sack of meal over the bluff.

The tension relieved, some of the crowd laughed, others looked over the embankment to see how Case had fared, and others remarked that for some reason he had gotten off better than they expected.

The borderman remained silent. He leaned against a post, with broad breast gently heaving, but his eyes sparkled as they watched Brandt, Williams, Mordaunt and Metzar. The Englishman alone spoke.

"Handily done," he said, cool and suave. "Sir, yours is an iron hand. I apologize for this unpleasant affair. My man is quarrelsome when under the influence of liquor."

"Metzar, a word with you," cried Colonel Zane curtly.

"Come inside, kunnel," said the innkeeper, plainly ill at ease.

"No; listen here. I'll speak to the point. You've got to stop running this kind of a place. No words, now, you've got to stop. Understand? You know as well as I, perhaps better, the character of your so-called inn. You'll get but one more chance."

"Wal, kunnel, this is a free country," growled Metzar. "I can't help these fellars comin' here lookin' fer blood. I runs an honest place. The men want to drink an' gamble. What's law here? What can you do?"

"You know me, Metzar," Colonel Zane said grimly. "I don't waste words. 'To hell with law!' so you say. I can say that, too. Remember, the next drunken boy I see, or shady deal, or gambling spree, out you go for good."

Metzar lowered his shaggy head and left the porch. Brandt and his friends, with serious faces, withdrew into the bar-room.

The borderman walked around the corner of the inn, and up the lane. The colonel, with Silas and Sheppard, followed in more leisurely fashion. At a shout from some one they turned to see a dusty, bloody figure, with ragged clothes, stagger up from the bluff.

"There's that blamed sailor now," said Sheppard. "He's a tough nut. My! What a knock on the head Jonathan gave him. Strikes me, too, that tomahawk came almost at the right time to save me a whole skin."

"I was furious, but not at all alarmed," rejoined Colonel Zane.

"I wondered what made you so quiet."

"I was waiting. Jonathan never acts until the right moment, and then—well, you saw him. The little villain deserved killing. I could have shot him with pleasure. Do you know, Sheppard, Jonathan's aversion to shedding blood is a singular thing. He'd never kill the worst kind of a white man until driven to it."

"That's commendable. How about Wetzel?"

"Well, Lew is different," replied Colonel Zane with a shudder. "If I told him to take an ax and clean out Metzar's place—God! what a wreck he'd make of it. Maybe I'll have to tell him, and if I do, you'll see something you can never forget."

CHAPTER IX.

On Sunday morning under the bright, warm sun, the little hamlet of Fort Henry lay peacefully quiet, as if no storms had ever rolled and thundered overhead, no roistering ever disturbed its stillness, and no Indian's yell ever horribly broke the quiet.

"'Tis a fine morning," said Colonel Zane, joining his sister on the porch. "Well, how nice you look! All in white for the first time since—well, you do look charming. You're going to church, of course."

"Yes, I invited Helen and her cousin to go. I've persuaded her to teach my Sunday-school class, and I'll take another of older children," replied Betty.

"That's well. The youngsters don't have much chance to learn out here. But we've made one great stride. A church and a preacher means very much to young people. Next shall come the village school."

"Helen and I might teach our classes an hour or two every afternoon."

"It would be a grand thing if you did! Fancy these tots growing up unable to read or write. I hate to think of it; but the Lord knows I've done my best. I've had my troubles in keeping them alive."

"Helen suggested the day school. She takes the greatest interest in everything and everybody. Her energy is remarkable. She simply must move, must do something. She overflows with kindness and sympathy. Yesterday she cried with happiness when Mabel told her Alex was eager to be married very soon. I tell you, Eb, Helen is a fine character."

"Yes, good as she is pretty, which is saying some," mused the colonel. "I wonder who'll be the lucky fellow to win her."

"It's hard to say. Not that Englishman, surely. She hates him. Jonathan might. You should see her eyes when he is mentioned."

"Say, Betts, you don't mean it?" eagerly asked her brother.

"Yes, I do," returned Betty, nodding her head positively. "I'm not easily deceived about those things. Helen's completely fascinated with Jack. She might be only a sixteen-year-old girl for the way she betrays herself to me."

"Betty, I have a beautiful plan."

"No doubt; you're full of them."

"We can do it, Betty, we can, you and I," he said, as he squeezed her arm.

"My dear old matchmaking brother," returned Betty, laughing, "it takes two to make a bargain. Jack must be considered."

"Bosh!" exclaimed the colonel, snapping his fingers. "You needn't tell me any young man—any man, could resist that glorious girl."

"Perhaps not; I couldn't if I were a man. But Jack's not like other people. He'd never realize that she cared for him. Besides, he's a borderman."

"I know, and that's the only serious obstacle. But he could scout around the fort, even if he was married. These long, lonely, terrible journeys taken by him and Wetzel are mostly unnecessary. A sweet wife could soon make him see that. The border will be civilized in a few years, and because of that he'd better give over hunting for Indians. I'd like to see him married and settled down, like all the rest of us, even Isaac. You know Jack's the last of the Zanes, that is, the old Zanes. The difficulty arising from his extreme modesty and bashfulness can easily be overcome."

"How, most wonderful brother?"

"Easy as pie. Tell Jack that Helen is dying of love for him, and tell her that Jack loves——"

"But, dear Eb, that latter part is not true," interposed Betty.

"True, of course it's true, or would be in any man who wasn't as blind as a bat. We'll tell her Jack cares for her; but he is a borderman with stern ideas of duty, and so slow and backward he'd never tell his love even if he had overcome his tricks of ranging. That would settle it with any girl worth her salt, and this one will fetch Jack in ten days, or less."

"Eb, you're a devil," said Betty gaily, and then she added in a more sober vein, "I understand, Eb. Your idea is prompted by love of Jack, and it's all right. I never see him go out of the clearing but I think it may be for the last time, even as on that day so long ago when brother Andrew waved his cap to us, and never came back. Jack is the best man in the world, and I, too, want to see him happy, with a wife, and babies, and a settled occupation in life. I think we might weave a pretty little romance. Shall we try?"

"Try? We'll do it! Now, Betts, you explain it to both. You can do it smoother than I, and telling them is really the finest point of our little plot. I'll help the good work along afterwards. He'll be out presently. Nail him at once."

Jonathan, all unconscious of the deep-laid scheme to make him happy, soon came out on the porch, and stretched his long arms as he breathed freely of the morning air.

"Hello, Jack, where are you bound?" asked Betty, clasping one of his powerful, buckskin-clad knees with her arm.

"I reckon I'll go over to the spring," he replied, patting her dark, glossy head.

"Do you know I want to tell you something, Jack, and it's quite serious," she said, blushing a little at her guilt; but resolute to carry out her part of the plot.

"Well, dear?" he asked as she hesitated.

"Do you like Helen?"

"That is a question," Jonathan replied after a moment.

"Never mind; tell me," she persisted.

He made no answer.

"Well, Jack, she's—she's wildly in love with you."

The borderman stood very still for several moments. Then, with one step he gained the lawn, and turned to confront her.

"What's that you say?"

Betty trembled a little. He spoke so sharply, his eyes were bent on her so keenly, and he looked so strong, so forceful that she was almost afraid. But remembering that she had said only what, to her mind, was absolutely true, she raised her eyes and repeated the words:

"Helen is wildly in love with you."

"Betty, you wouldn't joke about such a thing; you wouldn't lie to me, I know you wouldn't."

"No, Jack dear."

She saw his powerful frame tremble, even as she had seen more than one man tremble, during the siege, under the impact of a bullet.

Without speaking, he walked rapidly down the path toward the spring.

Colonel Zane came out of his hiding-place behind the porch and, with a face positively electrifying in its glowing pleasure, beamed upon his sister.

"Gee! Didn't he stalk off like an Indian chief!" he said, chuckling with satisfaction. "By George! Betts, you must have got in a great piece of work. I never in my life saw Jack look like that."

Colonel Zane sat down by Betty's side and laughed softly but heartily.

"We'll fix him all right, the lonely hill-climber! Why, he hasn't a ghost of a chance. Wait until she sees him after hearing your story! I tell you, Betty— why—damme! you're crying!"

He had turned to find her head lowered, while she shaded her face with her hand.

"Now, Betty, just a little innocent deceit like that—what harm?" he said, taking her hand. He was as tender as a woman.

"Oh, Eb, it wasn't that. I didn't mind telling him. Only the flash in his eyes reminded me of—of Alfred."

"Surely it did. Why not? Almost everything brings up a tender memory for some one we've loved and lost. But don't cry, Betty."

She laughed a little, and raised a face with its dark cheeks flushed and tear-stained.

"I'm silly, I suppose; but I can't help it. I cry at least once every day."

"Brace up. Here come Helen and Will. Don't let them see you grieved.

469

My! Helen in pure white, too! This is a conspiracy to ruin the peace of the masculine portion of Fort Henry."

Betty went forward to meet her friends while Colonel Zane continued talking, but now to himself. "What a fatal beauty she has!" His eyes swept over Helen with the pleasure of an artist. The fair richness of her skin, the perfect lips, the wavy, shiny hair, the wondrous dark-blue, changing eyes, the tall figure, slender, but strong and swelling with gracious womanhood, made a picture he delighted in and loved to have near him. The girl did not possess for him any of that magnetism, so commonly felt by most of her admirers; but he did feel how subtly full she was of something, which for want of a better term he described in Wetzel's characteristic expression, as "chain-lightning."

He reflected that as he was so much older, that she, although always winsome and earnest, showed nothing of the tormenting, bewildering coquetry of her nature. Colonel Zane prided himself on his discernment, and he had already observed that Helen had different sides of character for different persons. To Betty, Mabel, Nell, and the children, she was frank, girlish, full of fun and always lovable; to her elders quiet and earnestly solicitous to please; to the young men cold; but with a penetrating, mocking promise haunting that coldness, and sometimes sweetly agreeable, often wilful, and changeable as April winds. At last the colonel concluded that she needed, as did all other spirited young women, the taming influence of a man whom she loved, a home to care for, and children to soften and temper her spirit.

"Well, young friends, I see you count on keeping the Sabbath," he said cheerily. "For my part, Will, I don't see how Jim Douns can preach this morning, before this laurel blossom and that damask rose."

"How poetical! Which is which?" asked Betty.

"Flatterer!" laughed Helen, shaking her finger.

"And a married man, too!" continued Betty.

"Well, being married has not affected my poetical sentiment, nor impaired my eyesight."

"But it has seriously inconvenienced your old propensity of making love to the girls. Not that you wouldn't if you dared," replied Betty with mischief in her eye.

"Now, Will, what do you think of that? Isn't it real sisterly regard? Come, we'll go and look at my thoroughbreds," said Colonel Zane.

"Where is Jonathan?" Helen asked presently. "Something happened at Metzar's yesterday. Papa wouldn't tell me, and I want to ask Jonathan."

"Jack is down by the spring. He spends a great deal of his time there. It's shady and cool, and the water babbles over the stones."

"How much alone he is," said Helen.

Betty took her former position on the steps, but did not raise her eyes while she continued speaking. "Yes, he's more alone than ever lately, and quieter, too. He hardly ever speaks now. There must be something on his mind more serious than horse-thieves."

"What?" Helen asked quickly.

"I'd better not tell—you."

A long moment passed before Helen spoke.

"Please tell me!"

"Well, Helen, we think, Eb and I, that Jack is in love for the first time in his life, and with you, you adorable creature. But Jack's a borderman; he is stern in his principles, thinks he is wedded to his border life, and he knows that he has both red and white blood on his hands. He'd die before he'd speak of his love, because he cannot understand that would do any good, even if you loved him, which is, of course, preposterous."

"Loves me!" breathed Helen softly.

She sat down rather beside Betty, and turned her face away. She still held the young woman's hand which she squeezed so tightly as to make its owner wince. Betty stole a look at her, and saw the rich red blood mantling her cheeks, and her full bosom heave.

Helen turned presently, with no trace of emotion except a singular brilliance of the eyes. She was so slow to speak again that Colonel Zane and Will returned from the corral before she found her voice.

"Colonel Zane, please tell me about last night. When papa came home to supper he was pale and very nervous. I knew something had happened. But he would not explain, which made me all the more anxious. Won't you please tell me?"

Colonel Zane glanced again at her, and knew what had happened. Despite her self-possession those tell-tale eyes told her secret. Ever-changing and shadowing with a bounding, rapturous light, they were indeed the windows of her soul. All the emotion of a woman's heart shone there, fear, beauty, wondering appeal, trembling joy, and timid hope.

"Tell you? Indeed I will," replied Colonel Zane, softened and a little remorseful under those wonderful eyes.

No one liked to tell a story better than Colonel Zane. Briefly and graphically he related the circumstances of the affair leading to the attack on Helen's father, and, as the tale progressed, he became quite excited, speaking with animated face and forceful gestures.

"Just as the knife-point touched your father, a swiftly-flying object knocked the weapon to the floor. It was Jonathan's tomahawk. What followed was so sudden I hardly saw it. Like lightning, and flexible as steel, Jonathan jumped over the table, smashed Case against the wall, pulled him up and threw him over the bank. I tell you, Helen, it was a beautiful piece of action; but not, of course, for a woman's eyes. Now that's all. Your father was not even hurt."

"He saved papa's life," murmured Helen, standing like a statue.

She wheeled suddenly with that swift bird-like motion habitual to her, and went quickly down the path leading to the spring.

* * * * *

Jonathan Zane, solitary dreamer of dreams as he was, had never been in as strange and beautiful a reverie as that which possessed him on this Sabbath morning.

Deep into his heart had sunk Betty's words. The wonder of it, the sweetness, that alone was all he felt. The glory of this girl had begun, days past, to spread its glamour round him. Swept irresistibly away now, he soared aloft in a dream-castle of fancy with its painted windows and golden walls.

For the first time in his life on the border he had entered the little glade and had no eye for the crystal water flowing over the pebbles and mossy stones, or the plot of grassy ground inclosed by tall, dark trees and shaded by a canopy of fresh green and azure blue. Nor did he hear the music of the soft rushing water, the warbling birds, or the gentle sighing breeze moving the leaves.

Gone, vanished, lost to-day was that sweet companionship of nature. That indefinable and unutterable spirit which flowed so peacefully to him from his beloved woods; that something more than merely affecting his senses, which existed for him in the stony cliffs, and breathed with life through the lonely aisles of the forest, had fled before the fateful power of a woman's love and beauty.

A long time that seemed only a moment passed while he leaned against a stone. A light step sounded on the path.

A vision in pure white entered the glade; two little hands pressed his, and two dark-blue eyes of misty beauty shed their light on him.

"Jonathan, I am come to thank you."

Sweet and tremulous, the voice sounded far away.

"Thank me? For what?"

"You saved papa's life. Oh! how can I thank you?"

No voice answered for him.

"I have nothing to give but this."

A flower-like face was held up to him; hands light as thistledown touched his shoulders; dark-blue eyes glowed upon him with all tenderness.

"May I thank you—so?"

Soft lips met his full and lingeringly.

Then came a rush as of wind, a flash of white, and the patter of flying feet. He was alone in the glade.

CHAPTER X.

June passed; July opened with unusually warm weather, and Fort Henry had no visits from Indians or horse-thieves, nor any inconvenience except the hot sun. It was the warmest weather for many years, and seriously dwarfed the settlers' growing corn. Nearly all the springs were dry, and a drouth menaced the farmers.

The weather gave Helen an excuse which she was not slow to adopt. Her pale face and languid air perplexed and worried her father and her friends. She explained to them that the heat affected her disagreeably.

Long days had passed since that Sunday morning when she kissed the borderman. What transports of sweet hope and fear were hers then! How shame had scorched her happiness! Yet still she gloried in the act. By that kiss had she awakened to a full consciousness of her love. With insidious stealth and ever-increasing power this flood had increased to full tide, and, bursting its bonds, surged over her with irresistible strength.

During the first days after the dawning of her passion, she lived in its sweetness, hearing only melodious sounds chiming in her soul. The hours following that Sunday were like long dreams. But as all things reach fruition, so this girlish period passed, leaving her a thoughtful woman. She began to gather up the threads of her life where love had broken them, to plan nobly, and to hope and wait.

Weeks passed, however, and her lover did not come. Betty told her that Jonathan made flying trips at break of day to hold council with Colonel Zane; that he and Wetzel were on the trail of Shawnees with stolen horses, and both bordermen were in their dark, vengeful, terrible moods. In these later days Helen passed through many stages of feeling. After the exalting mood of hot, young love, came reaction. She fell into the depths of despair. Sorrow paled her face, thinned her cheeks and lent another shadow, a mournful one, to her great eyes. The constant repression of emotion, the strain of trying to seem cheerful when she was miserable, threatened even her magnificent health. She answered the solicitude of her friends by

473

evasion, and then by that innocent falsehood in which a sensitive soul hides its secrets. Shame was only natural, because since the borderman came not, nor sent her a word, pride whispered that she had wooed him, forgetting modesty.

Pride, anger, shame, despair, however, finally fled before affection. She loved this wild borderman, and knew he loved her in return although he might not understand it himself. His simplicity, his lack of experience with women, his hazardous life and stern duty regarding it, pleaded for him and for her love. For the lack of a little understanding she would never live unhappy and alone while she was loved. Better give a thousand times more than she had sacrificed. He would return to the village some day, when the Indians and the thieves were run down, and would be his own calm, gentle self. Then she would win him, break down his allegiance to this fearful border life, and make him happy in her love.

While Helen was going through one of the fires of life to come out sweeter and purer, if a little pensive and sad, time, which waits not for love, nor life, nor death, was hastening onward, and soon the golden fields of grain were stored. September came with its fruitful promise fulfilled.

Helen entered once more into the quiet, social life of the little settlement, taught her class on Sundays, did all her own work, and even found time to bring a ray of sunshine to more than one sick child's bed. Yet she did not forget her compact with Jonathan, and bent all her intelligence to find some clew that might aid in the capture of the horse-thief. She was still groping in the darkness. She could not, however, banish the belief that the traitor was Brandt. She blamed herself for this, because of having no good reasons for suspicion; but the conviction was there, fixed by intuition. Because a man's eyes were steely gray, sharp like those of a cat's, and capable of the same contraction and enlargement, there was no reason to believe their owner was a criminal. But that, Helen acknowledged with a smile, was the only argument she had. To be sure Brandt had looked capable of anything, the night Jonathan knocked him down; she knew he had incited Case to begin the trouble at Metzar's, and had seemed worried since that time. He had not left the settlement on short journeys, as had been his custom before the affair in the bar-room. And not a horse had disappeared from Fort Henry since that time.

Brandt had not discontinued his attentions to her; if they were less ardent it was because she had given him absolutely to understand that she could be his friend only. And she would not have allowed even so much except for Jonathan's plan. She fancied it was possible to see behind Brandt's courtesy, the real subtle, threatening man. Stripped of his kindliness, an assumed virtue, the iron man stood revealed, cold, calculating, cruel.

Mordaunt she never saw but once and then, shocking and pitiful, he lay dead drunk in the grass by the side of the road, his pale, weary, handsome face exposed to the pitiless rays of the sun. She ran home weeping over this wreck of what had once been so fine a gentleman. Ah! the curse of rum! He had learned his soft speech and courtly bearing in the refinement of a home where a proud mother adored, and gentle sisters loved him. And now, far from the kindred he had disgraced, he lay in the road like a log. How it hurt her! She almost wished she could have loved him, if love might have redeemed. She was more kind to her other admirers, more tolerant of Brandt, and could forgive the Englishman, because the pangs she had suffered through love had softened her spirit.

During this long period the growing friendship of her cousin for Betty had been a source of infinite pleasure to Helen. She hoped and believed a romance would develop between the young widow and Will, and did all in her power, slyly abetted by the matchmaking colonel, to bring the two together.

One afternoon when the sky was clear with that intense blue peculiar to bright days in early autumn, Helen started out toward Betty's, intending to remind that young lady she had promised to hunt for clematis and other fall flowers.

About half-way to Betty's home she met Brandt. He came swinging round a corner with his quick, firm step. She had not seen him for several days, and somehow he seemed different. A brightness, a flash, as of daring expectation, was in his face. The poise, too, of the man had changed.

"Well, I am fortunate. I was just going to your home," he said cheerily. "Won't you come for a walk with me?"

"You may walk with me to Betty's," Helen answered.

"No, not that. Come up the hillside. We'll get some goldenrod. I'd like to have a chat with you. I may go away—I mean I'm thinking of making a short trip," he added hurriedly.

"Please come."

"I promised to go to Betty's."

"You won't come?" His voice trembled with mingled disappointment and resentment.

"No," Helen replied in slight surprise.

"You have gone with the other fellows. Why not with me?" He was white now, and evidently laboring under powerful feelings that must have had their origin in some thought or plan which hinged on the acceptance of his invitation.

"Because I choose not to," Helen replied coldly, meeting his glance fully.

A dark red flush swelled Brandt's face and neck; his gray eyes gleamed balefully with wolfish glare; his teeth were clenched. He breathed hard and trembled with anger. Then, by a powerful effort, he conquered himself; the villainous expression left his face; the storm of rage subsided. Great incentive there must have been for him thus to repress his emotions so quickly. He looked long at her with sinister, intent regard; then, with the laugh of a desperado, a laugh which might have indicated contempt for the failure of his suit, and which was fraught with a world of meaning, of menace, he left her without so much as a salute.

Helen pondered over this sudden change, and felt relieved because she need make no further pretense of friendship. He had shown himself to be what she had instinctively believed. She hurried on toward Betty's, hoping to find Colonel Zane at home, and with Jonathan, for Brandt's hint of leaving Fort Henry, and his evident chagrin at such a slip of speech, had made her suspicious. She was informed by Mrs. Zane that the colonel had gone to a log-raising; Jonathan had not been in for several days, and Betty went away with Will.

"Where did they go?" asked Helen.

"I'm not sure; I think down to the spring."

Helen followed the familiar path through the grove of oaks into the glade. It was quite deserted. Sitting on the stone against which Jonathan had leaned the day she kissed him, she gave way to tender reflection. Suddenly she was disturbed by the sound of rapid footsteps, and looking up, saw the hulking form of Metzar, the innkeeper, coming down the path. He carried a bucket, and meant evidently to get water. Helen did not desire to be seen, and, thinking he would stay only a moment, slipped into a thicket of willows behind the stone. She could see plainly through the foliage. Metzar came into the glade, peered around in the manner of a man expecting to see some one, and then, filling his bucket at the spring, sat down on the stone.

Not a minute elapsed before soft, rapid footsteps sounded in the distance. The bushes parted, disclosing the white, set face and gray eyes of Roger Brandt. With a light spring he cleared the brook and approached Metzar.

Before speaking he glanced around the glade with the fugitive, distrustful glance of a man who suspects even the trees. Then, satisfied by the scrutiny he opened his hunting frock, taking forth a long object which he thrust toward Metzar.

It was an Indian arrow.

Metzar's dull gaze traveled from this to the ominous face of Brandt.

"See there, you! Look at this arrow! Shot by the best Indian on the border into the window of my room. I hadn't been there a minute when it came from the island. God! but it was a great shot!"

"Hell!" gasped Metzar, his dull face quickening with some awful thought.

"I guess it is hell," replied Brandt, his face growing whiter and wilder.

"Our game's up?" questioned Metzar with haggard cheek.

"Up? Man! We haven't a day, maybe less, to shake Fort Henry."

"What does it mean?" asked Metzar. He was the calmer of the two.

"It's a signal. The Shawnees, who were in hiding with the horses over by Blueberry swamp, have been flushed by those bordermen. Some of them have escaped; at least one, for no one but Ashbow could shoot that arrow across the river."

"Suppose he hadn't come?" whispered Metzar hoarsely.

Brandt answered him with a dark, shuddering gaze.

A twig snapped in the thicket. Like foxes at the click of a trap, these men whirled with fearsome glances.

"Ugh!" came a low, guttural voice from the bushes, and an Indian of magnificent proportions and somber, swarthy features, entered the glade.

CHAPTER XI.

The savage had just emerged from the river, for his graceful, copper-colored body and scanty clothing were dripping with water. He carried a long bow and a quiver of arrows.

Brandt uttered an exclamation of surprise, and Metzar a curse, as the lithe Indian leaped the brook. He was not young. His swarthy face was lined, seamed, and terrible with a dark impassiveness.

"Paleface-brother-get-arrow," he said in halting English, as his eyes flashed upon Brandt. "Chief-want-make-sure."

The white man leaned forward, grasped the Indian's arm, and addressed him in an Indian language. This questioning was evidently in regard to his signal, the whereabouts of others of the party, and why he took such fearful risks almost in the village. The Indian answered with one English word.

"Deathwind!"

Brandt drew back with drawn, white face, while a whistling breath escaped him.

"I knew it, Metz. Wetzel!" he exclaimed in a husky voice.

The blood slowly receded from Metzar's evil, murky face, leaving it haggard.

"Deathwind-on-Chief's-trail-up-Eagle Rock," continued the Indian. "Deathwind-fooled-not-for-long.   Chief-wait-paleface-brothers   at Two Islands."

The Indian stepped into the brook, parted the willows, and was gone as he had come, silently.

"We know what to expect," said Brandt in calmer tone as the daring cast of countenance returned to him. "There's an Indian for you! He got away, doubled like an old fox on his trail, and ran in here to give us a chance at escape. Now you know why Bing Legget can't be caught."

"Let's dig at once," replied Metzar, with no show of returning courage such as characterized his companion.

Brandt walked to and fro with bent brows, like one in deep thought.

478

Suddenly he turned upon Metzar eyes which were brightly hard, and reckless with resolve.

"By Heaven! I'll do it! Listen. Wetzel has gone to the top of Eagle Mountain, where he and Zane have a rendezvous. Even he won't suspect the cunning of this Indian; anyway it'll be after daylight to-morrow before he strikes the trail. I've got twenty-four hours, and more, to get this girl, and I'll do it!"

"Bad move to have weight like her on a march," said Metzar.

"Bah! The thing's easy. As for you, go on, push ahead after we're started. All I ask is that you stay by me until the time to cut loose."

"I ain't agoin' to crawfish now," growled Metzar. "Strikes me, too, I'm losin' more'n you."

"You won't be a loser if you can get back to Detroit with your scalp. I'll pay you in horses and gold. Once we reach Legget's place we're safe."

"What's yer plan about gittin' the gal?" asked Metzar.

Brandt leaned forward and spoke eagerly, but in a low tone.

"Git away on hoss-back?" questioned Metzar, visibly brightening. "Wal, that's some sense. Kin ye trust ther other party?"

"I'm sure I can," rejoined Brandt.

"It'll be a good job, a good job an' all done in daylight, too. Bing Legget couldn't plan better," Metzar said, rubbing his hands,

"We've fooled these Zanes and their fruit-raising farmers for a year, and our time is about up," Brandt muttered. "One more job and we've done. Once with Legget we're safe, and then we'll work slowly back towards Detroit. Let's get out of here now, for some one may come at any moment."

The plotters separated, Brandt going through the grove, and Metzar down the path by which he had come.

* * * * *

Helen, trembling with horror of what she had heard, raised herself cautiously from the willows where she had lain, and watched the innkeeper's retreating figure. When it had disappeared she gave a little gasp of relief. Free now to run home, there to plan what course must be pursued, she conquered her fear and weakness, and hurried from the glade. Luckily, so far as she was able to tell, no one saw her return. She resolved that she would be cool, deliberate, clever, worthy of the borderman's confidence.

First she tried to determine the purport of this interview between Brandt and Metzar. She recalled to mind all that was said, and supplied what she thought had been suggested. Brandt and Metzar were horse-thieves, aids of Bing Legget. They had repaired to the glade to plan. The Indian had been a surprise. Wetzel had routed the Shawnees, and was now on the trail of this chieftain. The Indian warned them to leave Fort Henry and to meet him at a place called Two Islands. Brandt's plan, presumably somewhat changed by the advent of the red-man, was to steal horses, abduct a girl in broad daylight, and before tomorrow's sunset escape to join the ruffian Legget.

"I am the girl," murmured Helen shudderingly, as she relapsed momentarily into girlish fears. But at once she rose above selfish feelings.

Secondly, while it was easy to determine what the outlaws meant, the wisest course was difficult to conceive. She had promised the borderman to help him, and not speak of anything she learned to any but himself. She could not be true to him if she asked advice. The point was clear; either she must remain in the settlement hoping for Jonathan's return in time to frustrate Brandt's villainous scheme, or find the borderman. Suddenly she remembered Metzar's allusion to a second person whom Brandt felt certain he could trust. This meant another traitor in Fort Henry, another horse-thief, another desperado willing to make off with helpless women.

Helen's spirit rose in arms. She had their secret, and could ruin them. She would find the borderman.

Wetzel was on the trail at Eagle Rock. What for? Trailing an Indian who was then five miles east of that rock? Not Wetzel! He was on that track to meet Jonathan. Otherwise, with the redskins near the river, he would have been closer to them. He would meet Jonathan there at sunset to-day, Helen decided.

She paced the room, trying to still her throbbing heart and trembling hands.

"I must be calm," she said sternly. "Time is precious. I have not a moment to lose. I will find him. I've watched that mountain many a time, and can find the trail and the rock. I am in more danger here, than out there in the forest. With Wetzel and Jonathan on the mountain side, the Indians have fled it. But what about the savage who warned Brandt? Let me think. Yes, he'll avoid the river; he'll go round south of the settlement, and, therefore, can't see me cross. How fortunate that I have paddled a canoe many times across the river. How glad that I made Colonel Zane describe the course up the mountains!"

Her resolution fixed, Helen changed her skirt for one of buckskin, putting on leggings and moccasins of the same serviceable material. She filled the pockets of a short, rain-proof jacket with biscuits, and, thus equipped, sallied forth with a spirit and exultation she could not subdue. Only one thing she feared, which was that Brandt or Metzar might see her cross the river. She launched her canoe and paddled down stream, under cover of the bluff, to a point opposite the end of the island, then straight across, keeping the island between her and the settlement. Gaining the other shore, Helen pulled the canoe into the willows, and mounted the bank. A thicket of willow and alder made progress up the steep incline difficult, but once out of it she faced a long stretch of grassy meadowland. A mile beyond began the green, billowy rise of that mountain which she intended to climb.

Helen's whole soul was thrown into the adventure. She felt her strong young limbs in accord with her heart.

"Now, Mr. Brandt, horse-thief and girl-snatcher, we'll see," she said with scornful lips. "If I can't beat you now I'm not fit to be Betty Zane's friend; and am unworthy of a borderman's trust."

She traversed the whole length of meadowland close under the shadow of the fringed bank, and gained the forest. Here she hesitated. All was so wild and still. No definite course through the woods seemed to invite, and yet all was open. Trees, trees, dark, immovable trees everywhere. The violent trembling of poplar and aspen leaves, when all others were so calm, struck her strangely, and the fearful stillness awed her. Drawing a deep breath she started forward up the gently rising ground.

As she advanced the open forest became darker, and of wilder aspect. The trees were larger and closer together. Still she made fair progress without deviating from the course she had determined upon. Before her rose a ridge, with a ravine on either side, reaching nearly to the summit of the mountain. Here the underbrush was scanty, the fallen trees had slipped down the side, and the rocks were not so numerous, all of which gave her reason to be proud, so far, of her judgment.

Helen, pressing onward and upward, forgot time and danger, while she reveled in the wonder of the forestland. Birds and squirrels fled before her; whistling and wheezing of alarm, or heavy crashings in the bushes, told of frightened wild beasts. A dull, faint roar, like a distant wind, suggested tumbling waters. A single birch tree, gleaming white among the black trees, enlivened the gloomy forest. Patches of sunlight brightened the shade. Giant ferns, just tinging with autumn colors, waved tips of sculptured perfection. Most wonderful of all were the colored leaves, as they floated downward with a sad, gentle rustle.

Helen was brought to a realization of her hazardous undertaking by a sudden roar of water, and the abrupt termination of the ridge in a deep gorge. Grasping a tree she leaned over to look down. It was fully an hundred feet deep, with impassable walls, green-stained and damp, at the bottom of which a brawling, brown brook rushed on its way. Fully twenty feet wide, it presented an insurmountable barrier to further progress in that direction.

But Helen looked upon it merely as a difficulty to be overcome. She studied the situation, and decided to go to the left because higher ground was to be seen that way. Abandoning the ridge, she pressed on, keeping as close to the gorge as she dared, and came presently to a fallen tree lying across the dark cleft. Without a second's hesitation, for she knew such would be fatal, she stepped upon the tree and started across, looking at nothing but the log under her feet, while she tried to imagine herself walking across the water-gate, at home in Virginia.

She accomplished the venture without a misstep. When safely on the ground once more she felt her knees tremble and a queer, light feeling came into her head. She laughed, however, as she rested a moment. It would take more than a gorge to discourage her, she resolved with set lips, as once again she made her way along the rising ground.

Perilous, if not desperate, work was ahead of her. Broken, rocky ground, matted thicket, and seemingly impenetrable forest, rose darkly in advance. But she was not even tired, and climbed, crawled, twisted and turned on her way upward. She surmounted a rocky ledge, to face a higher ridge covered with splintered, uneven stones, and the fallen trees of many storms. Once she slipped and fell, spraining her wrist. At length this uphill labor began to weary her. To breathe caused a pain in her side and she was compelled to rest.

Already the gray light of coming night shrouded the forest. She was surprised at seeing the trees become indistinct; because the shadows hovered over the thickets, and noted that the dark, dim outline of the ridges was fading into obscurity.

She struggled on up the uneven slope with a tightening at her heart which was not all exhaustion. For the first time she doubted herself, but it was too late. She could not turn back. Suddenly she felt that she was on a smoother, easier course. Not to strike a stone or break a twig seemed unusual. It might be a path worn by deer going to a spring. Then into her troubled mind flashed the joyful thought, she had found a trail.

Soft, wiry grass, springing from a wet soil, rose under her feet. A little rill trickled alongside the trail. Mossy, soft-cushioned stones lay imbedded here and there. Young maples and hickories grew breast-high on either side, and the way wound in and out under the lowering shade of forest monarchs.

Swiftly ascending this path she came at length to a point where it was possible to see some distance ahead. The ascent became hardly noticeable. Then, as she turned a bend of the trail, the light grew brighter and brighter, until presently all was open and clear. An oval space, covered with stones, lay before her. A big, blasted chestnut stood near by. Beyond was the dim, purple haze of distance. Above, the pale, blue sky just faintly rose-tinted by the setting sun. Far to her left the scraggly trees of a low hill were tipped with orange and russet shades. She had reached the summit.

Desolate and lonely was this little plateau. Helen felt immeasurably far away from home. Yet she could see in the blue distance the glancing river, the dark fort, and that cluster of cabins which marked the location of Fort Henry. Sitting upon the roots of the big chestnut tree she gazed around. There were the remains of a small camp-fire. Beyond, a hollow under a shelving rock. A bed of dry leaves lay packed in this shelter. Some one had been here, and she doubted not that it was the borderman.

She was so tired and her wrist pained so severely that she lay back against the tree-trunk, closed her eyes and rested. A weariness, the apathy of utter exhaustion, came over her. She wished the bordermen would hurry and come before she went to sleep.

Drowsily she was sinking into slumber when a long, low rumble aroused her. How dark it had suddenly become! A sheet of pale light flared across the overcast heavens.

"A storm!" exclaimed Helen. "Alone on this mountain-top with a storm coming. Am I frightened? I don't believe it. At least I'm safe from that ruffian Brandt. Oh! if my borderman would only come!"

Helen changed her position from beside the tree, to the hollow under the stone. It was high enough to permit of her sitting upright, and offered a safe retreat from the storm. The bed of leaves was soft and comfortable. She sat there peering out at the darkening heavens.

All beneath her, southward and westward was gray twilight. The settlement faded from sight; the river grew wan and shadowy. The ruddy light in the west was fast succumbing to the rolling clouds. Darker and darker it became, until only one break in the overspreading vapors admitted the last crimson gleam of sunshine over hills and valley, brightening the river until it resembled a stream of fire. Then the light failed, the glow faded. The intense blackness of night prevailed.

Out of the ebon west came presently another flare of light, a quick, spreading flush, like a flicker from a monster candle; it was followed by a long, low, rumbling roll.

Helen felt in those intervals of unutterably vast silence, that she must shriek aloud. The thunder was a friend. She prayed for the storm to break. She had withstood danger and toilsome effort with fortitude; but could not brave this awful, boding, wilderness stillness.

Flashes of lightning now revealed the rolling, pushing, turbulent clouds, and peals of thunder sounded nearer and louder.

A long swelling moan, sad, low, like the uneasy sigh of the sea, breathed far in the west. It was the wind, the ominous warning of the storm. Sheets of light were now mingled with long, straggling ropes of fire, and the rumblings were often broken by louder, quicker detonations.

Then a period, longer than usual, of inky blackness succeeded the sharp flaring of light. A faint breeze ruffled the leaves of the thicket, and fanned Helen's hot cheek. The moan of the wind became more distinct, then louder, and in another instant like the far-off roar of a rushing river. The storm was upon her. Helen shrank closer against the stone, and pulled her jacket tighter around her trembling form.

A sudden, intense, dazzling, blinding, white light enveloped her. The rocky promontory, the weird, giant chestnut tree, the open plateau, and beyond, the stormy heavens, were all luridly clear in the flash of lightning. She fancied it was possible to see a tall, dark figure emerging from the thicket. As the thunderclap rolled and pealed overhead, she strained her eyes into the blackness waiting for the next lightning flash.

It came with brilliant, dazing splendor. The whole plateau and thicket were as light as in the day. Close by the stone where she lay crept the tall, dark figure of an Indian. With starting eyes she saw the fringed clothing, the long, flying hair, and supple body peculiar to the savage. He was creeping upon her.

Helen's blood ran cold; terror held her voiceless. She felt herself sinking slowly down upon the leaves.

CHAPTER XII.

The sun had begun to cast long shadows the afternoon of Helen's hunt for Jonathan, when the borderman, accompanied by Wetzel, led a string of horses along the base of the very mountain she had ascended.

"Last night's job was a good one, I ain't gainsayin'; but the redskin I wanted got away," Wetzel said gloomily.

"He's safe now as a squirrel in a hole. I saw him dartin' among the trees with his white eagle feathers stickin' up like a buck's flag," replied Jonathan. "He can run. If I'd only had my rifle loaded! But I'm not sure he was that arrow-shootin' Shawnee."

"It was him. I saw his bow. We ought'er taken more time an' picked him out," Wetzel replied, shaking his head gravely. "Though mebbe that'd been useless. I think he was hidin'. He's precious shy of his red skin. I've been after him these ten year, an' never ketched him nappin' yet. We'd have done much toward snuffin' out Legget an' his gang if we'd winged the Shawnee."

"He left a plain trail."

"One of his tricks. He's slicker on a trail than any other Injun on the border, unless mebbe it's old Wingenund, the Huron. This Shawnee'd lead us many a mile for nuthin', if we'd stick to his trail. I'm long ago used to him. He's doubled like an old fox, run harder'n a skeered fawn, an', if needs be, he'll lay low as cunnin' buck. I calkilate once over the mountain, he's made a bee-line east. We'll go on with the hosses, an' then strike across country to find his trail."

"It 'pears to me, Lew, that we've taken a long time in makin' a show against these hoss-thieves," said Jonathan.

"I ain't sayin' much; but I've felt it," replied Wetzel.

"All summer, an' nothin' done. It was more luck than sense that we run into those Injuns with the hosses. We only got three out of four, an' let the best redskin give us the slip. Here fall is nigh on us, with winter comin' soon, an' still we don't know who's the white traitor in the settlement."

"I said it's be a long, an' mebbe, our last trail."

485

"Why?"

"Because these fellars red or white, are in with a picked gang of the best woodsmen as ever outlawed the border. We'll get the Fort Henry hoss-thief. I'll back the bright-eyed lass for that."

"I haven't seen her lately, an' allow she'd left me word if she learned anythin'."

"Wal, mebbe it's as well you hain't seen so much of her." In silence they traveled and, arriving at the edge of the meadow, were about to mount two of the horses, when Wetzel said in a sharp tone:

"Look!"

He pointed to a small, well-defined moccasin track in the black earth on the margin of a rill.

"Lew, it's a woman's, sure's you're born," declared Jonathan.

Wetzel knelt and closely examined the footprint; "Yes, a woman's, an' no Injun."

"What?" Jonathan exclaimed, as he knelt to scrutinize the imprint.

"This ain't half a day old," added Wetzel. "An' not a redskin's moccasin near. What d'you reckon?"

"A white girl, alone," replied Jonathan as he followed the trail a short distance along the brook. "See, she's makin' upland. Wetzel, these tracks could hardly be my sister's, an' there's only one other girl on the border whose feet will match 'em! Helen Sheppard has passed here, on her way up the mountain to find you or me."

"I like your reckonin'."

"She's suddenly discovered somethin', Injuns, hoss-thieves, the Fort Henry traitor, or mebbe, an' most likely, some plottin'. Bein' bound to secrecy by me, she's not told my brother. An' it must be call for hurry. She knows we frequent this mountain-top; said Eb told her about the way we get here."

"I'd calkilate about the same."

"What'll you do? Go with me after her?" asked Jonathan.

"I'll take the hosses, an' be at the fort inside of an hour. If Helen's gone, I'll tell her father you're close on her trail. Now listen! It'll be dark soon, an' a storm's comin'. Don't waste time on her trail. Hurry up to the rock. She'll be there, if any lass could climb there. If not, come back in the mornin', hunt her trail out, an' find her. I'm thinkin', Jack, we'll find the Shawnee had somethin' to do with this. Whatever happens after I get back to the fort, I'll expect you hard on my trail."

Jonathan bounded across the brook and with an easy lope began the gradual ascent. Soon he came upon a winding path. He ran along this for perhaps a quarter of an hour, until it became too steep for rapid traveling, when he settled down to a rapid walk. The forest was already dark. A slight rustling of the leaves beneath his feet was the only sound, except at long intervals the distant rumbling of thunder.

The mere possibility of Helen's being alone on that mountain seeking him, made Jonathan's heart beat as it never had before. For weeks he had avoided her, almost forgot her. He had conquered the strange, yearning weakness which assailed him after that memorable Sunday, and once more the silent shaded glens, the mystery of the woods, the breath of his wild, free life had claimed him. But now as this evidence of her spirit, her recklessness, was before him, and he remembered Betty's avowal, a pain, which was almost physical, tore at his heart. How terrible it would be if she came to her death through him! He pictured the big, alluring eyes, the perfect lips, the haunting face, cold in death. And he shuddered.

The dim gloom of the woods soon darkened into blackness. The flashes of lightning, momentarily streaking the foliage, or sweeping overhead in pale yellow sheets, aided Jonathan in keeping the trail.

He gained the plateau just as a great flash illumined it, and distinctly saw the dark hollow where he had taken refuge in many a storm, and where he now hoped to find the girl. Picking his way carefully over the sharp, loose stones, he at last put his hand on the huge rock. Another blue-white, dazzling flash enveloped the scene.

Under the rock he saw a dark form huddled, and a face as white as snow, with wide, horrified eyes.

"Lass," he said, when the thunder had rumbled away. He received no answer, and called again. Kneeling, he groped about until touching Helen's dress. He spoke again; but she did not reply.

Jonathan crawled under the ledge beside the quiet figure. He touched her hands; they were very cold. Bending over, he was relieved to hear her heart beating. He called her name, but still she made no reply. Dipping his hand into a little rill that ran beside the stone, he bathed her face. Soon she stirred uneasily, moaned, and suddenly sat up.

"'Tis Jonathan," he said quickly; "don't be scared."

Another illuminating flare of lightning brightened the plateau.

"Oh! thank Heaven!" cried Helen. "I thought you were an Indian!"

Helen sank trembling against the borderman, who enfolded her in his long arms. Her relief and thankfulness were so great that she could not speak. Her hands clasped and unclasped round his strong fingers. Her tears flowed freely.

The storm broke with terrific fury. A seething torrent of rain and hail came with the rushing wind. Great heaven-broad sheets of lightning played across the black dome overhead. Zigzag ropes, steel-blue in color, shot downward. Crash, and crack, and boom the thunder split and rolled the clouds above. The lightning flashes showed the fall of rain in columns like white waterfalls, borne on the irresistible wind.

The grandeur of the storm awed, and stilled Helen's emotion. She sat there watching the lightning, listening to the peals of thunder, and thrilling with the wonder of the situation.

Gradually the roar abated, the flashes became less frequent, the thunder decreased, as the storm wore out its strength in passing. The wind and rain ceased on the mountain-top almost as quickly as they had begun, and the roar died slowly away in the distance. Far to the eastward flashes of light illumined scowling clouds, and brightened many a dark, wooded hill and valley.

"Lass, how is't I find you here?" asked Jonathan gravely.

With many a pause and broken phrase, Helen told the story of what she had seen and heard at the spring.

"Child, why didn't you go to my brother?" asked Jonathan. "You don't know what you undertook!"

"I thought of everything; but I wanted to find you myself. Besides, I was just as safe alone on this mountain as in the village."

"I don't know but you're right," replied Jonathan thoughtfully. "So Brandt planned to make off with you to-morrow?"

"Yes, and when I heard it I wanted to run away from the village."

"You've done a wondrous clever thing, lass. This Brandt is a bad man, an' hard to match. But if he hasn't shaken Fort Henry by now, his career'll end mighty sudden, an' his bad trails stop short on the hillside among the graves, for Eb will always give outlaws or Injuns decent burial."

"What will the colonel, or anyone, think has become of me?"

"Wetzel knows, lass, for he found your trail below."

"Then he'll tell papa you came after me? Oh! poor papa! I forgot him. Shall we stay here until daylight?"

"We'd gain nothin' by startin' now. The brooks are full, an' in the dark we'd make little distance. You're dry here, an' comfortable. What's more, lass, you're safe."

"I feel perfectly safe, with you," Helen said softly.

"Aren't you tired, lass?"

"Tired? I'm nearly dead. My feet are cut and bruised, my wrist is sprained, and I ache all over. But, Jonathan, I don't care. I am so happy to have my wild venture turn out successfully."

"You can lie here an' sleep while I keep watch."

Jonathan made a move to withdraw his arm, which was still between Helen and the rock but had dropped from her waist.

"I am very comfortable. I'll sit here with you, watching for daybreak. My! how dark it is! I cannot see my hand before my eyes."

Helen settled herself back upon the stone, leaned a very little against his shoulder, and tried to think over her adventure. But her mind refused to entertain any ideas, except those of the present. Mingled with the dreamy lassitude that grew stronger every moment, was a sense of delight in her situation. She was alone on a wild mountain, in the night, with this borderman, the one she loved. By chance and her own foolhardiness this had come about, yet she was fortunate to have it tend to some good beyond her own happiness. All she would suffer from her perilous climb would be aching bones, and, perhaps, a scolding from her father. What she might gain was more than she had dared hope. The breaking up of the horse-thief gang would be a boon to the harassed settlement. How proudly Colonel Zane would smile! Her name would go on that long roll of border honor and heroism. That was not, however, one thousandth part so pleasing, as to be alone with her borderman.

With a sigh of mingled weariness and content, Helen leaned her head on Jonathan's shoulder and fell asleep.

The borderman trembled. The sudden nestling of her head against him, the light caress of her fragrant hair across his cheek, revived a sweet, almost-conquered, almost-forgotten emotion. He felt an inexplicable thrill vibrate through him. No untrodden, ambushed wild, no perilous trail, no dark and bloody encounter had ever made him feel fear as had the kiss of this maiden. He had sternly silenced faint, unfamiliar, yet tender, voices whispering in his heart; and now his rigorous discipline was as if it were not, for at her touch he trembled. Still he did not move away. He knew she had succumbed to weariness, and was fast asleep. He could, gently, without awakening her, have laid her head upon the pillow of leaves; indeed, he thought of doing it, but made no effort. A woman's head softly lying against him was a thing novel, strange, wonderful. For all the power he had then, each tumbling lock of her hair might as well have been a chain linking him fast to the mountain.

With the memory of his former yearning, unsatisfied moods, and the unrest and pain his awakening tenderness had caused him, came a determination to look things fairly in the face, to be just in thought toward this innocent, impulsive girl, and be honest with himself.

Duty commanded that he resist all charm other than that pertaining to his life in the woods. Years ago he had accepted a borderman's destiny, well content to be recompensed by its untamed freedom from restraint; to be always under the trees he loved so well; to lend his cunning and woodcraft in the pioneer's cause; to haunt the savage trails; to live from day to day a menace to the foes of civilization. That was the life he had chosen; it was all he could ever have.

In view of this, justice demanded that he allow no friendship to spring up between himself and this girl. If his sister's belief was really true, if Helen really was interested in him, it must be a romantic infatuation which, not encouraged, would wear itself out. What was he, to win the love of any girl? An unlettered borderman, who knew only the woods, whose life was hard and cruel, whose hands were red with Indian blood, whose vengeance had not spared men even of his own race. He could not believe she really loved him. Wildly impulsive as girls were at times, she had kissed him. She had been grateful, carried away by a generous feeling for him as the protector of her father. When she did not see him for a long time, as he vowed should be the case after he had carried her safely home, she would forget.

Then honesty demanded that he probe his own feelings. Sternly, as if judging a renegade, he searched out in his simple way the truth. This big-eyed lass with her nameless charm would bewitch even a borderman, unless he avoided her. So much he had not admitted until now. Love he had never believed could be possible for him. When she fell asleep her hand had slipped from his arm to his fingers, and now rested there lightly as a leaf. The contact was delight. The gentle night breeze blew a tress of hair across his lips. He trembled. Her rounded shoulder pressed against him until he could feel her slow, deep breathing. He almost held his own breath lest he disturb her rest.

No, he was no longer indifferent. As surely as those pale stars blinked far above, he knew the delight of a woman's presence. It moved him to study the emotion, as he studied all things, which was the habit of his borderman's life. Did it come from knowledge of her beauty, matchless as that of the mountain-laurel? He recalled the dark glance of her challenging eyes, her tall, supple figure, and the bewildering excitation and magnetism of her presence. Beauty was wonderful, but not everything. Beauty belonged to her, but she would have been irresistible without it. Was it not because she was a woman? That was the secret. She was a woman with all a woman's charm to bewitch, to twine round the strength of men as the ivy encircles the oak; with all a woman's weakness to pity and to guard; with all a woman's wilful burning love, and with all a woman's mystery.

At last so much of life was intelligible to him. The renegade committed his worst crimes because even in his outlawed, homeless state, he could not exist without the companionship, if not the love, of a woman. The pioneer's toil and privation were for a woman, and the joy of loving her and living for her. The Indian brave, when not on the war-path, walked hand in hand with a dusky, soft-eyed maiden, and sang to her of moonlit lakes and western winds. Even the birds and beasts mated. The robins returned to their old nest; the eagles paired once and were constant in life and death. The buck followed the doe through the forest. All nature sang that love made life worth living. Love, then, was everything.

The borderman sat out the long vigil of the night watching the stars, and trying to decide that love was not for him. If Wetzel had locked a secret within his breast, and never in all these years spoke of it to his companion, then surely that companion could as well live without love. Stern, dark, deadly work must stain and blot all tenderness from his life, else it would be unutterably barren. The joy of living, of unharassed freedom he had always known. If a fair face and dark, mournful eyes were to haunt him on every lonely trail, then it were better an Indian should end his existence.

The darkest hour before dawn, as well as the darkest of doubt and longing in Jonathan's life, passed away. A gray gloom obscured the pale, winking stars; the east slowly whitened, then brightened, and at length day broke misty and fresh.

The borderman rose to stretch his cramped limbs. When he turned to the little cavern the girl's eyes were wide open. All the darkness, the shadow, the beauty, and the thought of the past night, lay in their blue depths. He looked away across the valley where the sky was reddening and a pale rim of gold appeared above the hill-tops.

"Well, if I haven't been asleep!" exclaimed Helen, with a low, soft laugh.

"You're rested, I hope," said Jonathan, with averted eyes. He dared not look at her.

"Oh, yes, indeed. I am ready to start at once. How gray, how beautiful the morning is! Shall we be long? I hope papa knows."

In silence the borderman led the way across the rocky plateau, and into the winding, narrow trail. His pale, slightly drawn and stern, face did not invite conversation, therefore Helen followed silently in his footsteps. The way was steep, and at times he was forced to lend her aid. She put her hand in his and jumped lightly as a fawn. Presently a brawling brook, over-crowding its banks, impeded further progress.

"I'll have to carry you across," said Jonathan.

"I'm very heavy," replied Helen, with a smile in her eyes.

She flushed as the borderman put his right arm around her waist. Then a clasp as of steel enclosed her; she felt herself swinging easily into the air, and over the muddy brook.

Farther down the mountain this troublesome brook again crossed the trail, this time much wider and more formidable. Helen looked with some vexation and embarrassment into the borderman's face. It was always the same, stern, almost cold.

"Perhaps I'd better wade," she said hesitatingly.

"Why? The water's deep an' cold. You'd better not get wet."

Helen flushed, but did not answer. With downcast eyes she let herself be carried on his powerful arm.

The wading was difficult this time. The water foamed furiously around his knees. Once he slipped on a stone, and nearly lost his balance. Uttering a little scream Helen grasped at him wildly, and her arm encircled his neck. What was still more trying, when he put her on her feet again, it was found that her hair had become entangled in the porcupine quills on his hunting-coat.

She stood before him while with clumsy fingers he endeavored to untangle the shimmering strands; but in vain. Helen unwound the snarl of wavy hair. Most alluring she was then, with a certain softness on her face, and light and laughter, and something warm in her eyes.

The borderman felt that he breathed a subtle exhilaration which emanated from her glowing, gracious beauty. She radiated with the gladness of life, with an uncontainable sweetness and joy. But, giving no token of his feeling, he turned to march on down through the woods.

From this point the trail broadened, descending at an easier angle.

Jonathan's stride lengthened until Helen was forced to walk rapidly, and sometimes run, in order to keep close behind him. A quick journey home was expedient, and in order to accomplish this she would gladly have exerted herself to a greater extent. When they reached the end of the trail where the forest opened clear of brush, finally to merge into the broad, verdant plain, the sun had chased the mist-clouds from the eastern hill-tops, and was gloriously brightening the valley.

With the touch of sentiment natural to her, Helen gazed backward for one more view of the mountain-top. The wall of rugged rock she had so often admired from her window at home, which henceforth would ever hold a tender place of remembrance in her heart, rose out of a gray-blue bank of mist. The long, swelling slope lay clear to the sunshine. With the rays of the sun gleaming and glistening upon the variegated foliage, and upon the shiny rolling haze above, a beautiful picture of autumn splendor was before her. Tall pines, here and there towered high and lonely over the surrounding trees. Their dark, green, graceful heads stood in bold relief above the gold and yellow crests beneath. Maples, tinged from faintest pink to deepest rose, added warm color to the scene, and chestnuts with their brown-white burrs lent fresher beauty to the undulating slope.

The remaining distance to the settlement was short. Jonathan spoke only once to Helen, then questioning her as to where she had left her canoe. They traversed the meadow, found the boat in the thicket of willows, and were soon under the frowning bluff of Fort Henry. Ascending the steep path, they followed the road leading to Colonel Zane's cabin.

A crowd of boys, men and women loitering near the bluff arrested Helen's attention. Struck by this unusual occurrence, she wondered what was the cause of such idleness among the busy pioneer people. They were standing in little groups. Some made vehement gestures, others conversed earnestly, and yet more were silent. On seeing Jonathan, a number shouted and pointed toward the inn. The borderman hurried Helen along the path, giving no heed to the throng.

But Helen had seen the cause of all this excitement. At first glance she thought Metzar's inn had been burned; but a second later it could be seen that the smoke came from a smoldering heap of rubbish in the road. The inn, nevertheless, had been wrecked. Windows stared with that vacantness peculiar to deserted houses. The doors were broken from their hinges. A pile of furniture, rude tables, chairs, beds, and other articles, were heaped beside the smoking rubbish. Scattered around lay barrels and kegs all with gaping sides and broken heads. Liquor had stained the road, where it had been soaked up by the thirsty dust.

Upon a shattered cellar-door lay a figure covered with a piece of rag carpet. When Helen's quick eyes took in this last, she turned away in horror. That motionless form might be Brandt's. Remorse and womanly sympathy surged over her, for bad as the man had shown himself, he had loved her.

She followed the borderman, trying to compose herself. As they neared Colonel Zane's cabin she saw her father, Will, the colonel, Betty, Nell, Mrs. Zane, Silas Zane, and others whom she did not recognize. They were all looking at her. Helen's throat swelled, and her eyes filled when she got near enough to see her father's haggard, eager face. The others were grave. She wondered guiltily if she had done much wrong.

In another moment she was among them. Tears fell as her father extended his trembling hands to clasp her, and as she hid her burning face on his breast, he cried: "My dear, dear child!" Then Betty gave her a great hug, and Nell flew about them like a happy bird. Colonel Zane's face was pale, and wore a clouded, stern expression. She smiled timidly at him through her tears. "Well! well! well!" he mused, while his gaze softened. That was all he said; but he took her hand and held it while he turned to Jonathan.

The borderman leaned on his long rifle, regarding him with expectant eyes.

"Well, Jack, you missed a little scrimmage this morning. Wetzel got in at daybreak. The storm and horses held him up on the other side of the river until daylight. He told me of your suspicions, with the additional news that he'd found a fresh Indian trail on the island just across from the inn. We went down not expecting to find any one awake; but Metzar was hurriedly packing some of his traps. Half a dozen men were there, having probably stayed all night. That little English cuss was one of them, and another, an ugly fellow, a stranger to us, but evidently a woodsman. Things looked bad. Metzar told a decidedly conflicting story. Wetzel and I went outside to talk over the situation, with the result that I ordered him to clean out the place."

Here Colonel Zane paused to indulge in a grim, meaning laugh.

"Well, he cleaned out the place all right. The ugly stranger got rattlesnake-mad, and yanked out a big knife. Sam is hitching up the team now to haul what's left of him up on the hillside. Metzar resisted arrest, and got badly hurt. He's in the guardhouse. Case, who has been drunk for a week, got in Wetzel's way and was kicked into the middle of next week. He's been spitting blood for the last hour, but I guess he's not much hurt. Brandt flew the coop last night. Wetzel found this hid in his room."

Colonel Zane took a long, feathered arrow from where it lay on a bench, and held it out to Jonathan.

"The Shawnee signal! Wetzel had it right," muttered the borderman.

"Exactly. Lew found where the arrow struck in the wall of Brandt's room. It was shot from the island at the exact spot where Lew came to an end of the Indian's trail in the water."

"That Shawnee got away from us."

"So Lew said. Well, he's gone now. So is Brandt. We're well rid of the gang, if only we never hear of them again."

The borderman shook his head. During the colonel's recital his face changed. The dark eyes had become deadly; the square jaw was shut, the lines of the cheek had grown tense, and over his usually expressive countenance had settled a chill, lowering shade.

"Lew thinks Brandt's in with Bing Legget. Well, d—— his black traitor heart! He's a good man for the worst and strongest gang that ever tracked the border."

The borderman was silent; but the furtive, restless shifting of his eyes over the river and island, hill and valley, spoke more plainly than words.

"You're to take his trail at once," added Colonel Zane. "I had Bess put you up some bread, meat and parched corn. No doubt you'll have a long, hard tramp. Good luck."

The borderman went into the cabin, presently emerging with a buckskin knapsack strapped to his shoulder. He set off eastward with a long, swinging stride.

The women had taken Helen within the house where, no doubt, they could discuss with greater freedom the events of the previous day.

"Sheppard," said Colonel Zane, turning with a sparkle in his eyes. "Brandt was after Helen sure as a bad weed grows fast. And certain as death Jonathan and Wetzel will see him cold and quiet back in the woods. That's a border saying, and it means a good deal. I never saw Wetzel so implacable, nor Jonathan so fatally cold but once, and that was when Miller, another traitor, much like Brandt, tried to make away with Betty. It would have chilled your blood to see Wetzel go at that fool this morning. Why did he want to pull a knife on the borderman? It was a sad sight. Well, these things are justifiable. We must protect ourselves, and above all our women. We've had bad men, and a bad man out here is something you cannot yet appreciate, come here and slip into the life of the settlement, because on the border you can never tell what a man is until he proves himself. There have been scores of criminals spread over the frontier, and some better men, like Simon Girty, who were driven to outlaw life. Simon must not be confounded with Jim Girty, absolutely the most fiendish desperado who ever lived. Why, even the Indians feared Jim so much that after his death his skeleton remained unmolested in the glade where he was killed. The place is believed to be haunted now, by all Indians and many white hunters, and I believe the bones stand there yet."

"Stand?" asked Sheppard, deeply interested.

"Yes, it stands where Girty stood and died, upright against a tree, pinned, pinned there by a big knife."

"Heavens, man! Who did it?" Sheppard cried in horror.

Again Colonel Zane's laugh, almost metallic, broke grimly from his lips.

"Who? Why, Wetzel, of course. Lew hunted Jim Girty five long years. When he caught him—God! I'll tell you some other time. Jonathan saw Wetzel handle Jim and his pal, Deering, as if they were mere boys. Well, as I said, the border has had, and still has, its bad men. Simon Girty took McKee and Elliott, the Tories, from Fort Pitt, when he deserted, and ten men besides. They're all, except those who are dead, outlaws of the worst type. The other bad men drifted out here from Lord only knows where. They're scattered all over. Simon Girty, since his crowning black deed, the massacre of the Christian Indians, is in hiding. Bing Legget now has the field. He's a hard nut, a cunning woodsman, and capable leader who surrounds himself with only the most desperate Indians and renegades. Brandt is an agent of Legget's and I'll bet we'll hear from him again."

CHAPTER XIII.

Jonathan traveled toward the east straight as a crow flies. Wetzel's trail as he pursued Brandt had been left designedly plain. Branches of young maples had been broken by the borderman; they were glaring evidences of his passage. On open ground, or through swampy meadows he had contrived to leave other means to facilitate his comrade's progress. Bits of sumach lay strewn along the way, every red, leafy branch a bright marker of the course; crimson maple leaves served their turn, and even long-bladed ferns were scattered at intervals.

Ten miles east of Fort Henry, at a point where two islands lay opposite each other, Wetzel had crossed the Ohio. Jonathan removed his clothing, and tying these, together with his knapsack, to the rifle, held them above the water while he swam the three narrow channels. He took up the trail again, finding here, as he expected, where Brandt had joined the waiting Shawnee chief. The borderman pressed on harder to the eastward.

About the middle of the afternoon signs betokened that Wetzel and his quarry were not far in advance. Fresh imprints in the grass; crushed asters and moss, broken branches with unwithered leaves, and plots of grassy ground where Jonathan saw that the blades of grass were yet springing back to their original position, proved to the borderman's practiced eye that he was close upon Wetzel.

In time he came to a grove of yellow birch trees. The ground was nearly free from brush, beautifully carpeted with flowers and ferns, and, except where bushy windfalls obstructed the way, was singularly open to the gaze for several hundred yards ahead.

Upon entering this wood Wetzel's plain, intentional markings became manifest, then wavered, and finally disappeared. Jonathan pondered a moment. He concluded that the way was so open and clear, with nothing but grass and moss to mark a trail, that Wetzel had simply considered it waste of time for, perhaps, the short length of this grove.

Jonathan knew he was wrong after taking a dozen steps more. Wetzel's trail, known so well to him, as never to be mistaken, sheered abruptly off to the left, and, after a few yards, the distance between the footsteps widened perceptibly. Then came a point where they were so far apart that they could only have been made by long leaps.

On the instant the borderman knew that some unforeseen peril or urgent cause had put Wetzel to flight, and he now bent piercing eyes around the grove. Retracing his steps to where he had found the break in the trail, he followed up Brandt's tracks for several rods. Not one hundred paces beyond where Wetzel had quit the pursuit, were the remains of a camp fire, the embers still smoldering, and moccasin tracks of a small band of Indians. The trail of Brandt and his Shawnee guide met the others at almost right angles.

The Indian, either by accident or design, had guided Brandt to a band of his fellows, and thus led Wetzel almost into an ambush.

Evidence was not clear, however, that the Indians had discovered the keen tracker who had run almost into their midst.

While studying the forest ahead Jonathan's mind was running over the possibilities. How close was Wetzel? Was he still in flight? Had the savages an inkling of his pursuit? Or was he now working out one of his cunning tricks of woodcraft? The borderman had no other idea than that of following the trail to learn all this. Taking the desperate chances warranted under the circumstances, he walked boldly forward in his comrade's footsteps.

Deep and gloomy was the forest adjoining the birch grove. It was a heavy growth of hardwood trees, interspersed with slender ash and maples, which with their scanty foliage resembled a labyrinth of green and yellow network, like filmy dotted lace, hung on the taller, darker oaks. Jonathan felt safer in this deep wood. He could still see several rods in advance. Following the trail, he was relieved to see that Wetzel's leaps had become shorter and shorter, until they once again were about the length of a long stride. The borderman was, moreover, swinging in a curve to the northeast. This was proof that the borderman had not been pursued, but was making a wide detour to get ahead of the enemy. Five hundred yards farther on the trail turned sharply toward the birch grove in the rear.

The trail was fresh. Wetzel was possibly within signal call; surely within sound of a rifle shot. But even more stirring was the certainty that Brandt and his Indians were inside the circle Wetzel had made.

Once again in sight of the more open woodland, Jonathan crawled on his hands and knees, keeping close to the cluster of ferns, until well within the eastern end of the grove. He lay for some minutes listening. A threatening silence, like the hush before a storm, permeated the wilderness. He peered out from his covert; but, owing to its location in a little hollow, he could not see far. Crawling to the nearest tree he rose to his feet slowly, cautiously.

No unnatural sight or sound arrested his attention. Repeatedly, with the acute, unsatisfied gaze of the borderman who knew that every tree, every patch of ferns, every tangled brush-heap might harbor a foe, he searched the grove with his eyes; but the curly-barked birches, the clumps of colored ferns, the bushy windfalls kept their secrets.

For the borderman, however, the whole aspect of the birch-grove had changed. Over the forest was a deep calm. A gentle, barely perceptible wind sighed among the leaves, like rustling silk. The far-off drowsy drum of a grouse intruded on the vast stillness. The silence of the birds betokened a message. That mysterious breathing, that beautiful life of the woods lay hushed, locked in a waiting, brooding silence. Far away among the somber trees, where the shade deepened into impenetrable gloom, lay a menace, invisible and indefinable.

A wind, a breath, a chill, terribly potent, seemed to pass over the borderman. Long experience had given him intuition of danger.

As he moved slightly, with lynx-eyes fixed on the grove before him, a sharp, clear, perfect bird-note broke the ominous quiet. It was like the melancholy cry of an oriole, short, deep, suggestive of lonely forest dells. By a slight variation in the short call, Jonathan recognized it as a signal from Wetzel. The borderman smiled as he realized that with all his stealth, Wetzel had heard or seen him re-enter the grove. The signal was a warning to stand still or retreat.

Jonathan's gaze narrowed down to the particular point whence had come the signal. Some two hundred yards ahead in this direction were several large trees standing in a group. With one exception, they all had straight trunks. This deviated from the others in that it possessed an irregular, bulging trunk, or else half-shielded the form of Wetzel. So indistinct and immovable was this irregularity, that the watcher could not be certain. Out of line, somewhat, with this tree which he suspected screened his comrade, lay a huge windfall large enough to conceal in ambush a whole band of savages.

Even as he gazed a sheet of flame flashed from this covert.

Crack!

A loud report followed; then the whistle and zip of a bullet as it whizzed close by his head.

"Shawnee lead!" muttered Jonathan.

Unfortunately the tree he had selected did not hide him sufficiently. His shoulders were so wide that either one or the other was exposed, affording a fine target for a marksman.

A quick glance showed him a change in the knotty tree-trunk; the seeming bulge was now the well-known figure of Wetzel.

Jonathan dodged as some object glanced slantingly before his eyes.

Twang. Whizz. Thud. Three familiar and distinct sounds caused him to press hard against the tree.

A tufted arrow quivered in the bark not a foot from his head.

"Close shave! Damn that arrow-shootin' Shawnee!" muttered Jonathan. "An' he ain't in that windfall either." His eyes searched to the left for the

498

source of this new peril.

Another sheet of flame, another report from the windfall. A bullet sang, close overhead, and, glancing on a branch, went harmlessly into the forest.

"Injuns all around; I guess I'd better be makin' tracks," Jonathan said to himself, peering out to learn if Wetzel was still under cover.

He saw the tall figure straighten up; a long, black rifle rise to a level and become rigid; a red fire belch forth, followed by a puff of white smoke.

Spang!

An Indian's horrible, strangely-breaking death yell rent the silence.

Then a chorus of plaintive howls, followed by angry shouts, rang through the forest. Naked, painted savages darted out of the windfall toward the tree that had sheltered Wetzel.

Quick as thought Jonathan covered the foremost Indian, and with the crack of his rifle saw the redskin drop his gun, stop in his mad run, stagger sideways, and fall. Then the borderman looked to see what had become of his ally. The cracking of the Indian's rifle told him that Wetzel had been seen by his foes.

With almost incredible fleetness a brown figure with long black hair streaming behind, darted in and out among the trees, flashed through the sunlit glade, and vanished in the dark depths of the forest.

Jonathan turned to flee also, when he heard again the twanging of an Indian's bow. A wind smote his cheek, a shock blinded him, an excruciating pain seized upon his breast. A feathered arrow had pinned his shoulder to the tree. He raised his hand to pull it out; but, slippery with blood, it afforded a poor hold for his fingers. Violently exerting himself, with both hands he wrenched away the weapon. The flint-head lacerating his flesh and scraping his shoulder bones caused sharpest agony. The pain gave away to a sudden sense of giddiness; he tried to run; a dark mist veiled his sight; he stumbled and fell. Then he seemed to sink into a great darkness, and knew no more.

When consciousness returned to Jonathan it was night. He lay on his back, and knew because of his cramped limbs that he had been securely bound. He saw the glimmer of a fire, but could not raise his head. A rustling of leaves in the wind told that he was yet in the woods, and the distant rumble of a waterfall sounded familiar. He felt drowsy; his wound smarted slightly, still he did not suffer any pain. Presently he fell asleep.

Broad daylight had come when again he opened his eyes. The blue sky was directly above, and before him he saw a ledge covered with dwarfed pine trees. He turned his head, and saw that he was in a sort of amphitheater of about two acres in extent enclosed by low cliffs. A cleft in the stony wall let out a brawling brook, and served, no doubt, as entrance to the place. Several rude log cabins stood on that side of the enclosure. Jonathan knew he had been brought to Bing Legget's retreat.

Voices attracted his attention, and, turning his head to the other side, he saw a big Indian pacing near him, and beyond, seven savages and three white men reclining in the shade.

The powerful, dark-visaged savage near him he at once recognized as Ashbow, the Shawnee chief, and noted emissary of Bing Legget. Of the other Indians, three were Delawares, and four Shawnees, all veterans, with swarthy, somber faces and glistening heads on which the scalp-locks were trimmed and tufted. Their naked, muscular bodies were painted for the war-path with their strange emblems of death. A trio of white men, nearly as bronzed as their savage comrades, completed the group. One, a desperate-looking outlaw, Jonathan did not know. The blond-bearded giant in the center was Legget. Steel-blue, inhuman eyes, with the expression of a free but hunted animal; a set, mastiff-like jaw, brutal and coarse, individualized him. The last man was the haggard-faced Brandt.

"I tell ye, Brandt, I ain't agoin' against this Injun," Legget was saying positively. "He's the best reddy on the border, an' has saved me scores of times. This fellar Zane belongs to him, an' while I'd much rather see the scout knifed right here an' now, I won't do nothin' to interfere with the Shawnee's plans."

"Why does the redskin want to take him away to his village?" Brandt growled. "All Injun vanity and pride."

"It's Injun ways, an' we can't do nothin' to change 'em."

"But you're boss here. You could make him put this borderman out of the way."

"Wal, I ain't agoin' ter interfere. Anyways, Brandt, the Shawnee'll make short work of the scout when he gits him among the tribe. Injuns is Injuns. It's a great honor fer him to git Zane, an' he wants his own people to figger in the finish. Quite nat'r'l, I reckon."

"I understand all that; but it's not safe for us, and it's courting death for Ashbow. Why don't he keep Zane here until you can spare more than three Indians to go with him? These bordermen can't be stopped. You don't know them, because you're new in this part of the country."

"I've been here as long as you, an' agoin' some, too, I reckon," replied Legget complacently.

"But you've not been hunted until lately by these bordermen, and you've had little opportunity to hear of them except from Indians. What can you learn from these silent redskins? I tell you, letting this fellow get out of here alive, even for an hour is a fatal mistake. It's two full days' tramp to the Shawnee village. You don't suppose Wetzel will be afraid of four savages? Why, he sneaked right into eight of us, when we were ambushed, waiting for him. He killed one and then was gone like a streak. It was only a piece of pure luck we got Zane."

"I've reason to know this Wetzel, this Deathwind, as the Delawares call him. I never seen him though, an' anyways, I reckon I can handle him if ever I get the chance."

"Man, you're crazy!" cried Brandt. "He'd cut you to pieces before you'd have time to draw. He could give you a tomahawk, then take it away and split your head. I tell you I know! You remember Jake Deering? He came from up your way. Wetzel fought Deering and Jim Girty together, and killed them. You know how he left Girty."

"I'll allow he must be a fighter; but I ain't afraid of him."

"That's not the question. I am talking sense. You've got a chance now to put one of these bordermen out of the way. Do it quick! That's my advice."

Brandt spoke so vehemently that Legget seemed impressed. He stroked his yellow beard, and puffed thoughtfully on his pipe. Presently he addressed the Shawnee chief in the native tongue.

"Will Ashbow take five horses for his prisoner?"

The Indian shook his head.

"How many will he take?"

The chief strode with dignity to and fro before his captive. His dark, impassive face gave no clew to his thoughts; but his lofty bearing, his measured, stately walk were indicative of great pride. Then he spoke in his deep bass:

"The Shawnee knows the woods from the Great Lakes where the sun sets, to the Blue Hills where it rises. He has met the great paleface hunters. Only for Deathwind will Ashbow trade his captive."

"See? It ain't no use," said Legget, spreading out his hands, "Let him go. He'll outwit the bordermen if any redskin's able to. The sooner he goes the quicker he'll git back, an' we can go to work. You ought'er be satisfied to git the girl——"

"Shut up!" interrupted Brandt sharply.

"'Pears to me, Brandt, bein' in love hes kinder worked on your nerves. You used to be game. Now you're afeerd of a bound an' tied man who ain't got long to live."

"I fear no man," answered Brandt, scowling darkly. "But I know what you don't seem to have sense enough to see. If this Zane gets away, which is probable, he and Wetzel will clean up your gang."

"Haw! haw! haw!" roared Legget, slapping his knees. "Then you'd hev little chanst of gittin' the lass, eh?"

"All right. I've no more to say," snapped Brandt, rising and turning on his heel. As he passed Jonathan he paused. "Zane, if I could, I'd get even with you for that punch you once gave me. As it is, I'll stop at the Shawnee village on my way west——"

"With the pretty lass," interposed Legget.

"Where I hope to see your scalp drying in the chief's lodge."

The borderman eyed him steadily; but in silence. Words could not so well have conveyed his thought as did the cold glance of dark scorn and merciless meaning.

Brandt shuffled on with a curse. No coward was he. No man ever saw him flinch. But his intelligence was against him as a desperado. While such as these bordermen lived, an outlaw should never sleep, for he was a marked and doomed man. The deadly, cold-pointed flame which scintillated in the prisoner's eyes was only a gleam of what the border felt towards outlaws.

While Jonathan was considering all he had heard, three more Shawnees entered the retreat, and were at once called aside in consultation by Ashbow. At the conclusion of this brief conference the chief advanced to Jonathan, cut the bonds round his feet, and motioned for him to rise. The prisoner complied to find himself weak and sore, but able to walk. He concluded that his wound, while very painful, was not of a serious nature, and that he would be taken at once on the march toward the Shawnee village.

He was correct, for the chief led him, with the three Shawnees following, toward the outlet of the enclosure. Jonathan's sharp eye took in every detail of Legget's rendezvous. In a corral near the entrance, he saw a number of fine horses, and among them his sister's pony. A more inaccessible, natural refuge than Legget's, could hardly have been found in that country. The entrance was a narrow opening in the wall, and could be held by half a dozen against an army of besiegers. It opened, moreover, on the side of a barren hill, from which could be had a good survey of the surrounding forests and plains.

As Jonathan went with his captors down the hill his hopes, which while ever alive, had been flagging, now rose. The long journey to the Shawnee town led through an untracked wilderness. The Delaware villages lay far to the north; the Wyandot to the west. No likelihood was there of falling in with a band of Indians hunting, because this region, stony, barren, and poorly watered, afforded sparse pasture for deer or bison. From the prisoner's point of view this enterprise of Ashbow's was reckless and vainglorious. Cunning as the chief was, he erred in one point, a great warrior's only weakness, love of show, of pride, of his achievement. In Indian nature this desire for fame was as strong as love of life. The brave risked everything to win his eagle feathers, and the matured warrior found death while keeping bright the glory of the plumes he had won.

Wetzel was in the woods, fleet as a deer, fierce and fearless as a lion. Somewhere among those glades he trod, stealthily, with the ears of a doe and eyes of a hawk strained for sound or sight of his comrade's captors. When he found their trail he would stick to it as the wolf to that of a bleeding buck's. The rescue would not be attempted until the right moment, even though that came within rifle-shot of the Shawnee encampment. Wonderful as his other gifts, was the borderman's patience.

CHAPTER XIV.

"Good morning, Colonel Zane," said Helen cheerily, coming into the yard where the colonel was at work. "Did Will come over this way?"

"I reckon you'll find him if you find Betty," replied Colonel Zane dryly.

"Come to think of it, that's true," Helen said, laughing. "I've a suspicion Will ran off from me this morning."

"He and Betty have gone nutting."

"I declare it's mean of Will," Helen said petulantly. "I have been wanting to go so much, and both he and Betty promised to take me."

"Say, Helen, let me tell you something," said the colonel, resting on his spade and looking at her quizzically. "I told them we hadn't had enough frost yet to ripen hickory-nuts and chestnuts. But they went anyhow. Will did remember to say if you came along, to tell you he'd bring the colored leaves you wanted."

"How extremely kind of him. I've a mind to follow them."

"Now see here, Helen, it might be a right good idea for you not to," returned the colonel, with a twinkle and a meaning in his eye.

"Oh, I understand. How singularly dull I've been."

"It's this way. We're mighty glad to have a fine young fellow like Will come along and interest Betty. Lord knows we had a time with her after Alfred died. She's just beginning to brighten up now, and, Helen, the point is that young people on the border must get married. No, my dear, you needn't laugh, you'll have to find a husband same as the other girls. It's not here as it was back east, where a lass might have her fling, so to speak, and take her time choosing. An unmarried girl on the border is a positive menace. I saw, not many years ago, two first-rate youngsters, wild with border fire and spirit, fight and kill each other over a lass who wouldn't choose. Like as not, if she had done so, the three would have been good friends, for out here we're like one big family. Remember this, Helen, and as far as Betty and Will are concerned you will be wise to follow our example: Leave them to themselves. Nothing else will so quickly strike fire between a boy and a girl."

"Betty and Will! I'm sure I'd love to see them care for each other." Then with big, bright eyes bent gravely on him she continued, "May I ask, Colonel Zane, who you have picked out for me?"

"There, now you've said it, and that's the problem. I've looked over every marriageable young man in the settlement, except Jack. Of course you couldn't care for him, a borderman, a fighter and all that; but I can't find a fellow I think quite up to you."

"Colonel Zane, is not a borderman such as Jonathan worthy a woman's regard?" Helen asked a little wistfully.

"Bless your heart, lass, yes!" replied Colonel Zane heartily. "People out here are not as they are back east. An educated man, polished and all that, but incapable of hard labor, or shrinking from dirt and sweat on his hands, or even blood, would not help us in the winning of the West. Plain as Jonathan is, and with his lack of schooling, he is greatly superior to the majority of young men on the frontier. But, unlettered or not, he is as fine a man as ever stepped in moccasins, or any other kind of foot gear."

"Then why did you say—that—what you did?"

"Well, it's this way," replied Colonel Zane, stealing a glance at her pensive, downcast face. "Girls all like to be wooed. Almost every one I ever knew wanted the young man of her choice to outstrip all her other admirers, and then, for a spell, nearly die of love for her, after which she'd give in. Now, Jack, being a borderman, a man with no occupation except scouting, will never look at a girl, let alone make up to her. I imagine, my dear, it'd take some mighty tall courting to fetch home Helen Sheppard a bride. On the other hand, if some pretty and spirited lass, like, say for instance, Helen Sheppard, would come along and just make Jack forget Indians and fighting, she'd get the finest husband in the world. True, he's wild; but only in the woods. A simpler, kinder, cleaner man cannot be found."

"I believe that, Colonel Zane; but where is the girl who would interest him?" Helen asked with spirit. "These bordermen are unapproachable. Imagine a girl interesting that great, cold, stern Wetzel! All her flatteries, her wiles, the little coquetries that might attract ordinary men, would not be noticed by him, or Jonathan either."

"I grant it'd not be easy, but woman was made to subjugate man, and always, everlastingly, until the end of life here on this beautiful earth, she will do it."

"Do you think Jonathan and Wetzel will catch Brandt?" asked Helen, changing the subject abruptly.

"I'd stake my all that this year's autumn leaves will fall on Brandt's grave." Colonel Zane's calm, matter-of-fact coldness made Helen shiver.

"Why, the leaves have already begun to fall. Papa told me Brandt had gone to join the most powerful outlaw band on the border. How can these two men, alone, cope with savages, as I've heard they do, and break up such an outlaw band as Legget's?"

"That's a question I've heard Daniel Boone ask about Wetzel, and Boone, though not a borderman in all the name implies, was a great Indian fighter. I've heard old frontiersmen, grown grizzled on the frontier, use the same words. I've been twenty years with that man, yet I can't answer it. Jonathan, of course, is only a shadow of him; Wetzel is the type of these men who have held the frontier for us. He was the first borderman, and no doubt he'll be the last."

"What have Jonathan and Wetzel that other men do not possess?"

"In them is united a marvelously developed woodcraft, with wonderful physical powers. Imagine a man having a sense, almost an animal instinct, for what is going on in the woods. Take for instance the fleetness of foot. That is one of the greatest factors. It is absolutely necessary to run, to get away when to hold ground would be death. Whether at home or in the woods, the bordermen retreat every day. You wouldn't think they practiced anything of the kind, would you? Well, a man can't be great in anything without keeping at it. Jonathan says he exercises to keep his feet light. Wetzel would just as soon run as walk. Think of the magnificent condition of these men. When a dash of speed is called for, when to be fleet of foot is to elude vengeance-seeking Indians, they must travel as swiftly as the deer. The Zanes were all sprinters. I could do something of the kind; Betty was fast on her feet, as that old fort will testify until the logs rot; Isaac was fleet, too, and Jonathan can get over the ground like a scared buck. But, even so, Wetzel can beat him."

"Goodness me, Helen!" exclaimed the colonel's buxom wife, from the window, "don't you ever get tired hearing Eb talk of Wetzel, and Jack, and Indians? Come in with me. I venture to say my gossip will do you more good than his stories."

Therefore Helen went in to chat with Mrs. Zane, for she was always glad to listen to the colonel's wife, who was so bright and pleasant, so helpful and kindly in her womanly way. In the course of their conversation, which drifted from weaving linsey, Mrs. Zane's occupation at the tune, to the costly silks and satins of remembered days, and then to matters of more present interest, Helen spoke of Colonel Zane's hint about Will and Betty.

"Isn't Eb a terror? He's the worst matchmatcher you ever saw," declared the colonel's good spouse.

"There's no harm in that."

"No, indeed; it's a good thing, but he makes me laugh, and Betty, he sets her furious."

"The colonel said he had designs on me."

"Of course he has, dear old Eb! How he'd love to see you happily married. His heart is as big as that mountain yonder. He has given this settlement his whole life."

"I believe you. He has such interest, such zeal for everybody. Only the other day he was speaking to me of Mr. Mordaunt, telling how sorry he was for the Englishman, and how much he'd like to help him. It does seem a pity a man of Mordaunt's blood and attainments should sink to utter worthlessness."

"Yes,'tis a pity for any man, blood or no, and the world's full of such wrecks. I always liked that man's looks. I never had a word with him, of course; but I've seen him often, and something about him appealed to me. I don't believe it was just his handsome face; still I know women are susceptible that way."

"I, too, liked him once as a friend," said Helen feelingly. "Well, I'm glad he's gone."

"Gone?"

"Yes, he left Fort Henry yesterday. He came to say good-bye to me, and, except for his pale face and trembling hands, was much as he used to be in Virginia. Said he was going home to England, and wanted to tell me he was sorry—for—for all he'd done to make papa and me suffer. Drink had broken him, he said, and surely he looked 'a broken man. I shook hands with him, and then slipped upstairs and cried."

"Poor fellow!" sighed Mrs. Zane.

"Papa said he left Fort Pitt with one of Metzar's men as a guide."

"Then he didn't take the 'little cuss,' as Eb calls his man Case?"

"No, if I remember rightly papa said Case wouldn't go."

"I wish he had. He's no addition to our village."

Voices outside attracted their attention. Mrs. Zane glanced from the window and said: "There come Betty and Will."

Helen went on the porch to see her cousin and Betty entering the yard, and Colonel Zane once again leaning on his spade.

"Gather any hickory-nuts from birch or any other kind of trees?" asked the colonel grimly.

"No," replied Will cheerily, "the shells haven't opened yet."

"Too bad the frost is so backward," said Colonel Zane with a laugh. "But I can't see that it makes any difference."

"Where are my leaves?" asked Helen, with a smile and a nod to Betty.

"What leaves?" inquired that young woman, plainly mystified.

"Why, the autumn leaves Will promised to gather with me, then changed his mind, and said he'd bring them."

"I forgot," Will replied a little awkwardly.

Colonel Zane coughed, and then, catching Betty's glance, which had begun to flash, he plied his spade vigorously.

Betty's face had colored warmly at her brother's first question; it toned down slightly when she understood that he was not going to tease her as usual, and suddenly, as she looked over his head, it paled white as snow.

"Eb, look down the lane!" she cried.

Two tall men were approaching with labored tread, one half-supporting his companion.

"Wetzel! Jack! and Jack's hurt!" cried Betty.

"My dear, be calm," said Colonel Zane, in that quiet tone he always used during moments of excitement. He turned toward the bordermen, and helped Wetzel lead Jonathan up the walk into the yard.

From Wetzel's clothing water ran, his long hair was disheveled, his aspect frightful. Jonathan's face was white and drawn. His buckskin hunting coat was covered with blood, and the hand which he held tightly against his left breast showed dark red stains.

Helen shuddered. Almost fainting, she leaned against the porch, too horrified to cry out, with contracting heart and a chill stealing through her veins.

"Jack! Jack!" cried Betty, in agonized appeal.

"Betty, it's nothin'," said Wetzel.

"Now, Betts, don't be scared of a little blood," Jonathan said with a faint smile flitting across his haggard face.

"Bring water, shears an' some linsey cloth," added Wetzel, as Mrs. Zane came running out.

"Come inside," cried the colonel's wife, as she disappeared again immediately.

"No," replied the borderman, removing his coat, and, with the assistance of his brother, he unlaced his hunting shirt, pulling it down from a wounded shoulder. A great gory hole gaped just beneath his left collar-bone.

Although stricken with fear, when Helen saw the bronzed, massive shoulder, the long, powerful arm with its cords of muscles playing under the brown skin, she felt a thrill of admiration.

"Just missed the lung," said Mrs. Zane. "Eb, no bullet ever made that hole."

Wetzel washed the bloody wound, and, placing on it a wad of leaves he took from his pocket, bound up the shoulder tightly.

"What made that hole?" asked Colonel Zane.

Wetzel lifted the quiver of arrows Jonathan had laid on the porch, and, selecting one, handed it to the colonel. The flint-head and a portion of the shaft were stained with blood.

"The Shawnee!" exclaimed Colonel Zane. Then he led Wetzel aside, and began conversing in low tones while Jonathan, with Betty holding his arm, ascended the steps and went within the dwelling.

Helen ran home, and, once in her room, gave vent to her emotions. She cried because of fright, nervousness, relief, and joy. Then she bathed her face, tried to rub some color into her pale cheeks, and set about getting dinner as one in a trance. She could not forget that broad shoulder with its frightful wound. What a man Jonathan must be to receive a blow like that and live! Exhausted, almost spent, had been his strength when he reached home, yet how calm and cool he was! What would she not have given for the faint smile that shone in his eyes for Betty?

The afternoon was long for Helen. When at last supper was over she changed her gown, and, asking Will to accompany her, went down the lane toward Colonel Zane's cabin. At this hour the colonel almost invariably could be found sitting on his doorstep puffing a long Indian pipe, and gazing with dreamy eyes over the valley.

"Well, well, how sweet you look!" he said to Helen; then with a wink of his eyelid, "Hello, Willie, you'll find Elizabeth inside with Jack."

"How is he?" asked Helen eagerly, as Will with a laugh and a retort mounted the steps.

"Jack's doing splendidly. He slept all day. I don't think his injury amounts to much, at least not for such as him or Wetzel. It would have finished ordinary men. Bess says if complications don't set in, blood-poison or something to start a fever, he'll be up shortly. Wetzel believes the two of 'em will be on the trail inside of a week."

"Did they find Brandt?" asked Helen in a low voice.

"Yes, they ran him to his hole, and, as might have been expected, it was Bing Legget's camp. The Indians took Jonathan there."

"Then Jack was captured?"

Colonel Zane related the events, as told briefly by Wetzel, that had taken place during the preceding three days.

"The Indian I saw at the spring carried that bow Jonathan brought back. He must have shot the arrow. He was a magnificent savage."

"He was indeed a great, and a bad Indian, one of the craftiest spies who ever stepped in moccasins; but he lies quiet now on the moss and the leaves. Bing Legget will never find another runner like that Shawnee. Let us go indoors."

He led Helen into the large sitting-room where Jonathan lay on a couch, with Betty and Will sitting beside him. The colonel's wife and children, Silas Zane, and several neighbors, were present.

"Here, Jack, is a lady inquiring after your health. Betts, this reminds me of the time Isaac came home wounded, after his escape from the Hurons. Strikes me he and his Indian bride should be about due here on a visit."

Helen forgot every one except the wounded man lying so quiet and pale upon the couch. She looked down upon him with eyes strangely dilated, and darkly bright.

"How are you?" she asked softly.

"I'm all right, thank you, lass," answered Jonathan.

Colonel Zane contrived, with inimitable skill, to get Betty, Will, Silas, Bessie and the others interested in some remarkable news he had just heard, or made up, and this left Jonathan and Helen comparatively alone for the moment.

The wise old colonel thought perhaps this might be the right time. He saw Helen's face as she leaned over Jonathan, and that was enough for him. He would have taxed his ingenuity to the utmost to keep the others away from the young couple.

"I was so frightened," murmured Helen.

"Why?" asked Jonathan.

"Oh! You looked so deathly—the blood, and that awful wound!"

"It's nothin', lass."

Helen smiled down upon him. Whether or not the hurt amounted to anything in the borderman's opinion, she knew from his weakness, and his white, drawn face, that the strain of the march home had been fearful. His dark eyes held now nothing of the coldness and glitter so natural to them. They were weary, almost sad. She did not feel afraid of him now. He lay there so helpless, his long, powerful frame as quiet as a sleeping child's! Hitherto an almost indefinable antagonism in him had made itself felt; now there was only gentleness, as of a man too weary to fight longer. Helen's heart swelled with pity, and tenderness, and love. His weakness affected her as had never his strength. With an involuntary gesture of sympathy she placed her hand softly on his.

Jonathan looked up at her with eyes no longer blind. Pain had softened him. For the moment he felt carried out of himself, as it were, and saw things differently. The melting tenderness of her gaze, the glowing softness of her face, the beauty, bewitched him; and beyond that, a sweet, impelling gladness stirred within him and would not be denied. He thrilled as her fingers lightly, timidly touched his, and opened his broad hand to press hers closely and warmly.

"Lass," he whispered, with a huskiness and unsteadiness unnatural to his deep voice.

Helen bent her head closer to him; she saw his lips tremble, and his nostrils dilate; but an unutterable sadness shaded the brightness in his eyes.

"I love you."

The low whisper reached Helen's ears. She seemed to float dreamily away to some beautiful world, with the music of those words ringing in her ears. She looked at him again. Had she been dreaming? No; his dark eyes met hers with a love that he could no longer deny. An exquisite emotion, keen, strangely sweet and strong, yet terrible with sharp pain, pulsated through her being. The revelation had been too abrupt. It was so wonderfully different from what she had ever dared hope. She lowered her head, trembling.

The next moment she felt Colonel Zane's hand on her chair, and heard him say in a cheery voice:

"Well, well, see here, lass, you mustn't make Jack talk too much. See how white and tired he looks."

509

CHAPTER XV.

In forty-eight hours Jonathan Zane was up and about the cabin as though he had never been wounded; the third day he walked to the spring; in a week he was waiting for Wetzel, ready to go on the trail.

On the eighth day of his enforced idleness, as he sat with Betty and the colonel in the yard, Wetzel appeared on a ridge east of the fort. Soon he rounded the stockade fence, and came straight toward them. To Colonel Zane and Betty, Wetzel's expression was terrible. The stern kindliness, the calm, though cold, gravity of his countenance, as they usually saw it, had disappeared. Yet it showed no trace of his unnatural passion to pursue and slay. No doubt that terrible instinct, or lust, was at white heat; but it wore a mask of impenetrable stone-gray gloom.

Wetzel spoke briefly. After telling Jonathan to meet him at sunset on the following day at a point five miles up the river, he reported to the colonel that Legget with his band had left their retreat, moving southward, apparently on a marauding expedition. Then he shook hands with Colonel Zane and turned to Betty.

"Good-bye, Betty," he said, in his deep, sonorous voice.

"Good-bye, Lew," answered Betty slowly, as if surprised. "God save you," she added.

He shouldered his rifle, and hurried down the lane, halting before entering the thicket that bounded the clearing, to look back at the settlement. In another moment his dark figure had disappeared among the bushes.

"Betts, I've seen Wetzel go like that hundreds of times, though he never shook hands before; but I feel sort of queer about it now. Wasn't he strange?"

Betty did not answer until Jonathan, who had started to go within, was out of hearing.

"Lew looked and acted the same the morning he struck Miller's trail," Betty replied in a low voice. "I believe, despite his indifference to danger, he realizes that the chances are greatly against him, as they were when he began the trailing of Miller, certain it would lead him into Girty's camp. Then I know Lew has an affection for us, though it is never shown in ordinary ways. I pray he and Jack will come home safe."

"This is a bad trail they're taking up; the worst, perhaps, in border warfare," said Colonel Zane gloomily. "Did you notice how Jack's face darkened when his comrade came? Much of this borderman-life of his is due to Wetzel's influence."

"Eb, I'll tell you one thing," returned Betty, with a flash of her old spirit. "This is Jack's last trail."

"Why do you think so?"

"If he doesn't return he'll be gone the way of all bordermen; but if he comes back once more he'll never get away from Helen."

"Ugh!" exclaimed Zane, venting his pleasure in characteristic Indian way.

"That night after Jack came home wounded," continued Betty, "I saw him, as he lay on the couch, gaze at Helen. Such a look! Eb, she has won."

"I hope so, but I fear, I fear," replied her brother gloomily. "If only he returns, that's the thing! Betts, be sure he sees Helen before he goes away."

"I shall try. Here he comes now," said Betty.

"Hello, Jack!" cried the colonel, as his brother came out in somewhat of a hurry. "What have you got? By George! It's that blamed arrow the Shawnee shot into you. Where are you going with it? What the deuce—Say—Betts, eh?"

Betty had given him a sharp little kick.

The borderman looked embarrassed. He hesitated and flushed. Evidently he would have liked to avoid his brother's question; but the inquiry came direct. Dissimulation with him was impossible.

"Helen wanted this, an' I reckon that's where I'm goin' with it," he said finally, and walked away.

"Eb, you're a stupid!" exclaimed Betty.

"Hang it! Who'd have thought he was going to give her that blamed, bloody arrow?"

As Helen ushered Jonathan, for the first time, into her cosy little sitting-room, her heart began to thump so hard she could hear it.

She had not seen him since the night he whispered the words which gave such happiness. She had stayed at home, thankful beyond expression to learn every day of his rapid improvement, living in the sweetness of her joy, and waiting for him. And now as he had come, so dark, so grave, so unlike a lover to woo, that she felt a chill steal over her.

"I'm so glad you've brought the arrow," she faltered, "for, of course, coming so far means that you're well once more."

"You asked me for it, an' I've fetched it over. To-morrow I'm off on a trail I may never return from," he answered simply, and his voice seemed cold.

An immeasurable distance stretched once more between them. Helen's happiness slowly died.

"I thank you," she said with a voice that was tremulous despite all her efforts.

"It's not much of a keepsake."

"I did not ask for it as a keepsake, but because—because I wanted it. I need nothing tangible to keep alive my memory. A few words whispered to me not many days ago will suffice for remembrance—or—or did I dream them?"

Bitter disappointment almost choked Helen. This was not the gentle, soft-voiced man who had said he loved her. It was the indifferent borderman. Again he was the embodiment of his strange, quiet woods. Once more he seemed the comrade of the cold, inscrutable Wetzel.

"No, lass, I reckon you didn't dream," he replied.

Helen swayed from sick bitterness and a suffocating sense of pain, back to her old, sweet, joyous, tumultuous heart-throbbing.

"Tell me, if I didn't dream," she said softly, her face flashing warm again. She came close to him and looked up with all her heart in her great dark eyes, and love trembling on her red lips.

Calmness deserted the borderman after one glance at her. He paced the floor; twisted and clasped his hands while his eyes gleamed.

"Lass, I'm only human," he cried hoarsely, facing her again.

But only for a moment did he stand before her; but it was long enough for him to see her shrink a little, the gladness in her eyes giving way to uncertainty and a fugitive hope. Suddenly he began to pace the room again, and to talk incoherently. With the flow of words he gradually grew calmer, and, with something of his natural dignity, spoke more rationally.

"I said I loved you, an' it's true, but I didn't mean to speak. I oughtn't have done it. Somethin' made it so easy, so natural like. I'd have died before letting you know, if any idea had come to me of what I was sayin'. I've fought this feelin' for months. I allowed myself to think of you at first, an' there's the wrong. I went on the trail with your big eyes pictured in my mind, an' before I'd dreamed of it you'd crept into my heart. Life has never been the same since—that kiss. Betty said as how you cared for me, an' that made me worse, only I never really believed. Today I came over here to say goodbye, expectin' to hold myself well in hand; but the first glance of your eyes unmans me. Nothin' can come of it, lass, nothin' but trouble. Even if you cared, an' I don't dare believe you do, nothin' can come of it! I've my own life to live, an' there's no sweetheart in it. Mebbe, as Lew says, there's one in Heaven. Oh! girl, this has been hard on me. I see you always on my lonely tramps; I see your glorious eyes in the sunny fields an' in the woods, at gray twilight, an' when the stars shine brightest. They haunt me. Ah! you're the sweetest lass as ever tormented a man, an' I love you, I love you!"

He turned to the window only to hear a soft, broken cry, and a flurry of skirts. A rush of wind seemed to envelop him. Then two soft, rounded arms encircled his neck, and a golden head lay on his breast.

"My borderman! My hero! My love!"

Jonathan clasped the beautiful, quivering girl to his heart.

"Lass, for God's sake don't say you love me," he implored, thrilling with contact of her warm arms.

"Ah!" she breathed, and raised her head. Her radiant eyes darkly wonderful with unutterable love, burned into his.

He had almost pressed his lips to the sweet red ones so near his, when he drew back with a start, and his frame straightened.

"Am I a man, or only a coward?" he muttered. "Lass, let me think. Don't believe I'm harsh, nor cold, nor nothin' except that I want to do what's right."

He leaned out of the window while Helen stood near him with a hand on his quivering shoulder. When at last he turned, his face was colorless, white as marble, and sad, and set, and stern.

"Lass, it mustn't be; I'll not ruin your life."

"But you will if you give me up."

"No, no, lass."

"I cannot live without you."

"You must. My life is not mine to give."

"But you love me."

"I am a borderman."

"I will not live without you."

"Hush! lass, hush!"

"I love you."

Jonathan breathed hard; once more the tremor, which seemed pitiful in such a strong man, came upon him. His face was gray.

"I love you," she repeated, her rich voice indescribably deep and full. She opened wide her arms and stood before him with heaving bosom, with great eyes dark with woman's sadness, passionate with woman's promise, perfect in her beauty, glorious in her abandonment.

The borderman bowed and bent like a broken reed.

"Listen," she whispered, coming closer to him, "go if you must leave me; but let this be your last trail. Come back to me, Jack, come back to me! You have had enough of this terrible life; you have won a name that will never be forgotten; you have done your duty to the border. The Indians and outlaws will be gone soon. Take the farm your brother wants you to have, and live for me. We will be happy. I shall learn to keep your home. Oh! my dear, I will recompense you for the loss of all this wild hunting and fighting. Let me persuade you, as much for your sake as for mine, for you are my heart, and soul, and life. Go out upon your last trail, Jack, and come back to me."

"An' let Wetzel go always alone?"

"He is different; he lives only for revenge. What are those poor savages to you? You have a better, nobler life opening."

"Lass, I can't give him up."

"You need not; but give up this useless seeking of adventure. That, you know, is half a borderman's life. Give it up, Jack, it not for your own, then for my sake."

"No-no-never-I can't-I won't be a coward! After all these years I won't desert him. No-no———"

"Do not say more," she pleaded, stealing closer to him until she was against his breast. She slipped her arms around his neck. For love and more than life she was fighting now. "Good-bye, my love." She kissed him, a long, lingering pressure of her soft full lips on his. "Dearest, do not shame me further. Dearest Jack, come back to me, for I love you."

She released him, and ran sobbing from the room.

Unsteady as a blind man, he groped for the door, found it, and went out.

CHAPTER XVI.

The longest day in Jonathan Zane's life, the oddest, the most terrible and complex with unintelligible emotions, was that one in which he learned that the wilderness no longer sufficed for him.

He wandered through the forest like a man lost, searching for, he knew not what. Rambling along the shady trails he looked for that contentment which had always been his, but found it not. He plunged into the depths of deep, gloomy ravines; into the fastnesses of heavy-timbered hollows where the trees hid the light of day; he sought the open, grassy hillsides, and roamed far over meadow and plain. Yet something always eluded him. The invisible and beautiful life of all inanimate things sang no more in his heart. The springy moss, the quivering leaf, the tell-tale bark of the trees, the limpid, misty, eddying pools under green banks, the myriads of natural objects from which he had learned so much, and the manifold joyous life around him, no longer spoke with soul-satisfying faithfulness. The environment of his boyish days, of his youth, and manhood, rendered not a sweetness as of old.

His intelligence, sharpened by the pain of new experience, told him he had been vain to imagine that he, because he was a borderman, could escape the universal destiny of human life. Dimly he could feel the broadening, the awakening into a fuller existence, but he did not welcome this new light. He realized that men had always turned, at some time in their lives, to women even as the cypress leans toward the sun. This weakening of the sterner stuff in him; this softening of his heart, and especially the inquietude, and lack of joy and harmony in his old pursuits of the forest trails bewildered him, and troubled him some. Thousands of times his borderman's trail had been crossed, yet never to his sorrow until now when it had been crossed by a woman.

Sick at heart, hurt in his pride, darkly savage, sad, remorseful, and thrilling with awakened passion, all in turn, he roamed the woodland unconsciously visiting the scenes where he had formerly found contentment.

515

He paused by many a shady glen, and beautiful quiet glade; by gray cliffs and mossy banks, searching with moody eyes for the spirit which evaded him.

Here in the green and golden woods rose before him a rugged, giant rock, moss-stained, and gleaming with trickling water. Tangled ferns dressed in autumn's russet hue lay at the base of the green-gray cliff, and circled a dark, deep pool dotted with yellow leaves. Half-way up, the perpendicular ascent was broken by a protruding ledge upon which waved broad-leaved plants and rusty ferns. Above, the cliff sheered out with many cracks and seams in its weather-beaten front.

The forest grew to the verge of the precipice. A full foliaged oak and a luxuriant maple, the former still fresh with its dark green leaves, the latter making a vivid contrast with its pale yellow, purple-red, and orange hues, leaned far out over the bluff. A mighty chestnut grasped with gnarled roots deep into the broken cliff. Dainty plumes of goldenrod swayed on the brink; red berries, amber moss, and green trailing vines peeped over the edge, and every little niche and cranny sported fragile ferns and pale-faced asters. A second cliff, higher than the first, and more heavily wooded, loomed above, and over it sprayed a transparent film of water, thin as smoke, and iridescent in the sunshine. Far above where the glancing rill caressed the mossy cliff and shone like gleaming gold against the dark branches with their green and red and purple leaves, lay the faint blue of the sky.

Jonathan pulled on down the stream with humbler heart. His favorite waterfall had denied him. The gold that had gleamed there was his sweetheart's hair; the red was of her lips; the dark pool with its lights and shades, its unfathomable mystery, was like her eyes.

He came at length to another scene of milder aspect. An open glade where the dancing, dimpling brook raced under dark hemlocks, and where blood-red sumach leaves, and beech leaves like flashes of sunshine, lay against the green. Under a leaning birch he found a patch of purple asters, and a little apart from them, by a mossy stone, a lonely fringed gentian. Its deep color brought to him the dark blue eyes that haunted him, and once again, like one possessed of an evil spirit, he wandered along the merry water-course.

But finally pain and unrest left him. When he surrendered to his love, peace returned. Though he said in his heart that Helen was not for him, he felt he did not need to torture himself by fighting against resistless power. He could love her without being a coward. He would take up his life where it had been changed, and live it, carrying this bitter-sweet burden always.

Memory, now that he admitted himself conquered, made a toy of him, bringing the sweetness of fragrant hair, and eloquent eyes, and clinging arms, and dewy lips. A thousand-fold harder to fight than pain was the seductive thought that he had but to go back to Helen to feel again the charm of her presence, to see the grace of her person, to hear the music of her voice, to have again her lips on his.

Jonathan knew then that his trial had but begun; that the pain and suffering of a borderman's broken pride and conquered spirit was nothing; that to steel his heart against the joy, the sweetness, the longing of love was everything.

So a tumult raged within his heart. No bitterness, nor wretchedness stabbed him as before, but a passionate yearning, born of memory, and unquenchable as the fires of the sun, burned there.

Helen's reply to his pale excuses, to his duty, to his life, was that she loved him. The wonder of it made him weak. Was not her answer enough? "I love you!" Three words only; but they changed the world. A beautiful girl loved him, she had kissed him, and his life could never again be the same. She had held out her arms to him—and he, cold, churlish, unfeeling brute, had let her shame herself, fighting for her happiness, for the joy that is a woman's divine right. He had been blind; he had not understood the significance of her gracious action; he had never realized until too late, what it must have cost her, what heartburning shame and scorn his refusal brought upon her. If she ever looked tenderly at him again with her great eyes; or leaned toward him with her beautiful arms outstretched, he would fall at her feet and throw his duty to the winds, swearing his love was hers always and his life forever.

So love stormed in the borderman's heart.

Slowly the melancholy Indian-summer day waned as Jonathan strode out of the woods into a plain beyond, where he was to meet Wetzel at sunset. A smoky haze like a purple cloud lay upon the gently waving grass. He could not see across the stretch of prairie-land, though at this point he knew it was hardly a mile wide. With the trilling of the grasshoppers alone disturbing the serene quiet of this autumn afternoon, all nature seemed in harmony with the declining season. He stood a while, his thoughts becoming the calmer for the silence and loneliness of this breathing meadow.

When the shadows of the trees began to lengthen, and to steal far out over the yellow grass, he knew the time had come, and glided out upon the plain. He crossed it, and sat down upon a huge stone which lay with one shelving end overhanging the river.

Far in the west the gold-red sun, too fiery for his direct gaze, lost the brilliance of its under circle behind the fringe of the wooded hill. Slowly the red ball sank. When the last bright gleam had vanished in the dark horizon Jonathan turned to search wood and plain. Wetzel was to meet him at sunset. Even as his first glance swept around a light step sounded behind him. He did not move, for that step was familiar. In another moment the tall form of Wetzel stood beside him.

"I'm about as much behind as you was ahead of time," said Wetzel. "We'll stay here fer the night, an' be off early in the mornin'."

Under the shelving side of the rock, and in the shade of the thicket, the bordermen built a little fire and roasted strips of deer-meat. Then, puffing at their long pipes they sat for a long time in silence, while twilight let fall a dark, gray cloak over river and plain.

"Legget's move up the river was a blind, as I suspected," said Wetzel, presently. "He's not far back in the woods from here, an' seems to be waitin' fer somethin' or somebody. Brandt an' seven redskins are with him. We'd hev a good chance at them in the mornin'; now we've got 'em a long ways from their camp, so we'll wait, an' see what deviltry they're up to."

"Mebbe he's waitin' for some Injun band," suggested Jonathan.

"Thar's redskins in the valley an' close to him; but I reckon he's barkin' up another tree."

"Suppose we run into some of these Injuns?"

"We'll hev to take what comes," replied Wetzel, lying down on a bed of leaves.

When darkness enveloped the spot Wetzel lay wrapped in deep slumber, while Jonathan sat against the rock, watching the last flickerings of the camp-fire.

CHAPTER XVII.

Will and Helen hurried back along the river road. Beguiled by the soft beauty of the autumn morning they ventured farther from the fort than ever before, and had been suddenly brought to a realization of the fact by a crackling in the underbrush. Instantly their minds reverted to bears and panthers, such as they had heard invested the thickets round the settlement.

"Oh! Will! I saw a dark form stealing along in the woods from tree to tree!" exclaimed Helen in a startled whisper.

"So did I. It was an Indian, or I never saw one. Walk faster. Once round the bend in the road we'll be within sight of the fort; then we'll run," replied Will. He had turned pale, but maintained his composure.

They increased their speed, and had almost come up to the curve in the road, marked by dense undergrowth on both sides, when the branches in the thicket swayed violently, a sturdy little man armed with a musket appeared from among them.

"Avast! Heave to!" he commanded in a low, fierce voice, leveling his weapon. "One breeze from ye, an' I let sail this broadside."

"What do you want? We have no valuables," said Will, speaking low.

Helen stared at the little man. She was speechless with terror. It flashed into her mind as soon as she recognized the red, evil face of the sailor, that he was the accomplice upon whom Brandt had told Metzar he could rely.

"Shut up! It's not ye I want, nor valuables, but this wench," growled Case. He pushed Will around with the muzzle of the musket, which action caused the young man to turn a sickly white and shrink involuntarily with fear. The hammer of the musket was raised, and might fall at the slightest jar.

"For God's sake! Will, do as he says," cried Helen, who saw murder in Case's eyes. Capture or anything was better than sacrifice of life.

"March!" ordered Case, with the musket against Will's back.

Will hurriedly started forward, jostling Helen, who had preceded him. He was forced to hurry, because every few moments Case pressed the gun to his back or side.

Without another word the sailor marched them swiftly along the road, which now narrowed down to a trail. His intention, no doubt, was to put as much distance between him and the fort as was possible. No more than a mile had been thus traversed when two Indians stepped into view.

"My God! My God!" cried Will as the savages proceeded first to bind Helen's arms behind her, and then his in the same manner. After this the journey was continued in silence, the Indians walking beside the prisoners, and Case in the rear.

Helen was so terrified that for a long time she could not think coherently. It seemed as if she had walked miles, yet did not feel tired. Always in front wound the narrow, leaf-girt trail, and to the left the broad river gleamed at intervals through open spaces in the thickets. Flocks of birds rose in the line of march. They seemed tame, and uttered plaintive notes as if in sympathy.

About noon the trail led to the river bank. One of the savages disappeared in a copse of willows, and presently reappeared carrying a birch-bark canoe. Case ordered Helen and Will into the boat, got in himself, and the savages, taking stations at bow and stern, paddled out into the stream. They shot over under the lee of an island, around a rocky point, and across a strait to another island. Beyond this they gained the Ohio shore, and beached the canoe.

"Ahoy! there, cap'n," cried Case, pushing Helen up the bank before him, and she, gazing upward, was more than amazed to see Mordaunt leaning against a tree.

"Mordaunt, had you anything to do with this?" cried Helen breathlessly.

"I had all to do with it," answered the Englishman.

"What do you mean?"

He did not meet her gaze, nor make reply; but turned to address a few words in a low tone to a white man sitting on a log.

Helen knew she had seen this person before, and doubted not he was one of Metzar's men. She saw a rude, bark lean-to, the remains of a camp-fire, and a pack tied in blankets. Evidently Mordaunt and his men had tarried here awaiting such developments as had come to pass.

"You white-faced hound!" hissed Will, beside himself with rage when he realized the situation. Bound though he was, he leaped up and tried to get at Mordaunt. Case knocked him on the head with the handle of his knife. Will fell with blood streaming from a cut over the temple.

The dastardly act aroused all Helen's fiery courage. She turned to the Englishman with eyes ablaze.

"So you've at last found your level. Border-outlaw! Kill me at once. I'd rather be dead than breathe the same air with such a coward!"

"I swore I'd have you, if not by fair means then by foul," he answered, with dark and haggard face.

"What do you intend to do with me now that I am tied?" she demanded scornfully.

"Keep you a prisoner in the woods till you consent to marry me."

Helen laughed in scorn. Desperate as was the plight, her natural courage had arisen at the cruel blow dealt her cousin, and she faced the Englishman with flashing eyes and undaunted mien. She saw he was again unsteady, and had the cough and catching breath habitual to certain men under the influence of liquor. She turned her attention to Will. He lay as he had fallen, with blood streaming over his pale face and fair hair. While she gazed at him Case whipped out his long knife, and looked up at Mordaunt.

"Cap'n, I'd better loosen a hatch fer him," he said brutally. "He's dead cargo fer us, an' in the way."

He lowered the gleaming point upon Will's chest.

"Oh-h-h!" breathed Helen in horror. She tried to close her eyes but was so fascinated she could not.

"Get up. I'll have no murder," ordered Mordaunt. "Leave him here."

"He's not got a bad cut," said the man sitting on the log. "He'll come to arter a spell, go back to ther fort, an' give an alarm."

"What's that to me?" asked Mordaunt sharply. "We shall be safe. I won't have him with us because some Indian or another will kill him. It's not my purpose to murder any one."

"Ugh!" grunted one of the savages, and pointed eastward with his hand. "Hurry-long-way-go," he said in English. With the Indians in the lead the party turned from the river into the forest.

Helen looked back into the sandy glade and saw Will lying as they had left him, unconscious, with his hands still bound tightly behind him, and blood running over his face. Painful as was the thought of leaving him thus, it afforded her relief. She assured herself he had not been badly hurt, would recover consciousness before long, and, even bound as he was, could make his way back to the settlement.

Her own situation, now that she knew Mordaunt had instigated the abduction, did not seem hopeless. Although dreading Brandt with unspeakable horror, she did not in the least fear the Englishman. He was mad to carry her off like this into the wilderness, but would force her to do nothing. He could not keep her a prisoner long while Jonathan Zane and Wetzel were free to take his trail. What were his intentions? Where was he taking her? Such questions as these, however, troubled Helen more than a little. They brought her thoughts back to the Indians leading the way with lithe and stealthy step. How had Mordaunt associated himself with these savages? Then, suddenly, it dawned upon her that Brandt also might be in this scheme to carry her off. She scouted the idea; but it returned. Perhaps Mordaunt was only a tool; perhaps he himself was being deceived. Helen turned pale at the very thought. She had never forgotten the strange, unreadable, yet threatening, expression which Brandt had worn the day she had refused to walk with him.

Meanwhile the party made rapid progress through the forest. Not a word was spoken, nor did any noise of rustling leaves or crackling twigs follow their footsteps. The savage in the lead chose the open and less difficult ground; he took advantage of glades, mossy places, and rocky ridges. This careful choosing was, evidently, to avoid noise, and make the trail as difficult to follow as possible. Once he stopped suddenly, and listened.

Helen had a good look at the savage while he was in this position. His lean, athletic figure resembled, in its half-clothed condition, a bronzed statue; his powerful visage was set, changeless like iron. His dark eyes seemed to take in all points of the forest before him.

Whatever had caused the halt was an enigma to all save his red-skinned companion.

The silence of the wood was the silence of the desert. No bird chirped; no breath of wind sighed in the tree-tops; even the aspens remained unagitated. Pale yellow leaves sailed slowly, reluctantly down from above.

But some faint sound, something unusual had jarred upon the exquisitely sensitive ears of the leader, for with a meaning shake of the head to his followers, he resumed the march in a direction at right angles with the original course.

This caution, and evident distrust of the forest ahead, made Helen think again of Jonathan and Wetzel. Those great bordermen might already be on the trail of her captors. The thought thrilled her. Presently she realized, from another long, silent march through forest thickets, glades, aisles, and groves, over rock-strewn ridges, and down mossy-stoned ravines, that her strength was beginning to fail.

"I can go no further with my arms tied in this way," she declared, stopping suddenly.

"Ugh!" uttered the savage before her, turning sharply. He brandished a tomahawk before her eyes.

Mordaunt hurriedly set free her wrists. His pale face flushed a dark, flaming red when she shrank from his touch as if he were a viper.

After they had traveled what seemed to Helen many miles, the vigilance of the leaders relaxed.

On the banks of the willow-skirted stream the Indian guide halted them, and proceeded on alone to disappear in a green thicket. Presently he reappeared, and motioned for them to come on. He led the way over smooth, sandy paths between clumps of willows, into a heavy growth of alder bushes and prickly thorns, at length to emerge upon a beautiful grassy plot enclosed by green and yellow shrubbery. Above the stream, which cut the edge of the glade, rose a sloping, wooded ridge, with huge rocks projecting here and there out of the brown forest.

Several birch-bark huts could be seen; then two rough bearded men lolling upon the grass, and beyond them a group of painted Indians.

A whoop so shrill, so savage, so exultant, that it seemingly froze her blood, rent the silence. A man, unseen before, came crashing through the willows on the side of the ridge. He leaped the stream with the spring of a wild horse. He was big and broad, with disheveled hair, keen, hard face, and wild, gray eyes.

Helen's sight almost failed her; her head whirled dizzily; it was as if her heart had stopped beating and was become a cold, dead weight. She recognized in this man the one whom she feared most of all—Brandt.

He cast one glance full at her, the same threatening, cool, and evil-meaning look she remembered so well, and then engaged the Indian guide in low conversation.

Helen sank at the foot of a tree, leaning against it. Despite her weariness she had retained some spirit until this direful revelation broke her courage. What worse could have happened? Mordaunt had led her, for some reason that she could not divine, into the clutches of Brandt, into the power of Legget and his outlaws.

But Helen was not one to remain long dispirited or hopeless. As this plot thickened, as every added misfortune weighed upon her, when just ready to give up to despair she remembered the bordermen. Then Colonel Zane's tales of their fearless, implacable pursuit when bent on rescue or revenge, recurred to her, and fortitude returned. While she had life she would hope.

The advent of the party with their prisoner enlivened Legget's gang. A great giant of a man, blond-bearded, and handsome in a wild, rugged, uncouth way, a man Helen instinctively knew to be Legget, slapped Brandt on the shoulder.

"Damme, Roge, if she ain't a regular little daisy! Never seed such a purty lass in my life."

Brandt spoke hurriedly, and Legget laughed.

All this time Case had been sitting on the grass, saying nothing, but with his little eyes watchful. Mordaunt stood near him, his head bowed, his face gloomy.

"Say, cap'n, I don't like this mess," whispered Case to his master. "They ain't no crew fer us. I know men, fer I've sailed the seas, an' you're goin' to get what Metz calls the double-cross."

Mordaunt seemed to arouse from his gloomy reverie. He looked at Brandt and Legget who were now in earnest council. Then his eyes wandered toward Helen. She beckoned him to come to her.

"Why did you bring me here?" she asked.

"Brandt understood my case. He planned this thing, and seemed to be a good friend of mine. He said if I once got you out of the settlement, he would give me protection until I crossed the border into Canada. There we could be married," replied Mordaunt unsteadily.

"Then you meant marriage by me, if I could be made to consent?"

"Of course. I'm not utterly vile," he replied, with face lowered in shame.

"Have you any idea what you've done?"

"Done? I don't understand."

"You have ruined yourself, lost your manhood, become an outlaw, a fugitive, made yourself the worst thing on the border—a girl-thief, and all for nothing."

"No, I have you. You are more to me than all."

"But can't you see? You've brought me out here for Brandt!"

"My God!" exclaimed Mordaunt. He rose slowly to his feet and gazed around like a man suddenly wakened from a dream. "I see it all now! Miserable, drunken wretch that I am!"

Helen saw his face change and lighten as if a cloud of darkness had passed away from it. She understood that love of liquor had made him a party to this plot. Brandt had cunningly worked upon his weakness, proposed a daring scheme; and filled his befogged mind with hopes that, in a moment of clear-sightedness, he would have seen to be vain and impossible. And Helen understood also that the sudden shock of surprise, pain, possible fury, had sobered Mordaunt, probably for the first time in weeks.

The Englishman's face became exceedingly pale. Seating himself on a stone near Case, he bowed his head, remaining silent and motionless.

The conference between Legget and Brandt lasted for some time. When it ended the latter strode toward the motionless figure on the rock.

"Mordaunt, you and Case will do well to follow this Indian at once to the river, where you can strike the Fort Pitt trail," said Brandt.

He spoke arrogantly and authoritatively. His keen, hard face, his steely eyes, bespoke the iron will and purpose of the man.

Mordaunt rose with cold dignity. If he had been a dupe, he was one no longer, as could be plainly read on his calm, pale face. The old listlessness, the unsteadiness had vanished. He wore a manner of extreme quietude; but his eyes were like balls of blazing blue steel.

"Mr. Brandt, I seem to have done you a service, and am no longer required," he said in a courteous tone.

Brandt eyed his man; but judged him wrongly. An English gentleman was new to the border-outlaw.

"I swore the girl should be mine," he hissed.

"Doomed men cannot be choosers!" cried Helen, who had heard him. Her dark eyes burned with scorn and hatred.

All the party heard her passionate outburst. Case arose as if unconcernedly, and stood by the side of his master. Legget and the other two outlaws came up. The Indians turned their swarthy faces.

"Hah! ain't she sassy?" cried Legget.

Brandt looked at Helen, understood the meaning of her words, and laughed. But his face paled, and involuntarily his shifty glance sought the rocks and trees upon the ridge.

"You played me from the first?" asked Mordaunt quietly.

"I did," replied Brandt.

"You meant nothing of your promise to help me across the border?"

"No."

"You intended to let me shift for myself out here in this wilderness?"

"Yes, after this Indian guides you to the river-trail," said Brandt, indicating with his finger the nearest savage.

"I get what you frontier men call the double-cross'?"

"That's it," replied Brandt with a hard laugh, in which Legget joined.

A short pause ensued.

"What will you do with the girl?"

"That's my affair."

"Marry her?" Mordaunt's voice was low and quiet.

"No!" cried Brandt. "She flaunted my love in my face, scorned me! She saw that borderman strike me, and by God! I'll get even. I'll keep her here in the woods until I'm tired of her, and when her beauty fades I'll turn her over to Legget."

Scarcely had the words dropped from his vile lips when Mordaunt moved with tigerish agility. He seized a knife from the belt of one of the Indians.

"Die!" he screamed.

Brandt grasped his tomahawk. At the same instant the man who had acted as Mordaunt's guide grasped the Englishman from behind.

Brandt struck ineffectually at the struggling man.

"Fair play!" roared Case, leaping at Mordaunt's second assailant. His long knife sheathed its glittering length in the man's breast. Without even a groan he dropped. "Clear the decks!" Case yelled, sweeping round in a circle. All fell back before that whirling knife.

Several of the Indians started as if to raise their rifles; but Legget's stern command caused them to desist.

The Englishman and the outlaw now engaged in a fearful encounter. The practiced, rugged, frontier desperado apparently had found his match in this pale-faced, slender man. His border skill with the hatchet seemed offset by Mordaunt's terrible rage. Brandt whirled and swung the weapon as he leaped around his antagonist. With his left arm the Englishman sought only to protect his head, while with his right he brandished the knife. Whirling here and there they struggled across the cleared space, plunging out of sight among the willows. During a moment there was a sound as of breaking branches; then a dull blow, horrible to hear, followed by a low moan, and then deep silence.

CHAPTER XVIII.

A black weight was seemingly lifted from Helen's weary eyelids. The sun shone; the golden forest surrounded her; the brook babbled merrily; but where were the struggling, panting men? She noticed presently, when her vision had grown more clear, that the scene differed entirely from the willow-glade where she had closed her eyes upon the fight. Then came the knowledge that she had fainted, and, during the time of unconsciousness, been moved.

She lay upon a mossy mound a few feet higher than a swiftly running brook. A magnificent chestnut tree spread its leafy branches above her. Directly opposite, about an hundred feet away, loomed a gray, ragged, moss-stained cliff. She noted this particularly because the dense forest encroaching to its very edge excited her admiration. Such wonderful coloring seemed unreal. Dead gold and bright red foliage flamed everywhere.

Two Indians stood near by silent, immovable. No other of Legget's band was visible. Helen watched the red men.

Sinewy, muscular warriors they were, with bodies partially painted, and long, straight hair, black as burnt wood, interwoven with bits of white bone, and plaited around waving eagle plumes. At first glance their dark faces and dark eyes were expressive of craft, cunning, cruelty, courage, all attributes of the savage.

Yet wild as these savages appeared, Helen did not fear them as she did the outlaws. Brandt's eyes, and Legget's, too, when turned on her, emitted a flame that seemed to scorch and shrivel her soul. When the savages met her gaze, which was but seldom, she imagined she saw intelligence, even pity, in their dusky eyes. Certain it was she did not shrink from them as from Brandt.

Suddenly, with a sensation of relief and joy, she remembered Mordaunt's terrible onslaught upon Brandt. Although she could not recollect the termination of that furious struggle, she did recall Brandt's scream of mortal agony, and the death of the other at Case's hands. This meant, whether

526

Brandt was dead or not, that the fighting strength of her captors had been diminished. Surely as the sun had risen that morning, Helen believed Jonathan and Wetzel lurked on the trail of these renegades. She prayed that her courage, hope, strength, might be continued.

"Ugh!" exclaimed one of the savages, pointing across the open space. A slight swaying of the bushes told that some living thing was moving among them, and an instant later the huge frame of the leader came into view. The other outlaw, and Case, followed closely. Farther down the margin of the thicket the Indians appeared; but without the slightest noise or disturbance of the shrubbery.

It required but a glance to show Helen that Case was in high spirits. His repulsive face glowed with satisfaction. He carried a bundle, which Helen saw, with a sickening sense of horror, was made up of Mordaunt's clothing. Brandt had killed the Englishman. Legget also had a package under his arm, which he threw down when he reached the chestnut tree, to draw from his pocket a long, leather belt, such as travelers use for the carrying of valuables. It was evidently heavy, and the musical clink which accompanied his motion proclaimed the contents to be gold.

Brandt appeared next; he was white and held his hand to his breast. There were dark stains on his hunting coat, which he removed to expose a shirt blotched with red.

"You ain't much hurt, I reckon?" inquired Legget solicitously.

"No; but I'm bleeding bad," replied Brandt coolly. He then called an Indian and went among the willows skirting the stream.

"So I'm to be in this border crew?" asked Case, looking up at Legget.

"Sure," replied the big outlaw. "You're a handy fellar, Case, an' after I break you into border ways you will fit in here tip-top. Now you'd better stick by me. When Eb Zane, his brother Jack, an' Wetzel find out this here day's work, hell will be a cool place compared with their whereabouts. You'll be safe with me, an' this is the only place on the border, I reckon, where you can say your life is your own."

"I'm yer mate, cap'n. I've sailed with soldiers, pirates, sailors, an' I guess I can navigate this borderland. Do we mess here? You didn't come far."

"Wal, I ain't pertikuler, but I don't like eatin' with buzzards," said Legget, with a grin. "Thet's why we moved a bit."

"What's buzzards?"

"Ho! ho! Mebbe you'll hev 'em closer'n you'd like, some day, if you'd only know it. Buzzards are fine birds, most particular birds, as won't eat nothin' but flesh, an' white man or Injun is pie fer 'em."

"Cap'n, I've seed birds as wouldn't wait till a man was dead," said Case.

"Haw! haw! you can't come no sailor yarns on this fellar. Wal, now, we've got ther Englishman's gold. One or t'other of us might jest as well hev it all."

"Right yer are, cap'n. Dice, cards, anyways, so long as I knows the game."

"Here, Jenks, hand over yer clickers, an' bring us a flat stone," said Legget, sitting on the moss and emptying the belt in front of him. Case took a small bag from the dark blue jacket that had so lately covered Mordaunt's shoulders, and poured out its bright contents.

"This coat ain't worth keepin'," he said, holding it up. The garment was rent and slashed, and under the left sleeve was a small, blood-stained hole where one of Brandt's blows had fallen. "Hullo, what's this?" muttered the sailor, feeling in the pocket of the jacket. "Blast my timbers, hooray!"

He held up a small, silver-mounted whiskey flask, unscrewed the lid, and lifted the vessel to his mouth.

"I'm kinder thirsty myself," suggested Legget.

"Cap'n, a nip an' no more," Case replied, holding the flask to Legget's lips.

The outlaw called Jenks now returned with a flat stone which he placed between the two men. The Indians gathered around. With greedy eyes they bent their heads over the gamblers, and watched every movement with breathless interest. At each click of the dice, or clink of gold, they uttered deep exclamations.

"Luck's again' ye, cap'n," said Case, skilfully shaking the ivory cubes.

"Hain't I got eyes?" growled the outlaw.

Steadily his pile of gold diminished, and darker grew his face.

"Cap'n, I'm a bad wind to draw," Case rejoined, drinking again from the flask. His naturally red face had become livid, his skin moist, and his eyes wild with excitement.

"Hullo! If them dice wasn't Jenks's, an' I hadn't played afore with him, I'd swear they's loaded."

"You ain't insinuatin' nothin', cap'n?" inquired Case softly, hesitating with the dice in his hands, his evil eyes glinting at Legget.

"No, you're fair enough," growled the leader. "It's my tough luck."

The game progressed with infrequent runs of fortune for the outlaw, and presently every piece of gold lay in a shining heap before the sailor.

"Clean busted!" exclaimed Legget in disgust.

"Can't you find nothin' more?" asked Case.

The outlaw's bold eyes wandered here and there until they rested upon the prisoner.

"I'll play ther lass against yer pile of gold," he growled. "Best two throws out 'en three. See here, she's as much mine as Brandt's."

"Make it half my pile an' I'll go you."

"Nary time. Bet, or give me back what yer win," replied Legget gruffly.

"She's a trim little craft, no mistake," said Case, critically surveying Helen. "All right, cap'n, I've sportin' blood, an' I'll bet. Yer throw first."

Legget won the first cast, and Case the second. With deliberation the outlaw shook the dice in his huge fist, and rattled them out upon the stone. "Hah!" he cried in delight. He had come within one of the highest score possible. Case nonchalantly flipped the little white blocks. The Indians crowded forward, their dusky eyes shining.

Legget swore in a terrible voice which re-echoed from the stony cliff. The sailor was victorious. The outlaw got up, kicked the stone and dice in the brook, and walked away from the group. He strode to and fro under one of the trees. Gruffly he gave an order to the Indians. Several of them began at once to kindle a fire. Presently he called Jenks, who was fishing the dice out of the brook, and began to converse earnestly with him, making fierce gestures and casting lowering glances at the sailor.

Case was too drunk now to see that he had incurred the enmity of the outlaw leader. He drank the last of the rum, and tossed the silver flask to an Indian, who received the present with every show of delight.

Case then, with the slow, uncertain movements of a man whose mind is befogged, began to count his gold; but only to gather up a few pieces when they slipped out of his trembling hands to roll on the moss. Laboriously, seriously, he kept at it with the doggedness of a drunken man. Apparently he had forgotten the others. Failing to learn the value of the coins by taking up each in turn, he arranged them in several piles, and began to estimate his wealth in sections.

In the meanwhile Helen, who had not failed to take in the slightest detail of what was going on, saw that a plot was hatching which boded ill to the sailor. Moreover, she heard Legget and Jenks whispering.

"I kin take him from right here 'atwixt his eyes," said Jenks softly, and tapped his rifle significantly.

"Wal, go ahead, only I ruther hev it done quieter," answered Legget. "We're yet a long ways, near thirty miles, from my camp, an' there's no tellin' who's in ther woods. But we've got ter git rid of ther fresh sailor, an' there's no surer way."

Cautiously cocking his rifle, Jenks deliberately raised it to his shoulder. One of the Indian sentinels who stood near at hand, sprang forward and struck up the weapon. He spoke a single word to Legget, pointed to the woods above the cliff, and then resumed his statue-like attitude.

"I told yer, Jenks, that it wouldn't do. The redskin scents somethin' in the woods, an' ther's an Injun I never seed fooled. We mustn't make a noise. Take yer knife an' tomahawk, crawl down below the edge o' the bank an' slip up on him. I'll give half ther gold fer ther job."

Jenks buckled his belt more tightly, gave one threatening glance at the sailor, and slipped over the bank. The bed of the brook lay about six feet below the level of the ground. This afforded an opportunity for the outlaw to get behind Case without being observed. A moment passed. Jenks disappeared round a bend of the stream. Presently his grizzled head appeared above the bank. He was immediately behind the sailor; but still some thirty feet away. This ground must be covered quickly and noiselessly. The outlaw began to crawl. In his right hand he grasped a tomahawk, and between his teeth was a long knife. He looked like a huge, yellow bear.

The savages, with the exception of the sentinel who seemed absorbed in the dense thicket on the cliff, sat with their knees between their hands, watching the impending tragedy.

Nothing but the merest chance, or some extraordinary intervention, could avert Case's doom. He was gloating over his gold. The creeping outlaw made no more noise than a snake. Nearer and nearer he came; his sweaty face shining in the sun; his eyes tigerish; his long body slipping silently over the grass. At length he was within five feet of the sailor. His knotty hands were dug into the sward as he gathered energy for a sudden spring.

At that very moment Case, with his hand on his knife, rose quickly and turned round.

The outlaw, discovered in the act of leaping, had no alternative, and spring he did, like a panther.

The little sailor stepped out of line with remarkable quickness, and as the yellow body whirled past him, his knife flashed blue-bright in the sunshine.

Jenks fell forward, his knife buried in the grass beneath him, and his outstretched hand still holding the tomahawk.

"Tryin' ter double-cross me fer my gold," muttered the sailor, sheathing his weapon. He never looked to see whether or no his blow had been fatal. "These border fellars might think a man as sails the seas can't handle a knife." He calmly began gathering up his gold, evidently indifferent to further attack.

Helen saw Legget raise his own rifle, but only to have it struck aside as had Jenks's. This time the savage whispered earnestly to Legget, who called the other Indians around him. The sentinel's low throaty tones mingled with the soft babbling of the stream. No sooner had he ceased speaking than the effect of his words showed how serious had been the information, warning or advice. The Indians cast furtive glances toward the woods. Two of them melted like shadows into the red and gold thicket. Another stealthily slipped from tree to tree until he reached the open ground, then dropped into the grass, and was seen no more until his dark body rose under the cliff. He stole along the green-stained wall, climbed a rugged corner, and vanished amid the dense foliage.

Helen felt that she was almost past discernment or thought. The events of the day succeeding one another so swiftly, and fraught with panic, had, despite her hope and fortitude, reduced her to a helpless condition of piteous fear. She understood that the savages scented danger, or had, in their mysterious way, received intelligence such as rendered them wary and watchful.

"Come on, now, an' make no noise," said Legget to Case. "Bring the girl, an' see that she steps light."

"Ay, ay, cap'n," replied the sailor. "Where's Brandt?"

"He'll be comin' soon's his cut stops bleedin'. I reckon he's weak yet."

Case gathered up his goods, and, tucking it under his arm, grasped Helen's arm. She was leaning against the tree, and when he pulled her, she wrenched herself free, rising with difficulty. His disgusting touch and revolting face had revived her sensibilities.

"Yer kin begin duty by carryin' thet," said Case, thrusting the package into Helen's arms. She let it drop without moving a hand.

"I'm runnin' this ship. Yer belong to me," hissed Case, and then he struck her on the head. Helen uttered a low cry of distress, and half staggered against the tree. The sailor picked up the package. This time she took it, trembling with horror.

"Thet's right. Now, give ther cap'n a kiss," he leered, and jostled against her.

Helen pushed him violently. With agonized eyes she appealed to the Indians. They were engaged tying up their packs. Legget looked on with a lazy grin.

"Oh! oh!" breathed Helen as Case seized her again. She tried to scream, but could not make a sound. The evil eyes, the beastly face, transfixed her with terror.

Case struck her twice, then roughly pulled her toward him.

Half-fainting, unable to move, Helen gazed at the heated, bloated face approaching hers.

When his coarse lips were within a few inches of her lips something hot hissed across her brow. Following so closely as to be an accompaniment, rang out with singular clearness the sharp crack of a rifle.

Case's face changed. The hot, surging flush faded; the expression became shaded, dulled into vacant emptiness; his eyes rolled wildly, then remained fixed, with a look of dark surprise. He stood upright an instant, swayed with the regular poise of a falling oak, and then plunged backward to the ground. His face, ghastly and livid, took on the awful calm of death.

A very small hole, reddish-blue round the edges, dotted the center of his temple.

Legget stared aghast at the dead sailor; then he possessed himself of the bag of gold.

"Saved me ther trouble," he muttered, giving Case a kick.

The Indians glanced at the little figure, then out into the flaming thickets. Each savage sprang behind a tree with incredible quickness. Legget saw this, and grasping Helen, he quickly led her within cover of the chestnut.

Brandt appeared with his Indian companion, and both leaped to shelter behind a clump of birches near where Legget stood. Brandt's hawk eyes flashed upon the dead Jenks and Case. Without asking a question he seemed to take in the situation. He stepped over and grasped Helen by the arm.

"Who killed Case?" he asked in a whisper, staring at the little blue hole in the sailor's temple.

No one answered.

The two Indians who had gone into the woods to the right of the stream, now returned. Hardly were they under the trees with their party, when the savage who had gone off alone arose out of the grass in the left of the brook, took it with a flying leap, and darted into their midst. He was the sentinel who had knocked up the weapons, thereby saving Case's life twice. He was lithe and supple, but not young. His grave, shadowy-lined, iron visage showed the traces of time and experience. All gazed at him as at one whose wisdom was greater than theirs.

"Old Horse," said Brandt in English. "Haven't I seen bullet holes like this?"

The Chippewa bent over Case, and then slowly straightened his tall form.

"*Deathwind!*" he replied, answering in the white man's language.

His Indian companions uttered low, plaintive murmurs, not signifying fear so much as respect.

Brandt turned as pale as the clean birch-bark on the tree near him. The gray flare of his eyes gave out a terrible light of certainty and terror.

"Legget, you needn't try to hide your trail," he hissed, and it seemed as if there was a bitter, reckless pleasure in these words.

Then the Chippewa glided into the low bushes bordering the creek. Legget followed him, with Brandt leading Helen, and the other Indians brought up the rear, each one sending wild, savage glances into the dark, surrounding forest.

CHAPTER XIX.

A dense white fog rose from the river, obscuring all objects, when the bordermen rolled out of their snug bed of leaves. The air was cool and bracing, faintly fragrant with dying foliage and the damp, dewy luxuriance of the ripened season. Wetzel pulled from under the protecting ledge a bundle of bark and sticks he had put there to keep dry, and built a fire, while Jonathan fashioned a cup from a green fruit resembling a gourd, filling it at a spring near by.

"Lew, there's a frosty nip in the water this mornin'," said Jonathan.

"I reckon. It's gettin' along into fall now. Any clear, still night'll fetch all the leaves, an' strip the trees bare as burned timber," answered Wetzel, brushing the ashes off the strip of meat he had roasted. "Get a stick, an' help me cook the rest of this chunk of bison. The sun'll be an hour breakin' up thet mist, an' we can't clear out till then. Mebbe we won't have no chance to light another fire soon."

With these bordermen everything pertaining to their lonely lives, from the lighting of a fire to the trailing of a redskin, was singularly serious. No gladsome song ever came from their lips; there was no jollity around their camp-fire. Hunters had their moments of rapturous delight; bordermen knew the peace, the content of the wilderness, but their pursuits racked nerve and heart. Wetzel had his moments of frenzied joy, but they passed with the echo of his vengeful yell. Jonathan's happiness, such as it was, had been to roam the forests. That, before a woman's eyes had dispelled it, had been enough, and compensated him for the gloomy, bloody phantoms which haunted him.

The bordermen, having partaken of the frugal breakfast, stowed in their spacious pockets all the meat that was left, and were ready for the day's march. They sat silent for a time waiting for the mist to lift. It broke in places, rolled in huge billows, sailed aloft like great white clouds, and again hung tenaciously to the river and the plain. Away in the west blue patches of sky shone through the rifts, and eastward banks of misty vapor reddened

533

beneath the rising sun. Suddenly from beneath the silver edge of the rising pall the sun burst gleaming gold, disclosing the winding valley with its steaming river.

"We'll make up stream fer Two Islands, an' cross there if so be we've reason," Wetzel had said.

Through the dewy dells, avoiding the wet grass and bushes, along the dark, damp glades with their yellow carpets, under the thinning arches of the trees, down the gentle slopes of the ridges, rich with green moss, the bordermen glided like gray shadows. The forest was yet asleep. A squirrel frisked up an oak and barked quarrelsomely at these strange, noiseless visitors. A crow cawed from somewhere overhead. These were the only sounds disturbing the quiet early hour.

As the bordermen advanced the woods lightened and awoke to life and joy. Birds sang, trilled, warbled, or whistled their plaintive songs, peculiar to the dying season, and in harmony with the glory of the earth. Birds that in earlier seasons would have screeched and fought, now sang and fluttered side by side, in fraternal parade on their slow pilgrimage to the far south.

"Bad time fer us, when the birds are so tame, an' chipper. We can't put faith in them these days," said Wetzel. "Seems like they never was wild. I can tell, 'cept at this season, by the way they whistle an' act in the woods, if there's been any Injuns along the trails."

The greater part of the morning passed thus with the bordermen steadily traversing the forest; here, through a spare and gloomy wood, blasted by fire, worn by age, with many a dethroned monarch of bygone times rotting to punk and duff under the ferns, with many a dark, seamed and ragged king still standing, but gray and bald of head and almost ready to take his place in the forest of the past; there, through a maze of young saplings where each ash, maple, hickory and oak added some new and beautiful hue to the riot of color.

"I just had a glimpse of the lower island, as we passed an opening in the thicket," said Jonathan.

"We ain't far away," replied Wetzel.

The bordermen walked less rapidly in order to proceed with more watchfulness. Every rod or two they stopped to listen.

"You think Legget's across the river?" asked Jonathan.

"He was two days back, an' had his gang with him. He's up to some bad work, but I can't make out what. One thing, I never seen his trail so near Fort Henry."

They emerged at length into a more open forest which skirted the river. At a point still some distance ahead, but plainly in sight, two small islands rose out of the water.

"Hist! What's that?" whispered Wetzel, slipping his hand in Jonathan's arm.

A hundred yards beyond lay a long, dark figure stretched at full length under one of the trees close to the bank.

"Looks like a man," said Jonathan.

"You've hit the mark. Take a good peep roun' now, Jack, fer we're comin' somewhere near the trail we want."

Minutes passed while the patient bordermen searched the forest with their eyes, seeking out every tree within rifle range, or surveyed the level glades, scrutinized the hollows, and bent piercing eyes upon the patches of ferns.

"If there's a redskin around he ain't big enough to hold a gun," said Wetzel, moving forward again, yet still with that same stealthy step and keen caution.

Finally they were gazing down upon the object which had attracted Wetzel's attention.

"Will Sheppard!" cried Jonathan. "Is he dead? What's this mean?"

Wetzel leaned over the prostrate lad, and then quickly turned to his companion.

"Get some water. Take his cap. No, he ain't even hurt bad, unless he's got some wound as don't show."

Jonathan returned with the water, and Wetzel bathed the bloody face. When the gash on Will's forehead was clean, it told the bordermen much.

"Not an hour old, that blow," muttered Wetzel.

"He's comin' to," said Jonathan as Will stirred uneasily and moaned. Presently the lad opened his eyes and sat bolt upright. He looked bewildered for a moment, and felt of his head while gazing vaguely at the bordermen. Suddenly he cried:

"I remember! We were captured, brought here, and I was struck down by that villain Case."

"We? Who was with you?" asked Jonathan slowly.

"Helen. We came after flowers and leaves. While in full sight of the fort I saw an Indian. We hurried back," he cried, and proceeded with broken, panting voice to tell his story.

Jonathan Zane leaped to his feet with face deathly white and eyes blue-black, like burning stars.

"Jack, study the trail while I get the lad acrost the river, an' steered fer home," said Wetzel, and then he asked Will if he could swim.

"Yes; but you will find a canoe there in those willows."

"Come, lad, we've no time to spare," added Wetzel, sliding down the bank and entering the willows. He came out almost immediately with the canoe which he launched.

Will turned that he might make a parting appeal to Jonathan to save Helen; but could not speak. The expression on the borderman's face frightened him.

Motionless and erect Jonathan stood, his arms folded and his white, stern face distorted with the agony of remorse, fear, and anguish, which, even as

Will gazed, froze into an awful, deadly look of fateful purpose.

Wetzel pushed the canoe off, and paddled with powerful strokes; he left Will on the opposite bank, and returned as swiftly as he could propel the light craft.

The bordermen met each other's glance, and had little need of words. Wetzel's great shoulders began to sag slightly, and his head lowered as his eyes sought the grass; a dark and gloomy shade overcast his features. Thus he passed from borderman to Deathwind. The sough of the wind overhead among the almost naked branches might well have warned Indians and renegades that Deathwind was on the trail!

"Brandt's had a hand in this, an' the Englishman's a fool!" said Wetzel.

"An hour ahead; can we come up with them before they join Brandt an' Legget?"

"We can try, but like as not we'll fail. Legget's gang is thirteen strong by now. I said it! Somethin' told me—a hard trail, a long trail, an' our last trail."

"It's over thirty miles to Legget's camp. We know the woods, an' every stream, an' every cover," hissed Jonathan Zane.

With no further words Wetzel took the trail on the run, and so plain was it to his keen eyes that he did not relax his steady lope except to stop and listen at regular intervals. Jonathan followed with easy swing. Through forest and meadow, over hill and valley, they ran, fleet and tireless. Once, with unerring instinct, they abruptly left the broad trail and cut far across a wide and rugged ridge to come again upon the tracks of the marching band. Then, in open country they reduced their speed to a walk. Ahead, in a narrow valley, rose a thicket of willows, yellow in the sunlight, and impenetrable to human vision. Like huge snakes the bordermen crept into this copse, over the sand, under the low branches, hard on the trail. Finally, in a light, open space, where the sun shone through a network of yellow branches and foliage, Wetzel's hand was laid upon Jonathan's shoulder.

"Listen! Hear that!" he whispered.

Jonathan heard the flapping of wings, and a low, hissing sound, not unlike that made by a goose.

"Buzzards!" he said, with a dark, grim smile. "Mebbe Brandt has begun our work. Come."

Out into the open they crawled to put to flight a flock of huge black birds with grisly, naked necks, hooked beaks, and long, yellow claws. Upon the green grass lay three half-naked men, ghastly, bloody, in terribly limp and lifeless positions.

"Metzar's man Smith, Jenks, the outlaw, and Mordaunt!"

Jonathan Zane gazed darkly into the steely, sightless eyes of the traitor. Death's awful calm had set the expression; but the man's whole life was there, its better part sadly shining forth among the cruel shadows.

His body was mutilated in a frightful manner. Cuts, stabs, and slashes told the tale of a long encounter, brought to an end by one clean stroke.

"Come here, Lew. You've seen men chopped up; but look at this dead Englishman," called Zane.

Mordaunt lay weltering in a crimson tide. Strangely though, his face was uninjured. A black bruise showed under his fair hair. The ghost of a smile seemed to hover around his set lips, yet almost intangible though it was, it showed that at last he had died a man. His left shoulder, side and arm showed where the brunt of Brandt's attack had fallen.

"How'd he ever fight so?" mused Jonathan.

"You never can tell," replied Wetzel. "Mebbe he killed this other fellar, too; but I reckon not. Come, we must go slow now, fer Legget is near at hand."

Jonathan brought huge, flat stones from the brook, and laid them over Mordaunt; then, cautiously he left the glade on Wetzel's trail.

Five hundred yards farther on Wetzel had ceased following the outlaw's tracks to cross the creek and climb a ridge. He was beginning his favorite trick of making a wide detour. Jonathan hurried forward, feeling he was safe from observation. Soon he distinguished the tall, brown figure of his comrade gliding ahead from tree to tree, from bush to bush.

"See them maples an' chestnuts down thar," said Wetzel when Jonathan had come up, pointing through an opening in the foliage. "They've stopped fer some reason."

On through the forest the bordermen glided. They kept near the summit of the ridge, under the best cover they could find, and passed swiftly over this half-circle. When beginning once more to draw toward the open grove in the valley, they saw a long, irregular cliff, densely wooded. They swerved a little, and made for this excellent covert.

They crawled the last hundred yards and never shook a fern, moved a leaf, or broke a twig. Having reached the brink of the low precipice, they saw the grassy meadow below, the straggling trees, the brook, the group of Indians crowding round the white men.

"See that point of rock thar? It's better cover," whispered Wetzel.

Patiently, with no hurry or excitement, they slowly made their difficult way among the rocks and ferns to the vantage point desired. Taking a position like this was one the bordermen strongly favored. They could see everywhere in front, and had the thick woods at their backs.

"What are they up to?" whispered Jonathan, as he and Wetzel lay close together under a mass of grapevine still tenacious of its broad leaves.

"Dicin'," answered Wetzel. "I can see 'em throw; anyways, nothin' but bettin' ever makes redskins act like that."

"Who's playin'? Where's Brandt?"

"I can make out Legget; see his shaggy head. The other must be Case. Brandt ain't in sight. Nursin' a hurt perhaps. Ah! See thar! Over under the big tree as stands dark-like agin the thicket. Thet's an Injun, an' he looks too quiet an' keen to suit me. We'll have a care of him."

"Must be playin' fer Mordaunt's gold."

"Like as not, for where'd them ruffians get any 'cept they stole it."

"Aha! They're gettin' up! See Legget walk away shakin' his big head. He's mad. Mebbe he'll be madder presently," growled Jonathan.

"Case's left alone. He's countin' his winnin's. Jack, look out fer more work took off our hands."

"By gum! See that Injun knock up a leveled rifle."

"I told you, an' thet redskin has his suspicions. He's seen us down along ther ridge. There's Helen, sittin' behind the biggest tree. Thet Injun guard, 'afore he moved, kept us from seein' her."

Jonathan made no answer to this; but his breath literally hissed through his clenched teeth.

"Thar goes the other outlaw," whispered Wetzel, as if his comrade could not see. "It's all up with Case. See the sneak bendin' down the bank. Now, thet's a poor way. It'd better be done from the front, walkin' up natural-like, instead of tryin' to cover thet wide stretch. Case'll see him or hear him sure. Thar, he's up now, an' crawlin'. He's too slow, too slow. Aha! I knew it— Case turns. Look at the outlaw spring! Well, did you see thet little cuss whip his knife? One more less fer us to quiet. Thet makes four, Jack, an' mebbe, soon, it'll be five."

"They're holdin' a council," said Jonathan.

"I see two Injuns sneakin' off into the woods, an' here comes thet guard. He's a keen redskin, Jack, fer we did come light through the brush. Mebbe it'd be well to stop his scoutin'."

"Lew, that villain Case is bullyin' Helen!" cried Jonathan.

"Sh-sh-h," whispered Wetzel.

"See! He's pulled her to her feet. Oh! He struck her! Oh!"

Jonathan leveled his rifle and would have fired, but for the iron grasp on his wrist.

"Hev you lost yer senses? It's full two hundred paces, an' too far fer your piece," said Wetzel in a whisper. "An' it ain't sense to try from here."

"Lend me your gun! Lend me your gun!"

Silently Wetzel handed him the long, black rifle.

Jonathan raised it, but trembled so violently that the barrel wavered like a leaf in the breeze.

"Take it, I can't cover him," groaned Jonathan. "This is new to me. I ain't myself. God! Lew, he struck her again! *Again!* He's tryin' to kiss her! Wetzel, if you're my friend, kill him!"

"Jack, it'd be better to wait, an'——"

"I love her," breathed Jonathan.

The long, black barrel swept up to a level and stopped. White smoke belched from among the green leaves; the report rang throughout the forest.

"Ah! I saw him stop an' pause," hissed Jonathan. "He stands, he sways, he falls! Death for yours, you sailor-beast!"

CHAPTER XX.

The bordermen watched Legget and his band disappear into the thicket adjoining the grove. When the last dark, lithe form glided out of sight among the yellowing copse, Jonathan leaped from the low cliff, and had hardly reached the ground before Wetzel dashed down to the grassy turf.

Again they followed the outlaw's trail darker-faced, fiercer-visaged than ever, with cocked, tightly-gripped rifles thrust well before them, and light feet that scarcely brushed the leaves.

Wetzel halted after a long tramp up and down the ridges, and surveyed with keen intent the lay of the land ahead.

"Sooner or later we'll hear from that redskin as discovered us a ways back," whispered he. "I wish we might get a crack at him afore he hinders us bad. I ain't seen many keener Injuns. It's lucky we fixed ther arrow-shootin' Shawnee. We'd never hev beat thet combination. An' fer all of thet I'm worrin' some about the goin' ahead."

"Ambush?" Jonathan asked.

"Like as not. Legget'll send thet Injun back, an' mebbe more'n him. Jack, see them little footprints? They're Helen's. Look how she's draggin' along. Almost tuckered out. Legget can't travel many more miles to-day. He'll make a stand somewheres, an' lose all his redskins afore he gives up the lass."

"I'll never live through to-night with her in that gang. She'll be saved, or dead, before the stars pale in the light of the moon."

"I reckon we're nigh the end for some of us. It'll be moonlight an hour arter dusk, an' now it's only the middle of the arternoon; we've time enough fer anythin'. Now, Jack, let's not tackle the trail straight. We'll split, an' go round to head 'em off. See thet dead white oak standin' high over thar?"

Jonathan looked out between the spreading branches of a beech, and saw, far over a low meadow, luxuriant with grasses and rushes and bright with sparkling ponds and streams, a dense wood out of which towered a bare, bleached tree-top.

"You slip around along the right side of this meader, an' I'll take the left

540

side. Go slow, an' hev yer eyes open. We'll meet under thet big dead tree. I allow we can see it from anywhere around. We'll leave the trail here, an' take it up farther on. Legget's goin' straight for his camp; he ain't losin' an inch. He wants to get in that rocky hole of his'n."

Wetzel stepped off the trail, glided into the woods, and vanished.

Jonathan turned to the right, traversed the summit of the ridge, softly traveled down its slope, and, after crossing a slow, eddying, quiet stream, gained the edge of the forest on that side of the swamp. A fringe of briars and prickly thorns bordered this wood affording an excellent cover. On the right the land rose rather abruptly. He saw that by walking up a few paces he could command a view of the entire swamp, as well as the ridge beyond, which contained Wetzel, and, probably, the outlaw and his band.

Remembering his comrade's admonition, Jonathan curbed his unusual impatience and moved slowly. The wind swayed the tree-tops, and rustled the fallen leaves. Birds sang as if thinking the warm, soft weather was summer come again. Squirrels dropped heavy nuts that cracked on the limbs, or fell with a thud to the ground, and they scampered over the dry earth, scratching up the leaves as they barked and scolded. Crows cawed clamorously after a hawk that had darted under the tree-tops to escape them; deer loped swiftly up the hill, and a lordly elk rose from a wallow in the grassy swamp, crashing into the thicket.

When two-thirds around this oval plain, which was a mile long and perhaps one-fourth as wide, Jonathan ascended the hill to make a survey. The grass waved bright brown and golden in the sunshine, swished in the wind, and swept like a choppy sea to the opposite ridge. The hill was not densely wooded. In many places the red-brown foliage opened upon irregular patches, some black, as if having been burned over, others showing the yellow and purple colors of the low thickets and the gray, barren stones.

Suddenly Jonathan saw something darken one of these sunlit plots. It might have been a deer. He studied the rolling, rounded tree-tops, the narrow strips between the black trunks, and the open places that were clear in the sunshine. He had nearly come to believe he had seen a small animal or bird flit across the white of the sky far in the background, when he distinctly saw dark figures stealing along past a green-gray rock, only to disappear under colored banks of foliage. Presently, lower down, they reappeared and crossed an open patch of yellow fern. Jonathan counted them. Two were rather yellow in color, the hue of buckskin; another, slight of stature as compared with the first, and light gray by contrast. Then six black, slender, gliding forms crossed the space. Jonathan then lost sight of them, and did not get another glimpse. He knew them to be Legget and his band. The slight figure was Helen.

Jonathan broke into a run, completed the circle around the swamp, and slowed into a walk when approaching the big dead tree where he was to wait for Wetzel.

Several rods beyond the lowland he came to a wood of white oaks, all giants rugged and old, with scarcely a sapling intermingled with them. Although he could not see the objective point, he knew from his accurate sense of distance that he was near it. As he entered the wood he swept its whole length and width with his eyes, he darted forward twenty paces to halt suddenly behind a tree. He knew full well that a sharply moving object was more difficult to see in the woods, than one stationary. Again he ran, fleet and light, a few paces ahead to take up a position as before behind a tree. Thus he traversed the forest. On the other side he found the dead oak of which Wetzel had spoken.

Its trunk was hollow. Jonathan squeezed himself into the blackened space, with his head in a favorable position behind a projecting knot, where he could see what might occur near at hand.

He waited for what seemed to him a long while, during which he neither saw nor heard anything, and then, suddenly, the report of a rifle rang out. A single, piercing scream followed. Hardly had the echo ceased when three hollow reports, distinctly different in tone from the first, could be heard from the same direction. In quick succession short, fierce yells attended rather than succeeded, the reports.

Jonathan stepped out of the hiding-place, cocked his rifle, and fixed a sharp eye on the ridge before him whence those startling cries had come. The first rifle-shot, unlike any other in its short, spiteful, stinging quality, was unmistakably Wetzel's. Zane had heard it, followed many times, as now, by the wild death-cry of a savage. The other reports were of Indian guns, and the yells were the clamoring, exultant cries of Indians in pursuit.

Far down where the open forest met the gloom of the thickets, a brown figure flashed across the yellow ground. Darting among the trees, across the glades, it moved so swiftly that Jonathan knew it was Wetzel. In another instant a chorus of yelps resounded from the foliage, and three savages burst through the thicket almost at right angles with the fleeing borderman, running to intercept him. The borderman did not swerve from his course; but came on straight toward the dead tree, with the wonderful fleetness that so often had served him well.

Even in that moment Jonathan thought of what desperate chances his comrade had taken. The trick was plain. Wetzel had, most likely, shot the dangerous scout, and, taking to his heels, raced past the others, trusting to his speed and their poor marksmanship to escape with a whole skin.

When within a hundred yards of the oak Wetzel's strength apparently gave out. His speed deserted him; he ran awkwardly, and limped. The savages burst out into full cry like a pack of hungry wolves. They had already emptied their rifles at him, and now, supposing one of the shots had taken effect, redoubled their efforts, making the forest ring with their short, savage yells. One gaunt, dark-bodied Indian with a long, powerful, springy stride easily distanced his companions, and, evidently sure of gaining the coveted scalp of the borderman, rapidly closed the gap between them as he swung aloft his tomahawk, yelling the war-cry.

The sight on Jonathan's rifle had several times covered this savage's dark face; but when he was about to press the trigger Wetzel's fleeting form, also in line with the savage, made it extremely hazardous to take a shot.

Jonathan stepped from his place of concealment, and let out a yell that pealed high over the cries of the savages.

Wetzel suddenly dropped flat on the ground.

With a whipping crack of Jonathan's rifle, the big Indian plunged forward on his face.

The other Indians, not fifty yards away, stopped aghast at the fate of their comrade, and were about to seek the shelter of trees when, with his terrible yell, Wetzel sprang up and charged upon them. He had left his rifle where he fell; but his tomahawk glittered as he ran. The lameness had been a trick, for now he covered ground with a swiftness which caused his former progress to seem slow.

The Indians, matured and seasoned warriors though they were, gave but one glance at this huge, brown figure bearing down upon them like a fiend, and, uttering the Indian name of *Deathwind*, wavered, broke and ran.

One, not so fleet as his companion, Wetzel overtook and cut down with a single stroke. The other gained an hundred-yard start in the slight interval of Wetzel's attack, and, spurred on by a pealing, awful cry in the rear, sped swiftly in and out among the trees until he was lost to view.

Wetzel scalped the two dead savages, and, after returning to regain his rifle, joined Jonathan at the dead oak.

"Jack, you can never tell how things is comin' out. Thet redskin I allowed might worry us a bit, fooled me as slick as you ever saw, an' I hed to shoot him. Knowin' it was a case of runnin', I just cut fer this oak, drew the redskins' fire, an' hed 'em arter me quicker 'n you'd say Jack Robinson. I was hopin' you'd be here; but wasn't sure till I'd seen your rifle. Then I kinder got a kink in my leg jest to coax the brutes on."

"Three more quiet," said Jonathan Zane. "What now?"

"We've headed Legget, an' we'll keep nosin' him off his course. Already he's lookin' fer a safe campin' place for the night."

"There is none in these woods, fer him."

"We didn't plan this gettin' between him an' his camp; but couldn't be better fixed. A mile farther along the ridge, is a campin' place, with a spring in a little dell close under a big stone, an' well wooded. Legget's headin' straight fer it. With a couple of Injuns guardin' thet spot, he'll think he's safe. But I know the place, an' can crawl to thet rock the darkest night thet ever was an' never crack a stick."

* * * * *

In the gray of the deepening twilight Jonathan Zane sat alone. An owl hooted dismally in the dark woods beyond the thicket where the borderman crouched waiting for Wetzel. His listening ear detected a soft, rustling sound like the play of a mole under the leaves. A branch trembled and swung back; a soft footstep followed and Wetzel came into the retreat.

"Well?" asked Jonathan impatiently, as Wetzel deliberately sat down and laid his rifle across his knees.

"Easy, Jack, easy. We've an hour to wait."

"The time I've already waited has been long for me."

"They're thar," said Wetzel grimly.

"How far from here?"

"A half-hour's slow crawl."

"Close by?" hissed Jonathan.

"Too near fer you to get excited."

"Let us go; it's as light now as in the gray of mornin'."

"Mornin' would be best. Injuns get sleepy along towards day. I've ever found thet time the best. But we'll be lucky if we ketch these redskins asleep."

"Lew, I can't wait here all night. I won't leave her longer with that renegade. I've got to free or kill her."

"Most likely it'll be the last," said Wetzel simply.

"Well, so be it then," and the borderman hung his head.

"You needn't worry none, 'bout Helen. I jest had a good look at her, not half an hour back. She's fagged out; but full of spunk yet. I seen thet when Brandt went near her. Legget's got his hands full jest now with the redskins. He's hevin' trouble keepin' them on this slow trail. I ain't sayin' they're skeered; but they're mighty restless."

"Will you take the chance now?"

"I reckon you needn't hev asked thet."

"Tell me the lay of the land."

"Wal, if we get to this rock I spoke 'bout, we'll be right over 'em. It's ten feet high, an' we can jump straight amongst 'em. Most likely two or three'll be guardin' the openin' which is a little ways to the right. Ther's a big tree, the only one, low down by the spring. Helen's under it, half-sittin', half-leanin' against the roots. When I first looked, her hands were free; but I saw Brandt bind her feet. An' he had to get an Injun to help him, fer she kicked like a spirited little filly. There's moss under the tree an' there's where the redskins'll lay down to rest."

"I've got that; now out with your plan."

"Wal, I calkilate it's this. The moon'll be up in about an hour. We'll crawl as we've never crawled afore, because Helen's life depends as much on our not makin' a noise, as it does on fightin' when the time comes. If they hear us afore we're ready to shoot, the lass'll be tomahawked quicker'n lightnin'. If they don't suspicion us, when the right moment comes you shoot Brandt, yell louder'n you ever did afore, leap amongst 'em, an' cut down the first Injun thet's near you on your way to Helen. Swing her over your arm, an' dig into the woods."

"Well?" asked Jonathan when Wetzel finished.

"That's all," the borderman replied grimly.

"An' leave you all alone to fight Legget an' the rest of 'em?"

"I reckon."

"Not to be thought of."

"Ther's no other way."

"There must be! Let me think; I can't, I'm not myself."

"No other way," repeated Wetzel curtly.

Jonathan's broad hand fastened on Wetzel's shoulder and wheeled him around.

"Have I ever left you alone?"

"This's different," and Wetzel turned away again. His voice was cold and hard.

"How is it different? We've had the same thing to do, almost, more than once."

"We've never had as bad a bunch to handle as Legget's. They're lookin' fer us, an' will be hard to beat."

"That's no reason."

"We never had to save a girl one of us loved."

Jonathan was silent.

"I said this'd be my last trail," continued Wetzel. "I felt it, an' I know it'll be yours."

"Why?"

"If you get away with the girl she'll keep you at home, an' it'll be well. If you don't succeed, you'll die tryin', so it's sure your last trail."

Wetzel's deep, cold voice rang with truth.

"Lew, I can't run away an' leave you to fight those devils alone, after all these years we've been together, I can't."

"No other chance to save the lass."

Jonathan quivered with the force of his emotion. His black eyes glittered; his hands grasped at nothing. Once more he was between love and duty. Again he fought over the old battle, but this time it left him weak.

"You love the big-eyed lass, don't you?" asked Wetzel, turning with softened face and voice.

"I have gone mad!" cried Jonathan, tortured by the simple question of his friend. Those big, dear, wonderful eyes he loved so well, looked at him now from the gloom of the thicket. The old, beautiful, soft glow, the tender light, was there, and more, a beseeching prayer to save her.

Jonathan bowed his head, ashamed to let his friend see the tears that dimmed his eyes.

"Jack, we've follered the trail fer years together. Always you've been true an' staunch. This is our last, but whatever bides we'll break up Legget's band to-night, an' the border'll be cleared, mebbe, for always. At least his race is run. Let thet content you. Our time'd have to come, sooner or later, so why not now? I know how it is, that you want to stick by me; but the lass draws you to her. I understand, an' want you to save her. Mebbe you never dreamed it; but I can tell jest how you feel. All the tremblin', an' softness, an' sweetness, an' delight you've got for thet girl, is no mystery to Lew Wetzel."

"You loved a lass?"

Wetzel bowed his head, as perhaps he had never before in all his life.

"Betty—always," he answered softly.

"My sister!" exclaimed Jonathan, and then his hand closed hard on his comrade's, his mind going back to many things, strange in the past, but now explained. Wetzel had revealed his secret.

"An' it's been all my life, since she wasn't higher 'n my knee. There was a time when I might hev been closer to you than I am now. But I was a mad an' bloody Injun hater, so I never let her know till I seen it was too late. Wal, wal, no more of me. I only told it fer you."

Jonathan was silent.

"An' now to come back where we left off," continued Wetzel. "Let's take a more hopeful look at this comin' fight. Sure I said it was my last trail, but mebbe it's not. You can never tell. Feelin' as we do, I imagine they've no odds on us. Never in my life did I say to you, least of all to any one else, what I was goin' to do; but I'll tell it now. If I land uninjured amongst thet bunch, I'll kill them all."

The giant borderman's low voice hissed, and stung. His eyes glittered with unearthly fire. His face was cold and gray. He spread out his brawny arms and clenched his huge fists, making the muscles of his broad shoulders roll and bulge.

"I hate the thought, Lew, I hate the thought. Ain't there no other way?"

"No other way."

"I'll do it, Lew, because I'd do the same for you; because I have to, because I love her; but God! it hurts."

"Thet's right," answered Wetzel, his deep voice softening until it was singularly low and rich. "I'm glad you've come to it. An' sure it hurts. I want you to feel so at leavin' me to go it alone. If we both get out alive, I'll come many times to see you an' Helen. If you live an' I don't, think of me sometimes, think of the trails we've crossed together. When the fall comes with its soft, cool air, an' smoky mornin's an' starry nights, when the wind's sad among the bare branches, an' the leaves drop down, remember they're fallin' on my grave."

Twilight darkened into gloom; the red tinge in the west changed to opal light; through the trees over a dark ridge a rim of silver glinted and moved.

The moon had risen; the hour was come.

The bordermen tightened their belts, replaced their leggings, tied their hunting coats, loosened their hatchets, looked to the priming of their rifles, and were ready.

Wetzel walked twenty paces and turned. His face was white in the moonlight; his dark eyes softened into a look of love as he gripped his comrade's outstretched hand.

Then he dropped flat on the ground, carefully saw to the position of his rifle, and began to creep. Jonathan kept close at his heels.

Slowly but steadily they crawled, minute after minute. The hazel-nut bushes above them had not yet shed their leaves; the ground was clean and hard, and the course fatefully perfect for their deadly purpose.

A slight rustling of their buckskin garments sounded like the rustling of leaves in a faint breeze.

The moon came out above the trees and still Wetzel advanced softly, steadily, surely.

The owl, lonely sentinel of that wood, hooted dismally. Even his night eyes, which made the darkness seem clear as day, missed those gliding figures. Even he, sure guardian of the wilderness, failed the savages.

Jonathan felt soft moss beneath him; he was now in the woods under the trees. The thicket had been passed.

Wetzel's moccasin pressed softly against Jonathan's head. The first signal!

Jonathan crawled forward, and slightly raised himself.

He was on a rock. The trees were thick and gloomy. Below, the little hollow was almost in the wan moonbeams. Dark figures lay close together. Two savages paced noiselessly to and fro. A slight form rolled in a blanket lay against a tree.

Jonathan felt his arm gently squeezed.

The second signal!

Slowly he thrust forward his rifle, and raised it in unison with Wetzel's. Slowly he rose to his feet as if the same muscles guided them both.

Over his head a twig snapped. In the darkness he had not seen a low branch.

The Indian guards stopped suddenly, and became motionless as stone.

They had heard; but too late.

With the blended roar of the rifles both dropped, lifeless.

Almost under the spouting flame and white cloud of smoke, Jonathan leaped behind Wetzel, over the bank. His yells were mingled with Wetzel's vengeful cry. Like leaping shadows the bordermen were upon their foes.

An Indian sprang up, raised a weapon, and fell beneath Jonathan's savage blow, to rise no more. Over his prostrate body the borderman bounded. A dark, nimble form darted upon the captive. He swung high a blade that shone like silver in the moonlight. His shrill war-cry of death rang out with Helen's scream of despair. Even as he swung back her head with one hand in her long hair, his arm descended; but it fell upon the borderman's body. Jonathan and the Indian rolled upon the moss. There was a terrific struggle, a whirling blade, a dull blow which silenced the yell, and the borderman rose alone.

He lifted Helen as if she were a child, leaped the brook, and plunged into the thicket.

The noise of the fearful conflict he left behind, swelled high and hideously on the night air. Above the shrill cries of the Indians, and the furious yells of Legget, rose the mad, booming roar of Wetzel. No rifle cracked; but sodden blows, the clash of steel, the threshing of struggling men, told of the dreadful strife.

Jonathan gained the woods, sped through the moonlit glades, and far on under light and shadow.

The shrill cries ceased; only the hoarse yells and the mad roar could be heard. Gradually these also died away, and the forest was still.

CHAPTER XXI.

Next morning, when the mist was breaking and rolling away under the warm rays of the Indian-summer sun, Jonathan Zane beached his canoe on the steep bank before Fort Henry. A pioneer, attracted by the borderman's halloo, ran to the bluff and sounded the alarm with shrill whoops. Among the hurrying, brown-clad figures that answered this summons, was Colonel Zane.

"It's Jack, kurnel, an' he's got her!" cried one.

The doughty colonel gained the bluff to see his brother climbing the bank with a white-faced girl in his arms.

"Well?" he asked, looking darkly at Jonathan. Nothing kindly or genial was visible in his manner now; rather grim and forbidding he seemed, thus showing he had the same blood in his veins as the borderman.

"Lend a hand," said Jonathan. "As far as I know she's not hurt."

They carried Helen toward Colonel Zane's cabin. Many women of the settlement saw them as they passed, and looked gravely at one another, but none spoke. This return of an abducted girl was by no means a strange event.

"Somebody run for Sheppard," ordered Colonel Zane, as they entered his cabin.

Betty, who was in the sitting-room, sprang up and cried: "Oh! Eb! Eb! Don't say she's——"

"No, no, Betts, she's all right. Where's my wife? Ah! Bess, here, get to work."

The colonel left Helen in the tender, skilful hands of his wife and sister, and followed Jonathan into the kitchen.

"I was just ready for breakfast when I heard some one yell," said he. "Come, Jack, eat something."

They ate in silence. From the sitting-room came excited whispers, a joyous cry from Betty, and a faint voice. Then heavy, hurrying footsteps, followed by Sheppard's words of thanks-giving.

"Where's Wetzel?" began Colonel Zane.

The borderman shook his head gloomily.

"Where did you leave him?"

"We jumped Legget's bunch last night, when the moon was about an hour high. I reckon about fifteen miles northeast. I got away with the lass."

"Ah! Left Lew fighting?"

The borderman answered the question with bowed head.

"You got off well. Not a hurt that I can see, and more than lucky to save Helen. Well, Jack, what do you think about Lew?"

"I'm goin' back," replied Jonathan.

"No! no!"

The door opened to admit Mrs. Zane. She looked bright and cheerful, "Hello, Jack; glad you're home. Helen's all right, only faint from hunger and over-exertion. I want something for her to eat—well! you men didn't leave much."

Colonel Zane went into the sitting-room. Sheppard sat beside the couch where Helen lay, white and wan. Betty and Nell were looking on with their hearts in their eyes. Silas Zane was there, and his wife, with several women neighbors.

"Betty, go fetch Jack in here," whispered the colonel in his sister's ear. "Drag him, if you have to," he added fiercely.

The young woman left the room, to reappear directly with her brother. He came in reluctantly.

As the stern-faced borderman crossed the threshold a smile, beautiful to see, dawned in Helen's eyes.

"I'm glad to see you're comin' round," said Jonathan, but he spoke dully as if his mind was on other things.

"She's a little flighty; but a night's sleep will cure that," cried Mrs. Zane from the kitchen.

"What do you think?" interrupted the colonel. "Jack's not satisfied to get back with Helen unharmed, and a whole skin himself; but he's going on the trail again."

"No, Jack, no, no!" cried Betty.

"What's that I hear?" asked Mrs. Zane as she came in. "Jack's going out again? Well, all I want to say is that he's as mad as a March hare."

"Jonathan, look here," said Silas seriously. "Can't you stay home now?"

"Jack, listen," whispered Betty, going close to him. "Not one of us ever expected to see either you or Helen again, and oh! we are so happy. Do not go away again. You are a man; you do not know, you cannot understand all a woman feels. She must sit and wait, and hope, and pray for the safe return of husband or brother or sweetheart. The long days! Oh, the long sleepless nights, with the wail of the wind in the pines, and the rain on the roof! It is maddening. Do not leave us! Do not leave me! Do not leave Helen! Say you will not, Jack."

To these entreaties the borderman remained silent. He stood leaning on his rifle, a tall, dark, strangely sad and stern man.

"Helen, beg him to stay!" implored Betty.

Colonel Zane took Helen's hand, and stroked it. "Yes," he said, "you ask him, lass. I'm sure you can persuade him to stay."

Helen raised her head. "Is Brandt dead?" she whispered faintly.

Still the borderman failed to speak, but his silence was not an affirmative.

"You said you loved me," she cried wildly. "You said you loved me, yet you didn't kill that monster!"

The borderman, moving quickly like a startled Indian, went out of the door.

* * * * *

Once more Jonathan Zane entered the gloomy, quiet aisles of the forest with his soft, tireless tread hardly stirring the leaves.

It was late in the afternoon when he had long left Two Islands behind, and arrived at the scene of Mordaunt's death. Satisfied with the distance he had traversed, he crawled into a thicket to rest.

Daybreak found him again on the trail. He made a short cut over the ridges and by the time the mist had lifted from the valley he was within stalking distance of the glade. He approached this in the familiar, slow, cautious manner, and halted behind the big rock from which he and Wetzel had leaped. The wood was solemnly quiet. No twittering of birds could be heard. The only sign of life was a gaunt timber-wolf slinking away amid the foliage. Under the big tree the savage who had been killed as he would have murdered Helen, lay a crumpled mass where he had fallen. Two dead Indians were in the center of the glade, and on the other side were three more bloody, lifeless forms. Wetzel was not there, nor Legget, nor Brandt.

"I reckoned so," muttered Jonathan as he studied the scene. The grass had been trampled, the trees barked, the bushes crushed aside.

Jonathan went out of the glade a short distance, and, circling it, began to look for Wetzel's trail. He found it, and near the light footprints of his comrade were the great, broad moccasin tracks of the outlaw. Further searching disclosed the fact that Brandt must have traveled in line with the others.

With the certainty that Wetzel had killed three of the Indians, and, in some wonderful manner characteristic of him, routed the outlaws of whom he was now in pursuit, Jonathan's smoldering emotion burst forth into full flame. Love for his old comrade, deadly hatred of the outlaws, and passionate thirst for their blood, rioted in his heart.

Like a lynx scenting its quarry, the borderman started on the trail, tireless and unswervable. The traces left by the fleeing outlaws and their pursuer were plain to Jonathan. It was not necessary for him to stop. Legget and Brandt, seeking to escape the implacable Nemesis, were traveling with all possible speed, regardless of the broad trail such hurried movements left behind. They knew full well it would be difficult to throw this wolf off the scent; understood that if any attempt was made to ambush the trail, they must cope with woodcraft keener than an Indian's. Flying in desperation, they hoped to reach the rocky retreat, where, like foxes in their burrows, they believed themselves safe.

When the sun sloped low toward the western horizon, lengthening Jonathan's shadow, he slackened pace. He was entering the rocky, rugged country which marked the approach to the distant Alleghenies. From the top of a ridge he took his bearings, deciding that he was within a few miles of Legget's hiding-place.

At the foot of this ridge, where a murmuring brook sped softly over its bed, he halted. Here a number of horses had forded the brook. They were iron-shod, which indicated almost to a certainty, that they were stolen horses, and in the hands of Indians.

Jonathan saw where the trail of the steeds was merged into that of the outlaws. He suspected that the Indians and Legget had held a short council. As he advanced the borderman found only the faintest impression of Wetzel's trail. Legget and Brandt no longer left any token of their course. They were riding the horses.

All the borderman cared to know was if Wetzel still pursued. He passed on swiftly up a hill, through a wood of birches where the trail showed on a line of broken ferns, then out upon a low ridge where patches of grass grew sparsely. Here he saw in this last ground no indication of his comrade's trail; nothing was to be seen save the imprints of the horses' hoofs. Jonathan halted behind the nearest underbrush. This sudden move on the part of Wetzel was token that, suspecting an ambush, he had made a detour somewhere, probably in the grove of birches.

All the while his eyes searched the long, barren reach ahead. No thicket, fallen tree, or splintered rocks, such as Indians utilized for an ambush, could be seen. Indians always sought the densely matted underbrush, a windfall, or rocky retreat and there awaited a pursuer. It was one of the borderman's tricks of woodcraft that he could recognize such places.

Far beyond the sandy ridge Jonathan came to a sloping, wooded hillside, upon which were scattered big rocks, some mossy and lichen-covered, and one, a giant boulder, with a crown of ferns and laurel gracing its flat surface. It was such a place as the savages would select for ambush. He knew, however, that if an Indian had hidden himself there Wetzel would have discovered him. When opposite the rock Jonathan saw a broken fern hanging over the edge. The heavy trail of the horses ran close beside it.

Then with that thoroughness of search which made the borderman what he was, Jonathan leaped upon the rock. There, lying in the midst of the ferns, lay an Indian with sullen, somber face set in the repose of death. In his side was a small bullet hole.

Jonathan examined the savage's rifle. It had been discharged. The rock, the broken fern, the dead Indian, the discharged rifle, told the story of that woodland tragedy.

Wetzel had discovered the ambush. Leaving the trail, he had tricked the redskin into firing, then getting a glimpse of the Indian's red body through the sights of his fatal weapon, the deed was done.

With greater caution Jonathan advanced once more. Not far beyond the rock he found Wetzel's trail. The afternoon was drawing to a close. He could not travel much farther, yet he kept on, hoping to overtake his comrade before darkness set in. From time to time he whistled; but got no answering signal.

When the tracks of the horses were nearly hidden by the gathering dusk, Jonathan decided to halt for the night. He whistled one more note, louder and clearer, and awaited the result with strained ears. The deep silence of the wilderness prevailed, suddenly to be broken by a faint, far-away, melancholy call of the hermit-thrush. It was the answering signal the borderman had hoped to hear.

Not many moments elapsed before he heard another call, low, and near at hand, to which he replied. The bushes parted noiselessly on his left, and the tall form of Wetzel appeared silently out of the gloom.

The two gripped hands in silence.

"Hev you any meat?" Wetzel asked, and as Jonathan handed him his knapsack, he continued, "I was kinder lookin' fer you. Did you get out all right with the lass?"

"Nary a scratch."

The giant borderman grunted his satisfaction.

"How'd Legget and Brandt get away?" asked Jonathan.

"Cut an' run like scared bucks. Never got a hand on either of 'em."

"How many redskins did they meet back here a spell?"

"They was seven; but now there are only six, an' all snug in Legget's place by this time."

"I reckon we're near his den."

"We're not far off."

Night soon closing down upon the bordermen found them wrapped in slumber, as if no deadly foes were near at hand. The soft night wind sighed dismally among the bare trees. A few bright stars twinkled overhead. In the darkness of the forest the bordermen were at home.

CHAPTER XXII.

In Legget's rude log cabin a fire burned low, lightening the forms of the two border outlaws, and showing in the background the dark forms of Indians sitting motionless on the floor. Their dusky eyes emitted a baleful glint, seemingly a reflection of their savage souls caught by the firelight. Legget wore a look of ferocity and sullen fear strangely blended. Brandt's face was hard and haggard, his lips set, his gray eyes smoldering.

"Safe?" he hissed. "Safe you say? You'll see that it's the same now as on the other night, when those border-tigers jumped us and we ran like cowards. I'd have fought it out here, but for you."

"Thet man Wetzel is ravin' mad, I tell you," growled Legget. "I reckon I've stood my ground enough to know I ain't no coward. But this fellar's crazy. He hed the Injuns slashin' each other like a pack of wolves round a buck."

"He's no more mad than you or I," declared Brandt. "I know all about him. His moaning in the woods, and wild yells are only tricks. He knows the Indian nature, and he makes their very superstition and religion aid him in his fighting. I told you what he'd do. Didn't I beg you to kill Zane when we had a chance? Wetzel would never have taken our trail alone. Now they've beat me out of the girl, and as sure as death will round us up here."

"You don't believe they'll rush us here?" asked Legget.

"They're too keen to take foolish chances, but something will be done we don't expect. Zane was a prisoner here; he had a good look at this place, and you can gamble he'll remember."

"Zane must hev gone back to Fort Henry with the girl."

"Mark what I say, he'll come back!"

"Wal, we kin hold this place against all the men Eb Zane may put out."

"He won't send a man," snapped Brandt passionately. "Remember this, Legget, we're not to fight against soldiers, settlers, or hunters; but bordermen—understand—bordermen! Such as have been developed right here on this bloody frontier, and nowhere else on earth. They haven't fear in

554

them. Both are fleet as deer in the woods. They can't be seen or trailed. They can snuff a candle with a rifle ball in the dark. I've seen Zane do it three times at a hundred yards. And Wetzel! He wouldn't waste powder on practicing. They can't be ambushed, or shaken off a track; they take the scent like buzzards, and have eyes like eagles."

"We kin slip out of here under cover of night," suggested Legget.

"Well, what then? That's all they want. They'd be on us again by sunset. No! we've got to stand our ground and fight. We'll stay as long as we can; but they'll rout us out somehow, be sure of that. And if one of us pokes his nose out to the daylight, it will be shot off."

"You're sore, an' you've lost your nerve," said Legget harshly. "Sore at me 'cause I got sweet on the girl. Ho! ho!"

Brandt shot a glance at Legget which boded no good. His strong hands clenched in an action betraying the reckless rage in his heart. Then he carefully removed his hunting coat, and examined his wound. He retied the bandage, muttering gloomily, "I'm so weak as to be light-headed. If this cut opens again, it's all day for me."

After that the inmates of the hut were quiet. The huge outlaw bowed his shaggy head for a while, and then threw himself on a pile of hemlock boughs. Brandt was not long in seeking rest. Soon both were fast asleep. Two of the savages passed out with cat-like step, leaving the door open. The fire had burned low, leaving a bed of dead coals. Outside in the dark a waterfall splashed softly.

The darkest hour came, and passed, and paled slowly to gray. Birds began to twitter. Through the door of the cabin the light of day streamed in. The two Indian sentinels were building a fire on the stone hearth. One by one the other savages got up, stretched and yawned, and began the business of the day by cooking their breakfast. It was, apparently, every one for himself.

Legget arose, shook himself like a shaggy dog, and was starting for the door when one of the sentinels stopped him. Brandt, who was now awake, saw the action, and smiled.

In a few moments Indians and outlaws were eating for breakfast roasted strips of venison, with corn meal baked brown, which served as bread. It was a somber, silent group.

Presently the shrill neigh of a horse startled them. Following it, the whip-like crack of a rifle stung and split the morning air. Hard on this came an Indian's long, wailing death-cry.

"Hah!" exclaimed Brandt.

Legget remained immovable. One of the savages peered out through a little port-hole at the rear of the hut. The others continued their meal.

"Whistler'll come in presently to tell us who's doin' thet shootin'," said Legget. "He's a keen Injun."

"He's not very keen now," replied Brandt, with bitter certainty. "He's what the settlers call a good Indian, which is to say, dead!"

Legget scowled at his lieutenant.

"I'll go an' see," he replied and seized his rifle.

He opened the door, when another rifle-shot rang out. A bullet whistled in the air, grazing the outlaw's shoulder, and imbedded itself in the heavy door-frame.

Legget leaped back with a curse.

"Close shave!" said Brandt coolly. "That bullet came, probably, straight down from the top of the cliff. Jack Zane's there. Wetzel is lower down watching the outlet. We're trapped."

"Trapped," shouted Legget with an angry leer. "We kin live here longer'n the bordermen kin. We've meat on hand, an' a good spring in the back of the hut. How'er we trapped?"

"We won't live twenty-four hours," declared Brandt.

"Why?"

"Because we'll be routed out. They'll find some way to do it, and we'll never have another chance to fight in the open, as we had the other night when they came after the girl. From now on there'll be no sleep, no time to eat, the nameless fear of an unseen foe who can't be shaken off, marching by night, hiding and starving by day, until——! I'd rather be back in Fort Henry at Colonel Zane's mercy."

Legget turned a ghastly face toward Brandt. "Look a here. You're takin' a lot of glee in sayin' these things. I believe you've lost your nerve, or the lettin' out of a little blood hes made you wobbly. We've Injuns here, an' ought to be a match fer two men."

Brandt gazed at him with a derisive smile.

"We kin go out an' fight these fellars," continued Legget. "We might try their own game, hidin' an' crawlin' through the woods."

"We two would have to go it alone. If you still had your trusty, trained band of experienced Indians, I'd say that would be just the thing. But Ashbow and the Chippewa are dead; so are the others. This bunch of redskins here may do to steal a few horses; but they don't amount to much against Zane and Wetzel. Besides, they'll cut and run presently, for they're scared and suspicious. Look at the chief; ask him."

The savage Brandt indicated was a big Indian just coming into manhood. His swarthy face still retained some of the frankness and simplicity of youth.

"Chief," said Legget in the Indian tongue. "The great paleface hunter, Deathwind, lies hid in the woods."

"Last night the Shawnee heard the wind of death mourn through the trees," replied the chief gloomily.

"See! What did I say?" cried Brandt. "The superstitious fool! He would begin his death-chant almost without a fight. We can't count on the redskins. What's to be done?"

The outlaw threw himself upon the bed of boughs, and Legget sat down with his rifle across his knees. The Indians maintained the same stoical composure. The moments dragged by into hours.

"Ugh!" suddenly exclaimed the Indian at the end of the hut.

Legget ran to him, and acting upon a motion of the Indian's hand, looked out through the little port-hole.

The sun was high. He saw four of the horses grazing by the brook; then gazed scrutinizingly from the steep waterfall, along the green-stained cliff to the dark narrow cleft in the rocks. Here was the only outlet from the inclosure. He failed to discover anything unusual.

The Indian grunted again, and pointed upward.

"Smoke! There's smoke risin' above the trees," cried Legget. "Brandt, come here. What's thet mean?"

Brandt hurried, looked out. His face paled, his lower jaw protruded, quivered, and then was shut hard. He walked away, put his foot on a bench and began to lace his leggings.

"Wal?" demanded Legget.

"The game's up! Get ready to run and be shot at," cried Brandt with a hiss of passion.

Almost as he spoke the roof of the hut shook under a heavy blow.

"What's thet?" No one replied. Legget glanced from Brandt's cold, determined face to the uneasy savages. They were restless, and handling their weapons. The chief strode across the floor with stealthy steps.

"Thud!"

A repetition of the first blow caused the Indians to jump, and drew a fierce imprecation from their outlaw leader.

Brandt eyed him narrowly. "It's coming to you, Legget. They are shooting arrows of fire into the roof from the cliff. Zane is doin' that. He can make a bow and draw one, too. We're to be burned out. Now, damn you! take your medicine! I wanted you to kill him when you had the chance. If you had done so we'd never have come to this. Burned out, do you get that? Burned out!"

"Fire!" exclaimed Legget. He sat down as if the strength had left his legs.

The Indians circled around the room like caged tigers.

"Ugh!" The chief suddenly reached up and touched the birch-bark roof of the hut.

His action brought the attention of all to a faint crackling of burning wood.

"It's caught all right," cried Brandt in a voice which cut the air like a blow from a knife.

"I'll not be smoked like a ham, fer all these tricky bordermen," roared Legget. Drawing his knife he hacked at the heavy buckskin hinges of the rude door. When it dropped free he measured it against the open space. Sheathing the blade, he grasped his rifle in his right hand and swung the door on his left arm. Heavy though it was he carried it easily. The roughly hewn planks afforded a capital shield for all except the lower portion of his legs and feet. He went out of the hut with the screen of wood between himself and the cliff, calling for the Indians to follow. They gathered behind him, breathing hard, clutching their weapons, and seemingly almost crazed by excitement.

Brandt, with no thought of joining this foolhardy attempt to escape from the inclosure, ran to the little port-hole that he might see the outcome. Legget and his five redskins were running toward the narrow outlet in the gorge. The awkward and futile efforts of the Indians to remain behind the shield were almost pitiful. They crowded each other for favorable positions, but, struggle as they might, one or two were always exposed to the cliff. Suddenly one, pushed to the rear, stopped simultaneously with the crack of a rifle, threw up his arms and fell. Another report, differing from the first, rang out. A savage staggered from behind the speeding group with his hand at his side. Then he dropped into the brook.

Evidently Legget grasped this as a golden opportunity, for he threw aside the heavy shield and sprang forward, closely followed by his red-skinned allies. Immediately they came near the cliff, where the trail ran into the gorge, a violent shaking of the dry ferns overhead made manifest the activity of some heavy body. Next instant a huge yellow figure, not unlike a leaping catamount, plunged down with a roar so terrible as to sound inhuman. Legget, Indians, and newcomer rolled along the declivity toward the brook in an indistinguishable mass.

Two of the savages shook themselves free, and bounded to their feet nimbly as cats, but Legget and the other redskin became engaged in a terrific combat. It was a wrestling whirl, so fierce and rapid as to render blows ineffectual. The leaves scattered as if in a whirlwind. Legget's fury must have been awful, to judge from his hoarse screams; the Indians' fear maddening, as could be told by their shrieks. The two savages ran wildly about the combatants, one trying to level a rifle, the other to get in a blow with a tomahawk. But the movements of the trio, locked in deadly embrace, were too swift.

Above all the noise of the contest rose that strange, thrilling roar.

"Wetzel!" muttered Brandt, with a chill, creeping shudder as he gazed upon the strife with fascinated eyes.

"Bang!" Again from the cliff came that heavy bellow.

The savage with the rifle shrunk back as if stung, and without a cry fell limply in a heap. His companion, uttering a frightened cry, fled from the glen.

The struggle seemed too deadly, too terrible, to last long. The Indian and the outlaw were at a disadvantage. They could not strike freely. The whirling conflict grew more fearful. During one second the huge, brown, bearish figure of Legget appeared on top; then the dark-bodied, half-naked savage, spotted like a hyena, and finally the lithe, powerful, tiger-shape of the borderman.

Finally Legget wrenched himself free at the same instant that the bloody-stained Indian rolled, writhing in convulsions, away from Wetzel. The outlaw dashed with desperate speed up the trail, and disappeared in the gorge. The borderman sped toward the cliff, leaped on a projecting ledge, grasped an overhanging branch, and pulled himself up. He was out of sight almost as quickly as Legget.

"After his rifle," Brandt muttered, and then realized that he had watched the encounter without any idea of aiding his comrade. He consoled himself with the knowledge that such an attempt would have been useless. From the moment the borderman sprang upon Legget, until he scaled the cliff, his movements had been incredibly swift. It would have been hardly possible to cover him with a rifle, and the outlaw grimly understood that he needed to be careful of that charge in his weapon.

"By Heavens, Wetzel's a wonder!" cried Brandt in unwilling admiration. "Now he'll go after Legget and the redskin, while Zane stays here to get me. Well, he'll succeed, most likely, but I'll never quit. What's this?"

He felt something slippery and warm on his hand. It was blood running from the inside of his sleeve. A slight pain made itself felt in his side. Upon examination he found, to his dismay, that his wound had reopened. With a desperate curse he pulled a linsey jacket off a peg, tore it into strips, and bound up the injury as tightly as possible.

Then he grasped his rifle, and watched the cliff and the gorge with flaring eyes. Suddenly he found it difficult to breathe; his throat was parched, his eyes smarted. Then the odor of wood-smoke brought him to a realization that the cabin was burning. It was only now he understood that the room was full of blue clouds. He sank into the corner, a wolf at bay.

Not many moments passed before the outlaw understood that he could not withstand the increasing heat and stifling vapor of the room. Pieces of burning birch dropped from the roof. The crackling above grew into a steady roar.

"I've got to run for it," he gasped. Death awaited him outside the door, but that was more acceptable than death by fire. Yet to face the final moment when he desired with all his soul to live, required almost super-human courage. Sweating, panting, he glared around. "God! Is there no other way?" he cried in agony. At this moment he saw an ax on the floor.

Seizing it he attacked the wall of the cabin. Beyond this partition was a hut which had been used for a stable. Half a dozen strokes of the ax opened a hole large enough for him to pass through. With his rifle, and a piece of venison which hung near, he literally fell through the hole, where he lay choking, almost fainting. After a time he crawled across the floor to a door. Outside was a dense laurel thicket, into which he crawled.

The crackling and roaring of the fire grew louder. He could see the column of yellow and black smoke. Once fairly under way, the flames rapidly consumed the pitch-pine logs. In an hour Legget's cabins were a heap of ashes.

The afternoon waned. Brandt lay watchful, slowly recovering his strength. He felt secure under this cover, and only prayed for night to come. As the shadows began to creep down the sides of the cliffs, he indulged in hope. If he could slip out in the dark he had a good chance to elude the borderman. In the passionate desire to escape, he had forgotten his fatalistic words to Legget. He reasoned that he could not be trailed until daylight; that a long night's march would put him far in the lead, and there was just a possibility of Zane's having gone away with Wetzel.

When darkness had set in he slipped out of the covert and began his journey for life. Within a few yards he reached the brook. He had only to follow its course in order to find the outlet to the glen. Moreover, its rush and gurgle over the stones would drown any slight noise he might make.

Slowly, patiently he crawled, stopping every moment to listen. What a long time he was in coming to the mossy stones over which the brook dashed through the gorge! But he reached them at last. Here if anywhere Zane would wait for him.

With teeth clenched desperately, and an inward tightening of his chest, for at any moment he expected to see the red flame of a rifle, he slipped cautiously over the mossy stones. Finally his hands touched the dewy grass, and a breath of cool wind fanned his hot cheek. He had succeeded in reaching the open. Crawling some rods farther on, he lay still a while and listened. The solemn wilderness calm was unbroken. Rising, he peered about. Behind loomed the black hill with its narrow cleft just discernible. Facing the north star, he went silently out into the darkness.

CHAPTER XXIII.

At daylight Jonathan Zane rolled from his snug bed of leaves under the side of a log, and with the flint, steel and punk he always carried, began building a fire. His actions were far from being hurried. They were deliberate, and seemed strange on the part of a man whose stern face suggested some dark business to be done. When his little fire had been made, he warmed some slices of venison which had already been cooked, and thus satisfied his hunger. Carefully extinguishing the fire and looking to the priming of his rifle, he was ready for the trail.

He stood near the edge of the cliff from which he could command a view of the glen. The black, smoldering ruins of the burned cabins defaced a picturesque scene.

"Brandt must have lit out last night, for I could have seen even a rabbit hidin' in that laurel patch. He's gone, an' it's what I wanted," thought the borderman.

He made his way slowly around the edge of the inclosure and clambered down on the splintered cliff at the end of the gorge. A wide, well-trodden trail extended into the forest below. Jonathan gave scarcely a glance to the beaten path before him; but bent keen eyes to the north, and carefully scrutinized the mossy stones along the brook. Upon a little sand bar running out from the bank he found the light imprint of a hand.

"It was a black night. He'd have to travel by the stars, an' north's the only safe direction for him," muttered the borderman.

On the bank above he found oblong indentations in the grass, barely perceptible, but owing to the peculiar position of the blades of grass, easy for him to follow.

"He'd better have learned to walk light as an Injun before he took to outlawin'," said the borderman in disdain. Then he returned to the gorge and entered the inclosure. At the foot of the little rise of ground where Wetzel had leaped upon his quarry, was one of the dead Indians. Another lay partly submerged in the brown water.

Jonathan carried the weapons of the savages to a dry place under a projecting ledge in the cliff. Passing on down the glen, he stopped a moment where the cabins had stood. Not a log remained. The horses, with the exception of two, were tethered in the copse of laurel. He recognized Colonel Zane's thoroughbred, and Betty's pony. He cut them loose, positive they would not stray from the glen, and might easily be secured at another time.

He set out upon the trail of Brandt with a long, swinging stride. To him the outcome of that pursuit was but a question of time. The consciousness of superior endurance, speed, and craft, spoke in his every movement. The consciousness of being in right, a factor so powerfully potent for victory, spoke in the intrepid front with which he faced the north.

It was a gloomy November day. Gray, steely clouds drifted overhead. The wind wailed through the bare trees, sending dead leaves scurrying and rustling over the brown earth.

The borderman advanced with a step that covered glade and glen, forest and field, with astonishing swiftness. Long since he had seen that Brandt was holding to the lowland. This did not strike him as singular until for the third time he found the trail lead a short distance up the side of a ridge, then descend, seeking a level. With this discovery came the certainty that Brandt's pace was lessening. He had set out with a hunter's stride, but it had begun to shorten. The outlaw had shirked the hills, and shifted from his northern course. Why? The man was weakening; he could not climb; he was favoring a wound.

What seemed more serious for the outlaw, was the fact that he had left a good trail, and entered the low, wild land north of the Ohio. Even the Indians seldom penetrated this tangled belt of laurel and thorn. Owing to the dry season the swamps were shallow, which was another factor against Brandt. No doubt he had hoped to hide his trail by wading, and here it showed up like the track of a bison.

Jonathan kept steadily on, knowing the farther Brandt penetrated into this wilderness the worse off he would be. The outlaw dared not take to the river until below Fort Henry, which was distant many a weary mile. The trail grew more ragged as the afternoon wore away. When twilight rendered further tracking impossible, the borderman built a fire in a sheltered place, ate his supper, and went to sleep.

In the dim, gray morning light he awoke, fancying he had been startled by a distant rifle shot. He roasted his strips of venison carefully, and ate with a hungry hunter's appreciation, yet sparingly, as befitted a borderman who knew how to keep up his strength upon a long trail.

Hardly had he traveled a mile when Brandt's footprints covered another's. Nothing surprised the borderman; but he had expected this least of all. A hasty examination convinced him that Legget and his Indian ally had fled this way with Wetzel in pursuit.

The morning passed slowly. The borderman kept to the trail like a hound. The afternoon wore on. Over sandy reaches thick with willows, and through long, matted, dried-out cranberry marshes and copses of prickly thorn, the borderman hung to his purpose. His legs seemed never to lose their spring, but his chest began to heave, his head bent, and his face shone with sweat.

At dusk he tired. Crawling into a dry thicket, he ate his scanty meal and fell asleep. When he awoke it was gray daylight. He was wet and chilled. Again he kindled a fire, and sat over it while cooking breakfast.

Suddenly he was brought to his feet by the sound of a rifle shot; then two others followed in rapid succession. Though they were faint, and far away to the west, Jonathan recognized the first, which could have come only from Wetzel's weapon, and he felt reasonably certain of the third, which was Brandt's. There might have been, he reflected grimly, a good reason for Legget's not shooting. However, he knew that Wetzel had rounded up the fugitives, and again he set out.

It was another dismal day, such a one as would be fitting for a dark deed of border justice. A cold, drizzly rain blew from the northwest. Jonathan wrapped a piece of oil-skin around his rifle-breech, and faced the downfall. Soon he was wet to the skin. He kept on, but his free stride had shortened. Even upon his iron muscles this soggy, sticky ground had begun to tell.

The morning passed but the storm did not; the air grew colder and darker. The short afternoon would afford him little time, especially as the rain and running rills of water were obliterating the trail.

In the midst of a dense forest of great cottonwoods and sycamores he came upon a little pond, hidden among the bushes, and shrouded in a windy, wet gloom. Jonathan recognized the place. He had been there in winter hunting bears when all the swampland was locked by ice.

The borderman searched along the banks for a time, then went back to the trail, patiently following it. Around the pond it led to the side of a great, shelving rock. He saw an Indian leaning against this, and was about to throw forward his rifle when the strange, fixed, position of the savage told of the tragedy. A wound extended from his shoulder to his waist. Near by on the ground lay Legget. He, too, was dead. His gigantic frame weltered in blood. His big feet were wide apart; his arms spread, and from the middle of his chest protruded the haft of a knife.

The level space surrounding the bodies showed evidence of a desperate struggle. A bush had been rolled upon and crushed by heavy bodies. On the ground was blood as on the stones and leaves. The blade Legget still clutched was red, and the wrist of the hand which held it showed a dark, discolored band, where it had felt the relentless grasp of Wetzel's steel grip. The dead man's buckskin coat was cut into ribbons. On his broad face a demoniacal expression had set in eternal rigidity; the animal terror of death was frozen in his wide staring eyes. The outlaw chief had died as he had lived, desperately.

Jonathan found Wetzel's trail leading directly toward the river, and soon understood that the borderman was on the track of Brandt. The borderman had surprised the worn, starved, sleepy fugitives in the gray, misty dawn. The Indian, doubtless, was the sentinel, and had fallen asleep at his post never to awaken. Legget and Brandt must have discharged their weapons ineffectually. Zane could not understand why his comrade had missed Brandt at a few rods' distance. Perhaps he had wounded the younger outlaw; but certainly he had escaped while Wetzel had closed in on Legget to meet the hardest battle of his career.

While going over his version of the attack, Jonathan followed Brandt's trail, as had Wetzel, to where it ended in the river. The old borderman had continued on down stream along the sandy shore. The outlaw remained in the water to hide his trail.

At one point Wetzel turned north. This move puzzled Jonathan, as did also the peculiar tracks. It was more perplexing because not far below Zane discovered where the fugitive had left the water to get around a ledge of rock.

The trail was approaching Fort Henry. Jonathan kept on down the river until arriving at the head of the island which lay opposite the settlement. Still no traces of Wetzel! Here Zane lost Brandt's trail completely. He waded the first channel, which was shallow and narrow, and hurried across the island. Walking out upon a sand-bar he signaled with his well-known Indian cry. Almost immediately came an answering shout.

While waiting he glanced at the sand, and there, pointing straight toward the fort, he found Brandt's straggling trail!

CHAPTER XXIV.

Colonel Zane paced to and fro on the porch. His genial smile had not returned; he was grave and somber. Information had just reached him that Jonathan had hailed from the island, and that one of the settlers had started across the river in a boat.

Betty came out accompanied by Mrs. Zane.

"What's this I hear?" asked Betty, flashing an anxious glance toward the river. "Has Jack really come in?"

"Yes," replied the colonel, pointing to a throng of men on the river bank.

"Now there'll be trouble," said Mrs. Zane nervously. "I wish with all my heart Brandt had not thrown himself, as he called it, on your mercy."

"So do I," declared Colonel Zane.

"What will be done?" she asked. "There! that's Jack! Silas has hold of his arm."

"He's lame. He has been hurt," replied her husband.

A little procession of men and boys followed the borderman from the river, and from the cabins appeared the settlers and their wives. But there was no excitement except among the children. The crowd filed into the colonel's yard behind Jonathan and Silas.

Colonel Zane silently greeted his brother with an iron grip of the hand which was more expressive than words. No unusual sight was it to see the borderman wet, ragged, bloody, worn with long marches, hollow-eyed and gloomy; yet he had never before presented such an appearance at Fort Henry. Betty ran forward, and, though she clasped his arm, shrank back. There was that in the borderman's presence to cause fear.

"Wetzel?" Jonathan cried sharply.

The colonel raised both hands, palms open, and returned his brother's keen glance. Then he spoke. "Lew hasn't come in. He chased Brandt across the river. That's all I know."

"Brandt's here, then?" hissed the borderman.

The colonel nodded gloomily.

"Where?"

"In the long room over the fort. I locked him in there."

"Why did he come here?"

Colonel Zane shrugged his shoulders. "It's beyond me. He said he'd rather place himself in my hands than be run down by Wetzel or you. He didn't crawl; I'll say that for him. He just said, 'I'm your prisoner.' He's in pretty bad shape; barked over the temple, lame in one foot, cut under the arm, starved and worn out."

"Take me to him," said the borderman, and he threw his rifle on a bench.

"Very well. Come along," replied the colonel. He frowned at those following them. "Here, you women, clear out!" But they did not obey him.

It was a sober-faced group that marched in through the big stockade gate, under the huge, bulging front of the fort, and up the rough stairway. Colonel Zane removed a heavy bar from before a door, and thrust it open with his foot. The long guardroom brilliantly lighted by sunshine coming through the portholes, was empty save for a ragged man lying on a bench.

The noise aroused him; he sat up, and then slowly labored to his feet. It was the same flaring, wild-eyed Brandt, only fiercer and more haggard. He wore a bloody bandage round his head. When he saw the borderman he backed, with involuntary, instinctive action, against the wall, yet showed no fear.

In the dark glance Jonathan shot at Brandt shone a pitiless implacability; no scorn, nor hate, nor passion, but something which, had it not been so terrible, might have been justice.

"I think Wetzel was hurt in the fight with Legget," said Jonathan deliberately, "an' ask if you know?"

"I believe he was," replied Brandt readily. "I was asleep when he jumped us, and was awakened by the Indian's yell. Wetzel must have taken a snap shot at me as I was getting up, which accounts, probably, for my being alive. I fell, but did not lose consciousness. I heard Wetzel and Legget fighting, and at last struggled to my feet. Although dizzy and bewildered, I could see to shoot; but missed. For a long time, it seemed to me, I watched that terrible fight, and then ran, finally reaching the river, where I recovered somewhat."

"Did you see Wetzel again?"

"Once, about a quarter of a mile behind me. He was staggering along on my trail."

At this juncture there was a commotion among the settlers crowding behind Colonel Zane and Jonathan, and Helen Sheppard appeared, white, with her big eyes strangely dilated.

"Oh!" she cried breathlessly, clasping both hands around Jonathan's arm. "I'm not too late? You're not going to——"

"Helen, this is no place for you," said Colonel Zane sternly. "This is business for men. You must not interfere."

Helen gazed at him, at Brandt, and then up at the borderman. She did not loose his arm.

"Outside some one told me you intended to shoot him. Is it true?"

Colonel Zane evaded the searching gaze of those strained, brilliant eyes. Nor did he answer.

As Helen stepped slowly back a hush fell upon the crowd. The whispering, the nervous coughing, and shuffling of feet, ceased.

In those around her Helen saw the spirit of the border. Colonel Zane and Silas wore the same look, cold, hard, almost brutal. The women were strangely grave. Nellie Douns' sweet face seemed changed; there was pity, even suffering on it, but no relenting. Even Betty's face, always so warm, piquant, and wholesome, had taken on a shade of doubt, of gloom, of something almost sullen, which blighted its dark beauty. What hurt Helen most cruelly was the borderman's glittering eyes.

She fought against a shuddering weakness which threatened to overcome her.

"Whose prisoner is Brandt?" she asked of Colonel Zane.

"He gave himself up to me, naturally, as I am in authority here," replied the colonel. "But that signifies little. I can do no less than abide by Jonathan's decree, which, after all, is the decree of the border."

"And that is?"

"Death to outlaws and renegades."

"But cannot you spare him?" implored Helen. "I know he is a bad man; but he might become a better one. It seems like murder to me. To kill him in cold blood, wounded, suffering as he is, when he claimed your mercy. Oh! it is dreadful!"

The usually kind-hearted colonel, soft as wax in the hands of a girl, was now colder and harder than flint.

"It is useless," he replied curtly. "I am sorry for you. We all understand your feelings, that yours are not the principles of the border. If you had lived long here you could appreciate what these outlaws and renegades have done to us. This man is a hardened criminal; he is a thief, a murderer."

"He did not kill Mordaunt," replied Helen quickly. "I saw him draw first and attack Brandt."

"No matter. Come, Helen, cease. No more of this," Colonel Zane cried with impatience.

"But I will not!" exclaimed Helen, with ringing voice and flashing eye. She turned to her girl friends and besought them to intercede for the outlaw. But Nell only looked sorrowfully on, while Betty met her appealing glance with a fire in her eyes that was no dim reflection of her brother's.

"Then I must make my appeal to you," said Helen, facing the borderman. There could be no mistaking how she regarded him. Respect, honor and love breathed from every line of her beautiful face.

"Why do you want him to go free?" demanded Jonathan. "You told me to kill him."

"Oh, I know. But I was not in my right mind. Listen to me, please. He must have been very different once; perhaps had sisters. For their sake give him another chance. I know he has a better nature. I feared him, hated him, scorned him, as if he were a snake, yet he saved me from that monster Legget!"

"For himself!"

"Well, yes, I can't deny that. But he could have ruined me, wrecked me, yet he did not. At least, he meant marriage by me. He said if I would marry him he would flee over the border and be an honest man."

"Have you no other reason?"

"Yes." Helen's bosom swelled and a glory shone in her splendid eyes. "The other reason is, my own happiness!"

Plain to all, if not through her words, from the light in her eyes, that she could not love a man who was a party to what she considered injustice.

The borderman's white face became flaming red.

It was difficult to refuse this glorious girl any sacrifice she demanded for the sake of the love so openly avowed.

Sweetly and pityingly she turned to Brandt: "Will not you help me?"

"Lass, if it were for me you were asking my life I'd swear it yours for always, and I'd be a man," he replied with bitterness; "but not to save my soul would I ask anything of him."

The giant passions, hate and jealousy, flamed in his gray eyes.

"If I persuade them to release you, will you go away, leave this country, and never come back?"

"I'll promise that, lass, and honestly," he replied.

She wheeled toward Jonathan, and now the rosy color chased the pallor from her cheeks.

"Jack, do you remember when we parted at my home; when you left on this terrible trail, now ended, thank God! Do you remember what an ordeal that was for me? Must I go through it again?"

Bewitchingly sweet she was then, with the girlish charm of coquetry almost lost in the deeper, stranger power of the woman.

The borderman drew his breath sharply; then he wrapped his long arms closely round her. She, understanding that victory was hers, sank weeping upon his breast. For a moment he bowed his face over her, and when he lifted it the dark and terrible gloom had gone.

"Eb, let him go, an' at once," ordered Jonathan. "Give him a rifle, some meat, an' a canoe, for he can't travel, an' turn him loose. Only be quick about it, because if Wetzel comes in, God himself couldn't save the outlaw."

It was an indescribable glance that Brandt cast upon the tearful face of the girl who had saved his life. But without a word he followed Colonel Zane from the room.

The crowd slowly filed down the steps. Betty and Nell lingered behind, their eyes beaming through happy tears. Jonathan, long so cold, showed evidence of becoming as quick and passionate a lover as he had been a borderman. At least, Helen had to release herself from his embrace, and it was a blushing, tear-stained face she turned to her friends.

When they reached the stockade gate Colonel Zane was hurrying toward the river with a bag in one hand, and a rifle and a paddle in the other. Brandt limped along after him, the two disappearing over the river bank.

Betty, Nell, and the lovers went to the edge of the bluff.

They saw Colonel Zane choose a canoe from among a number on the beach. He launched it, deposited the bag in the bottom, handed the rifle and paddle to Brandt, and wheeled about.

The outlaw stepped aboard, and, pushing off slowly, drifted down and out toward mid-stream. When about fifty yards from shore he gave a quick glance around, and ceased paddling. His face gleamed white, and his eyes glinted like bits of steel in the sun.

Suddenly he grasped the rifle, and, leveling it with the swiftness of thought, fired at Jonathan.

The borderman saw the act, even from the beginning, and must have read the outlaw's motive, for as the weapon flashed he dropped flat on the bank. The bullet sang harmlessly over him, imbedding itself in the stockade fence with a distinct thud.

The girls were so numb with horror that they could not even scream.

Colonel Zane swore lustily. "Where's my gun? Get me a gun. Oh! What did I tell you?"

"Look!" cried Jonathan as he rose to his feet.

Upon the sand-bar opposite stood a tall, dark, familiar figure.

"By all that's holy, Wetzel!" exclaimed Colonel Zane.

They saw the giant borderman raise a long, black rifle, which wavered and fell, and rose again. A little puff of white smoke leaped out, accompanied by a clear, stinging report.

Brandt dropped the paddle he had hurriedly begun plying after his traitor's act. His white face was turned toward the shore as it sank forward to rest at last upon the gunwale of the canoe. Then his body slowly settled, as if seeking repose. His hand trailed outside in the water, drooping inert and lifeless. The little craft drifted down stream.

"You see, Helen, it had to be," said Colonel Zane gently. "What a dastard! A long shot, Jack! Fate itself must have glanced down the sights of Wetzel's rifle."

CHAPTER XXV.

A year rolled round; once again Indian summer veiled the golden fields and forests in a soft, smoky haze. Once more from the opal-blue sky of autumn nights, shone the great white stars, and nature seemed wrapped in a melancholy hush.

November the third was the anniversary of a memorable event on the frontier—the marriage of the younger borderman.

Colonel Zane gave it the name of "Independence Day," and arranged a holiday, a feast and dance where all the settlement might meet in joyful thankfulness for the first year of freedom on the border.

With the wiping out of Legget's fierce band, the yoke of the renegades and outlaws was thrown off forever. Simon Girty migrated to Canada and lived with a few Indians who remained true to him. His confederates slowly sank into oblivion. The Shawnee tribe sullenly retreated westward, far into the interior of Ohio; the Delawares buried the war hatchet, and smoked the pipe of peace they had ever before refused. For them the dark, mysterious, fatal wind had ceased to moan along the trails, or sigh through tree-tops over lonely Indian camp-fires.

The beautiful Ohio valley had been wrested from the savages and from those parasites who for years had hung around the necks of the red men.

This day was the happiest of Colonel Zane's life. The task he had set himself, and which he had hardly ever hoped to see completed, was ended. The West had been won. What Boone achieved in Kentucky he had accomplished in Ohio and West Virginia.

The feast was spread on the colonel's lawn. Every man, woman and child in the settlement was there. Isaac Zane, with his Indian wife and child, had come from the far-off Huron town. Pioneers from Yellow Creek and eastward to Fort Pitt attended. The spirit of the occasion manifested itself in such joyousness as had never before been experienced in Fort Henry. The great feast was equal to the event. Choice cuts of beef and venison, savory viands, wonderful loaves of bread and great plump pies, sweet cider and old

570

wine, delighted the merry party.

"Friends, neighbors, dear ones," said Colonel Zane, "my heart is almost too full for speech. This occasion, commemorating the day of our freedom on the border, is the beginning of the reward for stern labor, hardship, silenced hearths of long, relentless years. I did not think I'd live to see it. The seed we have sown has taken root; in years to come, perhaps, a great people will grow up on these farms we call our homes. And as we hope those coming afterward will remember us, we should stop a moment to think of the heroes who have gone before. Many there are whose names will never be written on the roll of fame, whose graves will be unmarked in history. But we who worked, fought, bled beside them, who saw them die for those they left behind, will render them all justice, honor and love. To them we give the victory. They were true; then let us, who begin to enjoy the freedom, happiness and prosperity they won with their lives, likewise be true in memory of them, in deed to ourselves, and in grace to God."

By no means the least of the pleasant features of this pleasant day was the fact that three couples blushingly presented themselves before the colonel, and confided to him their sudden conclusions in regard to the felicitousness of the moment. The happy colonel raced around until he discovered Jim Douns, the minister, and there amid the merry throng he gave the brides away, being the first to kiss them.

It was late in the afternoon when the villagers dispersed to their homes and left the colonel to his own circle. With his strong, dark face beaming, he mounted the old porch step.

"Where are my Zane babies?" he asked. "Ah! here you are! Did anybody ever see anything to beat that? Four wonderful babies! Mother, here's your Daniel—if you'd only named him Eb! Silas, come for Silas junior, bad boy that he is. Isaac, take your Indian princess; ah! little Myeerah with the dusky face. Woe be to him who looks into those eyes when you come to age. Jack, here's little Jonathan, the last of the bordermen; he, too, has beautiful eyes, big like his mother's. Ah! well, I don't believe I have left a wish, unless———"

"Unless?" suggested Betty with her sweet smile.

"It might be———" he said and looked at her.

Betty's warm cheek was close to his as she whispered: "Dear Eb!" The rest only the colonel heard.

"Well! By all that's glorious!" he exclaimed, and attempted to seize her; but with burning face Betty fled.

* * * * *

"Jack, dear, how the leaves are falling!" exclaimed Helen. "See them floating and whirling. It reminds me of the day I lay a prisoner in the forest glade praying, waiting for you."

The borderman was silent.

They passed down the sandy lane under the colored maple trees, to a new cottage on the hillside.

"I am perfectly happy to-day," continued Helen. "Everybody seems to be content, except you. For the first time in weeks I see that shade on your face, that look in your eyes. Jack, you do not regret the new life?"

"My love, no, a thousand times no," he answered, smiling down into her eyes. They were changing, shadowing with thought; bright as in other days, and with an added beauty. The wilful spirit had been softened by love.

"Ah, I know, you miss the old friend."

The yellow thicket on the slope opened to let out a tall, dark man who came down with lithe and springy stride.

"Jack, it's Wetzel!" said Helen softly.

No words were spoken as the comrades gripped hands.

"Let me see the boy?" asked Wetzel, turning to Helen.

Little Jonathan blinked up at the grave borderman with great round eyes, and pulled with friendly, chubby fingers at the fringed buckskin coat.

"When you're a man the forest trails will be corn fields," muttered Wetzel.

The bordermen strolled together up the brown hillside, and wandered along the river bluff. The air was cool; in the west the ruddy light darkened behind bold hills; a blue mist streaming in the valley shaded into gray as twilight fell.

BEST GHOST
STORIES

AND HORROR TALES OF

ALGERNON
BLACKWOOD

Best Ghost Stories and Horror Tales of Algernon Blackwood

ISBN-13: 978-1480110670

ISBN-10:1480110671

JOHN
CARTER

OF MARS SERIES

EDGAR RICE
BURROUGHS

John Carter of Mars Series (5 Books in 1)

ISBN-13: 978-1480104754

ISBN-10: 1480104752

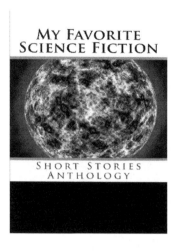

My Favorite Science Fiction Short Stories Anthology

ISBN-13: 978-1480115934

ISBN-10: 1480115932

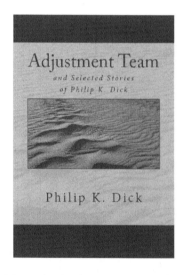

Adjustment Team And Selected Stories of Philip K. Dick

ISBN-13: 978-1479379248

ISBN-10: 1479379247

The Best Man

ISBN: 1479297372

ISBN-13: 978-1479297375

The story is about the love between Celia Hathaway and Cyril Gordon. Cyril Gordon is a handsome Secret Service Agent who stumbles in upon a wedding ceremony while he is being chased by his pursuers. He is being forced to walk down the aisle as the best man as he was being mistaken by the people in the church. But to his surprise, he was not the best man, but the groom!

ABOUT THE AUTHOR

Zane Grey (1872 – 1939) was a prolific author best known for his Western adventurous fictions. Born in Zanesville, Ohio in 1872, he was the fourth child of Lewis M. Gray and Alice Josephine Zane. His deep interests and enthusiasm in fishing, baseball and traveling contributed majorly to his writing success. His works had been adapted into over one hundred films. Near the end of his life, Grey looked into the future and wrote:

The so-called civilization of man and his works shall perish from the earth, while the shifting sands, the red looming walls, the purple sage, and the towering monuments, the vast brooding range show no perceptible change.